Continental Extensional Tectonics

Geological Society Special Publications
Series Editor K. COE

FRONTISPIECE Albert Quennell

GEOLOGICAL SOCIETY SPECIAL PUBLICATION NO 28

Continental Extensional Tectonics

EDITED BY

M. P. Coward
Department of Geology
Royal School of Mines
Imperial College
London

J. F. Dewey
Department of
Geological Sciences
The University of Durham
Durham

P. L. Hancock
Department of Geology
Wills Memorial Building
University of Bristol
Bristol

1987

Published for

The Geological Society by

Blackwell Scientific Publications

OXFORD LONDON EDINBURGH
BOSTON PALO ALTO MELBOURNE

Published for
The Geological Society by
Blackwell Scientific Publications
Osney Mead, Oxford OX2 0EL
8 John Street, London WC1N 2ES
23 Ainslie Place, Edinburgh EH3 6AJ
52 Beacon Street, Boston,
  Massachusetts 02108, USA
667 Lytton Avenue, Palo Alto,
  California 94301, USA
107 Barry Street, Carlton, Victoria 3053,
  Australia

First published 1987

Set by Downdell Ltd., Oxford
Printed and bound in Great Britain by
Butler & Tanner Ltd, Frome and London

DISTRIBUTORS

USA and Canada
  Blackwell Scientific Publications Inc.
  PO Box 50009, Palo Alto
  California 94303

Australia
  Blackwell Scientific Publications
  (Australia) Pty Ltd.
  107 Barry Street, Carlton,
  Victoria 3053

British Library Cataloguing in Publication Data

Continental extensional tectonics.—
  (Geological Society special publication,
  ISSN 0305-8719; v.28)
  1. Plate tectonics
  I. Coward, M.P.   II. Dewey, J.F.
  III. Hancock, P.L.   IV. Geological Society
  of London   V. Series
  551.1′36   QE511.4

  ISBN 0-632-01605-1

Library of Congress Cataloging-in-Publication Data

Continental extensional tectonics.

  (Geological Society special publication; no. 28)
  Papers from a conference held at the University
of Durham, April 18–20, 1985 under the auspices of
the Geological Society of London.
  1. Geology, Structural—Congresses.
I. Coward, M.P.   II. Dewey, J.F. (John F.)
III. Hancock, Paul L.   IV. Geological Society of
London.   V. Series.
QE601.C66   1987   551.8   87-309
ISBN 0-632-01605-1

Contents

Contents

Extension in the NW European Continental Shelf

Extension in the Middle East

Extension in Thrust Belts

Preface

A conference on Continental Extensional Tectonics was held at the University of Durham, during April 18 to 20 1985, under the auspices of the Geological Society of London and with financial support from The Royal Society. The meeting was well attended, in fact some people had to be turned away as the lecture rooms were packed. Forty-four papers were given as lectures, 44 as posters; this volume contains 39 of the papers presented.

The conference aimed to examine the geometry and mechanics of continental extension and their effects on basin development and plutonic and metamorphic processes. The resurgence of British interest in extensional tectonics has arisen from recent hydrocarbon exploration on the NW European continental shelf and North Sea, together with deep seismic reflection studies of British offshore basins undertaken by the BIRPS group and summarized in this volume by Cheadle *et al.* The importance of extensional tectonics in the Basin and Range region of the western USA has also been realized in the past few years and a large number of papers in this volume summarize the results of recent studies in this area. As can be seen, there is as yet no simple consensus of opinion on the geometry or driving mechanisms of Basin and Range extension. Other regions of crustal extension described in this volume, range from the Aegean and Red Sea to SE Australia and Antarctica. Some papers describe the geometry of extensional faulting as seen from earthquake seismology; others use analogue models. Several papers discuss the mechanisms of middle- to lower-crustal extension and the control on extension exerted by initial crustal thickness and geothermal gradient.

Papers by Allmendinger *et al.*, Beach *et al.*, Cheadle *et al.*, Gibbs and Kirton & Hitchen emphasize the recent advances in our understanding of continental extension based on seismic data, especially those shot to depths of 15 seconds (TWT) or over. Some of these data were obtained during commercial exploration programmes and we hope that in future there will be further growth in such cooperation and interchange of ideas and data between industry and academic institutions.

The organization in Durham fell to John Dewey and especially to Lois Karner who dealt with the detailed preliminary planning and day to day running of the conference.

The conference and this volume are dedicated to Bert Quennell who had long inspired work on the African extensional fields and had planned to present a paper on the North Tanzanian graben but who sadly passed away shortly before the meeting.

MICHAEL P. COWARD, Department of Geology, Royal School of Mines, Imperial College, Prince Consort Road, London SW7 2BP.

JOHN F. DEWEY, Department of Geological Sciences, Science Laboratories, South Road, Durham SH1 3LG.

PAUL L. HANCOCK, Department of Geology, Wills Memorial Building, University of Bristol, Queen's Road, Bristol BS8 1RJ.

Appreciation: A. M. Quennell—a prescient tectonician

Bert Quennell completed preparing his poster on the 'North Tanzanian Graben Field' on Sunday April 14th 1985, four days before the Continental Extensional Tectonics meeting. The next day he visited the doctor's surgery about a routine matter and while there died suddenly but peacefully. He was 78 and anticipating, with that blend of excitement and anxiety more typical of a scientist 50 years younger, presenting his latest research findings to a large and well-informed audience. This book honours not only his more formal and unusually farsighted contributions but also his infectious enthusiasm for geology and total lack of pretension.

Albert Mathieson Quennell was born in Dunedin, Otago, on 27 November 1906 and although he only worked in New Zealand for two short periods after 1946 he remained a New Zealander all his life. Bert was educated at Otago Boy's High School, Dunedin (1921–23) and then successively at King Edward Technical College, Dunedin (1923–27), the School of Mines, Otago University (1928–35) and Victoria University, Wellington (1936–37).

His initial vocational training led him to becoming a Member of the Institute of Civil Engineers (London), a qualification gained while working as an engineering cadet with the Otago Harbour Board. In 1931 he enrolled as a full-time student at Otago University, graduating in 1935 with two degrees, a B.Sc. in physics and geology and an Associateship of the Otago School of Mines in mining and geology.

During his student days he was taught by F.J. Turner, among others. An M.Sc. thesis, 'The Physiography and Structure of the Porirua District', prepared under the guidance of C.A. Cotton of Victoria University, followed in 1937. The influence of Cotton and growing to geological maturity among the youthful landscapes of New Zealand must have shaped Bert's outlook and 20 years later enabled him to recognize the significance of tectonic landforms in Palestine.

After gaining his first degrees, Bert joined the New Zealand Geological Survey, initially at the grade of Geologist but later being promoted to District Geologist. He remained with the survey until 1946, but for the period 1937–39 he was seconded to work on petroleum exploration for the Shell Group, and from 1940 to 45 he served with the New Zealand forces in the Middle East and Italy. With the rank of Captain he commanded sound-ranging and field artillery units and was mentioned in despatches.

The first phase of Bert's professional career can be thought of as ending in 1946, when, aged 40, he was appointed Assistant Director of the Lands and Surveys Department of what was then Trans-Jordan. He was returning to a land he knew, having triangulated the country in 1941 in preparation for an aerial survey. While there for the second time he conducted the first systematic geological survey of Trans-Jordan. His seminal paper on the Dead Sea rift did not, however, appear until 10 years later and after experience of the East African rift system. Another move followed in 1948, this time to the Tanganyika (now Tanzania) Geological Survey with whom he stayed until 1960, having become their Director. For the years 1960–65 he worked in Auckland as a consulting geologist; an occupation he would resume, again in Auckland, from 1967 to 1971. Between these two self-employed episodes he worked as mineral exploration Project Manager for the United Nations, initially in Nigeria (1965–67) and then in Sudan (1967–69).

In 1971, ostensibly having retired, Bert and Maidie, his wife, moved to Bristol in order to live near two of their four children. Soon after arriving in England he became a part-time Senior Scientific Officer with the Institute of Geological Sciences (now the British Geological Survey). His responsibilities were editing their *Journal of Overseas Geology and Mineral Resources* and preparing for publication related memoirs and maps. Because such work was only part-time and his remaining energy could not be entirely expended on perfecting his loudspeakers, he returned to thinking about the tectonics of the Middle East, especially the evolution of the Dead Sea rift. Not long after leaving the survey in 1974, Bert found another editing job; this time with Hutchinson Ross for whom he prepared two volumes in their 'Benchwork Series' (Quennell 1982, 1985), the second published shortly after his death.

It was while he was living in Bristol that I first met him. Bert became a frequent visitor to the university and a popular member of its geology department, in which he was an Honorary Research Associate. Seeing him in the corridor, the unsuspecting might have mistaken him for an unusually genial Somerset farmer come to enquire why his patch of the 'Levels' was sinking. Despite an easy affable charm and countryman's physique he was, however, very much a scientist and, in its fullest sense, a student. His enthusiasm for extensional and strike-slip tectonics was prodigious and characterized by a receptivity to new ideas.

Selecting for commentary a handful of publications from a lifetime's work is bound to result in a somewhat unbalanced view of a man's total output but I believe many would agree that Quennell's (1958, 1959) papers on the Dead Sea rift are those which will be most recalled by historians of geology. Both papers first surfaced at meetings in 1956: the one published in 1959 being read in early September at the International Geological Congress in Mexico and the 1958 article being delivered at the Geological Society at London on 12th December. In the 1959 article, Quennell argued from geological evidence that there had been two phases of left-lateral displacement along the Palestinian sector of the Dead Sea rift. The post-Senonian–pre-Miocene earlier phase achieved 62 km of slip, the later phase, beginning in the Pleistocene but still continuing, added another 45 km he thought. To postulate at an international meeting in 1956 such large horizontal displacements must have taken professional courage at a time when undergraduates, at least, were still being required to write essays with titles such as 'The permanence of the ocean basins'. Not only did Quennell argue for a then radical amount of motion but he also provided us with the first description of a pole of rotation, concluding that the Arabian block had, relative to the Sinai–Palestine block, rotated 5.5° about a pole situated at 33° N, 24° E, approximately 1100 km distant from the fault zone. With wisdom of hindsight it is interesting to note that in the report of the discussion following the session in which Quennell spoke there was relatively little reaction to his ideas, other papers, now largely forgotten, seem to have excited more comment.

In the article published in 1958, Quennell explored the large-scale physiographic consequences of his model, and his fig. 1 contains a clear illustration of a feature that would now be called a pull-apart basin, although he preferred the older and less inelegant name, rhomb graben. When, much later, Quennell (1984) returned to the theme of the Dead Sea rift system at the Geological Society's meeting

on 'The Geological Evolution of the Eastern Mediterranean' he integrated his original ideas with those expounded more recently by Israeli workers. At the same time, he argued that by the late Pliocene the entire length of the rift system, which stretches from the Red Sea to SE Anatolia, had become divided into three segments which operated independently. He proposed that the southern (Palestinian) and northern (Syrian) segments continued to be sinistral strike-slip faults, although with different amounts of displacement on them, but that the central (Lebanese) segment was principally a zone of oblique folding and thrusting with only the very young Yammoune fault transecting it.

In the context of the present debate about funding for geological research in the UK it is noteworthy that Bert's ideas on the Dead Sea rift arose from field work which was carried out in his leisure time.

While working for the Lands and Surveys Department Bert had met His Majesty King Abdulla. When news of his death reached Jordan a telegram of sympathy from Crown Prince Hassan was promptly despatched to Maidie. The local scientific community demonstrated its esteem by making him the first honorary member of the Jordanian Geologists' Association and by inviting him and Maidie to be guests at their first conference (Amman, 6–8 September 1982).

Bert Quennell showed his prescience not only by anticipating the importance of intracontinental transforms and poles of rotation but he also foresaw the significance of some of the criteria which it was later realized were necessary for identifying allochthonous (suspect) terranes. In an admirably concise two-page 'letter', Quennell & Hay (1964) documented the characteristics of the chaotic Tangihua Group of Northland, New Zealand; characteristics which they concluded indicated that the volcanic rocks of the group were derived from seamounts (now thought to be mainly of late-Jurassic age) surrounded by Late Cretaceous and Tertiary marine sediments. Quennell's & Hay's observations were later elaborated by other workers some of whom interpret the Tungihua Volcanics and surrounding sediments as being far travelled.

Selected bibliography

Quennell, A.M. 1958. The structural and geomorphic evolution of the Dead Sea rift. *Q. J. geol. Soc. London*, **114**, 1–24.

Quennell, A.M. 1959. Tectonics of the Dead Sea rift. *Proc. 20th International Geological Congress, Mexico, 1956, Associacion de Servicos Geologicos Africanos*, pp. 385–403.

Quennell, A.M. (ed.) 1982. *Rift Valleys: Afro-Arabian*, 419 pp. Hutchinson Ross, Pennsylvania.

Quennell, A.M. 1984. The Western Arabia rift-system. In: Dixon, J.F. & Robertson, A.H.F. (eds) *The Geological Evolution of the Eastern Mediterranean, Geol. Soc. Spec. Publ.* **17**, 775–88.

Quennell, A.M. (ed.) 1985. *Continental Rifts*, 346 pp. Hutchinson Ross, Pennsylvania.

Quennell, A.M. & Hay, R.F. 1964. Origin of the Tangihua Group of North Auckland. *N.Z.J. Geol. Geophys.* **7**, 638–9.

PAUL HANCOCK, Department of Geology, Wills Memorial Building, University of Bristol, Queen's Road, Bristol BS8 1RJ.

Fault Geometry
and Associated Processes

Active normal faulting and crustal extension

J.A. Jackson

SUMMARY: A world-wide review of fault-plane solutions and focal depths for large normal-faulting earthquakes on the continents shows that the overwhelming majority of such earthquakes nucleate in the depth range 6–15 km on faults dipping between 30 and 60°. In the few cases where levelling or seismic data are good enough, these normal faults are shown to be approximately planar from the surface to their nucleation depth at the base of the brittle crust. There is evidence that, in some cases, as a result of the enormous transitory increase in strain rate during large earthquakes, rupture continues into the normally 'ductile' lower crust on surfaces with substantially gentler dips. These low-angle surfaces may be analogous to some of the 'detachments' seen in metamorphic core complexes of the western USA, but the nature of the motion on them depends on strain rate as well as on rheological contrasts between the 'detachments' and the blocks on either side. Such contrasts, however, are unlikely to introduce substantial curvature to an originally planar shear zone.

If the observed spread in active normal-fault dips is caused by rotation of the faults and the blocks they bound during extension, then a maximum β value of 1.7 can be accommodated by *seismic* activity on a single generation of normal faults. With continued extension, either a new generation of steeper faults, cutting the rotated first faults, is likely to form, or the deformation will continue aseismically on faults dipping at less than 30°.

Large earthquakes have not been observed to nucleate on very low-angle ($<20°$) normal faults within the continental crust anywhere in the world. Such faults can of course move aseismically, but are unlikely to do so on a large scale within the upper crust in areas where steep normal faults are seismically active. Thus extensional models that require concentrated simple shear on large sub-horizontal faults within the brittle upper crust will also require a spatial separation between aseismic, very low-angle faulting and seismic high-angle faulting. Since seismogenic high-angle faults dominate the topography of extending regions, upper-crustal very-low-angle faulting, if it occurs on a large scale, presumably does so in areas that are relatively flat.

There is now little doubt that the formation of many continental sedimentary basins and passive margins has involved a considerable amount of both lithospheric and crustal stretching. At shallow levels, at least some, and perhaps the majority, of the crustal extension in these basins is accommodated by normal faults. Attempts to reconcile the observed normal faulting with estimates of overall crustal extension deduced from heat flow, subsidence or crustal thickness have proved difficult (see e.g. de Charpal *et al.* 1978; Le Pichon & Sibuet 1981; Wood & Barton 1983; Ziegler 1983), and there are profound disagreements about the nature of the normal faulting itself, particularly in the Basin and Range Province (e.g. Wernicke 1981; Gans & Miller 1983).

There are several continental areas where seismically active normal faulting is occurring today. This paper is an attempt to review the information available from seismological (and to some extent geomorphological) data, which throws light on the geometry and kinematics of the normal faults in these actively deforming regions. There are several advantages to be gained from studying large earthquakes.

1 Earthquakes larger than magnitude (M_s) 5.5 have source (fault) dimensions of at least 10–15 km, which are comparable with the thickness of the brittle upper crust. The faulting associated with such earthquakes usually dominates the topography, and thus there is no doubt that we are dealing with the major structures in a region and are not concerned with the minor accommodation structures that are always present.

2 By studying active faults we can see their geometry and orientation at the time of movement: information which may not be easy to deduce from the older geological record where original orientations may have been changed by tilting or uplift.

3 The interaction between adjacent faults is much more obvious in actively deforming areas than in the older geological record, where the resolution of timing creates its own difficulties.

4 Vertical movements associated with faulting can only be detected in the presence of a horizontal reference level. In the case of active faults this may either be sea-level (e.g. in the Aegean) or surveyed levelling lines. The absence of such reference levels in older geological records can

From COWARD, M.P., DEWEY, J.F. & HANCOCK, P.L. (eds), 1987, *Continental Extensional Tectonics.* Geological Society Special Publication No. 28, pp. 3–17.

make absolute vertical movements almost impossible to deduce.

A basic tenet of this paper is that seismically active normal faulting looks much the same wherever it is occurring in the continents today. This appears to be true in spite of the fact that the actively extending regions differ dramatically in both scale and altitude (e.g. Tibet and the Aegean), and almost certainly differ also in the nature and magnitude of the forces responsible for their extension. Thus the kinematics of normal faulting appear to be largely independent of dynamics, and, for this reason, older, now static extended areas are likely to have been stretched by normal faults in the same way as currently active regions. This paper first reviews the geometry of active normal faults, and then goes on to discuss plausible models for crustal extension that are compatible with these observations. Finally, it examines the problems faced when trying to reconcile some interpretations of older, now static, structures, especially in the Basin and Range Province, with the data from seismically active normal faults. This paper does not intend to imply that any such interpretations of static structures are wrong: it merely attempts to highlight the apparent incompatibility between some proposed mechanisms of crustal extension and active-fault geometries, in the belief that eventual understanding of this incompatibility will also increase our understanding of extensional processes.

Active normal faults

The nature of the data

Figure 1 shows cross-sections through two active normal faults in Greece, both of which broke the surface in earthquakes of $M_s > 6.0$. In both cases the dip of the surface slip vector was measured in the field, the dip of the fault at the hypocentre (nucleation point of the earthquake) was well constrained by the fault-plane solution, the focal depth was estimated from waveform modelling, and the epicentre (projection of the hypocentre to the surface) was determined by a relative location technique using a well-located aftershock as a reference. The data used in Fig. 1 are described fully by Soufleris & Stewart (1981), Soufleris *et al.* (1982), Mercier *et al.* (1979) and Jackson *et al.* (1982). The point of Fig. 1 is simply this: in spite of the uncertainties involved, the seismogenic faults (both of which were major structures extending 12–15 km along strike) cannot have had dips of less than

about 40–50° at depths shallower than about 6–8 km. The simplest interpretation of the data is that the faults are, to a first approximation, planar with a dip of 40–50° from the surface to a depth of at least 6–8 km. It is, of course, possible that the faults have minor curvature (the most extreme is shown by the dashed lines) and they could even have small changes of curvature, inflexions, or ramp-and-flat geometries, all of which are certainly sufficient to cause minor accommodation structures, antithetic faults and some curvature to bedding in the hanging wall (see e.g. Gibbs 1984; White *et al.* 1986). However, the degree of overall curvature is strongly limited by the seismic data: if the fault dip becomes horizontal, it does so *below* the nucleation point of the earthquake.

It is clear that the main constraints on the geometry shown in Fig. 1 are the dip of the fault at the hypocentre and the focal depth. Fortunately both are easily obtainable from the seismic waveforms generated by the earthquakes, which are recorded, and are thus available for study, world-wide.

Figures 2 & 3 present focal depths and dips for normal-faulting earthquakes in Greece, Turkey, western USA, the Gulf of Suez, Tibet, Baykal, NE China, Yunnan and East Africa. Much of this data is from published sources, the main ones being Chen & Molnar (1983a), Tapponnier & Molnar (1977, 1979), McKenzie (1972, 1978b), Eyidogan & Jackson (1985) and Shudofsky (in press), but much is as yet unpublished and will be reported in greater detail with fuller references elsewhere. All of the events used in these figures have magnitudes (M_s or m_b) greater than 5.2.

Focal depths

Focal depths reported by international agencies (e.g. USGS, ISC) are usually based on arrival-time data and are notoriously unreliable. Since about 1975, a different technique has become available, which models the shape of the observed seismic waveform by generating synthetic seismograms on a computer. This method is usually capable of estimating focal depths to within about 2 km (see e.g. Langston & Helmberger 1975; Chen & Molnar 1983a).

Figure 2 shows a histogram of focal depths determined from waveform modelling for 43 normal-faulting earthquakes in the continental regions listed above. The depths range from about 6–18 km and thus occur in the upper part of the continental crust. Moreover, where local seismic networks have been installed to locate aftershocks accurately, it is clear that large

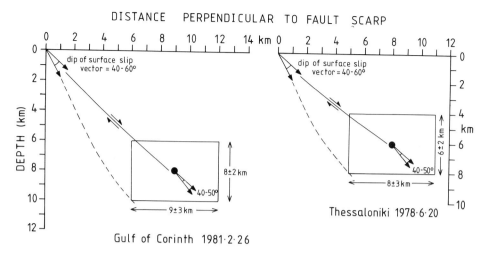

FIG. 1. Cross-sections through two active normal faults in Greece. References to the data used in this figure are given in the text. The hypocentre (focus) of each earthquake is marked by a filled circle surrounded by a rectangle indicating the uncertainty in its depth and epicentre. The uncertainties in the fault dip at the surface and at the hypocentre are marked by arrows. The position of the hypocentre as marked is consistent with a roughly planar geometry, but the hypocentre could lie anywhere within the rectangle indicated. The fault must pass through its outcrop and the focus and have correct dip at each of these positions. The most listric (concave upward) geometry allowable within these constraints is shown by a dashed line. From Eyidogan & Jackson (1985).

normal-faulting earthquakes nucleate at or near the base of the aftershock zone (e.g., Soufleris *et al.* 1982; King *et al.* 1984; Smith & Bruhn 1984; Lahr *et al.* 1976; Doser & Smith 1985). Below the depth to which aftershocks occur, deformation evidently takes place aseismically, presumably by some form of creep. There is mounting evidence that the depth of this tran-

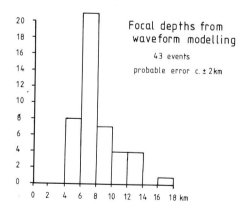

FIG. 2. Histogram of focal depths for normal faulting earthquakes. Detailed tabulation of the data will be published elsewhere.

sition from apparently 'brittle' (and seismic) to apparently 'ductile' (and aseismic) behaviour is controlled principally by the temperature gradient in the crust (e.g. Sibson 1982, 1984; Meissner & Strehlau 1982; Chen & Molnar 1983b; Wiens & Stein 1983). Variations in temperature gradient are probably responsible for variations in the focal depths from region to region; for example events in Greece and western Turkey appear to nucleate at depths as shallow as 6–8 km, whereas those in the Basin and Range Province appear to have focal depths of up to 15 km (see e.g. Doser 1985; Doser & Smith 1985). Thus Fig. 2 confirms the general view that the lower crust is largely aseismic and that the largest earthquakes nucleate at or near the base of the 'brittle' upper crust. Figure 2 does not include five significantly deeper normal-faulting earthquakes: two in southern Tibet (at 85 and 90 km; Chen & Molnar 1983a) and three in East Africa (at 25, 27 and 29 km; Shudofsky, 1985). All of these earthquakes nucleated in or near the uppermost upper mantle beneath continental crust and their interpretation is not clear. Under some thermal gradients it is possible that the uppermost mantle may deform in a brittle (seismic) fashion even though the lower crust deforms aseismically (see e.g. Chen & Molnar 1983b). Such deep events do not appear to be common, and their source dimensions (about 15 km) are small compared with their focal depths, making it unlikely that they will correlate directly with any structures visible at the surface.

Fault dips from fault-plane solutions

It is well known that either of the two nodal planes in a first-motion fault-plane solution for an earthquake could be the actual fault plane. For this reason, in the histogram of Fig. 3(a) both nodal planes are plotted for all the 82 normal-faulting earthquakes whose fault-plane solutions have been collected. All these fault-plane solutions have been constructed using a crustal *P*-wave velocity (of either 6.5 or 6.8 km sec^{-1}) at the focus. Although half the dips shown in Fig. 3(a) must be from auxiliary rather than fault planes, it is clear that both nodal

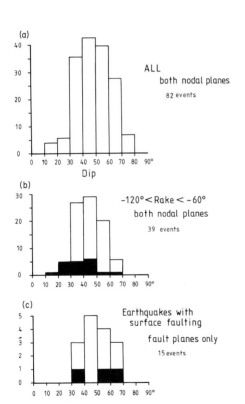

FIG. 3. Dips of nodal planes for normal faulting earthquakes measured from fault-plane solutions. Note that these dips indicate the orientation of the normal fault at the focus of the earthquake. The black regions of histograms (b) and (c) are explained in the text.

planes in normal-faulting earthquakes commonly dip in the range 30–70°. Nodal planes with dips less than 20° or more than 70° are very rare. Uncertainties in nodal-plane dips are variable and difficult to estimate. In places with good station coverage, such as the Mediterranean and western USA, both the dip and strike of the nodal planes is usually well constrained, whereas in remote parts of central Asia the dips may be much better constrained than the strikes. In particular, the uncertainty in dip usually depends on the dip itself: very low-angle faulting requires an almost vertical (auxiliary) nodal plane to pass near the centre of the focal sphere, which is the part of the radiation pattern best sampled by teleseismic observations. In almost all the earthquakes shown in Fig. 3(a), dilatational first motions dominate the teleseismic distance range (30–80°), thereby excluding the possibility of an almost-vertical nodal plane, and thus also excluding the possibility of a very low-angle fault plane. Molnar & Chen (1982) give a useful discussion of these uncertainties for those unfamiliar with these types of data. Fault-plane solutions the dips of which are very poorly constrained are not included in Fig. 3, where the majority of the dips are probably correct to within 10–15°.

Figure 3(b) shows a sub-set of Fig. 3(a) in which again the dips of both nodal planes are plotted, but this time only earthquakes for which the strike-slip component is constrained by the data to be small (i.e. with rake, as defined by Aki & Richards 1980, in the range −60 to −120°) are included. The dark parts of each column represent nodal planes the slip vectors of which are well determined unlike the dips. These have been drawn (and plotted) as almost pure normal faults but they could include a slightly greater component of strike-slip motion, i.e. they could have steeper but not gentler dips. Figure 3(b) shows that for normal-faulting earthquakes whose strike-slip motion is small, nodal planes (and hence fault planes) with dips less than 20° or more than 70° are virtually unknown, and that the great majority dip in the range 30–60°.

Finally, Fig. 3(c) shows dips for those earthquakes whose faulting was observed to break the ground surface, allowing one of the nodal planes of the fault-plane solution to be unambiguously chosen as the fault plane. In a few cases (shaded black) this choice was made from the very obvious pattern of the aftershock distribution. Note that in Fig. 3(c), unlike in Fig. 3(a) & (b), *only fault-plane dips* at the focus (and not auxiliary planes) are plotted. Figure 3(c) confirms what is suggested by Fig. 3(a) & (b): that, above m_b 5.5, seismic activity on normal faults with dips gentler than about 30° is almost unknown.

Conclusions

The data from active normal faults is quite unequivocal: in Greece, Turkey, the western USA, central Asia and Africa active normal faults nucleate at or near the base of the 'brittle' (seismogenic) upper crust with relatively steep dips (in the range 30–60°). The earthquakes discussed in this paper have source dimensions comparable to or bigger than their focal depths and thus break through most of the brittle upper continental crust. From the 82 normal-faulting earthquakes studied in this paper (as well as the five deeper events in Tibet and East Africa) there is *not one single example* of seismic activity on a sub-horizontal fault. From Fig. 3 we must conclude that normal faults with dips much less than 30° do not move seismically.

There are few examples where the fault geometry is as well constrained as in Fig. 1: generally because the earthquake epicentre is not sufficiently well determined. Other examples include the Dixie Valley (1954) and Borah Peak (1983) earthquakes in the western USA where levelling as well as seismic data support an approximately planar fault geometry from the surface to the nucleation depth (Eddington & Smith, this volume; Stein & Barrientos, in press; Doser & Smith 1985), though once again, minor departures from a planar geometry, sufficient to cause internal deformation of the hanging wall block, cannot be excluded by the available data. Thus, although the data in Fig. 3 permit the faults to steepen as they approach the surface, the evidence from the few earthquakes in Greece and the western USA for which the observations are good enough suggests that they do not steepen: i.e. that the faults are approximately planar. This does not, of course, deny the existence of faults that flatten abruptly with depth and even become horizontal; but it does put constraints on the nature of the movement on them, as such faults have never been seen to move *seismically* in the upper continental crust. A number of points can now be made.

1   There are many well-documented examples of large normal faults that are strongly curved in cross-section and become almost flat at depths within the upper crust. The best known are those within thick sedimentary sequences such as the Gulf of Mexico and Niger Delta. Most of these do not contribute to extension of the entire crustal thickness as the material beneath the fault surface is generally undeformed, and the extension in the up-dip direction is usually accommodated by shortening in the down-dip direction; achieved by either thrusting, folding or lateral compaction. Such faults represent a readjustment of the sediment load above the basement. However, the presence of such 'superficial' faults in places where the basement has genuinely been extended by other deeper faults can lead to confusion: especially where the sedimentary carapace is decoupled from the basement by salt (see e.g. Gibbs 1984).

2   It is, of course, possible that the steep upper-crustal seismogenic faults (of the type shown in Fig. 1) flatten abruptly below the hypocentre into the lower crust, where motion on them is aseismic. This possibility is discussed in a later section.

3   The data shown in Figs 2 & 3 cannot exclude the possibility of substantial *aseismic* motion on large extensional faults with dips less than 30° in the upper crust.

4   In the geological literature the term 'high-angle normal fault' is associated with a dip greater than 45° and 'low-angle normal fault' with a dip of less than 45° (e.g. Hobbs *et al.* 1976). This is unfortunate in the sense that seismically active normal faults are common throughout the dip range 30–60°. In this paper I will use the term 'very low-angle normal fault' when referring to a dip of less than 20° and 'steep normal fault' when referring to the dip range 30–60°.

Rotation and crustal extension

There is no doubt that substantial movement on roughly planar faults dipping at 30–60° throughout the upper crust occurs in extensional terranes. A direct and inevitable consequence of this is the rotation of both the faults and the blocks they bound about a horizontal axis. There are two main reasons for such rotation, the first being strain compatibility. Movement on planar faults represents simple shear yet the overall result of such movement must be pure shear: i.e. extending the crust in the horizontal direction by thinning it in the vertical. Overall pure shear can be achieved by a combination of simple shear and rotation (Fig. 4). The second reason is that substantial movement on crustal-scale, planar non-rotational faults over the width of an entire sedimentary basin would produce a massive isostatic disequilibrium and a long-wavelength gravity anomaly much larger than is ever observed. Where good gravity data exist, such as in the North Sea (Barton & Wood 1984), there is positive evidence that the

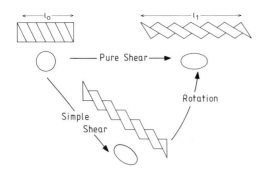

FIG. 4. Cartoon to illustrate the accomplishment of pure shear by simple shear and rotation, and to illustrate how planar non-rotational faulting on a crustal scale will inevitably lead to a large gravity anomaly. The relative extension is $\beta = l_1/l_0$ (as defined by McKenzie 1978a).

continental crust in sedimentary basins has no significant strength at all on wavelengths larger than the separation of major fault-bounded blocks; which may be 25 km or more in central Greece and the Basin and Range Province (Jackson & McKenzie 1983; Fletcher & Hallett 1983). In addition to a large gravity anomaly, planar non-rotational faults that cut the entire crust would lead to a depression of the Moho depth beneath the thickest sediments in the basin, rather than the elevation that is usually observed. Reconciliation with the gravity and Moho data is possible if the planar non-rotational faults are restricted to the upper crust: but then only if considerable flow is allowed in the lower crust.

It is therefore unlikely that planar non-rotational faults contribute significantly to major crustal extension processes, though on a small scale, especially in sediment cover, they certainly exist. Instead, faults and fault-bounded blocks rotate as they move, producing the tilted terranes characteristic of extended regions. This is the basis of the rotating block or 'domino' model for crustal extension, described by Ransome *et al.* (1910) and subsequently by many others (e.g. Morton & Black 1975; Le Pichon & Sibuet 1981; Wernicke & Burchfiel 1982; Jackson & McKenzie 1983). This model does not need elaboration here, though it is worth noting that the rotation of blocks in the extending terrane requires either a curved fault or substantial internal deformation of the hanging wall block where the extending terrane adjoins a non-extending stable region (see Wernicke & Burchfiel 1982).

Of interest here is whether the data in Fig. 3 put any quantitative constraints on the block-rotation process that accommodates stretching in the upper crust. Let us suppose that the spread in fault dips of 30–60°, implied by Fig. 3, is caused by rotation of the faults as they move. This would mean that the maximum rotation (and hence stretching) is achieved by a fault which starts with a dip of 60° and rotates to 30°. Such a rotation implies a relative extension, β, of 1.7 (see Fig. 4 and Jackson & McKenzie 1983 for relevant algebraic expressions). Indeed a value for β of 1.7 is the maximum extension that can be achieved with a single set of faults if they are to be seismically active. If stretching is to continue beyond $\beta = 1.7$ there are three possibilities:

1 A second generation of steep faults becomes active, cutting the first generation faults, which have rotated to a dip of 30°, making them inactive.
2 The faults continue to move at dips of less than 30°, but do so aseismically.
3 The faults become inactive once their dips reach 30°, and extension, with new faults, continues somewhere else nearby.

Note that $\beta = 1.7$ is the *maximum* value beyond which some change in the nature of extension must occur; if the faults start moving with dips of less than 60°, such a change will occur at smaller values of β.

The first of the three possibilities listed above is well documented as a process: there is good reason to think that as normal faults become flatter gravity will impede, rather than help, movement on them, and this is generally suggested as the reason why a second generation of steep faults may initiate. It is encouraging to note that, where values for stretching factors exceeding $\beta = 1.7$ on land have been suggested, two generations of normal faults have usually been described: e.g. in Afar (Morton & Black 1975); Yerrington, and the Snake Range in Nevada (Proffett 1977; Gans & Miller 1983); and parts of Mexico (Angelier & Colletta 1983). However, most sedimentary basins in which β exceeds 1.7 are in deep water and relatively unexplored. It is not certain whether an earlier generation of faults within the blocks bounded by the youngest faults would be revealed by seismic reflection, and resolution of fault structure in places like the Bay of Biscay (de Charpal *et al.* 1978) may have to await drilling. By contrast, in places where β is less than 1.7, such as the North Sea, there is no reason to expect to find anything other than a single generation of tilted fault blocks. If a rotation from an initial fault dip of 60° to one of 30° is all that can be expected from a single generation of faults, this in turn implies a maximum sedimentary tilt of 30° and a maximum throw on each fault equal to the initial spacing between adjacent faults.

It is perhaps worth noting that 'Andersonian' fault mechanics (Anderson 1951) predicts that normal faults should initiate in intact crust with dips of about 60°, which might explain the upper boundary to the observed range of seismically active normal fault dips. Furthermore, Sibson (1985 & pers. comm.) points out that, for a typical static rock-friction coefficient of 0.75, provided the maximum compressive stress (σ_1), remains vertical, *frictional* normal-slip failure cannot occur on planes dipping less than 37° unless the least principal compressive stress (σ_3) becomes effectively tensile, perhaps through abnormally high fluid pressures. This may go some way to explaining the lower observed boundary of seismically active normal fault dips: though in fact dips as gentle as 30° are known.

Faults in the lower crust

While it is clear that extension in the upper 'brittle' (i.e. seismogenic) crust occurs by rotating fault blocks it is less certain what happens in the lower crust. Several deep seismic reflection profiles have suggested the presence of discontinuities in the lower crust (e.g. Brewer & Smythe 1984), and two observations from actively extending areas strongly support the presence of faults below the seismogenic zone, at least in some cases.

The asymmetry of vertical movements in normal faulting

Figure 5 shows a cross-section of the eastern Gulf of Corinth: an active graben in Greece. In 1981 normal faults on both sides of the Gulf moved in earthquakes of $M_s > 6.4$, creating observed surface breaks about 12 km long in each event. Figure 4 is contructed from data reported in Jackson *et al.* (1982) and Kim *et al.* (1984). The section is approximately perpendicular to fault strike and the hypocentre of each event lay about 5 km to the side of the line of section.

The faults on both sides of the Gulf can be projected downwards to their respective hypocentres, which are both in the middle of the Gulf at roughly the same depth. The asymmetry of the vertical motions, however, clearly indicates that the southern fault projects northwards under the northern fault at a depth below that of the deepest aftershocks (see Jackson *et al.* 1982; King *et al.* 1984). Only this can explain the emergent nature of the southern shore (with

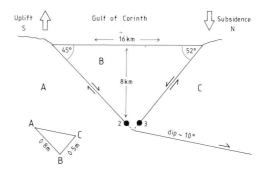

FIG. 5 A cross-section through the eastern Gulf of Corinth (Greece) constructed from seismic and surface data obtained from the earthquakes in 1981. Note the asymmetry of the vertical movement of the coastline. The dip of the very low-angle fault below the hypocentres of events 2 (1981.2.26) and 3 (1981.3.4) was estimated from the vector triangle on the left, showing the directions and amounts of the relative motions between blocks A, B and C. (see King *et al.* 1984).

raised beaches and uplifted solution notches in limestone) and the rapidly sinking northern shore. An estimate of the dip of the lower part of the southern fault can be made by vector addition, assuming that all the motion is transferred, presumably aseismically, on to this fault at depth (see King *et al.* 1984). This estimate suggests a dip of 10°, which is significantly less than the 45° dip observed in the upper crust. The change in dip of the slip vector is presumably responsible for the internal deformation of the hanging wall block, manifested by numerous small aftershocks and the presence of the main antithetic fault itself.

Earthquake faulting with a very similar geometry occurred in Bulgaria in 1928, where again the asymmetry of the vertical movements, this time revealed by levelling, clearly implies that the graben is asymmetrical at depth, with one fault continuing beneath the other. This work by Jankhof (1945: in Bulgarian) is reported by Richter (1958) and Jackson & McKenzie (1983).

Low-angle normal faulting in earthquakes

In a recent study, Eyidogon & Jackson (1985) investigated the normal faulting associated with several large earthquakes in western Turkey. All the events studied nucleated at depths of 6–10 km and broke through the upper crust on faults dipping between 30 and 45°. However, the seismograms of two of these events, at Gediz (1970.3.28) and Alasehir (1969.3.28), contain large-amplitude, long-period signals which originated *after* the faulting that broke through the upper crust. The extremely directional nature of these signals allows resolution of the fault orientation responsible for them. Eyidogan & Jackson (1985) concluded that these signals were caused by movement on almost flat (less than 10°) normal faults nucleating 15–25 sec after the start of the main shock and at the base of the seismogenic upper crust. As shown in Fig. 3, such faults are never seen in *first-motion* fault-plane solutions of earthquakes, and yet in Turkey they are apparently seen to move seismically during or immediately after earthquakes on steep normal faults in the upper crust. The explanation suggested by Eyidogan & Jackson (1985) for these observations is as follows. During the periods between large earthquakes the lower crust deforms by aseismic creep at strain rates in the region of 10^{-11} to 10^{-14} sec^{-1}. Meanwhile the upper crust deforms only by microearthquakes, whose source dimensions are small compared to the 'brittle' thickness of the crust, and therefore do not affect the lower crust beneath. When a large earthquake occurs, on a fault that breaks right through the 'brittle' upper crust, the top part of the lower crust suddenly experiences strain rates of about 10^{-4} sec^{-1}. With an increase in strain rate of 10 orders of magnitude, the lower crust is unlikely to respond by creep alone and will probably fail in a brittle fashion, but rupture will be attenuated as it propagates downwards into the 'ductile' layer. This behaviour is similar to that of toffee, which at slow strain rates will flow, and when hit with a hammer will shatter. In short, because of the extreme increase in strain rates during earthquakes, it is likely that rupture propagates down as well as up, and, under these special circumstances, the uppermost lower crust behaves in a brittle rather than a ductile fashion: but only for

a short time. This brief display of brittle behaviour is sufficient to radiate seismic energy and thus reveal the geometry of the faults in the lower crust.

This behaviour is illustrated in Fig. 6, taken from Eyidogan & Jackson (1985). The fault geometry is clearly very similar to that proposed for the Gulf of Corinth (Fig. 5). It is not clear how widespread such behaviour is. The later part of the *P*-wave seismograms have hitherto attracted less attention than the first cycle, which is sufficient to estimate the fault depth and seismic moment. Moreover, the *P*-wave radiation from flat faults is much more directional than that from faults dipping at 45°, and helps greatly in their detection. If the upper-crustal faults propagated downwards at a constant dip, they would be much more difficult to detect in the lower crust. Yielding (1985) and Nabelek (1985) both suggest a similar flattening of a fault, from a steep dip in the upper crust to a gentler dip in the uppermost lower crust, during the 1980 El Asnam earthquake in Algeria: though it should be noted that this was a thrust (reverse fault).

Rheology and the nature of faults in the lower crust

Both examples in the preceding section suggest that, at least for the short time during or immediately after large earthquakes, faults exist as discrete surfaces of concentrated simple shear in the lower crust beneath the depth at which earthquakes nucleate. Such faults are easier to detect if they decrease their dip with depth (because of the directional radiation they emit and the accompanying internal deformation of the hanging wall block); but there is no particular reason why they should do so.

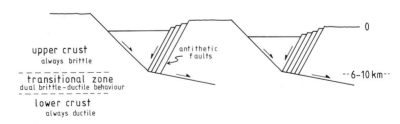

FIG. 6. Summary cross-section to illustrate the gross geometry of the normal faults investigated by Eyidogan & Jackson (1985). Note the change of dip at the base of the 'always brittle' crust. This section is designed to show the crude geometry of the faults and basement only. The effects of tilting, sediment fill and footwall uplift are not shown. Although the faults are shown as planar segments, they may in reality have limited curvature. Note that the very low-angle surface in the 'transitional zone' may only be a 'fault' (*sensu stricto*) at high strain rates.

The behaviour suggested in Figs 5 & 6 raises problems of terminology as well as rheology. The 'ductile' lower crust is only aseismic at low strain rates, and there will clearly be a transition zone in which the deformation is brittle (i.e. seismic) during big earthquakes and ductile (i.e. aseismic) otherwise. In this region, pseudo-tachylites are likely to intermix and be reworked by mylonites, as described by Sibson (1980). Some ultramylonites may consist almost entirely of reworked pseudotachylite created by this process. But what is the nature of the aseismic creep that occurs in the lower crust, and how is it distributed between the shear zones (or 'faults') and the blocks either side? This is a question of some importance, because if the deformation is partly distributed within the blocks either side of the shear zones (e.g. by pure shear) it will not be possible to restore a cross-section to its original configuration by simply reversing movement on the lower-crustal 'faults'. In short, are lower-crustal shear zones 'faults' in the same sense as is used in the upper crust?

A combination of reduced grain size, retrogressive mineral assemblages and crystallographic fabrics is likely to make a lower-crustal mylonite zone weaker than the surrounding rock (see e.g. White 1976; Etheridge, in press). The magnitude of this difference in strength will presumably govern how much the deformation in the lower crust is distributed between simple shear on the mylonite zone and pure shear within the blocks on either side. As discussed by Jackson & McKenzie (1983), both pure and simple shear produce rotations, but, for given values of total extension, β_{TOT}, and the initial dip of a fault or passive marker, the amount of rotation is different for each shear type. For a model in which the faults in the upper 'brittle' crust rotate by toppling (like dominoes) and the faults in the lower crust rotate as passive markers it is easy to calculate the difference in dip between the fault above and the passive marker below (see Fig. 7 and Jackson & McKenzie 1983). Such a model corresponds to an extremely weak lower crust, with no simple shear concentrated on the lower crustal 'fault zone'. What Jackson & McKenzie (1983) omitted to point out was the extremely small magnitude of this effect: for faults with initial dips in the range 30–60° the difference in dip (or 'curvature') between top and bottom layers is less than 8° for all values of β_{TOT} less than 3 (Fig. 7). Moreover, if the the dip of the fault in the brittle layer is restricted to be more than 30° (as implied by Fig. 3) the maximum 'curvature' is less than 4°. If the amount of simple shear, β_B, decreases gradually with depth, and the amount of pure shear, β_D, corres-

pondingly increases to maintain the same overall extension at all depths (such that $\beta_{TOT} = \beta_B \times \beta_D$), then the change of dip is gradual rather than abrupt, but is still the same amount, in total, between top and bottom.

A number of conclusions can be drawn from the discussion in this section.
1 A change in rheology with depth, leading to either an abrupt or a gradual change in the ratio of pure to simple shear, is not an efficient way to produce fault curvature, if the overall extension, β_{TOT}, is to stay the same at all levels. The change of dip produced in this way is always very small, though is probably sufficient to require internal deformation, antithetic faults, and curved sedimentary horizons within hanging wall blocks. Geometries such as those shown in Figs 5 & 6 will not be produced unless a second-generation fault in the upper crust continues to use an original first-generation fault in the lower crust. For example, a fault initially dipping at 60° throughout the crust will rotate to 30° in both upper and lower crust if $\beta_{TOT} = 1.7$ (using the expressions in Fig. 7). If a new generation of faults in the upper crust, again rotating from 60 to 30°, now contributes a further β of 1.7 (so that the total

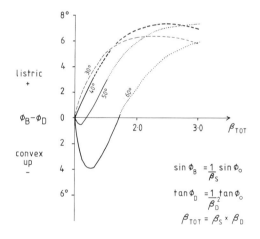

FIG. 7. Graph to show the maximum difference between the dip in the brittle and ductile portions of an originally planar surface, as a function of starting dip (ϕ_0) and extension (β_{TOT}). ϕ_B and ϕ_D are the final dips in the brittle and ductile layers respectively. β_B and β_D are the extensions achieved by simple shear (and rotation) and pure shear, respectively. The curves correspond to the case where $\beta_{TOT} = \beta_B$ and $\beta_D = 1$ in the brittle layer, and $\beta_{TOT} = \beta_D$ and $\beta_B = 1$ in the ductile layer. The expressions used are from Jackson & McKenzie (1983). The solid parts of the curves indicate regions where the dip in the brittle layer is greater than 30° (i.e. the fault may be seismically active).

stretching factor is $\beta_{TOT} = 1.7 \times 1.7 = 2.9$), then the original fault in the lower crust will have rotated by pure shear to a dip of 12°. Such a geometry would resemble that shown in Figs 5 & 6, though this process remains hypothetical. There is no evidence for this amount of extension in either central Greece or Western Turkey.

2 A planar fault in the crust is likely to stay approximately planar as deformation proceeds if β_{TOT} is to be the same at all levels. As a consequence, the shape of the 'fault' or shear zone is very little guide as to how the deformation is distributed between the 'faults' and the blocks either side. This is particularly relevant to the interpretation and restoration of deep seismic reflection sections from the lower crust.

3 If a weak layer exists at the base of the seismogenic crust, then a sub-horizontal decoupling of the layers above and below this layer is possible. Under these circumstances an abrupt change in dip is possible between the weak layer and the steep faults in the upper crust. Clearly, the nature of the weak layer itself is important in this case. If it marks an abrupt change from simple shear on rotating faults to penetrative pure shear below, as suggested by Gans & Miller (1983) for the Snake Range Decollement, then β_{TOT} may remain the same at all levels and the weak zone may have little or no simple shear concentrated on it. If, on the other hand, significant simple shear is concentrated on the weak layer, this movement will make the shear zone rotate towards the horizontal in all cases except where it is horizontal already.

In summary, gradual changes in rheology with depth are likely to control the distribution of deformation between simple shear on faults or mylonite zones and pure shear within the blocks in between. But this distribution will hardly affect the curvature of a planar shear zone at all: planar features, once formed, are there to stay.

Very low-angle normal faulting, detachments and decollements

In the last few years there has been considerable interest in the 'Cordilleran Metamorphic Core Complexes' of the western USA, and in particular in surfaces or zones of mylonitization, referred to variously as 'low-angle normal faults', 'detachments' or 'decollements', which are currently gently dipping or sub-horizontal, and are thought to have played an important role in crustal extension (see e.g. Crittenden *et al.* 1980; Frost & Martin 1982; Armstrong 1982). Of interest here is: (i) the nature of movement on or across these zones; (ii) how they were

lifted from the depths of 10–15 km needed to form mylonites to be exposed at the surface today; and (iii) whether the present-day active faulting in extensional regions throws any light on their origin. The examples cited below are chosen because they illustrate different possible extension mechanisms. This paper does not imply any view as to whether they are appropriate to the particular area they were designed to explain.

Second-generation normal faults

Any normal faulting on discrete fault zones, if it is to achieve major crustal extension, will involve rotation of the faults and the blocks they bound. There clearly exists a class of faults in the Basin and Range Province, which, though now almost horizontal, were much steeper when they were active, and have subsequently been passively rotated by a later generation of steep faults. Such faulting has been described in Nevada by Proffett (1977) and Gans & Miller (1983), who claim that the faults, when active, had relatively steep dips of 30–60° and were approximately planar from the surface to depths of about 10 km. This interpretation is clearly compatible with observations of seismically active normal faulting, in that it requires no large fault to be active outside the dip range 30–60°.

Brittle-ductile decoupling zones

In the northern Snake Range of Nevada, Gans & Miller (1983) and Gans *et al.* (1985) suggested that beneath the rotating fault blocks in the upper 'brittle' plate was a weak layer (the northern Snake Range Decollement), originally at a depth of about 7 km, which completely decoupled the fault movement above from penetrative ductile flow (pure shear) below. In this model, the upper-plate faults end abruptly and at steep angles against the decollement, but because the total extension in the upper and lower plates is approximately the same there need be little or no discrete simple shear on the decollement itself. A similar model was suggested by Rehrig & Reynolds (1980) for some of the core complexes in Arizona. In such interpretations no active very low-angle faulting is expected, except conceivably of the type described by Eyidogan & Jackson (1985) (Fig. 6), in which rupture during earthquakes on steep upper-plate faults propagates momentarily downwards, directed along the decollement surface by the strong *L–S* mylonite fabrics.

Large earthquakes are not seen to nucleate at depths shallower than about 5 km, presumably because the rocks at such levels are not strong enough to store the necessary elastic strain. Thus, as stretching proceeds and (in the absence of sedimentation) the upper plate thins, the decollement approaches the surface, and at some stage the upper-plate faults presumably become aseismic as their vertical extent is reduced. This type of model is not in conflict with observations of seismically active normal faulting.

Low-angle 'brittle' detachment faults

More problematic and interesting are the types of structure described by Wernicke (1981), who suggested that large-scale extension may occur by discrete simple shear on very low-angle fault zones that penetrate the whole crust (or even lithosphere). If such structures move only below the depth at which large earthquakes nucleate there is no difficulty reconciling them with the data shown in Fig. 3, and they may even represent the low-angle faults detected by Eyidogan & Jackson (1985) (Fig. 6). Possible origins for such structures in the lower crust may be either: (i) through rotation—where second-generation upper-crustal faults continue to transfer motion on to old first-generation faults in the lower crust; or (ii) as weak layers. However, weak layers that are controlled by temperature are likely to be roughly horizontal, and are unlikely to cut downwards through the entire lower crust unless they follow, or are influenced by, older pre-existing weak layers such as thrust faults. Alternatively, some *a priori* appeal to rupture propagation must be made, requiring a fault to form *ab initio* at a very gentle dip.

But what if such very low-angle faults do indeed move at extremely gentle dips right through the brittle upper crust? A fault dipping at 10° will have an across-strike width of 85 km from the surface to a depth of 15 km. Faults with dips less than 10° will occupy an even greater across-strike width in the upper crust. Eighty-five kilometres is considerably larger than the average spacing between the active high-angle normal faults that bound range fronts in the Basin and Range Province (Fletcher & Hallett 1983) or the Aegean (Jackson & McKenzie 1983). Since all large seismically active normal faults appear to be steep and to cut right through the brittle upper crust, they would cut, and render inactive, any very low-angle faults in the same vicinity (as described by Proffett 1977 and Gans & Miller 1983). Thus, not only are the very low-angle faults likely to be aseismic (Fig. 3), but they must also be in an area of almost no seismicity at all. The inevitable conclusion is that, if large-scale very low-angle normal faulting in the brittle upper crust really does occur *and contributes to significant crustal extension* (unlike, for instance, in the Gulf of Mexico), then extending regions may be expected to contain separate provinces in each of which one of two quite different types of upper-crustal deformation occurs: one in which very low-angle (<30°) normal faulting is accompanied by an almost total lack of sizeable earthquakes, and the other in which large earthquakes accompany movement on steep (30–60°) normal faults. The scale on which this spatial separation must occur clearly depends on the dip of the very low-angle faults and the thickness of the upper brittle layer. Note that both areas, because simple shear is involved, will exhibit rotations about the horizontal axis, though in the very low-angle terrains, because the faults are flatter, the tilting will be less.

The conclusion that upper-crustal extension by aseismic or creep processes does not occur in the same place as seismic faulting has other implications. In particular, steep normal faults produce high topography that dominates seismically active extending regions. Large-scale very low-angle normal faulting in the upper crust will presumably occur in regions that are relatively flat. The vertical movements in such areas will depend on the nature of the very low-angle 'faulting' itself, and whether the footwall or hanging wall (or both) deform internally: either uplift or subsidence could result.

In regions of continental shortening, a spatial separation of seismic and aseismic deformation is most unlikely. In Iran for example, it is known that only about 10% of the convergence between Arabia and Eurasia is manifest by seismic faulting (North 1977; Ambraseys & Melville 1982). Because the regions of active seismicity (mostly thrusting) totally dominate the topography, and relatively aseismic regions like the Southern Caspian Sea, central Iran and Western Afghanistan are almost flat, it is usually assumed that the aseismic creep occurs in the same geographical regions as the seismicity. In short, it is unlikely that 10% of the shortening produces all of the topography while 90% produces no elevation at all. The same remarks apply further E in Asia, where aseismic regions within the deforming belt (such as the Tarim basin and Ordos plateau) have very little topography.

Uplifting very low-angle detachments and decollements to the surface

While aseismic simple shear on flat or gently dipping shear zones below the nucleation depth of earthquakes is compatible with observed

---

---

siesmic faulting, it is not clear how these shear zones are uplifted from depths of about 10–15 km to the surface, where they are now observed. Both progressive rotation (Davis 1983) and unroofing of the footwall under a gently dipping fault (Spencer 1984) have been suggested; but both require faults dipping less than 30° to be active in the upper crust. They will presumably move aseismically, and so this mechanism leads inevitably to the spatial separation of the very low- and steep-angle faulting discussed earlier.

A second possibility involves extreme progressive thinning of the upper crust by several generations of rotating faults. This will, in the absence of sedimentation, bring a weak decoupling horizon at the base of the brittle crust closer to the surface, as envisaged by Rehrig & Reynolds (1980) and Gans et al. (1985). A combination of the resultant high heat flow and small vertical extent of the upper-crustal faults is likely to make this process aseismic as well.

A third possibility, alluded to by Davis (this volume) is that very low-angle faults that were originally active below the seismogenic depth, perhaps having been partially uplifted by one of the above-mentioned processes, are finally raised to the surface by structural uplift and rotation in the footwalls of later, steep (seismically active), range-bounding faults. This mechanism has the merit of not requiring aseismic movement on very low-angle faults at shallow crustal levels.

A note on terminology

The processes described in this paper merit a short plea for a less casual use of various common terms. In particular, the terms 'brittle' and 'ductile' are frequently used to mean 'seismic' and 'aseismic' and to imply 'strong' and 'weak'. They are often generalized to apply to the whole of a crustal layer even when the data on which they are based is from the seismicity (or lack of it) on faults or shear zones: where, as for example White (1976) and Etheridge (in press) point out, grain size, mineralogy and fabrics are likely to make rheological behaviour quite different from that in the blocks either side of the fault zone. Moreover, it is clear that some fault zones which are usually 'ductile' (and aseismic) may deform in a 'brittle' (and seismic) fashion during the high strain rates associated with earthquakes.

Similar difficulties surround the word 'listric' which is applied sometimes to faults whose dips become horizontal with depth and at other times to those with any concave-up curvature at all. Are the faults shown in Figs 1, 5 & 6 listric? This is

more than a semantic question—a certain amount of curvature above the hypocentre in Fig. 1 is certainly allowed by the data, but if the surfaces become flat (as in Figs 5 & 6) they do so below the hypocentre, in a region where deformation is assumed to have a 'ductile' character. Here it is questionable whether they should be called faults at all, because if *any* deformation occurs by penetrative flow in the blocks either side, it will not be possible to restore the section to its pre-deformation state by reversing simple shear on these surfaces alone. Thus lower-crustal 'shear zones', 'detachments' and 'decollements' may or may not behave like 'faults' in the usual sense, depending on the nature and strain rate of the deformation on them and in their surrounding blocks.

Conclusions

1 Normal faults that move in large earthquakes on the continents break through the entire upper (seismically active) crust with dips apparently restricted to the range 30–60°. It is, of course, possible to take the view that 20 years' data (on which Fig. 3 is based) is not long enough to obtain a representative picture of normal faulting in earthquakes. This may be so, but does not explain why 20 years is long enough to reveal seismogenic faults in the dip range 30–60° and not a single example (to date) where large-scale seismic motion on a normal fault dipping less than 20° in the upper crust can be proven. Nor does it explain why, seismically, the Basin and Range Province looks no different from any other actively extending terrain on the continents. Very low-angle normal faults, if they contribute to extension of the upper crust, are clearly something special.

2 Although limited curvature of large seismogenic faults (in cross-section) is permitted by the seismic observations, the few examples where the data are sufficiently good suggest that the faults are approximately planar from the surface to the base of the seismogenic upper crust.

3 Such limited curvature is expected if changing rheology with depth simply varies the distribution of extension between simple shear on the faults and pure shear in the blocks either side.

4 If the observed spread of active fault dips (30–60°) is caused by rotation, this suggests that either, (i) a second generation of steeper normal faults is initiated when (or before) β reaches a value of 1.7, or (ii) when β exceeds 1.7, extension occurs aseismically by motion on faults dipping less than 30°.

5 To avoid intersecting faults being simultaneously active, the second alternative (above) requires a spatial separation, within extending regions, of seismically active areas where steep (30–60°) faulting occurs and almost totally aseismic areas where very low-angle faulting occurs. The scale on which this separation must take place depends on the dip of the very low-angle faults and the thickness of the upper seismogenic layer.

6 There is evidence from both vertical movements at the surface and seismic waveforms for very low-angle normal faulting in the uppermost lower crust, beneath the depth at which earthquakes nucleate: at least during the momentarily high strain rates associated with earthquakes in the upper crust. The long-term effects of such lower-crustal motions depend on whether, at slow strain rates, deformation concentrates on these 'faults' or is spread penetratively throughout the lower crust. If the latter occurs it will not be possible to restore cross-sections to their pre-deformation states by reversing simple-shear movement on these lower-crustal 'faults' alone.

7 A remaining problem is that of lifting the low-angle 'shear zones', decollements' or 'detachments', found in the metamorphic core complexes of the western USA, from the depths of 10–15 km to the surface. Mechanisms that require them to be active at gentle (<30°) dips in the upper crust as they rise will also require them to be aseismic: leading to the difficulties expressed in (5) above.

ACKNOWLEDGMENTS: R. Sibson, B. Wernicke and P. Gans provided helpful reviews of this paper for which I am grateful. I have also benefitted from many useful discussions of this subject with D. McKenzie and G. Yielding. D. Doser, R. Smith and G. Shudofsky kindly sent me preprints of their work prior to publication. This work was supported by a grant from NERC and Cambridge University Department of Earth Sciences Contribution No. 791.

References

AKI, K. & RICHARDS, P. 1980. Quantitative Seismology, 932 pp. W. H. Freeman & Co., San Francisco.

AMBRASEYS, N.N. & MELVILLE, C.P. 1982. *A History of Persian Earthquakes* 219 pp. Cambridge University Press.

ANDERSON, E.M. 1951. *The Dynamics of Faulting*, 2nd edn, 206 pp. Oliver & Boyd, Edinburgh.

ANGELIER, J. & COLLETTA, B. 1983. Tensional fractures and extensional tectonics. *Nature*, **301**, 49–51.

ARMSTRONG, R.L. 1982. Cordilleran Metamorphic Core Complexes. *Ann. Rev. Earth planet. Sci.* **10**, 129–54.

BARTON, P. & WOOD, R. 1984. Tectonic evolution of the North Sea Basin: crustal stretching and subsidence. *Geophys. J. R. astron. Soc.* **79**, 987–1022.

BREWER, J.A. & SMYTHE, D.K. 1984. MOIST and the continuity of reflector geometry along the Caledonian–Appalachian orogen. *J. geol. Soc. London*, **141**, 105–20.

DE CHARPAL, O., GUENNOC, P., MONTADERT, L. & ROBERTS, D.G. 1978. Rifting, crustal attenuation and subsidence in the Bay of Biscay. *Nature*, **275**, 706–11.

CHEN, W-P. & MOLNAR, P. 1983a. Focal depths and fault plane solutions of earthquakes under the Tibetan plateau. *J. geophys. Res.* **88**, 1180–96.

—— —— 1983b. The depth distribution of intra-continental and intraplate earthquakes and its implications for the thermal and mechanical properties of the lithosphere. *J. geophys. Res.* **88**, 4183–214.

CRITTENDEN, M.D., JR, CONEY, P.J. & DAVIS, G.H. (eds) 1980. Cordilleran Metamorphic Core Complexes. *Mem. geol. Soc. Am.* **153**, 490 pp.

DAVIS, G.H. 1983. Shear zone model for the origin of Metamorphic Core Complexes. *Geology*, **11**, 342–7.

—— This volume. A shear-zone model for the structural evolution of metamorphic core complexes in southeastern Arizona, 247–66.

DOSER, D.I. 1985. Source parameters and faulting processes of the 1959 Hebgen Lake, Montana, earthquake sequence. *J. geophys. Res.* **90**, 4537–55.

—— & SMITH, R.B. 1985. Source parameters of the 28 October 1983 Borah Peak, Idaho, earthquake from body wave analysis. *Bull. seism. Soc. Am.* **75**, 1041–51.

EDDINGTON, P.K. & SMITH, R.B. This volume. Kinematics of Basin and Range intraplate extension, 371–92.

ETHERIDGE, M.A. In press. On the reactivation of extensional fault systems. *Phil. Trans. R. Soc. London*.

EYIDOGAN, H. & JACKSON, J.A. 1985. A seismological study of normal faulting in the Demirci, Alasehir and Gediz earthquakes of 1969–70 in western Turkey: implications for the nature and geometry of deformation in the continental crust. *Geophys. J. R. astron. Soc.* **81**, 569–607.

FLETCHER, R.C. & HALLETT, B. 1983. Unstable extension of the lithosphere: a mechanical model for Basin-and-Range structure. *J. geophys. Res.* **88**, 7457–66.

FROST, E.G. & MARTIN, D.L. (eds) 1982. *Mesozoic–Cenozoic evolution of the Colorado River region, California, Arizona and Utah.* Cordilleran Publishers, San Diego, California.

GANS, P.B. & MILLER, E.L. 1983. Style of mid-Tertiary extension in east-central Nevada. *In*:

Guidebook Part 1, Geol. Soc. Am. Rocky Mt. & Cordilleran Sections meeting: Utah Geol. & Mining Surv. Spec. Studies, **59**, 107–60.

——, —— ,McCarthy, J. & Ouldcott, M.L. 1985. Tertiary extensional faulting and evolving ductile-brittle transition zones in the northern Snake Range and vicinity: new insights from seismic data. *Geology*, **13**, 189–93.

Gibbs, A.D. 1984. Structural evolution of extensional basin margins. *J. geol. Soc. London*, **141**, 609–20.

Hobbs, B.E., Means, W.D. & Williams, P.F. 1976. *An outline of structural geology*, 571 pp. John Wiley & Sons.

Jackson, J.A. & McKenzie, D.P. 1983. The geometrical evolution of normal fault systems. *J. struct. Geol.* **5**, 471–82.

——, Gagnepain, J., Houseman, G., King, G., Papadimitriou, P., Soufleris, C. & Virieux, J. 1982. Seismicity, normal faulting and the geomorphological evolution of the Gulf of Corinth, (Greece): the Corinth earthquakes of February and March 1981. *Earth planet. Sci. Lett.* **57**, 377–97.

Jankhof, K. 1945. Changes in ground level produced by the earthquakes of April 14 to 18 1928 in southern Bulgaria. *In: Tremblements de Terre en Bulgarie, Nos 29–31* (in Bulgarian), pp. 131–136. Institute meteorologique central de Bulgarie, Sofia.

Kim, W-Y, Kulhanek, O. & Meyer, K. 1984. Source processes of the 1981 Gulf of Corinth earthquake sequence from body wave analysis. *Bull. seism. Soc. Am.* **74**, 459–77.

King, G., Ouyang, Z., Papadimitriou, P., Deschamps, A., Gagnepain, J., Houseman, G., Jackson, J., Soufleris, C. & Virieux, J. 1984. The evolution of the Gulf of Corinth (Greece): an aftershock study of the 1981 earthquake. *Geophys. J.R. astron. Soc.* **80**, 677–93.

Lahr, K.M., Lahr, J.C., Lindh, A.G., Bufe, C.G. & Lester, F.W. 1976. The August 1975 Oroville earthquakes. *Bull. seism. Soc. Am.* **66**, 1085–99.

Langston, C.A. & Helmberger, D.V. 1975. A procedure for modelling shallow dislocation sources. *Geophys. J.R. astron. Soc.* **42**, 117–30.

Le Pichon, X. & Sibuet, J.C. 1981. Passive margins: a model of formation. *J. geophys. Res.* **86**, 3708–21.

McKenzie, D.P. 1972. Active tectonics of the Mediterranean region. *Geophys. J.R. astron. Soc.* **30**, 109–85.

—— 1978a. Some remarks on the development of sedimentary basins. *Earth planet. Sci. Lett.* **40**, 25–32.

—— 1978b. Active tectonics of the Alpine–Himalayan belt: the Aegean Sea and surrounding regions. *Geophys. J. R. astron. Soc.* **55**, 217–54.

Meissner, R. & Strehlau, J. 1982. Limits of stress in continental crusts and their relation to depth—frequency distribution of shallow earthquakes. *Tectonics*, **1**, 73–89.

Mercier, J-L., Mouyaris, N., Simeakis, C., Roundoyannis, T. & Angelidhis, C. 1979. Intraplate deformation: a quantitative study of the faults activated by the 1978 Thessaloniki earthquakes. *Nature*, **278**, 45–8.

Molnar, P. & Chen, W-P. 1982. Seismicity and mountain Building. *In*: Hsu, K. J. (ed.) *Mountain Building Processes*, pp. 41–57. Academic Press.

Morton, W.H. & Black, R. 1975. Crustal attenuation in Afar. *In*: Pilger, A. & Rosler, A. (eds) *Afar depression of Ethiopia, Inter-union comm. Geodyn. Sci. Rep. No. 14.* pp. 55–65. E. Schweizerbart'sche Verlagsbuchhandlung, Stuttgart.

Nabelek, J. 1985. Geometry and mechanism of faulting of the 1980 El Asnam, Algeria, earthquake from inversion of teleseismic body waves and comparison with field observations. *J. geophys. Res.* **90**, 12,713–28.

North, R.G. 1974. Seismic slip rates in the Mediterranean and Middle East. *Nature*, **252**, 560–3.

Proffett, J.M. 1977. Cenozoic geology of the Yerington district, Nevada, and implications for the nature of Basin and Range faulting. *Bull. geol. Soc. Am.* **88**, 247–66.

Ransome, F.L. Emmons, W.H. & Garrey, G.H. 1910. Geology and ore deposits of the Bullfrog district, Nevada. *Bull. U. S. geol. Surv.* **407**, 130 pp.

Rehrig, W.A. & Reynolds, S.J. 1980. Geologic reconnaissance of a northwest trending zone of metamorphic core complexes in southern and western Arizona. *In*: Crittenden, M.D. jr, Coney, P.J. & Davis, G.H. (eds) *Cordilleran Metamorphic Core Complexes, Mem. geol. Soc. Am.* **153**, 131–57.

Richter, C.F. 1958. *Elementary Seismology*. W.H. Freeman, San Francisco.

Shudofsky, G.N. 1985. Source mechanisms and focal depths of east African earthquakes using Rayleigh wave inversion and body wave modelling. *Geophys. J. R. astron. Soc.* **83**, 563–614.

Sibson, R. H. 1980. Transient discontinuities in ductile shear zones. *J. struct. Geol.* **2**, 165–71.

——1982. Fault zone models, heat flow and depth distribution of earthquakes in the continental crust of the United States. *Bull. seism. Soc. Am.* **72**, 151–63.

—— 1984. Roughness at the base of the seismogenic zone: contributing factors. *J. geophys. Res.* **89**, 5791–800

—— 1985. A note on fault reactivation. *J. struct. Geol.* **7**, 751–4.

Smith, R.B. & Bruhn, R.L. 1984. Intraplate extensional tectonics of the eastern Basin–Range: inferences on structural style from seismic reflection data, regional tectonics and thermal–mechanical models of brittle–ductile deformation. *J. geophys. Res.* **89**, 5733–62.

Soufleris, C. & Stewart, G.S. 1981. A source study of the Thessaloniki (northern Greece) earthquake sequence. *Geophys. J. R. astron. Soc.* **67**, 343–58.

Soufleris, C., Jackson, J., King, G., Spencer, C. & Scholz, C. 1982. The 1978 earthquake sequence near Thessaloniki (northern Greece). *Geophys. J. R. astron. Soc.* **68**, 429–58.

Spencer, J.E. 1984. Role of tectonic denudation in warping and uplift of low angle normal faults. *Geology*, **12**, 95–8.

Stein, R.S. & Barrientos, S.E. In press. The 1983 Borah Peak, Idaho, earthquake: geodetic evidence for deep rupture on a planar fault. *In*: Stein, R. &

BUCKNAM, R. (eds) *Workshop XXVIII on the Borah Peak Earthquake*, US. Geol. Surv. Open-File Rep.

TAPPONIER, P. & MOLNAR, P. 1977. Active faulting and tectonics in China. *J. geophys. Res.* **82**, 2905–30.

—— & —— 1979. Active faulting and Cenozoic tectonics of the Tien Shan, Mongolia and Baykal regions. *J. geophys. Res.* **84**, 3425–59.

WERNICKE, B. 1981. Low angle normal faults in the Basin and Range province: nappe tectonics in an extending orogen. *Nature*, **291**, 645–8.

—— & BURCHFIEL, B.C. 1982. Modes of extensional tectonics. *J. struct. Geol.* **4**, 105–15.

WHITE, N.J., JACKSON, J.A. & McKENZIE, D.P. In press. The relationship between the geometry of normal faults and that of the sedimentary layers in their hanging walls. *J. struct. Geol.*

WHITE, S. 1976. The effects of strain on the micro-structures, fabrics and deformation mechanisms in quartzites. *Phil. Trans. R. Soc. London,* **A283**, 69–86.

WIENS, D.A. & STEIN, S. 1983. Age dependence of oceanic intraplate seismicity and implications for lithospheric evolution. *J. geophys. Res.* **88**, 6455–68.

WOOD, R. & BARTON, P. 1983. Crustal thinning and subsidence in the North Sea. *Nature*, **302**, 134–6.

YIELDING, G. 1985. Control of rupture by fault geometry during the 1980 El Asnam (Algeria) earthquake. *Geophys. J. R. astron. Soc.* **81**, 641–70.

ZIEGLER, P. 1983. Crustal thinning and subsidence in the North Sea. *Nature*, **304**, 561.

J.A. JACKSON, Department of Earth Sciences, Bullard Laboratories, Madingley Rise, Madingley Road, Cambridge CB3 0EZ, UK.

Development of extension and mixed-mode sedimentary basins

A. Gibbs

SUMMARY: Analysis of onshore and offshore basins using a variety of techniques including deep seismic reflection profiles has shown that basins develop above linked fault systems. These fault systems comprise both steep and gently dipping faults which can have either dip- or strike-slip displacements. Whilst linked fault systems are common to all basins they are developed to different degrees and hence produce a variety of structural expressions within, and between the basins. This allows basins to be classified either in terms of their dominant structural elements or seen as a mechanical and geological continuum.

As the basins grow, changes in crustal thickness in the upper brittle crust can take place, on staircase arrays of low-angle listric faults, on steeper planar (domino) faults or commonly on a combination of both linked by crustally conservative strike-slip systems.

The development of the controlling basement elements affects the distribution and pattern of internal deformation in the evolving sedimentary fill resulting in a characteristic basin architecture. This resulting architecture has profound implications for models of the stratigraphy and sedimentology of basins, and provides an insight into the occurrence of certain facies and stratigraphic changes.

A general model for the evolution of such basin architectures is presented in this paper including both the basement structural elements and the overlying carapace of sediments with both stratigraphic and structural components.

Sedimentary basins and their component fault systems have been described by a number of workers using observational data such as the deep seismic profiles acquired in the UK by the BIRPS group and in the United States by the COCORP group, from theoretical modelling and from field and industry data (see for example Allmendinger *et al.* 1983; Brewer & Smythe 1984; Chadwick *et al.* 1984; Cooke *et al.* 1981; Finckh *et al.* 1984; Graciansky *et al.* 1985; Harding 1984; Jackson & McKenzie 1983; McKenzie 1978). Such work suggests that we can distinguish different tectono-structural categories of basins which operate by extending on linked fault systems. Although apparently simple end members exist, few, if any, basins can be described completely in terms of a single structural style. All, to a greater or lesser extent, must share the same architectural elements. Changes in plate stresses with time and rotational strains may in some cases mean that a basin progresses from one end member to another and complex mixed-mode systems can occur. A first-order classification of basins into extensional on listric faults, extensional on domino faults (pure shear), strike-slip (simple shear), and mixed-mode (general strain) systems is useful. This classification serves to focus attention on the dominant kinematics of the basin architecture and also on the way in which the sedimentary fill may have responded to, and been involved in, basin development. In the UK,

on and offshore there is increasing evidence from commercial seismic data that most basins are not simply extensional but are of mixed-mode types (transpressional and transtensional basins, cf. Sanderson & Marchini 1984; Harland 1971).

Basin architecture

As the basement structure evolves with time the sedimentary fill becomes involved in the crustal deformation process as a 'carapace' overlying the basement architecture. The term 'carapace' is used to include both the sedimentary fill with its stratigraphic elements such as unconformities, growth faults etc. and its developing tectonic structure. Hence a basin will consist of some controlling basement structural pattern, a sediment and deformed sediment shell, the 'carapace', and an overlying undeformed or relatively little deformed 'upper carapace'. The latter corresponding to sedimentation during thermal subsidence of the basin. Together these elements make up the architecture of the basin. In North Sea terms, this division can be seen between basement structures in the upper Palaeozoic and older 'basement', carapace development through the Jurassic and Early Cretaceous, and subsidence phase from mid-Cretaceous to Tertiary times (Sclater & Christie 1980; Gibbs 1984a, figs 8 & 9). This carapace deformation interacts

From COWARD, M.P., DEWEY, J.F., & HANCOCK, P.L. (eds), 1987, *Continental Extensional Tectonics*, Geological Society Special Publication No. 28, pp. 19–33.

with the sedimentary processes resulting in the control of the development of sedimentary facies by the tectonic processes which in turn may inherit their style from an earlier basement structure.

A simplified North Sea model for the internal collapse of a sediment wedge as the hanging wall continues to move off on the extension fault is shown in Fig. 1. The sediment may collapse on a series of faults detaching in a low-strength layer such as shale or salt (see Gibbs 1984a) and the roll-overs produced in this way will control the distribution of continuing marginal and axial deposition. This idea can be taken a stage further where a stacked set of detachments develops in a half-graben with zones of shale flowage allowing disharmonic faulting. As the basin margin grows and subsides the sediment overlying these internally faulted wedges may show a variety of gravity driven structures and further complicate margins such as those described by Todd & Mitchum (1977) and Graciansky *et al.* (1985, fig. 16).

Basins dominated by ramp and flat 'staircase' fault arrays

The work of the BIRPS group published on the MOIST reflection profile (Brewer & Smythe 1984) demonstrates extension on older, reactivated thrust faults producing simple half-graben basins. Such extensional basins develop by dip-slip on staircase-like detachment faults made up of flats and ramps. This is similar to models of some of the Basin and Range type of structure such as the Sevier Desert basin (Allmendinger *et al.* 1983) and the Diamond Valley basins (Effimoff & Pinezich 1981). Gibbs discussed the structural evolution of basins of this type in terms of sequential development of hanging wall synclines and footwall collapse to produce a complex graben cross-section (Gibbs 1984b fig. 9). Where lower ramps collapse, core complex geometries can be generated and extensional chaos zones (Wernicke & Burchfiel 1982) and extensional duplexes will be common.

The characteristic of such basins is that they are controlled by low-angle extensional faults which remain active throughout basin development. The sole detachment of the staircase must eventually penetrate the brittle upper part of the crust, the 'elastic lid' and detach in a sub-horizontal ductile shear zone. Such fault systems are, as pointed out by Gibbs (1983, 1984b), analogous in the development of their fault systems and hanging wall structures with contractional thrusting.

Mixed-mode examples of these basins can develop where oblique-slip occurs on the detach-

(a)

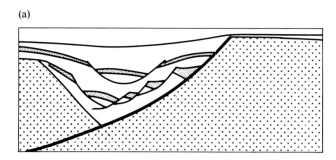

(b)

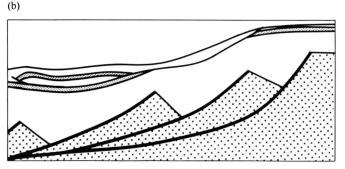

Fig. 1. Structures developed above basement extension faults. The geometries shown are seismic sections, but can be developed at all scales. (a) Distributed extension within sedimentary wedge coupled to basement faults; the faults in the wedge detach on low-strength and over-pressured shales. Tops of basement blocks are eroded. (b) Gravity slide on starved basin margin above extended basement. Note repetition of section.

ment fault with wrench, reverse faults and folding components of deformation in the hanging wall plate (Fig. 2). These will map out systematically in relation to a simple ellipse where its long axis on the map defines the direction of oblique stretch across the basin-margin fault. This geometry can be used to explain many of the apparent anomalies in seismically derived maps and sections of graben margins where the structure does not seem explicable in terms of either a simple dip-slip or strike-slip model. Figures 5 & 6 of Pegrum & Ljones (1984) show part of the eastern margin of the S Viking graben. Their model for this area of extension, then contraction, will work mechanically only where their sections are reinterpreted with gently dipping oblique-slip faults which would allow first extension, and then contraction of the basin. Similar structural patterns may account for some of the features described in the North Sea which cannot be explained by a simple extension model (e.g. Badley *et al.* 1984; Gabrielsen 1984; Price & Rattey 1984).

The general geometry of this class of basin is illustrated in the interpretation of part of the WINCH line shown in Fig. 3. The figure shows a low-angle detachment with the hanging wall

plate moving down a deep-crustal fault detaching at Moho level. The offshore Solway basin, developed above this fault, has relatively steep faults along its northern margin which can be shown in the field to have a strike-slip component. Observed rotations across faults dipping and throwing down towards the basin axis are not entirely compatible with a dip-slip listric extensional model. Steps or transfer faults (Gibbs 1984b) along this margin controlled fan growth in the Carboniferous (Fig. 4) and in the field faulting of the fanglomerates can be shown to be synsedimentary. This same set of Carboniferous transfer faults was reactivated during Permo/Triassic basin growth and was active again in the mid Jurassic and, offshore, in the Tertiary. Further to the E, in the Canonbie and Bewcastle areas, thrusts and thrust-related folds can be identified both in the field and on Survey maps. Thrusts active during Carboniferous times are the result of transpressive shortening in progressive strike-slip. Taken as a whole the evidence indicates that the Carboniferous basin grew dominantly by extension and strike-slip on older faults in a linked system similar to that shown in Fig. 2. A significant component of oblique-slip during deposition of the basin fill is necessary to explain the observed

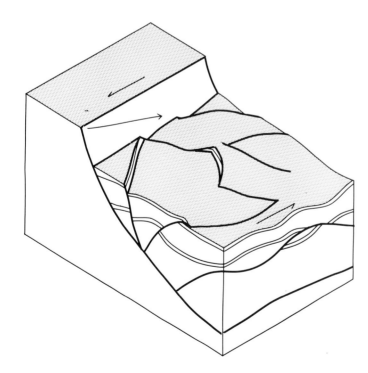

FIG. 2. Pattern of reverse and normal faults developed in the hanging wall block of a sinuous oblique-slip extension fault.

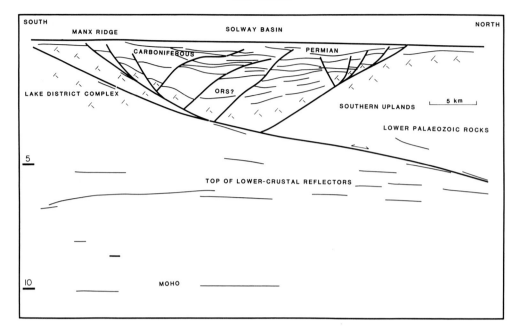

FIG. 3. Schematic interpretation of part of the WINCH deep seismic profile across the outer Solway Firth. Interpretation shows major detachment fault dipping N upon which the basin rides and the steeper North Solway fault system cutting down to join the detachment.

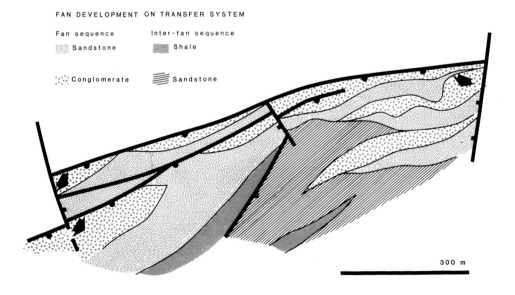

FIG. 4. Simplified map of the fan sequence developed on transfer faults on part of the North Solway fault to the S of Dalbeattie. Arrows show direction of sediment transport from the footwall.

thrusts, folds and obliquely trending normal faults. The basin filled and deformed as the hanging wall moved obliquely down and across the footwall fault. The depositional systems and sediments produced, therefore, became involved in the deformation. Hence gently dipping fault arrays allow for both dip-slip and oblique-slip across the sole detachment. Where the detachment fault is stepped, along-strike combinations of frontal and oblique ramps (Butler 1983) are possible as with thrust faulting, and give rise to apparently complex patterns of thrusts and folds in otherwise extensional basins.

Fault blocks on the margins of extensional basins may develop sequentially (e.g. Beach 1984; Gibbs 1984b). In these cases the locus of sedimentary deposition will be tied closely to the developing footwall fault. As the footwall and hanging wall collapse sequentially there will be a progressive rotation of planar stratigraphic markers across the faults. Changes in age of the sediment fill allow the footwall collapse to be dated and correlated with a corresponding rotation of the sediment wedges as described by Beach (1984).

Continuing growth of the sole fault leads to the development of growth faulting in the sediment fill. This is illustrated in Fig. 5 where depocentres may be stacked in the offset pattern indicated. When a ramp is present in the extension fault the ramp may collapse. Figure 5 shows how arrays of sedimentary wedges are developed, back-rotated, and then moved considerable distances away from later depocentres. The 'asterisk' and 'diamond' ornaments in the figure mark the positions of the axial depocentres in the first two stages of sediment fill. This model is particularly powerful in explaining the structural control of sedimentation axial to and down dip from major extension fault margins. In several areas of the UK continental shelf, complex sand-distribution patterns in the Jurassic were probably controlled by this process of carapace development. Several examples of this stacking of axial and marginal facies linked to a staircase-controlling fault occur onshore in the UK. Some particularly impressive occurrences of this process can be mapped in the Carboniferous of the Midland Valley of Scotland and in the New Red sandstones of the Solway basin (Gibbs & Page in prep.).

The structural similarity of staircase-basin fault systems and contractional thrust faults may suggest that the former are simply inherited from the latter (Coward 1983; Hossack 1984). It is not yet clear whether such systems can evolve in areas where the staircase elements are not already keyed into the pre-extension basement.

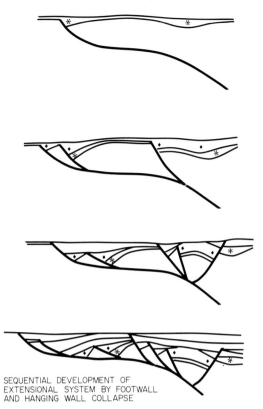

SEQUENTIAL DEVELOPMENT OF
EXTENSIONAL SYSTEM BY FOOTWALL
AND HANGING WALL COLLAPSE

FIG. 5. Development of faults and sedimentary wedges on a stepped extensional fault. Asterisk and diamond ornaments mark the sequential positions of the axial depositional systems deposited in the first two stages of development.

Indeed those areas where this form of basin seems best represented are just those areas with an earlier history of thrust faulting. An added consequence of the mechanistic similarity of such systems is that staircase basins are easily inverted by driving the system back up the flats and ramps, reversing the geometric development of the hanging wall as illustrated in Fig. 6 (see also Jackson 1980; Davies 1983).

Where faults are used as extensional systems the bed-lengths in the roll-over are increased (see Gibbs 1984a) and sedimentation in the half-graben on the roll-over will, in cross-section, have a longer bed-length section than the pre-extension marker. If the same faults are later recompressed, as for example in the Wessex Basin (Stoneley 1982), this extra bed-length must undergo considerable shortening before the pre-extension marker moves back to its 'null position'. Where the extensional system emerges at

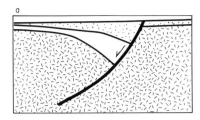

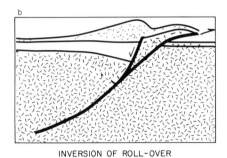

INVERSION OF ROLL-OVER

Fig. 6. Schematic sections showing collapse of roll-over with the development of back-thrusts and a shallower compressional ramp breaking through under the extensional block. The model is developed from field work and seismic data across Purbeck-type fold and fault zones in southern England and the English Channel.

the palaeosurface the ramp will be too steep for the hanging wall to translate over the step and fold simply. Back-thrusting, folding and possible detachment along post-extension sedimentary fill are a geometrical necessity. Purbeck-type monoclines may be the result of pushing a sedimentary growth sequence back up an extensional surface without necessarily pushing the pre-extension marker into net contraction. Figure 6 is a schematic model across a fault such as that shown by Stoneley (1982, fig. 3) with net extension preserved at lower stratigraphic levels (Sherwood sandstone) but with southerly directed back-thrusting at intermediate (Kimmeridgian) and northerly overthrusting at higher levels (Cretaceous). The formation of a new thrust ramp may be critical in developing the prospective structures in this area. These jacked up and back-thrust 'monocline' structures are common at varying scales in many of the UK basins and seem, as in the Wessex Basin example, to be associated either with inversion or oblique-slip on listric extension faults.

Where the step in the extensional system is relatively gently dipping (possibly 20–30° or less) simple roll-off roll-on structures (Fig. 7) may

result without significant development of structural complexity at the emergent ramp. Basins formed by the hanging wall moving off, and then back on to the footwall are the extensional and transtensional equivalents of Ori & Friend's (1984) piggy-back basins seen in thrust systems. These simpler roll-ons occurred in the East Midlands Carboniferous basins during regional transtension and basin formation in the Carboniferous—a modification and mechanistic explanation of the old 'tilt-block' concept. The controlling ramps must, however, have been relatively gently dipping and this may in part be due to the extensive development of overpressured shales throughout much of the Carboniferous sequence. Depths to controlling detachments and ramp positions can be estimated by the construction of regional balanced sections making allowances for oblique-slip where possible. Where the ramp is steeper new faults and folding will nucleate around the old ramp and Purbeck-type monoclines with complex associations of minor folds and faults will result. The Don monocline is probably an example of such a fold produced by shortening obliquely across an older ramp. The dominant features of basins controlled by staircase faults are that they may develop on sites of older basins or re-extended thrust-fold belts (e.g. Chadwick et al. 1984). Surprisingly complex patterns of stratigraphic build-ups result from sequential footwall and hanging wall collapse. Additionally the basins can be re-shortened using the same fault array with new faults being largely confined to modifications of the earlier extensional ramps.

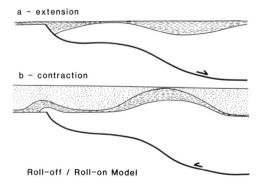

Fig. 7. Cartoon of hanging wall basins developed during extension (a) and contraction (b) on a stepped fault system during regional subsidence. The depositional highs and lows are inverted.

Sag basins and major hanging wall syncline basins

Basins which develop without appreciable extension of their floors and which in cross-section have simple saucer shapes may be termed 'sag basins'. In the UK continental shelf, onshore and offshore these are probably common but have not yet been described in the literature. A sag basin can only develop if material is removed from lower in the lithosphere by some process which does not stretch the upper leaf of the crust on which the basin sits. At a regional scale this may occur if the thinning of the elastic lid and the ductile lower plate are linked by a low-angle detachment fault (Fig. 8). This diagram, which is derived from regional analysis of North Sea data, shows three types of extensional basin linked by a common detachment. Wernicke (1985) published a similar model derived from analysis of Basin and Range structures.

A gently dipping detachment, as shown in Fig. 9, may result in the faulted basins in the upper crust being offset from the later thermal basin above the thinned lower lithosphere. The inversion of the basement and simple overlap geometry of the basin fill are diagnostic of this type of basin. Faulting will be limited to compactional features in the fill and there may be minor faulting within the basin system. These basin types may be large and remain as yet unidentified, as the crustal geometries and controlling detachments can only be mapped by the use of regional deep seismic grids.

Where the crust is thinned at an intermediate level by the detachment fault, simple hanging wall basins are formed. These occur as synclines above either mid-crustal ramps or above pulled-out wedges of material similar in geometry to under-thrust wedges. The hanging wall syncline basins so formed exhibit a large variation in size from major sub-basins such as the Beryl Embayment on the western margin of the Viking graben system (Fig. 9) to some of the local sub-

basins and 'gulfs' in the onshore English Carboniferous.

Figure 9 is a simplified line drawing from a Western Geophysical non-exclusive seismic survey. The base Cretaceous, base Permian and Jurassic seismic markers are identified on the basis of character and only some of the basement seismic markers are shown. In the central part of the diagram the fault planes are picked out along markers on the seismic record, elsewhere they are interpretations. Over the area covered by this survey many of the seismic lines show gently dipping markers in the basement upon which the later extensional faults apparently detached. Half-graben sedimentary basins of Devonian age are present to the S and W of the line illustrated and these seem to have geometries similar to those suggested by Hossack (1984) for the W coast of Norway and to those illustrated from the MOIST profile by Brewer & Smythe (1984) to the NW of Scotland. A similar interpretation of extension and relaxation of Caledonian thrusts to allow the development of Devonian basins is proposed for this area. Some of the gently dipping basement markers can be interpreted as Caledonian thrusts or shear zones.

Following the Devonian extension, Permian basins developed on the sites of the older basins and subsequently the Mesozoic basins appeared to utilize many of the same basement structures. The main Jurassic basin in this area is the S Viking graben which occurs just to the E of the basement high shown at the eastern end of Fig. 10. The margin of the Jurassic graben was probably controlled by a major basement structure of the sort shown by Beach *et al.* (this volume) controlling the development of the N Viking graben. This system therefore forms a double ramp with half-grabens detaching on shallow structures at the western end, a major hanging wall basin and then the main half-graben on a deeper detachment at the western end of the section. The line drawing and seismic profile shown by Allmendinger *et al.*

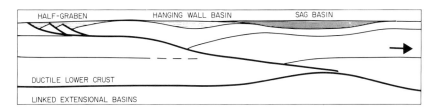

FIG. 8. Linked extensional basins showing possible relationship between a half-graben, hanging wall and sag basins on a crustal detachment. Horizontal length of section variable, ≈ 2–300 km.

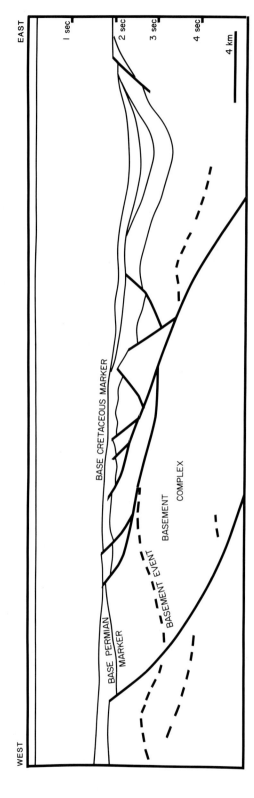

FIG. 9. Interpreted section across part of the Beryl embayment (Viking graben) based on Western Geophysical non-exclusive seismic line FGS 24.

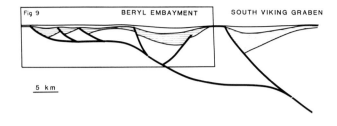

FIG. 10. Model for development of ramp basins on different levels of detachment. Compare with Fig. 9 (shown in area of box).

(1983) for the Sevier desert of Nevada could be interpreted in a similar way. Erosion and further footwall collapse of such a stepped detachment may be responsible for producing some core complex geometries on the upper, shallower detachment (cf. Spencer 1984; Wernicke & Burchfiel 1982; Wernicke 1985).

Basins developed by planar 'domino' fault arrays

Extensive data from currently active seismic faults (Jackson *et al.* 1981; Jackson & McKenzie 1983) suggest that the faults which penetrate the crust in some extensional basins are planar, that is 'domino' faults. These detach at around 10 to 15 km on a ductile zone which in terms of lithospheric structural geometry is a 'fault'.

Several authors (e.g. Wernicke & Burchfiel 1982; Bally 1981) have pointed out that a domino fault array must resolve the 'space problem' not only on its sole detachment, but at the end of the array, and Wernicke & Burchfiel suggested that this may be accomplished by a combined 'listric' and domino array. There is a clear and simple stratigraphic test for this. If the domino array has evolved by unfolding a listric fault system the fill above each successive fault block should young towards the footwall. In a true domino array as described by Jackson and his coworkers, all elements must rotate at the same time. The same stratigraphic sequences will be seen on each fault block. Moreover, the increasing rotations apparent between adjacent blocks as the footwall is approached, which are a necessary characteristic of a listric array, will not be seen in a domino array.

Extension on domino faults, while leading to rapid thinning of the crust, will also flatten the faults progressively and the system will tend to lock up (e.g. Gibbs 1984b). A new set of dominoes may be expected to develop at some

stage and these will re-fault the earlier set. Repetition of this process will rapidly result in geometries similar to those described by Proffett (1977) in the Yerington district of the Basin and Range Province. The important implication of this process for the analysis of offshore basins is that only the latest faults will be apparent on conventional seismic data, and that these will form a domino array on already thinned crust.

On reflection seismic data the early faults will appear as sub-horizontal basement events broken by steeper, later faults. As in the Yerington district the early rift-stage sediments must develop very high dips at quite low extensions. Although these would not be imaged directly on reflection data it should be possible to test this where an adequate number of wells reach 'basement'. It is also unlikely that significant internal complexity of the carapace will develop. The sediment cover will simply rotate on top of the basement dominoes. Observation of relative rotation between adjacent basement blocks; stratigraphic younging of fill across the basement; lack of steep (80°) dips in early sediments; and lack of internal carapace faulting in the sediment fill can be employed to suggest that a sequential development of domino faults is not operative in a particular basin. These features are relatively easily tested by conventional geological and geophysical data.

Domino fault arrays which do not end in listric elements must be bounded by zones of more complex strike-slip deformation. Once formed, domino faults may slip laterally in later deformation but will probably not easily restack to rethicken the crust. Cyclic reuse of domino faults other than as strike-slip systems may not be possible. Jackson *et al.* (1982b) reported dips of about 40° for the Aegean fault arrays and these would probably be too steep to act as ramps in compression. Changes in the regional stress field will therefore result in the generation of new faults.

Segmentation of extensional basins —transfer or compartmental faults

Along-strike, in both dip-slip ramp and flat staircase faults and domino extensional arrays, transfer faults (Bally 1981; Gibbs 1984a) segment the structure. They act as lateral and side-wall ramps and in staircase arrays will detach not only at the base of the elastic lid but at intermediate detachment levels. In this way they again resemble lateral ramps in thrust systems and may also be confined to either the footwall or hanging wall plate. Figure 11 shows a stepped detachment with a transfer fault joining two detachment levels. Transfer faults have the important attribute of being the longest-lived single fault elements in an extensional array while slip is localized on the sole fault of the extensional array. This process leads to footwall collapse and 'piggy-back' deformation of the overlying plate with the earlier extensional faults becoming inactive. In the case of domino arrays the second extensional fault array will develop bounded by the same transfer fault zone. The transfer system must therefore remain active as long as there is any extension within the compartment.

This longevity of the transfer elements means that they will be important in controlling sediment movement in the basin throughout the basin's history. Brooks *et al.* (1984) argued that in the northern North Sea the transfer elements effectively controlled Palaeocene sand build-ups and the fluid migration routes of hydrocarbons generated late in the burial history of the basin. A more overt effect early in basin development is seen when the transfers act as input channels for sand build-ups derived directly from the tilted fault blocks on the basin margins, as may be the case in the Brae Field of the S Viking graben.

The 'flower' type geometry in cross-section of the transfers as they develop up into the sediment fill is also important. The cross-sectional geometry and evolution of transfer-fault flowers will be as described for strike-slip flower structures (e.g. Harding & Lowell 1979). As the faults propagate upwards into unconsolidated sediment they will flatten into low-strength layers within the carapace. *En échelon* patterns of folding and both reverse and normal faults will occur riding on these concave-downwards faults. Figure 12, a section across the Vale of Pickering, is an example of a steep transfer zone branching upwards into flat-lying fault 'petals' in the carapace of Mesozoic and upper Palaeozoic sediments above a fairly simple basement tear fault. The basement fault allows displacement transfer between the strike-slip zones offshore to the E (Gibbs 1986) and the tilted block and basin geometry of northern England.

Basin formed by a 'mixed-mode' combination of strike-slip and dip-slip arrays—'leaf tectonics'

Many basins seem to be developed not only on gently dipping listric staircase or domino arrays but in association with steeply dipping faults. In the simplest cases these are strike-slip pull-apart basins (e.g. Reading 1980). Deep seismic profiles across such faults do not normally directly image the fault plane. In some cases these faults separate lower crust of different character. They are therefore very deep rooted, possibly at or near Moho level. Faults such as the Great Glen, the Highland Boundary and Southern Uplands Faults of Scotland are examples of such structures. In other cases the deep structure appears unaffected by the strike-slip zone and the fault may ride on an intermediate detachment.

A system of fault-bounded leaves which link to the deep-rooted strike-slip elements are necessary to allow the crust to thin under a pull-apart basin. The deep-rooted faults do not serve to thin or thicken during deformation. Figure 13 shows a composite basin bounded by a deep-rooted strike-slip fault and a gently dipping

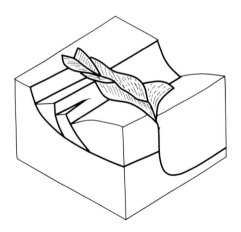

FIG. 11. Isometric model of transfer fault with strike-slip 'flower zone' (shaded) developed in the overlying sediments by differential movement of the blocks in the extensional compartments. The transfer fault steps the level of the extensional detachment and separates compartments with different structural styles.

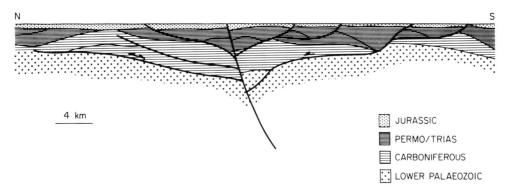

N   S

4 km

JURASSIC

PERMO/TRIAS

CARBONIFEROUS

LOWER PALAEOZOIC

FIG. 12. Simplified geological cross-section across the Vale of Pickering along easting '80'. Section drawn from plunge projections and a detachment geometry derived from balanced-section techniques, applied to series of sections through the basin. Note the development of fault leaves within the sedimentary basin linking on to, and driven by, a deep-crustal strike-slip fault zone along the basin axis which inverted the basin by changing slip on the detachment faults.

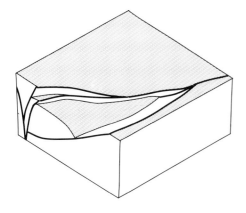

FIG. 13. Isometric sketch of model of linked extensional leaf and strike- or oblique-slip fault system. Compare front panel with Fig. 12.

listric fault forming the floor fault of the basin. This would define the lowest leaf in the fully evolved system. These leaves have a sole fault active during sedimentary growth and then develop a roof fault which forms the sole fault for the next stratigraphic sequence. Later leaves will show less rotation than those formed early in the development of the strike-slip basin. Gibbs (1984b) called these systems partial duplexes because of the stratigraphic break between the development of the sole and roof to the duplex. The results of this process can be

observed throughout the Midland Valley of Scotland. Figure 14 is a composite section parallel to the E coast of Arran crossing the Highland Boundary Fault. The Carboniferous and New Red Sandstone sections are developed on a growing fault-controlled unconformity and form an upper leaf to a duplex at Old Red Sandstone levels (Page & Gibbs in prep.). Further eastwards (Fig. 15) complete duplexes are preserved in the Carboniferous section and the Oil Shale and Cementstone sections form an intermediate leaf lying on top of the Old Red Sandstone, overlain in turn by the fault leaf carrying the coalfield. Field work in Scotland on new road sections and in open cast workings provides ample evidence for the gently dipping detachments in low-strength shales that this model requires.

In these mixed-mode basins the whole of the carapace continues to be involved in faulting driven by the deep-crustal faults as the basin develops. This contrasts with dip-slip extensional basins where deformation localizes on the footwall margin. The distinction between this type of basin and a dominantly dip-slip basin is that in the former case although the crust thins on the ramps and flats, the crustal-penetrating faults are essentially strike-slip elements. A simple division of basin-forming faults into extensional and transfer types is not appropriate.

Both the basement and the sedimentary carapace deform by the same structural process of steep ramp faults and compartmental leaves. The dominance of this structural style over

A. Gibbs

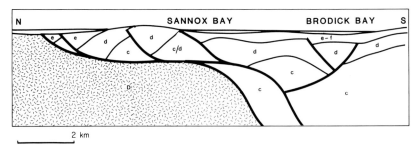

FIG. 14. Simplified composite section along the E coast of Arran across the Highland Boundary fault zone. The section was constructed by projecting out-crop patterns down-plunge on to the plane of section and constraining these plunge predictions with offshore seismic interpretations. (D = Dalradian; d = ORS; c = Carboniferous: e–f = Permo/Trias).

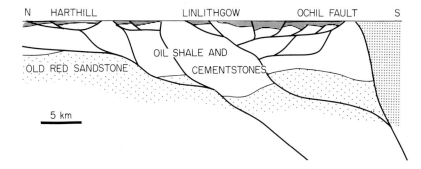

FIG. 15. Simplified geological cross-section of the Central Coal Basin of the Midland Valley of Scotland showing intermediate and upper fault leaves developed as a 'carapace' to the simpler basement strike-slip shears.

deep-rooted domino or listric basin-forming mechanisms is probably controlled by the predominance of layered upper and lower crust beneath the UK continental shelf inherited from Caledonian and Hercynian deformations and by the stratigraphic layering within the carapace.

Composite systems where the crustal-penetrating faults are dominantly strike-slip, but with dips less than 90° and linked to staircase or domino fault-bounded leaves seem to have been important in the development of many UK basins. Variants of this model have been recently proposed for the development of a linked fault system through the Carboniferous province of England into the Gas Area of the Southern North Sea for a dominantly strike-slip basin (Gibbs 1986) and by Beach *et al.* (this volume) for the dominantly extensional Viking graben. Figure 17 is a generalized section across such a basin where the basin has stretched obliquely. Carapace faulting allows the sediment-fill to stretch to accommodate changes in displacement of the basement faults as the basin grows.

In some cases the upper part of the basement may also be involved in these carapace structures as, for example, possibly occurs in the area shown in Fig. 9. Figure 16 illustrates a map of such a mixed extensional and strike-slip basin with an overlying carapace. In this cartoon the

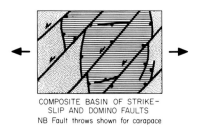

COMPOSITE BASIN OF STRIKE-
SLIP AND DOMINO FAULTS
NB Fault throws shown for carapace

FIG. 16. Schematic map of basin such as that illustrated in Fig. 17. The line of section runs from top left to bottom right. Fault throws on this cartoon are as they would be seen at a structural level in the sediment fill. At basement level the faults would all throw the same way as shown in Fig. 17.

section (Fig. 17a) runs from NW to SE and the basement faults define oblique-slip dominoes. The extension seen on the faults at basement level, basin subsidence, and crustal thinning need not balance on a single cross-section of such a basin. Throws on the map indicate the possible geometry of the carapace and it may not simply correspond to basement geometry.

Linked fault systems of this nature appear to provide a more general structural framework for upper-crustal deformation. Not only can older fault systems be reutilized but the crust can extend both across and along the basin axis. It also allows a clear linkage between the crustal-penetrating vertical, or dipping domino faults (evinced by neotectonic data) and other types of arrays which are amply supported by geological observations and interpretations of reflection seismic data. Furthermore, this structural pattern precludes neither domino nor staircase dip-slip basins with simple transfer elements, but gives an added dimension of mixing these components with large strike-slip zones.

Conclusions

Basins form on a variety of linked fault arrays which must ultimately join ductile shear zones in the mid and lower lithosphere. The variety of shallow structural geometries and their effect on the sedimentation and deformation of the sedimentary fill can be used to begin to understand the main structural elements and the patterns of linked fault arrays at depth. Deep

seismic reflection profiles provide a means of testing these models. Reflection seismic profiles may show only certain of the geologically necessary elements and important steeper dipping faults with small vertical offsets can be missed unless the basin development is examined regionally. Where the basins have developed in this way, on what are essentially two or more interfering staircase systems, the distinction between transfer and dip-slip elements is one of degree.

The analysis of basin dynamics necessitates merging and reconciling apparently conflicting data from theoretical and observational branches of tectonics, stratigraphy, and geophysics. Ultimately our models must be predictive and be capable of being tested. The implications of such basin models are important in that they begin to show how stratigraphy can evolve in response to structure and how the sediments may distribute with time. This approach provides a new suite of structural and stratigraphic models which have major economic implications to the distribution of, and exploration for, hydrocarbons.

ACKNOWLEDGMENTS: I wish to thank Western Geophysical for permission to publish the line drawing of non-exclusive survey Line FGS-24 (Fig. 9) and British Institutes Seismic Profiling Syndicate (BIRPS) for permission to publish an interpretation of part of the WINCH data (Fig. 3). I would also like to thank those who have contributed to the development of these ideas through their discussions, particularly John Nicholson and Alastair Beach.

(a)

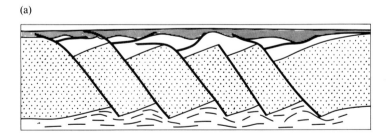

(b)

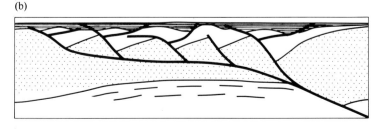

FIG. 17. Schematic cartoon of basin developed on (a) extensional domino faults and (b) extensional ramp system with considerable strike-slip occuring during basin filling. Carapace faults detach in low-strength sediments.

References

ALLMENDINGER, R.W., SHARP, J.W., VON TISH, D., SERPA, L., BROWN, L., KAUFMAN, S., OLIVER, J., & SMITH, R.B. 1983. Cenozoic and Mesozoic structure of the eastern Basin and Range province, Utah, from COCORP seismic-reflection data. *Geology,* **11,** 532–6.

BADLEY, M.E., EGEBERG, T. & NIPEN, O. 1984. Development of rift basins illustrated by the structural evolution of the Oseberg feature, Block 30/6, offshore Norway. *J. geol. Soc. London,* **141,** 639–51.

BALANCE, P.F. & READING, H.G. (eds) 1980. Sedimentation in oblique slip mobile zones. *Spec. Publ. Int. Assoc. Sed. 4.* 337pp.

BALLY, A. W. 1981. Atlantic Type Margins. *In*: BALLY *et al.* (eds) *Geology of Passive Continental Margins, AAPG Course Note Series,* **19,** 1–48.

—— , BERNOULLI, D., DAVIS, G.A. & MONTADENT, A. 1981. Listric Normal Faults. *Oceanologica Acta, 4. Proc. 26th Int. Geol. Cong., Geology of Continental Margins Symp.* Paris. Colloque C3 Geology of Continental Margins. pp. 87–101.

BEACH, A. 1984. Structural evolution of the Wytch Ground Graben, *J. geol. Soc. London,* **141,** 621–8.

BEACH, A. *et al.*

BOYER, S.M. & ELLIOT, D.W. 1982. Thrust systems. *Bull. Am. Assoc. Pet. Geol.* **66,** 1196–230.

BREWER, J.A. & SMYTHE, D.K. 1984. MOIST and the continuity of crustal geometry along the Caledonian–Appalachian orogen. *J. geol. Soc. London,* **141,** 105–20.

BROOKS, J., CORNFORD, C., GIBBS, A.D. & NICHOLSON, J. 1984. Geologic controls on occurrence and composition of Tertiary Heavy Oils, Northern, North sea. *Bull. Am. Assoc. Pet. Geol.* **68,** 793 (abstract).

BUTLER, R.W.H. 1982. The terminology of structures in thrust belts. *J. struct. Geol.* **4,** 239–45.

—— 1983. Balanced cross-sections and their implications for the deep structure of the northwest Alps. *J. struct. Geol.* **5,** 125–37.

CHADWICK, R.A., KENOLTY, N. & WHITTAKER, A. 1984. Crustal structure beneath southern England from deep seismic reflection profiles. *J. geol. Soc. London,* **140,** 893–912.

COOK, F., BROWN, D., KAUFMAN, S., OLIVER, J. & PETERSEN, T. 1981. COCORP seismic profiling of the Appalachian orogene beneath the Coastal Plain of Georgia. *Bull. geol. Soc. Am.* **92,** 738–48.

COWARD, M.P. 1983. Thrust tectonics, thin skinned or thick skinned, and the continuation of thrusts to deep in the crust. *J. struct. Geol.* **5,** 113–23.

DAVIES, V.M. 1983 Interaction of thrusts and basement faults in the French external Alps. *Tectonophysics,* **88,** 325–31.

EFFIMOFF, I. & PINEZICH, A.R. 1981. Tertiary structural development of Celeste Valleys based on seismic data: Basin and Range Province, North-eastern Nevada. *Phil. Trans. R. Soc. London,* **A.283,** 289–312.

FINCKH, P., ANSORGE, J., ST MUELLER, J. & SPRECHER, CHR. 1984. Deep crustal reflections from a vibroseis survey in Northern Switzerland. *Tectonophysics,* **109,** 1–14.

GABRIELSEN, R.H. 1984. Long-lived fault zones and their influence on the tectonic development of southwestern Barents Sea. *J geol. Soc. London,* **141,** 651–63.

GIBBS, A.D. 1983. Balanced cross-section constructions from seismic sections in areas of extensional tectonics. *J. struct. Geol.* **5,** 152–60.

—— 1984a. Clyde Field Growth Fault secondary detachment above basement faults in the North Sea. *Bull. Am. Assoc. Pet. Geol.* **68,** 1029–39.

—— 1984b. Structural Evolution of extensional basin margins. *J. geol. Soc. London,* **141,** 609–20.

—— 1986. Strike-slip basins and inversion: a possible model for the Southern North Sea Gas Area. *In*: BROOKS, J., GOFF, J.C. & VAN HORN, B. (eds) *Spec. publ. geol. Soc. London,* **23,** 23–36.

GRACIANSKY, P.C., POAG, C.W., CUNNINGHAM, R., LOUBERE, P., MASSON, D.G., MAZZULLO, J.M., MONTADERT, L., MULLER, C., OTSUKA, K., REYNOLDS, L.A., SIGAL, J., SNYDER, S.W., TOWNSEND, H.A., VAOS, S.P. & WAPLES, D. 1985. The Goban Spur transect: Geological evolution of a sediment-starved passive continental margin. *Bull. geol. Soc. Am.* **96,** 58–76.

HARDING, T.P. 1984. Graben hydrocarbon occurrences and structural style. *Bull. Am. Assoc. Pet.* **68,** 333–62.

—— & LOWELL, J.D. 1979. Structural styles, their plate tectonic habitats, and petroleum traps in petroleum provinces. *Bull. Am. Assoc. Pet. Geol.* **63,** 1016–59.

HARLAND, W.B. 1971 Tectonic transpression in Caledonian Spitsbergen. *Geol. Mag.* **108,** 27–42.

HOSSACK, J.R. 1984. The geometry of listric growth faults in the Devonian basins of Sunnfjord, W Norway. *J. geol. Soc. London,* **141,** 629–38.

JACKSON, J.A. 1980. Reactivation of basement faults and crustal shortening in orogenic belts. *Nature, Lond.* **283,** 343–6.

—— & MCKENZIE, D. 1983. The geometrical evolution of normal fault systems. *J. struct. Geol.* **5,** 471–82.

—— , KING G. & VITA-FINZI, C. 1982a. The neotectonics of the Aegean: an alternative view. *Earth planet. Sci. Lett.* **61,** 303-18.

—— , GAGNEPAIN, J., HOUSEMAN, G., KING, G.C.P., PAPADIMITRIOU, P., SOUFLERIS, C. & VIRIEUX, J. 1982b. Seismicity, normal faulting, and the geomorphological development of the Gulf of Corinth (Greece): the Corinth earthquakes of February and March 1981. *Earth planet. Sci. Lett.* **57,** 377–97.

MCKENZIE, D.P. 1978. Some remarks on the development of sedimentary basins. *Earth planet. Sci. lett.* **40,** 25–32.

ORI, G.G. & FRIEND, P.F. 1984. Sedimentary Basins formed and carried piggyback on active thrust sheets. *Geology*, **12**, 475–8.

PEGRUM. R.M. & LJONES, T.E. 1984. 15/9 Gamma Gas Field offshore Norway, new trap style for North Sea Basin with regional structural implications. *Bull. Am. Assoc. Pet. Geol.* **68**, 874–902

PRICE, I. & RATTEY R.P. 1984. Cretaceous tectonics off mid-Norway: implications for Rockall and Faeroe-Shetland troughs. *J. geol. Soc. London*, **141**, 985–92.

PROFFETT, J.M. 1977. Cenozoic geology of the Yerington district, Nevada, and implications for the nature and origin of Basin and Range faulting. *Bull. geol. Soc. Am.* **88**, 247–66

READING, H.G. 1980. Characteristics and recognition of strike-slip fault systems. pp. 7–26. *In*: BALLANCE, P.F. & READING, H.G. (eds) *Sedimentation in obliques slip mobile zones. Spec. Publ. 4 Int. Assoc. Sed.*

SANDERSON, J. & MARCHINI, W.R.D. 1984. Transpression. *J. struct. Geol.* **6**, 449–58.

SCLATER, J.G. & CHRISTIE, P.A.F. 1980. Continental stretching: an explanation of the post mid-Cretaceous subsidence of the Central North Sea Basin. *J. geophys. Res.* **85**, B.

SPENCER, J. 1984. Role of tectonic denudation in warping and uplift of low angle normal faults. *Geology*, **12**, 95–8.

STONELEY, R. 1982. The structural development of the Wessex Basin. *J. geol. Soc. London*, **139**, 543–54.

TODD, R.G. & MITCHUM, R.M. 1977. Seismic Stratigraphy and Global Changes of Sea level, part 8; Identification of Upper Triassic, Jurassic, and Lower Cretaceous Seismic Sequences in the Gulf of Mexico and offshore West Africa. *In*: PAYTON, C.E. (ed.) *Seismic Stratigraphy—Applications to hydrocarbon exploration, Mem. Am. Assoc. Pet. Geol.* **26**, 145–63.

WERNICKE, B. 1985. Uniform sense of normal simple shear of the continental lithosphere. *Can. J. Earth Sci.* **22**, 108–25.

—— & BURCHFIEL, B.C. 1982. Modes of extensional tectonics. *J. struct. Geol.* **4**, 105–15.

ALAN GIBBS, Midland Valley Exploration, 14 Park Circus, Glasgow G3 6AX, UK.

The extensional strength of the continental lithosphere: its dependence on geothermal gradient, and crustal composition and thickness

N.J. Kusznir & R.G. Park

SUMMARY: The response of lithosphere to an applied tectonic tensile force and the resulting stress distribution with depth has been investigated using a mathematical model incorporating the elastic, plastic and brittle behaviour of lithospheric material. Lithospheric strength is shown to be primarily controlled by lithospheric rheology and as a consequence is critically dependent on geothermal gradient and lithospheric composition. The rheologies of the upper crust, lower crust and mantle are assumed to be controlled by dislocation creep in quartz, plagioclase and olivine respectively.

The critical level of tensional tectonic force required to generate geologically significant strains has been calculated as a function of surface heat flow, and the predicted lithosphere strength compared with available levels of tensile tectonic force arising from subduction plate boundaries and isostatically compensated plateau uplift loads. The model predicts significant extensional deformation in regions with surface heat flow >65 mWm^{-2} subjected to a tensile tectonic force of 3×10^{12} N m^{-1} and is in good agreement with observed examples of intraplate extension.

Lithosphere strength is critically controlled by the crustal thickness since the quartzo-feldspathic rheology of the crust is weaker than the olivine rheology of the mantle. A decrease in crustal thickness thus increases the strength of the lithosphere. However, lithospheric extension also increases the geothermal gradient serving to weaken the lithosphere. The rate of extension is critical in determining which of these processes predominates. Fast strain rates ($>5 \times 10^{-15}$ sec^{-1}) produce a weakening of the lithosphere (i.e. strain softening) while slower strain rates lead to strengthening of the lithosphere (strain hardening). Extensional style is consequently controlled by the lithospheric extension rate; fast extension producing, through strain softening, intense localized lithospheric extension with high (potentially infinite) β values, and slow extension, through strain hardening, giving broader regions of lithosphere extension with finite β values of the order of 1.5.

For intermediate geothermal gradients ($q = 55$–70 mWm^{-2}) the model predicts a low stress–low strength region at the base of the crust due to the contrast between plagioclase and olivine rheology at the Moho. Other low-strength regions are predicted within the crust at major compositional (and rheological) boundaries. These low-strength zones are expected to control the location of detachment horizons by which crustal extension occurs particularly at slower strain rates. High geothermal gradients favour the shallower detachment horizons at the expense of the deeper horizons. The reverse is true for low geothermal gradients.

The strength of the continental lithosphere controls both the initiation and subsequent evolution of extensional deformation. The response of a piece of lithosphere to an applied tectonic force is dependent on the vertical distribution of both brittle and ductile strength, which in turn is controlled by the varying rheology of lithosphere material with depth. Whereas brittle strength is controlled primarily by lithostatic pressure and increases with depth, ductile strength is controlled by temperature and decreases with depth because of the geothermal gradient. In tectonically stable lithosphere subjected to an applied force, an upper region of brittle deformation and a lower region of ductile deformation will be separated by a competent elastic region (Fig. 1). With an increase in the magnitude of the applied force, geothermal gradient or with time, the regions of brittle and ductile deformation will extend downwards and upwards respectively, reducing the elastic core to zero and thereby enabling geologically significant strain to take place. At this point, *whole lithosphere failure* (WLF) may be said to occur.

The variation of both brittle and ductile strength with depth controls the vertical distribution of stress resulting from an applied force and defines the critical value of that force which must be applied to the lithosphere in order to produce geologically significant strain rates. The mathematical model used to calculate the stress distribution is more fully described in

From COWARD, M.P., DEWEY, J.F. & HANCOCK, P.L. (eds), 1987, *Continental Extensional Tectonics*, Geological Society Special Publication No. 28, pp. 35–52.

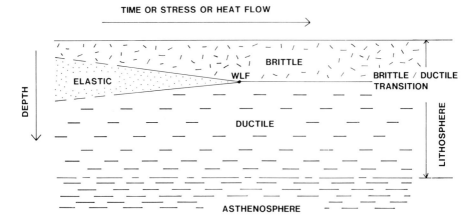

FIG. 1. A diagrammatic representation of the regions of brittle, elastic and ductile deformation within lithosphere subjected to a horizontal tectonic force. With increase in time, the level of the applied stress, or geothermal gradient, the elastic core of the lithosphere may be reduced to zero giving Whole Lithosphere Failure (WLF). Only after WLF can geologically significant strains occur.

Kusznir & Park (1984). The model examines the elastic, ductile and brittle response of the lithosphere to a lateral applied stress, assuming conservation of the total horizontal force arising from that stress, and that the lithosphere undergoes a uniform horizontal strain with depth. A Maxwell visco-elastic model is used for each infinitesimal component of the lithosphere. Brittle failure is predicted by Griffith theory (Griffith 1924) as modified by McClintock & Walsh (1962). Ductile deformation is assumed to be controlled by non-Newtonian power-law creep: dislocation creep in quartz for the upper crust and plagioclase for the lower crust; and a combination of dislocation and Dorn law creep in olivine for the mantle. The main stress-strain equations and values of constants used are given in the Appendix.

In Fig. 2, the strain rates of some minerals and rocks relevant to ductile lithosphere deformation are plotted against temperature. The curves, based on experimental data, assume a dislocation-creep mechanism and correspond to a stress difference of 50 MPa. Temperature is seen to have a marked effect on strain rate. The increase from 600 to 800°C for dry olivine for example, increases the strain rate from 10^{-20} to 10^{-15} sec^{-1}. At the same temperatures, quartz is very much weaker than olivine. At 600°C, the strain rates of dry quartz and dry olivine are roughly 10^{-11} and 10^{-20} sec^{-1} respectively. Typical strain rates for significant tectonic deformation are in the range 10^{-16} to 10^{-14} sec^{-1} (10^{-15} sec^{-1} produces 30% strain in 10 My). For quartz subjected to a differential stress of 50 MPa, a temperature of about

300°C would produce a strain rate of 10^{-15} sec^{-1}, whereas for dry olivine, a temperature of about 800°C would be required.

In the upper crust, deformation will be controlled by the behaviour of quartz (e.g. see White 1976). The rheology of the lower crust, however, is more likely to be controlled by the ductile deformation of plagioclase, which deforms more readily than pyroxene or olivine—quartz is unlikely to be present in sufficient quantity to control the deformation there. A model with a two-layer crustal rheology consisting of 50% wet quartz above 40% plagioclase is therefore used as the basis for the strength calculations. An alternative model with a three-layer rheology consisting of 50% wet quartz overlying 50% dry quartz overlying 40% plagioclase is also investigated.

The critical temperatures required to generate significant strain rates for these different rheologies are reached at different depths depending on the geotherm. For the purpose of the model, the geotherms have been calculated using a steady-state temperature model in which the geothermal gradient is characterized by the surface heat flow, q. The values of conductivity and radiogenic heat productivity, which vary with depth, are as given by Pollack & Chapman (1977).

Figure 3 shows how the model may be used to calculate stress–depth profiles at various times from 10^3 to 10^6 y after application of a tensile force of 10^{12} N m^{-1} to continental lithosphere with a surface heat flow of 60 mWm^{-2} (corresponding to the continental average). As time progresses ductile creed in the lower lithosphere

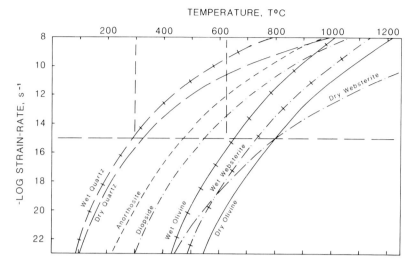

FIG. 2. Strain-rate plotted logarithmically against temperature for a number of rocks and minerals important in lithospheric plastic deformation. The curves assume a dislocation creep mechanism and correspond to a stress difference ($\sigma_1 - \sigma_3$) of 50 MPa. The curves are derived from experimental data as follows: Quartz (Koch *et al.* 1980), Dry Olivine (Goetze 1978), Wet Olivine (Bodine, Steckler & Watts 1981), Websterite and Diopside (Avé Lallement 1978) and Anorthosite (plagioclase) (Shelton & Tullis 1981).

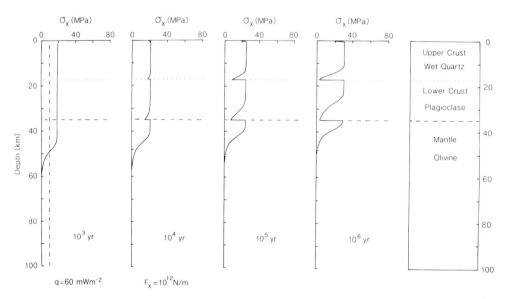

FIG. 3. Stress plotted against depth at various times after the application of a tensile tectonic force of 10^{12} N m^{-1} to continental lithosphere with a surface heat flow of 60 mWm^{-2}. Note the development of low stress–low strength regions above compositional (and therefore rheological) boundaries.

results in the dissipation of stress there and its transfer to the cooler non-ductile upper lithosphere, where it becomes amplified to levels sufficient to generate brittle failure. By 1 Ma after application of the initial force, stress levels in the upper lithosphere have increased by a factor of 4. Two major stress–depth discontinuities are apparent at the rheology changes between the upper and lower crust, and at the Moho.

Since lithosphere rheology is strongly temperature dependent, the geothermal gradient is critical in determining the variation of ductile strength with depth, and also the position and relative importance of the main strength discontinuities on which subsequent major tectonic displacements may take place. The rheological behaviour of the lithosphere is also dependent on the relative proportions of the weaker quartz–plagioclase rheologies of the crust and the olivine rheology of the mantle lithosphere. The relationship between *strength, crustal composition* and *thickness*, and *geothermal gradient* is therefore the key to the tectonic behaviour of the continental lithosphere, and the purpose of this paper is to explore and seek to quantify this.

The strength of the lithosphere

The control of strength by the geothermal gradient

˙The control of the stress–depth relationship by the geothermal gradient is illustrated in Fig. 4 where stress arising from an applied tensile force of 10^{12} N m^{-1} is shown as a function of depth for lithosphere models with a range of geothermal gradients (characterized by surface heat flow). For the coolest lithosphere models with $q = 45$ mWm^{-2}, corresponding to a shield-type geotherm, the applied force is carried to a depth of the order of 75 km leading to relatively small stress levels in the middle and upper lithosphere. As the geothermal gradient (and surface heat flow) increases ductile deformation within the upper mantle and crust extends upwards concentrating stresses within the upper crust and mantle. The large levels of stress associated with the larger heat-flow values are sufficient to produce brittle failure. The model with $q = 80$ mWm^{-2} shows the applied force carried almost completely in the top 10 km of the lithosphere with brittle failure almost completely penetrating the stress-carrying layer. A small elastic core still remains, however. For $q = 90$ mWm^{-2} the elastic core has been annihilated and WLF has occurred. The models with intermediate heat flows in the range 60–80 mWm^{-2} show pronounced low-strength regions in the lower and middle crust respectively, arising from the rheology discontinuities associated with the transition from plagioclase to olivine and wet quartz to plagioclase mineralogy.

The effect of increasing the level of the applied tensile tectonic force is shown in Fig. 5. Stress is shown as a function of depth for a lithosphere model with surface heat flow $q = 70$ mWm^{-2} subjected to a tensile force of 1.0×10^{12}, 1.5×10^{12} and 2.0×10^{12} N m^{-1}. The effect of increasing the value of the applied tensile force is to increase the level of the stress in the upper lithosphere resulting in deeper penetration of the region of brittle failure. For the model subjected to an applied force of 2.0×10^{12} N m^{-1}, the elastic core of the upper lithosphere has been eliminated and WLF has occurred. Only after WLF can extensive brittle and ductile deformation take place and lead to geologically significant strains.

The mathematical model can also be used to calculate the horizontal strains associated with the deformation arising from an applied tectonic force. In Fig. 6(a) horizontal strain is shown as a function of time for lithosphere models, with a range of surface heat flows, subjected to an applied tensile force of 2×10^{12} N m^{-1}. Strains are greater at a given time for models with larger geothermal gradients. Only models with $q > 70$ mWm^{-2} show WLF by 10 My and have geologically significant strain rates. In Fig. 6(b) horizontal strain is shown as a function of time for lithosphere models with a surface heat flow of 70 mWm^{-2} and a range of tensile applied forces. The models subjected to the larger applied forces show larger strains. A force of 2×10^{12} N m^{-1} or greater is required to give WLF by 10 My.

In order to generate WLF within a certain time, a critical level of applied force and a critical geothermal gradient must be exceeded. In Fig. 7 the critical tensile force required to generate WLF within 1 My is plotted as a function of heat flow. This critical force, which can also be regarded as the strength of the lithosphere, shows a very strong dependence on the geothermal gradient and decreases with increase in heat flow. Estimates of the tensile force arising from subduction suction and plateau uplift are also shown together with an estimate of the likely resultant level of tensile tectonic force. It can be seen that only lithosphere with a heat flow >65–70 mWm^{-2} is likely to undergo significant extensional deformation.

These model predictions may be compared with the heat-flow data and tectonic status of a number of representative regions (Fig. 8) divided into, (a) stable continental shields (Precambrian cratons), (b) regions of Palaeozoic orogenic crust, and (c) thermally active regions undergoing current or recent rifting and volcanicity. None of group (a) with heat-flow values in the range 34–49 mWm^{-2} show signs of significant tectonic deformation. In group (b) with heat-flow values in the range 57–75 mWm^{-2} local extensional failure occurs in Central Europe (Rhine–Ruhr rift system—see group (c)) and in

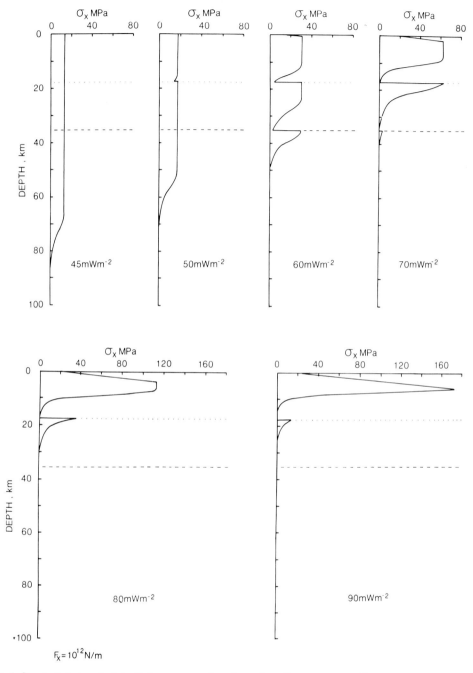

FIG. 4. Stress plotted against depth for a range of geothermal gradients, corresponding to surface heat flows of 45 to 90 mWm^{-2}, at 1 My after the application of a tensile tectonic force of 10^{12} N m^{-1}.

North China (Shansi graben system) both with heat flows of over 70 mWm^{-2}. In group (c) high heat flows (92–107 mWm^{-2}) are associated with the active rifts but lower heat flows occur in the flanking areas.

The model can be strictly applied only to the initial stage of rifting, starting from 'normal' lithosphere. Once crustal thinning has taken place, both the geometry and the rheology of the lithosphere are changed by the emplacement of

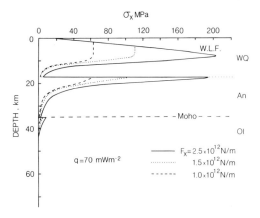

FIG. 5. Stress plotted against depth at 1My after the application of tensile forces of 10^{12}, 1.5×10^{12} and 2×10^{12} N m^{-1} to lithosphere with surface heat flow 70 mWm^{-2}. Increasing the magnitude of the applied force increases stress levels in the upper lithosphere causing brittle deformation to penetrate deeper until WLF occurs as in the case of the 2×10^{12} N m^{-1} model.

warmer asthenospheric material (cf. McKenzie 1978) and by the development of volcanicity. The flank values may thus probably be taken as minimum estimates and the rift values as maximum estimates of the heat flow at the time of rift initiation.

The data of Fig. 8 taken as a whole suggest a critical heat-flow band between 60 and 70 mWm^{-2} above which significant tectonic deformation may take place, which is consistent with the predictions of the model (see Fig. 7).

The control of lithosphere strength by crustal composition

The strength of the lithosphere is strongly controlled by the rheology of the lower crust, which is dependent not only on the geothermal gradient but also on composition and metamorphic grade. The continental crust is an extremely heterogeneous body, and in its lower part may vary from ultrabasic to acidic in composition and from granulite to amphibolite in facies. In Fig. 9(a) stress is plotted against depth for three models with different crustal compositions and rheologies. The effect of introducing a dry-quartz rheology into the lower crust is to considerably weaken the lower crust leading to larger stress levels in the upper crust compared with the model with a plagioclase-rheology lower crust. The stress–depth distribution arising from a three-layer wet-quartz–dry-quartz–plagioclase crust is also shown. In Fig. 9(b) the

strength of the lithosphere as a function of heat flow is compared for models with a plagioclase and dry-quartz lower crust. At 70 mWm^{-2} the model with the plagioclase lower crust is approximately twice as strong as that with the dry-quartz rheology. The strengths of all olivine and all wet-quartz models are also shown. For high geothermal gradients ($q > 90$ mWm^{-2}) the rheology of the wet-quartz upper crust completely controls lithosphere strength. For low geothermal gradients ($q < 50$ mWm^{-2}) strength is controlled by the much stronger olivine rheology of the mantle.

The control of lithosphere strength by crustal thickness

The quartzo–feldspathic rheologies of the crust are significantly weaker than the olivine rheology of the mantle. As a consequence, the strength of the lithosphere will be dependent on the relative proportions of quartzo–feldspathic and olivine material that it contains and therefore on crustal thickness. In Fig. 10(a) stress is shown as a function of depth for lithosphere models with crustal thicknesses of 20, 35 and 60 km. The thinner crust models (20 and 35 km) show stress being carried to greater depths than the thick-crust model (60 km) where the weaker quartzo–feldspathic rheology extends deeper. The 60-km crust model shows more than twice the maximum level of stress in the upper crust than the 20-km crust model. In Fig. 10(b) lithosphere strength as a function of heat flow is shown for models with a range of crustal thicknesses. The lithosphere is appreciably stronger for models with thinner crust. For a heat flow of 70 mWm^{-2}, a 20-km thick crust model is three to four times stronger than the 35-km thick model. At higher geothermal gradients, however, (for all but the zero crustal-thickness model) the lithosphere strength is independent of crustal thickness since the brittle–ductile transition has moved out of the olivine mantle and plagioclase lower crust into the quartz rheology upper crust. At low geothermal gradients too the strength of the lithosphere is independent of crustal thickness and is controlled only by the olivine rheology of the mantle. In this region of low geothermal gradients, however, the lithosphere is so strong compared with available levels of tectonic force that it is never likely to fail.

The evolution of lithosphere strength during extension

During extension the stretching of the lithosphere results in thinning of the crust and an

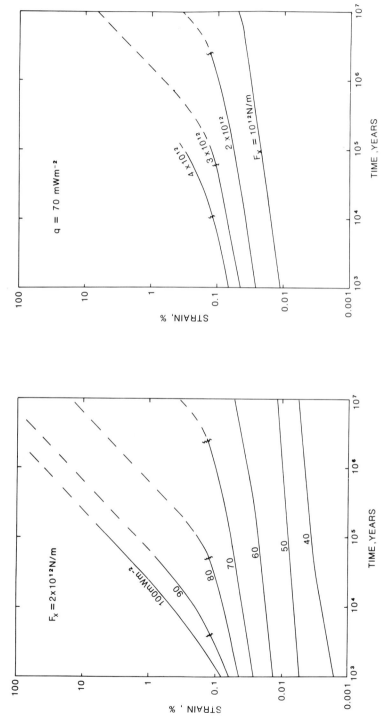

FIG. 6. Horizontal strain (%) plotted against time for: (a) lithosphere with a range of geothermal gradients subjected to a tensile force of 2×10^{12} N m^{-1}. (b) Lithosphere with a geothermal gradient corresponding to $q = 70$ mWm^{-2} subjected to a range of tensile force levels.

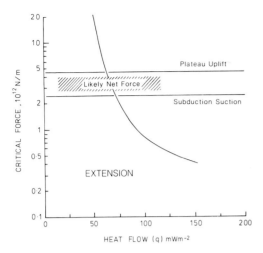

FIG. 7. Lithosphere extensional strength, defined as the critical tensile force required to generate WLF within 1 My, plotted against surface heat flow and compared with available levels of tensile tectonic force. Only lithosphere with a heat flow greater than 65–70 mWm^{-2} is likely to undergo significant extensional deformation.

increase in the geothermal gradient. Both crustal thickness and geothermal gradient have been seen to effect a strong control on lithosphere strength. In Fig. 11(a) the extensional strength of the lithosphere (defined as the applied tensile tectonic force required to generate WLF in 1 My) is shown contoured in crustal thickness–heat-flow space. Increasing the geothermal gradient during extension serves to weaken the lithosphere, while the simultaneous thinning of the crust will act to strengthen it. The lithosphere may show either a net strengthening (i.e. strain 'hardening') or a net weakening (i.e. strain 'softening') during extension depending on which effect dominates.

During extension at a finite strain rate, the increase in geothermal gradient due to lithosphere stretching will be partly offset by heat loss as the geothermal gradient endeavours to re-equilibrate. The behaviour of the geothermal gradient during extension will therefore be controlled by the extensional strain rate; fast strain rates producing a larger increase in geothermal gradient than slow strain rates for the same amount of stretching. In Fig. 11(b) typical tra-

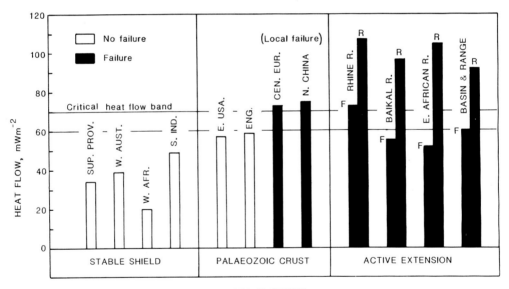

FIG. 8. Comparison of heat-flow values and tectonic status for a number of representative regions grouped into: stable shield (Precambrian cratons), Palaeozoic orogenic crust, and areas of active extensional rifting. Heat-flow data, in mWm^{-2}, are: Superior Province[1] 34±8; West Australia[1] 39±8; West Africa (Niger)[1] 20±8; South India[1] 49±8; E USA[1] 57±17; England and Wales[1] 59±23; Central Europe (Bohemian massif)[1] 73±18; Northern China[2] 75±15; Rhine graben[3] 107±35 (rift) and 73±20 (flanks – Rhenish massif); Baikal rift[3] 97±22 (SE flank 55±10); East African rift[3] 105±51 (flanks 52±17); Basin and Range Province[1] 92±33 (E flank – Colorado plateau[4] 60). Data from Viterello & Pollack (1980)[1], Pollack & Chapman (1977)[2] and Morgan (1982[3]; 1984[4]). For regions undergoing active extension both Rift (R) and Flank (F) heat flows are given.

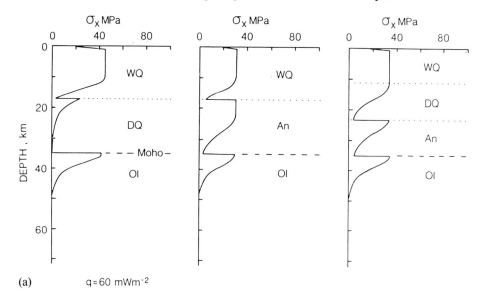

(a)   q=60 mWm⁻²

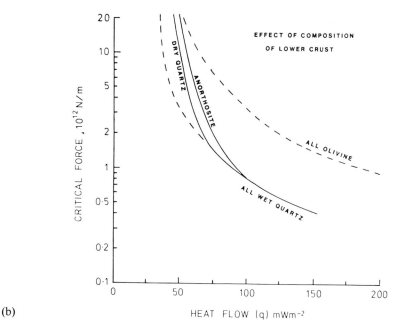

(b)   HEAT FLOW (q) mWm⁻²

FIG. 9. (a) Stress plotted against depth for a range of crustal compositions and rheologies at 1 My after the application of a tensile tectonic force of 10^{12} N m⁻¹ to lithosphere with heat flow $q = 60$ mWm⁻². WQ = Wet Quartz; DQ = Dry Quartz; An = Anorthosite (Plagioclase); Ol = Olivine. (b) Lithosphere strength plotted against heat flow compared for models with anorthosite (plagioclase) and dry-quartz lower-crustal rheology. Strength curves for lithosphere models with all olivine and all wet-quartz rheology are also shown.

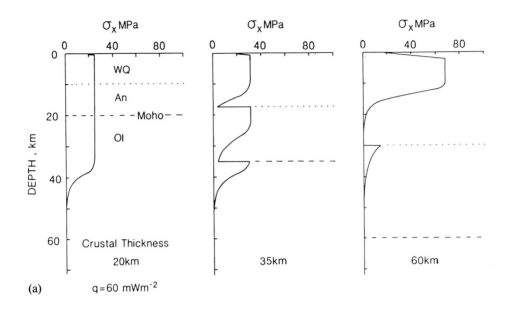

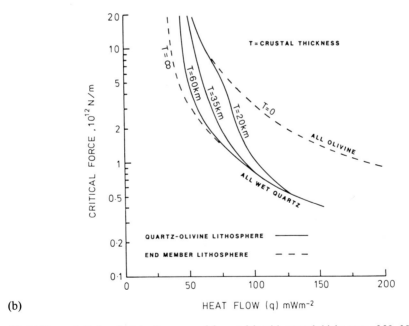

Fig. 10. (a) Stress plotted against depth compared for models with crustal thicknesses of 20, 35 and 60 km at 1 My after the application of a tensile tectonic force of 10^{12} N m^{-1} to lithosphere with heat flow $q = 60$ mWm^{-2}. (b) Lithosphere strength plotted against heat flow compared for models with different crustal thicknesses. Decreasing crustal thickness increases lithosphere strength.

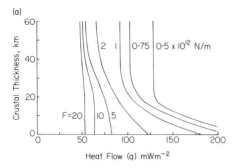

(a)

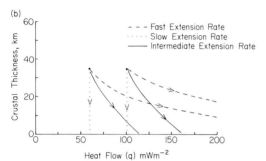

(b)

FIG. 11. (a) Contours of lithosphere extensional strength (the critical force required to generate WLF in 1 My) plotted in crustal thickness–heat-flow space. (b) Schematic trajectories in crustal thickness–heat-flow space for fast, slow and intermediate lithosphere extension rates.

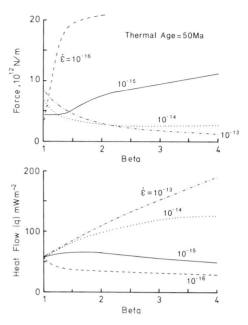

FIG. 12. Lithosphere strength (defined as the force required to maintain the respective strain rate) and surface heat flow plotted against β, the lithosphere extension factor, for a range of strain rates ($\dot{\epsilon} = 10^{-13}$ to 10^{-16} sec^{-1}). The initial model temperature structure corresponds to that of lithosphere with a thermal age of 50 My.

jectories in crustal thickness–heat flow space are shown for very fast and very slow extensional strain rates. Whether or not lithosphere strengthens ('hardens') or weakens ('softens') during extension will depend on whether the actual extension trajectories in crustal thickness–heat flow space ascend or descend the contours of lithosphere strength. As a consequence, the evolution of lithosphere strength during extension will depend critically on the extensional strain rate. For very fast strain rates a net weakening of the lithosphere will occur, while for slow strain rates there will be a net strengthening.

The quantitative control by strain rate on the evolution of lithosphere strength during extension can be calculated using a model which incorporates both the transient behaviour of the geotherm during extension and the thinning of the quartzo–feldspathic crust. In Fig. 12 lithosphere strength and heat flow during extension are plotted against Beta (β), the lithosphere stretching factor (McKenzie 1978), for a range of strain rates. The initial temperature structure of continental lithosphere has been calculated using a cooling-plate thermal model and has a

'thermal age' of 50 Ma. (The thermal structure is determined using a lithosphere thickness of 125 km and an initial uniform temperature at zero thermal age of 1300°C. Crust and mantle thermal conductivities and radiogenic productivities are those given by Sclater *et al.* (1981).) For slow strain rates, $\dot{\epsilon} = 10^{-16}$ sec^{-1}, the lithosphere hardens with extension, while for fast strain rates, $\dot{\epsilon} = 10^{-13}$ and 10^{-14} sec^{-1}, the lithosphere softens. The strain-rate curve for 10^{-15} sec^{-1} shows an almost constant lithosphere strength up to $\beta = 1.5$ followed by hardening. The behaviour of heat flow during extension is also shown to be controlled by strain rate, faster strain rates producing larger heat-flow values. The decrease in heat flow with β, shown for the strain rate of 10^{-16} sec^{-1} is caused by the thinning of the upper-crustal radiogenic heat producing layer during extension.

The effect of the initial geothermal gradient on the behaviour of lithosphere strength during extension is shown in Fig. 13 where lithosphere strength and heat flow are plotted against β, the lithosphere stretching factor, for a range of initial thermal ages of the model. All curves in Fig. 13 correspond to a strain rate of 10^{-15} sec^{-1}

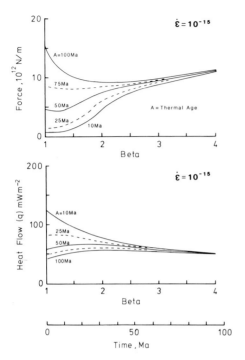

FIG. 13. Lithosphere strength (the force required to maintain the given strain rate) and surface heat flow plotted against β for a strain rate of 10^{-15} sec^{-1} compared for models with different initial temperature structures as characterized by lithosphere thermal age.

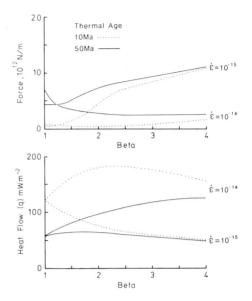

FIG. 14. A summary and comparison of the effect of both strain rate and the initial thermal age (i.e. temperature structure) of the lithosphere on lithosphere strength and heat flow as extension proceeds. β is the lithosphere extension factor. As extension proceeds both lithosphere strength and heat flow depend only on the strain rate not on the initial lithosphere temperature structure.

(and since a constant strain rate is used, time is also shown). The evolution of lithosphere strength during extension is shown to be strongly dependent on the initial thermal state of the lithosphere; thermally young, hot lithosphere tending to harden and thermally old, cool lithosphere to soften as extension proceeds. The cool models with thermal ages of 75 and 100 Ma are unrealistic, however, in that tensile tectonic forces of sufficient magnitude to initiate lithosphere deformation do not exist. The curves for thermal ages of 10, 25 and 50 Ma show an approximately constant lithosphere strength up to $\beta = 1.5$ before hardening occurs. The inter-relationship between extensional strength, strain rate and β, and between heat-flow, strain rate and β is summarized in Fig. 14 for the 'fast' (10^{-14} sec^{-1}) and 'slow' (10^{-15} sec^{-1}) strain rates for two models with thermal ages of 10 and 50 Ma respectively. It can be seen that the values of strength and heat flow become increasingly controlled by the strain rate as β increases, and independent of the initial thermal state of the lithosphere.

It is again evident that there is a critical β value of about 1.5 above which slow strain rates lead to rapid strain hardening for both hot and cool thermal models. It is also significant that a fast strain rate can only be initiated with the hotter thermal model since the cooler model requires an unrealistically high force.

The hardening of a piece of lithosphere during extension would be expected to lead to the cessation of extension in that section of lithosphere and its transfer to an adjacent weaker region and would therefore generate finite maximum values of β. The model, as shown in Fig. 13, suggests a maximum β value of ≈ 1.5. This figure is consistent with the β values of a representative set of intracontinental extensional basins with an average of 1.4–1.5 (Table 1). It is clear from the above that the mode of development of lithosphere extension will be dependent on extension rate (see Fig. 15). Fast extension rates are expected to lead to locally intense extension with large β values and large geothermal gradients, whereas slow strain rates are expected to produce smaller β values, distributed over a much wider region, with much lower geothermal gradients (see Fig. 18 also).

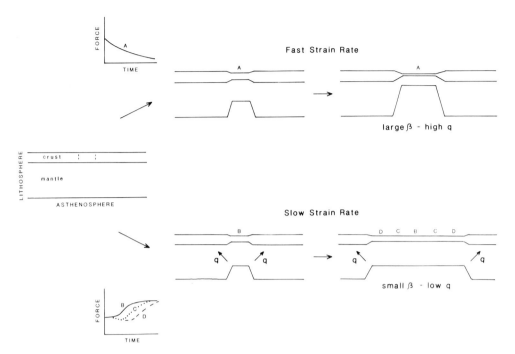

FIG. 15. Schematic diagram showing the effect of extensional strain rate on the style of extension and lithosphere temperature structure. *Fast strain rates*, through lithosphere strain softening, lead to intense localized extension with (locally) large β values and high heat flow. *Slow strain rates*, through lithosphere strain hardening, generates a broad region of extension with small β values and low surface heat flow.

The Rheological control of detachment horizons in extension

For intermediate geothermal gradients ($q = 60$–70 mWm^{-2}) the distribution of stress with depth shows pronounced zones of low stress and low ductile strength in the middle and lower crust (see Figs 4, 9(a) & 16). These zones result from the contrast in rheological strength between adjacent layers of different composition and would be expected to provide sites for the development of detachment horizons during extension. The two-layer crustal model (Fig. 4) shows low-strength zones between the quartz upper crust and plagioclase lower crust, and between the latter and the olivine mantle, respectively. The three-layer crust model (Fig. 16) shows low-strength zones between wet-quartz upper crust and dry-quartz middle crust, between dry-quartz middle crust and plagioclase lower crust, and between plagioclase lower crust and olivine mantle.

An example of such a three-layer rheological crust is found in northern Scotland where the LISPB seismic refraction line (Bamford 1979) is

TABLE 1. *Continental lithosphere extension.*

	β
North Sea basin – Central Graben	1.55–1.9
– Flanks	1.2–1.3
Rhine Graben	1.1–1.3
Pannonian Basin	1.8–2.7
Aegean	1.4
Vienna Basin	1.6–1.8
Paris Basin	1.3
Wessex Basin	1.1–1.25
Worcester Basin	1.2
Bass Basin	1.25–1.5
Gippsland Basin	1.8
East Siberian Basin	<1.5
Michigan Basin	<1.5
Illinois Basin	<1.5
Basin and Range	1.5–2
Representative average	$\beta = 1.4$–1.5

Data from G. D. Karner (1985 pers. comm.)

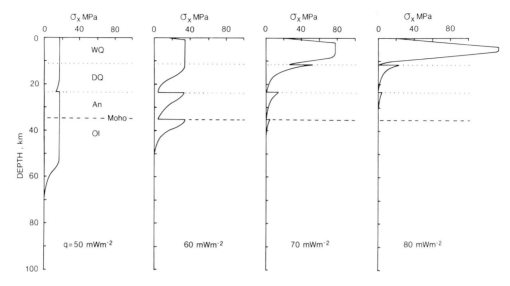

FIG. 16. Stress plotted against depth for a three-layer crustal model with a range of surface heat flows, showing the development of low-stress–low-strength regions in the middle and lower crust. The stress–depth distributions correspond to 1 My after the application of a tensile force of 10^{12} N m^{-1}. The low-strength regions represent the probable sites of detachment horizons. WQ = Wet Quartz; DQ = Dry Quartz; An = Anorthosite (Plagioclase); Ol = Olivine.

interpreted as indicating a Caledonian metamorphic upper crustal layer, above a Lewisian acid gneiss middle crustal layer, overlying a mafic granulite lower crust (Fig. 17). The boundaries between these layers may well represent tectonic detachment levels. The BIRPS MOIST deep reflection line (Brewer & Smythe 1984) shows that the major faults flatten out around 20 km cor-

responding to the base of the mid-crustal Lewisian acid gneiss layer.

The existence of these low stress, low-strength regions in the lower, middle and upper crust is very sensitive to the geothermal gradient (Fig. 16). For example, increasing the geothermal gradient from 60 to 70 mWm^{-2} introduces a third low-strength zone in the upper crust, while a

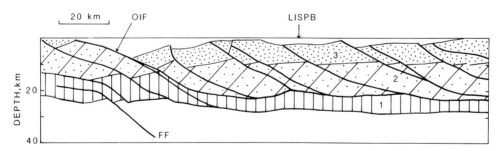

FIG. 17. Model of the MOIST profile across north Scotland after Blundell *et al.* (1984) showing the three main crustal layers recognized by Bamford *et al.* (1979). 1 – *lower crust* (7 km sec^{-1} – probably basic granulite); 2 – *middle crust* (6.4 km sec^{-1} – intermediate granulite-facies Lewisian); 3 – *upper crust* (6.15 km sec^{-1} – amphibolite-facies Caledonian metamorphics – mainly Moine in the E and Lewisian in the W). The uppermost (un-ornamented) layer corresponds to unmetamorphosed sediments from Torridonian to Mesozoic age. FF = Flannan 'fault', OIF = Outer Isles fault. Note that most of the major low-angle extensional faults (or shear zones) sole out along the top of layer 1 at about 20 km depth which therefore represents a key detachment horizon during post-Caledonian extension. A branch of the Outer Isles fault and the fault to the W appear to sole out along the Moho which may also have acted as a detachment horizon in the W (cf. Blundell *et al.* 1984).

further increase from 70 to 80 mWm^{-2} destroys the lowest zone at the base of the crust. Lower geothermal gradients therefore would favour the development of basal and mid-crustal detachment horizons whereas higher geothermal gradients would favour mid- and upper-crustal detachments (see Blundell *et al.* 1985).

Conclusion

The model demonstrates that the extensional strength of intraplate continental lithosphere is critically dependent on geothermal gradient, crustal composition and thickness. Of these, geothermal gradient exerts the strongest control on lithosphere strength; strength decreasing with increase in geothermal gradient. For likely levels of tectonic force, only lithosphere with heat flow >65–70 mWm^{-2} would be expected to undergo significant extension. This is consistent with heat-flow data from currently active and inactive tectonic regions.

Both the bulk strength of the lithosphere and the strength distribution with depth are conrolled by crustal composition. Large variations in the predicted strength of the lithosphere are produced by substituting plagioclase rheology for dry quartz in the lower crust, or wet quartz for dry quartz in the upper crust. A three-layer crustal rheology model (wet quartz above dry quartz above plagioclase), corresponding approximately to the present crustal structure of northern Scotland (see Blundell 1985), predicts major strength discontinuities at each compositional boundary. These weak zones represent potential detachment horizons during extension. Lower geothermal gradients (heat flows in the range 60–70 mWm^{-2}) favour the development of basal and mid-crustal detachments, whereas higher geothermal gradients (70–80 mWm^{-2}) favour mid- and upper-crustal detachments. The BIRPS MOIST deep reflection section across northern Scotland indicates that the lower two boundaries appear to have acted as detachment horizons during Mesozoic extension (Fig. 17), which is consistent with the model predictions.

Because the quartzo-feldspathic rheology of the crust is weaker than the olivine rheology of the mantle, crustal thickness exercises a significant control on bulk lithosphere strength. The lithosphere is appreciably stronger for models with thinner crust. For lithosphere with surface heat flow of 70 mWm^{-2}, a 20-km thick crust model is three to four times stronger than a 35-km thick crust. For very high and very low heat flows however, the strength of the lithosphere is independent of crustal thickness being controlled by the quartz rheology of the upper crust and the olivine rheology of the mantle respectively.

The process of lithosphere extension causes both a thinning of the crust, which has a strengthening effect (strain 'hardening'), and an increase in the geothermal gradient, which has a weakening effect (strain 'softening'). The rate of extension is critical in determining which process predominates. Fast strain rates (e.g. 10^{-14} sec^{-1}) produce a net weakening, while slow strain rates (e.g. 10^{-16} sec^{-1}) produce a net strengthening. For an intermediate strain rate of 10^{-15} sec^{-1}, lithosphere with a thermal age of 10–50 Ma shows an almost constant lithosphere strength up to a β value of 1.5, then hardens. This figure corresponds with the average β values of a representative set of intracontinental extensional basins.

It follows that slower extension rates would lead to the cessation of extension at one place when the critical β value was reached, and the spreading of the deformation laterally to an adjoining region, whereas faster strain rates with progressive softening would lead to a concentration of deformation in one section of lithosphere and potentially to infinite β values with crustal separation. Figure 18 is an illustrative model demonstrating the different tectonic styles which might be expected with fast and slow extension rates. Fast strain rates might be expected to lead to narrowing of the zone of active deformation and a progressive increase in β value, whereas slow strain rates should lead to progressive widening of the zone of active deformation as each section reaches the critical β value of around 1.5. The use of major mid- and lower-crustal detachment horizons would be favoured by the slow-extension model.

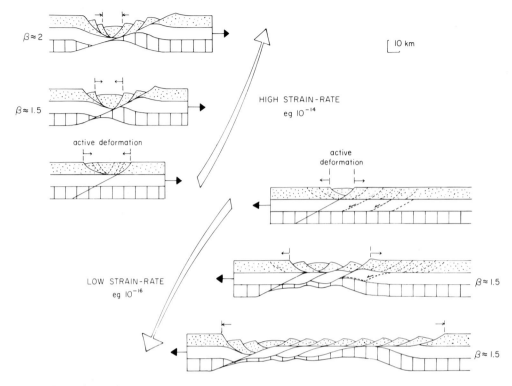

FIG. 18. Illustrative models showing the different styles of extensional deformation expected with fast and slow rates of extension. At *fast strain rates* (e.g. 10^{-14}) strain softening might be expected to localize the deformation near the original site of complete lithosphere failure causing progressive narrowing and intensification of the active deformation and leading potentially to high β values and complete crustal separation. At *slow strain rates* (e.g. 10^{-16}) local strain hardening might be expected to transfer deformation laterally to previously undeformed areas thus progressively widening the zone of active deformation but with a limiting β value of around 1.5. Note in the slow strain-rate model the use of detachment horizons between the crustal layers to transfer the deformation.

References

AVÉ LALLEMENT, H.G. 1978. Experimental deformation of diopside and websterite. *Tectonophysics*, **48**, 1–27.

BAMFORD, D. 1979. Seismic Constraints on the deep geology of the Caledonides of Northern Britain. *In*: HARRIS, A.L., HOLLAND, C.H. & LEAKE, B. E. (eds) *The Caledonides of the British Isles –reviewed. Spec. publ. geol. Soc. London*, **8**, 93–6.

BLUNDELL, D.J., HURICH, C.A. & SMITHSON, S. B. 1985. A model for the Moist seismic reflection profile, N. Scotland. *J. geol. Soc. London*, **142**, 245–58.

BODINE, J.H., STECKLER, M.S. & WATTS, A.B. 1981. Observations of flexure and the rheology of the oceanic lithosphere. *J. geophys. Res.* **86**, 3695–707.

BREWER, J.A. & SMYTHE, D.K. 1984. Moist and the continuity of crustal reflector geometry along the Caledonian-Appalachian orogen. *J. geol. Soc. London*, **141**, 105–20.

GOETZE, C. 1978. The mechanisms of creep in olivine. *Phil. Trans. R. Soc.* **A288**, 99–119.

GRIFFITH, A.A. 1924. Theory of rupture. *Proc. 1st int. Congr. Applied Mechanics*, Delft, **A221**, 163–98.

KOCH, P.S., CHRISTIE, J.M. & GEORGE, R.P. 1980. Flow law of 'wet' quartzite in the α-quartz field. *Eos.* **61**, 376.

KOHLSTEDT, D.L. & GOETZE, C. 1974. Low-stress high-temperature creep in olivine single crystals. *J. geophys. Res.* **79**, 2045–51.

KUSZNIR, N.J. 1982. Lithosphere response to externally and internally derived stresses: a viscoelastic stress guide with amplification. *Geophys. J.R. astron. Soc.* **70**, 399–414.

—— & PARK, R.G. 1984. Intraplate lithosphere deformation and the strength of the lithosphere. *Geophys. J.R. astron. Soc.* **79**, 513–38.

McCLINTOCK, F.A. & WALSH, J.B. 1962. Friction on Griffith cracks under pressure. *Proc. 4th U.S. Nat. Congr. Applied Mechanics*, pp. 1015–21.

McKENZIE, D. 1978. Some remarks on the development of sedimentary basins. *Earth planet. Sci. Lett.* **40**, 25–32.

MORGAN, P. 1982. Heat flow in rift zones, In: PALMASON, G. (ed.) *Continental and Oceanic Rifts. Am. Geophys. Union Geodyn. Ser.* 8, 107–22.

MORGAN, P. 1984. The thermal structure and thermal evolution of the Continental Lithosphere. *Phys. Chem. Earth. Preprint.*

POLLACK, H.N. & CHAPMAN, D.S. 1977. On the regional variation of heat flow, geotherms and lithosphere thickness. *Tectonophysics,* 38, 279–96.

POST, R.L. 1977. High temperature creep of Mt Burnet Dunite. *Tectonophysics.* 42, 75–110.

SCLATER, J.G., PARSONS, B. & JAUPART, C. 1981.

Oceans and Continents: similarities and differences in the mechanism of heat loss. *J. geophys. Res.* 86, 535–52.

SHELTON, G. & TULLIS, J. 1981. Experimental flow laws for crustal rocks. *Eos.* 62, 396.

VITORELLO, I. & POLLACK, H.N. 1980. On the variation of continental heat flow with age and the thermal evolution of continents. *J. geophys. Res.* 85, 983–95.

WHITE, S.H. 1976. The effects of strain on the microstructures, fabrics and deformation mechanisms of quartzites. *Phil. Trans. R. Soc. London,* A283, 69–86.

N.J. KUSZNIR, Department of Geological Sciences, University of Liverpool, Liverpool L69 3BX, UK.
R.G. PARK, Department of Geology, University of Keele, Keele, Staffs ST5 5BG, UK.

Appendix

The mathematical model considers the horizontal stresses arising from a tectonic force applied to the lithosphere in the horizontal direction, defined as the x-axis, at time $t = 0$. The perpendicular horizontal axis is labelled y and the vertical axis z (measured positive downwards). Fundamental to the model is the conservation of the horizontal tectonic force applied to the lithosphere and this gives the equation:

$$\int_0^L \sigma_x \, dz = \text{constant},$$

where σ_x is the horizontal stress in the lithosphere and L is the lithosphere thickness. Differentiation of this equation with respect to time gives:

$$\int_0^L \dot{\sigma}_x \, dz = 0.$$

The assumption that the various layers of the lithosphere are welded together and that the lithosphere undergoes a uniform horizontal strain with depth gives the equation:

$$\frac{d\epsilon_x}{dz} = 0,$$

or differentiating with respect to time

$$\frac{d\dot{\epsilon}_x}{dz} = 0$$

Each infinitesimal component of the lithosphere is assumed to behave as a Maxwell visco-elastic material capable of brittle deformation. Stress and strain for such a material are linked by the equation:

$$\epsilon_x = \frac{1}{E}(\sigma_x - \sigma_x^0) - \frac{\nu}{E}(\sigma_y - \sigma_y^0) - \frac{\nu}{E}(\sigma_z - \sigma_z^0) + \epsilon_x^\nu$$

where ϵ_x is the total horizontal strain, σ_x is the total stress in the x-direction, σ_x^0 is the initial stress, ϵ_x^ν is the ductile creep in the x-direction, E is Young's modulus and ν is Poisson's ratio. Initial stresses σ_x^0, σ_z^0 and σ_y^0 are used for modelling stress release by brittle fracture. Similar equations exist for strains ϵ_y and ϵ_z.

Plane strain in the y-direction gives the additional equation $\epsilon_y = 0$ while the vertical stress σ_z arising from the applied stress is zero, i.e. $\sigma_z = 0$. Manipulation and integration of the above equations gives the final equations for the temporal and spatial variations of σ_x and σ_y

$$\sigma_x = \int_0^t \left(\frac{1}{L} \int_0^L k\dot{\epsilon}_y dz - k\dot{\epsilon}_y \right) dt' - \frac{1}{L} \int_0^L \sigma_x^0 \times dz + \sigma_x^0,$$

$$\sigma_y = \int_0^t \left[\nu\dot{\sigma}_x - E \frac{(2\sigma_y - \sigma_x)}{6\eta} \right] dt' + \sigma_y^0 - \nu\sigma_x^0$$

where $k = E/(1 - \nu^2)$.

The derivation of these equations is decribed in greater detail by Kusznir (1982).

Following Kohlstedt & Goetze (1974), Goetze (1978), Post (1977) and Bodine *et al.* (1981) the following relationship between creep rate, stress and temperature for dislocation, and Dorn law creep for the olivine rheology of the mantle is used:

dislocation creep,

$$\dot{\epsilon} = 7 \times 10^{10} \exp\left(\frac{-53030}{T}\right)(\sigma_1 - \sigma_3)^3 \text{ sec}^{-1}$$

$$\text{for } (\sigma_1 - \sigma_3) < 2 \text{ kb};$$

Dorn law,

$$\dot{\epsilon} = 5.7 \times 10^{11} \exp\left(\frac{-55556}{T} \left(1 - \frac{(\sigma_1 - \sigma_3)}{85}\right)^2\right) \text{sec}^{-1}$$

$$\text{for } (\sigma_1 - \sigma_3) > 2 \text{ kb,}$$

where $(\sigma_1 - \sigma_3)$ is in kb (1 kb = 100 MPa).

The creep rate used for the wet-quartz, dry-quartz and plagioclase rheologies of the crust are as follows and are based on the experimental work of Koch, Christie & George (1980) and Shelton & Tullis (1981):

wet quartz,

$$\dot{\epsilon} = 4.36 \exp\left(\frac{-19332}{T}\right) (\sigma_1 - \sigma_3)^{2.44} \text{ sec}^{-1};$$

dry quartz,

$$\dot{\epsilon} = 0.126 \exp\left(\frac{-18245}{T}\right) (\sigma_1 - \sigma_3)^{2.86} \text{ sec}^{-1};$$

plagioclase,

$$\dot{\epsilon} = 8.2 \times 10^2 \exp\left(\frac{-28788}{T}\right) (\sigma_1 - \sigma_3)^{3.2} \text{ sec}^{-1},$$

where $(\sigma_1 - \sigma_3)$ is in kb.

Brittle deformation within the lithosphere has been predicted by the use of Griffith's theory (1924) as modified by McClintock & Walsh (1962). Three failure domains have been used—tensional failure, open-crack compressional, and closed-crack compressional. The physical parameters, within the modified Griffith theory, which control failure are tensile strength, T_0; the frictional coefficient, μ; and the critical stress, σ_{gc}, required to close the Griffith crack. Of these parameters T_0 and μ have the greatest influence on brittle failure.

The following values for these brittle-failure parameters have been used: $\mu = 0.5$, $T_0 = 0.2$ kb (20 MPa) and $\sigma_{gc} = 1.0$ kb (100 MPa). The justification for these chosen values and the effect of varying μ and T_0 on lithosphere strength is discussed in Kusznir & Park (1984).

Failure is dependent on stresses σ_x and σ_z. The stress σ_y, being the intermediate stress, is not required in the two-dimensional Griffith–McClintock and Walsh formulation. At failure the stress σ_x is returned to the failure envelope (the stress σ_z is simply lithostatic).

The tensile strength of the lithosphere and the localization of extension

H.D. Lynch & P. Morgan

SUMMARY: Continents appear to rift in preference to oceans. Furthermore, some areas of continents appear to be more susceptible to rifting than others. Experimental rock mechanics data are used to estimate lithospheric strength for lithospheres of different structure, thereby to investigate the possible causes of rift localization. Using optimum creep parameters for silicic, mafic and ultramafic rocks, we find that lithospheric strength is inversely related to both crustal thickness and heat flow. By virtue of its thinner crust, oceanic lithosphere is inherently stronger than continental lithosphere. We find that oceanic lithosphere older than about 10 Ma should be able to withstand the lithospheric forces exerted on it by gravity sliding and plate interactions. Rifting or ridge-jumps are therefore only likely to occur in very young oceanic lithosphere. Low heat flow continental shields should also be able to withstand likely lithospheric forces without significant deformation. As the heat flow increases, however, the lithosphere is weakened dramatically. A smaller amount of weakening is associated with crustal thickening. Thus, unless rifting is localized by a strongly heterogeneous stress field, it will be by anomalously weak lithosphere. This lithosphere is likely to have anomalously high heat flow and/or crustal thickness prior to extension.

Localization of extension

Rifts or zones of extension are ubiquitous in the continents. It is rare that extension originates in oceanic lithosphere, although new oceans are the product of successful continental rifts and oceanic rifts maintain extension. Crough (1983) has suggested that extensional deviatoric stresses associated with topography are greater in continents than oceans which may in part explain preferential rifting of continents. Lynch (1983) and Vink *et al.* (1984) have calculated that continental lithosphere is inherently weaker than oceanic lithosphere providing an additional mechanism for the preferential rifting of continents.

There is also evidence that some continental areas are rifted in preference to others. For example, the pre-1100 Ma cratons of Africa (Clifford 1970) were not cut by Mesozoic Atlantic rifting nor Cenozoic East African rifting. The Colorado Plateau has remained essentially undeformed during two Cenozoic episodes of rifting which surround it on three sides (Morgan & Swanberg 1985). Vink *et al.* (1984) concluded that the lithosphere becomes progressively weaker as the crust thickens, and some rifting is undoubtedly associated with thick crust (e.g. Morgan & Burke 1985). Some extension, however, develops in locally thin crust (even accounting for extensional thinning), such as the southern Rio Grande rift (Morgan *et al.* 1986).

Extensional tectonics are commonly associated with magmatism, and it is often observed that magmatic activity precedes rifting (Ramberg & Morgan 1984). This observation suggests that lateral variations in the geotherm may be associated with the localization of rifting. In this contribution, we present an analysis of the relationship between the geotherm and the tensile strength of the lithosphere.

Tensile strength of the lithosphere

Non-elastic deformation within the lithosphere is a complex function of a number of mechanisms. These mechanisms, however, can be classified as either brittle failure or ductile creep and at any depth the lithosphere can be assigned a brittle yield strength and a ductile yield strength. The yield stress for the lithosphere at any depth is given by the lesser of the brittle and ductile yield strengths (Tapponier & Francheteau 1978; Goetze & Evans 1979; Brace & Kohlstedt 1980), and this yield stress can be plotted as a function of depth giving a yield stress profile, as shown in Fig. 1. The integral of this profile over depth is the total yield stress of the lithosphere, or the horizontal deviatoric force, per unit horizontal length, required to cause non-elastic extension or compression. The point where the brittle and ductile yield strengths are equal is referred to as a brittle–ductile transition, and there can be more than one brittle–ductile transition in the lithosphere, as shown in Fig. 1. Yield stress profiles for the lithosphere can be extrapolated from the results of experimental rock mechanics in good agreement with geological observations.

From COWARD, M.P., DEWEY, J.F. & HANCOCK, P.L. (eds), 1987, *Continental Extensional Tectonics*, Geological Society Special Publication No. 28, pp. 53–65.

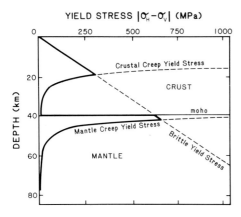

FIG. 1. Yield stress versus depth for continental lithosphere extending at a rate of 10^{-14} sec^{-1}. Temperatures correspond to a reduced heat flow of 42 mW m^{-2}, and the creep rheologies are for a mafic crust and ultramafic mantle. Crustal thickness is 40 km. The lithospheric yield strength profile is shown by the heavy curve. Between 0 and 19 km, the crust is deforming by brittle processes; between 19 and 40 km, the crust is deforming by creep. Between 40 and 42 km, the mantle is deforming brittlely and below 42 km it is deforming by creep. An increase in strain rate of a factor of 10 depresses the creep curves and brittle–ductile transitions by about 4 km, and vice versa for a decrease in strain rate (see Morgan & Golombek 1984).

Dependence of yield stress on depth

Evidence from drill holes, electrical conductivity and outcrops suggests that crustal rocks are extensively fractured, with a wide range of fracture orientations at any given locality (e.g. Brace 1972). Thus, for brittle failure, rock is modelled as a frictional plastic material. Resistance to sliding on fractures increases with pressure, and thus depth, but appears to be independent of strain rate, temperature and rock type (e.g. Byerlee 1978; Jamison & Cook 1980; McGarr 1980; Stetsky 1978). Accordingly, we have assumed that brittle yield strength, $(\sigma_H - \sigma_V)_{by}$ (the stress difference required for brittle failure), is given by

$$(\sigma_H - \sigma_V)_{by} = \beta z, \qquad (1)$$

where z is depth and β is the yield stress gradient given by 16 MPa km^{-1} for extension and 40 MPa km^{-1} for compression.

Ductile flow in rock, or creep, occurs whenever a deviatoric stress is present, but need only be considered when significant deformation occurs over geological time. The ductile yield

strength, $(\sigma_H - \sigma_V)_{dy}$ (the stress deviation required to produce a given creep rate), for a particular rock type, decreases with temperature, and thus decreases with depth (e.g. Carter 1976; Goetze & Brace 1972; Weertman & Weertman 1975), and we have assumed a power-law steady-state-flow creep equation (e.g. Weertman & Weertman 1975) of the form

$$(\sigma_H - \sigma_V)_{dy} = (\dot{\epsilon}/\dot{\epsilon}_0)^{1/n}$$
$$\exp[(Q^* + PV^*)/3RT], \qquad (2)$$

where $\dot{\epsilon}$ is strain rate, R is the gas constant, T is absolute temperature, $\dot{\epsilon}_0$, n and Q^* are constants dependent on rock type, P is pressure and V^* is the activation volume. Experimental determinations of the paramters $\dot{\epsilon}_0$, n and Q^* for various rocks and minerals, and representative values of these parameters, for silicic, mafic and ultramafic rock, adopted in this study are given in Table 1. An activation volume of 11×10^3 mm^3 mole^{-1} (Kohlstedt et al. 1980) results in the depth dependence (assuming a pressure gradient of 26.5 MPa km^{-1})

$$PV^* = 293 \, z \, \text{J mole}^{-1} \, \text{km}^{-1} \qquad (3)$$

where z is depth in km. Examples of ductile yield stress curves are shown in Figs 1 & 2, which illustrate that ductile yield stress is strongly dependent upon strain rate, temperature and composition.

Figure 2 shows the effect of the geothermal gradient on the yield stress level, the main focus of the present study. Geotherms, $T(z)$, were calculated using the equilibrium geotherm equation of Lachenbruch & Sass (1978) for steady-state conductive heat flow with radiogenic heat production near the surface:

$$T(z) = \frac{1}{k} \{q_r A_0 + D^2 [1 - \exp(-z/D)]\} \qquad (4)$$

where k is the thermal conductivity, A_0 is the surface heat production, and D is the characteristic depth of heat production. The reduced heat flow, q_r, represents heat flow from depth, and is the parameter used here to define the geothermal regime, with a low value of 25 mW m^{-2} representing a very cool continental shield, and a high value, 59 mW m^{-2} representing a hot geotherm typical of the Basin and Range Province. The value of A_0 varies from location to location, and can have a strong effect on lithospheric temperatures (Morgan 1984; Morgan & Sass 1984); however, this parameter was not varied in our study. The parameters of Lachenbruch & Sass (1978), $k = 2.5$ W m^{-1}K^{-1},

TABLE 1. *Steady-state creep parameters for rocks and minerals from experimental data and representative average creep parameters used in this study*

Rock or Mineral	$\log \dot{\epsilon}_0$	n	Q^*	Reference
Rocks and minerals common in upper crust (silicic)				
Aplite	−6.5±0.3	3.1	163	1
Granite	−8.85	2.9	106	2
Granite	−8.58	3.4	139	3
Granite (wet)	−2.72	1.5	137	3
Quartzite	−10.1	5.7±0.6	242±21	4
Quartzite	−6.6±0.3	2.86±0.18	150±29	5
Quartzite	−2.96±0.18	2.0	167	1
Quartzite	−4.46	1.9	122	3
Quartzite (wet)	−1.4±1.1	2.6±0.4	230±29	6
Quartzite (wet)	−4.25±0.30	2.44±0.13	159±21	5
Rocks and minerals common in lower crust (mafic)				
Diabase	−3.66±0.7	3.4	259	1
Diabase	−1.21	3.05	276	7
Anothosite	−3.49±0.2	3.2	238	1
Albite	−5.63±0.3	3.9	234	1
Diorite	−1.42	2.4	219	3
Minerals in both lower crust and mantle (mafic)				
Enstatite	−0.5	2.4	293	8
Diopside	1.2±0.5	2.6	334	1
Rocks and minerals common in mantle (ultramafic)				
Dunite	3.1±2.0	3.3±0.5	464±59	9
Dunite	2.87	3.18	543	10
Olivine	5.43	3.0	523±21	11
Olivine	4.84	3.0	510	12
Olivine [110]	4.92	3.6±0.3	523	13
[101]	4.43	3.7±0.2	523	13
[011]	3.80	3.5±0.3	523	13
Forsterite [110]	6.02	2.6±0.2	460±59	14
[101]	6.31	3.6±0.4	573±63	14
[011]	7.04	2.7±0.3	598±54	14
Dunite (wet)	−1.0±0.7	2.1±0.2	226±2	9
Olivine (wet)	−2.35	5.1±0.3	392±11	15
Representative average values used in this study				
Silicic	−7.6±1.2	3.0	138±21	–
Mafic	−2.5±1.2	3.0	251±21	–
Ultramafic	3.0±0.1	3.0	523±21	–

See text for definition of creep parameters: $\dot{\epsilon}_0$ in MPa^{-n} sec^{-1}, n dimensionless, Q^* in kJ mole^{-1}. Indices in brackets indicate crystallographic orientation. Source references for experimental data: 1 Shelton & Tullis (1981); 2 Carter *et al.* (1981); 3 Hansen & Carter (1982); 4 Heard & Carter (1968); 5 Koch *et al.* (1980); 6 Parrish *et al.* (1976); 7 Caristan (1982); 8 Raleigh *et al.* (1971); 9 Carter & Ave'Lallement (1970); 10 Post & Griggs (1973); 11 Kohlstedt & Goetze (1974); 12 Goetze (1978); 13 Durham & Goetze (1977); 14 Darot & Gueguen (1981); 15 Post (1977).

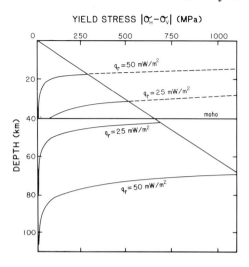

FIG. 2. Yield stress curves for different reduced heat flow values, q_r.

$A_0 = 2.1$ μW m^{-3}, and $D = 10$ km, were used to generate the geotherms used in this study. With these parameters, crustal heat production contributes 21 mW m^{-2} to the surface heat flow. The brittle–ductile transition(s) in crust occurs at a shallower depth for hot lithosphere than for cool lithosphere, and the area to the left of the yield stress curve (Fig. 2) increases as the lithosphere cools.

The curves shown in Figs 1 & 2 represent limits on deviatoric stress levels in the lithosphere (Brace & Kohlstedt 1980), and Goetze & Evans (1979) and Watts et al. (1980) successfully applied this type of yield stress limit to analyses of the mechanics of the bending of oceanic plates. Another situation in which these stress limits may be directly applied is the case of uniformly extending or compressing lithosphere.

Model assumptions for uniformly extending lithosphere

For models of lithospheric extension we have assumed two-dimensional flow or 'plane strain' deformation and constant volume, so the vertical strain rate is equal, but opposite in sign, to the horizontal strain rate. This is equivalent to assuming that Poisson's ratio is 0.5, in agreement with asymptotic steady-state flow of a visco-elastic substance. Thus, the horizontal strain rate determines the overall strain state at a point. Furthermore, it is assumed that the hor-

izontal strain rate is uniform throughout the portion of the lithosphere in question.

In order to obtain such a flow field it is necessary to meet several geological conditions. One condition is that the rock be laterally homogeneous; variations in rock-type and temperature occur only along the vertical coordinate. Another condition is that no shear stress is transmitted at the lithosphere/asthenosphere boundary. Finally, a state of steady-state flow is required, elastic stress variations have decayed, and deviatoric stresses in the creeping layers are determined entirely by creep laws.

Oceanic lithosphere meets these requirements fairly well; it is fairly uniformly layered with very gradual changes in sediment thickness and temperature in regions away from trenches and spreading centres. Global analyses of plate stresses by Forsyth & Uyeda (1975), and Chapple & Tullis (1977) suggest that the shear stress at the base of oceanic lithosphere is much less than 1 MPa. Continental lithosphere shows much greater lateral inhomogeneity than oceanic lithosphere but, to a crude approximation, it is fairly uniform over some geological provinces. In addition, there appears to be appreciable shear stress at the base of continental lithosphere, (Forsyth & Uyeda 1975; Chapple & Tullis 1977); indeed, asthenosphere may be entirely lacking beneath some continental shields (Chapman & Pollack 1974). For tectonically active lithosphere with a well-developed asthenosphere below it, the shear stress at the base of the lithosphere may be quite small, however.

Mercier (1980) presented stress- and strain-rate profiles for the United States Basin and Range Province and South African craton which he calculated on the basis of grain-size palaeopiezometers in mantle xenoliths. He found a fairly uniform strain rate of 10^{-15} sec^{-1} throughout the sampled depth of 50–80 km in the Basin and Range Province. This result is in basic agreement with a uniform stretching model for the Basin and Range. The South African craton, however, showed an extremely low strain rate of 10^{-18} sec^{-1}, at 80 km depth, which increased gradually to 10^{-14} sec^{-1} at 240 km depth. This is consistent with a model in which the Earth's rigid surface is translating relative to the asthenosphere, with the increasing strain rate with depth due to increasing temperature and creep rate. Thus, it appears that tectonically active lithosphere can meet the requirements of the simple stretching or compressing models, while basal shear effects may dominate strain beneath cratons; however, calculations will be made for lithosphere with cratonic temperatures, for purposes of comparison.

Depth and temperature of the brittle–ductile transition

Figure 3 displays the depth of the brittle-ductile transition as a function of strain rate. The curves represent models with reduced heat flows of 25, 42, and 59 mW m^{-2} with a two-layer crust. At the high value of reduced heat flow, typical of tectonically active regions, the mantle and lower crust deform entirely by creep mechanisms; the brittle–ductile transition is confined to the upper crust. With decreasing geothermal gradient, deeper layers of the lithosphere acquire a brittle zone as the deviatoric stress required to cause geological strain rates surpasses the brittle yield stress. The depth of the brittle–ductile transition increases with increasing strain rate.

The depth of the brittle–ductile transition, for a given type of rock, is surprisingly independent of temperature. In Fig. 4, temperature versus strain-rate curves are plotted for the same brittle–ductile transitions presented in Fig. 3. The curves for different geothermal gradients plot very close to one another.

To examine this phenomenon further, we solve equation (2) for temperature:

$$T = \frac{Q^* + PV^*}{R \cdot [\ln(\dot{\epsilon}_0/\dot{\epsilon}) = 3n(\sigma_H - \sigma_V)]} . \qquad (5)$$

At the brittle–ductile transition, the creep stress is equal to the brittle yield stress; so, inserting equation (1) into equation (2), and assuming that PV^* is proportional to depth (equation 3), we obtain

$$T_{BD} = \frac{Q^* + 293\,z}{R \cdot [\ln(\dot{\epsilon}_0/\dot{\epsilon}) + 3\ln(\beta z)]} , \qquad (6)$$

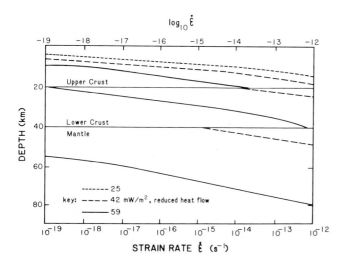

FIG. 3. Depth of the brittle-ductile transition as a function of strain rate for different values of reduced heat flow for a silicic upper crust, mafic lower crust, and ultramafic mantle.

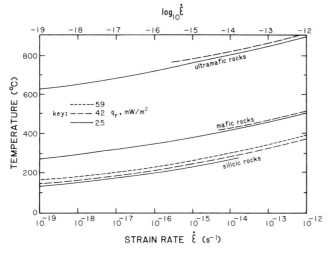

FIG. 4. Temperature of the brittle–ductile transition for different rock types as a function of strain rate for different values of reduced heat flow.

for the temperature of the brittle–ductile transition. The depth terms in the numerator and denominator tend to counteract each other, and at lithospheric depths, their variations tend to cancel. For example, the brittle–ductile ultramafic transition for a strain rate of 10^{-15} sec^{-1} changes from 815°C at a depth of 44 km to 807°C at a depth of 68 km for a reduction in reduced heat flow from 42 to 15 mW m^{-2}. Despite a substantial change in depth and thermal gradient, the temperature of the transition is essentially unchanged. The logarithmic strain-rate term of equation (6) produces the slight strain-rate dependence of the curves in Fig. 4. For geological strain rates of 10^{-14} to 10^{-17} sec^{-1}, the transitional temperature ranges from 700 to 800°C for ultramafic rock, 330 to 430°C for mafic rock, and 200 to 300°C for granitic rock.

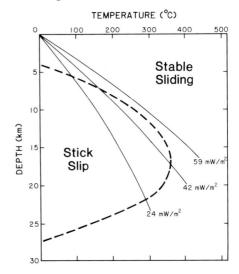

FIG. 5. Comparison of Brace's (1972) transition between stick-slip behaviour and stable sliding, for both granite and gabbro combined, with continental geotherms for different reduced heat flow values indicated by curves. The transition is not sharply defined, and is indicated by the dashed line.

The brittle–ductile transition and the maximum depth of earthquakes

Earthquakes represent a sudden slippage of rock along a fracture surface, and generally should be restricted to zones of brittle deformation. The maximum depth, in a region, at which earthquakes occur will delineate the brittle–ductile transition if there are a sufficient number of earthquakes and the entire brittle zone is seismically active. Unfortunately, the situation is complicated by two dominant modes of slippage, stick-slip behaviour (associated with earthquakes), and stable sliding (Jaeger & Cook 1976, Chapter 3).

The transition between stick-slip and stable sliding behaviour is poorly delineated, but has a strong temperature and pressure (depth) dependence, as well as dependence on mineralogy and details of the sliding surface (Brace 1972). Figure 5 presents this transition as a function of temperature and depth for granite and gabbro combined together with geotherms for different values of reduced heat flow. For reduced heat flows below 40 mW m^{-2}, the depth range of stick-slip behaviour is about 5 to 20 km. The geotherm for a reduced heat flow of 59 mW m^{-2}, typical of the Basin and Range Province, lies entirely outside the stick-slip range; however, earthquake activity is very common inside this province (Smith 1978). Thus, the actual range of stick-slip behaviour must be more extensive than shown in Fig. 5; the presence of such behaviour in the upper crust appears therefore, to be a reasonable assumption. Chen & Molnar (1981) analysed the depth distributions of continental and oceanic earthquakes and concluded that temperature was the

dominant factor in determining the maximum depth of earthquakes, with temperatures less than 250 to 450°C required for earthquakes to occur in the crust, while mantle earthquakes can occur at temperatures up to 600 to 800°C. These temperatures are in good agreement with those predicted for the brittle–ductile transition in Fig. 4. Good agreement between observed earthquake–depth distributions and yield stress model predictions for different thermal regimes has also been found by Meissner & Strehlau (1982) and Sibson (1982).

It should be pointed out that the laboratory data for creep and brittle yield stresses to deviatoric stresses are extrapolated above 100 MPa and are therefore uncertain. The brittle–ductile transition in the mantle occurs at the very point where these extrapolations are at their greatest; the agreement between the predicted temperature of this transition with the base of the observed mantle seismogenic layer may be fortuitous, but is consistent with the extrapolation. Uncertainty in the values of the creep equation parameters results in uncertainty in the ·value of the calculated brittle–ductile transition temperature. The uncertainties in the average creep parameters listed in Table 1 results in an uncertainty of 70°C for the brittle–ductile transitions in mafic and ultramafic rocks, and 100°C for the transition for granitic rock. These uncertainties are about the same as the uncertainty in the temperature which limits the depths of earthquakes.

Integrated stress difference and strength of the lithosphere

To model the lithosphere as a mechanical unit, Artyushkov (1973) introduced the integrated horizontal deviatoric stress,

$$\Sigma = \int_0^L (\sigma_H - \sigma_V)dz, \tag{7}$$

where L is the thickness of the lithosphere. He estimated values of Σ which should be caused by lateral density changes in the lithosphere. Σ represents the deviatoric force per unit length exerted by the lithosphere across a plane defined by the vertical stress axis and the intermediate stress axis (the y–z plane); it is the difference between the force required to resist lateral spreading under the force of gravity, and the actual force exerted on the lithosphere. With the convention that compressive stresses are positive, Σ is positive for deviatoric compression, and negative for deviatoric tension.

A similar integrated horizontal yield stress, S, can also be defined for the lithosphere:

$$S \equiv \int_0^L |\sigma_H - \sigma_V|_{yield}dz. \tag{8}$$

In general, S depends on the thermal and mineralogical structure of the lithosphere, as well as the strain rate, $\dot\Sigma$, and whether the lithosphere is in horizontal deviatoric compression or extension. Note that Σ, S, $\dot\epsilon$ and the class of deformation (compression or extension) describe the lithosphere as a whole, as opposed to the depth-dependent thermal and mineralogical variables.

Consider a section of lithosphere subjected to lithospheric forces generated some distance away. The definition of yield stress implies that the relationship

$$|\sigma_H - \sigma_V| \leq |\sigma_H - \sigma_V|_{yield} \tag{9}$$

holds at any point in the lithosphere. Integrating this equation with depth, and utilizing equations (7) and (8) produces the result

$$|\Sigma| \leq S, \tag{10}$$

where the value of S and sign of Σ depend on whether the lithosphere is in extension or com-

pression. If the lithospheric force is less than the yield strength, then lithospheric deformation is elastic, but if it equals the yield strength, non-recoverable non-elastic deformation takes place by creep and brittle sliding. Note that if the equality holds in equation (10), then it must also hold on the point by point basis implied in equation (9).

The state of deviatoric stress in the lithosphere is usually reported in the literature as an 'average deviatoric stress' calculated by determining a number similar to Σ, and dividing by an assumed lithospheric thickness. The strong variation of stress with depth predicted by rock mechanics suggests that this type of number is possibly a misleading description of the actual state of stress in the lithosphere, since the stress at most points is either significantly above or below the average value. Σ has the additional advantage that it is fairly independent of an assumed lithosphere thickness as the stress difference is low in the lower lithosphere.

Estimates of lithospheric forces

To interpret estimates of lithospheric yield strength it is important to consider deformation under geologically realistic conditions. If the strain rate is negligible on a geological time-scale, then deformation is essentially elastic, and we use a strain rate of 10^{-17} sec^{-1} (3% per 100 Ma) as a lower limit for significant non-elastic strain of the lithosphere. An upper limit on geologic strain rates is about 10^{-13} sec^{-1} (300% per Ma; Heard 1976; Pfiffner & Ramsey 1982), although these high strains are localized in narrow zones. An upper limit of 10^{-14} sec^{-1} (30% per Ma) is probably more appropriate to the distributed strain in the extension models for the present study.

Lithospheric forces must be sufficient to cause non-elastic extension. Regional forces are generated by lateral density variations in the lithosphere and asthenosphere associated primarily with mid-ocean ridges, subducting slabs and continental topography and most estimates of these forces per unit length lie in the range 1 to 5×10^{12} N m^{-1} (e.g. Jacoby 1980; McKenzie 1969; Schubert et al. 1975; Forsyth & Uyeda 1975; Richardson et al. 1976; Artyushkov 1973; Bott & Kusznir 1979; Solomon et al. 1980; Lynch 1983). Plate interactions may result in local stresses that exceed regional lithospheric forces (e.g. Atwater 1970; Molnar & Tapponier 1975; Lynch 1983), and we use an upper force limit of 10^{13} N m^{-1} per unit length for discussion of lithospheric deformation.

Strength of oceanic lithosphere

We have modelled oceanic plates as a thin mafic crust (8 km thick) overlying an ultramafic mantle, and the plate model of McKenzie (1967) was used to calculate temperatures in the oceanic lithosphere as a function of age and depth. Parameters for the model were taken from Parsons & Sclater's (1977) fit to global observations of heat flow and sea-floor topography and included a 125 km thick plate with a basal temperature of 1350°C. The integral in equation (8) was evaluated by using a simple rectangle rule; yield stresses were calculated at 100 m intervals, then summed. The oceanic yield stress curves for ages greater than 10 Ma are simpler than the continental yield stress curves shown in Figs 1 & 2, in that the entire crust is brittle and the yield stress curve is equivalent to that of a one-layer lithosphere.

Figure 6 shows lithospheric yield strength as a function of strain rate for extending oceanic lithosphere of different ages. The curve for 3 Ma differs from the other curves because of the presence of a ductile zone in the crust at this age. Beyond 100 Ma, the strength approaches an asymptotic value as the geotherm approaches its equilibrium state. The strength of the old lithosphere is 4×10^{13} in extension and 9×10^{13} in compression, an order of magnitude higher than probable imposed forces. Between 10 and about 70 Ma, the strength increases linearly with age, as shown in Fig. 7, a result that Lynch (1983) has also shown analytically. Above ages of 70 Ma, the thermal-equilibrium geotherm is approached and some deviation from the linear trend is evident as the lithosphere cools and strengthens at a less rapid rate. This linear increase of strength with age is quite interesting, especially in light of the fact that the compressive lithospheric force per unit length of ridge is also linear in age, for simple cooling models (Jacoby 1980).

Strength of continental lithosphere

The thermal structure of continental lithosphere cannot be simply related to age because of its complex thermal structure and evolution (Morgan 1984; Morgan & Sass 1984). We have therefore used reduced heat flow as the thermal parameter for continental lithosphere extension models for a variety of crustal structures. Generally areas which are tectonically active have reduced heat flows of greater than 40 mW m^{-2} while stable areas have reduced heat flows less than 35 mW m^{-2} (Morgan 1984). Lithospheric yield strength as a function of

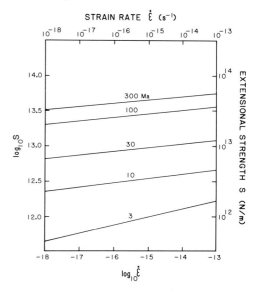

FIG. 6. Extensional strength of the oceanic lithosphere of different ages as a function of strain rate. Numbers on curves represent age in Ma.

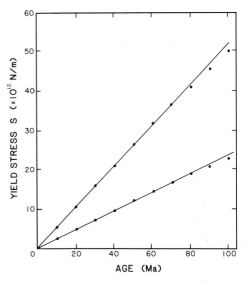

FIG. 7. Dependence of yield strength of oceanic lithosphere on age. Strength increases linearly to about 70 Ma, then increases at a less rapid rate as thermal equilibrium is approached. Lower curve—extension, upper curve—compression.

strain rate for four different crustal structures is shown in Figs 8–11 with families of curves representing a range of reduced heat flow values. These curves are considerably more complex than the oceanic yield strength curves (Fig. 6).

With a 40 km thick two-layer crust there is no brittle zone in the upper mantle for reduced heat flow values above about 40 mW m^{-2} and the lithospheric strength is relatively low, less than the likely range of geological forces (i.e. 5×10^{12} N m^{-1} or less) and thus susceptible to extensional deformation (see Fig. 8). For a low reduced heat flow of 25 mW m^{-2}, the extensional lithospheric strength is an order of magnitude greater than probable lithospheric forces and thus deformation can only occur if the forces are focused locally. For a reduced heat flow of 33 mW m^{-2}, the continental lithosphere is about a factor of 5 weaker than old oceanic lithosphere with an equivalent basal heat flux (Fig. 6), so deformation would still occur preferentially in continental rather than oceanic lithosphere.

The effect of crustal composition on continental lithospheric strength is shown by the comparison of the two-layer crust curves in Fig. 8 with the one-layer mafic crust curves in Fig. 9. For low reduced heat flow (less than 33 mW m^{-2}), the mantle dominates overall strength, and crustal composition is relatively unimportant. For higher reduced heat flow values, where upper-crustal strength dominates, the all-mafic crust is stronger than the two-layer crust, but its strength is still less than probable lithosphere forces and it is susceptible to extensional defor-

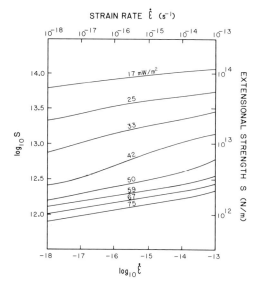

FIG. 9. Curves corresponding to Fig. 8 for a 40-km-thick mafic crust.

mation. Thickening the two-layer crust to 50 km has the same effect as increasing the reduced heat flow by 8–10 mW m^{-2} in the 40 km crust for the transition from 'strong' lithosphere to 'weak' lithosphere (Fig. 10). Crustal thickening weakens the lithosphere for the same geotherm, as relatively strong olivine mineralogy in the uppermost mantle is replaced by weaker crustal mineralogy. Thinning the crust has the opposite effect, and thinning the crust to 30 km is approximately equivalent to reducing the reduced heat flux by about 10 mW m^{-2} in the 40 km crust for the transition in lithospheric strength (Fig. 11). Thus, continental lithospheric strength is strongly dependent on reduced heat flow and crustal composition is only important with high geotherms. Changing crustal thickness by 10 km is roughly equivalent to changing the reduced heat flow by 10 mW m^{-2} in the opposite sense, a change which is similar to the strength uncertainty due to the creep parameter uncertainties in Table 1.

Implications for lithospheric extension

Oceanic lithosphere

The model of oceanic lithospheric strength (Fig. 6) suggests that oceanic lithosphere older than about 10 Ma should be able to withstand

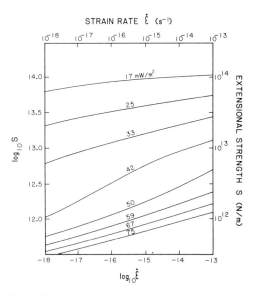

FIG. 8. Extensional continental yield strength as a function of strain rate and reduced heat flow. Numbers on curves indicate reduced heat flow in mW m^{-2}. This model consists of a 20-km-thick silicic upper crust over a 20-km-thick lower crust and ultramafic mantle.

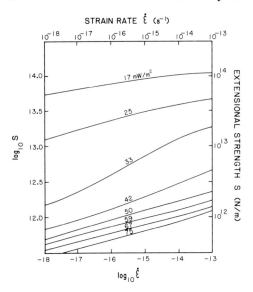

FIG. 10. Curves corresponding to Fig. 8 for a 50-km-thick crust (25 km silicic upper crust with 25 km mafic lower crust).

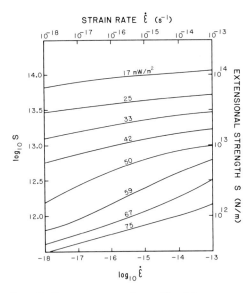

FIG. 11. Curves corresponding to Fig. 8 for a 30-km-thick crust (15 km silicic upper crust with 15 km mafic lower crust).

regional extensional lithospheric forces. Ridge-jumps of 50 to 100 km occur in response to energetically favourable re-orientations of spreading axes (Molnar *et al.* 1975; Shih & Molnar 1975; Lachenbruch, 1976; Hey *et al.* 1980), and these new spreading centres originate

in lithosphere less than a few Ma old assuming a spreading rate of 50 mm yr^{-1}. New spreading centres formed in lithosphere about 10 Ma old, near the hypothetical age limit for such activity, in a rearrangement of the East Pacific spreading system at 5 to 10 Ma (Atwater 1970; Sclater *et al.* 1971; Herron 1972), but such events are rare in the oceanic record. Most oceanic ridges can be traced to a continental origin (e.g. Sclater *et al.* 1981), and the overall observations of oceanic tectonics are in agreement with the predictions based upon experimental rock mechanics.

Continental lithosphere

Our results indicate that continental lithosphere is generally weaker and more likely to rift than oceanic lithosphere and that certain continental areas may be more prone to rifting than others. As noted by Vink *et al.* (1984), crustal thickening is one possible factor responsible for weakening lithosphere and localizing rifting. Our results suggest, however, that variations in the geotherm may have a stronger influence on localization of rifting than crustal thickening. For example, the Basin and Range Province of the US has a crust about 30 km thickness (Smith 1978), a reduced heat flow near 70 mW m^{-2} (Lachenbruch & Sass 1978), and a strain rate near 10^{-15} sec^{-1} (Mercier 1980), for which a force per unit length of about 10^{12} N m^{-1} is indicated (Fig. 11): the eastern US with a thicker 40 km crust and a reduced heat flow of 33 mW m^{-2} resists significant extension under this force, however as shown in Fig. 8, the lower geotherm compensates for the thicker crust in the eastern US in terms of lithospheric strength.

Without prejudice to cause or effect, the observation that volcanism commonly precedes rifting by several Ma (e.g. in East Africa, Baker *et al.* 1972; in the Rio Grande rift, Morgan *et al.* 1986), supports the concept that, at least in some rifts, the lithosphere is heated and weakened prior to rifting. Furthermore, in a detailed analysis of Cenozoic extension in the Rio Grande rift, Morgan & Golombek (1984) and Morgan *et al.* (1986) suggest that changes in the geotherm changing the depth of the brittle–ductile transition may also control the structural style of extension. Weakening of the lithosphere by preheating may be an important precursor to many extensional events.

We recognize that many uncertainties exist in our models. More realistic strength curves could perhaps be generated using dynamic strength models (e.g. Lynch 1983; Kusznir & Park 1984), but the comparative aspects of our results are unlikely to change. The implication that thermal and structural inhomogeneities may localize rifting to certain anomalously weak areas within continents suggests that the initial pre-rift state of the lithosphere must be carefully considered in rift-evolution models.

ACKNOWLEDGMENTS: H.D.L. was a visiting graduate fellow and P.M. was a staff scientist at the Lunar and Planetary Institute (LPI) for part of this study. K. Kincade, M.K. Morgan and J. Plappert are thanked for assistance in preparing this manuscript. LPI is operated by the Universities Space Research Association under Contract No. NASW-3389 for the National Aeronautics and Space Administration. This is LPI contribution no. 570.

References

ARTYUSHKOV, E.V. 1973. Stresses in the lithosphere caused by crustal thickness inhomogeneities. *J. geophys. Res.* **78**, 7675–708.

ATWATER, T. 1970. Implications of plate tectonics for the Cenozoic evaluation of North America. *Bull. geol. Soc. Am.* **81**, 3513–36.

BAKER, B.H., MOHR, P.A. & WILLIAMS, L.A.J. 1972. Geology of the Eastern Rift System of Africa. *Geol. Soc. Am. Spec. Pap. 136*, 67 pp. Boulder, Colorado.

BOTT, M.H.P. & KUSZNIR, N.J. 1979. Stress distributions associated with compensated plateau uplift structures, with applications to the continental splitting mechanism. *Geophys. J.R. astron. Soc.* **56**, 451–9.

BRACE, W.F. 1972. Laboratory studies of stick-slip, and their application to earthquakes. *Tectonophysics*, **14**, 189–200.

—— & KOHLSTEDT, D.L. 1980. Limits on lithospheric stress imposed by laboratory experiments. *J. geophys. Res.* **85**, 6248–52.

BYERLEE, J.D. 1978. Friction of rocks. *Pure appl. Geophys.* **116**, 615–26.

CARISTAN, Y. 1982. The transition from high temperature creep to fracture in Maryland Diabase. *J. geophys. Res.* **87**, 6781–90.

CARTER, N.L. 1976. Steady state flow of rocks. *Rev. Geophys. Space Phys.* **14**, 301–60.

—— & AVE'LALLEMANT, H.G. 1970. High temperature flow of dunite and peridotite. *Bull. geol. Soc. Am.* **81**, 2181–202.

——, ANDERSON, D.A., HANSEN, F.D. & KRANZ, R.L. 1981. Creep and rupture of granitic rocks. *In*: CARTER, N.L., FRIEDMAN, M., LOGAN, J.M. & STEARNS, V.W. (eds) *Mechanical Behavior of Crustal Rocks, Geophys. Mono. 24*, pp. 61–82. Am. Geophys. Union, Washington, DC.

CHAPMAN, D.S. & POLLACK, H.N. 1974. Cold spot in west Africa: Anchoring the African plate. *Nature*, **250**, 477–8.

CHAPPLE, W.M. & TULLIS, T.E. 1977. Evaluation of the forces which drive the plates. *J. geophys. Res.* **82**, 1967–84.

CHEN, WANG-PENG & MOLNAR, P. 1981. Depth distribution of earthquake foci and its possible implications for the rheological structure of the crust and upper mantle (abstract). *Eos.* **62**, 397.

CLIFFORD, T.N. 1970. The structural framework of Africa. *In*: CLIFFORD, T.N. & GASS, I.G. (eds) *Magmatism and Tectonics*, pp. 1–26. Oliver and Boyd, Edinburgh.

CROUGH, S.T. 1983. Rifts and swells: geophysical constraints on causality. *Tectonophysics*, **94**, 23–37.

DAROT, M. & GUEGUEN, Y. 1981. High-temperature creep of single forsterite crystals. *J. geophys. Res.* **86**, 6219–34.

DURHAM, W.B. & GOETZE, C. 1977. Plastic flow of oriented single crystals of olivine. *J. geophys. Res.* **82**, 5737–53.

FORSYTH, D. & UYEDA, S. 1975. On the relative importance of the driving forces of plate motion. *Geophys. J. R. astron. Soc.* **43**, 163–200.

GOETZE, C. 1978. The mechanisms of creep in olivine. *Phil. Trans. R. Soc. London*, **A288**, 99–119.

—— & BRACE, W.F. 1972. Laboratory observations of high-temperature rheology of rocks. *Tectonophysics*, **13**, 583–600.

—— & EVANS, B. 1979. Stress and temperature in the bending lithosphere as constrained by experimental rock mechanics. *Geophys. J. R. astron. Soc.* **59**, 463–78.

HANSEN, F.D. & CARTER, N.L. 1982. Creep of selected rocks at 1000 MPa (abstract). *Eos.* **63**, 437.

HEARD, H.C. 1976. Comparisons of the flow properties of rocks at crustal conditions. *Phil. Trans. R. Soc. London*, **A283**, 173–86.

—— & CARTER, N.L. 1968. Experimentally produced 'natural' intragranular flow in quartz and quartzite. *Am. J. Sci.* **266**, 1–42.

HERRON, E.M. 1972. Sea-floor spreading and the Cenozoic history of the east-central Pacific. *Geol. Soc. Am. Bull.* **83**, 1671–91.

HEY, R., DUENNEBIER, F.K. & MORGAN, W.J. 1980. Propagating rifts on mid-ocean ridges. *J. geophys. Res.* **85**, 3647–58.

JACOBY, W.B. 1980. Plate sliding and sinking in mantle convection and the driving mechanism. *In*: DAVIES, P.A. & RUNCORN, S.K. (eds) *Mechanisms of Continental Drift and Plate Tectonics*, pp. 159–72. Academic Press, New York.

JAEGER, J.C. & COOK, N.G.W. 1976. *Fundamentals of Rock Mechanics*, John Wiley, New York.

JAMISON, D.B. & COOK, N.G.W. 1980. Note on measured values for the state of stress in the Earth's crust. *J. geophys. Res.* **85**, 1833–8.

KOCH, P.S., CHRISTIE, J.M. & GEORGE, R.P. 1980. Flow law of 'wet' quartzite in the α-quartz field. *Eos, Trans. Am. geophys. Union*, **61**, 376.

KOHLSTEDT, D.L. & GOETZ, C. 1974. Low-stress high-temperature creep in single olivine crystals. *J. geophys. Res.* **79**, 2045–51.

——, NICHOLS, H.P.K. & HORNACK, P. 1980. The

effect of pressure on the rate of dislocation recovery in olivine. *J. geophys. Res.* **85**, 3122–30.

KUSZNIR, N.J. & PARK, R.G. 1984. Intraplate lithosphere deformation and the strength of the lithosphere. *Geophys. J. R. astr. Soc.* **79**, 513–38.

LACHENBRUCH, A.H. 1976. Dynamics of a passive spreading center. *J. geophys. Res.* **71**, 1883–1902.

—— & SASS, J.H. 1978. Models of extending lithosphere and heat flow in the Basin and Range Province. *In: Cenozoic Tectonics and Regional Geophysics of the Western Cordillera*, pp. 209–250. *Geol. Soc. Am. Mem.* **152**, Boulder, Colorado.

LYNCH, H.D. 1983. Numerical models of the formation of continental rifts by processes of lithospheric necking. *PhD dissertation*, New Mexico State University, Las Cruces, NM.

MCGARR, A. 1980. Some constraints on levels of shear stress in the crust from observations and theory. *J. geophys. Res.* **85**, 6231–8.

MCKENZIE, D.P. 1967. Some remarks on heat flow and gravity anomalies. *J. geophys. Res.* **72**, 6261–73.

—— 1969. Speculations on the consequences and causes of plate motion. *Geophys. J.R. astr. Soc.* **18**, 1–32.

MEISSNER, R. & STREHLAU, J. 1982. Limits of stresses in the continental crust and their relation to the depth-density distribution of shallow earthquakes. *Tectonics*, **1**, 73–90.

MERCIER, J.C. 1980. Magnitude of the continental lithosphere stresses inferred from rheomorphic petrology. *J. geophys. Res.* **85**, 6293–303.

MOLNAR, P. & TAPPONIER, P. 1975. Cenozoic tectonics of Asia: effects of a continental collision. *Science*, **189**, 419–26.

——, ATWATER, T., MAMMERICK, J. & SMITH, S. M. 1975. Magnetic anomalies bathymetry and the tectonic evolution of the South Pacific since the late Cretaceous. *Geophys. J.R. astr. Soc.* **40**, 383–420.

MORGAN, P. 1984. The thermal structure and thermal evolution of the continental lithosphere. *Phys. Chem. Earth*, **15**, 107–93.

—— & BURKE, K. 1985. Collisional plateaus, *Tectonophysics*, **119**, 137–51.

—— & GOLOMBEK, M. 1984. Factors controlling the phases and styles of extension in the northern Rio Grande rift. *Field Conf. Guidebook N. M. Geol. Soc.* **35**, 13–20.

—— & SASS, J.H. 1984. Thermal regime of the continental lithosphere. *J. Geodynamics*, **1**, 143–66.

—— & SWANBERG, 1985. On the Cenozoic uplift and tectonic stability of the Colorado Plateau. *J. Geodynamics*, **3**, 39–63.

——, SEAGER, W.R. & GOLOMBEK, M.P. 1986. Cenozoic thermal, mechanical and tectonic evolution of the Rio Grande rift. In press, *J. geophys. Res.*

PARRISH, D.K., KRIVIZ, A. & CARTER, N.L. 1976. Finite element folds of similar geometry. *Tectonophysics*, **32**, 183–207.

PARSONS, B. & SCLATER, J.C. 1977. An analysis of the variation of ocean floor bathymetry and heat flow

with age. *J. geophys. Res.* **82**, 803–27.

PFIFFNER, O.A. & RAMSEY, J.G. 1982. Constraints on geologic strain rates: arguments from finite strain rates of naturally deformed rocks. *J. geophys. Res.* **87**, 311–21.

POST, R.L., JR. 1977. High-temperature creep of Mt. Burnet dunite. *Tectonophysics*, **42**, 75–110.

—— & GRIGGS, D.T. 1973. The Earth's mantle: evidence of non-Newtonian flow. *Science*, **181**, 1242–4.

RALEIGH, C.B., KIRBY, S.H., CARTER, N.L. & AVE'LALLEMENT, H.G. 1971. Slip and the Clinoenstatite transformation as competing processes in enstatite. *J. geophys. Res.* **76**, 4011–22.

RAMBERG, I.B. & MORGAN, P. 1984. Physical characteristics and evolutionary trends of continental rifts. *Proc. 27th Int. Geol. Cong.* **7**, pp. 165–216. VNU Science Press, Amsterdam.

RICHARDSON, R.M., SOLOMON, S.C. & SLEEP, N.H. 1976. Intraplate stress as an indicator of plate tectonic driving forces. *J. geophys. Res.* **81**, 1847–56.

SCHUBERT, G., YUEN, D.A. & TURCOTTE, D.L. 1975. Role of phase transition in a dynamic mantle. *Geophys. J.R. astr. Soc.* **42**, 705–35.

SCLATER, J.G., ANDERSON, R.N. & BELL, M.L. 1971. Elevation of ridges and evolution of the central eastern Pacific. *J. geophys. Res.* **76**, 7888–915.

——, PARSONS, B. & JAUPART, C. 1981. Oceans and continents: similarities and differences in the mechanism of heat loss. *J. geophys. Res.* **86**, 11535–52.

SHELTON, G. & TULLIS, J. 1981. Experimental flow laws for crustal rocks. *Eos. Trans. Am. Geophys. Union*, **62**, 396.

SHIH, J. & MOLNAR, P. 1975. Analysis and interpretations of the ridge jumps that eliminated the Surveyor transform fault. *J. geophys. Res.* **80**, 4815–22.

SIBSON, R.H. 1982. Fault zone models, heat flow, and the depth distribution of earthquakes in the continental crust of the United States. *Bull. Seis. Soc. Am.* **72**, 151–63.

SMITH, R.B. 1978. Seismicity, crustal structure, and intraplate tectonics of the interior of the western Cordillera. *In: Cenozoic Tectonics and Regional Geophysics of the Western Cordillera*, pp. 111–144. *Geol. Soc. Am. Mem.* **152**, Boulder, Colorado.

SOLOMON, S.C., RICHARDSON, R.M. & BERGMAN, E.A. 1980. Tectonic stresses: models and magnitudes. *J. geophys. Res.* **85**, 6086–92.

STETSKY, R.M. 1978. Rock friction – the effect of confining pressure, temperature, and pore pressure. *Pure appl. geophys.* **116**, 690–704.

TAPPONIER, P. & FRANCHETEAU, J. 1978. Necking of the lithosphere and mechanics of slowly accreting plate boundaries. *J. geophys. Res.* **83**, 3955–70.

VINK, G.E., MORGAN, W.J. & ZHAO, W.-L. 1984. Preferential rifting of continents: a source of displaced terranes. *J. geophys. Res.* **89**, 10072–6.

WATTS, A.B., BODINE, J.H. & STECKLER, M.S. 1980. Observations of flexure and the state of stress in oceanic lithosphere. *J. geophys. Res.* **85**, 6369–76.

WEERTMAN, J. & WEERTMAN, J.R., 1975. High temperature creep of rock, and mantle viscosity. *In*: DONATH, F.A., STEHLI, F.G. & WETHERILL, G.W. (ed.) *Ann. Rev. Earth planet. Sci.* 3, 293–315.

H. DAVID LYNCH,* Department of Physics, Box 3D, New Mexico State University, Las Cruces, NM 88003, USA.

PAUL MORGAN, Department of Geosciences, Purdue University, West Lafayette, IN 47907, USA, and Lunar & Planetary Institute, 3303 NASA Road One, Houston, TX 77058, USA.

* Present address: Pecter International Co., PO Box 205, Houston, TX 77001, USA.

Some important consequences of lithospheric extension

C.E. Keen

SUMMARY: This paper briefly summarizes two of the important by-products of lithospheric extension during rifting. These are partial melting and the segregation and migration of basaltic melt to crustal levels, and the dynamical consequences of viscous flow in the lower lithosphere and asthenosphere. In both cases, the rift-stage subsidence may be significantly different from that predicted by a simple stretching model and may allow relative uplift of the rift zone, as well as subsidence. The dynamical model also predicts significant uplift of the rift shoulders, doming over the entire rift zone, and asymmetrical continental breakup at rifted continental margins. The relative importance of these predictions depends on the thermal and mechanical properties of the lithosphere. The model predictions help explain some of the discrepancies between the observed behaviour of rifts and results obtained from the simple stretching models.

Kinematic models of lithospheric stretching have been very successful in explaining observations of subsidence and thermal histories in many rifting environments (McKenzie 1978; Steckler & Watts 1982; Royden et al. 1980; Royden & Keen 1980; Sclater & Christie 1980; Sclater et al. 1980; LePichon & Sibuet 1981; Chenet et al. 1982; Beaumont et al. 1982; Sawyer et al. 1982; Hellinger & Sclater 1983; Barton & Wood 1984). The advantages of these models are that they are conceptually simple and are described by a minimal number of parameters. The models, however, are limited by their very simplicity, and there are a number of observed properties of rift basins which they cannot predict satisfactorily.

Among the more serious deficiencies of the simple stretching model is its inability to properly describe the geological history of the rifting process. This is manifested in the variety of geological styles exhibited by rift zones whose evolution may span some tens of millions of years. Examples of the behaviour of rifts which are not easily explained by simple stretching models include: (i) a complex history of vertical motions such as those causing the development of a breakup unconformity between the rift and post-rift phases of continental margin development; (ii) uplift of the shoulders of the rift zones; and (iii) the variable degree of volcanism observed during rifting.

In this paper, the results of quantitative modelling of two important consequences of extension are discussed. These are the role of partial melting in the stretching process and the dynamic behaviour of the lower, ductile lithosphere and asthenosphere during extension. The effect of these factors in modifying the predictions of extensional models is described, and compared with observation. The description given here is necessarily brief, and a full discussion of the methods and assumptions used to obtain the model results can be found elsewhere (Keen 1985; Foucher et al. 1982).

The role of partial melting

Any process which thins the lithosphere may be accompanied by partial melting of mantle asthenosphere. This melt may be the source of volcanism observed in many rift environments. Significant quantities of melt may accumulate when substantial thinning, such as that caused by stretching, occurs.

Consider the simple extension model (Fig. 1) in which extension and lithospheric thinning occur by an amount, β. As the lithosphere thins, asthenosphere rises beneath the thinned region. If the process is rapid enough to be considered adiabatic, then upwelling asthenosphere will experience a decreased pressure while maintaining a high temperature. The pressure drop enables partial melting of the more volatile (basaltic) fraction of the mantle rocks. The degree of partial melting will depend on the amount of extension and thinning, given by β, which determines the pressure decrease.

The amount and distribution of melt is illustrated in Fig. 2 where the solidus and degree of partial melt is shown for a pyrolite mantle composition. Superimposed on these melting curves is the temperature distribution in the lower lithosphere and asthenosphere, for several values of β. The solidus intersects the adiabatic thermal gradient for the asthenosphere (Ta) at a depth of about 75 km, so no melt is produced until the lithosphere/asthenosphere boundary is thinned to this depth, allowing us to define a critical β value for the onset of melting, β_c. The

From COWARD, M.P., DEWEY, J.F. & HANCOCK, P.L. (eds), 1987, *Continental Extensional Tectonics*, Geological Society Special Publication No. 28, pp. 67–73.

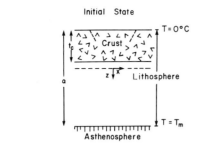

Initial State

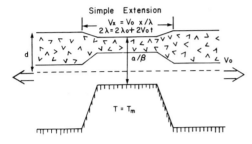

FIG. 1. Simple model of lithospheric stretching. Values for model parameters are given in Table 1. The factor β describes the amount of lithospheric stretching. Within the rift zone the horizontal velocity, v_x, is specified as a function of x. In all models discussed here a linear relationship between v_x and x is assumed. λ is the half-width of the rift zone, and increases in time, as indicated.

total amount of melt can be obtained by integrating over the melt zone, the shaded region in Fig. 2.

The numerical calculations are described in detail by Foucher et al. (1982). These calculations have been used here to show the rift-stage subsidence and the thickness, h_b, of a basaltic layer which could be produced by the volume of melt available (Fig. 3). These quantities are shown as a function of the amount of extension, assuming that extension is not instantaneous but occurs at a steady rate, given by V_0, across a rift zone of initial half width, λ_0. It is also assumed that there is no heat loss during rifting. Parameter values are given in Table 1.

The results show that while β increases steadily with time, the amount of melt (shown here as the equivalent thickness of a basaltic layer) approaches a maximum value of 5.5 km (as $\beta \to \infty$). This is the thickness of oceanic crust which would be produced in the case of complete rupture of the lithosphere. The rift-stage subsidence is rapid at first, becoming more gradual with time. Three cases are shown: (i) the effects of partial melting are not considered in the calculations; (ii) melt production, its segregation and migration from the asthenosphere, and its plutonic solidification at the base of or within the crust is assumed; and (iii) melt production is allowed but there is no migration of the melt (Fig. 3).

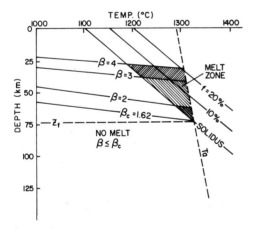

FIG. 2. Lines showing the degree of partial melting for a pyrolite mantle, plotted versus temperature and depth, and the temperature distribution in the lithosphere and asthenosphere. The temperatures within the lower lithosphere are shown for different values of stretching, β. The temperature of the asthenosphere is given by the line marked Ta, the adiabatic temperature. z_f is the level to which the base of the lithosphere must rise before melting can occur. The shaded region illustrates the region in which there is melting.

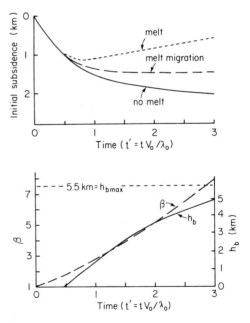

FIG. 3. Illustration of the rift subsidence, β, and amount of melt produced versus time, for a constant rate of extension.

TABLE 1. *Physical properties used in extension- and melt-model calculation.*

Meaning	Value
Density of basaltic melt	2600 kg m^{-3}
Density of basaltic rock	2862
Average crustal density	2862
Average mantle density	3237
Density of asthenosphere	3186
Density of water	1000
Maximum degree of partial melting	22%
Temperature at base of lithosphere (T_m)	1350°C
Coefficient of thermal expansion	$3.2 \times 10^{-5}/°C$
Initial crustal thickness (t_c)	35 km
Initial lithospheric thickness (a)	125 km
Initial thickness of brittle layer (d)	45 km
Critical value of β for onset of partial melting (β_c)	1.63
Adiabatic gradient — asthenosphere	0.5°C km^{-1}
Total thickness and width of the quarter-space used in the flow model (W)	700 km
Thermal activation energy for temperature dependent viscosity (Q)	250 kJ mol^{-1}
Exponent for stress, in power-law creep (n)	3
Initial half-width of rift zone (λ_0)	40 km
Extension rate (V_0)	1 cm a^{-1}

The 'no melt' subsidence curve exhibits the greatest rift-stage subsidence. The curves for models including melt production show less subsidence later in the rift stage. This reduction is caused by the change in isostatic balance which is, in turn, due to the lower density of the melt (see also Foucher *et al.* 1982). When the melt migrates and solidifies in the crust there is greater subsidence than when the melt remains in place, because of the density differences between solid basalt and basaltic melt (Table 1).

Two important conclusions can be drawn from the subsidence curves. First, all the curves exhibit an 'exponential' shape, similar in some respects to that of the thermal cooling subsidence of the post-rift phase of basin formation (McKenzie 1978). This characteristic shape is seen in the rift-stage subsidence of some rifted continental margins (Falvey & Middleton 1981). It has been used to support the hypothesis that a phase change in the crust is a primary cause of subsidence (Falvey & Middleton 1981). However, it is clear from these results that simple extension models will provide the same result.

Secondly, partial melting during extension could cause relative uplift in the late rift stage. This uplift might explain why breakup unconformities occur on many rifted continental margins (Royden & Keen 1980; Falvey & Middleton 1981). However, this is predicted only for values of $\beta > 3.5$ for the model parameters used here.

As shown in Fig. 4, the melt may rise through the lower lithosphere and intrude or underplate the crust. On many rifted margins and in many rift basins a high-velocity lower-crustal layer is observed, which could be the result of this process (LASE Study Group, in press). Alternatively if the melt is retained in the asthenosphere, it may migrate to the surface at the time of final continental rupture at rifted margins. This would produce large quantities of basaltic material extruded near the ocean/continent boundary, and could be the process responsible for margins such as the Vöring plateau and Rockall plateau. The association of dipping seismic reflectors with lava flows on these and other margins may suggest that such processes are widepsread (Hinz 1981; Mutter *et al.* 1982).

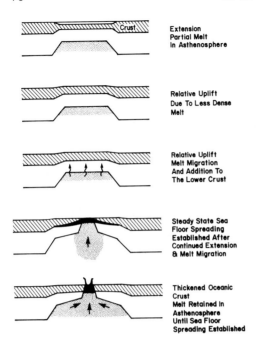

Extension
Partial Melt
In Asthenosphere

Relative Uplift
Due To Less Dense
Melt

Relative Uplift
Melt Migration
And Addition To
The Lower Crust

Steady State Sea
Floor Spreading
Established After
Continued Extension
& Melt Migration

Thickened Oceanic
Crust
Melt Retained In
Asthenosphere
Until Sea Floor
Spreading Established

FIG. 4. Cartoon of possible geological effects of partial melting.

The dynamics of flow below the brittle region

Model calculations

The model calculations will not be described in any detail here, as the basic methods are discussed by Keen (1985). However, the results presented in this paper were derived from an improved version of that earlier model, and so the method requires some brief description. The fundamental objective behind the numerical modelling was to obtain the deformation and thermal histories of the viscous lower lithosphere when subjected to extension, in order to test the assumptions implicit in the kinematic models. From the deformation and the temperature distribution, the subsidence was also computed, in a manner similar to that used in the kinematic models. The model (Fig. 5) is divided into three regions of different mechanical properties: (i) an upper, brittle region which was assumed to behave in a manner described by the simple extension model with stretching at a constant rate given by V_0; (iii) the lower lithosphere which is assumed to deform through viscous flow, with a temperature dependent viscosity; and (iii) the asthenosphere characterized by constant temperature and viscosity.

The thermal properties of the lithosphere are identical to those assumed in the simple extension model, except that the viscous flow can transport heat by convection as well as by conduction in the lower lithosphere. The initial, equilibrium thermal gradient in the lithosphere is linear and is not varied in the model calculations (Table 1).

This model was stepped through a number of time-steps, starting from the equilibrium state of the lithosphere. At each time step the flow velocities and resultant deformation within the viscous region of the model was computed, and the temperature and viscosity distributions in the lithosphere were updated, using these flow velocities. The specified extension rate, V_0, provided the driving force for extension. The post-rift thermal subsidence was computed after the specified time extent of the rift stage was reached, by setting $V_0 = 0$ at subsequent time-steps.

This model is similar to that described by Keen (1985). It is more realistic, however, in that a temperature-dependent viscosity is now included. Furthermore, flow within the asthenosphere is now considered. This is important as motion of the overlying lithosphere will induce flow within the asthenosphere, including upwelling of the asthenosphere below the thinning lithosphere.

Model results

There are two important consequences of flow in the lithosphere and asthenosphere, whose relative importance depend on the magnitude and distribution of viscosity in the lower lithosphere. Firstly, if viscosities are sufficiently low, $\eta_b \sim 2 \times 10^{19}$ Pa·s, lithospheric stretching will trigger small-scale convection near the base of the lithosphere, due to the lateral changes in temperature (and density) in that region (Fig. 6). Secondly, the flow will create dynamic stresses acting at the upper surface of the viscous region. These stresses can produce uplift or doming of the rift zone (Fig. 6).

Small-scale convection will thin the lower lithosphere during and after rifting, to an extent dependent primarily on the viscosity. For high viscosity values near the lithosphere/asthenosphere boundary ($\eta_b \sim 10^{21}$ Pa·s) there is no small-scale convection and the lithosphere deforms according to the predictions of the simple extension model. For low viscosity values ($\eta_b \sim 2 \times 10^{19}$ Pa·s), convective thinning of the lithosphere will be as great as that due to lithospheric stretching. This is one method of thinning the lower lithosphere more than the upper lithosphere, and therefore provides a physical explanation for depth-dependent extension (Hellinger &

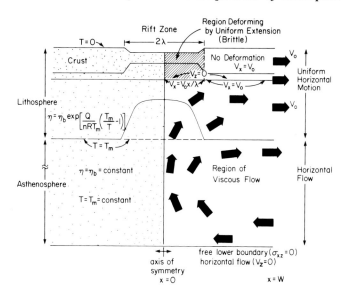

FIG. 5. Illustration of the various regions and parameters involved in the construction of the dynamic rifting model. To the left of the central line the thermal boundary conditions and temperature regions are shown, as well as the viscosity–temperature relationship in the lower lithosphere. On the right the region for which viscous flow and deformation are computed is shown, above which lies the brittle region. Parameter values are given in Table. 1.

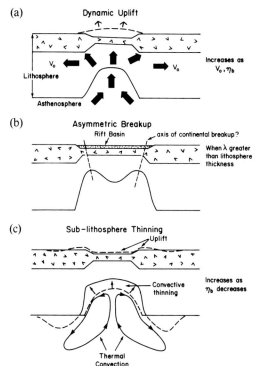

FIG. 6. A cartoon summary of the important results obtained when viscous flow occurs in the lower lithosphere and asthenosphere.

Sclater 1983; Royden & Keen 1980). Convection will also broaden the zone over which thinning occurs, so that the lower lithosphere is thinned beyond the region of stretching in the upper lithosphere. This causes uplift of the rift shoulders.

Convective thinning can occur during and after stretching, but its vigour will decrease as conductive cooling of the lithosphere increases the viscosities and reduces the lateral temperature gradients. However, the effects of convection can be observed in the surface elevations up to one thermal time-constant after rifting stops. This may explain why post-rift subsidence is sometimes delayed for some tens of millions of years and why breakup unconformities are developed on rifted continental margins. It may also explain why post-rift uplift occurs at the edges of some rifted continental margins (e.g. Srivastava *et al.* 1981).

When the width of the rift zone is greater than the thickness of the lithosphere, maximum lithospheric thinning may not occur in the centre of the rift zone because of small-scale convection (Fig. 6). Vigorous convection occurs where lateral temperature gradients are greatest, near the edges of the rift zone. For wide rifts, convective thinning will only affect the sides of the rift, thereby creating maximum thinning in these regions. This could explain why continental breakup does not occur symmetrically, about the centre of a rift, but at one edge. This eventually

C. E. Keen

leaves most of the rift basin on one side of the widening ocean basin (e.g. Jansa & Weidmann 1982).

A weakness of the above arguments in favour of convective thinning of the lower lithosphere is that the asthenosphere's viscosity has been varied, but not its temperature. This is an inconsistency of the model, which includes a temperature-dependent viscosity. In principle, the model should include convection in the Earth's mantle, which determines the initial viscosity and temperature distributions (see e.g. Fleitout & Yuen 1984). In practice, computations for such a model would be extremely time-consuming at present. Furthermore, results presented by Fleitout & Yuen (1984) suggest that a wide range of basal viscosity values, compatible with those quoted above, result from convection models when the viscosity is varied with temperature, pressure and strain rate. Therefore, the correct equation of state describing viscosity in the asthenosphere is still uncertain and it was considered both prudent and practical to keep the models, used here, as simple as possible.

The second important result from the dynamical models is the significance of dynamic stresses, acting on the upper surface of the viscous layer. These stresses may cause uplift which must be added to the rift-stage subsidence to obtain the actual elevation during rifting. Dynamic elevation is directly proportional to η_b and to the rate of extension. These stresses vanish when extension stops, unless there is significant small-scale convection during the post-rift period. Similar dynamical effects result from large-scale mantle convection (e.g. Jarvis & Peltier 1982).

These stresses can cause uplift during rifting (Fig. 6); however, the models are not yet realistic enough to provide adequate numerical esti-mates. An uplift of about 10 km is obtained using the present models, boundary conditions and parameter values. The point to emphasize at present is that flow during stretching can significantly change the simple-model predictions of elevation changes during rifting.

Conclusions

This brief summary of some of the consequences of lithospheric stretching illustrates the large gap which exists between observations in extensional environments and our understanding of the causal processes involved. Both melting in the upwelling asthenosphere and flow in the lower lithosphere and asthenosphere can cause some of the diversity of observations at rifts and rifted continental margins and therefore help to bridge this gap. The results presented here are of necessity oversimplified, and much remains to be done to improve the models and their conceptual basis. Of particular importance is an improved understanding of the mechanical and compositional nature of the lithosphere–asthenosphere system. It is interesting that many of the consequences of extension produce the same kind of geological effects as are predicted by models in which rifting is caused entirely by convection from below (Spohn & Schubert 1982; Yuen & Fleitout 1985). Thus the simple concept of 'active' and 'passive' rifts (Sengor & Burke 1978) may no longer be meaningful in discriminating amongst the various driving mechanisms proposed for rifting.

ACKNOWLEDGMENTS: I am grateful to W. Kay for his help in assembling the diagrams for this paper, and to I. Reid and S. Ojo for helpful comments on the text.

References

BARTON, P. & WOOD, R. 1984. Tectonic Evolution of the North Sea Basin: crustal stretching and subsidence. *Geophys. J.R. astron. Soc.* **79**, 987–1022.

BEAUMONT, C., KEEN, C.E. & BOUTILIER, R. 1982. Evolution of rifted continental margins; comparison of models and observations for the Nova Scotia margin. *Geophys J.R. astron. Soc.* **70**, 667–715.

CHENET, P., MONTADERT, L., GAIRAUD, H. & ROBERTS, D. 1982. Extension ratio measurements on the Galicia, Portugal and North Biscay continental margins; Implications for Evolutionary Models of Passive Continental Margins *In*: WATKINS, J. S. & DRAKE, C.L. (eds) *Studies in Continental Margin Geology. Am. Assoc. Pet. Geol. Mem.* **34**, 703–15.

FALVEY, D.A. & MIDDLETON, M.F. 1981. Passive continental margins; evidence for a pre-breakup deep crustal metamorphic subsidence mechanism. *Oceanologica Acta, Vol 4, SP Geology of Continental Margins Symposium*, pp. 103–14.

FLEITOUT, L. & YUEN, D.A. 1984. Steady state secondary convection beneath lithospheric plates with temperature and pressure dependent viscosity. *J. geophys. Res.* **89**, 9227–44.

FOUCHER, J.P., LEPICON, X. & SIBUET, J.G. 1982. The ocean–continent transition in the uniform lithospheric stretching model; role of partial melting in the mantle. *Phil. Trans. R. Soc. London*, **A305**, 27–43.

HELLINGER, S.J. & SCLATER, J.G. 1983. Some comments on two layer extensional models for the evolution of sedimentary basins. *J. geophys. Res.* **88**, 8251–70.

HINZ, K. 1981. A hypothesis on terrestrial catastrophes. Wedges of very thick oceanward dipping layers beneath passive continental margins—their origin and paleoenvironmental significance. *Geol. Jahrb. Reihe E.; Geophys.* **22**, 3–28.

JANSA, L.F. & WEIDMANN, J. 1982. Mesozoic–Cenozoic development of the eastern North American and northwest African continental margins: a comparison. *In:* VON RAD, U., HINZ, K., SARNTHEIN, M. & SEIBOLD, E. (eds) *Geology of the northwest African continental margin.* Springer-Verlag, 215–69.

JARVIS, G.T. & PELTIER, R. 1982. Mantle Convection as a boundary layer phenomenon. *Geophys. J. R. astron. Soc.* **68**, 385–424.

KEEN, C.E. 1985. The dynamics of rifting: deformation of the lithosphere by active and passive driving forces. *Geophys. J. R. astron. Soc.* **80**, 95–120.

LASE STUDY GROUP. In press. Deep structure of the U.S. East Coast Passive Margin from Large Aperture Seismic Experiments (LASE) *Geology.*

LEPICHON, X. & SIBUET, J.C. 1981. Passive margins; a model of formation. *J. geophys. Res.* **86**, 3708–20.

MCKENZIE, D.P. 1978. Some remarks on the development of sedimentary basins. *Earth Planet. Sci. Lett.* **40**, 25–32.

MUTTER, J.C., TALWANI, M. & STOFFA, P.L. 1982. Origin of seaward dipping reflectors in oceanic crust off the Norwegian margin by 'subaerial seafloor spreading'. *Geology*, **10**, 134–40.

ROYDEN, L. & KEEN, C.E. 1980. Rifting process and thermal evolution of the continental margin of eastern Canada determined from subsidence curves. *Earth planet. Sci. Lett.* **51**, 343–61.

ROYDEN, L., SCLATER, J.G. & VON HERZEN, R.P. 1980. Continental margin subsidence and heat flow; Important parameters in formation of petroleum hydrocarbons. *Am. Assoc. Pet. Geol. Bull.* **64**, 173–87.

SAWYER, D.S., TOKSÖZ, M.N., SCLATER, J.G. & SWIFT, G.A. 1982. Thermal evolution of the Baltimore Canyon Trough and Georges Bank Basin; *In:* WATKINS, J.S. & DRAKE, C.L. (eds) *Am. Assoc. Pet. Geol. Mem.* **34**, 743–62.

SCLATER, J.G. & CHRISTIE, P.A.F. 1980. Continental stretching; an explanation of the post Mid-Cretaceous subsidence of the central North Sea Basin. *J. geophys. Res.* **85**, 3711–39.

SCLATER, J.G., ROYDEN, L., HORVATH, F., BURCHFIEL, B.C., SEMKEN, S. & STEGENA, L. 1980. Subsidence and thermal evolution of the intraCarpathian Basins; *Earth planet. Sci. Lett.* **51**, 139–62.

SENGOR, A.H.C. & BURKE, K. 1978. Relative timing of rifting and volcanism on earth and its tectonic implications. *Geophys. Res. Lett.* **5**, 419–21.

SPOHN, T. & SCHUBERT, G. 1982. Convective thinning of the lithosphere; a mechanism for this initiation of continental rifting. *J. geophys. Res.* **87**, 4669–81.

SRIVASTAVA, S.P., FALCONER, K.H. & MACLEAN, B. 1981. Labrador Sea, Davis Strait, Baffin Bay: Geology and Geophysics—a review, *In:* KERR, J.W. & FERGUSSON, A.J. (eds) *Geology of the North Atlantic borderlands*; *Can. Soc. Pet. Geol. Mem.* **7**, 333–98.

STECKLER, M.S. & WATTS, A.B. 1982. Subsidence history and tectonic evolution of Atlantic-type continental margins; *In:* SCRUTTON, R.A. (ed.) *Dynamics of Passive Continental Margins*, *Am. geophys. Union Geodyn. Ser.* **6**, 184–96.

YUEN, D.A. & FLEITOUT, L. 1985. Thinning of the lithosphere by small-scale convective destabilization. *Nature*, **313**, 125–8.

C.E. KEEN, Atlantic Geoscience Centre, Geological Survey of Canada, Bedford Institute of Oceanography, Dartmouth, Nova Scotia, Canada.

Lithospheric stretching, detached normal faulting and footwall uplift

D. Barr

SUMMARY: Lithospheric stretching can successfully account for the overall evolution of many sedimentary basins, and detached normal faulting the detailed geometry of the upper crust. In an instantaneously stretched, isostatically compensated basin, the equations which describe these two processes can be combined to define a 'notional depth to decollement'. Only at this level can the sole to the normal fault system maintain a constant depth below sea-level during extension. The notional depth to decollement depends primarily on the mean density of the basin fill and for a constant-density basin fill (e.g. sea water) coincides with the level of no vertical motion during stretching. In a sediment-filled basin, the notional depth to decollement will increase with the stretching factor β as early-deposited sediments are compacted and the mean density of the sediment column increases. In general, a physical sole fault will not lie at the notional depth to decollement, and must move vertically to maintain isostatic equilibrium: such movement precludes the use of balanced cross-section techniques to determine the physical depth to decollement.

In typical crustal situations, uplift of the sole fault will be more common than subsidence and will in turn cause uplift of any residual, unfaulted basement blocks which rest upon it. Footwall uplift can also be modelled using area-balance constraints, referred to the notional depth to decollement rather than to the physical sole fault. The amount of uplift depends primarily on the initial fault spacing. Three fields can be distinguished: one in which footwalls subside at an increasing rate as β increases, one in which they are uplifted above sea-level then subside below sea-level, and one in which they are uplifted then subside, but always remain above sea-level. Similar relationships exist in an uncompensated basin, where the depth to the physical sole fault replaces the notional depth to decollement.

Curves showing uplift and subsidence versus β have been constructed in dimensionless form (referred to depth to decollement) and for a model basin with an exponential sediment compaction relationship. They agree closely with uplift/subsidence histories inferred from seismic and well data for the North Sea, and with published descriptions of other areas (the Armorican margin, the Aegean Sea).

Models of lithospheric stretching have successfully accounted for the broad geological evolution of several intracontinental basins, marginal seas and passive continental margins (e.g. McKenzie 1978; Steckler & Watts 1978; Sclater *et al.* 1980; Sclater & Christie 1980; Le Pichon & Sibuet 1981; Watts 1982; Hellinger & Sclater 1983). In these interpretations, an initial phase of fault-bounded subsidence S_i reflects the stretching episode. The base of the lithosphere is considered to be thermally controlled and is elevated as isotherm adjustment lags behind stretching. As isotherms recover, the lithosphere cools and thickens as a phase of near-exponential regional (thermal) subsidence S_t ensues. The simplest models (e.g. McKenzie 1978) assume instantaneous stretching. The effect of non-instantaneous stretching is to increase fault-bounded subsidence at the expense of regional subsidence (Jarvis & McKenzie 1980; Cochran 1983). Most estimates of the magnitude of lithospheric stretching have been obtained by modelling the thermal subsidence stage from well data (because there is little faulting, a few wells

can be considered representative of a given basin), with the degree of basement thinning being confirmed by interpretation of seismic refraction or gravity data (e.g. Barton & Wood 1984). Upper-crustal extension is usually inhomogeneous and accommodated by detached normal faulting, which may or may not be listric (cf. Chenet *et al.* 1983; Le Pichon *et al.* 1983). Estimates of upper-crustal extension during rifting, as measured on reflection seismic sections (Gibbs 1983), often appear to conflict with those of lithospheric stretching (cf. Christie & Sclater 1980; Smythe *et al.* 1980; Wood & Barton 1983; Ziegler 1983). This paper attempts to clarify the geometrical relationships between subsidence, lithospheric stretching and upper-crustal extensional faulting for the simple case of instantaneous stretching. Further consideration of these relationships permits semi-quantitative modelling of footwall uplift and hanging wall subsidence in extensional basins—a feature of obvious relevance to hydrocarbon exploration.

From COWARD, M.P., DEWEY, J.F. & HANCOCK, P.L. (eds), 1987, *Continental Extensional Tectonics*, Geological Society Special Publication No. 28, pp. 75–94.

Lithospheric stretching and detached normal faulting

The level of no vertical motion during stretching

Figure 1 is a schematic model of the lithosphere immediately following instantaneous stretching. The upper crust has deformed by faulting above a sub-horizontal decollement and the lower crust and mantle by homogeneous stretching. The average depth to the basin floor corresponds to S_i, the initial subsidence due to stretching. This model is admittedly over-simplified, but can serve as a starting point for more realistic models involving, for example, inhomogeneous stretching.

S_i can be obtained from equation 1 of McKenzie (1978), which simply expresses the requirement that stretched and unstretched lithosphere be in isostatic equilibrium with one another and with the mid-ocean ridge of Parsons & Sclater (1977):

$$S_i = \frac{a\{(\varrho_0 - \varrho_c)t_c/a[1 - (\alpha T_1 t_c)/2_a] - \alpha T_i \varrho_0/2\}}{\varrho_0 \times (1 - \alpha T_1) - \varrho_w}$$

$$\times \frac{(1 - 1/\beta)}{\varrho_0 \times (1 - \alpha T_1) - \varrho_w} \qquad (1)$$

Parameters are identified in Table 1. The conventional correction for sediment loading (e.g. Sclater & Christie 1980) makes the assumption that isostatic compensation takes place at the base of the crust. For the purposes of this paper, it is more convenient (and makes little difference to the result) to assume isostatic compensation at the base of the lithosphere, distributed over a horizontal distance comparable in magnitude to the dominant upper-crustal fault spacing. In that case, ϱ_w can be replaced by ϱ_s, the mean density of the sediment + water column after stretching.

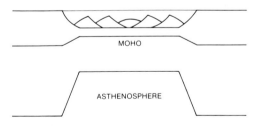

FIG. 1. Schematic model of stretched continental lithosphere, before thermal subsidence. The lower crust and mantle have deformed homogeneously, by ductile flow, while the brittle upper crust has deformed by detached normal faulting.

McKenzie (1978) measured initial subsidence S_i relative to the elevation of unstretched lithosphere and, if the other parameters are kept constant, S_i varies widely with crustal thickness. The thicker the crust the greater the subsidence, and if the crust is thinner than about 18 km, syn-stretching uplift occurs. However, isostatic constraints require such thin crust to lie below sea-level prior to stretching and thick crust to lie above sea level. If on the other hand the pre-stretching crustal elevation is specified, the parameters in equation 1 are no longer independent of one another. For example, a thin crust may be of unusually low density or may be compensated by a high heat flow and thin mantle lithosphere.

If the pre- and post-stretching elevations are measured *relative to a common reference level,* the factor relating S_i to $(1 - 1/\beta)$ is a constant with units of depth, and corresponds to the *level of no vertical motion within the lithosphere, d_n.* That this level lies within the continental crust is indicated by the general observation that the surface subsides and the Moho rises during stretching. It is convenient to choose present-day sea-level as a reference, in which case d_n corresponds to the predicted depth to a mid-ocean ridge if no oceanic crust were present. This is apparent from Fig. 2. At infinite extension, $(1 - 1/\beta) = 1$, $S_i = d_n$ and a notional column consisting of mantle asthenosphere directly overlain by sea water or sediments of constant density is in isostatic equilibrium with unstretched lithosphere and with all intervening stages (cf. Le

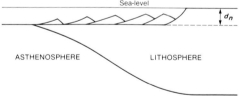

FIG. 2. Physical significance of the level of no vertical motion or 'notional depth to decollement' d_n. It corresponds to the level to which the asthenosphere would rise if loaded to sea-level by water or a sedimentary column of specified density; i.e. in the water-loaded case, to the mantle geoid of Turcotte *et al.* (1977). As the continental lithosphere undergoes instantaneous, homogeneous stretching, its mean density is unchanged and the proportion of its thickness which rises above d_n remains constant. The remaining column to sea-level is filled by water or sediments of the previously specified density. At infinite extension, the sea-water or sediment column would directly overlie the asthenosphere.

TABLE 1. *List of symbols used.*

a	Thickness of lithosphere
t_c	Thickness of continental crust
T_1	Temperature of asthenosphere
α	Thermal expansion coefficient of lithosphere
β	Stretching factor
ϱ_0	Mantle density at 0°C
ϱ_c	Crustal density at 0°C
ϱ_a	Density of asthenosphere
ϱ_l	Mean density of the pre-rifting lithosphere
ϱ_w	Density of sea water
ϱ_s	Mean density of a (sedimentary) basin fill
ϱ_{sg}	Density of sediment grains
f_0	Porosity of a sediment at sea level
f	Porosity of a sediment at depth
k	Post-exponential factor describing sediment compaction
S_i	Initial subsidence due to stretching
S_t	Subsequent (thermal) subsidence
S_∞	Total subsidence at infinite time
d_n	Notional depth to decollement in an isostatically compensated basin (= level of no vertical motion given a basin fill of constant density)
s	Approximate factor relating S_t to $(1-1/\beta)$
d'	Depth to the physical decollement surface in a system of detached normal faults
d_i	Initial (pre-stretching) depth to a physical decollement surface
ϕ_i	Initial (pre-stretching) dip of a 'domino' fault-plane
ϕ	Fault-plane dip after stretching
θ	Dip of the top basement surface after stretching
a'	Initial (pre-stretching) separation between 'domino' faults
c'	Final (post-stretching) separation between 'domino' faults
z_f	Magnitude of footwall uplift
z_h	Magnitude of hanging wall subsidence

TABLE 2. *Estimates of the notional depth to decollement* d_n *and of the thermal subsidence factor* s *for water-loaded and sediment-loaded* ($\varrho_s = 2200$ kgm^{-3}) *basins.*

Source for parameters	water-loaded		sediment-loaded	
	d_n	s	d_n	s
McKenzie (1978)	3.07	4.17	6.82	9.24
Sclater *et al.* (1980)	3.24	4.13	7.29	9.31
Le Pichon & Sibuet (1981)	3.61	4.21	7.83	9.12
Cochran (1983)	3.26	4.33	7.16	9.63

Pichon *et al.*'s (1982) discussion of a notional column of mantle asthenosphere directly overlain by sea water, and Turcotte *et al.*'s (1977) water-loaded mantle geoid).

Values of the level of no vertical motion d_n are quoted in Table 2 for various combinations of lithospheric parameters and for $\varrho_s = 1000$ kgm^{-3} (water-filled) and $\varrho_s = 2200$ kgm^{-3} (sediment-filled). The latter density corresponds to that of a quartz sand with 30% water-filled porosity and is a reasonable compromise for a mature basin containing a few kilometres of syn-rifting sediments. For example, Beach (1984) recorded

950 m of syn-rifting sediments with average density 2600 kgm^{-3} in part of the North Sea graben system, and concluded from the geometry of the graben that these had suffered 325 m of post-extensional compaction. Decompacting and assuming water-filled porosity yields a mean density of 2192 kgm^{-3}. For water-filled (sediment-starved) basins, $d_n = 3.1$–3.6 km, while for sediment-filled basins, $d_n = 6.8$–7.8 km. All the values for d_n quoted in Table 2 can be regarded as estimates of the same parameter (the depth to the mantle geoid at a mid-ocean ridge), so for the remainder of this paper,

average values of 3.3 and 7.3 km will be used. The differences between the estimates presumably arise from the specific mid-ocean ridge chosen and the correction (if any) made for oceanic crust.

This relationship severely restricts the extent to which variations in crustal parameters can explain inconsistencies between seismically measured β values and basement subsidence (e.g. by inferring an unusually thick crust where subsidence is excessive). As long as the crust was in isostatic equilibrium and close to sea-level before stretching, the amount of subsidence relative to a constant sea-level should be independent of crustal thickness.

Eustatic sea-level changes will have two main effects. If sea-level at the end of stretching is different from that before stretching, this will introduce an error into S_i of the order of the net sea-level change (short-period fluctuations *during* stretching tending to cancel out). If sea-level was constant during stretching but different from that at the present day, d_n will be increased or decreased by an amount equal to the sea-level change. Even changes of a few hundred metres will have only second-order effects in typical sedimentary basins (where S_i = a few kilometres, $d_n = 7.3$ km), so this effect will be ignored for the remainder of the discussion.

Where the mean thickness of syn-rift sediments can be inferred from seismic or other evidence, an approximate indication of the stretching factor can be obtained by assuming that $S_i = 7.3$ $(1 - 1/\beta)$. This approach is complementary to the more usual practice of modelling the thermal subsidence stage only (cf. Wood 1981; Angelier 1985). However, it is particularly important when dealing with the irregular sediment-thickness distributions found in typical half-grabens to measure *mean* sediment thickness over some area comparable in width to the deeper zone of ductile thinning. For example, much of the discrepancy which Beach (1984) found between β as calculated from the thickness of syn-rifting sediments, and extension ratios measured on reflection seismic sections can probably be attributed to the fact that he used sediment thicknesses from the deepest part of the Witchground graben, rather than the average thickness within the graben as a whole. Beach's β values imply that a 125 km thick lithosphere thins to 90 km across a horizontal distance of less than 10 km, a mechanically unlikely scenario which is contradicted by the distributed lower-crustal thinning recorded in a refraction survey by Christie & Sclater (1980).

Subsequent thermal subsidence will have depressed the level of no (syn-stretching) vertical

motion in fossil basins. Following Le Pichon & Sibeut (1981), the total subsidence $S_i + S_t$ at infinite time can be approximated within a few metres or tens of metres by:

$$S_\infty = \frac{t_c(\varrho_0 - \varrho_c)[1 - (\alpha T_1 t_c)/2a](1 - 1/\beta)}{\varrho_0 \times (1 - \alpha T_1) - \varrho_s} . \quad (2)$$

The thermal subsidence $S_t = S_\infty - S_i$ and so:

$$S_t = \frac{(a \times \alpha T_1 \varrho_0) \times (1 - 1/\beta)}{2[\varrho_0 \times (1 - \alpha T_1) - \varrho_s]}$$

$$= \frac{a}{2} \times \left(\frac{\varrho_0 - \varrho_a}{\varrho_a - \varrho_s}\right) \times (1 - 1/\beta)$$

$$= s \times (1 - 1/\beta), \quad (3)$$

and is essentially independent of crustal thickness. Water- and sediment-loaded values of s are quoted in Table 2. Average values of 4.2 and 9.3 km will be used in the remainder of this paper. For a basin in which stretching ceased at about 120 Ma (e.g. the North Sea, the Biscay margin), the thermal subsidence will have reached about 87% of its ultimate value (Le Pichon & Sibuet 1981), and so the subsidence at infinite time can be used with little loss of precision. Present-day depth to the fossil horizon of no vertical motion is given by $(d_n + S_t)$, and is displayed graphically in Fig. 4 for three extreme cases. In the outermost part of a sediment-starved continental margin with $\beta = 4$, this horizon should lie at ≈ 6.5 km below sea-level. Where the initial, rift-stage half-grabens are sediment-filled but subsequent thermal subsidence was largely water-loaded (e.g. the Biscay margin—Le Pichon & Sibuet 1981), this horizon should lie at ≈ 10 km for $\beta = 2-4$. Where sediment loading applied throughout (e.g. the North Sea), this horizon should lie at ≈ 12 km for $\beta = 2$.

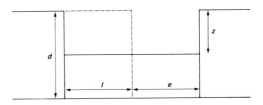

FIG. 3. Schematic balanced cross-section showing the relationship between extension ($\beta = l + e/l$), depth to decollement (d) and mean basin depth (z). See text for further details.

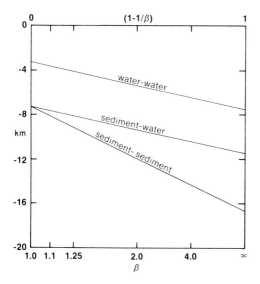

FIG. 4. Notional depth to decollement, after thermal subsidence, for three extreme models: (i) water-loaded throughout; (ii) sediment-loaded ($\varrho_s = 2200$ kgm^{-3}) during stretching, water-loaded during thermal subsidence; (iii) sediment-loaded throughout ($\varrho_s = 2200$ kgm^{-3}).

True and notional depths to decollement

The discussion so far has ignored the detailed geometry of the upper crust. Recent models of extensional basin formation (Wernicke & Burchfiel 1982; Le Pichon *et al.* 1983; Gibbs 1984) have emphasized the role of detached normal faulting above a gently dipping decollement surface, and have applied balanced cross-section techniques originally developed in compressional terraines (Dahlstrom 1969). Following Gibbs (1983), a simple geometric model can be constructed for faulting above a basal decollement at depth d (Fig. 3), whereby a line of original length l is extended to $l+e$, resulting in subsidence z. Assuming preservation of the cross-sectional area within the basement and no vertical movement of the basal decollement:

$$e \times d = (l+e) \times z \qquad (4)$$

and the stretching factor β is defined as $(l+e)/l$. Substituting $\beta \times l$ for $l+e$ and $l \times (\beta-1)$ for e in equation 4, and rearranging:

$$z = d \times (1-1/\beta). \qquad (5)$$

The analogy with equation 1 is obvious. In an isostatically compensated basin, any attempt to apply the area-balancing technique of Gibbs (1983) will yield a 'depth to decollement' which

corresponds to the level of no vertical motion d_n, rather than the depth to a physical sole fault. The depth to the sole fault will only be correctly determined where by coincidence it lies at or near the level of no vertical motion. Conversely, if the amount of basement subsidence is controlled only by the depth to a physical sole fault, the basin will be unable to maintain isostatic equilibrium during extension, its sediment fill will be uncompensated, and the simple stretching model of McKenzie (1978) will be inapplicable (as in the Inner Moray Firth basin, which is associated with a regional negative free-air gravity anomaly and lacks significant thermal subsidence—McQuillin *et al.* 1982; Barr 1985).

Thus the indiscriminate application of area-balancing techniques to syntectonic sediments in extensional basins should be discouraged. Where they have yielded results compatible with reflection seismic evidence, either this must be put down to pure coincidence, or the basin in question must be uncompensated. If in a compensated basin the calculated 'depth to decollement' (=the level of no vertical motion) deviates markedly from the values predicted in Table 2, the basin must have formed by some mechanism other than uniform stretching (e.g. the level of no vertical motion will be shallower if β(mantle) $>\beta$(crust), and deeper if β(crust) $> \beta$(mantle)). Calculating the level of no vertical motion may therefore help in determining the relative proportions of crust and mantle stretching and hence whether heat flow within the basin was significantly greater during stretching than it is today.

In many respects, the upper part of a compensated basin behaves during stretching as if it were an uncompensated basin with a basal decollement lying at the level of no vertical motion d_n. It is therefore convenient to introduce the alternative term 'notional depth to decollement'. This enables comparisons to be made between basins whose degree of compensation is unclear, but in which a real or notional depth to decollement can nevertheless be determined by area-balancing. As will be shown below, the term 'level of no vertical motion' is inappropriate to most sedimentary basins because the magnitude of d_n increases with β as the sediment density ϱ_s increases through compaction.

Comparison of notional and observed depths to decollement

Information on actual depth to decollement d' can be obtained from seismic reflection data (Fig. 5). Where a basal decollement is observed,

D. Barr

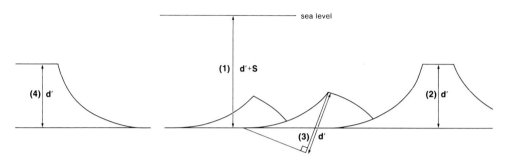

FIG. 5. Techniques for measuring actual depth to decollement: (1) by subtraction of thermal subsidence S_t; (2) from the height of major basement horsts; (3) by reconstructing the initial shape of large basement fault blocks; (4) by direct measurement from an unstretched graben margin.

$d' + S_t$ can be measured directly from sea-level (1) and d' obtained using the curves in Fig. 4, or d' can be reconstructed from large basement blocks whose bounding faults did not intersect above the sole fault (2, 3), or from the overall form of the graben (4). Using equation 5, depth to decollement can also be calculated in uncompensated basins from the decompacted thickness of the syn-rift sediments and a seismically measured β value (5). In several published cross-sections, d' appears to be close to the level of no vertical motion or notional depth to decollement (Table 3). In others, d' is either significantly deeper or shallower. This suggests that there is no mechanical reason for a sole fault to lie at the notional depth to decollement, in either compensated or uncompensated basins, and so in the general case we should expect sole faults in compensated basins to move vertically during stretching.

TABLE 3. *Estimates of the depth in kilometres to a physical decollement, based on seismic data.*

Area	d'	$d' + S_t$	β	method
North Sea (Beach 1984)	2	4.2	1.4	(4), (5)
West Orkney Basin (Brewer & Smythe 1984)	15–18		1.6	(2), (3)
Inner Moray Firth Basin (Barr 1985)	20–25		1.08	(5)
	>10		1.08	(2), (4)
Bay of Biscay (de Charpal et al. 1978)	5			(3)
	4	9		(1)
Armorican margin (Montadert et al. 1979)	6	9	2.5	(1)
	7		2.5	(3)
Aegean Sea (Jackson & McKenzie 1983)	c. 10			(8)
Sevier Desert, USA (McDonald 1976)	3		1.5–2	(2)
Snake Range, USA (Miller et al. 1983)	6–7		6	(6)
	1.1		6	(7)

Notes: Method of calculation (cf. Fig. 5 for (1) to (4)): (1) $d' + S_t$; (2) large horsts; (3) reconstructing fault blocks; (4) graben margin; (5) area-balance; (6) pre-rifting stratigraphic thickness in upper plate (a version of (3)); (7) present-day stratigraphic thickness of upper plate; (8) earthquake foci. Methods (1), (4), (5), (7) and (8) measure the present-day depth to decollement. Methods (2), (3) and (6) reconstruct the initial depth to decollement.

Vertical movement of the sole fault during extension

In practice, the physical depth to decollement will often be controlled by externally imposed factors. The 'sole fault' may correspond to a brittle–ductile transition (e.g. Miller *et al.* 1983) and so broadly to an isotherm within the crust, it may be localized in a weak horizon (e.g. evaporites) or at a basement/cover interface, or it may reactivate a pre-existing low-angle fault. In all these cases, it is likely that the sole fault, once initiated, will remain at essentially the same geological horizon during deformation. This horizon will, however, move passively upwards or downwards as isostatic equilibrium is maintained. Figure 6 represents the case where initial depth to decollement d_i is shallower than the notional depth d_n. As before, $z = d_n \times (1 - 1/\beta)$, but that part of the crust lying between d_i and d_n deforms homogeneously so that the decollement subsides to d'. Clearly, $\Delta d = (d_n - d_i) \times (1 - 1/\beta)$ and so:

$$d' = d_i + \Delta d = d_i + d_n - d_i - \frac{d_n}{\beta} + \frac{d_i}{\beta}$$

$$= d_n + \frac{(d_i - d_n)}{\beta}. \qquad (6)$$

The same equation applies if the sole fault is deeper than d_n.

If a sole fault can be observed on seismic records, then from a knowledge of β, the original (pre-stretching) depth to decollement can be calculated from:

$$d_i = d_n + \beta \times (d' - d_n), \qquad (7)$$

d_n being selected according to the nature of the basin fill. For large values of β, d_i is strongly dependent on the chosen value of d_n, which in turn depends on the detailed nature of the sedimentary fill. For this reason it is best to measure the initial depth to decollement directly, using methods (2) and (3) of Fig. 5.

In the Bay of Biscay cross-section quoted in Table 3, the volume of the sedimentary fill is insufficient, in relation to the volume of the intervening basement blocks, to accommodate Le Pichon & Sibuet's (1981) β estimate of 2.5. This suggests that, at least in the later stages of extension, the sediment/water interface lay well below sea-level and the system was in part water-loaded. This emphasizes the general point that the density of a sedimentary basin fill will vary with β—e.g. in the early stages of extension, uncompacted sediments will dominate and d_n will have a relatively low value. Even if the decollement surface initiated at the notional depth d_n, the value of d_n will change through time and the decollement surface will either have to switch to this new depth or, more likely, move vertically to maintain isostatic equilibrium. Because such vertical movement displaces the decollement surface and the top basement interface by the same amount, it is geometrically impossible for the physical decollement surface to track the notional depth to decollement, and so the area-balance constraints required for section-balancing cannot be maintained during stretching.

The effect of sediment compaction

An attempt will now be made to semi-rigorously model the instantaneous stretching phase for a sediment-filled, isostatically compensated basin. As the basin extends, early-deposited sediments will be buried and compacted and the mean density of the sediment column (ϱ_s) will increase. At any point during the basin evolution, the notional depth to decollement d_n will be controlled by the density of the basin fill. This in turn depends upon the mean height of the sediment column and the type of sediment involved. For this simple model, the uneven horizontal distribution of sediments implied by an irregular top basement interface will be ignored, so that the basin fill is represented by a sedimentary layer of uniform thickness S_i. An exponential compaction relationship will be assumed, of the form:

$$f = f_0 \times exp(-k \times z), \qquad (8)$$

where f is the porosity at depth z, f_0 porosity at sea-level and k a constant. By a procedure analogous to that followed by Christie & Sclater (1980), it can be shown that:

$$\varrho_s = \varrho_{sg} - \left(\frac{(\varrho_{sg} - \varrho_w) \times f_0 \cdot (1 - exp(-k \times S_i))}{k \times S_i} \right). \qquad (9)$$

FIG. 6. Construction to show how a physical decollement (broken line) moves relative to the notional decollement d_n during stretching (see text).

Taking Sclater & Christie's (1980) 'shaly sand' relationship ($\varrho_{sg} = 2680 \text{ kgm}^{-3}$, $\varrho_w = 1000 \text{ kgm}^{-3}$, $f = 0.56 \exp(-0.39z)$):

$$\varrho_s = 2680 - \left(\frac{940.8(1 - \exp(-0.39S_i))}{0.39S_i} \right). \quad (10)$$

(Depths are given in kilometres in this case).

For a given value of β, d_n can be obtained iteratively: S_i and hence ϱ_s are calculated for a reasonable value of d_n (e.g. 7 km), and the new value of ϱ_s provides a new estimate of d_n, which yields new values of S_i and ϱ_s, etc. The results of this calculation are displayed in Fig. 7, together with curves relating to footwall uplift which will be described later. d_n increases from 4.95 to 9.53 km, and lies in the range 7–8 km for moderate values of β. ϱ_s increases from 1740 to 2430 kgm^{-3}, and is close to 2200 kgm^{-3} for $\beta = 2$. To a first approximation, the curve representing the mean depth to basement can be used to predict β from a knowledge of the average thickness of syn-rifting sediments, corrected for post-rifting compaction. This is preferable to simply assuming a constant sediment density. For a given basin, a more accurate result could be obtained by constructing a similar set of curves for a local density/depth relationship derived from well data, or for a local extension/subsidence relationship derived from seismic and/or well data.

The behaviour of three physical decollement surfaces of initial depth 2.5, 4.95 and 10 km has also been investigated. Equation 6 was solved numerically by determining d_i after a small increment of $(1 - 1/\beta)$, using this as d_i for the next increment and selecting a new value for d_n from Fig. 7. The resulting curves are plotted on Fig. 7. Note how even the physical decollement which initiated at the notional depth to decollement departs from this depth as the basin evolves, and how the shallowest physical decollement only converges on the notional depth at very large β.

Footwall uplift

Geometric models

Vertical movement of the sole fault provides an additional mechanism for footwall uplift within a stretched basin, beyond those provided by lateral heat flow (Cochran 1983), inhomogeneous stretching (Royden & Keen 1980; Hellinger & Sclater 1983), lithospheric flexure (Watts *et al.* 1982), local isostatic effects (Jackson & McKenzie 1983) or area-balance constraints

(Barr *et al.* 1985). The first four mechanisms invoke modifications to the simple stretching model and can generate absolute uplift (above sea-level); the last mechanism only accounts for differential subsidence and applies to basins which do not maintain local isostatic equilibrium.

Consider a residual, unfaulted basement block resting on the sole fault. If isostatic equilibrium is maintained on a horizontal scale greater than that of the basement block, the block will either subside or be uplifted, depending on whether the initial depth to decollement d_i is shallower or deeper than the notional depth d_n. In general, a sole fault controlled by a brittle/ductile transition at 300–350°C (Chen & Molnar 1983; Sibson 1983) will lie at a depth of 10–20 km and so be deeper than d_n, therefore footwall uplift should be the rule. Smaller blocks may experience either net uplift or net subsidence, depending on how their detailed geometry interacts with that of the system of fault planes. The (signed) subsidence, averaged over the basin as a whole, should correspond to that predicted by the lithospheric stretching model (although strictly, a correction should be made for the additional isostatic load of emergent blocks). From Fig. 7, a sole fault initially at 10 km depth would be uplifted by ≈ 800 m for $\beta = 1.25$ and ≈ 1500 m for $\beta = 2$. This mechanism may explain the persistent uplift of major, internally unfaulted basement highs within extensional basins, such as the Halibut Horst within the Moray Firth basin (Johnson & Dingwall 1981). Gravity data indicate that even this 100×25 km horst is not locally compensated.

Uplift of minor blocks bounded by listric normal faults cannot readily be assessed quantitatively. However, footwall uplift in a system of rotated planar ('domino') fault blocks is amenable to calculation (Fig. 8—cf. Wernicke & Burchfiel 1982; Le Pichon *et al.* 1983). Assuming that all the 'dominoes' are the same size, and that some area-conserving, megascopically ductile process operates at the base of each (so that voids do not open up), it is only necessary to consider whether asperities on the top basement interface rise above sea-level. Figure 9 represents the geometry of this interface after stretching by a factor:

$$\beta = \frac{B'A'}{B'C} = \frac{c'}{a'} = \frac{\sin\phi_i}{\sin\phi} = \frac{\sin\phi_i}{\sin(\phi_i - \theta)}.$$

ϕ_i is the initial dip of a fault plane, ϕ its present-day dip and θ the dip of the top basement interface (initially horizontal). AB represents the

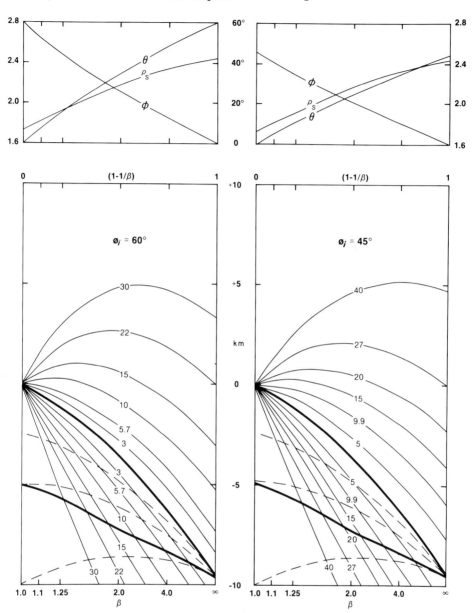

FIG. 7. Model set of curves representing the evolution of an instantaneously stretched, isostatically compensated, sediment-loaded basin with increasing β. Upper-crustal extension is accommodated by rotated planar ('domino') faults. Initial fault-plane dip ϕ_i is assumed to be (a) 60° or (b) 45°. The curves for sediment density, overall subsidence and depths to decollement (notional and physical) are independent of assumptions about the type of upper-crustal extension.

The sediment column is assumed to compact according to Sclater & Christie's (1980) 'shaly sand' relationship:

$$f = 0.56 \exp(-0.39z),$$

where f is porosity at depth z. The sediment grains are assigned a density of 2680 kgm^{-3}, and the pore space filled with water. The mean density of the sediment column is plotted as ϱ_s. The vertical scale is in specific gravity, e.g. 2.0 = 2000 kgm^{-3}. The upper heavy curve shows the mean depth to the basin floor, while the lower heavy curve represents the notional depth to decollement (see text). The broken curves show average basement elevation, such that excess area $AA'D$, is balanced by the deficiency ABC. Clearly, $\Delta h = 0.5h'$. Since

$$\sin \theta = \frac{h'}{a'},$$

$$h' = a' \times \sin \theta = \frac{c'}{\beta} \times \sin \theta.$$

The maximum footwall elevation above the mean basin floor is given by:

$$\Delta h = 0.5h' = 0.5a' \times \sin \theta = \frac{0.5c' \times \sin \theta}{\beta}, \quad (11)$$

FIG. 8. Schematic representation of a system of rotated planar ('domino' or 'pack of cards') detached normal faults. The fault planes rotate with bedding as extension progresses, and the lower portion of each fault block must undergo ductile deformation. All faults move simultaneously and a listric normal fault is required to separate the system from undeformed basement.

where c' and a' are respectively the present-day and original horizontal separations between major 'domino-bounding' faults.

If isostatic equilibrium is maintained on a horizontal scale greater than the distance between hanging wall and footwall cut-offs, the physical depth to decollement can be ignored since the *shape* of the top basement surface is unaffected by vertical uplift or subsidence. Relative to sea-level, footwall uplift z_f is given by $\Delta h - S_i$; if $\Delta h > S$, footwall blocks will be emergent. The corresponding hanging wall subsidence z_h is given by $\Delta h + S_i$. At large extensions, the space problem at the base of the 'dominoes' becomes more severe. Ultimately, the hanging wall intersects the sole fault and the model is clearly unrealistic. Extension can only continue if the hanging wall blocks slide as individual riders on the sole fault (e.g. the left-most fault-blocks in Fig. 2—cf. Gibbs 1984, fig. 11) or if new, high-angle faults are initiated (cf. Proffett 1977). In the former case, z_f will remain constant at the value which obtained when individual riders became detached from one another.

Since both S_i and θ are functions of β, there is a critical initial fault spacing a'_{crit} above which footwall uplift can give rise to islands:

$$a'_{crit} = \frac{2S_i}{\sin\theta}. \quad (12)$$

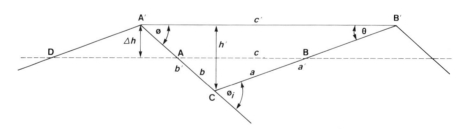

FIG. 9. Geometry of the top basement interface in a system of 'domino' faults (cf. Fig. 8). The broken line represents the mean depth to the basin floor, ϕ_i is the initial fault-plane dip, ϕ the present-day fault-plane dip, θ the dip of bedding, a' the initial fault spacing and c' the present-day fault spacing. For further discussion, see text.

FIG. 7 cont.

the behaviour of three different physical decollement surfaces. Note that they converge on the mean basin floor at large β, rather than on the notional depth to decollement, and how even the physical decollement which initiated at the notional depth, departs from it as extension proceeds. The 'domino-fault' model breaks down where the physical decollement surface appropriate to the basin under discussion intersects the hanging wall cut-off, e.g. at $\beta = 2$ for a sole fault initiated at 10 km depth with an initial 'domino-fault' spacing of 20 km.

The upper panels show how ϕ (fault-plane dip) and θ (bedding-plane dip) vary with β for 'domino-fault' models with $\phi_i = 60$ and $45°$. The labelled curves in the lower panels represent footwall uplift/subsidence (upper set) and hanging wall subsidence (lower set) for the indicated initial fault-spacings (labelled in kilometres). See text for details of their derivation. No correction has been made for the additional isostatic load of emergent footwalls.

The value of a'_{crit} for infinitesimal extension can be obtained from a consideration of Fig. 10. For very small values of β, angle $B'DC$ approaches a right angle, h^* approaches h' and $\tan\phi \simeq \dfrac{h'}{e}$ Thus:

$$\beta = \frac{(a'+e)}{a'} \simeq 1 + \left(\frac{h'}{a' \times \tan\phi}\right),$$

and

$$\Delta h = \frac{h'}{2} \simeq \frac{(\beta-1) \times a' \times \tan\phi}{2}.$$

Since $S_i = d_n \times \left(1 - \dfrac{1}{\beta}\right) = \dfrac{(\beta-1) \times d_n}{\beta}$,

then $\Delta h = S_i$ implies that:

$$a'_{crit} \simeq \frac{2d_n}{\beta \times \tan\phi}. \tag{13}$$

As $\beta \to 1$, $\phi \to \phi_i$
and

$$a'_{crit} \to \frac{2d_n}{\tan\phi_i}. \tag{14}$$

At infinite extension, $\phi \to 0$ and $\theta \to \phi_i$, so

$$a'_{crit} = \frac{2d_n \times (1-1/\beta)}{\sin\theta} \to \frac{2d_n}{\sin\phi_i}. \tag{15}$$

In general, a'_{crit} increases with β, so footwall uplift should be most widespread at low extensions, although the magnitude of the uplift on an individual fault will initially increase with β. Uplift is also favoured by a high initial fault-plane dip ϕ_i and a low-density basin fill, e.g. water. The initiation of new, high-angle faults (cf. Proffett 1977) in a sediment-filled basin will reset β and ϕ_i and provoke renewed uplift of both basement and lithified sediments.

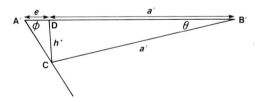

FIG. 10. Construction showing the geometry of a 'domino' fault at infinitesimal extension (labels correspond to those in Fig. 9, but the value of θ has been exaggerated for clarity). See text for further discussion.

In Fig. 11, critical values of a' for infinitesimal and infinite stretching are plotted against ϕ_i. For a particular density of basin fill, they define three fields: one in which footwalls always subside, one in which they are first uplifted then subside below sea-level with increasing extension, and one in which they are uplifted then subside, but always remain above sea-level. The curve for $\beta = 4$ is also shown in Fig. 11, as an alternative to that for $\beta = \infty$, since beyond this point oceanic crust may form and stretching cease (Le Pichon *et al.* 1982). Corresponding values of c'_{crit} define the present-day spacing of islands produced by this mechanism and are in the range 5–25 km for moderate values of β and ϕ_i. These figures are reasonably consistent with the present-day spacing of islands in the Aegean Sea (Jackson *et al.* 1982a, b) and of major fault blocks in the Brent province of the North Sea (Bowen 1975; Hay 1978) and in the Bay of Biscay (de Charpal *et al.* 1978), all areas where footwall uplift and erosion are well documented.

Figure 12 shows representative uplift/subsidence paths for a water-loaded basin. Where $a' < 3.8$ km, footwalls subside more slowly than the basin as a whole (which follows the curve for $a' = 0$). Where 3.8 km $< a' < 7.6$ km, footwalls are initially uplifted by a few hundred metres then subside below sea-level. Where $a' > 7.6$ km, footwalls are uplifted by between a few

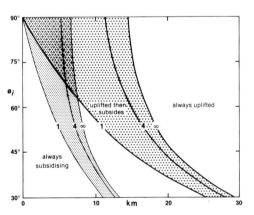

FIG. 11. Graph showing critical values of initial 'domino-fault' spacing for footwall uplift to occur, for initial fault-plane dips ϕ_i in the range 30 to 90°. Two sets of curves are shown, one for water loading (light shading) and one for sediment loading ($\varrho_s = 2200$ kgm^{-3}—dark shading). In each case, the three curves represent critical spacings for $\beta = 1$, $\beta = 4$ and $\beta = \infty$. The shaded and unshaded areas define three fields of contrasting footwall behaviour, which are labelled for the sediment-loaded case. See text for further discussion.

hundred metres and a few kilometres, then subside slightly but always remain above sea-level. Large-scale uplift (sufficient to leave a geological record) requires values of a' not much less than 7.6 km, i.e. the value of a'_{crit} for infinite stretching. Otherwise, footwall uplift is severely limited in both magnitude and duration (cf. the curve for $a' = 5$ km). Sediment-loaded curves will have the same general shape, if both the subsidence scale and a' are expressed in terms of d_n—e.g. for $\varrho_s = 2200$ kgm^{-3}, these will be increased by a factor of 2.206.

The curves in Fig. 12 can be used qualitatively to model the effects of footwall erosion. If erosion is 100% efficient, the footwall cut-offs should sink below sea-level at the apex of each curve rather than at the zero-crossing. However, because the topographic crest of the fault block migrates updip as it is eroded, final subsidence actually takes place where the curve is tangential to one of a family of straight lines radiating

from sea-level at $\beta = \infty$. For example, Fig. 13 represents a set of such curves constructed for a basin loaded by sediments with average density 2200 kgm^{-3}—footwalls are actively eroded over that part of each curve where $z_f = 0$, and fault-blocks with $a' > 17$ km are emergent to $\beta = \infty$.

The additional isostatic load imposed by emergent footwall blocks can be modelled as follows. Consider a column of width c' compensated within the asthenophere and filled to sea-level (or some other convenient datum) with sediments. If the top basement surface lies at or below sea-level, the areas and densities are as defined in Fig. 14a. Compare this with a column in which a footwall island of cross-sectional area A_3 rises above sea-level, but all other areas remain unchanged and the base of the lithosphere remains at the same depth (Fig. 14b). This is equivalent to removing basement of area A_3 from below sea-level, and to conserve area replacing it by sediments of area A_3. This column is now out of isostatic equilibrium with that of Fig. 14a. To restore equilibrium the column must subside, displacing a quantity of asthenosphere A_5 (Fig. 14c). An equivalent area of sediments is deposited. Balancing columns (a) and (c):

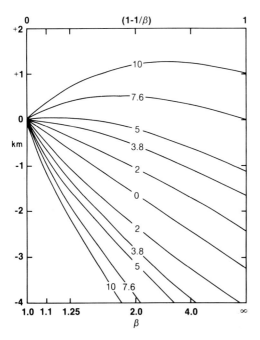

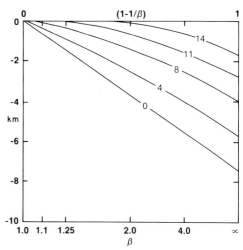

FIG. 12. Set of curves showing footwall uplift (upper set) and hanging wall subsidence (lower set) in an instantaneously stretched, isostatically compensated, water-loaded basin assuming upper-crustal extension to be accommodated by 'domino-faulting' with initial fault-place dip $\phi_i = 60°$. The labels on the curves correspond to the initial fault-plane spacing a' in kilometres. The curve for $a' = 0$ represents the mean basin floor. No correction has been made for the additional isostatic load of emergent footwall blocks.

FIG. 13. Set of curves showing footwall uplift in an instantaneously stretched, isostatically compensated basin, loaded by sediments of density 2200 kgm^{-3}, assuming complete erosion of emergent footwalls. Upper-crustal extension is by 'domino-faulting' with initial fault-plane dip $\phi_i = 60°$. The labels on the curves correspond to the initial fault-plane spacing a' in kilometres. The curve for $a' = 0$ represents the mean basin floor. Active erosion takes place where the footwalls are at sea-level.

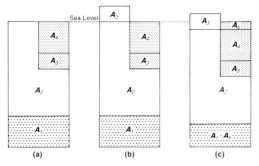

FIG. 14. Construction used to determine the additional isostatic load imposed by an emergent footwall block. Each column is of width c' (the wavelength of the 'domino' faults in Fig. 15), and areas A_1 to A_5 are the same in each case. Pre-stretching lithosphere (basement) of density ϱ_1 is unornamented, the asthenosphere of density ϱ_a is represented by coarse stipple and sediments of density ϱ_s by fine stipple. Column (a) is in isostatic balance (distributed over a width c') and reaches to sea-level. Column (b) is identical but for an island of area A_3 rising above sea-level and a correspondingly greater sediment fill. It is out of isostatic equilibrium with column (a). Column (c) is identical to column (b) except that it has been allowed to sink to reach isostatic equilibrium with column (a), displacing asthenosphere of area A_5 and permitting deposition of additional sediments.

$$A_1\varrho_a + A_2\varrho_1 = A_1\varrho_a - A_5\varrho_\alpha + A_2\varrho_1 + A_3\varrho_1 + A_3\varrho_s$$
$$+ A_3\varrho_1 + A_4\varrho_s \quad + A_4\varrho_s + A_5\varrho_s,$$

i.e. $A_5 = \dfrac{A_3\varrho_s}{(\varrho_a - \varrho_s)}$. (16)

Figure 15 shows a situation equivalent to that of Fig. 14b, where an island has risen above sea-level but no allowance has yet been made for its additional isostatic load. From Fig. 15,

$$\frac{AF}{AG} = \frac{BC}{DE}, \quad \text{i.e.} \quad \frac{z_f}{z_f + S_i} = \frac{BC}{0.5c'},$$

so

$$BC = \frac{c' \times z_f}{2(z_f + S_i)},$$

and the area of triangle ABC (equivalent to A_3 of Fig. 14) is

$$\frac{c' \times z_f^2}{4(z_f + S_i)}. \tag{17}$$

Thus

$$A_5 = \frac{\varrho_s \times c' \times z_f^2}{4(\varrho_a - \varrho_s) \times (z_f + S_i)}.$$

Treating A_5 as a uniform sediment blanket of width c', i.e. ignoring the slight interruptions caused by the islands, the additional subsidence caused by the emergent footwalls is given by:

$$z_a = \frac{\varrho_s \times z_f^2}{4(\varrho_a - \varrho_s) \times (z_f + S_i)}. \tag{18}$$

This component of subsidence is typically less than 10% of z_f, and even in the most extreme cases, only reaches $\approx 25\%$ of z_f. Given the other simplifications involved, correcting the curves was not considered worthwhile.

In a real basin, the density of the sedimentary fill will evolve through time, increasing as deeper sediments are compacted. This will amplify the subsidence component S_i at large β, and shorten both the amount and the duration of footwall uplift. For example, consider the isostatically compensated basin discussed in the previous section and represented in Fig. 7. Values of footwall uplift z_f and hanging wall subsidence z_h have been calculated for various initial fault spacings

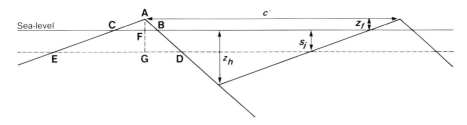

FIG. 15. Geometry of an emergent footwall block ABC. S_i is the initial subsidence due to stretching, c' the present-day fault-spacing, z_f the magnitude of footwall uplift and z_h the magnitude of hanging wall subsidence. See text for further explanation.

a' and for initial fault-plane dips ϕ_i of 45 and 60°. These curves are plotted in Fig. 7, together with those for θ and ϕ, the dips of bedding and the dips of 'domino-bounding' faults after stretching. No correction has been made for the isostatic load of emergent blocks.

Where $\theta_i = 60°$ (Fig. 7a), an initial fault spacing a' of ≈ 10 km is sufficient to yield a few hundred metres of footwall uplift, until subsidence ensues at around $\beta = 1.5$. A fault spacing of less than 5.7 km results in continuous subsidence, although the footwall subsides much less rapidly than the hanging wall. Values of a' significantly greater than 10 km result in major footwall uplift (>1 km). In contrast to the accelerating footwall subsidence, hanging wall subsidence is almost linear in $(1 - 1/\beta)$, and even moderate values of a' (e.g. 10 km) permit the hanging wall cut-off to be twice as deep as the average basin floor. This observation emphasizes the importance of using *mean* rather than *maximum* basin depth or sediment thickness in any isostatic or area-balance calculation.

The curves for $\phi_i = 45°$ (Fig. 7b) are similar to those in Fig. 7a, but a' is increased by about 50%. In both cases, geologically reasonable fault spacings permit widespread footwall uplift, which should be particularly evident at moderate values of β.

At high extensions, renewed steep faulting may rejuvenate the system and promote additional uplift. In such cases, the curves in Fig. 7 cannot strictly be re-applied by returning to $\beta = 1$. This is because compaction of the underlying column will create space for new sediments, over and above that produced by extension, and d_n will be depressed to greater depth.

To facilitate comparisons between basins, a final set of curves has been constructed in dimensionless form, referred to the notional depth to decollement (Fig. 16). They emphasize the fact that uplift of footwalls above sea-level requires a fault spacing several times greater than the notional depth to decollement. Figure 16 can also be applied to an uncompensated basin in which subsidence is controlled by the depth to a physical decollement surface—d_n is simply replaced by d', the actual depth to decollement. In that case, the forbidden zone places a strict limitation on the amount of extension which can be accommodated before the hanging wall intersects the sole fault, and d' is independent of the nature of the basin fill.

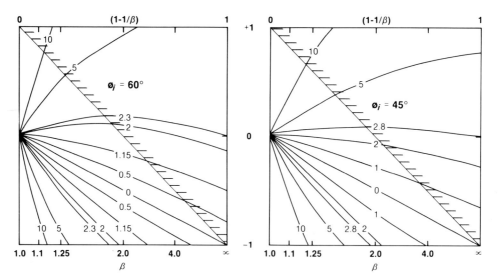

FIG. 16. Dimensionless set of curves showing footwall uplift (upper set) and hanging wall subsidence (lower set) in terms of the notional depth to decollement d_n, for a system of 'domino' faults with initial fault-plane dip $\phi_i = 60°$ (a) and 45° (b). The labels on the curves correspond to the ratio between the initial fault-spacing a' and the notional depth to decollement d_n. The curve for $a' = 0$ represents the mean basin floor. The curves can also be applied to uncompensated basins, where the notional depth to decollement is replaced by the depth to the physical sole fault. In that case, the 'forbidden zone' (to the right of the hatched line) sets an upper limit to the amount of extension which can be accommodated by 'domino' faulting before the hanging wall cut-off intersects the sole fault.

Basins produced by listric normal faulting can also be modelled, to the extent that the geometry of the top basement interface corresponds to that of Fig. 9. In the simplest case (Fig. 17), c'/a' will provide a slight over-estimate of β, but after allowing for this, a similar magnitude of uplift would be expected. Note that in Fig. 17, ϕ represents the dip of the fault plane at relatively shallow levels (down to the hanging wall cut-off), rather than at depth. If minor faulting is present within the hanging wall, this will tend to fill in the basin, at the expense of the height of the next footwall.

Examples from the geological record

North Sea

Inner Moray Firth

The Inner Moray Firth basin forms part of the North Sea graben system (Whiteman *et al.* 1975; McQuillin *et al.* 1982), and was produced by late Jurassic and Early Cretaceous extension. It is not isostatically compensated, and developed by listric normal faulting above a decollement whose depth d' is certainly greater than 10 km (the maximum penetration of available seismic reflection data) and probably lies at 20–25 km below sea-level (Barr 1985). Although footwalls within the basin have undergone relative uplift which is broadly proportional to the magnitude of fault displacement (Jackson & McKenzie 1983; Barr *et al.* 1985), there are no indications of significant emergence during rifting (Linsley *et al.* 1980). Present-day spacing, c', between major half-graben-bounding faults is 20–30 km, and the basin is filled by well-consolidated Jurassic and Cretaceous sediments. Barr (1985) determined a post-Triassic stretching factor β of ≈ 1.1 from reflection seismic data, and major faults have steep dips (45–60°) in their upper few

kilometres. Initial fault spacing a' is 18–27 km, i.e. 0.72–1.35 in dimensionless terms (taking the most extreme combinations of c' and d'). Assuming an initial fault-plane dip of 60° (or 45°) the model predicts a final footwall depth of -1000 m to $+75$ m (-1500 to -800 m) and a maximum basin depth of 3.5 to 3.7 km (2.4 to 3.0 km) at the hanging wall cut-off. The highest values of c' permit a few tens of metres of true uplift (above sea-level) during extension. In the other cases, footwall subsidence is lowest at low values of β. These figures agree reasonably well with observations. Released exploration well 12/23-1, drilled by Total on a footwall block, penetrated ≈ 750 m of syn-rifting sediments, most of which are of lower Cretaceous age and represent the later stages of rifting. A full Jurassic sequence is present, although the Lower to Middle Jurassic is thin and includes some hiatuses indicative of emergence or very shallow marine conditions. Jurassic and lower Cretaceous sediments typically attain 3 km in major half-grabens and locally reach 4 km (Chesher & Bacon 1975; McQuillin *et al.* 1982; Barr 1985). Thus the model successfully explains the accelerating footwall subsidence but broadly linear hanging wall subsidence, and attributes the general absence of footwall uplift to an abnormally deep decollement.

East Shetland basin

The East Shetland basin or Brent Province forms the northwestern part of the Viking graben and comprises a system of down-to-the-E tilted fault blocks which were active during the late Jurassic and perhaps the Early Cretaceous (Hay 1978; Johnson & Dingwall 1981). The sedimentary fill is isostatically compensated by thin crust (Donato & Tully 1981) and the basin was probably produced by lithospheric stretching. About 2.5 km of post-rifting sediments are present, suggesting a β factor of ≈ 1.5, in agreement with Donato & Tully's

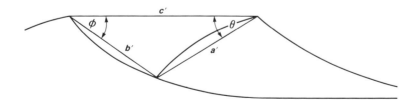

FIG. 17. Schematic representation of a system of listric normal faults. The curved top basement interface is approximated by the straight line segments a', b' and c'. To estimate footwall uplift, the listric normal faults are represented by a set of 'domino' faults with bedding-plane dip θ, fault-plane dip ϕ, and extension ratio $\beta = c'/a'$.

(1981) conclusions. The Brent oil field (Bowen 1975) occupies a footwall block which was emergent during extension. Upper Jurassic and lowermost Cretaceous sediments are absent from the crest of the structure, and the pre-rift Lower to Middle Jurassic section is deeply eroded. The amount of post-Middle-Jurassic erosion (600–1000 m) was estimated by taking Bowen's (1975) cross-section and projecting the top reservoir horizon beyond the unconformity until it intersected the main bounding fault.

In the Brent area, fault spacing c' is ≈ 25 km (Hay 1978) so a' is ≈ 17km. From Fig. 7a ($\phi_i = 60°$), footwall uplift $z_f = 1.5$ km and hanging wall subsidence z_h is in excess of 5 km. The peak of the uplift curve occurs at $\beta = 1.5$, so even if an erosional model like that of Fig. 13 were preferred, footwalls would be emergent throughout the stretching episode. An erosional model would require stretching to continue until the Albian/Aptian, when marine deposition resumed over the crest of the structure, but a model in which islands rose a significant height above sea-level would permit extension to cease somewhat earlier. Fig. 7b ($\phi_i = 45°$) predicts rather less uplift (≈ 500 m), but the curve for $a' = 17$ km remains above sea-level at $\beta = 1.5$.

The Heather oil field (Gray & Barnes 1981) lies 70 km W of Brent, and although the footwall block has suffered erosion, a thinned but continuous sequence of uppermost Jurassic and lower Cretaceous sediments is present. Fault spacing in the Heather area is 15–20 km (Hay 1978), i.e. $a' = 10$–13 km. For $\phi_i = 60°$ (Fig. 7a), a β value of 1.5 is past the crest of the uplift curve, and on an erosional model, footwalls would subside during the later stages of extension. The effect is even more marked for $\phi_i = 45°$ (Fig. 7b).

Although fault spacing in the Brent Province is similar to that in the Inner Moray Firth, isostatic compensation means that subsidence is controlled by a relatively shallow notional depth to decollement rather than a deep physical sole fault, so favouring footwall uplift. There is a suggestion (in comparing Heather and Brent) that variations in the severity of footwall erosion can be attributed to local variations in fault spacing.

Aegean Sea

The area around the Aegean Sea has undergone recent (post-middle Miocene) extension, with a stretching factor β close to 2 (Jackson & McKenzie 1983, and references therein). Islands within the Aegean correspond to the footwall blocks of major active normal faults (Jackson

et al. 1982a). Jackson & McKenzie (1983) attributed the absolute uplift (above sea-level) of these footwall blocks to a local isostatic mechanism (after Heiskanen & Vening Meinesz 1958). Their geometry can also be described in terms of the uplift model presented in this paper. Jackson & McKenzie (1983) state that the present-day fault spacing c' is 30–40 km, so the initial spacing a' was 15–20 km. They suggest that footwall uplift, z_f, is 500–1000 m and total fault throw 5–10 km, so hanging wall subsidence z_h is 4.5–9 km. Because the Aegean contains deep-water troughs (up to ≈ 1 km), subsidence must be partly water-loaded. The notional depth to decollement d_n should therefore be intermediate between those for sediment-loaded (Fig. 7) and water-loaded (Fig. 12) basins. A reasonable round-number estimate is 6 km, in which case a' corresponds to 2.5–3.5 times d_n, and S_i, the average sediment + water thickness, should be ≈ 3 km. If the fault blocks have a simple 'saw-tooth' geometry, Jackson & McKenzie's (1983) figures imply values for S_i of 2–4 km, and for $\beta = 2$, $d_n = 4$–8 km. From Fig. 16, ($\phi_i = 60°$, $a' = 3 \times d_n$), $z_f = 1.8$ km, $z_h = 4.8$ km, and the total throw on each fault is 6.6 km. For $\phi_i = 45°$, $z_f = 1$ km, $z_h = 4$ km and the total throw is 5 km. These results are reasonably consistent with Jackson & McKenzie's (1983) observations.

The 'forbidden zone' of Fig. 16 does not apply in this compensated basin, since earthquake foci imply that fault planes extend to ≈ 10 km depth (Jackson et al. 1982a), and so any physical decollement must be deeper than ≈ 10 km. However, the 'domino' model implies that the fault planes have shallow present-day dips ($\phi = 20$–30°), unless an unreasonably high value is chosen for ϕ_i. Evidence from the Corinth area (Jackson et al. 1982a) suggests a steeper present-day dip to 10 km depth ($\phi = 45°$), although it is of course possible that β is greater and ϕ lower in the Aegean proper. By analogy with Proffett's (1977) interpretation of the Basin and Range, Jackson & McKenzie (1983) suggested that old fault planes have been rotated to low dips and abandoned, and that new, steep fault planes dominate the topography. A crude assessment of the effects of this process can be made by assuming an initial dip ϕ_i of 60° and a present-day dip ϕ of 45°. From Fig. 7a, $\beta = 1.25$, and so three generations of faulting would be required to accommodate a total extension of $\beta = 2$ (since $1.25^3 = 1.95$). For the most recent set of faults, $c' = 30$–40 km, so $a' = 24$–32 km, i.e. 4 to 5 times d_n. From Fig. 16, $z_f = 2$–3 km, $z_h = 3.2$–4.2 km, and $S_i = 1.2$ km. This is probably too much uplift, even allowing for reduction by erosion.

Choosing a slightly higher value of d_n (e.g. 7 km, to allow for compaction of sediments deposited during earlier episodes of extension) decreases this uplift figure slightly ($a' = 3.5–4.5 \times d_n$, $z_f = 1.8–2.8$ km, $z_h = 3.2–4.2$ km, $S_i = 1.4$ km).

Major faults in the Corinth area are rather more closely spaced than 30 km (≈ 18 km— Jackson *et al.* 1982a). If a' is set to 15 km for $\beta = 1.25$ and $\phi_l = 60°$, then $z_f = 900$ m, $z_h = 2.1$ km and $S_i = 1.2$ km; figures in close agreement with local topography. As a final example, consider the Platea area, NE of Corinth. An old erosion surface is uplifted to 300 m at Platea and downfaulted to 900 m below sea-level in the Gulf of Corinth (Jackson *et al.* 1982a, p. 395). The mean depth of 300 m ($= S_i$) suggests that, for this increment of stretching, $\beta = 1.055$. Fault planes dip at 40–45° today, so given the low value of β, the curves for $\phi_i = 45°$ will be used ($\phi = 42°$ for $\beta = 1.055$). For a present-day fault spacing of ≈ 25 km, $a' = 24$ km $= 4 \times d_n$, $z_f = 300$ m and $z_h = 900$ m, in excellent agreement with the observations of Jackson *et al.* (1982a).

Thus the simple model of footwall uplift presented here can be applied in the Aegean area. Note that its success is without prejudice to other, mechanistic models based on an isostatic or elastic response (e.g. Jackson & McKenzie 1983). In its simplest terms, the model is purely geometric and should apply to any isostatically compensated basin with a regular, 'sawtooth-shaped' top basement interface. The breakdown of 'domino-fault' systems at large β, with initiation of new, steeper faults, precludes rigorous application of the model to predict a detailed history of uplift and subsidence versus β.

Armorican margin

Le Pichon & Sibuet (1981) and Le Pichon *et al.* (1983) have shown that the development of the Armorican continental margin is consistent with a model of lithospheric stretching. Extension ratios (β) range from 1.1 to 2.7, in a transect from continent to ocean, and subsidence has been largely water-loaded with a small sedimentary contribution. Le Pichon *et al.* (1983) have suggested that a 'domino-faulting' model can explain the geometry of upper-crustal fault blocks, the initial fault-plane dip ϕ_i being 45°. Le Pichon *et al.*'s (1983) fig. 2, based on Montadert *et al.*'s (1979) depth-converted seismic reflection section, implies a β value of ≈ 2.5. On the Armorican margin (unlike the Aegean?), it would appear that simple 'domino-faulting' has been effective even at large β, although as Le Pichon *et al.* (1983) pointed out,

it requires substantial ductile strain across a broad brittle–ductile transition, rather than a simple sole fault.

The thermal component of subsidence can be stripped off by applying equation 3, and assuming (following Le Pichon & Sibuet 1981) that S_t has reached 87% of its ultimate value. For water loading:

$$S_t = 3.65 \, (1 - 1/\beta) = 2.19 \text{ km.}$$

A ≈ 1 km thick layer of post-rift sediments is present; from Fig. 7, these probably have an average density of ≈ 1900 kgm^{-3}, so the average density of the actual post-rifting column (1 km of sediments + 1.19 km of water) is 1411 kgm^{-3}. By using this new density ($= \varrho_s$) to insert a new value of s into equation 3, and proceeding iteratively, it can be shown that $S_t = 4.34 \, (1 - 1/\beta) = 2.6$ km. The mean density of this sediment + water column is 1348 kgm^{-3}. On removing 2.6 km of thermal subsidence, 2.5 km of water + syn-rift sediments remains; from equation 1, $d_n = 4.17$ km, and ϱ_s (the mean density of the sediment + water column during stretching) is 1456 kgm^{-3}. These figures are consistent with the observation that subsidence was largely water-loaded, and with Le Pichon *et al.*'s independent reconstructions (1983, fig. 1).

Present-day fault-spacing c' is 18 km, so $a' = 7.2$ km $= 1.73 \times d_n$. From Fig. 16, this fault-spacing is not quite sufficient to permit footwall uplift. However, if the early stages of extension were water-loaded (Fig. 12), several hundred metres of uplift would be possible, and if β was somewhat lower (e.g. 2), even sediment-loaded uplift would be possible. Given the uncertainties involved, the uplift model is reasonably consistent with Montadert *et al.*'s (1979) cross-section, which shows only minor footwall erosion, and that probably at an early stage in the extension process.

The Armorican data can be used to assess the relationship between the physical depth to decollement d' and the notional depth d_n. Le Pichon *et al.* (1983, fig. 1) provide three reconstructions of the Armorican margin, prior to thermal subsidence, and imply that the initial depth to the 'sole fault' (actually a broad brittle–ductile transition) was 9 km. Their models have $\beta = 1.1$, 1.7 and 2.7, and from equation 6 ($d_n = 4.17$ km), $d' = 8.6$, 7 and 6 km; depths in close agreement with Le Pichon *et al.*'s reconstructions. On Montadert *et al.*'s (1979) cross-section, the physical decollement surface lies at ≈ 9 km below sea-level, and prior to 2.6 km of thermal subsidence, lay at a depth $d' = 6.4$ km. From equation 7, with $\beta = 2.5$ and $d_n = 4.17$ km, its initial depth d_i was 9.75 km. By inverting equation 5, it is simple to demonstrate the inapplicability of simple area-balancing techniques to this area (cf. Gibbs 1983). After stripping off the thermal subsidence, $z = S_i = 2.5$ km, $\beta = 2.5$ and the calculated (notional) depth to decollement is 4.17 km $(= d_n)$. This is very different to the physical depth to decollement, which ranges from $\approx$ 6 km to $\approx$ 10 km, depending on the magnitude of β.

Discussion

By comparing the equations for balancing cross-sections above a basal decollement with those for subsidence during lithospheric stretching, a geometric relationship has been identified between detached normal faulting and stretching. For an instantaneously stretched, isostatically compensated basin, area/bed length balancing yields a notional depth to decollement which is related to the 'mantle geoid' of Turcotte *et al.* (1977) and for a constant-density basin fill coincides with the level of no vertical motion within the lithosphere. Prior to thermal subsidence, this notional depth to decollement lies $\approx$ 3.3 km below sea-level for water-loaded basins. Sediment-loaded basins are most readily treated if the subsidence equations of McKenzie (1978) are modified to take explicit account of sediment density; the notional depth to decollement ranges from $\approx$ 5–10 km, increasing with the stretching factor β. The physical sole to a system of detached normal faults can take any depth, and is not predictable from extension and subsidence data; in general, it will move vertically, as extension proceeds, to maintain isostatic equilibrium. Paradoxically, the physical depth to decollement is more likely to be incorrectly calculated where a reliable sea-level reference is preserved. Where, as in many fossil basins, a datum surface is constructed from major fault blocks which have moved vertically with the sole fault, this datum will not correspond to the contemporary sea-level but may yield a correct depth to decollement.

Vertical movement of the sole fault provides a mechanism for the uplift of major basement horsts within extensional basins, since in general a sole fault localized in a brittle–ductile transition will lie below the notional depth to decollement and will be uplifted as stretching proceeds (provided isostatic compensation operates on a horizontal scale greater than that of the uplifted block). In a system of rotated planar ('domino' or 'pack of cards') detached normal faults, footwall uplift should be widespread for large initial fault spacings (several times the notional depth to decollement). Several sets of curves have been presented, which predict (with increasing β) either accelerating footwall subsidence, uplift followed by subsidence below sea-level, or uplift followed by subsidence to a final elevation above sea-level. These curves can be used to predict and explain footwall uplift/subsidence patterns in a variety of basins. Major fault systems in several basins appear to have had an initial fault spacing of 10–20 km, i.e. about the depth to the brittle–ductile transition. This may have implications for the mechanical behaviour of the brittle upper crust, and if it can be generalized, implies that footwall uplift should be a feature of most extensional basins.

The recognition that footwall uplift and erosion can take place during extension has implications for both neotectonic and palaeotectonic interpretations. It provides support for the suggestion of Jackson *et al.* (1982b) that recent uplift of islands in the Aegean Sea does not imply an episode of compression. Individual footwalls can be uplifted then subside during progressive extension, and footwall blocks from different parts of the same basin can record markedly different subsidence histories. This observation gains increased importance because information about the stratigraphy of most extensional basins is derived mainly from hydrocarbon exploration wells sited on footwall blocks. For example, the preservation in the Inner Moray Firth basin of a continuous sedimentary sequence through the end-Jurassic 'Cimmerian unconformity' is primarily attributable to the fact that the basin is not isostatically compensated, and has a relatively deep sole fault which inhibits footwall uplift. Elsewhere (e.g. the East Shetland basin), isostatic compensation was maintained, the notional depth to decollement remained shallower than 10 km regardless of the depth to the physical sole fault, and footwalls were uplifted above sea-level during extension.

The uplift model described in this paper is essentially geometric, and independent of mechanism—it requires only that the extended top basement interface approximates to the 'sawtooth' form produced by 'domino-faulting'. The local isostatic effects discussed by Jackson & McKenzie (1983) could be superimposed on this model, and listric normal faults can be accommodated if bedding surfaces in their hanging wall blocks are not excessively curved. The uplift model can be applied to detached normal faulting in uncompensated basins, where the notional depth to decollement is replaced by the constant depth to a physical sole fault. It can be extended to more complex basins, such as those produced by non-uniform or non-instantaneous stretching (Royden & Keen 1980; Jarvis & McKenzie 1980; Hellinger & Sclater 1983). For example, it is possible to envisage a situation where the level of no vertical motion lay *above* sea-level. Extreme attenuation of the mantle lithosphere relative to the continental crust (e.g. by heating during stretching) would give rise to overall uplift (cf. Royden & Keen 1980), implying the operation of a *negative* notional depth to decollement. Physical sole faults or decollement surfaces would be progressively uplifted and eroded, to eventually be exposed at the surface, as appears to have happened in the Basin and Range area (e.g. Miller *et al.* 1983). For any stretching model, it should be possible to define an instantaneous notional depth to decollement, based on the relationship between basement subsidence and β, and from this a set of curves like those of Fig. 7 could be generated. The observed history of individual fault blocks would then provide additional constraints on the validity of the basic stretching model.

ACKNOWLEDGMENTS: The ideas developed in this paper have benefited from discussions with colleagues in the British Geological Survey and their presentation from the comments of two anonymous referees. This work is published with the permission of the Director, British Geological Survey (N.E.R.C.).

References

ANGELIER, J. 1985. Extension and rifting: the Zeit region, Gulf of Suez. *J. struct. Geol.* 7, 605–12.

BARR, D. 1985. 3-D palinspastic restoration of normal faults in the Inner Moray Firth: implications for extensional basin development. *Earth planet. Sci. Lett.* 75, 191–203.

—— , McQUILLIN, R & DONATO, J.A. 1985. Footwall uplift in the Inner Moray Firth basin, offshore Scotland. *J. struct. Geol.* 7, 267–8.

BARTON, P. & WOOD, R. 1984. Tectonic evolution of the North Sea basin: crustal stretching and subsidence. *Geophys. J.R. astron. Soc.* 79, 987–1022.

BEACH, A. 1984. The structural evolution of the Witch Ground Graben. *J. geol. Soc. London,* 141, 621–8.

BOWEN, J.M. 1975. The Brent oil-field. *In:* WOODLAND, A.W. (ed.) *Petroleum and the continental shelf of North-west Europe,* 353–60. Applied Science Publishers, London.

BREWER, J.A. & SMYTHE, D.K. 1984. MOIST and the continuity of crustal reflector geometry along the Caledonian–Appalachian orogen. *J. geol. Soc. London,* 141, 105–20.

DE CHARPAL, O., MONTADERT, L., GUENNOC, P. & ROBERTS, D.G. 1978. Rifting, crustal attenuation and subsidence in the Bay of Biscay. *Nature, Lond.,* 275, 706–10.

CHEN, W-P. & MOLNAR, P. 1983. Focal depths of intracontinental and intraplate earthquakes and their implications for the thermal and mechanical properties of the lithosphere. *J. geophys. Res.* 88, 4183–214.

CHENET, P., MONTADERT, L., GAIRAUD, H. & ROBERTS, D. 1983. Extension ratio measurements on the Galicia, Portugal and northern Biscay continental margins: implications for evolutionary models of passive continental margins. *In:* WATKINS, J.S. & DRAKE, C.L. (eds) *Studies in continental margin geology. Mem. Am. Assoc. Pet. Geol.* 34, 703–15.

CHESHER, J.A. & BACON, M. 1975. A deep seismic survey of the Moray Firth. *Rep. Inst. geol. Sci. London, 75/11.*

CHRISTIE, P.A.F. & SCLATER, J.G. 1980. An extensional origin for the Buchan and Witchground graben in the North Sea. *Nature, Lond.,* 283, 729–32.

COCHRAN, J.R. 1983. Effects of finite rifting times on the development of sedimentary basins. *Earth planet. Sci. Lett.* 66, 289–302.

DAHLSTROM, C.D.A. 1969. Balanced cross-sections. *Can. J. Earth Sci.* 6, 743–57.

DONATO, J.A. & TULLY, M.C. 1981. A regional interpretation of North Sea gravity data. *In:* ILLING, L.V. & HOBSON, G.D. (eds) *Petroleum Geology of the Continental Shelf of North-west Europe,* pp. 65–75. Institute of Petroleum, London.

GIBBS, A.D. 1983. Balanced cross-section construction from seismic sections in areas of extensional tectonics. *J. struct. Geol.* 5, 471–82.

—— 1984. Structural evolution of extensional basin margins. *J. geol. Soc. London,* 141, 609–20.

GRAY, W.D.T. & BARNES, G. 1981. The Heather oil field. *In:* ILLING, L.V. & HOBSON, G.D. (eds) *Petroleum Geology of the Continental Shelf of North-West Europe,* pp. 335–41. Institute of Petroleum, London.

HAY, J.T.C. 1978. Structural development in the Northern North Sea. *J. Pet. Geol.* 1, 65–77.

HEISKANEN, W.A. & VENING MEINESZ, F.A. 1958. *The Earth and its Gravity Field.* McGraw-Hill, New York.

HELLINGER, S.J. & SCLATER, J.G. 1983. Some comments on two-layer extensional models for the evolution of sedimentary basins. *J. geophys. Res.* 88, 8251–69.

JACKSON, J.A. & McKENZIE, D. 1983. The geometrical evolution of normal fault systems. *J. struct. Geol.* 5, 471–82.

—— , GAGNEPAIN, J., HOUSEMAN, G., KING, G.C.P., PAPADIMITRIOU, P., SOUFLERIS, C. & VIRIEUX. J. 1982a. Seismicity, normal faulting and the geomorphological development of the Gulf of Corinth (Greece): the Corinth earthquakes of February and March 1981. *Earth planet. Sci. Lett.* 57, 377–97.

—— , KING, G. & VITA-FINZI, C. 1982b. The neotectonics of the Aegean: an alternative view. *Earth planet. Sci. Lett.* 61, 303–18.

JARVIS, G.T. & McKENZIE, D.P. 1980. Sedimentary basin formation with finite extension rates. *Earth planet. Sci. Lett.* **48**, 42–52.

JOHNSON, R.J. & DINGWALL, R.G. 1981. The Caledonides: their influence on the stratigraphy of the North-west European continental shelf. *In*: ILLING, L.V. & HOBSON, G.D. (eds) *Petroleum Geology of the Continental Shelf of North-west Europe*, pp. 85–97. Institute of Petroleum, London.

LE PICHON, X. & SIBUET, J-C. 1981. Passive margins: a model of formation. *J. geophys. Res.* **86**, 3708–20.

——, ANGELIER, J. & SIBUET, J-C. 1982. Plate boundaries and extensional tectonics. *Tectonophysics*, **81**, 239–56.

——, —— & —— 1983. Subsidence and stretching. *In*: WATKINS, J.S. & DRAKE, C.L. (eds) Studies in Continental Margin Geology. *Mem. Am. Assoc. Pet. Geol.* **34**, 731–41.

LINSLEY, P.N., POTTER, H.C., McNAB, J. & RACHER, D. 1980. The Beatrice Field, Inner Moray Firth. *In*: HALBOUTY, M.T. (ed.) *Giant Oil and Gas Fields of the Decade 1968–1978*, pp. 117–29. Am. Assoc. Pet. Geol. Tulsa.

McDONALD, R.E. 1976. Tertiary tectonics and sedimentary rocks along the transition, Basin and Range province to plateau and thrust province. *In*: HILL, J.G. (ed.) *Symposium on Geology of the Cordilleran Hingeline*, pp. 281–318. Rocky Mtn Assoc. Geol. Denver.

McKENZIE, D. 1978. Some remarks on the development of sedimentary basins. *Earth planet. Sci. Lett.* **40**, 25–32.

McQUILLIN, R., DONATO, J.A. & TULSTRUP, J. 1982. Development of basins in the Inner Moray Firth and the North Sea by crustal extension and dextral displacement of the Great Glen Fault. *Earth planet. Sci. Lett.* **60**, 127–39.

MILLER, E.L. GANS, P.B. & GARING, J. 1983. The Snake Range decollement: an exhumed mid-Tertiary ductile–brittle transition. *Tectonics*, **2**, 239–63.

MONTADERT, L., ROBERTS, D.G., DE CHARPAL, O. & GUENNOC, P. 1979. Rifting and subsidence of the northern continental margin of the Bay of Biscay. *In*: MONTADERT, L. & ROBERTS, D.G. (eds) *Init. Rep. D.S.D.P.* **48**, 1025–60.

PARSONS, B. & SCLATER, J.G. 1977. An analysis of the variation of ocean floor bathymetry and heat flow with age. *J. geophys. Res.* **82**, 803–27.

PROFFETT, J.M. 1977. Cenozoic geology of the Yerington district, Nevada, and implications for the nature of Basin and Range faulting. *Bull. geol. Soc. Am.* **88**, 247–66.

ROYDEN, L. & KEEN, C.E. 1980. Rifting process and thermal evolution of the continental margin of eastern Canada determined from subsidence curves. *Earth planet. Sci. Lett.* **51**, 343–61.

SCLATER, J.G. & CHRISTIE, P.A.F. 1980. Continental stretching: an explanation of the post-mid-Cretaceous subsidence of the Central North Sea. *J. geophys. Res.* **85**, 3711–39.

——, ROYDEN, L., HORVATH, F., BURCHFIEL, B.C., SEMKEN, S. & STEGENA, L. 1980. The formation of the intra-Carpathian basins as determined from subsidence data. *Earth planet. Sci. Lett.* **51**, 139–62.

SIBSON, R.H. 1983. Continental fault structure and the shallow earthquake source. *J. geol. Soc. London*, **140**, 741–67.

SMYTHE, D.K., SKUCE, A.G. & DONATO, J.A. 1980. Geological objections to an extensional origin for the Buchan and Withground Graben in the North Sea. *Nature, Lond.* **287**, 467.

STECKLER, M.S. & WATTS, A.B. 1978. Subsidence of the Atlantic-type continental margin off New York. *Earth planet. Sci. Lett.* **41**, 1–13.

TURCOTTE, D.L., HAXBY, W.F. & OCKENDOW, J.R. 1977. Lithospheric instabilities. *In*: TALWANI, M. & PITMAN, W.C. (eds) *Island Arcs, Deep-Sea Trenches and Back-Arc Basins. Am. geophys. Union Maurice Ewing Series*, **1**, 63–9.

WATTS, A.B. 1982. Tectonic subsidence, flexure and global changes in sea level. *Nature, Lond.* **297**, 469–74.

——, KARNER, G.D. & STECKLER, M.S. 1982. Lithospheric flexure and the evolution of sedimentary basins. *Phil. Trans. R. Soc. London*, **A305**, 249–81.

WERNICKE, B. & BURCHFIEL, B.C. 1982. Modes of extensional tectonics. *J. struct. Geol.* **4**, 105–15.

WHITEMAN, A., NAYLOR, D., PEGRUM, R. & REES, G. 1975. North Sea troughs and plate tectonics. *Tectonophysics*, **26**, 39–54.

WOOD, R. 1981. The subsidence history of Conoco well 15/30-1, central North Sea. *Earth planet. Sci. Lett.* **54**, 306–12.

—— & BARTON, P. 1983. Crustal thinning and subsidence in the North Sea. *Nature, Lond.* **302**, 134–6.

ZIEGLER, P. 1983. Crustal thinning and subsidence in the North Sea. *Nature, Lond.* **304**, 562.

DAVID BARR, British Geological Survey, 19 Grange Terrace, Edinburgh EH9 2LF, UK.
Present address: Britoil plc, 150 St Vincent Street, Glasgow G2 5LJ, UK.

Physical models of extensional tectonics at various scales

B. Vendeville, P.R. Cobbold, P. Davy, J.P. Brun & P. Choukroune

SUMMARY: In a preliminary series of experiments, using physical models mechanical processes of extensional tectonics have been investigated at various scales. By a suitable choice of model materials, experiments were performed at low cost in a natural gravity field. Upper layers of the lithosphere were modelled using sand; lower layers, using silicone putties of two different densities; the mantle asthenosphere was modelled using honey. The models deformed under their own weight or under absolute horizontal tension. Rates of extension were controlled using a stepper motor. Surface deformation and faulting were monitored using 35 mm time-lapse photography. Lower lithosphere topography was photographed through the transparent asthenosphere. Fault patterns in models with lithosphere only, were observed by serial sectioning. Otherwise, the brittle–ductile interface was observed after suctioning off the sand.

Simple experiments with uniformly extended sand layers only show that; (i) spacing of normal faults is a measure of the layer thickness; (ii) the length of fault trace increases with the amount of downthrow; and (iii) faults tend to form domino domains. Some experiments with a brittle layer on a ductile substrate show a mechanism of passive rifting where; (i) major faults occur in conjugate pairs, defining rift valleys; (ii) minor faults localize additional extension in rift-valley floors; and (iii) isostatic uplift of the viscous substrate causes uplift and tilting of rift rims. In freely floating continents, gravitational spreading leads to: (i) highly localized extension and thinning at continental margins and (ii) internal rifting.

Physical and numerical models of tectonic processes can provide insights into the mechanical and thermal processes that operate in nature. In favourable circumstances, they can even produce structures which exist in nature but have escaped detection.

For the last two years, the experimental tectonics group at Rennes has been engaged in pilot studies of physical modelling within a normal gravity field and at the scale of the Earth's lithosphere (Cobbold *et al.* unpublished manuscript). Since the pioneering work of Hubbert (1937) and Ramberg (1967), it has been known that this technique places severe restrictions on the strength of model materials used. For example, if a model has linear dimensions 10 million times smaller than its natural counterpart (so that 1 m represents 10,000 km), then the model material must also be 10 million times weaker than rock, if gravity is to have an equivalent effect on the model to that it has in nature. Thus for a brittle crust, obeying a simple frictional (Navier–Coulomb) failure law with no time dependence, the cohesive strength must be 10 million times smaller in the model. A lithified sedimentary rock must therefore be represented by a material such as dry sand. Similarly, if a laboratory experiment is to take place in a reasonable time (say, a day) and this is to represent a typical tectonic period (say, 20 Ma), then the viscosity of a ductile lower crust must be reduced by a factor of about 10^{16} and the cor-

responding model material must have the consistency of pitch. It has often been argued (e.g. Ramberg 1967, p. 44) that such consistencies make it difficult for the experimenter to construct and dissect his models, so that he would be better advised to use a centrifuge. We maintain that a centrifuge is neither necessary, nor even always desirable, but leave more detailed discussion of this topic to a companion paper (Cobbold *et al.* unpublished manuscript).

The purpose of what follows is to describe a number of pilot experiments covering the field of extensional tectonics at various scales. We illustrate the contrasting results of using models that (a) are purely brittle or (b) have a brittle layer underlain by a viscous substrate. In a broad sense, we are therefore studying extensional tectonics at the scale of (a) the upper crust only, or (b) the entire crust, if not the lithosphere. Because of current uncertainties regarding the rheology of the lithosphere (see, e.g. Kusznir & Park, this volume), it is not always easy to be definitive about what one is modelling. We have constructed simple (some would say oversimplified) models with materials of known rheology and have subjected them to simple conditions of boundary motion. No attempt has been made to introduce or study thermal effects. Our experiments are similar in this respect to those of Oertel (1965), Cloos (1955, 1968), Hoeppener *et al.* (1969) and to other more recent ones in the field of extensional tectonics

From COWARD, M.P., DEWEY, J.F. & HANCOCK, P.L. (eds), 1987, *Continental Extensional Tectonics*, Geological Society Special Publication No. 28, pp. 95–107.

(Horsfield 1980; Elmohandes 1981; Mulugeta 1985).

In this paper, we focus on the distribution of faults obtained in the brittle layer, including such geologically important aspects as (i) fault location and localization, (ii) fault spacing, (iii) fault vergence and (iv) relationships between fault length and amount of throw. Not enough experiments have been done to allow us to develop unequivocal mechanical interpretations in all cases. Nevertheless our preliminary experiments draw attention to some factors which control the geometry of fault systems during extensional tectonics.

Experimental procedure

Materials

Three kinds of material have been used: dry quartz sand, silicone putty and honey.

1 Dry quartz sand (Fontainebleau sand, well sorted, with grains of 200–300 μm, well rounded) was used to simulate the brittle behaviour of lithified rock in the upper crust. The sand fails according to a Navier–Coulomb law, with negligible cohesion and with an angle of internal friction, $\Phi = 30°$ (Mandl *et al.* 1977). Failure leads to formation of narrow planar shear bands or faults, orientated at about ± 30° to the compression direction. Bands form by pore-space dilatation, with accompanying strain-softening (Mandl *et al.* 1977). Once formed, the bands remain weaker than the surrounding non-dilatated sand. The density of the starting material ($\varrho = 1.3$ g cm^{-3}) can be reduced by mixing with ethyl-cellulose powder ($\varrho = 0.3$ g cm^{-3}) which has similar mechanical properties. The cohesion can be increased by mixing with dry cement powder. Finally, the colour can be changed by dyeing with methylene blue or other organic pigments.

2 Silicone putty (pink opaque gomme GS1R, manufactured by Rhone–Poulenc, France) was used to model the lower crust, or the lower lithosphere, depending on the scale of the problem considered. Rheological tests, performed by the manufacturer or by us using various viscometers, show that this silicone putty is an almost perfectly Newtonian fluid in the range of strain rates 10^{-6} sec$^{-1} < \dot{\epsilon} < 10^{-2}$ sec^{-1}, with a typical viscosity (batch dependent) of about 10^4 Pa s at 20°C. This behaviour contrasts with that of other makes of silicone putty (see Dixon & Summers 1985), which are non-Newtonian. The density of 1.16 g cm^{-3} can be increased to 1.37 g cm^{-3} by charging with finely powdered galena. This also increases the viscosity sevenfold, and imparts a grey colour to the silicone putty.

3 Natural clear honey ($\varrho = 1.40$ g cm^{-3}) was used to model the asthenosphere. The honey is nearly Newtonian, with a viscosity of about 10 Pa s at 20°C. It is transparent over a distance of about 5 cm and translucent over greater distances. This property is very convenient for the observation of an overlying layer of silicone putty representing the lithosphere.

The densities of sand, silicone and honey were chosen and adjusted so as to give a gravitationally stable density stratification representative of the crust, mantle lithosphere and asthenosphere. Similarly, the viscosity ratio of silicone and honey (greater than 100:1) is assumed to be representative of that between lithosphere and asthenosphere. For fuller discussion of these matters, see Cobbold *et al.* (in prep.)

Apparatus

Models were constructed and then deformed in two kinds of housings. The wide housing (Fig. 1a) is also shallow ($50 \times 50 \times 10$ cm^3) and suitable for one-layer or two-layer models; whereas the deep housing (Fig. 1b; $20 \times 20 \times 20$ cm^3) with its transparent base is suitable for three-layer models.

Model construction

Viscous layers were poured into the chosen housing and allowed to attain a horizontal upper surface under the spreading action of gravity. Because higher layers were successively less dense, no difficulties were encountered in this procedure.

Uppermost sand units were layered to reveal fault throws. Thin layers of uniform thickness and contrasting colours were poured sequentially by hand.

Model deformation

In most experiments, horizontal extension was either imposed or allowed by displacing one side wall of the housing at a constant velocity, in the range $1 < v < 10$ cm hr^{-1}, provided by a stepper motor and a screw-jack. In some experiments, basal stretching was rendered uniform by the use of a thin rubber sheet (1 mm), stretched between two moving walls. The other horizontal dimension of the rubber sheet was kept constant by the use of hooks along two stationary curtain rails.

Model observation

The motion of passive markers and the development of faults at the upper surface of the model were monitored using time-lapse photography (35 mm reflex Minolta camera with programmable back). For three-layer models, the topography of the silicone–honey interface was photographed occasionally through the honey and transparent base. No attempt was made to photograph the model through the transparent lateral glass walls, because boundary friction was judged to be too severe and the result not representative of the internal deformation. At the end of experiments with sand or sand/silicone models, the sand was wetted by carefully spraying the upper surface with water. This introduced extra cohesion and enabled vertical sections to be cut through both the sand and silicone.

The sections were then photographed. Some of the sectioned models were further hardened by cooling to −30°C in a commercial freezer. With three-layer models, no practical cutting or cooling techniques were discovered. Instead the geometry of the sand layers was observed by siphoning off the sand at selected sites using a vacuum pipe fitted with a thin nozzle (1 mm aperture).

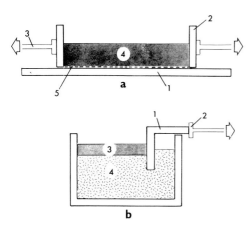

FIG. 1. Model housings and applied boundary motions. (a) Wide housing has rigid base (1) and mobile end walls (2) attached to pistons (3). Uniform basal extension of model (4) can be provided by rubber sheet (5). (b) Deep housing has one mobile wall (1) attached to a piston (2). Sand/silicone (3) floats on honey (4).

Uniform sand models

Seven experiments were performed using models made of sand alone, to investigate the effect of a uniform basal stretching on the development of faults. The models may represent the upper crust, or part of it, in areas subject to uniform ductile extension, without isostatic response. Uniform basal extension was achieved using a rubber sheet in the wide housing. Parameters that differed from one model to another were (i) the inclination of the stretched base with respect to the horizontal, and (ii) the thickness of the model.

Horizontal models

Cross-sections and a plan view (Fig. 2) illustrate typical patterns of normal faults obtained (in models initially 2.5 and 5 cm thick) after a stretch of $\lambda = 1.5$. Our principal observations are listed below.

(1) Fault spacing is strongly dependent on model thickness (cf. Figs 2b & c). (2) In a given model there are approximately equal numbers of faults with opposite senses of dip (vergence). (3) Faults with the same vergence are often but not always concentrated in domains, a result previously obtained by Oertel (1965), Hoeppener *et al.* (1969), Freund (1974), and Faugère & Brun (1984). (4) In fault domains bedding dips tend to be largest where fault dips are gentlest. We interpret this as evidence for block tilting, domino-fashion, as demonstrated in detail by Faugère & Brun (1984). (5) Domains are largest and more clearly defined in thin models (Fig. 2c), whereas thick models show more cross cutting faults as well as horst and rift blocks (Fig. 2b). The reason for this is not yet clear: it may be, for example, that the thinner models with their larger number of faults, are less constrained by the vertical end walls of the housing. (6) Major faults tend to be planar within domino domains; more sigmoidal (initially planar?) where they bound horsts or rifts. (7) At their widest parts, horst and rift blocks contain minor faults (Fig. 2b) also arranged with alternating vergences. These minor faults clearly are responsible for horizontal extension within the blocks. There is a possibility that extension is not constant with depth and this may explain the sigmoidal shape of the bounding major faults. (8) In plan view (Fig. 2d), deformed passive markers show that surface strain is remarkably homogeneous on a bulk scale, but heterogeneous at fault-block scale. (9) Fault traces appear longest where the throw is greatest. Fault

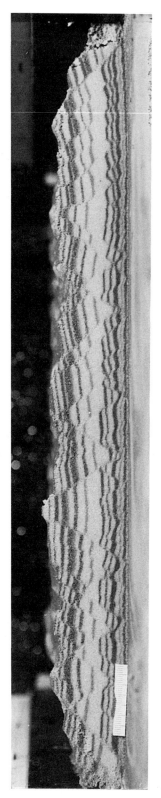

2a

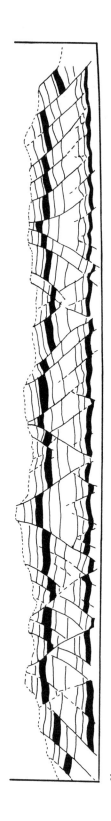

2b

2c

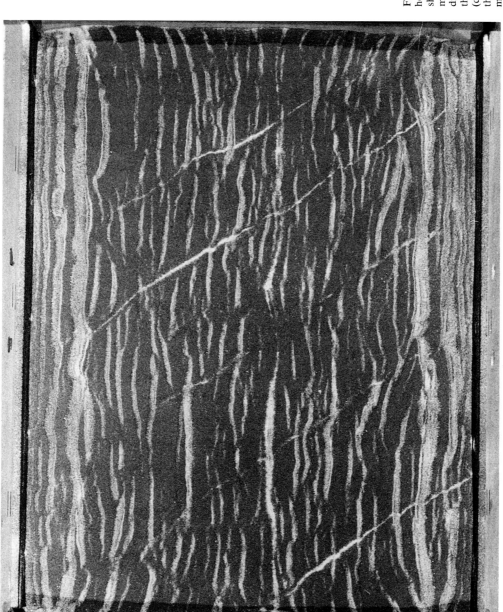

FIG. 2. Sand models uniformly and horizontally stretched at base ($\lambda = 1.5$), showing (a) longitudinal section through model initially 5 cm thick, (b) line drawing of same, (c) longitudinal section through model initially 2.5 cm thick, and (d) surface view of model initially 5 cm thick. Diagonal lines in (d) are passive markers (surface scratches).

2d

traces are locally slightly oblique to the bulk kinematic axes or slightly wavy.

The last observation is more readily understood if one examines a series of time-lapse photographs of the upper surface of a model. These show that the trace length and the throw of an individual fault increase together with time, so that a fault scarp maintains a characteristic pea-pod shape, unless it coalesces with another fault scarp.

Models with inclined bases

Two experiments were performed by making models as before (2.5 cm thick) and then inclining the housing at 7° or 14° to the horizontal *before* applying a basal extension. Sections through both models, after a stretch of $\lambda = 1.4$, show that practically all faults are nearly planar and dip downslope, forming a single domino domain (Fig. 3). Using the occasional conjugate pair, we find that the acute bisector is vertical to within a degree or so. This suggests that faults formed in response to a vertical principal stress, which itself resulted from gravitational loading. Although at the free surface the principal compressive stress must in theory have acted in a direction normal to that surface and not vertically, this stress state appears to have had no control on fault orientation. In fact, stress magnitudes at the sand surface were probably all close to zero. We infer that faults nucleated lower in the model or at its base and maintained their orien-

tation as they propagated upwards. Thus we attribute the dominance of one fault set over its conjugate to the non-parallelism of stress with the stretching base.

A third experiment was performed in the same way as the other two, except that whereas the base was inclined at 14° previously, the top was made horizontal. The model was thus of variable thickness (triangular in cross-section). As before, a dominant family of faults was obtained at $\lambda = 1.3$, but fault spacing varied directly with local thickness of the model. This confirms the thickness/spacing relationship established earlier.

Sand model with internal silicone layer

One experiment was performed in the wide housing to investigate the effect of having ductile horizons at the base and within a brittle system. The layers from bottom to top were pure silicone (3 mm), sand (18 mm), pure silicone (3 mm) and sand (20 mm). End-wall velocity was 3.5 cm hr^{-1} and total stretch was $\lambda = 1.25$. Uniform basal extension was achieved via a rubber sheet. A cross-section (Fig. 4) reveals notable differences with pure sand models. (1) The number of faults is smaller. (2) There is only one domino domain, affecting the lower sand layer. (3) Horst and rift blocks are common. They contain few minor faults. (4) The fault pattern is markedly different from one sand layer to

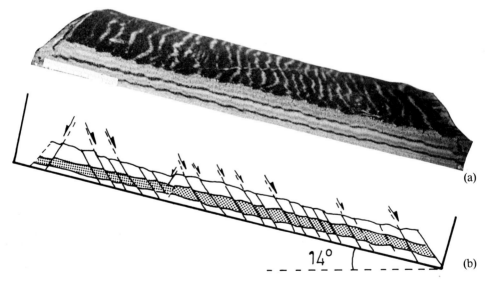

FIG. 3. (a) Sand model uniformly stretched to $\lambda = 1.4$ downslope inclined at 14° to the horizontal. (b) Line drawing of same.

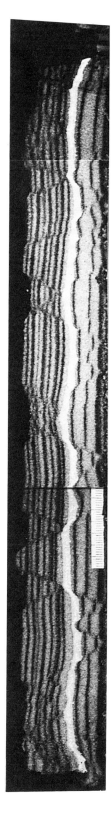

FIG. 4. Longitudinal section through sand model with internal silicone layer (thin, at mid-height), for λ = 1.26.

the other, as one crosses the intervening silicone layer. Indeed, large unfaulted blocks on one side of the silicone appear to face domains with smaller blocks on the other side. Some major fault traces appear to cut through the silicone without any offset; whereas others terminate at the silicone.

We infer that the ductile silicone layers acted as decoupling and accommodating horizons. They thus reduced the number of faults, facilitating horsts and rifts, reduced the need for domino domains and allowed subsurface fault patterns to be different from surface patterns. In spite of the presence of ductile horizons, we observed little tendency for faults to be curved (listric).

Two-layer models (sand/silicone)

Models were constructed with an upper layer of sand and a lower layer of charged silicone putty, in order to simulate the behaviour of an upper brittle crust above a lower ductile crust. In the absence of lateral constraint, the silicone spreads under its own weight and the overlying sand layer is extended.

In an early set of experiments (Faugère & Brun 1984; Faugère 1985; Brun & Choukroune 1983), the spreading rate was in no way constrained at the end of the model. Basal friction was rendered negligible by floating on mercury. In horizontal models the silicone tended to extrude out from under the sand, imparting a basal shear stress to the sand layer, revealed by observation of passive markers embedded in the silicone. In the central part of the sand layer, where basal shear stress was greatest, a domino domain appeared (Fig. 5a). If a model was tilted before spreading was allowed, thus reversing the sense of basal shear stress, a domino pattern was again obtained, but facing the other way, that is downslope (Fig. 5b).

More recently, we performed four new experiments in which the spreading rate was controlled via screw-jacks and a stepper motor. Velocities chosen were 1 to 1.8 cm hr^{-1}. Models were constructed and deformed in the wide housing. Basal friction was reduced using liquid soap. At these low spreading rates, we infer that shear stresses at the sand/silicone interface were smaller than in the experiments of Faugère & Brun (1984). We illustrate a section through one model at a stretch of λ = 1.21 (Fig. 6). It shows two major rifts, containing minor faults and limiting large blocks of almost unfaulted sand. Time-lapse photographs of the top surface revealed the following history. (1) The earliest

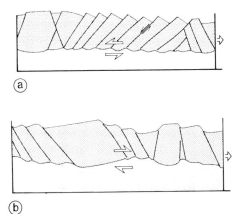

(a)

(b)

FIG. 5. Line drawings of longitudinal sections through two-layer models of sand (stippled) upon silicone (grey) extended in horizontal position (a), or inclined at about 10° to the right (b). Large arrows show slip sense of basal shear stress, small arrows show slip sense on faults (after Faugère & Brun 1984).

faults to form were a conjugate pair with initial dips of 60° and an intersection point at the sand/silicone interface, 5 cm from the mobile wall. They define a major rift valley. (2) Minor faults formed in the rift floor and accommodated localized extension. The rift widened. (3) At a bulk stretch of 1.2, the second rift developed 5 cm from the first one. (4) Both rifts widened.

The cross-section (Fig. 6) shows that rift development, in its late stages (left-hand side), resembles boudinage: the sand layer necking almost symmetrically and the silicone rising into the neck. We infer that this is the result of isostatic response beneath the rift. Other features to be noticed are the uplifted rims of the rift and the associated curvature of the intervening blocks. Notice the minor normal faults at the outer arcs. Neither major nor minor faults are listric.

Three-layer models (sand/silicone/honey)

Four experiments have so far been conducted in the deep housing to explore mechanisms of extension at lithospheric scale. In all experiments, honey was used for modelling the mantle asthenosphere; sand and silicone for the lithosphere. We distinguish the experiments on the basis of boundary motions and lithospheric

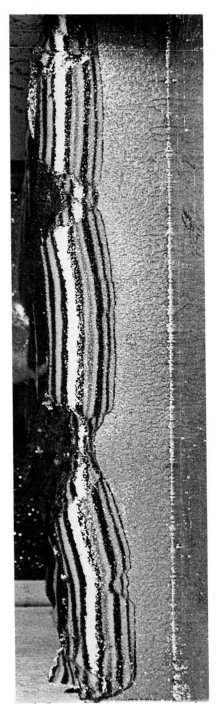

FIG. 6. Longitudinal section through two-layer model (sand upon silicone) at a stretch of $\lambda = 1.21$ and for an end-wall velocity of $v = 1.18$ cm hr^{-1}.

structure. These conditions lead to passive rifting (Sengör & Burke 1978).

Uniaxially stretched simple lithosphere

The lithosphere was modelled simply as a rigid crust (1.8 cm of lightened sand) resting on a heavier ductile mantle (2.1 cm of pink silicone). It was subjected to a uniaxial end-wall velocity of 4.6 cm hr^{-1}. This was greater than the spreading rate due to gravity alone and was obtained because of high adherence between the silicone and the end plate. Time-lapse photography (Fig. 7a & b) and a balanced cross-section (Fig. 7c) show that a single major rift formed near the moving end wall. Most of the extension then became localized within the rift floor. Notice the isostatic upwelling of the honey and the typical rift geometry with uplifted and tilted rims.

Uniaxially stretched complex lithosphere

The lithosphere was modelled as a brittle upper crust (0.7 cm of sand), ductile lower crust (1 cm of pink silicone) and ductile mantle (3.6 cm of heavy stiff grey silicone). It was subjected to a uniaxial end-wall velocity of 1.46 cm hr^{-1}, greater than the spreading rate due to gravity alone. Time-lapse photography (not illustrated) showed marginal major faults at the moving wall and also a zone of rifting in the central part of the model.

Uniaxially spreading simple lithosphere

The lithosphere was modelled simply (1.1 cm of lightened sand, 1.5 cm of pink silicone) and subjected to a low end-wall velocity (1.15 cm hr^{-1}), almost equal to the gravitational spreading velocity. In contrast with the uniaxially stretched simple lithosphere experiment, two major rifts appeared, affecting almost half the model length (Fig. 7d). This may have been a result of the low velocity, or it may have been due to other factors, such as unintentional variations in initial sand thickness. Further experiments are required to clarify these uncertainties. Notice, however, the clear correlation between depressions in the upper surface of the sand and upwelling of the honey; this contrasts with the undeflected nature of the sand/silicone interface. As in the first experiment, the rift floors localized most of the model extension. Notice again the typical rift geometry with tilted rims.

Biaxially spreading rectangular continent

Continental lithosphere within a rectangular continent (26 × 15 cm², equivalent to 1300 × 750 km²) was modelled as an upper brittle layer (0.8 cm of sand) and a lower ductile layer (1.5 cm of pink silicone) freely floating on an asthenosphere (honey) without any lateral constraint (Fig. 8a). There was no equivalent to an oceanic lithosphere.

The continent spread biaxially under its own weight. The initial velocity was about 1 cm hr^{-1}, diminishing rapidly. Most of the resulting extension occurred in marginal zones initially about 1–1.3 cm wide (equivalent to 50–65 km wide) and separated from the unextended interior by sharp breakaway faults (Fig. 8b). The margins attained stretches of about $\lambda = 3.0$ after 10 hours (10 Ma in nature), whereas the bulk stretch was only $\lambda = 1.3$. Notice that the margins and breakaway faults followed the initial rectangular shape, but corners became rounded. More strikingly perhaps, two corners became progressively rifted off, one completely, the other partially. The propagating rifts had stubby open tips, reminiscent of natural rift valleys. Rift width at initiation was about 0.5 cm (25 km), increasing to 1.5 cm (75 km).

Certain similarities can be seen between the pattern of extension and surface topography in this model and extension in the Basin and Range Province of the western United States. Thus the marginal zone, oblique rift valley and rifted-off corner in the model resemble the Great Basin, Rio Grande rift and Colorado plateau. This raises the question as to how much the pattern of extension in the western US may be due to faulting in a crust spreading under its own weight, with isostatic readjustment below.

Conclusions

Mechanical processes of lithospheric extension can be modelled at various scales and in three dimensions using physical models with brittle and ductile layers, deformed in a natural gravity field. From our preliminary range of experiments, we draw the following tentative conclusions. (i) In a strain-softening brittle upper crust, faults have a tendency to persist and if necessary, rotate or deform to accommodate finite deformation. (ii) Spacing of normal faults in a brittle layer is a measure of layer thickness. Faults propagate laterally as downthrow increases. (iii) Uniformly extended brittle layers with straight horizontal bases tend to develop domino domains. The sense of basal shear stress exerts considerable control on the sense of vergence. (iv) An underlying viscous substrate can favour the development in the upper brittle layer of localized rifts bounded by major conjugate faults. (v) Tilted rift margins can result

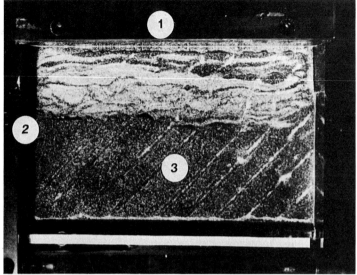

(a)

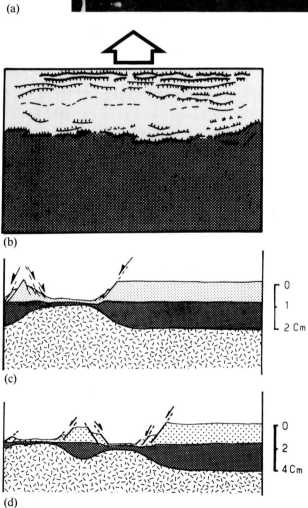

(b)

(c)

(d)

FIG. 7. Uniaxially extending three-layer models. Photograph of top surface of model uniaxially stretched at $v = 4.6$ cm hr^{-1} (a), shows moving and wall (1), stationary side wall (2) and lightened sand (3). Line drawing of above (b) shows fault scarps. Longitudinal balanced cross-section through same (c), shows sand (light stipple), silicone (heavy stipple), honey (ornament) and one major rift. Longitudinal balanced cross-section through another model (d), allowed to spread at 1.15 cm hr^{-1}, shows two major rifts.

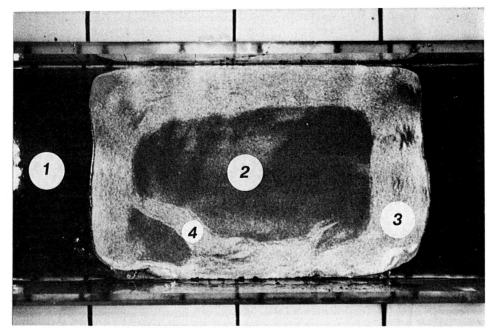

(a)

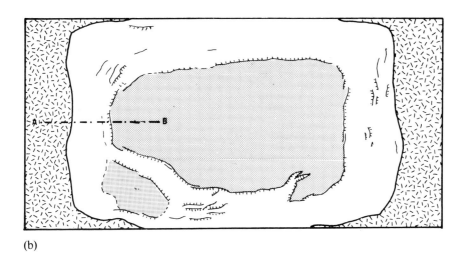

(b)

A B

(c)

FIG. 8. Biaxially spreading rectangular model. View of upper surface after 10 hours, equivalent to 10 Ma. (a) shows honey (1), unstretched sand (2), stretched margins (3) and rift (4). Line drawing of same (b), shows main faults and line of section A–B. Balanced cross-section along line A–B, (c), shows honey (ornament), silicone (heavy stipple) and sand (light stipple).

TABLE 1: *Summary of experimental conditions and parameters. All lengths are in cm; velocities in cm hr^{-1}; stretches, dimensionless*

Experiment	Layering	Basal slope (degrees)	Initial thickness (cm)		Initial length (cm)	Width (cm)	Velocity (cm hr^{-1})	Total stretch (λ)
Uniform horizontal sand model	Sand only	0		5.0	27.4	50		1.50
		0		2.5	29.0	50		1.48
		0		2.5	26.0	50		1.50
		0		1.25	28.0	50		1.50
Inclined uniform sand model	Sand only	14		2.5	21.5	25		1.40
		7		5.0→1.5	22.0	25		≃ 1.30
		14		2.0→8.0	23.0	25		≃ 1.30
Sand model with internal silicone layer	Sand Silicone	0	Sand: Silicone:	2.6 0.25	26.0	50	15.0	1.50
	Sand Silicone	0	Sand: Silicone:	1.8+2.0 0.3+0.3	28.7	50	3.5	1.25
Two-layer models (sand/silicone)	Sand	0	Sand: Silicone:	3.0 3.0	23.0	50	1.8	1.20
	Grey silicone	0	Sand: Silicone:	1.8 2.1	33.0	50	1.0	≃ 1.20
Three-layer models (stretching)	Lightened sand Pink silicone	0	Sand: Silicone:	1.1 1.5	10.5	20	1.15	1.60
	Honey	0	Sand: Silicone:	1.8 2.0	9.0	20	4.60	1.42
	Sand Pink silicone Grey silicone Honey	0	Sand: Pink silicone: Grey silicone:	0.7 1.0 3.6	10.7	20	1.46	1.31
Three-layer models (spreading)	Sand Pink silicone Honey	0	Sand: Silicone:	0.8 1.5	15.0	26	<1.0	1.33 × 1.25

quite simply from buoyancy effects (isostatic readjustment). (vi) Continued extension tends to become localized via minor faults in rift floors, leading eventually to very large extensions. (vii) Unconstrained continental margins spread under their own weight, becoming thinner than they were before continental breakup.

ACKNOWLEDGMENTS: This work was financed jointly by the Compagnie Française des Pétroles (C.F.P.) and the Institut Français du Pétrole (I.F.P.). We thank J.J. Kermarrec, C.N.R.S. technician, for expert technical asisstance in the design, construction and maintenance of laboratory equipment.

References

BRUN, J.P. & CHOUKROUNE, R. 1983. Normal faulting, block tilting and décollement in a stretched crust. *Tectonics*, **2**, 345–56.

CLOOS, E. 1955. Experimental analysis of fracture patterns. *Bull. geol. Soc. Am.* **66**, 241–56.

—— 1968. Experimental analysis of Gulf Coast fracture patterns. *Bull. Am. Assoc. Pet. Geol.* **52**, 420–44.

DIXON, J.M. & SUMMERS, J.M. 1985. Recent developments in centrifuge modelling of tectonic processes: equipment, model construction techniques and rheology of model materials. *J. struct. Geol.* **7**, 83–102.

ELMOHANDES, S.E. 1981. The Central European graben system: rifting imitated by clay modelling. *In*: ILLIES, J.H. (ed.) Mechanism in graben formation. *Tectonophysics*, **73**, 69–78.

FAUGÈRE, E. 1985. La tectonique en extension intracontinentale. Etude de terrain (le Sud Nevada, U.S.A.) et modélisation analogique. *Mémoire des sciences de la Terre, Université Pierre & Marie Curie, Paris*, **85-06.**

FAUGÈRE, E. & BRUN, J.P. 1984. Modélisation expérimentale de la distention continentale. *Compte Rendus de l'Académie des Sciences de Paris*, **299, Série II**, 365–70.

FREUND, R. 1974. Kinematics of transform and transcurrent faults. *Tectonophysics*, **21**, 93–134.

HOEPPENER, R., KALTHOFF, E., & SCHRADER, P. 1969. Zur physicalischen tectonik bruchbildung bei verschieden affinen deformationen im experiment. *Geol. Rdsch.* **59**, 179–93.

HORSFIELD, W.J. 1980. Contemporaneous movement along crossing conjugate faults. *J. struct. Geol.* **2**, 305–10.

HUBBERT, M.K. 1937. Theory of scale models as applied to the study of geologic structures. *Bull. geol. Soc. Am.* **48**, 1459–520.

KUSZNIR, N.J. & PARK, R.G. This volume. The extensional strength of the continental lithosphere: its dependence on geothermal gradient, and crustal composition and thickness.

MANDL, G., DE JONG, L.N.J. & MALTHA, A. 1977. Shear zones in granular material. *Rock Mech. Wien.* **9**, 95–144.

MULUGETA, G. 1985. Dynamic models of continental rift valley systems. *Tectonophysics*, **113**, 49–73.

OERTEL, G. 1965. The mechanism of faulting in clay experiments. *Tectonophysics*, **2**, 343–93.

RAMBERG, H. 1967. *Gravity, deformation and the Earth's crust*, 214 pp. Academic Press, London.

ŞENGOR, A.M.C. & BURKE, K. 1978. Relative timing of rifting and volcanism on earth and its tectonic implications. *Geophys. Res. Lett. Washington*, **5, 419–21.**

B.V. VENDEVILLE, P.R. COBBOLD, P. DAVY & P. CHOUKROUNE, Centre Armorican d'Etude Structurale des Socles, (Laboratoire C.N.R.S. Conventionné à l'Universite de Rennes), Campus de Beaulieu, 35042 RENNES Cédex, France.

J.P. BRUN, Laboratoire de Tectonique, Université de Paris VII, 4 Place Jussieu, 75007 PARIS, France.

Analogue models of extensional fault geometries

K.R. McClay & P.G. Ellis

SUMMARY: The progressive development of extensional fault geometries in a sedimentary cover sequence above a rigid or deforming basement has been experimentally investigated using analogue models. Quartz sand (700 μm) was used as a modelling material. The experiments were recorded using time-delay 16 mm cine photography and 35 mm photography. Final models were impregnated with resin and serially sectioned to investigate the three-dimensional fault geometry. Four series of experiments were carried out: (i) extension above a linear basement dislocation; (ii) extension above a uniformly stretching basement; (iii) extension controlled by a planar fault; and (iv) extension controlled by a listric fault.

Extension above a linear basement dislocation produced a single graben structure in which initial high-angle bounding faults were cut by later listric faults. Fault nucleation occurred into the hanging wall of the graben and only minor rotation occurred in the fault blocks within the graben. Extension above a uniformly extending basement produced a variety of fault structures. Heterogeneous nucleation of faults occurred with initial planar geometries giving way to more listric faults. Significant fault-block rotation was observed. In some instances rotation of pre-existing fault planes produced a negative (convex upward) listric-fault geometry. Extension controlled by a planar fault produced a single graben structure in which new faults developed into the graben. Little rotation of fault blocks occurred. Extension controlled by a predetermined listric fault showed the progressive development of a rollover anticline. The crest of the anticline collapsed producing a second-order crestal collapse graben. The nucleation of new faults was consistently in the hanging wall above the major detachment faults.

In all of the experiments carried out to date, once a major fault had developed the second-order fault nucleation was consistently in the hanging wall fault block. Footwall collapse and hence fault migration into the footwall was not significant. Listric faults produced considerable rotation of hanging wall blocks. In some instances heterogeneous rotation of pre-existing faults generated negative listric-fault shapes. In rollover structures collapse of the crestal region of the fold produced a second-order graben structure.

Recent research on the structural evolution of extensional basins (e.g. Gibbs 1984; Bally *et al.* 1981), of growth faulting in deltas (e.g. Crans *et al.* 1980), of metamorphic core complexes (e.g. Spencer 1984) and of the Basin and Range terrane (e.g. Wernicke & Burchfiel 1982) have emphasized the geometric relationships of the extensional fault systems. In particular, complex models of extensional-fault geometries and fault evolution patterns have been developed (Fig. 1).

In this paper we describe a series of simple analogue-model experiments designed to investigate the fault geometries and sequences of faulting in extensional terranes. Previous analogue models (H. Cloos 1928, 1931, 1939; Rettger 1935; Wunderlich 1957; E. Cloos 1955, 1968; Oertel 1962, 1965; Badgley 1965; Elmohandes 1981) have largely concentrated on final fault geometries. Horsfield (1977, 1980) examined the progressive development of basement-controlled faulting. Here we use techniques similar to those employed by Horsfield in order to simulate the progressive development of extensional fault geometries in a sedimentary cover sequence above a deforming basement.

The results from four series of experiments are presented: (i) extension above a linear basement dislocation; (ii) extension above a uniformly stretching basement; (iii) extension controlled by a planar fault; and (iv) extension controlled by a listric fault.

Attention is focused upon fault geometries and changes in fault geometries with time, fault nucleation (initiation of a new fault), fault propagation (growth of an existing fault surface) and rotation of passive marker beds between fault surfaces.

The experimental method

The deformation apparatus consisted of a 55 cm $\times$ 15 cm $\times$ 10 cm sliding box, with glass sides. The sliding box was seated on a static base, and deformation was achieved by moving the box relative to an internal end wall which was fixed to the static base (Fig. 2). In the four series of experiments deformation was controlled by various basement geometries. Deformation above a linear dislocation was achieved by the

From Coward, M.P., Dewey, J.F. & Hancock, P.L. (eds), 1987, *Continental Extensional Tectonics*, Geological Society Special Publication No. 28, pp. 109–125.

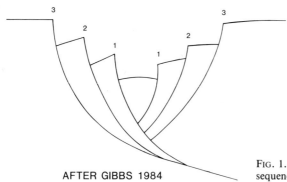

AFTER GIBBS 1984

FIG. 1. Footwall fault nucleation, generalized fault sequence (1–3) (after Gibbs 1984).

attachment of a thin 10 cm long base plate to the fixed wall of the apparatus, with the result that one half of the model remains stationary while the other half is extended away from the linear dislocation. Uniform extension was achieved by using a basement comprising a rubber sheet fixed between the stationary and moving walls of the deformation apparatus. The uniformity of the extension was verified using strain ellipses on the rubber sheet. There is, however, the probability of a small finite propagation time for stretching of the rubber sheet and this could determine the initial orientation of some faults, and lead to an apparent asymmetry of fault orientations. For the experiments with predetermined planar and listric detachment faults, deformation geometries were obtained by moulding the basement fault geometry in a plasticine block which was attached to the stationary end of the deformation apparatus. Extension was produced by movement of a thin flexible baseplate attached to the moving part of the deformation box.

To produce geologically valid results, the models must be appropriately scaled. If the initial model dimensions used in these experiments are taken to represent brittle upper crust between 1 and 10 km thick, this gives a scaling factor between 10^{-4} and 10^{-5}. Assuming a brittle Coulomb-type failure criterion for both the crust and the modelling material, a similar scaling factor must be applied to the modelling material properties. As a result, a weak, near-cohesionless material must be used. In these experiments a dry, cohesionless, bleached pottery sand, with an average grain size of 700 μm and an internal angle of friction of 31°, was used. We noted however, that the scaling was not perfect as the relatively large grain size resulted in the formation of narrow shear zones rather than discrete fault planes (Horsfield 1977).

The models were prepared within the sliding box by carefully sieving sand into layers until a composite model was constructed. Marker layers were made using sand dyed with different colours. The external force was applied via a motor-driven worm screw that moves at a constant displacement rate over a range of rates from 4×10^{-3} cm sec^{-1} to 8×10^{-5} cm sec^{-1}. Typical initial model dimensions were 20 cm × 15 cm × 10 cm to give an initial strain rate that varied from 2×10^{-4} sec^{-1} to 4×10^{-6} sec^{-1}. In addition to repeating experiments in order to establish their reproducibility, experiments were conducted with a variety of strain rates in order to determine their effects on the type and style of structures produced. Because the modelling material fails by a simple Coulomb-type failure criterion (which is unaffected by strain rate), no significant variation in structural style was expected nor found.

Data were recorded using 16 mm time-lapse cine photography and 35 mm time-lapse still photography. The completed models were impregnated with resin and sectioned in order to examine the three-dimensional fault goemetries. In the experiments described in this paper, the extensional structures were infilled with sand, as the experiments progressed, in order that a hor-

DEFORMATION RIG

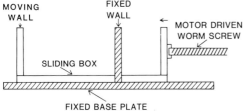

FIG. 2. The deformation apparatus.

izontal free upper-surface be maintained and to prevent the development of unstable surface slopes.

Results

Linear dislocation

A 20 cm × 15 cm × 8 cm colour-laminated sand block was deformed at a strain rate of 2×10^{-4} sec^{-1}, producing a total of 25% extension above a stationary linear dislocation with no vertical relief. The fault sequence, and fault geometries produced were as follows (Fig. 3a–f).

1   Steep (75–85°) extensional faults, propagated upwards from the base, with the stationary margin fault (right-hand side of the model) being marginally steeper (fault 1, Fig. 3e) than the moving margin fault (left-hand side). They both had a steepening-upwards (positive listric) geometry (Fig. 3a).

2   Footwall collapse (fault 2, Fig. 3e) on both the fixed and moving sides of the graben resulted in the flattening (60–70°) of the graben master faults (Fig. 3b).

3   Continued nucleation of near-planar faults (faults 3, 4 and 6, Fig. 3e) occurred in the hanging wall to the moving margin of the graben with new faults occurring progressively towards the centre of the graben (Fig. 3c & d).

The final structure was an asymmetric graben consisting of a simple master fault on the stationary wall of the graben margin, and a complementary series of antithetic faults on the moving-wall margin. There was little or no rotation associated with the near-planar faulting. Fault nucleation was dominantly into the hanging wall (Fig. 3e), although footwall collapse occurred where an initial high-angled fault formed. Serial sections (e.g. Fig. 3f), showed only minor edge effects, due to friction, along the glass walls of the deformation apparatus. The fault and shear-zone thicknesses remained constant, and the fault geometries and spacing showed only minor changes across the width of the model.

Uniform extension

A 20 cm × 15 cm × 10 cm colour-laminated sand block was deformed above a uniformly extending rubber sheet, at a strain rate of 2×10^{-4} sec^{-1}, producing a total of 50% extension, and the fault sequence and geometries produced were as follows (Fig. 4a–f).

1   With low extensions (10–15%), early heterogeneous extension of the rubber sheet produced

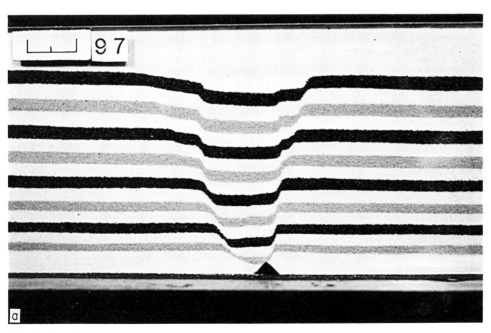

5% Extension

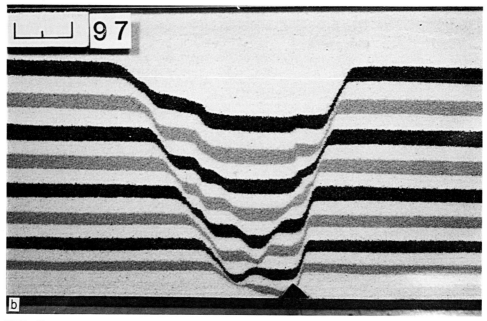

10% Extension

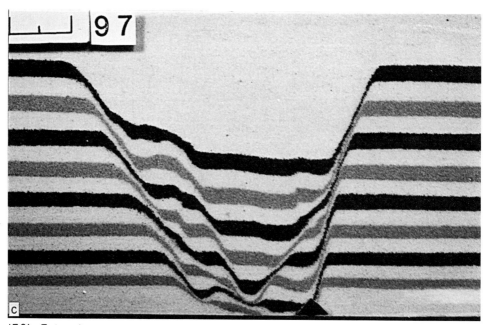

15% Extension

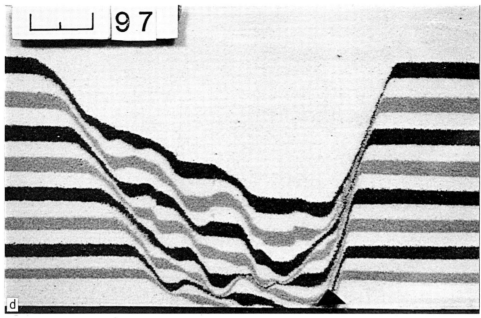

25% Extension

LINEAR DISLOCATION FAULT SEQUENCE

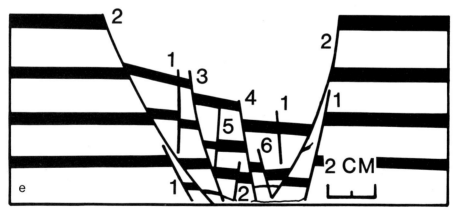

25% Extension

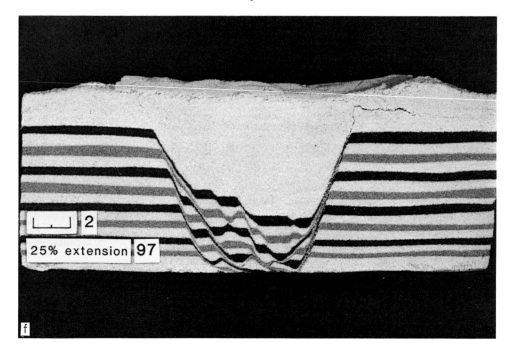

FIG. 3. (a)–(d) Fault development above a linear dislocation. The black triangle at the base of the model marks the end of the fixed baseplate on the right-hand side of the model. The left-hand side of the model moves progressively to the left. (e) Fault-sequence diagram, showing dominant nucleation of faults into the hanging wall of the graben. Minor footwall collapse has truncated the high-angled fault (1). (f) Serial section, cut 2 cm into the model showing continuity of structures across the model.

negative listric faults (faults 1 and 2, Fig. 4e) at the ends of the model (Fig. 4A).

2 With 20% extension a series of evenly spaced, steepening-upwards (positive) listric faults formed in the centre of the model (faults 2, 3 and 5, Fig. 4e). The layering was rotated progressively from the base. These faults separated two unrotated horst blocks (Fig. 4b).

3 As deformation continued, minor antithetic faults (faults 7 and 11, Fig. 4e) formed in the small right-hand graben (Fig. 4c).

4 With 40% extension there was limited nucleation (faults 8 and 10, Fig. 4d) into the footwall of the right-dipping, positive listric faults.

The final structure contained evenly spaced, positive listric fault-bounded panels, with associated rotation of the layering, separating two unrotated horst blocks (Fig. 4e). A serial section (Fig. 4f), cut 2 cm from the model margin showed a similar distribution of horst blocks and fault-bounded panels. In addition, some minor faults were found in the horst blocks (Fig. 4f).

Planar-fault geometry

A 15 cm × 15 cm × 10 cm colour-laminated sand block was deformed above a planar detachment at a strain-rate of $1.5 \times 10^{-4} \sec^{-1}$, to produce a total of 33% extension. The resulting fault sequence and geometries were as follows (Fig. 5a–f).

1 High-angled, near-planar faults (faults 1 and 2, Fig. 5e) developed progressively into the graben (Fig. 5a).

2 The planar, lower-angled fault 3 truncated fault 2 (Fig. 5b).

3 Planar faults (faults 4 and 5, Fig. 5e) developed in their hanging walls, progressively towards the centre of the graben (Fig. 5c & d). The initially planar-fault geometry produced a gross rollover structure. The induced faulting was predominantly planar and antithetic to the master fault. The layering showed minimal (6° max) rotation towards the master fault (Fig. 5e). Serial sectioning (Fig. 5f) showed consistent fault geometries across the whole width of the model.

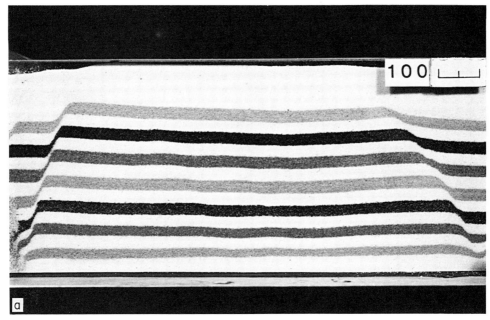

20% Extension

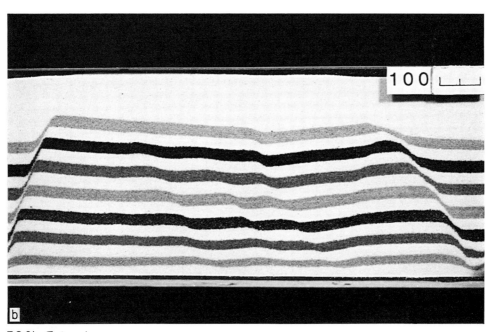

30% Extension

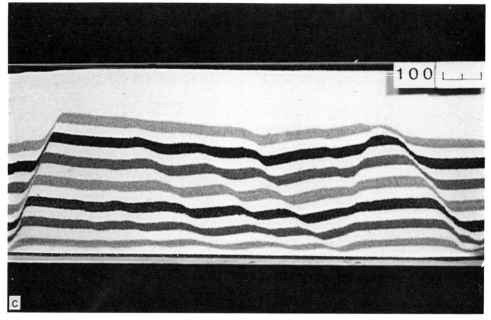

40% Extension

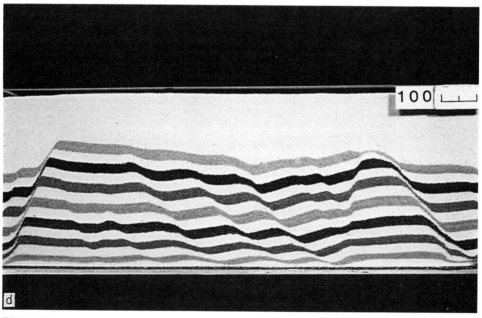

50% Extension

UNIFORM EXTENSION   FAULT SEQUENCE

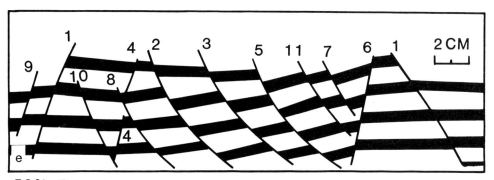

50% Extension

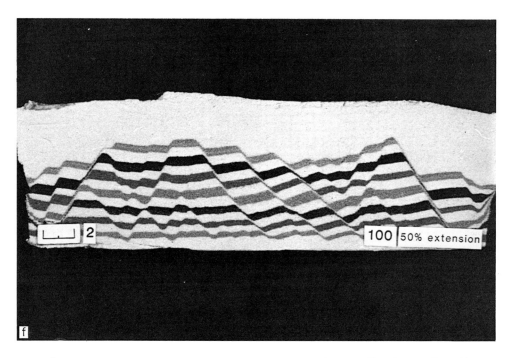

FIG. 4. (a)–(d) Fault development generated with uniform extension above a uniformly extending rubber sheet. (e) Fault-sequence diagram, showing the development of evenly spaced positive listric faults with rotated layering between the fault surfaces. (f) Serial section, cut 2 cm into the model.

Listric-fault geometry

A 15 cm × 15 cm × 10 cm colour-laminated sand block was deformed above a listric detachment at a strain-rate of 1.5×10^{-4} sec^{-1}, producing a total of 33% extension. The resulting fault sequence and geometries were as follows (Fig. 6a–f).

1 Two faults (faults 1 and 2, Fig. 6e) developed at the crest of the rollover, producing a small graben. They had markedly different geometries (Fig. 6a). The right-dipping fault developed with, and retained, a planar geometry. The left-dipping fault developed with a steepening-downwards or negative listric geometry. The

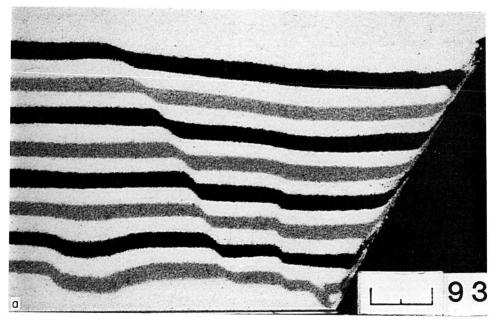

7.5% Extension

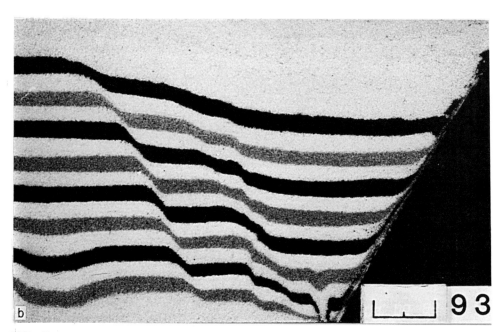

15% Extension

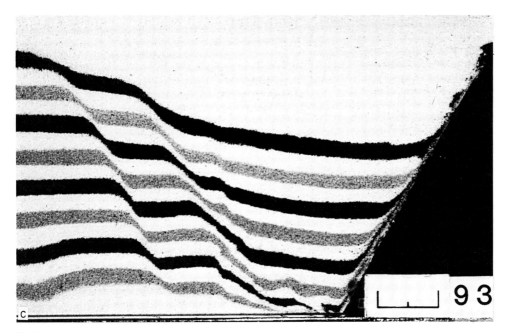

25% Extension

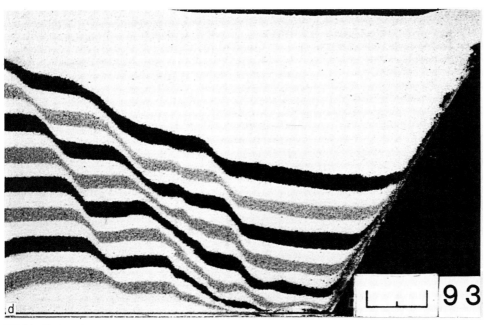

33% Extension

PLANAR FAULT GEOMETRY   FAULT SEQUENCE

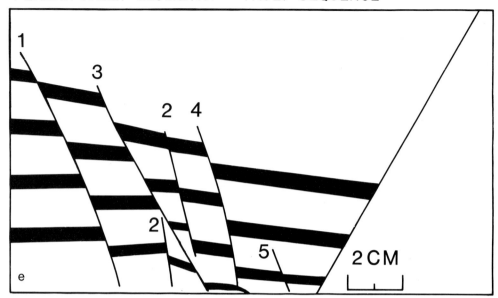

33% Extension

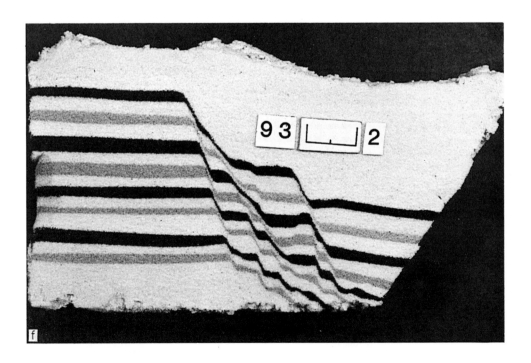

FIG. 5. (a)–(d) Fault development associated with a planar fault. The right-hand side of the model is stationary whereas the left-hand side moves away at a constant rate. (e) Fault-sequence diagram, showing dominant nucleation of faults into the hanging wall. There is very little rotation of the layering. (f) Serial section, cut 2 cm into the model.

curvature on this fault consistently increased with increased extension (Fig. 7).

2 Faulting nucleated progressively from both margins into the hanging wall of the crestal graben (faults 2, 3 and 4, Fig. 6e). The left-dipping, negative listric faults formed slightly earlier than, and were truncated by, the right-dipping planar faults (Fig. 6b & c).

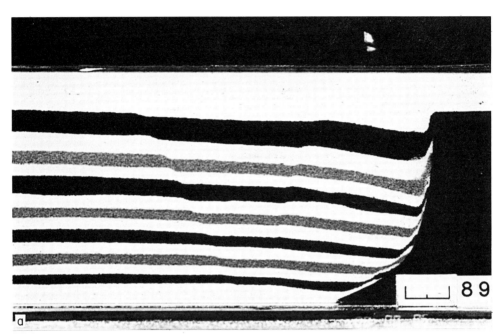

7.5% Extension

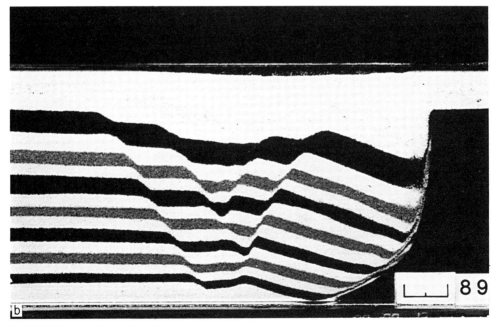

15% Extension

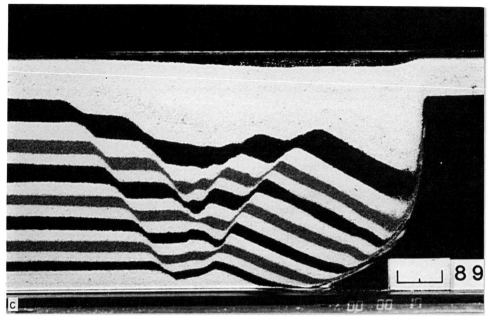

25% Extension

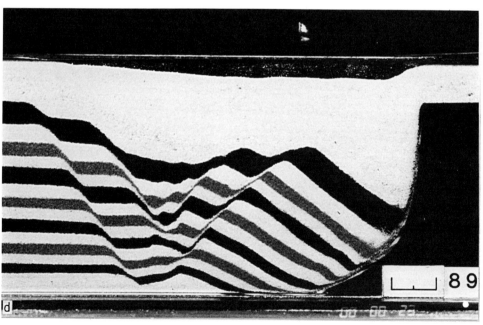

33% Extension

LISTRIC FAULT GEOMETRY   FAULT SEQUENCE

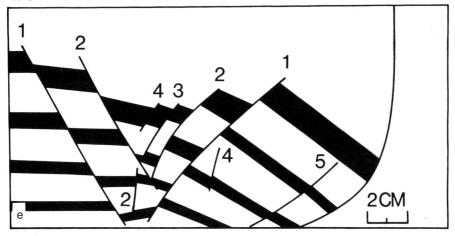

33% Extension

FIG. 6. (a)–(d) Fault development above a listric detachment fault. (e) Fault-sequence diagram, showing planar and negative listric-fault development in a crestal collapse graben. Fault nucleation is into the hanging wall. (f) Serial section, cut 2 cm into the model.

RELATIVE POSITION OF A NEGATIVE LISTRIC
FAULT IN A CRESTAL COLLAPSE STRUCTURE

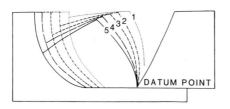

FIG. 7. Development of negative listric-fault
geometry due to heterogeneous rotation within a
rollover anticline.

3 Late-stage faults (4 and 5, Fig. 6e), not
associated with the crestal collapse graben,
developed (Fig. 6d). They were minor and synthetic to the major listric detachment.
The listric-fault geometry produced a well-
developed rollover anticline with highly rotated
(up to 35°) layering (Fig. 6e). The right-dipping
faults to the left of the crestal collapse graben
remained planar and marked the progressive
limit of rotation within the rollover. The left-
dipping, negative listric faults became progressively rotated into the master fault. Greater
rotation occurred towards the top of the model,
decreasing the fault angle and increasing the fault
curvature (Fig. 7). Serial sectioning (Fig. 6f),
showed a consistent fault geometry across the
entire width of the model.

Discussion and conclusions

The simple sand box experiments described in
this paper have produced three distinct
extensional-fault geometries: (i) planar faults;
(ii) positive listric faults and (iii) negative listric
faults.
   i Planar faulting occurred predominantly in
the planar fault block and linear-dislocation
models (Figs 3e & 5e). In both experiments,
extension only occurred over a very limited
distance and this may have inhibited the formation of listric geometries. Planar faulting was
also found at the outermost margin of the crestal
collapse graben of the listric-fault models (Fig.
6e), and in this case marked the limit of rotation
within the rollover anticline. In all the experiments described here planar faulting caused no
significant rotation of the layering.
   ii Positive listric faults occurred predominantly
in the uniform-extension experiment (Fig. 4e)
and to a lesser degree as the initial, large master

faults in the linear-dislocation model (Fig. 3e).
The rotation of the layering caused by this style
of faulting is well documented (e.g. Gibbs 1983,
1984; Wernicke & Burchfiel 1982; Crans *et al.*
1980). Fault displacements decreased upwards,
suggesting that the faults propagated from the
base.
   iii Negative listric-fault geometries were found
only on the rotating margin of the crestal collapse structure of the listric-fault geometry (Fig.
6e). They initiated as negative listric faults and
had their geometry accentuated by non-uniform rotation within the rollover anticline
(Fig. 7).

Rollover anticlines

   The models involving an individual fault plane
(the initially listric and planar faults and to a
lesser extent the linear dislocation) all produced
a gross rollover geometry. The initially listric
fault produced the classic rollover geometry of
Hamblin (1965), with a high degree of hanging
wall rotation. Accommodation within the
rollover was achieved by crestal collapse (Fig.
6e), producing a second-order graben. In contrast the uniform extension experiment produced
no rollover structure (Fig. 4e), as the uniformity
of the extension allowed a large number of
relatively closely spaced master faults to
develop, and there was insufficient distance
between these faults to allow a rollover to
develop.

Fault nucleation and propagation

Fault nucleation is the initiation of new fault
planes. Fault propagation is the increase in
length of a fault plane. These experiments have
shown that fault nucleation may occur in two
ways: (i) footwall collapse; and (ii) hanging wall
nucleation. Footwall collapse is a minor, localized event which caused a decrease in the fault
angle. It occurred primarily where the initial
faulting was at a very high angle (Fig. 3a). Hanging
wall nucleation was seen to dominate the fault
sequences found in these sand box experiments.
This was most noticeable in the linear-
dislocation, planar- and listric-fault geometries
(Figs 3e, 5e & 6e). In the linear-dislocation and
planar-fault geometries, nucleation occurred into
the hanging wall of the moving margin only
(Figs 3e & 5e). In the listric-fault geometry,
hanging wall nucleation occurred equally from
both margins of the crestal collapse graben (Fig.
6e).
   The fault generation sequences described
here, have an opposite sense to the footwall

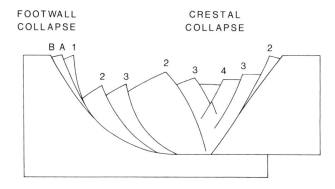

FIG. 8. Generalized fault sequence dominated by hanging wall nucleation of new faults with minor footwall collapse.

nucleation models proposed by Gibbs (1984) (Fig. 1). Using the data from the experiments described in this paper, a new generalized nucleation sequence is proposed (Fig. 8) involving dominant hanging wall nucleation, with minor footwall collapse.

ACKNOWLEDGMENTS: This research project has been funded by British Petroleum PLC and Goldsmiths College. Tom Easter assisted with the photography. Ian Vann, Rod Graham, Jake Hossack and Kevin Hill and thanked for discussions during the course of the research.

References

BADGLEY, P.C. 1965. Structual and tectonic principles, 521 pp. Harper and Row, New York.

BALLY, A.W., BERNOULLI, D., DAVIS, G.A. & MONTADERT, L. 1981. Listric normal faults. *Oceanologica Acta, 26th International Geological Congress, Paris, 1980*, pp. 87–102.

CLOOS, E. 1955. Experimental analysis of fracture patterns. *Bull. geol. Soc. Am.* **66**, 241–56.

—— 1968. Experimental analysis of Gulf Coast fracture patterns. *Bull. Am. Assoc. Pet. Geol.* **52**, 420–44.

CLOOS, H. 1928. Uber antithetische Beweguhgen. *Geol. Rdsch.* **30**, 246–51.

—— 1931. Zur experimentellen Tectonik, Bruche und Falten. *Naturwiss. Abh. Wien.* **19**, 242–47.

—— 1939. Hebung, spaltung, vulkanisimus. *Geol. Rdsch.* **30**, 405–527.

CRANS, W., MANDL, G., & HAREMBOURE, J. 1980. On the theory of growth faulting: A geomechanical delta model based on gravity sliding. *J. pet. Geol.* **2**, 265–307.

ELMOHANDES, S.E. 1981. The Central European graben system; rifting imitated by clay modelling. *In:* ILLIES, J.H. (ed.), Mechanism in Graben Formation. *Tectonophysics*, **73**, 69–78.

GIBBS, A.D. 1983. Balanced cross-section construction from seismic sections in areas of extensional tectonics. *J. struct. Geol.* **5**, 153–60.

—— 1984. Structural evolution of extensional basin margins. *J. geol. Soc. London,* **141**, 609–20.

HAMBLIN, W.K. 1965. Origin of 'reverse drag' on the down-thrown side of normal faults. *Bull. Am. Assoc. Pet. Geol.* **63**, 1016–59.

HORSFIELD, W.T. 1977. An experimental approach to basement contolled faulting. *Geol Mijnbouw*, **56(4)**, 363–70.

—— 1980. Contemporaneous movement along crossing conjugate normal faults. *J. struct. Geol.* **2(3)**, 305–10.

OERTEL, G. 1962. Stress, strain and fracture in clay models of geologic deformation. *Geotimes*, **6(8)**, 26–31.

—— 1965. The mechanism of faulting in clay experiments. *Tectonophysics*, **2**, 343–93.

RETTGER, R.E. 1935. Experiments in soft rock deformation. *Bull. Am. Assoc. Pet. Geol.* **19**, 271–92.

SPENCER, J.E. 1984. Role of tectonic denudation in warping and uplift of low angle normal faults. *Geology*, **12**, 95–8.

WERNICKE, B. & BURCHFIEL, B.C. 1982. Modes of extensional tectonics. *J. struct. Geol.* **4**, 105–15.

WUNDERLICH, H.G. 1957. Bruch und Graben im tektonischen Experiment. *Neues Jahrb. Geol. Palaeontol. Monatshefte.* **11**, 477–98.

K.R. MCCLAY, Department of Geology, Royal Holloway and Bedford New College, Egham, Surrey TW20 0EX, UK.

P.G. ELLIS, Department of Earth Sciences, University of London Goldsmiths College, London SE8 3BU, UK.

Brittle modes of foreland extension

P.L. Hancock & T.G. Bevan

SUMMARY: Complex systems of mesoscopic brittle fractures striking transversely to orogenic margins are characteristic upper-crustal structures in forelands (and hinterlands) that have experienced extension as a consequence of continental collision. They are especially well developed in foreland peripheries and some forelands lacking major grabens and strike-slip faults, the best-known expressions of horizontal extension. Despite the contribution of the mesofractures to foreland strain being less than that achieved by macrofault zones they are important structures because: (i) they are widespread and pervasive at outcrop scale, (ii) they influence the location of some major topographic lineaments and (iii) they permit regionally significant extension directions to be determined where macrostructures are absent.

The principal styles of mesoscopic brittle structures are planar normal faults, vertical extension joints and veins, and steeply inclined, conjugate hybrid and shear joints. Commonly, the strike of fracture sets is uniform throughout large areas and although it is generally normal to a deformation front, this simple relationship is not present everywhere, particularly distant from some markedly arcuate fronts.

Two examples of parts of forelands containing brittle extensional structures approximately coeval with late-Alpide events are the European platform in S England and N France, and the Arabian platform neighbouring the Gulf coast. In both regions, the fractures are superimposed obliquely on older Tertiary structures and comprise dominant sets of extension fractures accompanied locally by normal faults and hybrid joints. The dominance of extension and hybrid fractures among the failure modes indicates that differential stresses remained low throughout large areas of the forelands and that the effective minimum stress was tensile.

The aim of this paper is to focus attention on suites of small-scale (mesoscopic) fractures that are the products of several modes of brittle failure in forelands and hinterlands that have extended laterally, parallel to the margins of neighbouring collisional mountain belts. These intraplate brittle structures, striking transversely to deformation fronts, are well developed in horizontally bedded platform sequences, including those lacking genetically related large-scale (macroscopic) grabens or strike-slip faults. We follow Şengör (1984) by distinguishing between forelands and hinterlands according to whether a terrain is, or was, part of a subducting or overriding plate, respectively. We use 'foreland' as a collective name to embrace both forelands and hinterlands when the distinction between them is not known or is irrelevant.

Discussion is largely restricted to late Cenozoic structures cutting post-Palaeozoic rocks in 'forelands' external to Alpide mountain belts. This restriction means that the extensional structures, which are approximately coeval with the contractional structures in the neighbouring deformation belt, are not overprinted by younger structures with which they could be confused. An additional benefit of concentrating on young structures is that in some settings it is possible to compare geologically inferred extension directions with the contemporary stress field where it is known from *in situ* measurements or fault-plane solutions of earthquakes.

Antecedents

The notion that one response of 'forelands', to collision and post-collisional shortening in mountain belts, is their lateral extension is well established. The most publicized example of hinterland extension is central Asia N of the Himalayas (Molnar & Tapponnier 1975). The principles of indentation tectonics have also been applied to the lateral escape of other blocks in the Alpide system, in particular the Anatolian *scholle* (crustal flake) (McKenzie 1972; Tapponnier 1977; Dewey *et al.* 1986). The two-stage splitting of the central European foreland across the Rhine graben system is an example of foreland extension via the development of a collisional rift ('impactogen') (Şengör 1976; Şengör *et al.* 1978; Illies 1981). Şengör (1976) has also proposed that a phase of conjugate transcurrent faulting can follow rifting when collision has been achieved along a broad front. Although the role of macroscopic structures in 'foreland' extension is well documented, the contribution from mesofractures has received

From COWARD, M.P., DEWEY, J.F. & HANCOCK, P.L. (eds), 1987, *Continental Extensional Tectonics*, Geological Society Special Publication No. 28, pp. 127–137.

little attention in the context of tectonic hypotheses. In this section we review published examples of 'foreland' extensional structures of all scales.

Central Asian hinterland N of the Himalaya

Major left- and right-lateral faults are traditionally thought to be the principal structures achieving the lateral escape of blocks (Molnar & Tapponnier 1975; Tapponnier & Molnar 1976; Molnar & Chen 1982; Rothery & Drury 1984) (Fig. 1a). Molnar & Tapponnier have compared the strike-slip faults with displacement discontinuities that are the materialization of slip lines (maximum shear-stress trajectories) that would occur beneath the seismogenic zone in a rigid-plastic material experiencing plane indentation by a rigid die. The conjugate strike-slip faults of central Asia enclose an obtuse angle about the shortening direction and hence, despite penetrating the brittle carapace, their attitudes probably reflect ductile-failure mechanisms operating in the lower crust. In addition to plane-strain strike-slip faulting there was also lateral elongation combined with crustal attenuation as a consequence of the gravity-driven development of N–S-striking normal faults in the Quaternary (Tapponnier *et al.* 1981a; Tapponnier *et al.* 1981b; Molnar & Chen 1982; Rothery & Drury 1984). The orientations of P and T axes determined from fault-plane solutions (Molnar & Chen 1982) confirm the N–S or NNW–SSE compression and complementary E–W or ENE–WSW extension of the region.

Syrian–Turkish foreland S of the Bitlis thrust zone

The Syrian–Turkish foreland N of the Palmyra Ranges has experienced a different neotectonic history to the remainder of the Arabian platform, to which it belonged until the early Neogene (Dewey *et al.* 1986). Immediately S of the Bitlis thrust zone, the foreland rocks are deformed by relatively gentle folds in the Border Ranges, but S of them, in Syria, the sequence is largely undeformed. Within the foreland, late Cenozoic lavas were erupted from N–S fissures and the sequence was disrupted by faults and extension fractures related to post-collisional shortening (Letouzey & Trémolières 1980; Şengör & Yilmaz 1981; Dewey *et al.* 1986) (Fig. 1b). The horizontal direction of extension was arcuate and sub-parallel to the concave-S trace of the Bitlis thrust.

Central European foreland N of the Alps

Many workers perceive the evolution of the Rhine graben system as an extensional response to two principal episodes of Alpine convergence (Ahorner 1975; Baumann 1981; Illies 1977, 1981; Illies & Greiner 1978, 1979; Illies *et al.* 1981; Schmitt 1981; Şengör 1976; Şengör *et al.* 1978). NNE–SSW convergence in the medial Eocene–early Miocene generated the Upper Rhine graben system, and subsequent NW–SE convergence in the late Miocene–Recent propagated the system northwestwards into the Lower Rhine embayment (Fig. 1c). Synchronous with northwestwards rift propagation was the transformation of the Upper Rhine graben system into a sinistral shear zone. Conjugate strike-slip faults disrupting central Europe E of the Rhine also caused the foreland to extend NE–SW at the same time as shortening NW–SE (Şengör 1976; Şengör *et al.* 1978). Directions of compression and extension determined from fault-plane solutions of earthquakes and *in situ* stress measurements accord with those inferred from the neotectonic structures.

Unlike in the two Asiatic regions discussed earlier, there has been some study of brittle mesofractures in central Europe (e.g. Wagner 1964; Hoffers 1974; Greiner 1975; Buchner 1981). The youngest mesostructures are abundant extension fractures, stylolites and less-common strike-slip faults, the assemblage indicating that the direction of horizontal extension was NE–SW, accompanied locally by NW–SE shortening, especially in the S.

Aquitaine hinterland basin N of the Pyrenean front

Arthaud & Choukroune (1972) and Choukroune (1976) have described vertical stylolites, extension veins and strike-slip mesofaults cutting Mesozoic–Palaeogene rocks on the margins of the Aquitaine basin, up to 400 km distant from the Pyrenean front. In Fig. 1d only extension fracture trends are shown. The inferred direction of horizontal extension is generally E–W, but according to Arthaud & Choukroune (1972) it varies locally as a result of the influence of basement structures and the sedimentary evolution of the platform. The generalized E–W extension direction is sub-parallel to the Pyrenean front. Thrusting in the Pyrenees and development of the mesostructures on the northern and eastern margins of the Aquitaine basin are considered to have occurred in the Palaeogene.

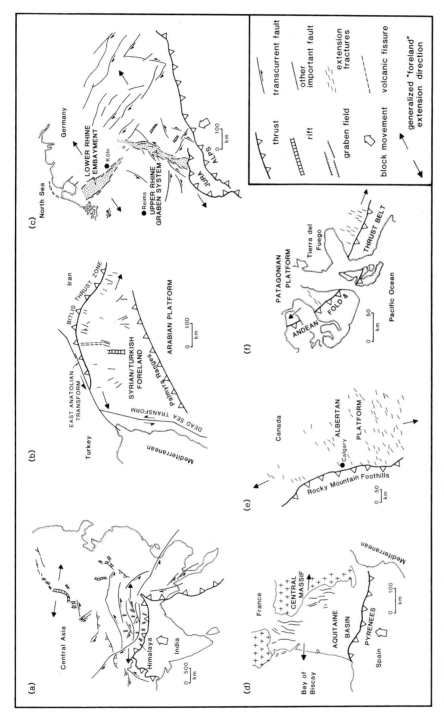

FIG. 1. Schematic maps of structures responsible for the lateral extension of forelands and hinterlands. (a) Central Asian hinterland (based on Molnar & Tapponnier 1975; Tapponnier *et al.* 1980; Şengör & Yilmaz 1981; Dewey *et al.* 1986). (b) Syrian–Turkish foreland (based on Letouzey & Trémolières 1981a; Rothery & Drury 1984). (c) Central European foreland (based on Ahorner 1975; Illies 1977, 1981; Şengör *et al.* 1978; Illies *et al.* 1981). (d) Aquitaine hinterland basin (based on Choukroune 1976). (e) Albertan hinterland platform (based on Babcock 1974b). (f) Patagonian hinterland platform (based on Winslow 1983).

Albertan hinterland platform E of the Rocky Mountain foothills

Babcock (1973, 1974a) described up to four sets of vertical joints cutting the nearly horizontal late Cretaceous–Palaeogene sandstones and siltstones in the southern and central parts of the Albertan platform. The set striking ENE–WSW in the S and NE–SW in the N is dominant at many localities (Fig. 1e), and was interpreted by Babcock as comprising extension fractures. The development of this set, which Babcock relates to the Laramide movements in the neighbouring Rocky Mountains, caused a small percentage of hinterland elongation parallel or sub-parallel to the gentle arc of foothill structures. The dominant extension-joint set is parallel to an important photolinear trend (Babcock 1974b) and the direction of the contemporary maximum horizontal stress determined from four-arm caliper logs of well break-outs (Bell & Gough 1979).

Patagonian hinterland platform E of the Andean front

According to Winslow (1983) the relatively undeformed Cenozoic rocks of the Patagonian hinterland platform in Chile are cut by cross-joints and veins, and localized swarms of intrusive clastic dykes (Fig. 1f). She interpreted the veins, which contain growth fibres normal to their walls, as extension fractures. As Fig. 1f shows, the strikes of the cross-joint and vein sets (extrapolated from equal-area diagrams in Winslow 1983) are arranged in a slightly convergent fan relative to the Andean frontal thrust, and hence the direction of lateral extension in the platform defines a gently concave arc. The clastic dykes occupy former cross-joints that were dilated and intruded by fluidized sediments during the advance of the Andean thrust sheets.

E Arabian foreland platform W of the Zagros front

Macrostructures disturbing the Phanerozoic sedimentary sequences of the E Arabian foreland platform are few, subdued and simple. Those of Mesozoic–Palaeogene age are the central Arabian arch, the central Arabian graben system and major N–S growth folds (Fig. 2) (Powers et al. 1966; Hancock et al. 1984). Superimposed obliquely on these older structures is a group of NE-trending lineaments, fault belts and mesofractures that are especially well expressed in the Neogene–Quaternary cover.

The principal element is Wadi Al Batin, a rectilinear gentle-sided wadi eroded in Neogene rocks except in the SW where it crosses outcrops of Cretaceous and Palaeogene formations. Planar NE-trending normal faults displace Palaeogene and Neogene sediments beneath and immediately to the E of the Kuwaiti sector of the wadi (Al Sawari 1980). Hancock et al. (1984) have argued that the large dimensions and straightness of Wadi Al Batin favour a tectonic control along its entire length. It is noteworthy that Wadi Al Batin, the longest and widest of the NE-trending lineaments, is directed towards the Khuzestan topographic embayment of the Zagros mountain front, a region which is also an embayment in the swarm of earthquake epicentres that define the Zagros seismic zone (Jackson & McKenzie 1984). A perturbation on the boundary between the Zagros fold-and-thrust belt and the Arabian craton may have controlled the location of the fault zone guiding Wadi Al Batin. Şengör (1976) emphasized the possibly analogous control on 'foreland' behaviour that can be exerted by salients or embayments on the leading edges of continents that are colliding along a suture zone.

Other NE-trending lineaments range in length from 10 to 150 km (Fig. 2) and correspond on the ground to subdued ridges, shallow wadis and narrow, abnormally trending outcrops of lithostratigraphic contacts. The pre-Neogene N–S Bahrain dome is crossed obliquely by five NE-trending troughs, each framed by inward-facing monoclines that, according to Doornkamp et al. (1980), overlie normal faults. Development of the normal faults caused Bahrain to elongate slightly in a NW–SE direction.

Within the E Arabian foreland platform it is possible to recognize three suites of mesofractures (Hancock et al. 1984). Two of the suites are restricted to Mesozoic–Palaeogene formations and are genetically related to the development of the central Arabian arch and graben system, while the third is superimposed obliquely on them. NE–SW striking mesofractures in the third suite also cut the previously unfractured Miocene–early Pliocene sequence, although they do not cut the overlying duricrust layer, dated by Chapman (in Al Sayari & Zötl 1978) as of latest Pliocene–Pleistocene age. It follows, therefore that they were initiated during a Miocene–medial Pliocene interval, that is, during the earlier part of the neotectonic history of the Gulf region. Thus the Batin-trend mesofractures (Fig. 2) are interpreted here as being related to Miocene (Berberian et al. 1982) collision in the Zagros domain with most of them probably being formed before the late Pliocene–

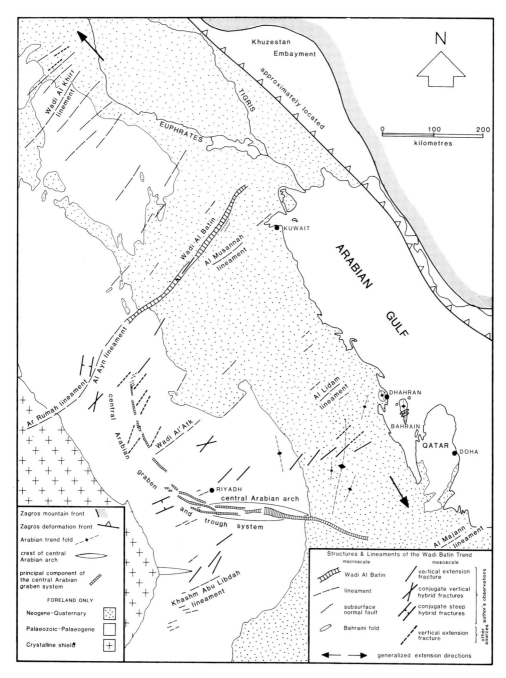

FIG. 2. Structures of Wadi Batin trend in the E Arabian platform. Data sources: author's (P.L.H.) observations; Doornkamp *et al.* (1980); Hancock *et al.* (1984); Sha'ath (1986); M.S. Atiya (pers. comm.);
A. Naqash (pers. comm.).

Pleistocene (Berberian & King 1981) climax of post-collisional amplification of the Zagros foothill structures.

Mesofractures in the neotectonic suite either strike NE–SW (the Batin trend) or they enclose an acute bisector about that direction. The following classes of structure are present: (i) vertical NE-striking extension joints; (ii) vertical NE-striking extension veins, a few of which contain growth fibres normal to their margins; (iii) steeply inclined, NE-striking conjugate hybrid (transitional tensile) joints enclosing an average acute dihedral angle (2θ) of $35°$; (iv) steeply inclined, planar NE-striking conjugate normal mesofaults; and (v) vertical NNE- and ENE-striking conjugate hybrid joints enclosing a 2θ angle of $31°$ about a NE-trending acute bisector. As Fig. 2 shows, the suite is mainly represented by a set of extension fractures, conjugate sets of hybrid fractures being rare and restricted to sites in Mesozoic–Palaeogene rocks N of the crest of the central Arabian arch. Because the Palaeogene direction of stretching N of the arch crest was also NW–SE, some of the conjugate structures in that area may be older than those of the neotectonic suite (Hancock *et al.* 1984). More than 90% of structures of Batin trend are joints; of the remainder the majority are calcite veins and only a few are normal mesofaults. Some of the joints are large surfaces (greater than 5000 m^2) and some are closely spaced and pervasive at outcrop scale.

Because lineaments and fractures of Batin trend are uniformly orientated throughout at least 750,000 km^2 and because they are superimposed obliquely on older structures we interpret them as the products of a regional strain field. The direction of horizontal extension derived from the normal to extension fractures, or the obtuse bisector between conjugate hybrid fractures, is everywhere orientated NW–SE, sub-parallel to the Zagros deformation front. There is a gentle arc in this generalized extension direction from 315–135° in the N to 325–145° in the S (Fig. 2). The extension-direction arc curves in sympathy with, but consistently 10–20° clockwise of, the orthogonal to slip-vectors determined by Jackson & McKenzie (1984) from fault-plane solutions of thrust-related earthquakes in the Zagros region.

European foreland in S England and N France

The NW European foreland platform in S England and N France is cut by a widespread, pervasive mesofracture system containing uniformly orientated sets trending NW–SE (Fig.

3) (Bevan & Hancock 1986). In Upper Cretaceous and Palaeogene rocks the system is dominated by vertical extension joints locally accompanied by normal mesofaults, conjugate sets of steeply inclined hybrid and shear joints (2θ angles 37 and 63°, respectively) and conjugate sets of vertical hybrid joints enclosing a 2θ angle of 35° about a NW-directed acute bisector. The fractures are best developed in SE England and N France where the extension joints are characteristically smooth, large surfaces. In addition, normal mesofaults are commoner and display greater displacements in N France than in S England.

The NW trend is also represented by a major lineament direction visible on Landsat images and topographic and geological maps (Bevan & Hancock 1986, fig. 4). It is especially well developed in N France where a wide outcrop of nearly horizontal chalk is not complicated by E–W flexures, such as those of S England, where NW-trending lineaments are shorter and less abundant. The majority of NW-trending lineaments in N France are coincident with major rectilinear drainage channels.

Abutting and cross-cutting relationships indicate that mesofractures in the NW-trending system are younger than those which accompany the E–W trending flexures (e.g. Isle of Wight and Purbeck monoclines). The E–W flexures, which formed in response to displacements on reactivated Variscan basement faults, are of Oligocene–early Miocene age and, according to Dewey (1982), reflect the 'Helvetic phase' in the Alpine domain. When convergence in that domain became NW–SE during the late Miocene–Quaternary (roughly coincident with Dewey's 'Jura' phase) it caused the Rhine graben system to propagate NW into the Lower Rhine embayment (Fig. 1c) and it transformed the Upper Rhine graben system into a sinistral-shear zone.

NW–SE shortening in the Alpine domain induced regional NE–SW extension in the foreland. We propose that this extension was responsible for propagating not only the Lower Rhine embayment normal faults, but also the NW-trending mesofractures in S England and N France. The westerly decrease in frequency and scale of the NW-trending mesofractures in S England can be correlated with increasing distance from the Lower Rhine embayment, the principal site of foreland rifting related to NW–SE convergence. The NW-trending lineaments of N France have been interpreted by Bevan & Hancock (1986) as reflecting the locations of joint swarms in the Cretaceous cover sequence. A comparable explanation for the presence of

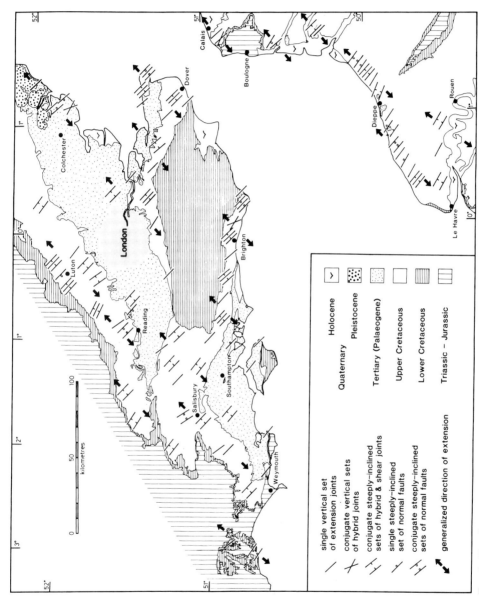

Fig. 3. Mesofracture sets of NW-trend cutting late Cretaceous–Palaeogene rocks in S England and N France. From Bevan & Hancock (1986, fig. 1).

analogous lineaments in Italy has also been advanced by Wise *et al.* (1985).

Discussion

The presence of fractures that cause 'forelands' to extend laterally, even in regions greater than 500 km from a deformation front, demonstrates, as argued earlier by Şengör (1976), that plates can transmit stresses for long distances from collision sites. Rather than the stresses responsible for failure in a platform sequence being transmitted directly through the sequence, it is more likely that they are transmitted by the main stress-carrying part of the lithosphere, which is ductile. Thus, although mesofracture attitudes and classes in foreland platforms will be controlled by brittle-failure criteria and the orientations of the principal stresses in the brittle carapace, the stresses themselves will be responses to behaviour in the underlying ductile crust (cf. Wise *et al.* 1985), which may contain old weakness zones capable of reactivation (cf. Arthaud & Choukroune 1972).

Figure 4 is a diagrammatic inventory of the principal varieties of structure that cause forelands to extend laterally. Although macroscale, but localized, structures (Fig. 4a–f) are separated from mesoscale, but distributed, structures (Fig. 4g–n) there are transitions between the two and commonly they occur in conjunction. Pervasive brittle mesofractures result in the homogeneous extension of 'forelands' by a few per cent in contrast to macrostructures which achieve substantial but local elongations. Major grabens striking at high angles to orogens are relatively uncommon and likewise conjugate transcurrent fault sets are not universally developed in advance of deformation fronts. Conversely, the joint and other mesofracture sets described by Babcock (1973, 1974a) from Alberta and by us from Arabia and SE England and N France are pervasive in regions lacking the macrostructures.

'Foreland' extension is generally parallel or sub-parallel to the margin of a neighbouring deformation belt (Fig. 5b, c). In S England and N France, however, the extension direction inferred from brittle mesofractures in a peripheral part of a foreland lacking macrostructures is uniformly oriented instead of arcing in sympathy with the Alpine deformation front (Fig. 5a). The NE–SW direction of extension is, nevertheless, everywhere normal to the sense of convergence responsible for the 'Jura' phase of the Alpine Orogeny. The very slight arc in the sense of extension in the E Arabian

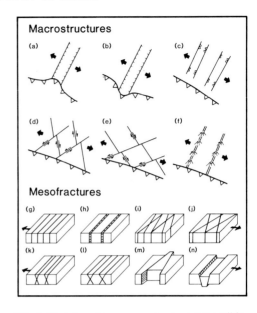

FIG. 4. Varieties of transverse structure responsible for lateral 'foreland' extension. *Macrostructures* (a) Graben located opposite a salient on the leading edge of a thrust sheet. (b) Graben located opposite an embayment on the leading edge of a thrust sheet. (c) Troughs bounded by inward-facing monoclines. (d) Conjugate brittle strike-slip faults. (e) Conjugate ductile strike-slip faults. (f) Fissure eruptions related to dykes. In each map the outcrop of the related thrust front is shown by a solid line with open triangles in the hanging wall and the regional direction of extension is depicted by outward-directed solid arrows. *Mesofractures* (g) Set of vertical extension joints. (h) Set of vertical extension veins. (i) Conjugate sets of vertical hybrid joints. (j) Conjugate sets of vertical shear joints. (k) Conjugate sets of steeply inclined hybrid joints. (l) Conjugate sets of steeply inclined shear joints. (m) Conjugate sets of strike-slip mesofaults. (n) Conjugate sets of normal mesofaults. The front of each block diagram is taken to be parallel or sub-parallel to the trend of a related deformation front, the solid arrows indicating directions of regional extension.

foreland platform correlates with the change in direction of normals to slip vectors across the Zagros belt, although there is a consistently 10–20° clockwise mismatch between slip vectors and fractures (Fig. 5d).

An important aspect of the development of 'foreland' extensional mesofractures is the timing of their initiation with respect to shortening in a neighbouring deformation belt. Winslow (1983) considered the cross-joints of the Patagonian hinterland to have formed before they were incorporated in thrust sheets that were advancing from the Andes. Field

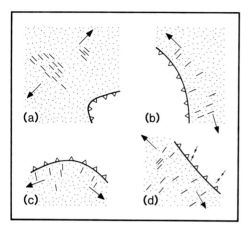

FIG. 5. Cartoons illustrating relationships in plan between directions of lateral 'foreland' extension inferred from mesofractures and shapes of neighbouring deformation fronts. (a) Uniform extension direction in the peripheral part of a foreland in advance of a markedly convex front. (b) Convex arc of extension directions sub-parallel to a gently convex front. (c) Concave arc of extension directions sub-parallel to a gently concave front. (d) Very gentle convex arc of extension directions in advance of an almost rectilinear front behind which shortening is either normal to the front or oblique to it. Note that the strikes of the transverse 'foreland' fractures sets are not precisely parallel to the shortening directions but nevertheless they rotate in sympathy with them. Solid line with open triangles in hanging wall—deformation front; short solid line—mesofracture set; large arrow—regional extension direction; inward-directed small arrows—slip vector; stipple—'foreland'.

evidence (Hancock *et al.* 1984) from E Arabia supports this view of some 'foreland' extensional fractures being older than the outermost contractional structures of an orogen. Joint initiation in E Arabia, which may have started in the Miocene, must have lasted until the medial Pliocene, whereas shortening in the Zagros foothills reached a climax in the late Pliocene–early Pleistocene. Thus transverse extensional failure in some 'foreland' platform sequences probably occurs before and ahead of an advancing thrust front. When a frontal thrust lurches via a flat and ramp into previously undeformed 'foreland' the transverse fractures will be absorbed and become active in shear or dilation. Elongation parallel to fold axes dilates cross-joints which may become occupied by vein minerals or clastic dyke material. Interconnected cross-joints or transverse normal faults could be transformed in some strain regimes into strike-

slip (i.e. tear) faults or lateral ramps within linked thrust systems.

The observation that most transverse brittle structures in the platform sequences of 'forelands' are either vertical extension fractures or steep hybrid and shear fractures, locally accompanied by normal and strike-slip faults and parallel joints (Fig. 4g–n), gives rise to four important inferences. (i) The direction of extension (minimum principal stress axis) during fracture initiation is generally horizontal. (ii) The magnitude of the differential stress generally remains small throughout a failure sequence. (iii) The effective minimum stress is generally tensile, probably aided by the influence of relatively high fluid pressures. (iv) The lateral elongation of 'forelands' is not accompanied by complementary horizontal shortening unless the structural assemblage also contains strike-slip faults and parallel shear or hybrid joints, possibly accompanied by coeval stylolitic seams bearing columns (teeth) orientated parallel to the strike of the extension fractures. Field evidence for horizontal shortening normal to the principal extension direction is common only in some 'forelands', and within these it is generally most abundant close to the neighbouring deformation belt.

Conclusions

1 Many forelands and hinterlands are traversed for hundreds of kilometres by sets of fractures that have caused lateral elongation parallel or sub-parallel to neighbouring collisional orogenic margins.
2 Although the major proportion of lateral 'foreland' strain is contributed by macrostructures such as grabens and transcurrent faults, whose attitudes may be related to ductile-failure criteria, a small fraction comes from complex systems of mesoscopic brittle fractures cutting platform sequences at high crustal levels.
3 The principal modes of mesoscopic brittle structures causing 'foreland' lateral extension are: (i) vertical extension joints and veins; (ii) vertical hybrid and shear joints; (iii) steeply inclined hybrid and shear joints; (iv) strike-slip mesofaults; and (v) steep, planar, normal mesofaults.
4 The majority of mesoscopic brittle structures causing the lateral elongation of 'foreland' platform sequences are extension and hybrid fractures indicating that differential stresses within the upper part of the brittle carapace are generally small and that the effective minimum stress is tensile. Because the structures are vertical or

steeply inclined it also follows that the direction of the minimum principal stress during their initiation was horizontal. Horizontal extension was accompanied by complementary horizontal shortening only where conjugate strike-slip faults or associated stylolites are present, generally in areas relatively close to orogenic fronts.

5 The direction of 'foreland' extension is generally parallel or sub-parallel to a related rectilinear or gently arcuate deformation belt, but where a belt is markedly arcuate the extension direction, in at least the more peripheral parts of the 'foreland', may be approximately uniform and normal to the regional sense of convergence.

6 Mesoscopic brittle fractures permit regional extension directions to be determined in 'forelands' lacking macrostructures.

7 Transverse extensional mesofractures of 'forelands' form before and in advance of a migrating deformation front.

8 Swarms of closely spaced extension and hybrid joints control the locations of topographic lineaments in some 'forelands'.

ACKNOWLEDGMENTS: We are grateful to the Natural Environment Research Council who provided a postgraduate award for one of us (T.G.B.) and funded fieldwork in N France for both of us. Fieldwork by P.L.H. in Saudi Arabia was funded by King Saud University. Mohammed Atiya and Adnan Naqash kindly gave us information about joint directions in SW Iraq, and Na'im Sha'ath permitted us to use data from his unpublished Ph.D. thesis on the northernmost part of the central Arabian graben system. Celâl Şengör and Robert Stoneley provided us with challenging but encouraging comments on a draft of the manuscript.

References

AHORNER, L. 1975. Present-day stress field and seismotectonic block movements along major fault zones in central Europe. *Tectonophysics*, **29**, 233–49.

AL SAWARI, A.M. 1980. Tertiary faulting beneath Wadi Al-Batin [Kuwait]. *Bull. geol. Soc. Am.* **91**, 610–18.

AL SAYARI, S.S. & ZOTL, J.G. (eds) 1978. *Quarternary Period in Saudi Arabia*. Springer, New York.

ARTHAUD, F. & CHOUKROUNE, P. 1972. Méthode d'analyse de la Tectonique cassante à l'aide des microstructures dans les zones peu déformées: Example de la Plateforme Nord Aquitaine. *Rev. Inst. Fr. Pét. Paris*, **25**, 715–32.

BABCOCK, E.A. 1973. Regional jointing in southern Alberta. *Can. J. Earth Sci.* **10**, 1769–81.

—— 1974a. Jointing in Central Alberta. *Can. J. Earth Sci.* **11**, 1181–6.

—— 1974b. Photolineaments and regional joints: lineament density and terrain parameters, south-central Alberta. *Bull. Can. Pet. Geol.* **22**, 89–105.

BAUMANN, H. 1981. Regional stress field and rifting in Western Europe. *Tectonophysics*, **73**, 105–11.

BELL, J.S. & GOUGH, D.I. 1979. Northeast-southwest compressive stress in Alberta: evidence from oil wells. *Earth planet. Sci. Lett.* **45**, 475–82.

BERBERIAN, F., MUIR, I.D., PANKHURST, R.J. & BERBERIAN, M. 1982. Late Cretaceous and early Miocene Andean-type plutonic activity in northern Makran and Central Iran. *J. geol. Soc. London*, **139**, 605–14.

BERBERIAN, M. & KING, G. 1981. Towards a palaeo-geography and tectonic evolution of Iran. *Can. J. Earth Sci.* **18**, 210–65.

BEVAN, T.G. & HANCOCK, P.L. 1986. A late Cenozoic regional mesofracture system in southern England and northern France. *J. geol. Soc. London*, **143**, 355–62.

BUCHNER, F. 1981. Rhinegraben: horizontal stylolites indicating stress regimes of earlier stages of rifting. *Tectonophysics*, **73**, 113–8.

CHOUKROUNE, P. 1976. Strain patterns in the Pyrenean chain. *Phil. Trans. R. Soc. London*, **A283**, 271–80.

DEWEY, J.F. 1982. Plate tectonics and the evolution of the British Isles. *J. geol. Soc. London*, **139**, 371–412.

——, HEMPTON, M.R., KIDD, W.S.F., SAROGLU, F. & ŞENGÖR, A.M.C. 1986. The neotectonics of Eastern Anatolia – a young collision zone; implications for the shortening of continental lithosphere. *In*: COWARD, M.P. & RIES, A. (eds) *Collision Tectonics. Spec. Publ. geol. Soc. London*, **19**, 3–36.

DOORNKAMP, J.C., BRUNSDEN, D. & JONES, D.K.C. (eds). 1980. *Geology, Geomorphology and Pedology of Bahrain*. Geo Abstracts, Norwich.

GREINER, G. 1975. In-situ stress measurements in southwest Germany. *Tectonophysics*, **29**, 265–74.

HANCOCK, P.L., AL KADHI, A. & SHA'AT, N.A. 1984. Regional joint sets in the Arabian platform as indicators of intraplate processes. *Tectonics*, **3**, 27–43.

HOFFERS, B. 1974. Horizontal Stylolithen, Klüfte, Alschiebungen und Harnische im Gebiet des Hohenzollerngrabens und ihre Altersverhaltnisse. *Oberrhein Geol. Abh.* **23**, 65–73.

ILLIES, J.H. 1977. Ancient and recent rifting in the Rhinegraben. *Geol. Mijnb.* **54**, 329–50.

—— 1981. Mechanism of graben formation. *Tectonophysics*, **73**, 249–66.

—— & GREINER, G. 1978. Rhinegraben and the Alpine system. *Bull. geol. Soc. Am.* **89**, 770–82.

—— & —— 1979. Holocene movements and state of stress in the Rhinegraben rift system. *Tectonophysics*, **52**, 349–59.

——, BAUMANN, H. & HOFFERS, B. 1981. Stress

pattern and strain release in the Alpine foreland. *Tectonophysics*, **71**, 157–72.

JACKSON, J. & McKENZIE, D. 1984. Active tectonics of the Alpine–Himalayan Belt between western Turkey and Pakistan. *Geophys. J.R. astron. Soc.* **77**, 185–264.

LETOUZEY, J. & TRÉMOLIÈRES, P. 1980. Palaeo-stress fields around the Mediterranean since the Mesozoic derived from microtectonics: comparison with plate tectonic data. *Mem. Bur. Rech. geol. Minieres*, **115**, 261–73.

McKENZIE, D.P. 1972. Active tectonics of the Mediterranean region. *Geophys. J.R. astron. Soc.* **30**, 109–86.

MOLNAR, P. & CHEN, W-P. 1982. Seismicity and mountain building. *In*: HSÜ, K.J. (ed.) *Mountain Building Processes*, pp. 41–57. Academic Press, London.

—— & TAPPONNIER, P. 1975. Cenozoic tectonics of Asia: effects of a continental collision. *Science*, **189**, 419–26.

POWERS, R.W., RAMIREX, L.F., REDMOND, C.D. & ELBERG, E.L. 1966. Geology of the Arabian Peninsula – sedimentary geology of Saudi Arabia. *Prof. Pap. U.S. geol. Surv.* **560D**, D1–D147.

ROTHERY, D.A. & DRURY, S.A. 1984. The neotectonics of the Tibetan Plateau. *Tectonics*, **3**, 19–26.

SCHMITT, T.J. 1981. The West European stress field: new data and interpretation. *J. struct. Geol.* **3**, 309–15.

ŞENGÖR, A.M.C. 1976. Collision of irregular continental margins: implications for foreland deformation of Alpine-type orogens. *Geology*, **4**, 779–82.

—— 1984. The Cimmeride orogenic system and the tectonics of Eurasia. *Spec. Pap. geol. Soc. Am.* **195**, 1–82.

—— & YILMAZ, Y. 1981. Tethyan evolution of Turkey: a plate tectonic approach. *Tectonophysics*, **75**, 181–241.

——, BURKE, K. & DEWEY, J.F. 1978. Rifts at high angles to orogenic belts: tests for their origin and the Upper Rhine graben as an example. *Am. J. Sci.* **278**, 24–40.

SHA'ATH, N.A. 1986. The structure of the Majma'ah graben complex. Unpubl. Ph.D. thesis, Univ. Bristol.

TAPPONNIER, P. 1977. Evolution tectonique du Système Alpin en Mediterrané: poinçonnement et ecrasement rigide-plastique. *Bull. Soc. géol. Fr.* **19**, 437–60.

—— & MOLNAR, P. 1976. Slip-line field theory and large-scale continental tectonics. *Nature, Lond.* **264**, 319–24.

——, MERCIER, J.L., ARMIJO, R., HAN, T. & ZHOU, J. 1981a. Field evidence for active normal faulting in Tibet. *Nature, Lond.* **294**, 410–14.

—— et al. 1981b. The Tibetan side of the India–Eurasia collision. *Nature, Lond.* **294**, 405–10.

WAGNER, H.G. 1964. Kleintektonishe Untersuchungen im Gebiet des Nördlinger Rieses. *Geol. Jahrb. Hannover*, **81**, 519–600.

WINSLOW, M.A. 1983. Clastic dike swarms and the structural evolution of the foreland fold and thrust belt of the southern Andes. *Bull. geol. Soc. Am.* **94**, 1073–80.

WISE, D.U., FUNICIELLO, R., PAROTTO, M. & SALVINI, F. 1985. Topographic lineament swarms: clues to their origin from domain analysis of Italy. *Bull. geol. Soc. Am.* **96**, 952–67.

P.L. HANCOCK & T.G. BEVAN*, Department of Geology, University of Bristol, Wills Memorial Building, Queen's Road, Bristol BS8 1RJ, UK.
*Present address: BP Petroleum Development Ltd, Farburn Industrial Estate, Aberdeen, AB2 0PB, UK.

Sedimentary models for extensional tilt-block/half-graben basins

M.R. Leeder & R.L. Gawthorpe

SUMMARY: Extensional tectonism produces characteristic half-graben/tilt-block systems whose facies mosaics are influenced by tectonically induced slopes resulting from hanging wall downtilting and footwall uplift. The characteristic asymmetrical subsidence vectors that therefore develop across the graben also exert a fundamental control upon facies distributions. A number of predictive tectono–sedimentary facies models are presented in which these various influences are explored. Alluvial fans and cones react to tilting by becoming segmented, those in the hanging wall showing down-dip hanging wall off-lap and those sourced in the footwall showing progradation from the apex. Lake and coastal waters react instantly to tilting, causing transgression and seiche-induced erosion. Axial through-flowing river channels and delta lobes tend to migrate or avulse towards the axis of maximum subsidence but may be constrained by the toes of footwall-sourced fans. Peat accumulation or soil development are accentuated up the hanging wall dip slope away from the locus of maximum deposition. In coastal areas, fan deltas sourced in the footwall pass offshore into small submarine fans whilst axial fans issue from delta fronts where individual fan lobes may migrate under fault control. In carbonate provinces the footwall scarp may become a bypass margin whilst the hanging wall dip slope may undergo a ramp-to-rimmed shelf evolution with time.

It has become apparent in the last few years that the process of lithospheric extension is characterized by a distinctive development of tilt blocks and half-grabens bounded by major normal faults (Morton & Black 1975; McKenzie 1978; Wernicke & Birchfiel 1982; Jackson et al. 1982a, b; Brun & Choukroune 1983; Gibbs 1984). These types of basins develop progressively during extension, and we recognize that during this time they exert a profound and logical influence upon geomorphology and sediment-transfer mechanisms in the vicinity. Examples of active basins of this sort occur in the Aegean back-arc (McKenzie 1978; Jackson et al. 1982b; Jackson & McKenzie 1983); in the Basin and Range Province of the western United States (Myers & Hamilton 1964; Wernicke & Birchfiel 1982; Anderson et al. 1983); in the lower Rhine basin (Illies & Fuchs 1983); in the Gulf of Suez (Sellwood & Netherwood 1984); and in Afar (Hutchinson & Engels 1970; Morton & Black 1975). Extinct fault-bounded extensional basins occur around the margins of almost all Atlantic-type passive continental margins (e.g. Surlyk 1977, 1978) and in continental areas where extension did not proceed to oceanic separation (failed arms) as in the Central African rift system (Browne & Fairhead 1983). These extinct basins usually lie buried beneath the later deposits of the thermal-contraction phase of extensional subsidence. One of the best known examples is the North Sea basin (Christie & Sclater 1980; Barton &

Wood 1984; Ziegler 1982). An increasing number of geologically ancient basins of this type are being recognized, e.g. the early Carboniferous extensional province of the British Isles (Leeder 1982; Dewey 1982; Gawthorpe, in press), and doubtless many others await recognition.

Recently major advances have been made concerning the dynamics and kinematics of normal faulting in areas of active extension (Wernicke & Birchfiel 1982; Jackson et al. 1982a, b; Gibbs 1984; Jackson & McKenzie 1983). It is the purpose of this paper to integrate such studies with analysis of sediment transfer and deposition, the resulting three-dimensional tectono–sedimentary-facies models being helpful in the study of ancient basin-fill successions. The models developed herein have been culled from an extensive but scattered geomorphological and sedimentological literature, our unpublished studies in active extensional terrains (Aegean, Basin and Range), our work in the ancient extensional graben-fill successions of the Lower Carboniferous in N Britain (Leeder 1982, 1986; Gawthorpe 1986, in press), and from previous stratigraphic-modelling contributions (Bridge & Leeder 1979).

Tilt-block/half-graben morphology and structure

Originally, Morton & Black (1975) envisaged domino-type fault blocks forming during active

From COWARD, M.P., DEWEY, J.F. & HANCOCK, P.L. (eds), 1987, *Continental Extensional Tectonics*, Geological Society Special Publication No. 28, pp. 139–152.

139

extension, with the further occurrence of progressive fault rotation causing nucleation of higher angle second- or third-generation normal faults which themselves become progressively rotated. Structural studies in the Basin and Range Province have confirmed this model (Proffett 1977) and led to a number of more detailed tectonic models involving basement thrust reactivation, listric-fault fans and extensional analogues to the ramp and flat models of thrust tectonics (Wernicke & Birchfiel 1982; Brun & Choukroune 1983; Anderson *et al.* 1983; Chamberlin 1983; see also the general papers of Gibbs 1983, 1984). These studies serve to stress the great complexities of extensional faulting, especially on an intrabasinal scale.

Whilst American workers in the Basin and Range Province have stressed the importance of shallow, 'domino-style' faulting, workers in the Aegean extensional province (McKenzie 1978; Jackson *et al.* 1982a, b) have shown the importance of major normal faults of mid-crustal penetration which bound 'bouyant' tilt blocks. Some examples of this type of fault also occur in the Basin and Range Province (Anderson *et al.* 1983). These major faults cause instantaneous unloading along the fault plane during fault motion leading to an instantaneous isostatic upwarp of the footwall block (Heiskanen & Vening Meinesz 1958; Savage & Hastie 1966; Bott 1976). Jackson & McKenzie (1983) calculate this footwall uplift to be around 10% of the hanging wall subsidence.

Whether small- or large-scale faulting develops seems to depend upon the extensional strain rate, the geothermal gradient and the

existence of crustal fractures ripe for rejuvenation (Anderson *et al.* 1983; Eaton 1982).

Reduced to their simplest form, tilt-block/half-graben structures can be considered to be bounded by single normal faults which penetrate to mid-crustal levels. As the hanging wall basement detaches from the footwall an asymmetrical basin progressively develops above the hanging wall. The fundamental controls upon geomorphology and sedimentation patterns are as follows (see Figs 1 & 2):

1 Tectonic slopes. These are produced by a combination of footwall uplift and hanging wall subsidence and comprise the steeper footwall scarp slope and the gentler hanging wall dip slope. The footwall area is the main sediment source for the adjacent basin although, due to the asymmetrical nature of the basin, the hanging wall-derived sediment may be spatially more extensive. Recent geomorphological studies (Hanks *et al.* 1984) demonstrate that the gradual decay of the scarp profile with time follows a decay equation of the error-function type. The periodic rejuvenation of the footwall scarp will give rise to important sedimentary consequences in the basin fill (q.v.). In examples where the basin-margin fault has a listric geometry, tilting of the surface during extension is accompanied by rotation and the development of a rollover structure.

2 Asymmetrical subsidence. This is due to the pivot-like motion of the hanging wall after individual extensional episodes. Asymmetrical subsidence following historic earthquakes is best documented for the Hebgen Lake area of Montana, USA. In Fig. 2a we reproduce the

FIG. 1. Nomenclature diagram for tectonic slopes associated with a simple tilt block/half-graben. The main tectonic slopes produced during basin development are the steep, spatially restricted footwall scarp associated with the footwall-to-hanging wall transition, and a broad, gentle slope, the hanging wall dip slope, characteristic of the hanging wall of the basin-forming fault. The fulcrum is the position where displacement of the hanging wall block is zero; either the limit of roll-over in isolate tilt block/half-grabens or the transition from areas of the hanging wall undergoing positive motion due to footwall uplift to areas undergoing negative motion due to hanging wall subsidence. The position of the fulcrum is governed by the relative displacement vectors across the half-graben-bounding fault(s), the presence of antithetic/synthetic intrabasin structures and the subsurface geometry of the faults.

a

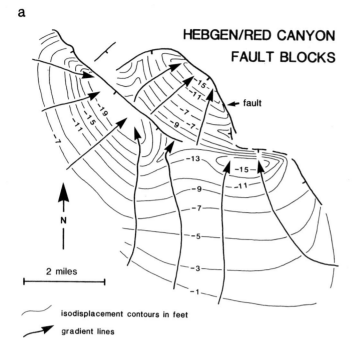

HEBGEN/RED CANYON
FAULT BLOCKS

← fault

N

2 miles

~~~ isodisplacement contours in feet

→ gradient lines

b

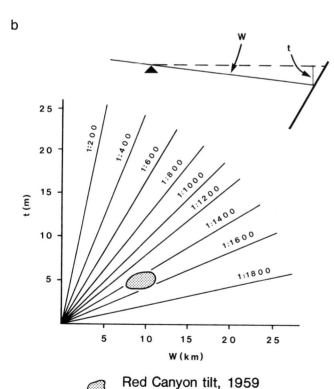

Red Canyon tilt, 1959
earthquake

FIG. 2. (a) Example of surface displacement associated with the 1959 earthquake in the Hebgen/Red Canyon tilt block, Montana, USA (after Fraser *et al.* 1964). Contours are of equal ground displacement associated with the earthquake and our arrows represent sketch gradients. (b) Our graph showing the approximate tectonic slopes produced by single motions of vertical magnitude (t) across tilt block of width (W).

isodisplacement contours of Fraser *et al.* (1964) drawn up following the 1959 earthquake, with an indication of the secondary gradients due to tilting. As shown in Fig. 2b, tectonic slopes produced by quite modest fault displacements have a great effect when superimposed on say, typical river gradients. Our fundamental starting point is thus emphasized: all sedimentary processes driven by gravity will be influenced by extensional tilting.

The point where the hanging wall displacement tends to zero may be called the fulcrum. The position of the fulcrum is not fixed but is controlled by the geometry of the basin-margin fault, the presence or absence of antithetic/synthetic intrabasin faults and time. In the simplest case of a tilt block/half-graben bounded by a listric normal fault, progressive extension will lead to the fulcrum moving away from the fault, i.e. up the hanging wall. This effect may be particularly important in the early stages of evolution of tilt blocks/half-grabens, leading to progressive on-lap onto the basement. The seismic section and line drawing across the Fallon basin by Anderson *et al.* (1983, fig. 5) displays such on-lap developed during progressive extension. In a linked series of tilt blocks the fulcrum divides areas undergoing positive motion due to footwall uplift from areas of negative motion arising from hanging wall subsidence. As shown below, we postulate that the location of fulcral lines will have considerable influence upon the sedimentary and geomorphic evolution of a tilt block and should also provide valuable clues concerning crustal dynamics.

In active half-grabens the simple tilt-block concept described above is complicated, to a greater or lesser extent, by the occurrence of both antithetic and synthetic faults which deform both the hanging wall basement and the developing sedimentary fill. Although these various structures have received descriptive attention in seismic studies (e.g. Gibbs 1983, 1984) in ancient basins it is by no means clear how they influenced topography and sedimentation at the depositional surface. Such structures will, however, clearly be of importance in modifying the sub-surface geometry of the sedimentary fill. Major intrabasinal normal faults define important 'mini' horsts and grabens in the Rio Grande rift (Velarde graben of Manley 1979: Ladron horst of Brown *et al.* 1979). Analogous structures are deduced from the extensional Carboniferous basins of northern England (Leeder 1986, in press; Gawthorpe 1986, in press).

At the Earth's surface, extensional normal faults are of finite extent and thus the asymmetrical basins so produced have a distinctive 'scoop' shape, at least in the early stages of extension. This is well seen in the Hebgen Lake area of Montana (Fraser *et al.* 1964, see our Fig. 1) and in the Rio Grande basin system of Colorado/New Mexico where continued extension along a N–S trend has led to the joining up of a series of originally isolated scoops into the present complex linear graben system (Chapin 1979; Bachman & Mehnert 1978).

Another consequence of the finite extent of normal faults at the surface (see Smith & Bruhn 1984) is that overlap zones exist between *en échelon* fault segments. In such zones, where the footwall zone of one fault passes into the hanging wall of an adjacent structure, an oblique monoclinal downbend develops at a high angle to the normal-fault trend. Large drainage systems may exploit the hinterland behind such areas, causing the development of larger-than-average depocentres in the main hanging wall basin (see Fig. 4). We have seen examples in the Greek Aegean, at Karrena Bourla in Locride, and in Montana, USA, along the Madison Front N of 'Quake Lake. Examples have also been described by Crossley (1984) from the East African graben in Malawi. Transform (Bally 1982) or transfer faults (Gibbs 1984) are other structures developed at a high angle to normal faults within half-grabens; indeed, the monoclines described above may be the surface expression of blind transfer faults. These faults separate areas of the basins deforming in different styles or at different rates and, in some instances, the sense of tilting may change polarity across them. Transfer faults also have an important role in sediment transfer, being the sites of major transport of sediment off both the hanging wall and footwall. In the Lower Carboniferous Bowland basin of northern England transfer faults were a major control on the location of coarse-grained carbonate debris-flow deposits that were derived off the hanging wall basin margin (Gawthorpe, in press).

Additional complications also arise because of the occurrence of layers of upwardly mobile partial melts in the shallow crust. These buoyant accumulations cause local areas of minor relative upwarp in an otherwise subsiding regime. Perhaps the most spectacular example occurs beneath the Rio Grande rift at Socorro, New Mexico (Sanford *et al.* 1977; Brown *et al.* 1979). Suspected ancient analogues existed in the Jurassic of the Central North Sea (Leeder 1983) and in the Lower Carboniferous Northumberland graben in the Scottish Borders (Leeder 1976, 1982). Major surface effects will also arise once this magma is erupted, with the production of lava plateaux, large-scale river damming, and local fan formation. Such effects are seen in the Rio Grande rift (Lipman & Mehnert 1979).

A dynamic feature of major importance in extensional basin evolution is the abandonment of one tilt-block/half-graben system because of the abandonment of one crustal-scale normal fault and the development of another (Jackson & McKenzie 1983). If the new fault develops on the hanging wall side of the now-extinct fault then the basin-fill is gradually uplifted in the footwall of the new fault. Examples occur in the Greek Aegean, particularly on the S side of the Gulf of Corinth and in Locride (Jackson *et al.* 1982a; Jackson & McKenzie 1983).

Stratigraphic and sedimentary consequences of extension— general remarks

As noted previously the occurrence of movement on an extensional normal fault causes surface tilting. Thus a tectonic gravity slope arises which will be superimposed upon the existing geomorphic slope. Since many sedimentary processes are gravity controlled it follows *a priori* that erosion, sediment transfer, deposition and soft-sediment deformation (see Leeder (in press) for a full discussion of this latter feature) will then have a tectonic influence, if not control. Once sedimentary systems become established in extensional basins then each slope component will contribute to the basin infill in a distinctive and, to some extent, predictable way. Of major importance are (i) *lateral-transport systems* that deposit sediment in high-gradient fans and low-gradient cones down the footwall and hanging wall slopes respectively, normal to the strike of the main bounding fault, and (ii) low seeking *axial-transport systems* that transfer sediment parallel to the strike of the main bounding faults. The effects of surface tilting on those lateral and axial systems give rise to marked basin-wide variations in lithology, facies and thickness. In the following sections the implications of these various general considerations are applied to particular sedimentary facies associations so that general and predictive basin-fill sequences may be proposed.

Before proceeding to the models it is essential at the outset to stress that there are many other variables (other than tectono–sedimentary, that is) which can affect the details of facies distributions. Thus climate and hinterland geology will also exert profound influences upon facies

associations in particular tectonic settings. These two variables will combine to determine the magnitude of clastic-sediment flux into an extensional basin. Clearly, a balance will then be set up between sediment deposition rate and subsidence rate as ultimately determined by the rate of extension. The relative position of sea-level with respect to the basin floor is also of obvious importance. Tilting is expected to have instantaneous and catastrophic effects upon both lake and marine shorelines. Such effects will give rise to a distinctive 'signal' in the basin-fill successions and may cause the production of distinctive sedimentary cycles. Such effects are of major importance to the geologist examining the fills of ancient basins. Here, in the absence of direct evidence for active extensional tectonics, it is essential to integrate the study of observed facies changes with structural information. The following models are proposed as basic templates for such studies.

Tectono-sedimentary facies model A— continental basin with interior drainage (Fig. 3)

This style of basin is a very characteristic one in the Basin and Range Province of the western USA where isolated fault-bounded depressions form local interior-drainage basins with no outlet to adjacent structures. The fundamental slopes are the relatively low-gradient hanging wall dip slope with broad alluvial cones and the relatively high-gradient footwall scarp slope which sources small alluvial fans whose depositional loci occur at the foot of the scarp on the lower hanging wall dip slope. As noted previously, large drainage systems frequently take advantage of transfer-fault zones and areas between *en échelon* fault terminations so that larger-than-average cones may preferentially form in such locations (Fig. 4). Should local climatic conditions allow, permanent or playa lake bodies will form in the basin as close to the locus of maximum subsidence as the footwall-sourced fans will allow. Such triplet cone-lake-fan systems have particularly dynamic interactions at their internal boundaries.

Perhaps the most studied example is Death Valley, California where the meticulous work of Hooke (1972), following on from the studies of Hunt & Mabey (1966), led to the first recognition of the effects of tilt movements on fan evolution and sedimentation. Hooke established beyond reasonable doubt that fan segmentation results from surface tilting and that characteristic off-lap sequences result if the tilting process is carried on periodically. These effects are

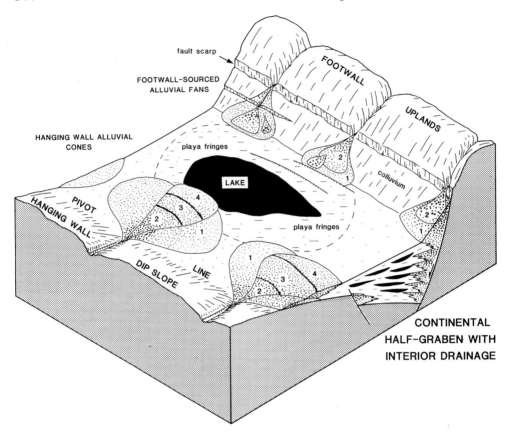

Fig. 3. Isometric diagram showing the main sedimentological features of facies model A: continental basin with interior drainage. Full discussion in text. Note: only the major basin-margin fault is shown; in natural examples the presence of antithetic, synthetic and transfer fault systems strongly modify certain depositional reactions to tilting. In addition, the sub-surface geometry is modified by differential compaction, thinning of the hanging wall associated with development of the roll-over and the presence of antithetic/synthetic fault systems within the sedimentary cover. 1, 2, 3 etc. indicate successive fan lobes.

generally predictable in terms of an extensional tilt-block model and may be amplified as follows.

Periods of fault motion cause the tectonic gradient and length of the footwall .scarp to increase instantaneously. Hanging valleys are produced as fan-head channel incision occurs progressively. The gradient of the fan surface in the hanging wall is decreased though, so that renewed sedimentation leads to the construction of a new fan segment close to the fan apex. This is expected to prograde gradually over the old fan segment with time, causing a crude upward-coarsening cycle to develop in response to the progradation of the downslope-thinning clastic wedge. Fault motion will also cause instantaneous lake transgression over the distal portions of the footwall-sourced fans, causing them to shrink substantially in area. Should subsequent

gradual fan progradation occur, these transgressive facies will be intercalated at the base of a tectonic fan cycle. Historic observations of lake-tilting, notable after the Hebgen Lake 'quake of 1959 (Myers & Hamilton 1964), show the occurrence of major seiches which may be expected to initiate erosive contacts and debris washover units over a much larger area than that covered by the permanent lake. The alluvial cones of the hanging wall dip slope react to tilting by incising their main fan-apex feeder channels close to the pivot line. The previous equilibrium-cone surface is tilted up by an amount determined by the magnitude of fault motion and a new active cone-lobe surface forms on a lower angle surface, often basinwards of the old cone lobe because of the steepening of the tilted dip-slope surface. Prominent breaks of slope occur at the junction of old and new surfaces, the older surface becoming depositionally defunct and subject to pedogenesis (calcretization in the case of Death Valley). Basinwards, the cones will prograde over the latero–distal portions of older fan surfaces forming off-lap sequences of downslope-thickening and fining wedges (see Hooke 1972, fig. 3). Thin units of lacustrine facies will be incorporated in these successions as progradation occurs over the upslope abandoned portions of the old lake shoreline. Examples of such effects are known from the hanging wall cones of Hebgen Lake (Alexander & Leeder, in press).

It seems clear that fault-induced tilting causes a number of rapid facies changes to occur. It should be borne in mind, however, that fan, cone and lake shrinkage and growth cycles may also be caused by climatic fluctuations, as is frequently seen in the Pleistocene history of the western USA (Hawley *et al.* 1976) and elsewhere (Talbot & Williams 1979). These more gradual sorts of effects must be separated from the purely tectonic effects discussed above. This may only be possible in very well-exposed terrains where good stratigraphic dating is present.

The basin-centre facies in the present model are certainly the most variable since evaporitic deposits may form from playa lakes as well as the non-evaporitic deposits of more permanent, possibly stratified lakes. The primary control here is obviously climatic. A further possibility, where run-off is very low and where regional sand-laden winds blow across the basin, is that small desert ergs may develop, particularly in the axis of maximum subsidence. In such areas the decelerating winds drop portions of their bedload before they accelerate up the hanging wall dip slope or the footwall scarp. Other geometrical possibilities of minor erg formation clearly exist. The Great Sand Dunes of the San Luis basin, Colorado are proposed as an example of this kind of facies association.

Tectono-sedimentary facies model B— continental basin with axial through-drainage (Fig. 4)

Active examples of this style of basin are well developed in the Aegean region, e.g. the River Axios in the Vardar graben, River Speriohos in the Lamia graben, and the Great Meander River in one of the Anatolian grabens. Other examples are the lower Rhine graben (particularly the River Erft in the Erft graben), the Rio Grande rift of Colorado/New Mexico and the Madison River graben of Montana. Certain features are shared in common with model A, namely the

occurrence of footwall and hanging wall derived fans and cones respectively. Some basins have, in fact, evolved from interior to through-drainage during their extensional evolution, notably the Rio Grande composite linear graben system which now comprises the once isolated San Luis, Taos, Sante Fe/Espanola and Albuquerque sub-basins (Bachman & Mehnert 1978; Kelley 1977; Manley 1979).

The most fundamental characteristic of this kind of model concerns the reaction of the axial river to episodes of tectonic tilting which influence river migration. The effect to be described was briefly noted by Russell (1954, p. 370) in his Anatolian geomorphological study and independently explored by Bridge & Leeder (1979) in their simulation models of alluvial stratigraphy ('architecture'). The latter authors postulated that periodic abrupt channel movements (avulsions) would cause the 'low-seeking' channel to persistently reoccupy the axis of maximum subsidence in statistical preference to other areas of the half-graben. Thus, with time, a preferential stacking of alluvial sand-bodies would be observed in the axis of the sub-surface basin fill (see discussion in Alexander & Leeder, in press).

A number of other factors will influence this simple model.

1 The actual position of the axial river will be displaced from the axis of maximum subsidence by alluvial fans issuing from the footwall scarp slope. This is well seen in the Anatolian grabens (Russell 1954) and at the margins of the ancestral Rio Grande rift (Hawley *et al.* 1976, p. 250; Bachman & Mehnert 1978, p. 288) where the axial fluvial-channel facies are inter-digitated with transverse piedmont facies.

2 Intrabasinal normal faulting may create mini-grabens within the main structure. Such features would tend to 'trap' the axial river and encourage the production of sharply defined fault-bounded sub-surface stacks of axial-channel sand or gravel units. A modern example is represented by the Velarde mini-graben in the Espanola portion of the Rio Grande rift (Reilinger *et al.* 1979, fig. 6; Manley 1979, fig. 2). Ancient examples occur in the axis of the Lower Carboniferous Northumberland graben, as discussed by Leeder (1986, in press).

3 Recent theoretical and field studies (Leeder & Alexander, in press) have shown that axial river channels also gradually respond to tectonic tilting by a process of preferential downslope cut-off and minor avulsion. This leads to the production of an abnormally wide channel belt sand-body,examples of which occur along the South Fork River in the Hebgen area of Montana

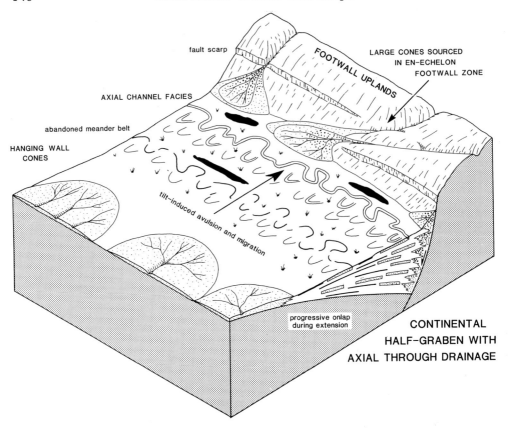

FIG. 4. Isometric diagram for facies model B: continental basin with axial through-drainage. Note the large alluvial fans sourced in the zone between two *en échelon* normal faults and preferential avulsion of the axial river channel(s) towards the faults. Full discussion in text.

(Myers & Hamilton 1964; Leeder & Alexander, in press) and along the Mississippi River in the New Madrid uplift area (Russ 1982; Alexander & Leeder, in press). Very large-scale examples of such behaviour were originally postulated by Mike (1975) in his analysis of channel migration over the Carpathian molasse plain.

4 It is also a possibility that instantaneous, low-seeking avulsion could occur as a direct result of a tilting movement.

A corollary of the tendency for channels to seek out the axis of subsidence by the various means outlined above is that fine-grained out-of-channel flood sediments should be deposited progressively more infrequently as the hanging wall dip slope is ascended. This is because, like the axial-channel system, surface floodwaters will always tend to follow the main basin gradient. In a suitable climatic regime, especially humid tropical, and in areas away from hanging

wall cones, this process will cause the formation of a broad belt of hanging wall dip-slope swamplands which will gradually lead to the occurrence of sub-surface peat layers and hence, ultimately, to the formation of coals which will tend to thicken into the basin axis. Minor intrabasinal faulting may cause abrupt thickness changes of the peats. Examples of these sorts of consequences of our model are illustrated by Teichmuller & Teichmuller (1968, figs 5 & 8) and by Brunnacker & Boenigk (1983, fig. 5) from the lower Rhine graben. As the hanging wall is further ascended it may be expected that the lowered water table should encourage the swamplands to peter out and let oxygenated soil horizons develop in their place as the pivot line of the tilted surface is approached. In a more arid climatic regime, the above facies mosaic would be replaced by calcrete-type soil-profile development away from the loci of active hanging wall dip-slope cones. Examples are seen in the Rio Grande rift (Llano de Albuquerque—Bachman & Mehnert 1978, p. 288).

Tectono-sedimentary facies model C—coastal marine gulf basin (Fig. 5)

Active examples of these basins occur at many localities around the margins of the Aegean e.g. the Gulf of Corinth, the Thermaic Gulf, and the Gulf of Euboea. As shown in Fig. 5, the gulf is often actively being infilled by axial drainage systems. Transverse fans and cones are characteristically present in all examples. The gulf morphology is a direct result of half-graben morphology, with the major bounding normal faults determining the position and characteristic cliffed morphology of the linear footwall shoreline. Ancient analogues are discussed by Surlyk & Clemmensen (1983).

Basins with axial drainage will closely follow certain behavioural tendencies proposed for the previous alluvial model. Thus the terminal deltaic lobes to the drainage system will migrate or avulse preferentially towards the axis of maximum tectonic subsidence, thereby leading to the preferential stacking of delta lobes in the sub-surface (Leeder & Strudwick 1986) and a tendency for maximum back-swamp peat development to occur some way up the hanging wall slope. Important additional features will result from instantaneous marine transgression over the delta lobe, and adjacent shorelines following motion along the normal fault. In general, the effects of such transgressions will lessen in importance up the hanging wall slope. In the footwall and on the footwall scarp slope, emergence will occur, as elegantly demonstrated from geomorphological features in the Corinth Gulf by Jackson *et al.* (1982b) after the 1981 earthquakes. The extent of instantaneous transgressions over the low-gradient axial gulf coastal plain may be very large indeed e.g. a 3 m fault throw in an axial coastal plain of gradient 1:500 would flood a maximum of 1.5 km inland.

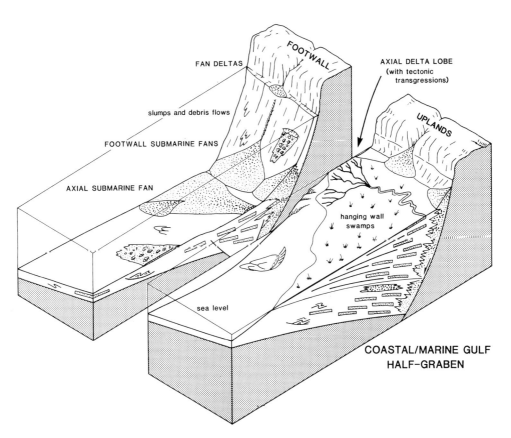

FIG. 5. Isometric diagram showing sedimentological characteristics of facies model C: coastal/marine gulf basin. Location of axial submarine fan, controlled by intrabasin synthetic and antithetic faults, is shown schematically. Full discussion in text.

Renewed clastic progradation after the period of fault motion would then give rise to a very distinctive abrupt transgressive and gradual regressive-facies sequence.

The hanging wall cones and footwall fans sourced in the exposed gulf-perimeter uplands will both show dynamic interactions with the marine-gulf coastal facies after periods of fault-induced subsidence. Footwall-sourced alluvial fans will be subject to the instantaneous effects of marine transgression across their distal aprons. Our observations in the Gulf of Corinth where the fans are largely inactive, being late-Wurmian features, reveal that fan aprons are often cliffed and are subject to marine erosion at present. Eventually, more active fans will prograde once more over such marine transgressive surfaces. Particularly distinctive facies occur in arid climates, where fan aprons may contain sabkha evaporites. Wave-modified shorelines and near-shore carbonate build-ups should provide characteristic markers of fault-generated transgression followed by renewed progradation. Examples of such fans are commonplace around the periphery of the Red Sea and in the Gulf of Eilat (Sellwood & Netherwood 1984).

The footwall alluvial fans may border particularly steep offshore slopes leading into the marine-gulf proper. Such fan systems define the fan-delta complexes of some authors (e.g. Westcott & Etheridge 1982) and these may source important submarine-fan complexes issuing from channels cut into the submarine margins of the faulted gulf margin. Examples were inferred from the Mesozoic tilt blocks of E Greenland by Surlyk (1977, 1978) and are also known in the North Sea (Stowe *et al.* 1982). On the gulf basin floor these transverse fan complexes may interact with axial fans sourced from the axial delta front. These environments are particularly susceptible to earthquake-induced liquefaction and provide a potent and active source for slumps, debris flows and turbidity currents issuing on to the gulf floor via major submarine fans (e.g. the Gulf of Corinth, Perissoratis *et al.* 1984). A major control of fan-lobe location by submarine topography is to be expected since each of these above-mentioned re-sedimentation processes is controlled by the gravity slope. Major episodes of tilting, and internal sub-basins formed by intragraben faults will closely control sand and gravel deposition. Subtle topographic effects on the faulted basin floor will thus cause important lateral changes in turbidite thickness and 'proximality'. Examples are revealed in Sparker surveys across the Gulf of Corinth by Brooks & Ferentinos (1984) and stacked offset fan lobes are seen in seismic

reflection charts across Californian borderland fans (Graham & Bachman 1983).

Tectono-sedimentary facies model D—coastal/shelf basins with carbonate facies (Fig. 6)

Once the hinterlands around a half-graben system become more-or-less submerged and the basin becomes part of an actively extending shelf (e.g. modern Aegean Sea) the rate of clastic input may become substantially reduced. Should the graben be located in low-latitude areas of high organic productivity then a purely carbonate facies mosaic will be superimposed upon the structural topographic template discussed previously. Since carbonate production and facies distributions are strongly depth and slope dependent we expect to see marked contrasts in depositional style across a half-graben system. The degree of facies contrast will depend critically upon the relative rates of subsidence versus carbonate production rates. In the following discussion we assume that an adequate differential exists to maintain water depths.

We postulate that the footwall scarp slope will ensure that the footwall-to-hanging wall margin develops into a bypass margin (McIlreath & James 1978) with the scarp fringed by peri-platform talus and the upper slope cut by gullies feeding debris flows and density currents on to the basin floor as allodapic carbonates. More extensive debris-flow units may also form from slumps of the talus fringe, particularly when directly activated by fault motion.

The footwall will be dominated by relatively shallow-water facies such as build-ups and carbonate sand shoals, the exact facies type being dependent upon scarp-slope orientation relative to prevailing winds, and upon the magnitude of the local tidal-current vectors. One important feature that will develop is minor cyclicity related to shallowing during periodic footwall uplift, with the possibility of periodic emergence giving rise to karstic surfaces and calcrete development. The minor cycles themselves should be markedly asymmetrical, with rapid upward shallowing followed by a more gradual deepening trend as subsidence due to thermal decay occurs. The hanging wall dip slope should initially develop into a ramp-type margin (Ahr 1973) deepening (sloping) towards the footwall scarp as a result of the induced tectonic tilt. This will gradually evolve into an up-dip shelf with a rimmed margin, following the evolutionary trend outlined by Read (1982, 1984), and pass downslope into basinal facies. The rimmed shelf margin may include reef build-ups and sand shoals and may eventually develop into a bypass

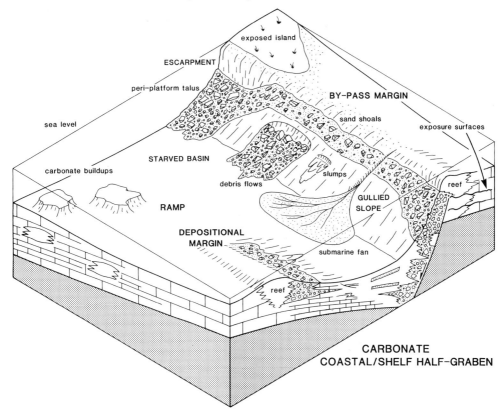

FIG. 6. Isometric diagram showing characteristic sedimentary features of facies model D: coastal/shelf basin with carbonate facies. The variety of carbonate margins associated with tilt block/half-grabens is shown; footwall scarp characterized by a bypass margin of gullied slope or escarpment type while the hanging wall may develop from a carbonate ramp into a rimmed shelf associated with a depositional slope. Full discussion in text.

margin, bordered downslope by talus fans, by now closely resembling the bypass margin on the opposite side of the basin. Thus at an advanced evolutionary stage the carbonate-shelf basin may show a symmetrical geometry, irrespective of the underlying basin geometry. The two margins have markedly different modes of origin, however; the footwall-to-hanging wall margin being predominantly controlled by tectonism and the hanging wall dip-slope margin largely the result of sedimentary processes.

The axial basin floor will in general be starved of sediment and of condensed aspect unless a distant source is available and axial transport of this sediment is possible. Clastic mud plumes may be important in such environments leading to thick mud-dominant sequences in the axial zone of carbonate-shelf basins.

Ancient examples of this type of tilt block/half-graben are present in the Lower Car-

boniferous (Dinantian) of central/northern England, in particular the Bowland basin and Derbyshire dome (Gawthorpe 1986, in press; Miller & Grayson 1982; Smith *et al.* in press) provide good examples.

Basin evolution and abandonment

During the development of an extensional basin it is clear that an evolutionary sequence of basin fills may develop, starting with continental-interior facies and ending up with shelf/coastal facies. Thus the various characteristic basin-fills noted above may succeed each other stratigraphically. It is becoming increasingly clear, however, following the work of Jackson *et al.* (1982a, b) and Jackson & McKenzie (1983), that entire tilt-block/half-graben systems may become inactive at any stage of their evolution due to a change in position of the major bounding crustal-scale normal-fault system. Should the new fault system propagate on the hanging wall side of the former active basin, then footwall uplift associated with the new fault may cause gradual uplift of the whole basin-fill. Such a process should lead to the occurrence of upward-shallowing trends in the highest sequences of the abandoned basin, followed by continental facies and finally by marked erosional dissection as uplift proceeds above the depositional base-line. Examples of such sequences have been observed by the authors in the footwall-uplifted basin of Alipohori in the Gulf of Corinth and in the Mygdonia area east of Thessaloniki.

Conclusions

We have tried to show how the characteristic kinematic features of extensional half-graben/tilt-block systems give rise to predictable surface effects due to the primary control on depositional processes exerted by imposed tectonic slopes. Such surface depositional controls thus exert a major influence upon resulting facies distributions in the sub-surface. We expect the general models presented above to have applicability in geologically ancient basins, but it is stressed, finally, that basin analysis must involve the tectonic analysis of fault trends and their relation to a mapped lithofacies pattern. Only an integrative study of this kind can truly reconstruct the once-active extensional basin system.

ACKNOWLEDGMENTS: M.R. Leeder wishes to thank Texaco USA and the University of Leeds for financial support. R.L. Gawthorpe wishes to thank BP Minerals International Limited for a postgraduate studentship (1982–1985). We are both indebted to numerous colleagues at Leeds University for frequent tectono-sedimentary discussions, particularly to Harry Clemmey and Jan Alexander. We are grateful to Dan McKenzie and James Jackson who provided the initial encouragement to explore the sedimentary consequences of extensional tectonics. We thank Cath Hunt for help with the figures and typing.

References

AHR, W.M. 1973. The carbonate ramp: an alternative to the shelf model. *Trans. Gulf Coast Ass. geol. Soc.* **23**, 221–5.

ALEXANDER, J. & LEEDER, M.R. In press. Active tectonic control of alluvial architecture. *In*: FLORES, R., ETHRIDGE, F. & HARVEY, M. (eds) *Recent Developments in Fluvial Sedimentology. Spec. Publ. Soc. Econ. Palaeont. Miner.*

ANDERSON, R.E., ZOBACK, M.L. & THOMPSON, G.A. 1983. Implications of selected subsurface data on the structural form and evolution of some basins in the northern Basin & Range province, Nevada & Utah. *Bull. geol. Soc. Am.* **94**, 1055–72.

BACHMAN, G.O. & MEHNERT, H.H. 1978. New K–Ar dates and the late Pliocene to Holocene geomorphic history of the central Rio Grande region, New Mexico. *Bull. geol. Soc. Am.* **89**, 283–92.

BALLY, A.W. 1982. Musings over sedimentary basin evolution. *Phil. Trans. R. Soc. London,* **A305**, 325–37.

BARTON, P. & WOOD, R. 1984. Tectonic evolution of the North Sea basin: crustal stretching and subsidence. *Geophys. J.R. astron. Soc.* **79**, 987–1022.

BOTT, M.H.P. 1976. Formation of sedimentary basins of graben type by extension of the continental crust. *Tectonophysics,* **36**, 77–86.

BRIDGE, J.S. & LEEDER, M.R. 1979. A simulation model of alluvial stratigraphy. *Sedimentology,* **26**, 617–44.

BROOKS, M. & FERENTINOS, G. 1984. Tectonics and sedimentation in the Gulf of Corinth and the Zakynthos and Kefallania channels, Western Greece. *Tectonophysics,* **101**, 25–54.

BROWN, L.D., KRUMHANSL, P.A., CHAPIN, C.E., SANFORD, A.R., COOK, F.A., KAUFMAN, S., OLIVER, J.E. & SCHILT, F.S. 1979. COCORP seismic reflection studies of the Rio Grande rift. *In*: RIEKER, R.E. (ed.) *Rio Grande rift – tectonics & magmatism,* pp. 169–84. Am. geophys. Union.

BROWNE, S.E. & FAIRHEAD, J.D. 1983. Gravity study of the Central African Rift System: a model of continental disruption 1. The Ngaoundere and Abu Gabra Rifts. *Tectonophysics,* **94**, 187–203.

BRUN, J-P, & CHOUKROUNE, P. 1983. Normal faulting, block tilting, and decollement in a stretched crust. *Tectonics,* **2**, 345–56.

BRUNNACKER, K. & BOENIGK, W. 1983. The Rhine Valley between the Neuwied Basin and the Lower Rhenish Embayment. *In*: FUCHS, K., VON GEHLEN, K., HALZER, H., MURAWSKI, H. & SEMMEL, A. (eds) *Plateau Uplift,* pp. 62–72. Springer-Verlag, Berlin.

CHAMBERLIN, R.M. 1983. Cenozoic domino-style crustal extension in the Lemitar Mountains. *In*: CHAPIN, C. (ed.) *Socorro Region II,* pp. 111–18. New Mex. geol. Soc.

CHAPIN, C.E. 1979. Evolution of the Rio Grande rift – a summary. *In*: RIECKER, R.E. (ed.) *Rio Grande rift – tectonics & magmatism,* pp. 1–5. Am. geophys. Union.

CHRISTIE, P.A.F. & SLATER, J.G. 1980. An extensional origin for the Buchan and Witchground graben in the North Sea. *Nature, London,* **283**, 729–32.

CROSSLEY, R. 1984. Controls of sedimentation in the Malawi Rift Valley, Central Africa. *Sediment. Geol.* **40**, 33–50.

DEWEY, J.F. 1982. Plate tectonics and the evolution of the British Isles. *J. geol. Soc. London*, **139**, 371–412.

EATON, G.P. 1982. The Basin and Range province: origin and tectonic significance. *Ann. Rev. Earth planet. Sci.* **10**, 409–40.

FRASER, G.D., WITKIND, I.J. & NELSON, W.H. 1964. A geological interpretation of the epicentral area – the dual-basin concept. *Prof. Pap. U.S. geol. Surv.* **435**, 99–106.

GAWTHORPE, R.L. 1986. Sedimentation during carbonate ramp-to-slope evolution in a tectonically active area: Bowland Basin (Dinantian), N. England. *Sedimentology*, **33**, 185–206.

—— In press. Tectono-sedimentary evolution of the Bowland Basin, northern England, during the Dinantian. *J. geol. Soc. London*.

GIBBS, A.D. 1983. Balanced cross-section construction from seismic sections in areas of extensional tectonics. *J. struct. Geol.* **5**, 153–60.

—— 1984. Structural evolution of extensional basin margins. *J. geol. Soc. London*, **141**, 609–20.

GRAHAM, S.A. & BACHMAN, S.B. 1983. Structural controls on submarine-fan geometry and internal architecture: Upper La Jolla Fan System, offshore S. California. *Bull. Am. Assoc. Pet. Geol.* **67**, 83–96.

HANKS, T.C., BUCKNAM, R.C., LAJOIE, K.R. & WALLACE, R.E. 1984. Modification of wave-cut and fault-controlled landforms. *J. geophys. Res.* **89**, 5771–90.

HAWLEY, J.W., BACHMAN, G.O. & MANLEY, K. 1976 Quaternary stratigraphy in the Basin and Range and Great Plains provinces, New Mexico and Western Texas. *In*: MAHANEY, W.C. (ed.) *Quarternary stratigraphy of North America*, pp. 235–74. Dowden, Hutchinson & Ross.

HEISKANEN, W.A. & VENING MEINESZ, F.A. 1958. *The Earth and its Gravity Field*. McGraw-Hill, New York.

HOOKE, R. LeB. 1972. Geomorphic evidence for late-Wisconsian and Holocene tectonic deformation, Death Valley, California. *Bull. geol. Soc. Am.* **83**, 2073–98.

HUNT, C.B. & MABEY, D.R. 1966. Stratigraphy and structure, Death Valley, California. *Prop. Pap. U.S. geol. Surv.* A494.

HUTCHINSON, R.W. & ENGELS, G.G. 1970. Tectonic significance of regional geology and evaporite lithofacies in NE Ethiopia. *Phil. Trans. R. Soc. London*, **267**, 313–29.

ILLES, J.H. & FUCHS, K. 1983. Plateau uplift of the Rhenish Massif. *In*: FUCHS, K., VONGEHLEN, K., MALZER, H., MURAWSKI, H. & SEMMEL, A. (eds) *Plateau Uplift*, pp. 62–72. Springer-Verlag, Berlin.

JACKSON, J.A., KING, G. & VITA-FINZI, C. 1982a. The neotectonics of the Aegean: an alternative view. *Earth planet. Sci. Lett.* **61**, 303–18.

—— & McKENZIE, D.P. 1983. The geometric evolution of normal fault systems. *J. struct. Geol.* **5**, 471–82.

—— , GAGNEPAIN, J., HOUSEMAN, G., KING, G.C.P., PAPDAIMITRIOU, P., SOUFLERIS, C. & VIRIEUX, J. 1982b. Seismicity, normal faulting, and the geomorphological development of the Gulf of Corinth (Greece): the Corinth earthquakes of February and March 1981. *Earth planet. Sci. Lett.* **57**, 377–97.

KELLEY, V.C. 1977. *Geology of the Albuquerque Basin. Mem.* **33**, New Mex. Bur. Mines Mineral Res.

LEEDER, M.R. 1976. Palaeogeographic significance of pedogenic carbonates in the topmost Upper Old Red Sandstone of the Scottish Border Basin. *Geol. J.* **11**, 21–8.

—— 1982. Upper Palaeozoic basins of the British Isles – Caledonide inheritance versus Hercynian plate margin processes. *J. geol. Soc. London,* **139**, 479–91.

—— 1983. Lithospheric stretching and North Sea Jurassic clastic sourcelands. *Nature, Lond.* **305**, 510–13.

—— 1986. Tectonic and palaeogeographic models for Lower Carboniferous Europe. *In*: MILLER, J., ADAMS, A.E. & WRIGHT, V.P. (eds) *European Dinantian Environments*, pp. 1–20. Wiley, London.

—— In press. Sediment deformation structures and the palaeotectonic analysis of ancient extensional sedimentary basis. *In*: JONES, N.E. & PRESTON, R.M.F. (eds) *Deformation of sediments and sedimentary rocks. Spec. Publ. geol. Soc. London*.

—— & ALEXANDER, J. In press. The origin and tectonic significance of asymmetrical meander belts. *Sedimentology*.

—— & STRUDWICK, A.E. 1986. Delta-marine interactions: a discussion of sedimentary models for Yoredale-type cyclicity in the Dinantian of N England. *In*: MILLER, J., ADAMS, A.E. & WRIGHT, V.P. (eds) *European Dinantian Environments*, pp. 115–30. Wiley, London.

LIPMAN, P.W. & MEHNERT, H.H. 1979. The Taos plateau volcanic field, northern Rio Grande rift, New Mexico. *In*: RIECKER, R.E. (ed.) *Rio Grande rift-tectonics & magmatism*, pp. 289–311. American geophysical Union.

McILREATH, I.A. & JAMES, N.P. 1978. Facies Models 13, Carbonate slopes. *Geoscience Can.*, **5**, 188–99.

McKENZIE, D.P. 1978. Some remarks on the development of sedimentary basins. *Earth planet. Sci. Lett.* **40**, 25–32.

MANLEY, K. 1979. Stratigraphy and structure of the Espanola basin, Rio Grande rift, New Mexico. *In*: RIECKER, R.E. (ed.) *Rio Grande rift – tectonics & magmatism*, pp. 71–86. American geophysical Union.

MIKE, K. 1975. Utilisation of the analysis of ancient river beds for the detection of Holocene crustal movements. *Tectonophysics*, **29**, 359–68.

MILLER, J. & GRAYSON, R.F. 1982. The regional context of Waulsortian facies in N. England. *In*: BOLTON, K., LANE, H.R. & LeMONE, D.V. (eds) *Symposium on the Environmental Setting and Distribution of the Waulsortian Facies*, pp. 17–33. El Paso geol. Soc. and University of Texas at El Paso.

MORTON, W.H. & BLACK, R. 1975. Crustal attenuation in Afar. *In*: PILGER, A. & ROSSLER, A. (eds) *Afar Depression of Ethopia*, pp. 55–65. Deutsche Forschauna, Stuttgart.

MYERS, W.B. & HAMILTON, W. 1964. Deformation associated with the Hebgen Lake earthquake of August 17, 1959. *Prof. Pap. U.S. geol. Surv.* **435**, 55–98.

PERISSORATIS, C., MITROPOULOS, D. & ANGELOPOULOS, I. 1984. The role of earthquakes in inducing sediment mass movement in the eastern Korinthiakos Gulf. An example from the February 24-March 4, 1981 activity. *Mar. Geol.* **55**, 35–45.

PROFFETT JR, J.M. 1977. Cenozoic geology of the Yerington district, Nevada, and implications for the nature and origin of Basin and Range faulting. *Bull. geol. Soc. Am.* **88**, 247–66.

READ, J.F. 1982. Carbonate platforms of passive (extensional) continental margins: types, characteristics and evolution. *Tectonophysics*, **81**, 195–212.

—— 1984. Carbonate platform facies models. *Bull. Am. Ass. Pet. Geol.* **69**, 1–21.

REILINGER, R.E., BROWN, L.D. & OLIVER, J.E. 1979. Recent vertical crustal movements from levelling observations in the vicinity of the Rio Grande rift. *In*: RIECKER, R.E. (ed.) *Rio Grande rift – tectonics and magmatism*, pp. 223–36. Am. geophys. Union.

—— OLIVER, J., BROWN, L., SANFORD, A. & BALAZS, E. 1980. New measurements of crustal doming over the Socorro magma body, New Mexico. *Geology*, **8**, 291–5.

RUSS, D.P. 1982. Style and significance of surface deformation in the vicinity of New Madrid, Missouri. *Prof. Pap. U.S. geol. Surv.* **H1236**, 95–114.

RUSSELL, R.J. 1954. Alluvial morphology of Anatolian rivers. *Ass. Am. Geog. Ann.* **44**, 363–91.

SANFORD, A.R., MOTT, R.P., SHULESKI, P.J., RINEHART, E.J., CARAVELLA, R., WARD, M. & WALLACE, T.C. 1977. Geophysical evidence for a magma body in the crust in the vicinity of Socorro, New Mexico. *In*: HEACOCK, J. (ed.) *The Earths Crust, Am. geophys. Union Mon.* **20**, 385–403.

SAVAGE, J.C. & HASTIE, L.M. 1966. Surface deformation associated with dip-slip faulting. *J. geophys. Res.* **71**, 4897–904.

SELLWOOD, B.W. & NETHERWOOD, R.E. 1984. Facies evolution in the Gulf of Suez area: Sedimentation history as an indicator of rift initiation and development. *Mod. Geol.* **9**, 43–69.

SMITH, K., SMITH, N.J.P. & HOLLIDAY, D.W. In press. The deep structure of Derbyshire. *Geol. J.*

SMITH, R.B. & BRUHN, R.L. 1984. Intraplate extensional tectonics of the eastern Basin–Range: Inferences on structural style from seismic reflection data, regional tectonics and thermal-mechanical models of brittle-ductile deformation. *J. geophys. Res.* **89**, 5733–62.

STOWE, D.A.V., BISHOP, C.D. & MILLS, S.J. 1982. Sedimentology of the Brae Oil Field, North Sea: fan models & controls. *J. Pet. Geol.* **5**, 129–48.

SURLYK, F. 1977. Stratigraphy, tectonics and palaeogeography of the Jurassic sediments of the areas north of Kong Oscars Fjord, E. Greenland. *Bull. Grønland. Geol. Unders.* **123**, 56pp.

—— 1978. Submarine fan sedimentation along fault scarps on tilted fault blocks (Jurassic–Cretaceous boundary, E. Greenland). *Bull. Grønland. Geol. Unders.* **128**, 108pp.

—— & CLEMMENSEN, L.B. 1983. Rift propagation and eustacy as controlling factors during Jurassic inshore and shelf sedimentation in northern East Greenland. *Sediment. Geol.* **34**, 119–43.

TALBOT, M.R. & WILLIAMS, M.A.S. 1979. Cyclic alluvial fan sedimentation on the flanks of fixed dunes, Janjari, Central Niger. *Catena,* **6**, 43–62.

TEICHMULLER, M. & TEICHMULLER, R. 1968. Cainozoic and Mesozoic coal deposits of Germany. *In*: MURCHISON, D. & WESTOLL, T.S. (eds) *Coal and Coal-bearing Strata*, pp. 347–80. Oliver & Boyd, Edinburgh.

WERNICKE, B. & BURCHFIEL, B.C. 1982. Modes of extensional tectonics. *J. struct. Geol.* **4**, 105–15.

WESTCOTT, W.A. & ETHERIDGE, F.G. 1982. Bathymetry and sediment dispersal dynamics along the Yallahs fan delta front, Jamaica. *Mar. Geol.* **46**, 245–60.

ZIEGLER, P.A. 1982. *Geological Atlas of Western and Central Europe*. Shell Internationale Petroleum Mij. BV, The Hague.

M.R. LEEDER & R.L. GAWTHORPE, Department of Earth Sciences, The University, Leeds LS2 9JT, UK.

Extension in the Basin and Range Province and East Pacific Margin

Crustal extension in the Basin and Range Province, southwestern United States

W. Hamilton

SUMMARY: Cenozoic extension of areally varying ages and amounts has on average doubled the width of the Basin and Range Province. Extensional structures that formed at all depths down to 20 km, and which range in age from Oligocene to Holocene, are widely exposed and are here interpreted in terms of a model of depth-varying deformation. The middle crust is extended by discontinuous ductile shear as internally undeformed lenses slide apart along gently dipping zones of mylonite. The tops of these lenses are undulating detachment faults, the composite area of which increases with time as deep lenses slide out from underneath shallower ones. Brittle blocks of upper-crust bedrock above the detachments respond first by rotating between range-front faults, the same direction of rotation being maintained across a series of lenses, and then by pulling completely apart, while basinal strata fill the gaps and are dragged directly on detachment faults. Some faults rise gently from the main detachment zones and surface as range-front faults. Most tilted-block ranges are isolated atop detachments.

Detachment faults cut out crust. Beneath them are mid-crustal rocks of any age and type and above them are mostly upper-crustal rocks, including extensive syndeformational basin sediments rotated to steep or moderate dips. As attenuation proceeds and components rise, detachment faults evolve from ductile to brittle, develop splays, and are themselves broken by steep brittle structures related to new, deeper detachments. Parts of detachment faults remain active even after exposure at the surface, but slip on them is then limited to the down-dip direction. It is inferred from seismic reflection profiles and rock-mechanic considerations that the unexposed lower crust is extended by more pervasive ductile flattening.

This paper develops a model of depth-varing extensional styles to account for the common denominators in Cenozoic geological structures exposed by erosion and tectonic denudation throughout the Basin and Range Province. The general model was suggested earlier (Hamilton 1982), and resembles in important aspects that of Davis (1980).

Oligocene to Quaternary extension of the style discussed in this paper has affected the Great Basin part of the province (Fig. 1), and also a region N of the Snake River Plain in E-central Idaho and SW Montana. Most of the similar extension in the Mojave and Sonoran Desert sectors of the province was of Oligocene to middle-Miocene age, correlating with early extension in the N. Middle-crust extensional structures are widely exposed in both N and S sub-provinces, whereas shallow structures are seen primarily in the N one. Topographic relief is high throughout the province. Exposures are excellent in the arid SW part, and good in the semi-arid SE and N parts.

Extension has about doubled the pre-Oligocene width of the province, now 350–700 km wide. Palinspastic reconstruction of Mesozoic tectonic and magmatic belts requires such extension (Hamilton 1978). Relationships between strike-slip and extensional faults in the southern Great Basin indicate late-Cenozoic extension to be at least 65% (Wernicke et al. 1982). Pre-Tertiary rocks and Cenozoic basin-fill materials comprise sub-equal amounts above exposed detachment faults, requiring 100% extension in many areas. Extension has, however, been erratic in space, time, and amount.

How has the hundreds of kilometres of extension been transmitted through the continental crust? The field data needed to answer this have been greatly expanded by many geologists, particularly those working with detachment structures within the last decade, but there is still much disagreement regarding extensional mechanisms. Although Ransome, Emmons & Garrey (1910) recognized that Basin and Range faulting required crustal extension (they also mapped a detachment fault), more than 50 years passed before extension was broadly accepted over alternatives of vertical jostling or even compression and it was not until almost 1980 that extension of more than 5 or 10% was widely regarded as likely. Among those with more advanced ideas were Hunt & Mabey (1966), probably first to recognize a complete domiform fault as extensional, Hamilton & Myers (1966), who argued for 100% extension and Armstrong (1972), first to see the regional extent of middle-crust extensional structures.

From COWARD, M.P., DEWEY, J.F. & HANCOCK, P.L. (eds), 1987, *Continental Extensional Tectonics*, Geological Society Special Publication No. 28, pp. 155–176.

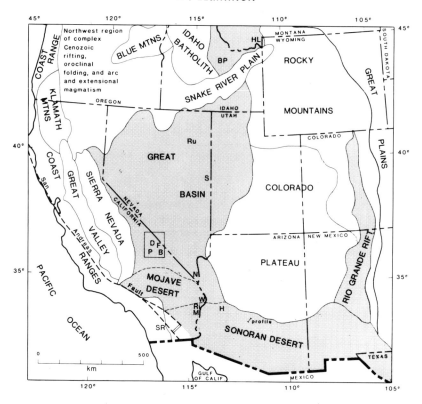

Fɪɢ. 1. Index map of part of the western United States. Basin and Range Province of extensional faulting is shaded, as are areas of similar structure in the Rio Grande rift system and in the region N of the Snake River Plain. Extensional faulting also affects much of the 'NW region', and the W and S margins of the Colorado Plateau; most boundaries shown are arbitrary. Death Valley region (Fig. 7) is located by a rectangle; reflection profile (Fig. 24) is located in Arizona. Localities noted in text and figures: B = Black Mts; BP = Borah Peak; D = Death Valley; F = Funeral Mts; H = Harcuvar Mts; HL = Hebgen Lake; M = Big Maria Mts; N = Newberry Mts; P = Panamint Mts; Ri = Riverside Mts; Ru = Ruby Mts; S = Snake Range; SR = Santa Rosa Mts; W = Whipple Mts.

Only a few of the many authors whose reports are integrated here can be cited. I also draw heavily on discussions and field trips with many geologists and on my own detailed and recon- naissance fieldwork. As the structures described here include types unfamiliar to many readers, I illustrate them with a number of photographs.

The model

The model sketched here (Fig. 2) is derived from the systematic variations of observed structures with the inferred depths and temperatures of their formation. Extension is accommodated within the brittle upper crust by rotation about sub-horizontal axes and fragmentation of large blocks that end abruptly downward against undulating regional *detachment faults* that

mostly initiated at depths greater than about 10 km. 'Detachment fault' has been used in this context by Davis *et al.* (1980) and many others. 'Denudation fault' (Armstrong 1972) and 'decollement' (Miller *et al.* 1983) are used with approximate synonymity. Upper-crust bedrock blocks are bounded laterally by downward-flat- tening listric faults, by rotated planar faults and by basin fills deposited in widening gaps between separating blocks. The detachment faults define the tops of great lenses that are separated by gently dipping, anastomosing ductile faults and that retain pre-faulting fabrics in their interiors. As the lenses slide apart the area of their com- posite top, the detachment faults, is increased and the middle crust is extended by discontin- uous ductile flow. Although most faults above the typically mid-crust detachments are probably listric, curving into the detachments, in

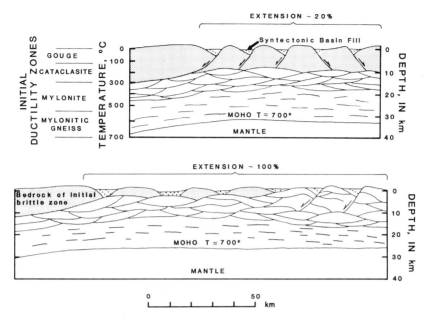

FIG. 2. Cross-sections of extending crust. Brittle upper-crust blocks rotate and separate. Middle-crust lenses slide apart along ductile shear zones; composite upper surface of lenses forms detachment faults that increase in total area with time. Lower crust flattens pervasively. Structural styles are superimposed as components rise to the surface with continuing attenuation. Attenuating crust is partly rebuilt by magmatism, and possibly also by phase change, so crust is thinned by a factor less than extension ratio. Ductility zones after Sibson (1983).

places major gently dipping faults rise for tens of kilometres laterally through upper-crust rocks and curve to steeper dips only at shallow depth.

COCORP reflection profiles (Allmendinger *et al.* 1983) across western Utah show a detachment fault of this upper-crust type, which crops out in the Canyon Range, dipping gently westward for a distance of 100 km or more in the sub-surface, to a depth of at least 13 km. In outcrop and at shallow depth, the fault separates Tertiary strata, rotated to moderate dips, from Palaeozoic strata. The fault most likely steepened into a range-front fault in its upper part, now removed by erosion. The broadly undulating Canyon Range detachment passes westward beneath the Sevier Desert, House Range, Tule Valley, Confusion Range, and Snake Valley, all of which are thus allochthonous above it, and appears to project westward beneath the thick crustal lens whose top is the Snake Range detachment fault. Discontinuous reflections beneath the Canyon Range detachment fault may in part image subdetachment ductile shear zones.

Detachment faults evolve from zones of ductile slip initially 10–20 km deep. Local variations in temperature, strain rate and lithology are reflected in variations in initial depth and configuration of the ductile faults that evolve into detachment faults. As extension progresses and the crust is thinned, most parts of the system rise toward the surface; ductility-facies boundaries rise as extension and possibly also shear heating, outpaces thermal conduction, but in general superimposed structures and fabrics indicate progressions from deformation under deep, hot conditions to deformation under shallow, cold conditions. Ductile faults become semi-ductile, then brittle and splays split away. Still further extension can no longer be accommodated on undulating faults, which then are broken by steep, brittle faults, related to new ductile faults at depth, but limited slip continues on detachment faults even after they are exposed at the surface. Extension in the lower crust is accomplished by more pervasive ductile flattening.

Middle-crust crystalline rocks beneath detachment faults are widely termed core complexes. I do not use the term, for it often incorporates the implication that detachments are necessarily related to local thermal anomalies which is not the case. Some detachments may indeed be related to synextensional magmatism, but most sub-detachment complexes represent nearly random samples of the middle crust, albeit in a region subjected to much synextensional magmatism.

Mathematical and mechanical analysis of depth-varying crustal deformation was presented by Kligfield *et al.* (1984) and Sibson (1983).

Tectonic setting

The middle Tertiary structures of the Basin and Range Province record extension mostly W-southwestward in the S and approximately westward in the N, relative to the continental interior. This extension was perpendicular to the continental margin of the time (Zoback *et al.* 1981) and was synchronous with subduction of Pacific lithosphere beneath most of that margin (Eaton 1984). There was thus great extension of the overriding continental plate in a convergent-plate regime. A common misconception is that overriding lithosphere plates generally undergo shortening and compression; actually, most undergo extension, although not generally as extreme as in the southwestern US. Trenches retreat and roll back into subducting plates. The inclination of a subducting slab marks a transient position, not a trajectory down a fixed slot; subduction occurs at an angle steeper than that inclination and the common regime above a slab is extensional, not compressional. The mid-Tertiary extension occurred after the slowing of the previously rapid westward motion of North America (as viewed in a whole-Earth, zero-sum frame).

Extension of similar style, mostly of mid-Tertiary age, but continuing through the Neogene, affected the Rio Grande rift. Extension there can be visualized as due to the clockwise rotation of the Colorado Plateau about 3° relative to interior North America, about a Euler pole near the Colorado–Wyoming border. Late Cenozoic extension represents oblique fragmentation of the crust in the NW direction of relative slip between the Pacific and North American Plates, due presumably to partial coupling between those plates (Atwater 1970, Eaton 1984). The structural style of extensional response is similar. There was much inheritance of mid-Tertiary structural grain from Mesozoic structures and from those by late-Cenozoic structures; structures of all of these ages typically have northerly trends in the Great Basin and northwesterly ones in the Mojave and Sonoran Deserts.

Sophisticated climatic analysis of palaeofloras by Axelrod (1985) indicates that surface altitude in the Great Basin, the sector now undergoing broad extension, has increased markedly during the late Cenozoic. This increase has been coincident both with extension and with the rise of much of western North America. Such palaeo-altitude data appear incompatible with speculation by Coney & Harms (1984), that high-standing thick crust spread gravitationally to produce extensional structures.

Magmatism

Mid-Tertiary extension was broadly coextensive in space and time with magmatism both of arc type and of more silicic type intermediate between typical arc and extensional assemblages. Volcanism of both types is now active above subducting lithosphere in the rapidly widening North Island, New Zealand. Thermal softening of the crust by magmatism probably expedited extension. The Colorado Plateau was bypassed by magmatism and left unextended, whereas the Rio Grande rift to the E was the site of extensive magmatism and severe extension. Integration of the high heat flow and widespread late-Cenozoic magmatism with the rates and amounts of extension indicates that these thermal manifestations are largely effects, not causes, of extension (Lachenbruch & Sass 1978) and are enhanced by asthenospheric convection as a by-product of the extension (cf. Steckler 1985). Late-Cenozoic magmatism has been mostly of bimodal basalt-and-rhyolite type that probably reflects the melting of lower-crustal materials by rift-related mantle magmas. Deep-crystallization products of magmas of both arc and rift types must have partly rebuilt attenuating crust.

Structures of the upper crust

The basic structural unit of the Basin and Range Province is commonly but mistakenly perceived to be a tilted bedrock block, which includes a mountain range and the basement of the adjacent basin and which rotates against the next block along a fault that either is flattened with time by rotation, or else flattens downward as a curving, listric surface and that ends as a detachment fault. Such juxtaposed blocks probably formed during an early stage of extension, but most of the province has evolved beyond this stage. The majority of ranges in the province represent a mature stage and are either tilted panels of resistant rocks isolated from one another atop detachment faults or else are raised sub-detachment complexes. Wernicke *et al.* (1985) came to similar conclusions. Examples from the Death Valley region are discussed below.

Major upper-plate panels typically are 70–150 km long and 10–25 km wide in the Great Basin. The width of a mature bedrock panel is markedly less than the distance between range-front faults of adjacent mountain blocks (mostly 20–35 km). Most bedrock blocks are separated from one another, the gaps being filled by syntectonic basin strata in direct contact with gently dipping faults that pass beneath the tilted blocks. Dips in basin fills increase markedly downward, both stratigraphically and along the beds, toward bounding and underlying faults (Allmendinger *et al.* 1983; Effimoff & Pinezich 1981; Smith & Bruhn 1984). Details are complex, for basin fill deposited during early extension can become the lithified bedrock of subsequent deformation. Blocks and basin fills are broken by lesser normal faults. Upper plates can be shattered into small rotated-domino sub-blocks (e.g. Ransome *et al.*. 1910; Miller *et al.* 1983), or they can be tilted blocks of crust 10-km thick and little deformed internally (Howard *et al.* 1982).

Upper-plate panels are tilted randomly on a provincial scale, but tend to be tilted mostly in single directions over domains of 10,000 km² or more (Stewart 1980, 1983b). These domain tilts may record initial coherence of blocks rotating in the same sense. Non-tilted horsts and grabens are uncommon and where present they generally separate domains of blocks of opposite tilt directions.

Young normal faults have dips mostly of 45–60° where they cut bedrock at the surface (Fig. 3). Faults refract upward to steeper dips in unconsolidated materials, in which extensional collapse features are developed (Myers & Hamilton 1964). Erosion of fast-rising scarps to slopes recording their angle of repose (Fig. 4) occurs largely by landsliding that results in the formation of extensive megabreccias along scarps (Fig. 5). In settings of rapid tilting and faulting, lacustrine strata also can be deposited almost directly against high scarps.

Rates and amounts of extension have been non-uniform in space and time. Extreme late-Miocene to Quaternary extension characterizes the Death Valley region. Most deformation more than 30 km across strike to the E of Death Valley pre-dates the late-Miocene, whereas the faulting that has defined the modern ranges

FIG. 3. Normal fault (arrow) between Proterozoic metadolomite (right) and slightly tilted Quaternary alluvium. N end Tucki Mountain, Panamint Mountains, California. The fault cuts only the upper plate, above the detachment fault (not in view). Exposure is 10 m high.

FIG. 4. Late Quaternary normal-fault scarp cutting middle- or upper-Miocene volcanic and tuffaceous rocks. The late-Holocene scarp, 6 m high, along base of mountain, displays structural dip, but the rest of face has been eroded back, mostly by landsliding. Miocene rocks dip steeply E (left) and are truncated at shallow depth by a detachment fault. Slide megabreccia (right foreground, blocky) is separated by broad collapse moat (low ground) from frontal fault. View SE—Artist's Drive fault, Black Mountains, California.

across strike to the W of Death Valley is of Pliocene and Quaternary age.

Gently dipping extensional faults formed in upper-crust, low-temperature rocks in a number of places in the Great Basin and commonly truncate rotated upper plates against lower plates. The western Utah example plumbed by COCORP was discussed previously. Wernicke *et al.*

FIG. 5. Small, Holocene slide megabreccia (centre), and upper edge of large late-Pleistocene slide megabreccia (far left), derived from middle- or upper-Miocene volcanic rocks of the Artist's Drive fault. View N—upper and lower plates and the fault are all truncated downward against the Badwater detachment fault in exposures to the S.

(1985) described a domiform example from southern Nevada, similar geometrically to the more common detachment faults atop mid-crust crystalline rocks but with almost unmetamorphosed Palaeozoic strata in the footwall. Some such high-level faults appear to have reactivated faults that initially were thrusts. Howard & John (this volume) show a detachment fault that splays to shallow normal faults that bound crystalline-block ranges in headwall fashion. It is not yet clear whether such headwall blocks are anchored to the deep crust or are adrift above detachment faults with which the shallow faults merge.

Earthquakes

Most small earthquakes in the Great Basin occur shallower than 8 km, whereas large ones typically nucleate at 10–15 km. Shear strength apparently increases below 8 km, then decreases rapidly across the brittle–ductile transition, which represents a temperature of 300–350°C and is no deeper than 15 km (Sibson 1983; Smith & Bruhn 1984). A major unresolved problem is the much greater depth extent suggested for steep faults by studies of seismicity than is permitted by the continuity of detachment faults seen on reflection seismic profiles.

Tilted blocks of bedrock commonly end downward against detachment faults which pass beneath the ranges, and generally only basin fill is in contact with frontal faults. Analyses of coseismic strain, that incorporate the assumption that adjacent tilted blocks of elastic bedrock are in direct contact at sub-surface frontal faults (e.g. Stein & Barrientos 1985) are probably incorrect. The best-documented deformation accompanying a normal-fault earth-

quake, that at Hebgen Lake, Montana, in 1958, $Ms = 7.5$, consisted largely of absolute subsidence which represented a net decrease of about 1 km^3 of crustal volume (Myers & Hamilton 1964). Coseismic subsidence also greatly excluded rise during the 1973 Borah Peak earthquake, $Ms = 7.3$, in Idaho (Stein & Barrientos 1985). Pre-seismic extensional strain high in the crust apparently is stored primarily as dilatation and released mostly as compaction.

Structures initiated in the middle crust

Detachment faults

Domiform or undulating detachment faults have been recognized in perhaps 50 ranges scattered far beyond the narrow zone depicted in some relatively early reports (e.g. Rehrig & Reynolds 1980). These faults are not thrusts, for they cut out, not duplicate, crust and their upper plates display abundant extensional features. Any middle-crust rocks can lie beneath detachment faults: rocks of various lithologies e.g. mid-crust granites, gneisses and migmatites, or metasedimentary or meta-igneous rocks of any grade from lowest greenschist, even slate, to highest amphibolite, and of ages ranging from Precambrian to Miocene. Non-metamorphosed supracrustal rocks occur primarily in upper plates and commonly are rotated steeply downward against the faults with truncation angles near 50°. Granitic rocks of Phanerozoic, mostly late-Mesozoic, age within upper plates are primarily of upper-crust types.

Upper-plate rocks tend to show the same sense of rotation over large domains. The direction of relative slip along a detachment surface, as defined by extensional structures low in the upper plate, is typically in the same sense as that rotation. In a domain of about 20,000 km^2 in SE California and SW Arizona (e.g. Fig. 6; Davis *et al.* 1980; Howard & John, this volume), upper-plate blocks slipped relatively NE over sub-detachment rocks and have general SW dips. As the unfaulted Colorado Plateau lies NE of this tract and as upper-plate structure requires extreme extension, upper-plate blocks must have moved relatively southwestward away from the plateau by amounts increasing with distance from the plateau. The southwestward offset of lower-plate rocks relative to the plateau must be still greater.

The amount of slip between juxtaposed upper and lower plates is commonly difficult to determine; half the province is covered by Quaternary

Fɪɢ. 6. Undulating Oligocene detachment fault, Riverside Mountains, SE California. Upper plate: light-coloured middle-Proterozoic granite (Ɛg) and dark Oligocene slide megabreccias and redbeds (T; direction of steep dip indicated); broken by spoon-shaped faults. Lower plate: (Pz), Palaeozoic metasediments; (Mz), Mesozoic metasedimentary and metavolcanic rock; and (Ɛm), retrograded and variably mylonitized middle-Proterozoic gneiss. View N—slip of upper plate relatively NE. Range mapped by author.

basin materials and too little of the other half displays optimal mixes of upper and lower plates, necessary for comparison. The outcrop overlap of 6 km of quite different crystalline assemblages in the Riverside Mountains (Fig. 6) requires an offset substantially greater than that distance; the geology of lower-plate ranges to the SW, from which relative direction the upper plate came, best fits an offset of 20–30 km. Howard *et al.* (1982) inferred 30–40 km of offset of a dyke swarm between upper and lower plates in the same tilt domain, 70 km NE across strike from the Riverside Mountains. The extreme extension within the intervening upper plate is apparently not matched by variations in slip on the detachment, so the area of the detachment surface probably increased with time. Bartley & Wernicke (1984) made a permissive argument for 60 km of slip on the Snake Range detachment, eastern Nevada. Note that in arguing for little slip on the same structure, Miller *et al.* (1983) invoked such improbabilities as regional metamorphism that ended abruptly at the level of the initial fault, and the formation of kyanite at a depth of only 6 km.

Equivalence of deep and shallow structures

Basin and Range detachment faults are regarded by many investigators (e.g. Davis 1980; Miller *et al.* 1983; Rehrig & Reynolds 1980; Reynolds 1985; Snoke *et al.* 1984) as having evolved from deep ductile structures to shallow brittle ones. Explanations diverge widely beyond this limited consensus. Some models infer that shallow deformation above the detachment faults was quite unlike that of presently active parts of the Great Basin and was typified, perhaps, by close-spaced normal faults of small individual displacements and by depositional basins larger than those of the modern system (e.g. Stewart 1983b). I infer, as do many other geologists (e.g. Wernike *et al.* 1985) that on the contrary, tilted Great Basin blocks are forming above detachments like the older ones now widely exposed and that those older structures had basin–range pairs above them.

Dimensions of basement and basin-fill assemblages above detachment faults (Fig. 7) resemble those of basin-range pairs. There is broad temporal and geographical overlap of structures

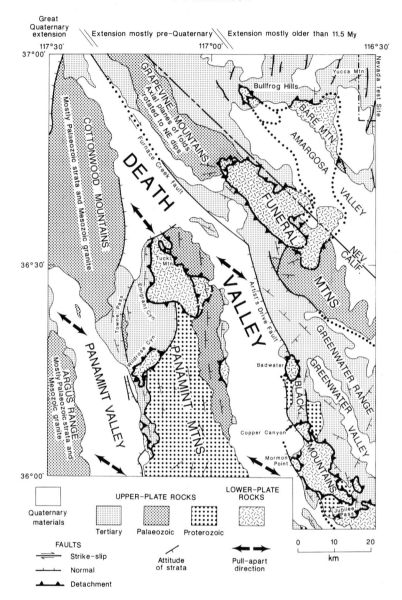

Fig. 7. Tectonic map of Death Valley region, California and Nevada. Most normal faults are omitted. Adapted from published maps, including those cited in text.

exposed as tilted blocks and as detachments. Continuing extension superimposed block structures on detachments at transition times that varied from early-Miocene to Quaternary. There are exposed detachment faults as young as Holocene, and block-bounding faults as old as early-Miocene, nearby within the southern Great Basin. Early-Miocene floras of Nevada indicate that basins and ranges then existing had a topographic relief comparable to modern basin–

range pairs (Axelrod 1985). Domains of same-direction tilting of upper-plate rocks above detachment faults are of sizes, typically 10,000–20,000 km^2, similar to those of Great Basin tilted-block domains (Stewart 1980; Fig. 7; Hamilton, unpubl. work). Scarp-facies sediments are widely present in basin strata truncated downward against detachment faults. Abundant, more or less monolithological, megabreccias (Figs 8, 9 & 10) must have slid

FIG. 8 Rotated normal fault. Stripped fault surface (smooth slope, right and foreground) on Cretaceous muscovite granite dips 30°W; light-coloured landslide megabreccias of granite and Proterozoic metasediments dip 20° E into fault. Pliocene or early Pleistocene range-front fault with 3 km of slip, rotated 25° with upper-plate block above detachment fault (not in view). Jail Canyon, Panamint Mountains; mapped by Albee *et al.* (1981).

FIG. 10. Mid-Tertiary detachment fault, SE Whipple Mountains, California. Oligocene volcanic rocks and slide megabreccias dip left (SW) to truncation against horizontal fault at top of Proterozoic (?) plutonic rocks. Mylonitic carapace shows as layering beneath fault.

FIG. 9. Oligocene landslide megabreccia, dip 60° right (SW), 100 m above Riverside Mountains detachment fault.

FIG. 11. View N across Sacramento Pass to sub-horizontal mid-Tertiary detachment fault (marked), Snake Range, Nevada. Upper plate consists of rotated blocks of unmetamorphosed Palaeozoic strata that dip to the left. Lower plate (including foreground) is of Cambrian and upper-Proterozoic strata metamorphosed to amphibolite facies (kyanite present) and intruded by muscovite granite. Light-coloured low ground is underlain by upper-plate Oligocene redbeds, which also dip moderately left above detachment fault. Area described by Miller *et al.* (1983).

from high, fast-rising scarps like those of Figs 4 & 5. Truncation angles of Cenozoic strata against faults are typically within the range 40–60°, regardless of the dips of strata and faults (Figs 3, 6, 8, 10, 11, 12, 13, 14); rocks now truncated by gently dipping faults have been rotated down from truncations against normal faults.

Rise with time

Most components in an extending system must rise toward the surface with time. Many investigators have cited evidence for the great rise of detachment faults from middle to upper crustal levels as slip on them progressed (e.g. Davis 1980, 1983; Rehrig & Reynolds 1980; Reynolds 1985; Snoke *et al.* 1984). Final major slip has always been at low temperatures and

FIG. 12. Late-Neogene Tucki Mountain detachment fault. Smooth bedrock slope is stripped fault, dipping gently W, on upper Proterozoic metasedimentary rocks and Cretaceous muscovite granite. Unconsolidated Pliocene alluvium dips (lines) E to truncation against detachment. Emigrant Wash, Panamint Mountains.

shallow depths. The faults are marked by brittle gouge and incoherent breccia, typically a few decimetres (Fig. 15) to a few metres thick, but ranging from a centimetre (Fig. 16) to tens of metres. Many gouge zones grade upward into decreasingly brecciated upper-plate rocks and small-scale extensional structures are widespread low down in upper plates (Fig. 17). Severe brecciation can extend 100 m into the upper plate.

The depth and temperature of slip decrease with time (cf. Fig. 2). Progressively older and more ductile-strain rocks, in the sequence gouge–cataclasite–mylonite–mylonitic gneiss, are displayed downward from many detachment faults. A detachment-fault gouge zone is commonly bounded sharply against a shear-polished pavement (Fig. 15) on a hard, chloritic

FIG. 13. Neogene detachment fault, W side Funeral Mountains, California. Sheared carapace (layering, right) was developed concordantly below detachment in middle-grade Proterozoic metasedimentary rocks. Arrow indicates dip of upper-plate mid-Tertiary redbeds beneath late Quaternary pediment. View N from Keane Wonder Mine.

FIG. 14. Truncation of upper-plate structures against active detachment fault, Black Mountains, California. Interbedded Pliocene clastic strata, slide breccias, and volcanic rocks (lower left) dip obliquely back and right towards the Quaternary normal-fault scarp along high-standing plutonic rocks (left and centre rear). Hanging wall, footwall, and fault are all truncated downward against the active Copper Canyon turtleback (detachment) fault, which forms the smooth face dipping obliquely left through the centre of the view. Light-coloured rocks

microbreccia that displays partial reconstitution at low greenschist facies. This cataclasite is typically a few metres thick and it may grade downward into a zone of sheared chloritic, epidotic rocks, tens of metres thick, Beneath these, or directly beneath the microbreccia in other cases, is rock typically recording more ductile shear. Such rock is laminated mylonite where quartzofeldspathic rocks are involved (Fig. 10) and foliated greenschist-facies rock where metasediments are present (Figs 13, 18, 19). These ductile zones typically fade out downward through thicknesses of tens or even hundreds of metres and define carapaces semi-concordant beneath the detachment faults. Mylonitic gneisses are widespread in the most-uplifted lower plates. The mylonitic carapaces and progressively lower-temperature cata-

on the turtleback are a discontinuous carapace of mylonitized dolomite. An active range-front normal fault truncates both upper and lower plates at the top of the alluvial fan.

FIG. 15. Close up of fault of Fig. 10. Hammer is on zone of breccia 0.4 m thick, above which (in shade) is a thin zone of gouge. Upper-plate Oligocene slide breccia dips steeply left. Lower plate displays several levels of shear-polished pavement in coherent cataclastic microbreccia.

FIG. 17. Small normal faults in variably brecciated Tertiary redbeds, 50 m above Riverside Mountains detachment fault.

FIG. 16. Mid-Miocene detachment fault, Newberry Mountains, Nevada. Proterozoic monzogranite both above and below. Upper-plate rock is altered red (in part by Precambrian (?) retrogression from granulite facies) and variably brecciated; lower-plate rock is grey and is stripped along its mylonitic carapace. Gouge zone is 1 cm thick.

FIG. 18. Calcite mylonite derived from marble, in carapace beneath Ruby Mountains detachment fault, Nevada. Quartzite and amphibolite form boudins and rotated blocks. Area studied by Snoke *et al.* (1984).

clasites are developed in some cases on Tertiary mid-crust granites, barely older than the detachment faults that cut them (e.g. Reynolds 1985; Snoke *et al.* 1984). Much debate centres on whether the ductile carapaces represent old zones of any origin affected latterly by extensional slip, or early slip on mid-crust zones that evolved into the shallow detachment faults. My conclusion, shared with many other investigators, is that the mylonites generally belong to the detachment systems, whereas the more regional and higher-grade mylonitic gneisses are in many cases older than extensional deformation.

Crustal level

There is typically great crustal omission across detachment faults, although large upper-plate blocks rotated down against detachment faults show much omission at their toes but little or none at their heels (Howard *et al.* 1982) Rocks exposed beneath detachment faults mostly dis-

FIG. 19. Retrograde carapace in right-central part of Fig. 13. Z folds (arrows to hinges) and small fault (offsets contact × 2 m) indicate shear of top-to-W (right) sense, same as slip of upper plate. b = boudin.

play petrological evidence for crystallization in the middle crust, whereas unmetamorphosed supracrustal rocks of any age are largely confined to upper plates of detachments younger than those rocks. Mesozoic and Tertiary granitic rocks of upper plates are mostly of upper-crustal type in cross-cutting plutons with contact-metamorphosed wall rocks, whereas correlating rocks beneath detachments include abundant mid-crust migmatites and muscovite granite. I have discussed elsewhere depth variations in granitic and migmatitic systems (Hamilton 1981). Kyanite occurs beneath detachment faults in many ranges, whereas andalusite is uncommon. Sedimentary rocks beneath detachment faults may be metamorphosed only to slate, but even this requires a temperature of 300°C and hence generally a mid-crustal depth. Quartzose mylonites, also requiring a minimum temperature of about 300°C, are widespread beneath detachment faults and uncommon in the young rocks above them. These and other indicators of temperature and pressure require a common minimum depth of erosion of 10 km for rocks beneath detachment faults and of 15 km for many of them, even where those rocks are as young as Miocene.

Rapid uplift generally accompanied extension. K–Ar and fission-track ages of rocks beneath detachments commonly approximate the age of tectonic denudation and record rapid uplift and cooling from ambient temperatures of the middle crust. The dates do not generally record mysterious 'thermal events' despite the over-use of that term in the literature. Slip on detachment faults, and hence local rates of ex-

tension, must correspondingly have reached at least 10 km 1,000,000 yr^{-1}, or 1 cm yr^{-1}. At any one time, extension was rapid in parts of the province, as in the modern Death Valley region, and much slower or inactive elsewhere. High strain rates may have resulted in the shear heating of ductile shear zones, expediting further strain.

Precambrian basement rocks were widely eroded to mid-crustal depths before the deposition of upper-Proterozoic and younger strata and so occur in both upper and lower plates. Precambrian basement rocks of upper plates, however, tend to be variably altered, brecciated, and oxidized (Fig. 16) whereas those of lower plates generally lack such low-grade alteration and show instead variable carapace retrogression to mineral assemblages of lower greenschist facies and of higher grades at greater depths.

Wernicke (1985) postulated that detachment faults are segments of ramps that cut through the entire crust. The prediction that depths of origin of terrains, juxtaposed by correlating detachments, vary systematically across-strike on a regional scale is not fulfilled, although local sectors of several ranges each, may show such progressions (e.g. Howard & John, this volume). The superb imaging by Klemperer (Klemperer *et al.* 1986) of the Mohorovicic discontinuity across northern Nevada shows the seismic base of the crust to be continuous and gently undulating, unbroken by ramps as postulated by Wernicke (1985). Upper-crust ramps do, however, apparently connect between mid-crust lenses and the surface, as in the Utah COCORP example.

Davis (1983) inferred that gently dipping detachment faults develop by domino rotation of blocks between faults of initially steep dips. The lack of unmetamorphosed basin fills and other upper-crust rocks beneath most detachment faults is evidence against this view.

Late-Cenozoic detachments of the Death Valley region

Most of the detachment-fault literature has described mid-Tertiary complexes and this has led to the erroneous impression that structures of that age are different from younger ones. Accordingly, I emphasize here the detachment faults of late-Neogene age in the Death Valley region (Fig. 7), which is within the most actively extending part of the Great Basin. Here are the highest steep scarps, the greatest deformation of Quaternary materials, the deepest topographic closures of structural depressions and the youngest exposed detachment faults of late-

Miocene to Holocene age. Unresistant Neogene upper-plate materials are widely preserved above the detachments and late-Quaternary valley fill hides much less structure than in less active regions. Mica K–Ar ages of 10–15 Ma for sub-detachment rocks in several ranges presumably date the early stage of vigorous tectonic denudation here as of late-middle-Miocene and early-late-Miocene age.

The domiform Tucki Mountain detachment fault in the Panamint Mountains has flank dips of 10–30° and a broad crest (Figs 20 & 12; Hunt & Mabey 1966). The fault is sub-parallel to the layering in lower-plate rocks, which are upper-Proterozoic metasedimentary rocks and Cretaceous muscovite granites. A retrograde, mylonitic carapace on these materials parallels the domiform fault, which is marked by gouge and incoherent breccia. The upper plate consists of unmetamorphosed Palaeozoic strata in the E, Pliocene (?) slide megabreccias on the crest and Pliocene fluvial strata, slide megabreccias, and basalt to the W, all steeply to moderately E-dipping to truncations downward against the detachment fault and broken by many W-dipping normal faults that end against the detachment.

I found in my own reconnaissance another small detachment dome in the Wildrose Canyon area, where E-dipping Pliocene strata and slide megabreccias are rotated down-to-the-SE against it. Detachment faults, with megabreccias in the upper plate, are exposed in several places to the S along the W base of the Panamint Range, where Albee *et al.* (1981) in part mapped them as 'slide surfaces'. Detachment faults are exposed also at the E foot of the range (the 'Amargosa thrust fault' of Hunt & Mabey 1966), where the lower plate is of mid-Proterozoic augen gneiss intruded by abundant Tertiary dykes.

K–Ar biotite ages of 11–14 Ma in the gneiss (Stern *et al.* 1966) presumably reflect rapid Miocene uplift by tectonic denudation. I infer from the alteration of the Tertiary dykes, that they were injected while the wall rocks were still at ambient mid-crust temperatures.

The central and southern Panamint Mountains form a great tipped crustal section, 10–12 km thick and dipping about 20° E, entirely alloch-thonous above these detachment faults that are exposed to the W, N, and E, as I interpret the reports of Albee *et al.* (1981), Hunt & Mabey (1966), and Labotka *et al.* (1980). The down-section progression of the overlying crustal block begins with upper-Miocene volcanics (Cemen *et al.* 1985) and unmetamorphosed Palaeozoic strata and continues W through increasingly metamorphosed Palaeozoic and Proterozoic rocks, first andalusitic and then sillimanitic (Labotka *et al.* 1980). A shallow, cross-cutting Miocene granite occurs in the middle of the section and a Cretaceous muscovite granite occurs at the same low crustal level as that of sub-detachment rocks. Normal faults dipping gently W through the E-dipping crustal section (Labotka *et al.* 1980), presumably merge with the underlying detachment (cf. Fig. 20). The range-front fault, that bounded this upper-plate has been tilted with the block and with the flanking hanging wall slide breccias (Fig. 5). The palaeo-range-front fault is exposed all along the W slope of the Panamint Mountains (Albee *et al.* 1981), has a slip of about 3 km (Labotka *et al.* 1980) and projects obliquely up the Tucki dome to its crest (Fig. 20). The hanging wall breccias are truncated downward against an exposed detachment fault. The whole assemblage has been raised along young normal faults at the W and N edges of the range, although even the modern faults appear to offset upper-plate

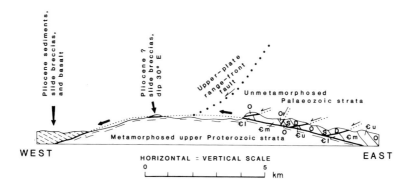

FIG. 20. Section across Tucki Mountain detachment fault, Panamint Mountains, California. Sense of slip of upper plate is the same in both flanks of dome. Palaeozoic strata: €1, €m and €u = lower, middle and upper Cambrian; O = Ordovician; S = Silurian; D = Devonian. Adapted from Hunt & Mabey (1966, their fig. 86).

materials more than lower-plate ones and hence may until recently have ended at the same detachment fault.

What I regard as a domiform detachment fault in the Funeral Mountains was mapped as many faults of diverse types by Hunt & Mabey (1966) McAllister (1971), B.W. Troxel and L.A. Wright (in Labotka 1980), and Giaramita (1984, who recognized its detachment character). Rocks inside the continuous elliptical trace of the detachment, so inferred, are upper-Proterozoic strata and possibly also older-Proterozoic basement rocks, metamorphosed during the Mesozoic to greenschist to uppermost amphibolite facies and intruded by muscovite granite. Kyanite occurs in rocks of all grades, and metamorphism occurred at a uniform depth of about 20 km (Labotka 1980, pers. comm. 1986). Upper-plate rocks are unmetamorphosed uppermost Proterozoic to Miocene strata, the latter including slide megabreccias rotated to steep to moderate E and SE dips and truncated against the detachment (Fig. 13). The Neogene stratigraphy is summarized by Cemen *et al.* (1985), who do not make a detachment interpretation. A greenschist-facies carapace on the lower plate displays isoclinal folding in the same shear sense as the slip direction of upper-plate rocks (Fig. 19) and opposite to vergence in unretrograded deeper lower-plate rocks (Fig. 21). Giaramita (1984) similarly recognized that W-verging folding and shearing (progressing with time from ductile and mylonitic to brittle) affected high lower-plate rocks at the N end of the dome synchronous with Tertiary detachment and denudation.

FIG. 21. Lower amphibolite facies Proterozoic metacarbonates, below carapace near area of Fig. 19. S folds (arrows to hinges) indicate shear of top-up-to-E (left) sense: Cretaceous synmetamorphic shearing had sense opposite to that in Neogene carapace. Exposure is 4m high.

Bare Mountain displays a detachment fault (The Tertiary thrust fault of Cornwall & Kleinhampl 1961; M.D. Carr & S.A. Monsen, unpubl. map; P.P. Orkild pers. comm., 1985) representing either another culmination on an undulating Funeral Mountains fault, or possibly the top of a separate mid-crustal lens. Miocene volcanic and clastic strata as young as about 12 Ma dip moderately to steeply E to their truncation at the gently dipping Bare Mountain fault atop Palaeozoic and upper-Proterozoic strata. These are metamorphosed to greenschist to lower amphibolite facies and are cut by gently dipping Tertiary faults. Biotite K–Ar ages of crystalline rocks beneath the Funeral Mountains and Bare Mountain detachments scatter from 10 to 50 Ma (M.D. Carr, pers. comm. 1985), so variations in synextensional and pre-extensional uplift and erosion are indicated. A composite detachment fault system exposed nearby in the Bullfrog Hills consists of an upper sheet of unmetamorphosed Palaeozoic strata intervening between downward-truncated Miocene rocks above and variably mylonitized gneisses beneath (Florian Maldonado, pers. comm. 1985).

The Black Mountains expose undulating detachment faults, of late-Neogene age, at two structural levels, as I interpret mapping and descriptions by: Drewes (1963—he recognized little extension); Otton (1977—summarized by Wright *et al.* 1974—who recognized great extension); and Wright & Troxel (1984—they inferred mostly imbricate listric normal faults where I identify undulating detachments). My inferences have been shaped also by my own reconnaissance and by discussions with B.W. Troxel. The structurally lower part consists of three small domiform masses, the NW-trending Badwater, Copper Canyon (Fig. 14), and Mormon Point turtlebacks, that are disconnected at present erosion levels and are separated by detachment faults from overlying Cenozoic materials in the W and plutonic rocks in the E. These masses consist of variably mylonitized mid-Proterozoic plutonic rocks capped by discontinuous carapaces of mylonitized and extremely attenuated upper-Proterozoic metasedimentary rocks (Otton 1977). The domiform turtlebacks might represent either giant mullions on a continuous detachment surface, or separate lenses above deeper faults. Drewes (1963) presented a lens-structure interpretation of a different sort. Above the turtleback detachments, to the E is a thick sheet forming a structurally higher lens of diorite and monzogranite of Mesozoic and (?) Tertiary age. Bounding this sheet on the top is the upper detachment fault, marked by breccias and lenses of upper- and lower-plate rocks in a zone as thick as 100 m. Above this zone, or elsewhere truncated sharply against the detachment, are variously mid-Proterozoic plutonic rocks, unmetamorphosed upper-Proterozoic and Cambrian sedimentary rocks and, mostly, mid-Miocene to Quaternary volcanic and sedimentary materials. The Cenozoic sections include extensive intercalated slide megabreccias (most 'chaos' and much 'Palaeozoic sedimentary rock' of Drewes 1963, and most 'megabreccia' and many 'fault slices' of Wright & Troxel 1984), from which I infer that high scarps were present, and hence that extension was very active, while they were being deposited. Around the southern Black Mountains, upper-Miocene rocks generally dip more steeply than do Pliocene rocks, although both are truncated by the same undulating faults, and mid-Quaternary strata are rotated to gentler dips in the same direction (Wright & Troxel 1984), whereas in the N, steep-dipping Pliocene strata are semi-concordant to upper-Miocene strata (Cemen *et al.* 1985; Hunt & Mabey 1966). Rotation synchronous with persistent faulting is indicated.

Each of the three exposed turtleback detachment faults is now active as a low-angle normal fault. A large, active normal fault, limited to upper-plate rocks, ends truncated downward against each turtleback (Fig. 7). Footwall Neogene volcanic rocks, hanging wall Quaternary slide breccias and the late-Quaternary Artist's Drive fault (Figs 4 & 5) are all truncated downward against the gently dipping Badwater turtleback. The Copper Canyon turtleback detachment truncates, from beneath, an upper-plate complex of footwall plutonic rocks, hanging wall tilted Pliocene strata and the intervening large normal fault (Fig. 14). Quaternary strata are rotated to steep truncations against the Mormon Point turtleback fault. In each case, the upper-plate rocks are slipping in the downhill direction on the turtleback detachments; gravitational sliding toward fast-deepening Death Valley is indicated. Faults that originated as zones of ductile slip in the middle crust have risen to the surface and have evolved until they now bound what are in effect giant landslides. Turtleback and upper-plate complexes alike are broken by normal faults that define parts of the present range front (Fig. 14).

Slip on the Bare Mountain detachment was largely completed before about 11.5 Ma, whereas detachments in the Bullfrog Hills continued to be active until perhaps 7 Ma; the Funeral Mountains were probably affected by considerable Pliocene slip and activity has continued throughout the Quaternary in the Black and Panamint Mountains. Late-Quaternary normal faults, with the usual 50° dips, break the Panamint and Black Mountains (Fig. 14) detachments. Major detachment faults must now be active at shallow depth beneath Death Valley, Panamint Valley, and areas W and NW of them.

Above all of these late-Neogene detachment faults, upper-plate strata, Proterozoic to lower-Pliocene, mostly display rotation to general steep to moderate E dips and hence a consistent slip relatively westward across both flanks of each detachment dome, up E flanks and down W flanks. Fault segments of opposite dips belong to continuous domiform or undulating structures, not, as they have often been interpreted, to kinematically unrelated structures sliding down the sides of domes, although the turtleback faults have evolved recently to the condition where such sliding is now occurring. Except for this final phase, which may be exemplified also by late slip on the Tucki Mountain (Fig. 12) and Wildrose Canyon detachments, the domes did not extrude upward, shedding slide masses off their flanks, for regional slip of upper plates requires continuous cover.

Tertiary strata comprise about half of the aggregate width of the upper plates truncated downward against detachment faults exposed in the Death Valley region (Fig. 7), and this requires at least 100% extension of the pre-Tertiary crust. Oligocene and Miocene strata may represent basins of markedly different configuration to that of the Pliocene ones, which in turn were quite different from modern ones (Cemen *et al.* 1985). Basin fills were dragged directly against detachment faults; pre-Tertiary upper-plate rocks did not underlie the basins. B.C. Burchfiel (pers. comm. 1985) regards his mapping as requiring similarly that the Quaternary fill of the actively widening northern Panamint Valley be dragging directly on a shallow detachment fault.

Throughout the region of Fig. 7, high, young fault scarps of the type commonly thought of as typifying Basin and Range structure are developed mostly in the upper-plate assemblages of detachment faults. The lower plates outcrop primarily as domiform masses and are broken into tilted fault blocks to only a minor extent. Relationships between modern and ancient basins and ranges and domiform detachment faults can be seen in Fig. 7. Most of the modern relief correlates with a position relative to the domes rather than with block faulting younger than the exposed detachment faults. The domiform sub-detachment masses and the resistant parts of the tilted upper-plate rocks above them form the modern ranges. The palaeobasins and the palaeoranges represented by, respectively, Tertiary and pre-Tertiary upper-plate materials are distributed randomly with regard to trough or crest positions across the domes. Perhaps initial basins and ranges were positioned systematically above lows and highs in underlying detachment faults (cf. Davis 1980) but were dragged across the expanding composite surface of sub-detachment lenses to their present positions. Where resistant rocks stand high atop a dome, normal faulting toward the adjacent lowlands is facilitated.

Active right-slip faults trend NW and serve as transforms between the modern obliquely separating, N-trending basin-range blocks. I infer that the sub-detachment crustal lenses, now active at depth, are sliding apart in a NW–SE direction beneath the modern blocks, that the northerly trends of those blocks are inherited from older extensional systems and that the strike-slip faults are restricted to upper plates allochthonous above detachments.

The detachment faults disappear beneath upper-plate materials at the E and W sides of the region discussed here. Rock assemblages of upper-plate type are broken by small to very large late-Cenozoic normal faults for about 75 km in both directions. As the age range of normal faulting differs across the region, the age range of major subjacent detachment faulting probably varies correspondingly.

Stewart (1983a) inferred that the part of the Panamint Mountains here regarded as the tilted upper-plate crustal block slipped about 45 km relatively westward from above the Black Mountains turtleback complexes. I concur with this conclusion; Cemen *et al.* (1985) do not.

Increasing area of detachment faults

If the analysis of detachment geometry summarized here is basically correct, then the widening of a normal-faulted terrain must be a response to an increase in area of the underlying detachment faults. The ages and intensities of detachment faulting over broad terrains vary complexly. Upper and lower plates do not display either systematic variations in initial crustal depth nor slips that increase undirectionally, both of which would be required were detachments planar faults cutting through the crust.

Sub-detachment structure

I infer that the middle crust is extended by the sliding apart, along ductile shear zones, of lenses that are little deformed internally. The area of

the composite top of these lenses thus increases as deeper lenses are pulled out from beneath shallower ones.

Beneath the cataclastic carapaces beneath detachment faults, lower-plate rocks largely retain pre-detachment fabrics: synextensional ductile shear occurred in discrete zones and was not pervasive. Still deeper, additional gently dipping zones of brittle or ductile shear, discordant metamorphically and structurally with the older rocks, have been recognized (Figs 22 & 23). Such zones divide sub-detachment complexes into lenses. Major faults beneath the upper

FIG. 22. Horizontal sub-detachment Tertiary fault, Big Maria Mountains, California. Permian Kaibab Marble (Pk) and Coconino Quartzite (Pc) are truncated downward against sub-horizontal Mesozoic metasedimentary rocks (Mz), all metamorphosed at upper greenschist facies. Overturning is a product of Cretaceous recumbent folding; slip on the fault is a few km.

FIG. 23. Internally isoclinal mylonite of low greenschist facies, in fault zone near and like that of Fig. 22. Layers and lenses are rich alternately in mylonitic marble (m) and mylonitic greenschist (g; note contortions in lowest mass) but the two types are finely mixed. Kaibab Marble (Pk) at top is · boudinaged but not mylonitized.

detachment faults in the Death Valley region were noted previously. John (1982) outlined a large sub-detachment lens with her Mohave Wash fault, and Spencer & Turner (1982) defined a smaller one with their 'lowest detachment fault'. Howard *et al.* (1982) found major sub-horizontal faults just above a detachment. I suspect that two very large lenses are in exposed contact in the Harcuvar Mountains of SW Arizona (cf. Rehrig & Reynolds 1980); a large eastern mass of deep-seated plutonic rocks has a domiform mylonitic carapace, which is overlain in the E by an exposed detachment fault and upper-plate assemblages, but in the W, at Cunningham Pass, by another sub-detachment mass, domiform in its topography, composed of granitic rocks typical of the upper part of the middle crust.

I infer that such lens-defining faults are common although relatively few have yet been mapped. I consider that junctions between detachment domiforms are mostly dihedral angles where deeper lenses emerge from beneath shallower ones; but such junctions in general are hidden beneath upper-plate rocks or beneath the alluvial fill of basins. Such lenses are shown in Fig. 24. In SE California, an undulating detachment fault dips S from the Riverside Mountains (Fig. 6) and another dips N from the Big Maria Mountains, the next range to the S; the distinctive lowerplate rock assemblages of the two ranges are very similar, except that markedly higher-grade Cretaceous metamorphism has affected the southern range, and it is possible that the Riverside lower plate moved about 25 km, relatively NE, from an initial position atop the Big Maria lower plate.

Domal form

Detachment faults can be irregular, undulating surfaces, but many outcrop as broad domes (e.g. Davis *et al.* 1980; Davis 1980; Rehrig & Reynolds 1980; Figs 7 & 20). Flank dips vary from a few to 25 degrees, locally more. Domes can be symmetrical or irregular, and typically have exposed dimensions of 10–20 by 20–40 km. Some are elongate in the direction of slip of overlying plates, as defined by the perpendicular to the axis of rotation of Tertiary rocks and by ductile-slip fabrics and, like parallel second-order corrugations of the surfaces, may be 'porpoising mullion structures' (John 1984; cf. Wright *et al.* 1974). Other domes are elongate at high angles to slip directions, or are irregular and I consider that these shapes record the interactions between diversely shaped lenses as they slid apart.

Other explanations that have been proposed for the domes do not appear to me to be broadly viable. Conjecture that the domes are products of the diapiric rise of hot cores that shrugged off their covers (e.g. Drewes 1981) is disproved because major offsets on bounding faults show no preference for down-dip directions, consistent senses of rotation of upper-plate rocks instead being maintained across series of domes (Fig. 7). Explanations invoking local heat sources (e.g. Miller *et al.* 1983) cannot generally be valid because many sub-detachment complexes were at only ambient middle-crust temperatures during extension. Plutonic rocks are present in many domiforms, as they are throughout the middle crust, but are of all ages from Precambrian to Miocene, whereas the domes were outlined in Cenozoic time and many domes expose little magmatic rock of any age. The common denominator of rocks beneath detachment faults is the depth, not the temperature or age, of their formation. Compressive folding could not have produced the domes, for it is incompatible with the continuing formation of extensional structures shown by many domes. Doming by isostatic uplift following differential tectonic denudation (Spencer 1984) would require, in view of the relatively steep flanks and small dimensions of many of the domes, an improbably low viscosity of the lithosphere.

Dykes

Sub-vertical mafic to silicic dykes of mid-Tertiary age, perpendicular to the direction of extension, are present in many ranges, mostly beneath detachment faults, but are generally sparse. Dyke swarms are present only locally (e.g. John 1982; Spencer & Turner 1982). The intrusion of dykes was therefore not a major contributor to regional extension at exposed crustal levels. Many lower-plate dykes exhibit static alteration to greenschist-facies minerals, which is thought to indicate emplacement at mid-crust depths and retention at greenschist temperatures.

Superimposed structures

Many detachment faults are broken by steep normal and strike-slip faults. Presumably the detachment complexes had risen to high crustal levels where further low-angle slip was not possible, and subsequent extension was accommodated

SSW

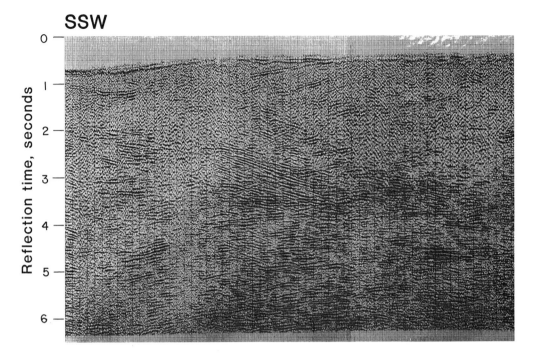

FIG. 24 (Above, and facing page). Deep-crustal seismic reflection profile in S-central Arizona (Fig. 1). The northern two-thirds of the line lies on or near outcrop of lower-plate middle-crust plutonic rocks, structurally beneath a mid-Tertiary detachment fault that outcrops with a northerly dip at the N end of the profile. The southern one-third lies on alluvial basin fill, and underlying bedrock may contain a detachment fault dipping SW. A well a few km W of the S end of the line penetrated 1 km of gravel and arkose, 2 km of upper-plate granitic rocks, a detachment fault at 3 km, and 2.5 km of sub-detachment plutonic rocks, including Tertiary muscovite granite, to bottom (Reif & Robinson 1981). Five biotite and hornblende K–Ar ages between the detachment fault and the bottom of the hole range only from 25 to 31 Ma (Reif & Robinson 1981), indicating rapid uplift from mid-crustal depths at the time of detachment faulting. The depth scale is based on regional refraction velocities. The profile is 40 km long; effective horizontal scale is 1.6 × vertical scale. The N end of line is near 33°05′ N, 111°00′ W; the S-end is near 32°50′ N, 111°10′ W. Profile provided by Pacific West Exploration and the Anschutz Corporation.

Interpretation: Reflectors represent variable mylonitization and shear transposition during Tertiary extension. The top 10 km (present upper crust, but middle crust before extension) is broken into great lenses which have slid apart; few reflections come from inside the lenses. The undulating apparent fabric of the lower 10 km (pre-extension lower crust) may, if real, record pervasive ductile flattening.

in the rotating-block, upper-crustal mode, new detachment faults being developed at depth (Figs 2 & 14).

Structures of the lower crust

The mode of extension deep in the crust cannot yet be inferred from field observations. Lower continental crust is exposed along the SW edge of the province, but deep extensional structures have not been recognized there.

Reflection profiles in Arizona yield information that may prove relevant to the behaviour of the deep crust. These profiles mostly remain proprietary, but a public one is reproduced as Fig. 24. The ground surface along most of this profile is eroded beneath a detachment fault, hence represents a crustal depth of at least 10 km before mid-Tertiary extension. The top 10 km of the profile displays anastomosing zones of apparent reflectors which I consider to be shear zones and to represent, in part, pre-existing lithologies transposed in the shear direction and, in part, velocity anisotropy in variably mylonitized rocks (cf. Fountain *et al.* 1984; Jones & Nur 1984). I conclude that the acoustically transparent rock between reflective zones consists of large lenses that retain pre-shearing massive or heterogeneous fabric. The lower half

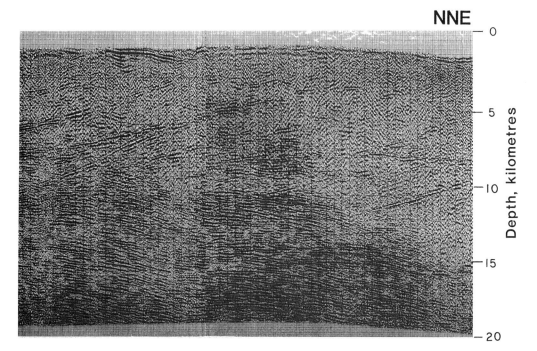

FIG. 24 cont. from facing page.

of this profile, like many of the other Arizona profiles, shows a strong fabric of gently undulating apparent reflectors. If such fabrics truly record varying velocity layering in the deep crust, and are not artefacts due to over-zealous processing or to such acoustic effects as reverberation, then pervasive ductile flattening may be indicated. Such pervasive deformation can be inferred also on theoretical grounds (Sibson 1983).

Other regions

The model advocated here may have a general application to extended continental crust. Domiform detachment faults separating steeply rotated upper-crustal rocks from mid-crustal complexes may be widespread around the world. Most have been interpreted in terms of thrust faulting because of their gentle dips, although this is disproved where thick crustal sections are omitted across them. A few examples are noted here.

The numerous 'Shuswap' domes of mid-crust rocks in NE Washington and interior British Columbia are bounded by detachment faults strikingly like those of the Basin and Range Province, except that those northern faults are

of Eocene age. The structures display the same progressions of ductile to brittle structures in carapaces on the lower plates (Lane 1984, and references therein). Lower plates consist of mid-crust crystalline rocks, varying from kyanite greenschist to migmatite and muscovite granite and, locally, granulite, of Proterozoic to Eocene age. Upper plates consist of little-metamorphosed Proterozoic to Eocene strata, often truncated steeply against the gently dipping detachment faults, and upper-crust cross-cutting granitic rocks and their contact-metamorphosed wall rocks. Eocene K–Ar ages in many lower-plate rocks indicate great uplift at that time. Most investigators have interpreted these structures as being due to Mesozoic thrusting or rising of plutons, with minor Tertiary complications. Fox & Beck (1985) are among the few who have explained the structures, largely in terms of Eocene extension, and with this I concur.

The island of Naxos in the Aegean Sea is a detachment complex of Basin and Range type in an extensional setting (Lister *et al.* 1984). Beneath a domiform detachment fault is a lower plate of melange, metamorphosed at blueschist facies in the Palaeogene and then metamorphosed and migmatized under mid-crustal conditions in the Miocene. The upper plate includes unmetamorphosed Palaeogene melange and upper-crustal

Miocene granitic rocks. Both Palaeogene and Miocene indicators thus require great crustal elision across the detachment.

The Betic Cordillera of SE Spain contain high-grade metamorphic rocks separated by gently domiform faults from overlying unmetamorphosed Mesozoic to mid-Tertiary strata, which have steep to moderate dips (Platt 1982; Volk 1967). The faults have generally been assumed to be thrusts despite their elision of thick crustal sections. Platt recognized their extensional nature, although he invoked a rising-dome, gravity-sliding model.

Similarity to thrust deformation

The middle continental crust may deform in the same general lenticular mode under compressive overthrusting as under extension. Late Cretaceous mylonite zones each hundreds of metres thick outline huge, overlapping lenses in a gently dipping stack in the Santa Rosa Mountains of SW California. Reflection profiling shows that the upper-crust basement Palaeogene thrust that bounds the Wind River Mountains of Wyoming flattens downward into a series of lens-defining splays at depths of 17–26 km (Sharry *et al.* 1986) acoustically

appropriate for mylonitic zones (Jones & Nur 1984). Such thrust lenses are defined by ductile shear zones in the Proterozoic Grenville crustal-thrust terrain of Ontario, where the pervasiveness of deformation increases with depth of exposure within the lower crust (Davidson 1984).

A great contrast between compressive and extensional regimes is that depth and temperature of mid-crust components increase with time in the former, but decrease with time in the latter.

ACKNOWLEDGMENTS: I started mapping what are now referred to as detachment faults, in SE California 25 years ago, when I termed them 'gravity thrust faults'; but it was not until I attended the 1977 Geological Society of America Penrose Conference on 'metamorphic core complexes', in Tucson, that I began to appreciate the common characteristics and regional prevalence of these remarkable structures. That fine conference was organized by M.D. Crittenden, Jr, P.J. Coney, and G.H. Davis. Discussions and field trips with, and papers written by, many geologists since then have profoundly influenced my views. My recent debt is greatest to G.A. Davis and K.A. Howard, whose interpretations in many ways overlap my own. This manuscript was much improved as a result of criticism by M.D. Carr, A.M.C. Sengor, and J.H. Stewart.

References

ALBEE, A.L., LABOTKA, T.C., LANPHERE, M.A. & McDOWELL, S.D., 1981. Geologic map of the Telescope Peak quadrangle, California. *U.S. geol. Surv. Map GQ 1532.*

ALLMENDINGER, R.W. *et al.* 1983. Cenozoic and Mesozoic structure of the eastern Basin and Range province, Utah, from COCORP seismic-reflection data. *Geology*, 11, 532–6.

ARMSTRONG, R.L. 1972. Low-angle (denudation) fault, hinterland of the Sevier orogenic belt, eastern Nevada and western Utah. *Bull. geol. Soc. Am.* 83, 1729–54.

ATWATER, T. 1970. Implications of plate tectonics for the Cenozoic tectonic evolution of western North America. *Bull. geol. Soc. Am.* 81, 3513–36.

AXELROD, D.I. 1985. Miocene floras from the Middlegate basin, west-central Nevada. *Univ. Calif. Publ. geol. Sci. 129.*

BARTLEY, J.M. & WERNICKE, B.P. 1984. The Snake Range decollement interpreted as a major extensional shear zone. *Tectonics*, 3, 647–57.

CEMEN, I., WRIGHT, L.A., DRAKE, R.E., & JOHNSON, F.C. 1985. Cenozoic sedimentation and sequence of deformational events at the southeastern end of the strike-slip Furnace Creek fault zone, Death Valley region, California. *Soc. econ. Paleontol. and Mineral., Spec. Publ.* 37, 127–41.

CONEY, P.J. & HARMS, T.A. 1984. Cordilleran metamorphic core complexes: Cenozoic extensional relics of Mesozoic compression. *Geology*, 12, 550–4.

CORNWALL, H.R. & KLEINHAMPL, F.J. 1961. Geology of Bare Mountain quadrangle, Nevada. *U.S. geol. Surv. Map GQ 157.*

DAVIDSON, A. 1984. Identification of ductile shear zones in the southwestern Grenville Province of the Canadian Shield. *In*: KRONER, A. & GREILING, R. (eds) *Precambrian tectonics illustrated*, pp. 263–79. Schweizerbart., Stuttgart.

DAVIS, G.A. ANDERSON, J.L., FROST, E.G. & SHACKELFORD, T.J. 1980. Mylonitization and detachment faulting in the Whipple-Buckskin-Rawhide Mountains terrane, southeastern California and western Arizona. *Mem. geol. Soc. Am.* 153, 79–129.

DAVIS, G.H. 1980. Structural characteristics of metamorphic core complexes, southern Arizona. *Mem. geol. Soc. Am.* 153, 35–77.

—— 1983. Shear-zone model for the origin of metamorphic core complexes. *Geology*, 11, 342–7.

DREWES, H.D. 1963. Geology of the Funeral Peak quadrangle, California, on the east flank of Death Valley. *U.S. geol. Surv. Prof. Pap. 413.*

—— 1981. Tectonics of southeastern Arizona. *U.S. geol. Surv. Prof. Pap. 1144.*

EATON, G.P. 1984. The Miocene Great Basin of western North America as an extending back-arc region. *Tectonophysics,* **102,** 275–95.

EFFIMOFF, I. & PINEZICH, A.R. 1981. Tertiary structural development of selected valleys based on seismic data: Basin and Range province, Nevada *Phil. Trans. R. Soc. London,* **A-300,** 435–42.

FOUNTAIN, D.M., HURICH, C.A. & SMITHSON, S.B. 1984. Seismic reflectivity of mylonite zones in the crust. *Geology,* **12,** 195–8.

FOX, K.F. & BECK, M.E., JR, 1985. Paleomagnetic results for Eocene volcanic rocks from northeastern Washington and the Tertiary tectonics of the Pacific Northwest. *Tectonics,* **4,** 323–341.

GIARAMITA, M.J. 1984. Structural evolution and metamorphic petrology of the northern Funeral Mountains, Death Valley, California. Unpubl. MSc. Thesis, Univ. California (Davis).

HAMILTON, W. 1978. Mesozoic tectonics of the western United States. *Soc. econ. Paleontol. and Mineral, Pac. sect. Paleogeog. Symp.* **2,** 33–70.

—— 1981. Crustal evolution by arc magmatism. *Phil. Trans. R. Soc. London,* **A-301,** 279–91.

—— 1982. Structual evolution of the Big Maria Mountains, Northeastern Riverside County, southeastern California. *In*: FROST, E.G. & MARTIN, D.L. (eds) *Mesozoic-Cenozoic ectonic evolution of the Colorado River region, California, Arizona, and Nevada (Anderson–Hamilton volume),* pp. 1–27. Cordilleran Publishers, San Diego.

—— & MYERS, W.B. 1966. Cenozoic tectonics of the western United States. *Rev. Geophys.* **4,** 509–49.

HOWARD, K.A. & JOHN, B.E. This volume. Crustal extension along a rooted system of imbricate low-angle faults: Colorado River extensional corridor, California and Arizona, pp. 299–311.

——, GOODGE, J.W. & JOHN, B.E. 1982. Detached crystalline rocks of the Mohave, Buck, and Bill Williams Mountains, western Arizona. *In*: FROST, G.C. & MARTIN, D.L. (eds) *Mesozoic–Cenozoic tectonic evolution of the Colorado River region, California, Arizona, and Nevada (Anderson–Hamilton volume),* pp. 377–90. Cordilleran Publishers, San Diego.

HUNT, C.B. & MABEY, D.R. 1966. Stratigraphy and structure, Death Valley, California. *U.S. geol. Surv. Prof. Pap. 494-A.*

JOHN, B.E. 1982. Geologic framework of the Chemehuevi Mountains, California. *In*: FROST, E.G. & MARTIN, D.L. (eds) *Mesozoic–Cenozoic tectonic evolution of the Colorado River region, California, Arizona and Nevada (Anderson–Hamilton volume),* pp. 317–25. Cordilleran Publishers, San Diego.

—— 1984. Primary corrugations in Tertiary low-angle normal faults, SE California: porpoising mullion structures? *Abstr. with Programs geol. Soc. Am.* **16,** 291.

JONES, T. & NUR, A. 1984. The nature of seismic reflections from deep crustal fault zones. *J. geophys. Res.* **89,** 3153–71.

KLEMPERER, S.L., HAUGE, T.A., HAUSER, E.C., OLIVER, J.E., & POTTER, C.J. 1986. The Moho in the northern Basin and Range Province, Nevada, along the COCORP 40°N seismic reflection transect. *Bull. geol. Soc. Am.* **97,** 603–18.

KLIGFIELD, R., CRESPI, J., NARUK, S. & DAVIS, G.H. 1984. Displacement and strain patterns of extensional orogens. *Tectonics,* **3,** 577–609.

LABOTKA, T.C. 1980. Petrology of a medium-pressure regional metamorphic terrane, Funeral Mountains, California. *Am. Min.* **65,** 670–89.

——, ALBEE, A.L., LANPHERE, M.A., & McDOWELL, S.D. 1980. Stratigraphy, structure, and metamorphism in the central Panamint Mountains (Telescope Peak quadrangle), Death Valley area, California. *Bull. geol. Soc. Am.* **I-91,** 125–9, **II-91,** 843–933.

LACHENBRUCH, A.H. & SASS, J.H. 1978. Models of an extending lithosphere and heat flow in the Basin and Range province. *Mem. geol. Soc. Am.* **152,** 209–50.

LANE, L.S. 1984. Brittle deformation in the Columbia River fault zone near Revelstoke, southeastern British Columbia. *Can. J. Earth Sci.* **21,** 584–98.

LISTER, G.S., BANGA, G. & FEENSTRA, A. 1984. Metamorphic core complexes of Cordilleran type in the Cyclades, Aegean Sea, Greece. *Geology,* **12,** 221–5.

McALLISTER, J.F. 1971. Preliminary geologic map of the Funeral Mountains in the Ryan quadrangle, Death Valley region, Inyo County, California. *U.S. geol. Surv. Open-File Rep. 71–187.*

MILLER, E.L., GANS, P.B. & GARING, J. 1983. The Snake Range decollement, an exhumed mid-Tertiary ductile-brittle transition. *Tectonics,* **2,** 239–63.

MYERS, W.B. & HAMILTON, W. 1964. Deformation accompanying the Hebgen Lake earthquake of August 17, 1959. *U.S. geol. Surv. Prof. Pap. 435-I.*

OTTON, J.K. 1977. Geology of the central Black Mountains, Death Valley, California: The turtleback terrane. Unpubl. PhD. Thesis, Pennsylvania State Univ.

PLATT, J.P. 1982. Emplacement of a fold-nappe, Betic orogen, southern Spain. *Geology,* **10,** 97–102.

RANSOME, F.L., EMMONS, W.H. & GARREY, G.H. 1910. Geology and ore deposits of the Bullfrog District, Nevada. *Bull. U.S. geol. Surv. 407.*

REHRIG, W.A. & REYNOLDS, S.J. 1980. Geologic and geochronologic reconnaissance of a northwest-trending zone of metamorphic core complexes in southern and western Arizona. *Mem. geol. Soc. Am.* **153,** 131–57.

REIF, D.M. & ROBINSON, J.P. 1981. Geophysical, geochemical, and petrographic data and regional correlation from the Arizona State A-1 Well, Pinal County, Arizona. *Ariz. geol. Soc. Dig.* **13,** 99–109.

REYNOLDS, S.J. 1985. Geology of the South Mountains, central Arizona. *Ariz. Bur. Geol. Min. Res. Bull. 195.*

SHARRY, J., LANGAN, R.T., JOVANOVICH, D.B., JONES, G.M., HILL, N.R. & GUIDISH, T.M.

1986. Enhanced imaging of the COCORP seismic line, Wind River Mountains. *Am. geophys. Union Geodyn. Ser.* **13**, 223–36.

SIBSON, R.H. 1983. Continental fault structure and the shallow earthquake source. *J. geol. Soc. London*, **140**, 741–67.

SMITH, R.B. & BRUHN, R.L. 1984. Intraplate extensional tectonics of the eastern Basin-Range: Inferences on structural style from seismic reflection data, regional tectonics and thermal mechanical models of brittle–ductile transition. *J. geophys. Res.* **89**, 5733–62.

SNOKE, A.W., LUSH, A.P. & HOWARD, K.A. 1984. Polyphase deformational history of northern Ruby Mountains-East Humboldt Range, Nevada. *In*: LINTZ, J., JR (ed.) *Univ. Nev. Dept. geol. Sci. Western geol. Exc.* **4**, 232–303.

SPENCER, J.E. 1984. Role of tectonic denudation in warping and uplift of low-angle normal faults. *Geology*, **12**, 95–8.

—— & TURNER, R.B. 1982. Dike swarms and low-angle faults, Homer Mountain and the northwestern Sacramento Mountains, southeastern California. *In*: FROST, E.G. & MARTIN, D.L. (eds) *Mesozoic-Cenozoic tectonic evolution of the Colorado River region, California, Arizona and Nevada. (Anderson–Hamilton volume)*, pp. 97–107. Cordilleran Publishers San Diego.

STECKLER, M.S. 1985. Uplift and extension at the Gulf of Suez: Indications of induced mantle convection. *Nature*, **317**, 135–9.

STEIN, R.S. & BARRIENTOS, S.E. 1985. Planar high-angle faulting in the Basin and Range: geodetic analysis of the 1983 Borah Peak, Idaho, earthquake. *J. geophys. Res.* **90**, 11, 355–66.

STERN, T.W., NEWELL, M.F. & HUNT, C.B. 1966. Uranium–lead and potassium–argon ages of parts of the Amargosa thrust complex, Death Valley,

California. *U.S. geol. Surv. Prof. Pap. 550-B.* pp. 142–7.

STEWART, J.H. 1980. Regional tilt patterns of late Cenozoic basin-range fault blocks, western United States. *Bull. geol. Soc. Am.* **91**, 460–4.

—— 1983a. Extensional tectonics in the Death Valley area, California: Transport of the Panamint Range structural block 80 km northwestward. *Geology*, **11**, 153–7.

—— 1983b. Cenozoic structure and tectonics of the northern Basin and Range Province, California, Nevada and Utah. *Geotherm. Res. Coun. Spec. Rep.* **13**, 25–40.

VOLK, H.R. 1967. Zur Geologie und Stratigraphie des Neogenbeckens von Vera, südost-Spanien, Unpubl. thesis. Univ. Amsterdam.

WERNICKE, B. 1985. Uniform-sense normal shear of the continental lithosphere. *Can J. Earth Sci.* **22**, 108–125.

—— , WALKER, J.D. & BEAUFAIT, M.S. 1985. Structural discordance between Neogene detachments and frontal Sevier thrusts, central Mormon Mountains, southern Nevada. *Tectonics*, **4**, 213–46.

—— , SPENCER, J.E., BURCHFIEL, B.C. & GUTH, P.L. 1982. Magnitude of crustal extension in the southern Great Basin. *Geology*, **10**, 499–502.

WRIGHT, L.A. & TROXEL, B.W. 1984. Geology of the north 1/2 Confidence Hills quadrangle, Inyo County, California. *Calif. Div. Mines Geol.* Map Sheet 34.

—— , OTTON, J.K. & TROXEL, B.W. 1974. Turtleback surfaces of Death Valley viewed as phenomena of extensional tectonics. *Geology*, **2**, 53–4.

ZOBACK, M.L., ANDERSON, R.E. & THOMPSON, G.A. 1981. Cainozoic evolution of stress and style of tectonism of the Basin and Range province of the western United States. *Phil. Trans. R. Soc. London*, **A-300**, 407–34.

WARREN HAMILTON, Branch of Geophysics, US Geological Survey, Denver, Colorado 80225, USA.

The regional tectonic setting and possible causes of Cenozoic extension in the North American Cordillera

P. J. Coney

SUMMARY: Timing and tectonic setting of middle Cenozoic crustal extension in the North American Cordillera supports the concept that an overthickened crustal welt formed behind or astride the thrust belts as a result of compression during the Mesozoic to early Cenozoic. At the end of the Laramide Orogeny the gravitationally unstable welt collapsed by deep-seated crustal extension. The extension was aided by a lowering of crustal viscosity resulting from a complex pattern of volcanism and a reduction in intraplate compressive stress. As plate regimes evolved along the Pacific margin during the late Cenozoic, subduction progressively ceased as did compressive stress also. An evolving transform boundary and a massive Cordilleran-wide lithospheric uplift allowed a second phase of extension to develop across the already thinned and thermally weakened crust to form the Basin and Range Province, being active up to the present time.

The principal manifestation of extensional tectonism in the North American Cordillera has been recognized for years as the Basin and Range Province (Stewart 1978). The Basin and Range Province formed in the central-western United States and northwestern Mexico by block faulting, some strike-slip faulting, and associated relative regional subsidence during the late Cenozoic. The crust has been thinned to less than normal, heat flow is high, and the extension has been accompanied by a sparse bimodal basaltic–rhyolitic volcanism. The Basin and Range Province remains active to this day, as evidenced in seismicity and landscape, but the nature of its origins remains controversial.

An earlier period of mid-Tertiary Cordilleran extensional tectonics has only recently been recognized. This extension affected a larger region than the younger Basin and Range Province extending from northern British Columbia across the western United States and southward into northern Mexico. The mid-Tertiary extension was originally recognized in the sub-horizontal younger on older detachment faults (Armstrong 1972) which juxtapose unmetamorphosed upper-plate Precambrian to Cenozoic sedimentary and volcanic rocks against lower-plate mylonitic gneiss in the peculiar metamorphic core complexes of the Cordilleran hinterland (Coney 1980; Armstrong 1982). Coeval everywhere with this middle-Tertiary extension was a voluminous outburst of generally caldera-centred ignimbrite eruptions (Lipman et al. 1971; Elston 1976; Coney & Reynolds 1977; Dickinson 1981). This has resulted today in the paradox of mountain ranges exposing thick ash-flow tuffs nested amongst ranges exposing mylonitic gneiss, both yielding the same mid-Tertiary K–Ar cooling ages. The middle-Tertiary extensional province was superimposed on widespread compressional features of Mesozoic and early-Tertiary age.

Although the earlier mid-Tertiary extension covered an area larger than the younger Basin and Range Province, the two provinces overlap to a very large degree in the western United States. In other words, the Basin and Range Province was superimposed over much of the same ground that had been extended in the middle Tertiary. Thus, the crust of this area was extended and thinned twice. It is important to realize the scale of these features: the combined area of mid- and late-Tertiary extension in western North America is about 10 times longer and five times wider than the Aegean extensional province of the eastern Mediterranean region (Le Pichon 1982) and would comfortably encompass much of western Europe.

The principal problem with Cenozoic extensional tectonics in western North America has been to explain why it took place. After a description of the regional tectonic setting of these two periods of continental extension we will review some possible explanations to this question.

Regional tectonic setting of Basin and Range extension

The Basin and Range Province (Stewart 1978; Eaton et al. 1978; Eaton 1982) includes the northern Basin and Range of Nevada and western Utah, the Arizona–Sonora Basin and Range of the southwestern United States and northwestern Mexico and the Mojave region of southeastern California (Fig. 1a). The northern Basin and Range is bounded to the W by the

From COWARD, M.P., DEWEY, J.F. & HANCOCK, P.L. (eds), 1987, *Continental Extensional Tectonics*, Geological Society Special Publication No. 28, pp. 177–186.

178   *P.J. Coney*

Sierra Nevada batholith and to the E by the Colorado Plateau. The northern boundary, which is quite transitional, is the Columbia Plateau and the mountains N of the Snake River Plain. The Arizona–Sonora Basin and Range lies E of the Peninsular Ranges batholith of southern California and the Gulf of California, and S of the Colorado Plateau. The province extends eastward into southern New Mexico and Chihuahua, Mexico and then extends northward into Colorado as the narrow Rio Grande rift. The Rio Grande rift is a conspicuous narrow finger of block faulting that extends northward from northern Mexico into the southern and central Rocky Mountains along the eastern margin of the Colorado Plateau. Although often ignored in conceptual models of Basin and

Range tectonics, the Rio Grande rift displays identical geometry and timing to the larger Basin and Range Province of which it is a part. The Mojave Desert is largely that region E of the San Andreas Fault, S of the Garlock fault, and W of the Colorado River. The Basin and Range Province is most characterized by a basin and range topography and a general elevation less than surrounding provinces. Both the Rio Grande rift and Basin and Range Province are young, certainly no older than the past 17 My. Both are also clearly the result of widespread extensional block faulting and associated strike-slip faulting which collapsed and fragmented large segments of the Cordillera during the late Tertiary.

The Basin and Range Province is superimposed over a wide variety of inherited, regional tec-

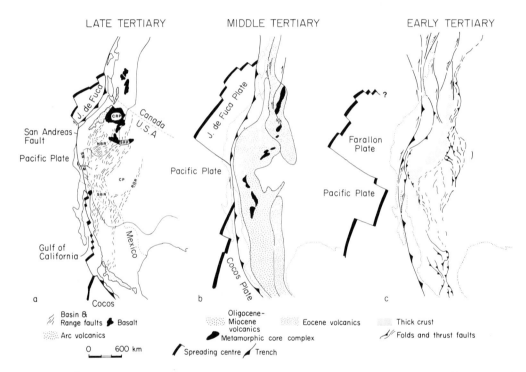

Fig. 1.(a) Regional and plate-tectonic setting of late-Tertiary Basin and Range extension. The Basin and Range Province is shown by fine lines depicting block faults in the western United States and northern Mexico. Heavy barbed line; subduction zone. Heavy line; spreading centres. V pattern; arc volcanic rocks. Black areas; late-Cenozoic flood basalt. Plate configuration is that of today. CRP = Columbia River plateau; SRP = Snake River Plain; SN = Sierra Nevada; NBR = northern Basin and Range; SBR = southern Basin and Range; CP = Colorado Plateau; M = Mojave Desert; RGR = Rio Grande rift. (b) Regional and plate-tectonic setting of mid-Tertiary extension. Dark areas are positions of the Cordilleran metamorphic core complexes. Subduction zones and spreading centres as in (a). Stippled area is the distribution of mainly Eocene volcanic rocks. V pattern is the distribution of mainly Oligocene–Miocene volcanics. The age of extension in each of the core complexes is the same as the age of the volcanic rocks with which each is associated. (c) The North American Cordillera at the end of Laramide Orogeny. Subduction zones and spreading centres as in (a) & (b). Fine lines and small barbed lines represent the fold and thrust belts of Laramide age. The pattern is the approximate position of the proposed thickened crustal welt due to crustal compression that later collapsed to form the belt of mid-Tertiary extension.

tonic domains. Most of the western half of the northern Basin and Range does not lie on ancient North American continental basement but instead extends well into the region of accreted 'suspect terranes' (Coney *et al.* 1980). In contrast, the eastern part of the northern Basin and Range and most of the Arizona–Sonora Basin and Range lie on ancient cratonic North America. The eastern part of the northern Basin and Range lies within the Palaeozoic miogeocline, the eastern hinge line of which coincides with the eastern edge of the Basin and Range and the western edge of the Colorado Plateau. On the other hand, the northern edge of the Arizona–Sonora Basin and Range is not a noticeable discontinuity in Palaeozoic stratigraphy. The Palaeozoic formations of the Colorado Plateau are essentially identical to those of the Basin and Range to the S. In both areas they are part of the thin interior cratonic sequence of southwestern North America.

The Basin and Range Province similarly has an interesting relationship to Mesozoic–early-Cenozoic compressional features. The eastern part of the northern Basin and Range developed in the mainly Cretaceous, pre-Laramide age, thin-skinned foreland fold and thrust belt which closely tracks the Cordilleran Palaeozoic miogeocline. The western part of the northern Basin and Range evolved in a region of early- to mid-Mesozoic thrusting and metamorphism probably associated with accretionary tectonics there. In contrast, the Arizona Basin and Range developed astride a wide belt of mainly Late Cretaceous–early-Tertiary Laramide deep-seated basement involved thrust faulting. Except for the narrow Rio Grande rift, the Basin and Range avoided the Colorado Plateau and the Rocky Mountains.

The Basin and Range Province is underlain by relatively thin (25 km thick) crust and experiences higher heat flow than adjacent regions (Thompson & Burke 1974; Eaton *et al.* 1978). The differentiation between the Basin and Range and adjacent provinces is particularly well known at the Colorado Plateau, which has a crust nearly 40 km thick, and the Sierra Nevada, which has a crust nearly 50 km thick. Both provinces have lower heat-flow values than the Basin and Range. A related geophysical fact is that the Bouguer gravity is slightly to considerably higher and the general elevation slightly to considerably lower in the Basin and Range as compared with the adjoining Colorado Plateau (Eaton *et al.* 1978). What is more important, however, is that general elevation is significantly higher and the Bouguer gravity is significantly lower over the entire region of the Basin and

Range, Colorado Plateau and Rocky Mountains than might be expected. This suggests the Basin and Range Province is simply a slightly collapsed part of a massive regional uplift which affects the entire Cordillera and even the Great Plains, as inspection of a continental relief map reveals.

The Basin and Range Province suffered extensional block faulting over the wide area described above (Stewart 1978) accompanied by scattered bimodal basaltic–rhyolitic volcanism (Christiansen & Lipman 1972). There was also some strike-slip faulting, particularly in the western part of the province, associated with growing transform faults along the Pacific margin. All this activity began, in some sectors at least, by 17 Ma (Eberly & Stanley 1978) and has continued, in some sectors at least, to the present time (Stewart 1978). There has been discussion as to whether the Basin and Range is time-transgressive and has grown northward with time. It is clear that large parts of the Arizona–Sonora region were not as recently active as the northern Basin and Range evidenced by much wide pedimentation, and a lack of evidence of recent faulting. Also, the general elevation there is significantly lower and the Bouguer gravity significantly higher than in the northern Basin and Range. This could suggest that the Arizona sector is now quiescent and perhaps cooling. The quiescence may coincide with the opening of the Gulf of California which might have transferred strain to Gulf spreading centres; whereas before, it had been distributed over the entire region, as it still is to the N in Nevada–Utah.

It is very clear that the Basin and Range Province, including the Rio Grande rift, results from late-Tertiary regional extension. Extension explains the thin crust and lithosphere, and the higher heat flow, and is compatible with normal faulting, present seismicity and general relative elevation. The amount of extension is much debated. Estimates have ranged from about 10 to over 100%, but the value probably lies in the range of 30 to 60% province-wide, with local variations (Stewart 1978; Coney & Harms 1984). If the extension were much more than 40%, some argue, the region would be below sea-level, although higher temperatures due to lithospheric thinning no doubt counteract the effect.

Late-Tertiary plate-tectonic settings of the Basin and Range Province evolved from late-Mesozoic to mid-Tertiary plate configurations (Atwater 1970). By the Late Cretaceous we know that at least three major plates, the Pacific, Farallon, and Kula, paved the eastern Pacific Ocean. Spreading centres lay between them and a trench formed along the accreting transpressive Pacific margin of North America. The trench was subducting first the Kula and then Farallon Plates, probably very obliquely, as these plates spread away from the East Pacific and related rises. Sometime after 30 Ma, but before 20 Ma, the East Pacific Rise made initial contact with North America, probably in the vicinity of southern California–northern Baja California. This placed the northwestward-moving Pacific Plate in direct contact with North America's westward moving margin, and the vector subtraction of these two motions produced right strike-slip transform faults between the two plates trending northwesterly parallel to the Pacific margin. As more and more of the rise crest was annihilated, the transform boundary developed to both N and S and subduction and arc activity ceased between the two separating triple junctions. Dickinson & Snyder (1979) have argued that this would produce a 'window' in the subducting slab NE of the growing transform boundary under the adjacent North American Plate. Their geometry depicts this window evolving directly under the Basin and Range Province.

The transform-fault boundary, which probably initially lay offshore, was nearly 1000 km long before Basin and Range rifting began ≈ 17 Ma during the Miocene (Atwater 1970; Engebretson *et al.* 1982). In any event, the annihilation of the East Pacific Rise has continued to the present and the entire evolution of Basin and Range extensional tectonics took place during this period. One major interruption in this progressive evolution occurred when the transform margin jumped inboard to open the Gulf of California and initiate the San Andreas fault system ≈ 6 Ma. This transferred Baja California and much of western California to the Pacific Plate, and probably stabilized the Arizona–Sonora sector of the Basin and Range. There was considerable clockwise rotation and northward translation of blocks within the coastal ranges of northwestern Mexico and California and in Washington and Oregon during this time.

Regional tectonic setting of mid-Tertiary extension

Mid-Tertiary extensional tectonism (Fig. 1b) in the North American Cordillera has been an illusive feature. It was overprinted and masked by the late-Tertiary extension of the Basin and Range (just discussed), and its resultant structures have been confused with those due to older

Mesozoic to early-Tertiary compression. Evidence of extensional tectonism in the mid-Tertiary was discovered only in the past 15 years and the controversy this discovery initiated has centred upon the so-called 'Cordilleran metamorphic core complexes' (Coney 1979, 1980; Davis & Coney 1979; Crittenden *et al.* 1980; Armstrong 1982; Coney & Harms 1984).

Cordilleran metamorphic core complexes occur in a sinuous discontinuous belt along the eastern part of the North American Cordillera extending from British Columbia in southern Canada S through the Cordillera into Sonora, Mexico over a distance of 3000 km. Over this distance all the complexes are characterized by similar rock type, structures and fabric. The complexes typically exhibit two distinctly different domains. These are a metamorphic–plutonic basement terrane and an overlying or adjacent unmetamorphosed cover. Separating the two is a sharp surface, or zone, of sub-horizontal shearing and detachment, usually with a younger on older geometry. The complexes are mostly domal or anticlinal in form and usually constitute the highest mountains in their respective regions.

The basement terranes of core complexes are characterized by low-dipping foliations and a distinctive 'stretching' lineation in mylonitic gneiss formed from protoliths that range from Precambrian basement to mid-Tertiary plutons. The unmetamorphosed cover terranes are replete with listric normal faults which have shattered protoliths, ranging across the entire spectrum of Phanerozoic sedimentary and volcanic rocks including mid-Tertiary continental volcanic and sedimentary rocks. The amount of extension in the cover terrane is often dramatic. Cover stratigraphy is usually strongly attenuated and the Tertiary rocks, the youngest of the original cover, are commonly brought down into tectonic contact with the mylonitic gneisses of the basement terrane. The detachment surface separating the basement and cover terranes is typically sharp and very visible in topography. The mylonitic fabrics of the basement terrane are commonly sub-parallel to the detachment surface, but rocks both above and below the detachment surface are usually intensely brecciated as a result of what appears to be the latest movement on the surface.

During the last few years the core complexes have generated a considerable controversy (Thorman 1977; DeWitt 1980; Brown & Read 1983). The debate has surrounded their age and tectonic significance. The age controversy (Armstrong 1982) stems from the fact that evidence for the age of deformation has seemed contradictory in that structural elements thought to result from one episode of deformation in one complex are identified as of a different age in another. The controversy surrounding tectonic significance is similar in that features that have been interpreted by some to be of compressional origin have been interpreted by others as extension-related. The debate became quite polarized for several years, but more recently has moved toward the realization that both processes have been important in the evolution of Cordilleran metamorphic core complexes (Armstrong 1982; Coney & Harms 1984).

From southern Nevada northward into southern Canada the metamorphic core complexes lie within a belt which extends about 200 km W of the eastern edge of the thin-skinned foreland fold and thrust belt so characteristic of the North American Cordillera (Fig. 1b & c). The complexes lie mostly within, or along the western edge of, the thick Palaeozoic miogeocline prisms. Here they form an infrastructural orogenic core zone of deep-seated metamorphism and associated plutonism behind the thrust belts to the E. They are in part due to some combination of mid-Mesozoic obduction of accreting terranes over the miogeoclinal margin and widespread intraplate telescoping which ramped the metamorphic core zone upward and eastward as the deformation moved eastward into the foreland during the late Mesozoic and early Cenozoic.

On the other hand, the metamorphic core complexes of Arizona and Sonora, Mexico are not in a 'hinterland' behind a foreland thrust belt, but are in the midst of a belt of rather deep-seated late Cretaceous to early-Tertiary, Laramide-age thrust faulting, which involved both the Precambrian basement as well as cover rocks. No infrastructural metamorphic core zone formed as it did to the N, but there is some syntectonic, rather low-grade, metamorphism found in areas of most severe deformation (Haxel *et al.* 1984).

Spatially associated with the belt of metamorphic core complexes is a suite of distinctive granitic plutons of the so-called two-mica type (Coney 1980). The majority of these are apparently of Cretaceous to early Tertiary age (Armstrong 1983).

Superimposed upon the compressional features, in both areas described above, are the features now nearly universally ascribed to mid-Tertiary extensional tectonics. As this extension began the previously tectonically uplifted hinterland began to collapse. Instead of being a source area, as it had been through the long preceding compressional periods, drainage

reversed and it became an area of deposition for continental sediments. Listric normal faulting became widespread, tilting the continental sediments to high angles. Eventually attenuation and tectonic denudation became so extreme that rocks once deeply buried were exposed in domal culminations to reveal mylonitic gneisses in which extensional fabrics are superimposed on earlier compressional features.

The age of mid-Tertiary extension is diachronous (Fig. 1b). The complexes N of the Snake River Plain in southern Idaho are mainly Eocene, whereas S of the plain they are mainly Oligocene–Miocene (Coney 1980). However, the extensional events in both areas occurred during a coeval period of spatially much more widespread volcanic eruptions and shallow plutonic emplacement (Elston 1976; 1984; Coney 1980; Dickinson 1981). This magmatic pulse is part of a very complex pattern of post-Laramide igneous activity that swept generally southwestward across the Cordillera from the Eocene Challis–Absaroka activity in the N to the Oligocene–Miocene 'ignimbrite flare-up' of the Great Basin and the American Southwest (Lipman *et al.* 1971; Armstrong 1974; Coney & Reynolds 1977).

Estimation of the amount of extension in the belt of metamorphic core complexes and associated listric normal faults is difficult, but it must have reached values of 40 to 75% (Coney & Harms 1984). The direction of extension, as revealed by pervasive stretching lineations in the basement terranes and tilted fault blocks in the cover, varies along-strike in the belt. To the N it was generally westward to slightly N of W, while in the central region it was more northwesterly. In the Arizona and Sonora sector the direction of extension was toward the SW.

The plate-tectonic setting of mid-Tertiary extension in the North American Cordillera is more difficult to reconstruct than that of the later Basin and Range extension, but there are reasonable limits on the options. There is considerable agreement that during the Late Cretaceous to early Tertiary Laramide Orogeny convergent rates between the Farallon and/or Kula Plates and the North America Plate were very elevated (9 to 15 cm yr^{-1}) and, particularly so in the case of the Kula Plate, oblique to the Cordilleran margin (Coney 1978; Engebretson *et al.* 1982). It is probable that the exact location of the triple junction between Kula–Farallon–North America will never be known for certain, but there is a growing consensus that it was initially far to the S off southern Mexico during the Late Cretaceous and that it then migrated northward to a more certain position near Vancouver Island by the late Eocene. Construction of vector circuits demonstrates that the convergent rate between the Farallon and North America Plates falls to nearly half of its Laramide value during the late Eocene. This is an artefact of the change in Pacific Plate motion over the Hawaii hot-spot represented by the elbow in the Hawaii-Emperor seamount chain now dated near 44 My. It could also have been due, in part, to a reduction in the North America Plate's westward motion at about this time (Coney 1971, 1978). This abrupt fall in rate has long been correlated with the end of the major compressional tectonics of the Laramide Orogeny in western North America (Coney 1971, 1978). Subduction of the Farallon Plate or its remaining fragments beneath North America's western margin continued at the reduced rate during the mid-Tertiary until the East Pacific Rise was progressively extinguished from near 30 Ma to the present. In other words, the compressional events of Laramide age correlate with high rates of plate convergence, while the extensional events of the mid-Tertiary correlate with reduced rates of convergence. It is important to emphasize that the extension of the middle Tertiary began before subduction ceased.

Analyses of the timing and distribution of structural features and igneous activity associated with the compressional Laramide Orogeny and subsequent extensional tectonics and associated igneous activity of the mid-Tertiary (Fig. 1b & c) have led to the hypothesis that the subducting plate progressively flattened in dip beneath the western United States during the Laramide to the point that it was nearly horizontal by the Eocene (Coney & Reynolds 1977). This geometry has been used to explain the presence of deep-seated, basement cored, thrust-bound uplifts, so typical of the Laramide Orogeny, as far E as Denver, over 1000 km from the assumed subduction zone (Dickinson & Snyder 1979). Likewise, the equally eastward sweep of presumed arc-related Laramide igneous activity to eventual near extinction by the Eocene is similarly explained (Coney & Reynolds 1977). This proposed flattening of the Laramide Benioff zone, and the destruction it is supposed to have produced, correlates with the high rates of convergence of the Laramide discussed above.

Then, during the Eocene, the compressional deformation ceased, ending the Laramide Orogeny, as convergent rates dropped. What followed was a striking retrograde sweep of the massive outburst of ignimbrites back toward the coast during the mid-Tertiary (Coney & Reynolds 1977) associated with the extensional tectonics of the metamorphic core complexes and listric normal faults. The retrograde sweep of presumed arc-like igneous activity has been correlated with a proposed collapse and/or steepening of the earlier flat-dipping Laramide subducting slab during the Eocene to Miocene.

Presumably, as the East Pacific Rise was progressively extinguished, causing a cessation of subduction and initiating the transform regimens between the Pacific and North America Plates during the late Tertiary, the extension of the mid-Tertiary merged and transposed itself into the extension of the Basin and Range. The two phases of extensional tectonics probably overlap in space and time in the southwesternmost United States where mid-Tertiary extension seems to be youngest, and the extension of the Basin and Range may be oldest. Further inland and northward, the two extensional phases must be separated by as much as 20 My or more. This fact, coupled with the observation that the structural styles, directions of extension, and type of igneous activity of the two extensional phases are so distinct seems to suggest that they are best kept separate in our minds and may have a different origin.

A search for a cause

Most models proposed to explain the extensional tectonic features of the mid-Tertiary and Basin and Range have been largely kinematic in character (Davis & Coney 1979; Stewart 1978; Wernicke 1981; Wernicke & Burchfiel 1982). The emphasis has been upon the geometry of the metamorphic core complexes and related listric normal faults in the case of the middle Tertiary, or upon the geometry of the horsts and grabens and related strike-slip faults in the case of the Basin and Range. There has been a general recognition that most of what we see is above the brittle–ductile transition and that the faulting probably shallows with depth to merge into sub-horizontal surfaces of ductile shear. Recent deep seismic sounding seems to confirm these concepts (Smith & Bruhn 1984).

Considering the problem at crustal scales, and assuming that intraplate continental deformation is essentially penetrative and approximates pure shear (England 1982), yields the conclusion that upper-crustal telescoping or extension must be matched by commensurate crustal thickening or thinning. If this approach is applied to western North America (Coney & Harms 1984), restoration of the estimates of extension during Basin and Range and mid-Tertiary time yields crustal geometry at the beginning of each period of extension. Most important, the process yields the crustal geometry at the end of the phase of Mesozoic to early-Cenozoic compressional tectonism at about 50 My BP before the initiation of extension. There are obvious weaknesses inherent in both the method and the data bases used, but the approach seems to give reasonable results that might be representative of the pattern of crustal conditions at Cordilleran scale.

The details of this procedure (Coney & Harms 1984) will not be reviewed here, but the broad results of restoration of Cenozoic crustal extension in the western United States yields a pre-Basin and Range palinspastic palaeocrustal thickness map where fairly uniform crustal thicknesses of 35–40 km are obtained based on extension values of about 40–60% across the width of the Basin and Range. If correct, the crustal thickness in the Basin and Range before rifting began was about the same as the crustal thickness of the Colorado Plateau today (Coney & Harms 1984, fig. 3). Quantification of extension during mid-Tertiary development of the mẽtamorphic core complexes is more difficult, but exposure of crystalline infrastructure suggests stripping of at least one complete thickness of the $\approx$ 10-km thick original sedimentary and volcanic cover. Extensional values of 40 to 75% are not unreasonable. The restoration of mid-Tertiary extension using these values results in a palinspastic and palaeocrustal thickness map representative of conditions just prior to Cenozoic extension and just after Laramide compression (Coney & Harms 1984, fig. 4). The principal feature of this map is an overthickened crustal welt along the trend of the belt of Cordilleran metamorphic core complexes (Fig. 1c).

The overthickened crustal welt is the result of mainly Middle Jurassic to early-Tertiary crustal telescoping iñ and behind the Cordilleran thrust belt and within the metamorphic hinterland. Estimates of shortening within the thrust belts range from 50% or more in the Canadian and northern Rocky Mountain thrust belts (Price & Mountjoy 1970; Royse *et al.* 1975) to about 30% in southwestern Arizona (Davis 1979). These amounts, particularly when added to comparable deep-seated telescoping through crustal-scale duplexing and ductile flow in the Cordilleran metamorphic hinterland, are ample to produce a 50–60 km thick crustal welt (see Coney 1979, pp. 21–22 and Fig. 2a). Armstrong's (1983) suggestion that the so-called two-mica granites typical of the Cordilleran hinterland core complex belt (Coney 1980), the majority of which are Cretaceous to early Tertiary in age, are produced by melting in overthickened crustal roots supports this proposition.

If we now combine the data on the regional and plate-tectonic setting of Cenozoic extension in western North America discussed in the previous sections with the inferences on the evolution of crustal geometry discussed above, we have before us most of the obvious elements which when summed somehow must have caused that extension. I will discuss in turn those factors that seem most important.

It was argued above that an overthickened crustal welt 50–60 km thick formed from intraplate telescoping in the hinterland behind, or astride, the belt of Middle Jurassic to early-Tertiary thrust faulting of the North American Cordillera. This welt became the site of deep-seated crustal extension in the core complexes during the Eocene through to the Miocene. A simple calculation (Le Pichon 1982) shows that an overthickened continental crustal welt at or near a continental margin, particularly when it has an isostatically generated topographic head, generates lithostatic pressures as a function of depth greater than those found at equivalent depths in the adjacent oceanic crust. The pressure difference reaches a maximum somewhere between 10 and 15 km depth. Several workers have recently suggested that overthickened continental welts produced by intraplate telescoping will spread laterally because of gravitational instability if there is sufficient lateral density variation, sufficient topographic head and sufficient lowering of viscosity (England 1982; Molnar & Chen 1983; see also Le Pichon 1982). Presumably the flow can occur only if the welt is not laterally confined by stronger regions or under high compressive boundary stress resulting from convergent plate margin and/or intraplate high compressive stress regimes. If all the flow is below the brittle-ductile transition, what we see at the surface in the core complexes and listric normal faults is a brittle 'raft' torn apart as the crust deforms by pure shear below.

A second factor which may have been very important is the observation discussed in the previous section that an extensive outburst of caldera-centred ash flows coexisted with the extending core complexes during the mid-Tertiary. The principal effect of this igneous activity was presumably to lower crustal viscosity through higher heat flow. As was mentioned above, the lowering of crustal viscosity could be a contributing factor in allowing the gravitationally unstable crustal welt to spread. Coney & Harms (1984) suggested that this magmatic pulse may have in fact triggered the crustal extension by providing the necessary ductility to permit flow. The higher heat flow would also have presumably raised the brittle–ductile transition to shallower than normal levels, perhaps placing it at, or even above, the levels of highest pressure gradients generated by the lateral density contrasts discussed above.

A third factor which may have contributed to the Cenozoic extension is the observation that compressive stress at the western margin of North America may have dropped significantly during the Eocene at the end of the Laramide Orogeny. Recall that this reduction in compressive stress derives from changes in plate kinematics in the Pacific realm (Coney 1978; Engebretson *et al.* 1982), and may have even been caused in part by a drop in North America's westward motion (Coney 1971). This stress drop may have been coupled with, or at least accompanied by, collapse and/or steepening of the previously flat-dipping Laramide subducting slab after the Eocene (Coney & Reynolds 1977). The collapse and/or steepening of the slab in itself would create a downward force which translates into the so-called 'roll-back' (Dewey 1980), or 'suction' force which tends to induce migration of the trench and its adjacent continental margin toward the ocean and away from the continent (Le Pichon 1982). In any event, these factors would presumably have reduced

the boundary stress to the W releasing the stored potential energy in the thickened welt and allowing it to spread laterally in that direction.

All of the above important factors, particularly when summed, seem adequate to generate the stresses necessary to cause the mid-Tertiary extension seen in the Cordilleran metamorphic core complex belt. It suggests that an over-thickened crustal welt formed by intraplate crustal telescoping which took place from the Cretaceous to the early Tertiary (Fig. 2a). It is important to realize that in the thin-skinned decollement-style thrust belt typical of the central and northern Cordillera most of the crustal thickening took place behind the foreland fold and thrust belt in the metamorphic hinterland. In areas where thrusting was more profound and involved the crystalline basement, such as in the Laramide belt of Arizona, the thickening took place within and beneath the telescoping and not behind it. It is also significant that the crustal welt may not have formed everywhere at the same time. For example, in Utah–Nevada it was probably late Jurassic to Cretaceous (Sevier) in age, whereas in southern Canada it was late Jurassic–Cretaceous and early Tertiary (Columbian–Laramide), and in Arizona it was Late Cretaceous to early Tertiary (Laramide).

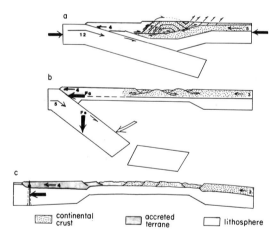

FIG. 2. Possible forces at work during Cenozoic Cordilleran tectonic evolution. (a) Late-Mesozoic–early Cenozoic Laramide compression. The North America Plate moves westward (left) at 5 cm yr^{-1} while the Farallon plate moves eastward at 12 cm yr^{-1} and subducts at a shallow angle. The opposed forces (heavy arrows) produce high intraplate compressive stress. Intraplate telescoping during Laramide compression is assumed to be about 1 cm yr^{-1} producing the crustal welt. Relative motion between the North America and Farallon Plates at the plate margin is thus 16 cm yr^{-1}. (b) Mid-Tertiary extension. North America Plate westward motion falls to 3 cm yr^{-1} and Farallon Plate eastward motion falls to 5 cm yr^{-1}. The crustal welt spreads westward at a rate of about 1 cm yr^{-1} yielding a relative motion between North America and Farallon Plates of 9 cm yr^{-1} at the plate margin. Fc is the spreading force of the extending crust; Fs is the suction force of the collapsing slab. (c) Late-Tertiary Basin and Range extension. The North America Plate continues to move westward at 3 cm yr^{-1} while the Pacific Plate moves into the figure and away on the other side of the San Andreas Fault at the left. A broad Cordilleran uplift produces a gradient down which the fragmenting orogen moves toward a 'free face' opening the Basin and Range.

Regardless, the unstable crustal welt remained until after its viscosity was lowered by the post-Laramide magmatic patterns and the regional intraplate stress was reduced (Fig. 2b). Under these conditions the welt spread laterally toward the coast in the direction of least resistance, reversing the earlier compression and producing the superposition of Tertiary extensional features on earlier structural and metamorphic features of Mesozoic–early-Tertiary crustal shortening (Coney & Harms 1984).

All of the above may offer an explanation for mid-Tertiary extension, but the extension of the Basin and Range remains. Recall that reversal of Basin and Range extension discussed in an earlier section generates a continental crustal section slightly in excess of normal, or at least about the same as the crust under the Colorado Plateau today. Recall also that the evolution of the Basin and Range seems inseparably tied to the progressive demise of the East Pacific Rise and development of a complex transform margin replacing a convergent one (Atwater 1970). This may have further reduced compressive stress, or made it even more extensional as the case may be, creating what amounts to a free face (Fig. 2c). Furthermore, it has been argued (Dickinson & Snyder 1979) that the progressive extinction of the East Pacific Rise would create a so-called slab 'window' beneath the southwestern Cordillera seemingly geometrically required by growth of the Pacific–North America transform margin as subduction ceased. This would allow hot asthenosphere to well up into the window heating the North American lithosphere above. Damon (1979) has suggested the progressive approach of the Earth Pacific Rise towards the North America margin translates into progressive subduction of younger and hotter lithosphere beneath that

margin. This also is a source of heat and both factors could have contributed to regional uplift. If we couple this to the observation that the only regional tectonic pattern the Basin and Range comes near to mimicking is the ground previously ignited by the mid-Tertiary magmatism, we are left with the possibility that enough thermally induced gravitational instability exists in a thermally weakened and uplifted lithosphere to be released by the free face. This includes the Colorado Plateau, which is beginning to act like a microplate, as it accelerates westward slightly ahead of a trailing North America Plate opening the Rio Grande rift behind it, and slightly behind the Basin and Range and the rest of the Cordillera W of it. This is beginning to sound like plate tectonics, instead of the intraplate tectonics of the mid-Tertiary, and suggests that the entire fragmenting Cordillera is moving westward down a deep-seated gradient. Such extension usually leads to the opening of oceans.

In conclusion, it should be pointed out, if it has not already been obvious, that all of the arguments proposed above to explain Cenozoic extension are 'passive' in a dynamic sense. The forces appealed to here are bouyancy and body forces generated by the plates themselves and occuring within the plates and perturbations from normality produced by plate interactions and intraplate response. One can think of all sorts of sub-lithospheric currents generated from descending slabs and particularly changes in dip of those slabs, asthenospheric flow patterns generated from delaminating slabs, slab windows, and the like. These would be more 'active' forces from below and may be quite real. They are not discussed here because they do not seem to be required and more importantly because they are so intractable.

References

ARMSTRONG, R. L. 1972. Low-angle (denudational) faults, hinterland of the Sevier orogenic belt, eastern Nevada and western Utah. *Bull. geol. Soc. Am.* **83**, 1729–54.
—— 1974. Geochronology of the Eocene volcanic-plutonic episode in Idaho. *Northwest Geol.* **3**, 1–14.
—— 1982. Cordilleran metamorphic core complexes – from Arizona to southern Canada. *Ann. Rev. Earth planet. Sci.* **10**, 129–54.
—— 1983. Cordilleran S- and I-type granites: indicators of lithosphere thickness. *Geol. Assoc. Canada Ann. Mtg. Prog.* **8**, A3.
ATWATER, T. 1970. Implications of place tectonics for the Cenozoic tectonic evolution of western North America. *Bull. geol. Soc. Am.* **81**, 3513–36.

BROWN, R.L. & READ, P.B. 1983. Shuswap terrane of British Columbia: a Mesozoic 'core complex'. *Geology*, **11**, 164–8.
CHRISTIANSEN, R.L. & LIPMAN, P.W. 1972. Cenozoic volcanism and plate tectonic evolution of western United States: 11. Late Cenozoic. *Phil. Trans. R. Soc. London*, **271**, 249–84.
CONEY, P.J. 1971. Cordilleran tectonic transitions and motion of the North American plate. *Nature*, **233**, 462–5.
—— 1978. Mesozoic–Cenozoic Cordilleran Plate Tectonics. *In*: SMITH, R.B. & EATON, G.I. (eds) *Cenozoic Tectonics and Regional Geophysics of the Western Cordillera. Mem. geol. Soc. Am.* **152**, 33–50.

186   *P.J. Coney*

—— 1979. Tertiary evolution of Cordilleran metamorphic core complexes. *In*: ARMENTROUT, J.W., COLE, M.R. & TERBEST, H. (eds) *Cenozoic Paleogeography of Western United States. Soc. econ. Paleontol. Min., Pac. sect. Symp. 111.*

—— 1980. Cordilleran metamorphic core complexes: an overview. *In*: CRITTENDEN, M.L., CONEY, P.J. & DAVIS, G.H. (eds) *Cordilleran Metamorphic Core Complexes. Mem. geol. Soc. Am.* **153**, 7–34.

—— & REYNOLDS, S.J. 1977. Cordilleran Benioff zones. *Nature*, **270**, 403–6.

—— & HARMS, T.A. 1984. Cordilleran metamorphic core complexes: Cenozoic extensional relics of Mesozoic compression. *Geology*, **12**, 550–4.

——, JONES, D.L. & MONGER, J.W.H. 1980. Cordilleran suspect terranes. *Nature*, **288**, 329–33.

CRITTENDEN, M.D., JR, CONEY, P.J. & DAVIS, G.H. 1980. *Cordilleran Metamorphic Core Complexes. Mem. geol. Soc. Am.* **153**, 490 pp.

DAMON, P.E. 1979. Continental uplift at convergent margins. *Tectonophysics*, **61**, 307–19.

DAVIS, G.H. 1979. Laramide folding and faulting in southeastern Arizona. *Am. J. Sci.* **279**, 543–69.

—— & CONEY, P.J. 1979. Geologic development of the Cordilleran metamorphic core complexes. *Geology*, **7**, 120–4.

DEWEY, J.F. 1980. Episodicity, sequence, and style of convergent plate boundaries. *In*: STRANGWAY, D.W. (ed.) *The Continental Crust and its Mineral Deposits. Spec. Pap. geol. Assoc. Canada,* '20, 553–73.

DEWITT, E. 1980. Comment on Geologic development of the Cordilleran metamorphic core complexes. *Geology*, **8**, 6–9.

DICKINSON, W.R. 1981. Plate tectonic evolution of the southern Cordillera. *In*: DICKINSON, W.R. & PAYNE, W.D. (eds) *Relations of Tectonics to Ore Deposits in the Southern Cordillera. Digest Ariz. geol. Soc.* **14**, 113–35.

—— & SNYDER, W.S. 1979. Geometry of subducted slabs related to San Andreas transform. *J. Geology*, **87**, 609–27.

EATON, G.P. 1982. The Basin and Range province: origin and tectonic significance. *Ann. Rev. Earth planet. Sci.* **10**, 409–40.

——, WAHL, R.R., PROTSKA, H.J., MAYBEY, D.R. & KLIENKOPF, M.D. 1978. Regional gravity and tectonic patterns: their relation to late Cenozoic epeirogeny and lateral spreading in the western Cordillera. *In*: SMITH, R.B. & EATON, G.L. (eds) *Cenozoic Tectonics and Regional Geophysics of the Western Cordillera. Mem. geol. Soc. Am.* **152**, 51–92.

EBERLY, L.D. & STANLEY, T.B. 1978. Cenozoic stratigraphy and geologic history of southwestern Arizona. *Bull. geol. Soc. Am.* **89**, 921–40.

ELSTON, W.E. 1976. Tectonic significance of mid-Tertiary volcanism in the Basin and Range province: a critical review with special reference to New Mexico. *In*: ELSTON, W.E. & NORTHRUP, S.A. (eds) *Cenozoic Volcanism in Southwestern New Mexico. Spec. Publ. New Mex. geol. Soc.* **5**, 93–151.

—— 1984. Subduction of young oceanic lithosphere and extensional orogeny in southwestern North America during mid-Tertiary time. *Tectonics*, **3**, 229–50.

ENGEBRETSON, D.C., COX, A.V. & THOMPSON, G.A. 1982. Convergence and tectonics: Laramide to Basin and Range. *Eos*. **63**, 911.

ENGLAND, P. 1982. Some numerical investigations of large scale continental deformation. *In*: HSU, K.J. (ed.) *Mountain Building Processes*, pp. 129–39. Academic Press, London.

HAXEL, G.B., TOSDAL, R.M., MAY, D.J. & WRIGHT, J.E. 1984. Latest Cretaceous and early Tertiary orogenesis in south-central Arizona: thrust faulting, regional metamorphism, and granite plutonism. *Bull. geol. Soc. Am.* **94**, 632–53.

LEPICHON, X. 1982. Land-locked oceanic basins and continental collision: the eastern Mediterranean as a case example. *In*: HSU, K.J. (ed.) *Mountain Building Processes*, pp. 201–12. Academic Press, London.

LIPMAN, P.W., PROTSKA, H.J. & CHRISTIANSEN, R.L. 1971. Evolving subduction zones in the western United States as interpreted from igneous rocks. *Science*, **174**, 821–5.

MOLNAR, P. & CHEN, W.-P. 1983. Focal depths and fault plane solutions of earthquakes under the Tibetan plateau. *J. geophys. Res.* **88**, 1180–96.

PRICE, R.A. & MOUNTJOY, E. W. 1970. Geologic structure of the Canadian Rocky Mountains between Bow and Athabasca Rivers – a progress report. *Sp. Pap. Geol. Assoc. Canada*, **6**, 7–25.

ROYSE, F., JR, WARNER, M.A. & REESE, D.L. 1975. Thrust belt structural geometry and related stratigraphic problems, Wyoming–Idaho–northern Utah. *Rocky Mnt. Assoc. Geol. 1975 Symposium*. 41–54.

SMITH, R.B. & BRUHN, R.L. 1984. Intraplate extensional tectonics of the eastern Basin and Range: inference on structural style from seismic reflection data, regional tectonics, and thermal–mechanical models of brittle–ductile deformation. *J. geophys. Res.* **89**, 5733–62.

STEWART, J.H. 1978. Basin and Range structure in western North America: a review. *In*: SMITH, R.B. & EATON, G.L. (eds) *Cenozoic Tectonics and Regional Geophysics of the Western Cordillera. Mem. geol. Soc. Am.* **152**, 1–31.

THOMPSON, G.A. & BURKE, D.B. 1974. Regional geophysics of the Basin and Range province. *Ann. Rev. Earth planet. Sci.* **2**, 213–38.

THORMAN, C.H. 1977. Gravity induced folding off a gneiss dome complex, Rincon Mountains, Arizona –a discussion. *Bull. geol. Soc. Am.* **88**, 1211–2.

WERNICKE, B. 1981. Low angle normal faults in the Basin and Range province: nappe tectonics in an extending orogen. *Nature*, **192**, 645–8.

—— & BURCHFIEL, B.C. 1982. Modes of extension tectonics. *J. struct. Geol.* **4**, 105–15.

P.J. CONEY, Department of Geosciences, University of Arizona, Tucson, AZ 85721, USA.

A physical model for Cenozoic extension of western North America

L.J. Sonder, P.C. England, B.P. Wernicke & R.L. Christiansen

SUMMARY: We investigate the possibility that the onset and development of Cenozoic extension in western North America was governed by the potential energy contrast within, and mechanical properties of, lithosphere that was previously thickened during the Sevier and Laramide Orogenies. The strength of the lithosphere can be defined by its vertically averaged properties; to a first approximation, this strength is too great for geologically significant extension to occur unless the Moho temperature exceeds about 700°C ($\pm 100°$). This means that there may be a delay between the end of compression and the beginning of extension, the length of which depends on the pre-thickening thermal structure and the compressional strain. Delays of up to 100 My may occur for the lowest initial Moho temperatures investigated (<450°C), or extension may follow immediately on release of compression if the initial Moho temperature exceeds about 700°C. The total extensional strain that is achieved depends on the potential-energy contrast between the thickened lithosphere and its surroundings. Partial melting of peridotite to produce basaltic magma is possible after small degrees of extension, but depends strongly on details of the initial temperature condition in the lower part of the lithosphere.

The results of these calculations agree with observations of the Cenozoic extensional history of North America: late-Mesozoic/early-Tertiary compression in the Pacific Northwest was accompanied by extensive calc-alkaline magmatic activity and was followed almost immediately by extension; in the northern and southern Great Basin—which show respectively, little and no evidence of syn-compressional igneous activity—the gap between compression and extension was 20–40 Ma (N) to about 70 Ma (S).

A number of explanations have been proposed for the Cenozoic extension in western North America. One view relates it to Pacific–Farallon–North American Plate interactions; for example, following Atwater (1970), the extension has often been ascribed to distributed shear resulting from transform motion along the North American Plate boundary. However, this is not easy to reconcile with the fact that the tectonic regime along western North America has been compressive to transpressive through much of the Cenozoic (see data summarized by Wernicke *et al.* this issue), and many details of geography and timing of extension are difficult to relate to any obvious features of Pacific or North American Plate motions. Other explanations rely on inherently untestable assumptions about the mantle underneath North America in the early Tertiary, such as the existence of hot-spots or buoyant subducted slabs.

By contrast, we use a simple quantitative model to consider the hypothesis that extension in the western Cordillera resulted not from forces acting on the base or edges of the North American Plate but from forces in the plate interior inherited from its pre-extensional tectonic history. Much of western North America experienced multiple episodes of compression and crustal thickening during the Mesozoic and earliest Cenozoic eras, and the subsequent extension occurred mainly in a N–S band that coincides with the locus of crustal thickening during the Sevier and Laramide Orogenies (Christiansen & Lipman 1972; Molnar & Chen 1983).

It has long been recognized (e.g. Love 1911; Jeffreys 1929) that regions of isostatically compensated thickened crust may be in a state of extensional deviatoric stress and this has provided the basis for many mechanical explanations of continental extension (e.g. Bott & Dean 1972; McKenzie 1972; Artyushkov 1973; Le Pichon 1982). Molnar & Chen (1983) suggest that extension of the Basin and Range Province resulted from such stresses in a manner analogous to, but more complete than, the present extension of the Tibetan Plateau.

Much of the published work on this topic has concentrated on the existence of potential energy contrasts that create a tendency for thickened crust to extend. Whether or not this tendency results in an appreciable extensional strain rate depends on the instantaneous strength of the lithosphere (a term to be defined later), and the degree of extension depends on the evolution of the potential energy and strength of the lithosphere during stretching. In

From COWARD, M.P., DEWEY, J.F. & HANCOCK, P.L. (eds), 1987, *Continental Extensional Tectonics*, Geological Society Special Publication No. 28, pp. 187–201.

this paper we use a simple mechanical model for the continental lithosphere to calculate the evolution of the strength and potential energy of the lithosphere during compressional and extensional strain. The amount of compressional strain experienced by the continental lithosphere and its post-compressional thermal profile largely determine the amount and timing of its subsequent extension. We investigate the dependence of the total extensional strain and the time of onset of extension on these parameters and attempt an interpretation of the variations in Cenozoic extensional history of western North America in terms of the results of these calculations. This analysis does not preclude contributions from other mechanisms to Cordilleran extension, but it does provide a coherent and testable basis for understanding the origin and timing of Cenozoic extension and related magmatism in western North America.

Evolution of lithospheric strength

To calculate the finite strain of the continental lithosphere we need to calculate strain rates at all points within it. In general this is a formidable problem, but a reasonable first approach is to neglect the (in any case ill-defined) effects of lateral variations in strain and consider the thermal and mechanical evolution of a single column of lithosphere that strains in the vertical and one horizontal direction in response to the potential energy contrast between itself and a reference column of continental lithosphere (see Fig. 3). In addition, we follow previous workers (Bird & Piper 1980; Bird & Baumgardner 1984; England & McKenzie 1982, 1983; England & Houseman 1986; Houseman & England 1986a; Sonder *et al.* 1986; Vilotte *et al.* 1982) and treat the lithosphere as an incompressible thin sheet overlying an inviscid substrate; only vertical integrals of stress and strain rate are considered.

Under these conditions, the strength of the lithosphere may be defined as the vertical integral of the deviatoric stress that is required to produce a given horizontal strain rate. This depends principally on the mineralogy of the rocks that make up the lithosphere, and on their temperatures.

For the purposes of these calculations we adopt the rheology for the continental lithosphere suggested by Brace & Kohlstedt (1980), which contains a brittle upper crust obeying Byerlee's law, a ductile lower crust, the deformation of which is governed by the power-law creep of quartz and a mantle, the deforma-

tion of which is governed by Byerlee's law, by high stress plasticity, or by power-law creep of olivine, depending on the strain rate, confining pressure, and temperature. The uncertainty in temperature attached to using these flow laws is discussed below.

Dependence of lithospheric strength on geotherm

Sonder & England (1986) show that for a wide choice of geothermal gradients, the vertically integrated strength of such a lithosphere depends primarily on the temperature at the Moho and on the stress difference at the brittle–ductile transition. This is illustrated in Fig. 1, which shows the dependence of the extensional strain rate on the Moho temperature and on the frictional (Byerlee's law) contribution to the strength for a fixed vertically integrated driving stress of 5×10^{12} N m^{-1}.

The primary geological application of this paper is the extension in the Cordillera of western North America; this has accomplished several tens of percent strain in 30 Ma, thus a relevant strain rate for this problem is a few

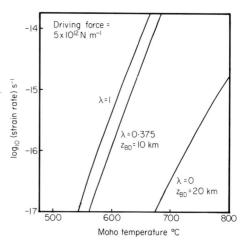

FIG. 1. Extensional strain rate resulting from a driving force of 5×10^{12} N m^{-1} acting on a thin sheet with a vertically averaged rheology containing friction on faults (Byerlee's law), power-law creep of quartz, and Dorn law creep and power-law creep of olivine (see Brace & Kohlstedt 1980). λ is the ratio of pore-fluid pressure to lithostatic pressure in the crust and z_{BD} is the depth to the brittle–ductile transition; when $\lambda = 1$ the deformation is controlled by creep in the upper mantle. Decreasing λ and increasing z_{BD} represent increasing contributions to the strength from friction on faults (see Sonder & England 1986).

times 10^{-16} sec^{-1}. In the cases illustrated in Fig. 1, this strain rate is reached at Moho temperatures between 550 and 750°C. This result is not strongly dependent upon the value of the driving force used and leads us to consider next a simple estimate of the length of time required for the lithosphere to be capable of straining at a geologically significant rate. Figure 1 shows that if a Moho temperature of 750° has been reached, a strain rate of at least 10^{-16} sec^{-1} is calculated for any of the conditions considered.

We assume an initial condition in which shortening is accomplished by uniformly thickening the lithosphere by a factor, f, so that the temperature at a depth, z, is equal to the pre-shortening temperature at depth z/f. We use the method of England & Thompson (1984, appendix B, equation B12) to calculate the approximate amount of time for the Moho to reach 750°C, as a function of the initial Moho temperature and the vertical compressional strain, f.

Figure 2 shows the results of this calculation, using the parameter values listed in Table 1; different initial Moho temperatures correspond to different steady-state mantle heat fluxes. The time required to reach 750°C decreases with the compressional strain and with the initial Moho temperature. Initially hot lithosphere (that had, for example, experienced continental arc volcanism during the compressional stage) could be capable of extending immediately after crustal shortening ends. Conversely, cold lithosphere may take some tens of millions of years to become weak enough to deform. If the amount of thickening is too small, lithosphere may remain cold and strong enough to support the extensional stresses without appreciable extensional strain. Figure 2 indicates that if the compressional strain, f, is less than approximately 1.25, extension will not begin in less than 60–100 My after the end of compression unless

the initial Moho temperature is greater than 650°C. Under these circumstances erosion is likely to be a more efficient means of reducing the crustal thickness.

Between these extremes lies a range of degrees of thickening and of Moho temperatures that are relevant to many orogenic belts, and this calculation indicates approximately the conditions under which one might expect such a belt to undergo either no post-compressional extension, extension during or immediately after compression, or extension beginning some tens of millions of years after the end of compression. However, this treatment neglects any influence of strain on the geotherm and provides no estimate of the amount of extension. In the following section we describe calculations that have a bearing on the thermal and mechanical evolution of such a lithosphere after extension begins.

A physical model for extension following compression of continental crust

Description of the model

We define a reference state for continental lithosphere by requiring it to be in isostatic and potential energy equilibrium with oceanic lithosphere and in thermal steady-state with basal temperature, T_1, and heat production, H_0, distributed uniformly throughout the crust (see Fig. 3). Instantaneous homogeneous thickening of the reference lithosphere perturbs the geotherm and changes the potential energy of the lithosphere. The contrast in potential energy between the thickened lithosphere and the reference lithosphere gives rise to deviatoric stresses that can drive extension if the strength of the lithosphere permits.

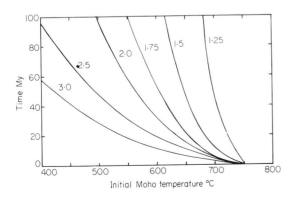

FIG. 2. Time required for the Moho temperature to reach 750°C, as a function of initial Moho temperature and compressional strain f using the method of England & Thompson (1984, appendix B, equation B12). The value of f is indicated beside each curve.

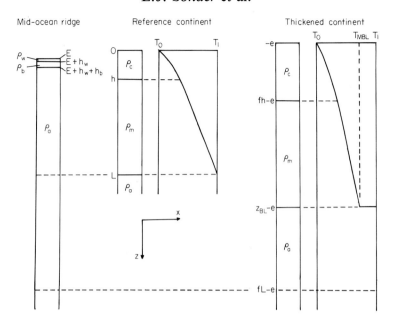

FIG. 3. Reference state and initial density and temperature conditions for the calculations of this paper. Reference lithosphere is in potential energy and isostatic equilibrium with mid-ocean ridge; under these conditions crustal density, ϱ_c, and elevation, E, are constrained once values for crustal thickness, h, and heat production, H_0, are chosen (see Table 1 for parameter values). Reference lithosphere is assumed to be in thermal steady-state with heat production H_0 distributed uniformly throughout the crust, and with surface and basal temperatures T_0 and T_1, respectively. Initial conditions are a consequence of uniformly and instantaneously thickening the reference continent by a factor f. The elevation change associated with isostatic response to the thickening is e. At depth z_{BL}, where the temperature is T_{MBL}, the lower portion of the lithosphere is assumed to detach and be replaced by asthenosphere with temperature T_1 (see text).

The thermal and mechanical evolution of thickened continental lithosphere depends strongly on the choice of a lower boundary condition. Since the lithosphere can be regarded as a mechanically rigid layer overlying a convecting asthenosphere, there must be a thermal boundary layer at the base of the lithosphere across which heat is transferred dominantly by conduction, but which is hotter, hence weaker, than the overlying mechanical lithosphere (see, e.g. Parsons & McKenzie 1978). Houseman *et al.* (1981) have shown that a lithospheric thickening event, such as occurred in the Mesozoic and early Cenozoic in western North America, can result in instability of the thickened thermal boundary layer, which consequently detaches from the mechanical lithosphere and is replaced by material at asthenospheric temperatures. The time at which detachment occurs depends on the intensity of mantle convection and, in the cases illustrated by Houseman *et al.*, lies between 0 and 100 My after the end of thickening.

We assume that during compression of the continent the mechanical lithosphere is thickened to the same extent as the crust; however, we follow Houseman *et al.* (1981) in recognizing the instability of the thickened thermal boundary layer. In the absence of any constraint on the timing of the detachment of the thermal boundary layer, we assume that it occurs at the end of compression. We define the base of the mechanical boundary layer (i.e. the depth at which detachment occurs) by an isotherm, T_{MBL}, which we take to be a free parameter. The exact form of the boundary and initial conditions, and a summary of the governing equations, are contained in the Appendix.

For the rest of this paper, we shall be concerned with the evolution of the potential energy and thermal profile of the lithosphere from these initial conditions, and the resulting strain history. In order to reduce the number of parameters investigated, we neglect the contribution of the crust to the strength of the lithosphere. Thus our results represent the maximum extension to be expected from the model discussed in this paper.

The extensional strain, β, is defined as the ratio of the crustal thickness immediately after the shortening event to its thickness at a subse-

TABLE 1. *Values of parameters used in the calculations.*

L	Reference lithosphere thickness	110 km
h	Reference crustal thickness	33.75 km
h_w	Water depth above mid-ocean ridge	2.5 km
h_b	Crustal thickness at mid-ocean ridge	5.0 km
ϱ_w	Density of water	1.03×10^3 kg m^{-3}
ϱ_b	Density of oceanic crust	2.96×10^3 kg m^{-3}
ϱ_c^0	Density of continental crust at $T = T_0$	2.82×10^3 kg m^{-3}
ϱ_m^0	Density of mantle at $T = T_0$	3.33×10^3 kg m^{-3}
ϱ_a	Density of asthenosphere at $T = T_1$	3.17×10^3 kg m^{-3}
α	Coefficient of thermal expansion	3.4×10^{-5} K^{-1}
C_p	Specific heat	1.2×10^3 J kg^{-1} K^{-1}
$\varkappa$	Thermal diffusivity	8×10^{-7} m^2 sec^{-1}
K	Thermal conductivity	2.6 W m^{-2} K^{-1}
H_0	Crustal heat production	1.15×10^{-6} W m^{-3}
T_0	Surface temperature	0°C
T_1	Asthensophere temperature	1400°C
T_{MBL}	Temperature at base of mechanical lithosphere	1120°C
g	Gravitational acceleration	9.8 m sec^{-2}
f	Compressional strain	2.0

quent time. The compressional strain, f, is the ratio of the crustal thickness immediately after compression to that of the crust in the reference continent (see Fig. 3).

Two other parameters are of importance in these calculations; they are the immediate post-thickening Moho temperature, $T_M(0)$, and the temperature T_{MBL} that defines the base of the mechanical lithosphere. Each of the values of the parameters in Table 1 is uncertain to $\pm 10\%$ at least, but the results of the calculations are most sensitive to the three parameters f, $T_M(0)$ and T_{MBL}. The values of the parameters used in the calculations are those given in Table 1, except where explicitly stated otherwise. $T_M(0)$ is varied by changing the crustal heat production, H_0.

Timing of extension

Figure 4 shows the evolution over time of the elevation, extensional strain, heat flow, effective viscosity (vertically averaged stress divided by strain rate), strain rate, and Moho temperature for a calculation using the parameter set defined in Table 1. Results can be divided into three phases: pre-extension, syn-extension, and post-extension.

The pre-extension phase lasts approximately 30 Ma and represents the period of time for the geotherm to relax to a stage where the strength of the lithosphere is low enough to permit deformation at an appreciable strain rate. During this time the Moho temperature increases from 600 to almost 700°C (cf. Fig. 2) and the strain rate increases by two orders of magnitude. The initial

elevation is slightly over 4 km as a result of isostatic compensation for almost 70 km of crust (compare with Tibet, where the elevation is mainly between 5 and 6 km, and with the Altiplano of western South America, where elevations reach about 4.5 km). Surface heat flow, which immediately after thickening is half that of the reference lithosphere, increases only slightly before major extension starts.

In the succeeding 20 Ma, 90% extension ($\beta = 1.9$) occurs, bringing the crustal thickness back almost to its pre-thickening value; the elevation drops sharply in isostatic compensation for the thinning of low-density crust, and the surface heat flux increases rapidly, reflecting the upward transport of hot material as the lithosphere thins. During the early phase of extension the Moho temperature continues to increase, but in the later stages (around 45–50 Ma elapsed time) the Moho temperature begins to fall as the Moho is brought close enough to the surface to begin cooling (see England 1983; Houseman & England 1986b).

Once deformation stops, the elevation subsides slowly as temperatures fall and the average densities of the crust and mantle increase. Because in this example the strain resulting from thickening, f, almost equals the extensional strain, β, the Moho temperature and the surface heat flow return to close to their pre-thickening values after a long time has elapsed.

Figures 5 & 6 show results from calculations starting with thermal profiles that are hotter and colder, respectively, than the initial thermal profile of Fig. 4. If the Moho temperature is suffi-

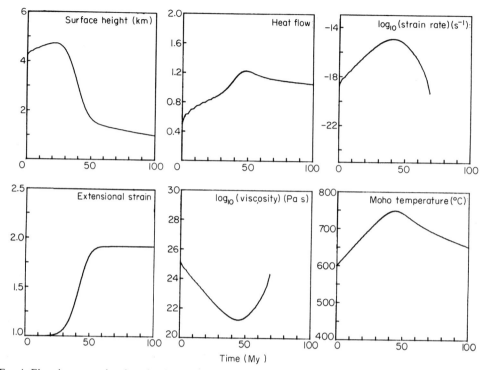

FIG. 4. Elevation, extensional strain (β), surface heat flow, effective viscosity (vertically averaged stress divided by strain rate), strain rate and Moho temperature as functions of time, for a calculation using parameter values listed in Table 1. Heat flow is normalized to that of the reference continent, which for this calculation is 67 mW m^{-2}, and initial Moho temperature, $T_M(0)$ is 600°C. Strain rate and effective viscosity are not plotted after the strain rate falls below 10^{-19} sec^{-1}.

ciently high, extension can begin immediately after shortening ends (see Fig. 2). This is shown in Fig. 5, where the initial Moho temperature is 700°C (other parameter values are as for Fig. 4). The strain rate is almost at its maximum value immediately after compression stops, rises slightly during the first part of the extension, then falls monotonically as the potential-energy contrast, and hence the deviatoric stress, decreases. Deformation has ceased by 25 Ma and results in approximately 110% extensional strain. Accompanying the extension, the elevation falls from almost 3.5 to less than 1 km. Because the deformation occurs rapidly compared with the time needed for the decay of thermal perturbations, temperatures change very little during extension; for example, the Moho temperature varies by less than 100°C.

The evolution of thickened lithosphere with a cold initial thermal structure is shown in Fig. 6. Parameters were chosen to give an initial Moho temperature of 550°C. The effect of such cold temperatures is to inhibit extension until about 50 Ma after the end of compression; however, by this time the Moho temperature has risen

close to 700°C (compare Fig. 4) and extension of about 70% is achieved in the next 25 Ma.

Figures 4–6 show that, as suggested by the approximate calculation of Fig. 2, the time at which extension begins depends on the thermal profile at the end of compression. Figure 7 illustrates this by plotting the time at which extensional strain rates exceed 10^{-16} sec^{-1} for a wider range of the parameters $T_M(0)$, f and T_{MBL}.

The curves of Figs 2 & 7 are qualitatively similar, and this suggests that the time interval required for the Moho temperature to reach 750°C (Fig. 2) is a useful approximation of the time required for extension to begin. There are quantitative differences between Figs 2 & 7, which result from the fact that in Fig. 7 the criterion for the onset of extension is strain rate, not Moho temperature, so that differences in the initial potential energy of the column influence the time at which the specified strain rate (10^{-16} sec^{-1}) is reached. The potential energy contrast is determined largely by the amount of compressional strain, f, and by the amount of lithosphere that detaches immediately after compression (see above). For Fig. 7(a), no

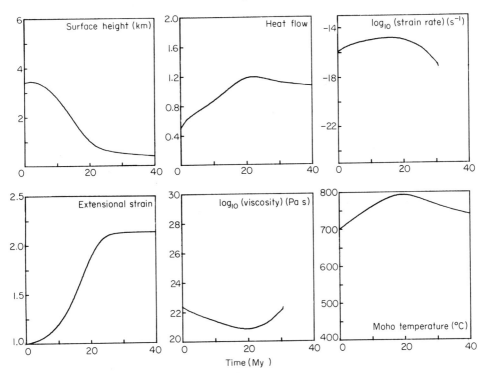

FIG. 5. Similar to Fig. 4, but with $H_0 = 1.9 \times 10^{-6}$ W m^{-3}, $T_M(0) = 700°$C. Heat flow is normalized to 88 mW m^{-2}.

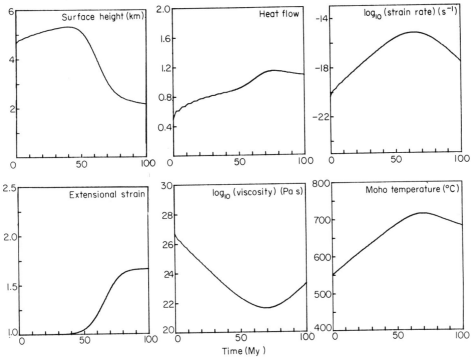

FIG. 6. As Fig. 4, but with $H_0 = 8.2 \times 10^{-7}$ W m^{-3}, $T_M(0) = 550°$C, and heat flow normalized to 57 mW m^{-2}.

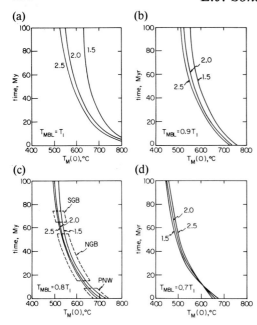

FIG. 7. Time required for extensional strain rate to reach 10^{-16} for calculations using the values of parameters given in Table 1, except that the initial Moho temperature, $T_M(0)$ is varied between 400 and 800°C by adjusting H_0, and T_{MBL} is varied from T_1 to $0.7 \times T_1$. Curves are shown for $f = 2.5$, 2 and 1.5. Boxes labelled PNW, NGB and SGB show the ranges of time and $T_M(0)$ for the Pacific Northwest, northern Great Basin and the 'amagmatic corridor' in the southern Great Basin.

lithosphere detaches, and curves differ from their counterparts in Fig. 2 mainly because of the variation in the initial potential energy contrasts. Figure 7(b), (c) and (d) represent cases in which detachment of a portion of the lithosphere occurs; this strongly affects the potential energy of the lithosphere column, and the time at which extension begins. When approximately 20% or more of the lithosphere is detached (i.e. $T_{MBL} \leq 0.8\ T_1$) the influence of this upon the potential energy is much greater than the effect of variations in compressional strain, so that there is a difference of less than 5 Ma in the time of onset of extension for different values of f (Fig. 7c & d).

Amount of extension

We have seen that the time required for extension to begin is strongly dependent upon the initial potential energy excess of the thickened lithosphere. If thermal diffusion were unimportant the same quantity would determine the *total* strain which the column of lithosphere could undergo. However, thermal diffusion influences the maximum extension in two ways: it affects the strength of the lithosphere, and it acts to change the density of the lithosphere, and hence its potential energy excess. Therefore, the total amount of extension that can be achieved depends not only upon the initial temperature and density structure, but upon the thermal and mechanical evolution through time. There is no

simple relationship between the maximum extensional strain and the thermal state of the lithosphere at the end of compression, but Fig. 8 shows the results of our calculations.

The maximum extensional strain increases with the initial potential energy excess—that is, with increasing crustal compressional strain or decreasing thickness of the mechanical boundary layer (i.e. decreasing T_{MBL}). The extensional strain decreases with lower initial Moho temperature, and this is mainly the result of the higher strength of cold lithosphere, which inhibits deformation even when the potential energy contrast is non-zero. (Lowering the Moho temperature also has the effect of slightly lowering the potential energy of the lithosphere, but this is a relatively unimportant factor.)

Figure 8 also indicates that there is a range of conditions in which the maximum extensional strain exceeds the compressional strain, resulting in a final crustal thickness less than that of the reference lithosphere.

Discussion

The model for extension of over-thickened continental lithosphere that we have presented in this paper depends only upon the observation that the potential energy stored during the thickening of continental crust will tend to be released by the extension of the thickened crust once the compressive stress required for orogeny

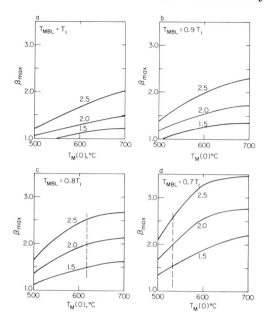

FIG. 8. Maximum extension, β_{max}, as a function of T_{MBL}, $T_M(0)$ and f. Other parameters as in Table 1. The dashed lines in (c) and (d) separate conditions for which $\beta_{max} > f$ from those in which $\beta_{max} < f$.

is removed (e.g. Molnar & Lyon-Caen in prep.). The purpose of this section is to investigate to what extent the Tertiary extensional history of western North America may be explained by such a model, and to see what features of that history demand the action of forces other than those arising from the late-Mesozoic crustal thickening which is known to have affected the region.

The extensional history calculated from the model presented above depends strongly upon two parameters—the Moho temperature and the excess potential energy of the lithospheric column immediately after the thickening episode. Neither of these parameters is well constrained by geological observations that we can make on the region 50 Ma or more after the end of compression. However, the calculations of Fig. 7 show that the inverse dependence on the initial Moho temperature, $T_M(0)$, of the time interval between the end of compression and the onset of extension is preserved almost independently of the initial potential energy excess. Consequently, if this model is relevant to the Tertiary history of western North America, we should expect a similar dependence of this time interval on Moho temperature. Although it is not possible to estimate absolute values of Moho temperature, observations summarized by Wernicke *et al.* (this issue) indicate that the relative timing of extension in three separate parts of the North American Cordillera is consistent with our calculations.

Relative timing of extension in the Pacific Northwest, and northern and southern Great Basin

Wernicke *et al.* (this issue, table 1) summarize the time intervals between the end of major compression and the onset of extension in these three regions. In the Pacific Northwest the latest major compressional event appears to have been no older than 58 Ma, and the onset of extension was no later than about 49 Ma, an interval of approximately 9 Ma. In the northern Great Basin, the equivalent interval was from mid-Eocene to early Miocene; although there was localized extension between 10 and 20 Ma after the end of thickening, the major extension occurred between 20 and 40 Ma after the end of compression. In the southern Great Basin, this interval is even longer, extending from 90 to 20 Ma.

An indication of the relative Moho temperatures in these terrains may be obtained from their pre-extensional tectonic histories. In the Pacific Northwest, extensive calc-alkaline plutonism and volcanism accompanied the crustal thickening, and it seems reasonable to assume high sub-Moho temperatures in this region at the end of shortening; indeed, the extensive calc-alkaline activity suggests that much of the lower crust may have been partially molten. In contrast, the northern Great Basin experienced only minor amounts of igneous activity towards the end of its Mesozoic compressional history, as would be consistent with the thickening of continental crust of average geothermal gradient (see, e.g. England & Thompson 1984, in press). The 'amagmatic corridor' in the southern Great Basin exhibited no magmatic activity during this time.

Figure 7(c) shows the lengths of the time intervals between compression and extension in these three regions, and indicates the approximate post-compressional Moho temperatures required if the model calculations are to yield the same time interval. The 65–75 Ma interval of the southern Great Basin would require Moho temperatures of 500–550°C, the 15–55 Ma of the northern Great Basin would require Moho temperatures of 525–650°C, and Moho temperatures in the range 625–725°C would give the interval of 20 Ma or shorter shown in the Pacific Northwest. These relative Moho temperatures are consistent with the late-Mesozoic/early-Cenozoic history of these regions but, of course, no absolute Moho temperatures can be determined. Although, as discussed below, there is an uncertainty, due to extrapolating laboratory flow laws, of ±100°C in the absolute values of temperatures shown in Figs 4–8, this does not affect the relative temperatures we discuss.

Magmatic activity

As discussed in our companion paper, the Tertiary extensional and magmatic histories of western North America are closely interlinked. Owing to three sources of uncertainty, it is impossible to make a quantitative calculation of the volume or chemistry of the magmas that would result from the thermal histories we discuss above. First, without a knowledge of the rates of ascent of various magma types through the lithosphere, the geothermal regimes that we calculate are schematic if a large proportion of the heat is carried by magma. Secondly, although we may calculate conductive temperature regimes and relate them to choices of solidus, we calculate strain histories by extrapolating laboratory flow laws over approximately six orders of magnitude in strain rate. There is an uncertainty of at least 100°C attached to this extrapolation if we wish to determine the temperatures at which the lithosphere will deform at a given strain rate; consequently a region that is characterized by a given strain history may well have experienced that strain under a regime where the Moho temperature was 100°C higher than would be calculated using the values of laboratory flow-law parameters listed in Table 1. Finally, the chemistry of magma that reaches the surface depends critically upon the composition of the lower crust and the time available for fractionation and mixing during the ascent of the magma through the lithosphere.

Extension of continental lithosphere of normal thickness is almost certain to result in basaltic magmatism as uppermost asthenosphere—initially close to the solidus—is decompressed nearly adiabatically (e.g. Beaumont et al. 1982). In the cases described here, the immediately post-compressional lithosphere is far thicker than normal, although its thickness is reduced by instability of the thermal boundary layer; diffusion of heat may also considerably raise the temperature of the lower lithosphere before extension begins.

Figures 9 & 10 compare the geotherms before and during extension with estimated crust and mantle solidi for calculations with two different sets of parameters.

In the case illustrated in Fig. 9, the isotherm defining the base of the mechanical lithosphere is taken to be 1000°C, and the bottom 70 km—the thermal boundary layer—of the thickened lithosphere is replaced by asthenosphere immediately after the compressional episode. The choice of asthenospheric temperature in this calculation is such that a small portion of the lowermost lithosphere is above the peridotite solidus even before extension begins at about 30 Ma. During extension, much more of the lithosphere passes above the peridotite solidus until at 43 Ma (the end of extension) the geotherm intersects the solidus at 70 km. In Fig. 10 the isotherm defining the base of the mechanical lithosphere is taken to be 1150°C, and the geotherm does not pass above the peridotite solidus until half the extension is accomplished, and even at maximum extension, the geotherm does not lie much above the solidus.

The generation of basaltic melt during extension thus depends on an indeterminate quantity: the ratio of the temperature at the base of the lithosphere at the onset of extension to the mantle solidus temperature at that depth. However, the observation that basaltic volcanism almost invariably post-dates the onset of extension in western North America (Wernicke et al. this issue) is in agreement with the model proposed here, provided that the lowermost 20–30% of the lithosphere is unstable in the fashion suggested above. The left-hand sides of Figs 9(a) & 10(a) show the relationships of the geotherms in the crust to various solidi for crustal materials; in each case the thermal relaxation before extension begins has been sufficient to raise the lowermost 5–15 km of the crust

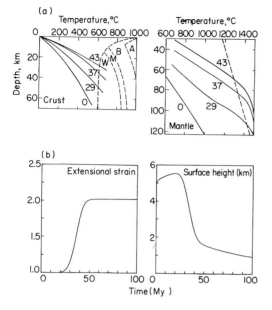

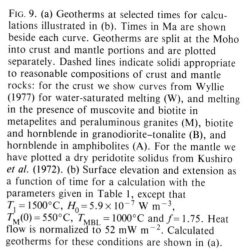

FIG. 9. (a) Geotherms at selected times for calculations illustrated in (b). Times in Ma are shown beside each curve. Geotherms are split at the Moho into crust and mantle portions and are plotted separately. Dashed lines indicate solidi appropriate to reasonable compositions of crust and mantle rocks: for the crust we show curves from Wyllie (1977) for water-saturated melting (W), and melting in the presence of muscovite and biotite in metapelites and peraluminous granites (M), biotite and hornblende in granodiorite–tonalite (B), and hornblende in amphibolites (A). For the mantle we have plotted a dry peridotite solidus from Kushiro *et al.* (1972). (b) Surface elevation and extension as a function of time for a calculation with the parameters given in Table 1, except that $T_1 = 1500°C$, $H_0 = 5.9 \times 10^{-7}$ W m^{-3}, $T_M(0) = 550°C$, $T_{MBL} = 1000°C$ and $f = 1.75$. Heat flow is normalized to 52 mW m^{-2}. Calculated geotherms for these conditions are shown in (a).

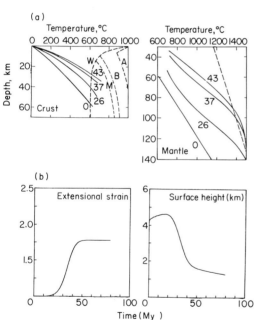

FIG. 10. As Fig. 9, except that $T_{MBL} = 1150°C$ and $H_0 = 1.0 \times 10^{-6}$ W m^{-3}, $T_M(0) = 630°C$, and heat flow is normalized to 64 mW m^{-2}. Initial Moho temperature has been adjusted to give total extension comparable with the calculation in Fig. 9.

above a temperature of 600°C. We emphasize again the uncertainty of ±100°C in the absolute values of these temperatures, but suggest that the syn-extensional bimodal magmatism in the Great Basin may be explained by the interaction of basaltic melt, produced in an adiabatically decompression upper mantle, with a lower crust that has been heated by thermal relaxation of the thickened lithosphere.

Comparison with the present Basin and Range Province

Figures 4–6 illustrate *possible* thermal and mechanical histories of the Pacific Northwest (Fig. 5), northern (Fig. 4) and southern (Fig. 6) Great Basin. We do not wish to imply that they represent the only conditions under which such extension could occur: Figs 7 & 8 show that

L.J. Sonder et al.

several other parameter combinations would produce similar results.

Here we compare the results of two calculations with observations of the crustal thickness, elevation, heat flow, seismic lithosphere thickness, and strain rate in the Great Basin. The calculations are those of Figs 4 & 9; each has an interval of 20–30 My between compression and extension and the calculations differ in that the initial conditions for Fig. 9 involved less crustal thickening, a lower Moho temperature and thinner lithosphere than for Fig. 4.

Crustal thickness in the Great Basin is between 25 and 30 km (Smith 1978); the elevation in the Great Basin is between 1.5 and 2 km (Eaton *et al.* 1978) and the average elevation of Nevada N of 38°N is 1.8 km (Navy Fleet Numerical Oceanography Center 1982); the average heat flow in the Basin and Range is 90 mW m^{-2} (Lachenbruch & Sass 1978); the depth to the top of the low-velocity zone for shear waves is about 65 km (Burdick & Helmberger 1978; Priestley *et al.* 1980). The present strain rate in the Basin and Range is poorly constrained; Minster & Jordan (1984) place an upper limit of 8 mm yr^{-1} on the extension of North America E of the San Andreas system and Smith (this issue) estimates extension rates of between 1 and 20 mm yr^{-1} within the Basin and Range. Divided by a width of 700 km for the province these estimates amount to strain rates of 3.5×10^{-16} sec^{-1} and 4.5×10^{-17} sec^{-1} to 9×10^{-16} sec^{-1} respectively.

Table 2 lists these estimates and compares them with the quantities calculated for Figs 4 & 9. It is not possible to quantify the uncertainty involved in comparing an estimate of lithospheric thickness based on calculated geotherms with an estimate based on the depth of the top of a shear-wave low-velocity zone. The only quantitative disagreement between the calculations and the observations is in the crustal thickness for Fig. 4; this figure could doubtless be adjusted, but it would serve no useful purpose, as better agreement may be obtained by adjusting one or more of the initial conditions (e.g. as has been done for Fig. 9), none of which is well constrained by observation.

Conclusions

The geological observations reviewed by Wernicke *et al.* (this issue) indicate that Cenozoic extension in western North America is not related in a simple way to plate-boundary forces; for much of the time that extension was operating in the continental interior, the strain on the western margin of North America was compressive or transpressive. This, together

TABLE 2. *Comparison between calculated and observed values of crustal thickness elevation, heat flow, lithosphere thickness and strain rate.*

	Great Basin[1]	Fig. 4[2]	Fig. 9[3]
Crustal thickness	25–30 km	37 km	31 km
Original crustal thickness[4]	—	33.75/67.5 km	33.75/59.1 km
Elevation	1.5–2 km, 1.8 km	1.7 km	1.7 km
Original elevation[5]	—	0.2 km	0.2 km
Heat flow	90 (±30) mW m^{-2}	80 mW m^{-2}	70 mW m^{-2}
Original heat flow[5]	—	65 mW m^{-2}	52 mW m^{-2}
Seismic lithospheric thickness	65 km	—[6](90 km)	70 km[6] (60 km)
Strain rate	$<3.5 \times 10^{-16}$ sec^{-1} $4.5 \times 10^{-17} - 9 \times 10^{-16}$ sec^{-1}	4.5×10^{-16} sec^{-1}	5×10^{-16} sec^{-1}

[1]See text for sources.
[2]Parameter values given in caption to Fig. 4 and Table 1. Time after end of thickening, 50 Ma; $\beta = 1.8$.
[3]Parameter values given in caption to Fig. 9 and Table 1. Time after end of thickening, 43 Ma; $\beta = 1.9$.
[4]First value, crustal thickness before compression; second value, crustal thickness immediately after compression.
[5]Values before compression.
[6]Depth to intersection of geotherm with peridotite solidus that is used in Figs 9 & 10. Numbers in parentheses indicate values obtained by taking depth at which geotherm reaches 100°C less than the solidus temperature.

with the observation that the locus of extension correspond to the locus of Mesozoic crustal thickening (e.g. Coney & Harms 1984), lends support to the suggestion that the buoyancy force associated with crustal thickening may have had a major influence on subsequent extensional tectonics of the region (e.g. McKenzie 1972; Molnar & Tapponnier 1978; Molnar & Chen 1983). However, the onset of extension in the Cordillera did not follow directly, nor indeed at any constant interval, after the end of compression. While a state of extensional deviatoric stress may have existed throughout much of the Cenozoic in this region, it was not expressed in appreciable extensional strain for a time that varied from less than 10 My in the Pacific Northwest to over 70 My in the southern Great Basin.

The physical model presented in this paper treats the continental lithosphere in terms of the vertical averages of its rheology and of the stresses acting upon it. The rheology is based on laboratory flow laws (see Description of Model, arrd Brace & Kohlstedt (1980)), and the stresses acting upon the lithosphere are solely those that arise from changing its thickness and thermal structure while maintaining isostatic balance with a reference continental column.

If such a continental lithosphere is thickened it is gravitationally unstable and will tend to spread under its own weight. The strength of the rheologically stratified lithosphere depends on its thermal regime, which may conveniently be characterized by the Moho temperature (Sonder & England 1986). Over the range of conditions discussed here, the deviatoric stresses associated with thickened lithosphere do not result in appreciable extensional strain until the Moho temperature is greater than about 700°C (see, e.g. Figs 4, 5 & 6). Consequently, there is a time interval between the end of compression and the onset of extension that depends on the time required for thermal relaxation to warm the

lithosphere and, to a lesser extent, on the excess potential energy stored in the thickened lithosphere (see Fig. 7). For the lowest initial Moho temperatures considered (<450°C) this length of time exceeds 100 My, and it is likely that erosion, rather than extension, would reduce the thickness of such a mountain belt. However, for initial Moho temperatures between 500 and 700°C, the time interval drops from around 100 Ma to zero (Fig. 7). In the calculations illustrated in Fig. 8, extension occurs until the lithosphere is in potential energy balance with the reference continental column, and in many cases (see Fig. 8c & d) the total extension may exceed the original compressional strain, leaving crust thinner than before compressional strain began. Under these conditions, the lithosphere is substantially thinner at the end of extension than it was originally, and it is likely that basaltic melts are produced by adiabatic decompression of the asthenosphere during extension; the intrusion of such melts into lower crust already close to its solidus could well result in bimodal magmatism during the extension.

The predominant testable feature of the physical model presented here is the inverse dependence of the time interval between compression and extension on the Moho temperature at the end of compression. Insofar as thermal regimes may be estimated from syncompressional magmatic activity, this is a feature that is shared by the Cenozoic extensional terrains of western North America (see above and Wernicke *et al.*, this volume).

ACKNOWLEDGMENTS: It is a pleasure to acknowledge the countless conversations and arguments with Peter Molnar that have raised the level of our understanding of the mechanics of mountain belts. This work was made much easier by Greg Houseman's generous help in writing the computer programs. We were supported by NSF grants EAR84-08352 and EAR83-19767. L.J.S. acknowledges support from an Exxon Teaching Fellowship.

References

ARTYUSHKOV, E.V. 1983. Stresses in the lithosphere caused by crustal thickness inhomogeneities. *J. geophys. Res.* **78**, 7675–708.

ATWATER, T. 1970. Implications of plate tectonics for the Cenozoic tectonic evolution of western North America. *Bull. geol. Soc. Am.* **81**, 3513–36.

BEAUMONT, C., KEEN, C.E. & BOUTILIER, R. 1982. On the evolution of rifted continental margins: comparision of models and observations for the Nova Scotian margin. *Geophys. J. R. astron. Soc.* **70**, 667–715.

BIRD, P. & BAUMGARDNER, J. 1984. Fault friction, regional stress, and crust–mantle coupling in southern California from finite element models. *J. geophys. Res.* **89**, 1932–44.

—— & PIPER, K. 1980. Plane-stress finite-element models of tectonic flow in southern California. *Phys. Earth planet. Inter.* **21**, 158–75.

BOTT, M.H.P. & DEAN, D.S. 1972. Stress systems at young continental margins. *Nature*, **235**, 23–5.

BRACE, W.F. & KOHLSTEDT, D.L. 1980. Limits on lithospheric stress imposed by laboratory experiments. *J. geophys. Res.* **85**, 6248–52.

BURDICK, L.J. & HELMBERGER, D.V. 1978. The upper mantle *P* velocity structure of the western United States *J. geophys. Res.* **83**, 1699–712.

CHRISTIANSEN, R.L. & LIPMAN, P.W. 1972. Cenozoic volcanism and plate tectonic evolution of the western United States II. Late Cenozoic. *In: A Discussion on Volcanism and the Structure of the Earth, Phil. Trans. R. Soc. London,* **A217**, 249–84.

CONEY, P.J. & HARMS, T.A. 1984. Cordilleran metamorphic core complexes: Cenozoic extensional relics of Mesozoic compression. *Geology,* **12**, 550–4.

EATON, G.P., WAHL, R.R., PROSTKA, H.J., MAHEY, D.R. & KLEINKOPF, M.D. 1978. Regional gravity and tectonic patterns: Their relation to late Cenozoic epeirogeny and lateral spreading in the western Cordillera. *In:* SMITH, R.B. & EATON, G.P. (eds) *Cenozoic Tectonics and Regional Geophysics of the Western Cordillera. Mem. geol. Soc. Am.* **152**, 51–91.

ENGLAND, P.C. 1983. Constraints on extension of continental lithosphere. *J. geophys. Res.* **88**, 1145–52.

—— & HOUSEMAN, G.A. 1986. Finite strain calculations of continental deformation II. Comparison with the India–Asia collision. *J. geophys. Res.* **91**, 3664–76.

—— & McKENZIE, D.P. 1982. A thin viscous sheet model for continental deformation. *Geophys. J.R. astron. Soc.* **70**, 295–321.

—— &—— 1983. Correction to: A thin viscous sheet model for continental deformation. *Geophys. J.R. astron. Soc.* **73**, 523–32.

—— & THOMPSON. A.B. 1984. Pressure–temperature–time paths of regional metamorphism I. Heat transfer during the evolution of regions of thickened continental crust. *J. Petrol.* **25**, 894–928.

—— &—— In press. Some thermal and tectonic models for crustal melting in continental collision zones. *J. geol. Soc. London.*

HOUSEMAN, G.A. & ENGLAND, P.C. 1986a. A dynamical model for lithosphere extension and sedimentary basin formation. *J. geophys. Res.* **91**, 719–29.

—— & —— 1986b. Finite strain calculations of continental deformation I. Method and general results for convergent zones. *J. geophys. Res.* **91**, 3651–63.

—— , McKENZIE, D.P. & MOLNAR, P. 1981. Convective instability of a thickened boundary layer and its relevance for the thermal evolution of continental convergent belts. *J. geophys. Res.* **86**, 6115–32.

JEFFREYS, H. 1929. *The Earth*, 346 pp. Cambridge University Press, Cambridge, England.

KUSHIRO, I., SHIMIZU, N. & NAKAMURA, Y. 1972. Compositions of coexisting liquid and solid phases formed upon melting of natural garnet and spinel lherzolites at high pressures: a preliminary report. *Earth planet. Sci. Lett.* **14**, 19–25.

LACHENBRUCH, A.H. & SASS, J.H. 1978. Models of an extending lithosphere and heat flow in the Basin and Range province. *In:* SMITH, R.B. & EATON, G.P. (eds) *Cenozoic Tectonics and Regional Geophysics of the Western Cordillera.*

Mem. geol. Soc. Am. **152**, 209–50.

LE PICHON, X. 1982. Land-locked oceanic basins and continental collision. *In:* HSU, K. (ed.) *Mountain Building Processes*, pp. 201–11. Academic Press, London.

LOVE, A.E.H. 1911. Some Problems of Geodynamics, pp. 180. Cambridge University Press, Cambridge.

McKENZIE, D.P. 1972. Active tectonics of the Mediterranean region. *Geophys. J.R. astron. Soc.* **30**, 109–85.

MINSTER, J.B. & JORDAN, T.H. 1984. Vector constraints on Quaternary deformation of the western United States east and west of the San Andreas fault. *In:* CROUCH, J.K. & BACHMAN, S.B. (eds) *Tectonics and Sedimentation along the California Margin. Soc. econ. Paleontol. and Mineral., Pac. sect.,* 1–16.

MOLNAR, P. & CHEN, W.-P. 1983. Focal depths and fault plane solutions of earthquakes under the Tibetan plateau. *J. geophys. Res.* **88**, 1180–96.

—— & TAPPONNIER, P. 1978. Active tectonics of Tibet. *J. geophys. Res.* **83**, 5361–75.

NAVY FLEET NUMERICAL OCEANOGRAPHY CENTER 1982. 10 Minute Elevation Data archived by National Center for Atmospheric Research, Boulder, Colorado, USA.

PARSON, B. & McKENZIE, D.P. 1978. Mantle convection and the thermal structure of the plates. *J. geophys. Res.* **83**, 4485–96.

PRIESTLEY, K., ORCUTT, J.A. & BRUNE, J.N. 1980. Higher-mode surface waves and structure of the Great basin of Nevada and western Utah. *J. geophys. Res.* **85**, 7166–74.

SMITH, R.B. 1978. Seismicity, crustal structure, and intraplate tectonics of the interior of the western Cordillera. *In:* SMITH, R.B. & EATON, G.P. (eds) *Cenozoic Tectonics and Regional Geophysics of the Western Cordillera. Mem. geol. Soc. Am.* **152**, 111–44.

—— This volume. Kinematics and dynamics of an extending lithosphere: The Basin-Range.

SONDER, L.J. & ENGLAND, P.C. 1986. Vertical averages of rheology of the continental lithosphere: relation to thin sheet parameters. *Earth planet. Sci. Lett.* **77**, 81–90.

—— ,—— & HOUSEMAN, G.A. 1986. Continuum calculations of continental deformation in transcurrent environments. *J. geophys. Res.* **91**, 4797–818.

VILOTTE, J.P., DAIGNIERES, M. & MADARIAGA, R. 1982. Numerical modeling of intraplate deformation: simple mechanical models of continental collision. *J. geophys. Res.* **87**, 10709–28.

WERNICKE, B.P., CHRISTIANSEN, R.L., ENGLAND, P.C. & SONDER, L.J. This volume. Tectonomagmatic evolution of Cenozoic extension in the North American Cordillera.

WYLLIE, P.J. 1977. Crustal anatexis: An experimental review. *Tectonophysics,* **43**, 41–71.

L.J. SONDER*, P.C. ENGLAND † , B.P. WERNICKE & R.L. CHRISTIANSEN † † , Department of Geological Sciences, Hoffman Laboratory, Harvard University, Cambridge, MA 02138, USA.

* Present address: Seismological Laboratory, California Institute of Technology, Pasadena, CA 91125, USA.

† Present address: Department of Earth Sciences, Parks Road, Oxford OX1 3PR, UK.

† † Present address: United States Geological Survey, 245 Middlefield Road, Menlo Park, CA 94025, USA.

Appendix

The method used by Houseman & England (1986b) and in this paper adopts the thin-sheet approximation of England & McKenzie (1982, 1983), which amounts to neglecting the stress components τ_{xz} and τ_{yz} (where z is the vertical direction) and letting all other deviatoric stress components represent quantities averaged over the thickness of the lithosphere. We make the further assumption that the deformation is two-dimensional; hence the only non-zero components of the deviatoric stress tensor are the vertically averaged components $\bar{\tau}_{xx}$ and $\bar{\tau}_{zz}$. With the assumption of incompressibility, the horizontal deviatoric stress may be expressed as

$$\bar{\tau}_{xx} = \frac{1}{2L}\left[F_x - \int_{z_t}^{L}\sigma_{zz}\,dz\right],\qquad(A1)$$

where L is the thickness of the lithosphere, z_t is the top of the lithosphere, and σ_{zz} equals the lithostatic load. F_x is a constant and may be calculated from the density structure of a reference lithosphere that is in potential energy and isostatic equilibrium with the mid-ocean ridges (see Fig. 3). For isostatically compensated lithosphere columns, differences in $\bar{\tau}_{xx}$ are proportional to differences in their gravitational potential energy (Molnar & Lyon-Caen in prep.).

Once a constitutive relationship is assumed, the horizontal strain rate $\dot{\epsilon}_{xx}$ may be calculated. We use the rheological model of Brace & Kohlstedt (1980), in which the lithosphere deforms by a combination of brittle and ductile mechanisms that depend on temperature, strain rate and depth. For the calculations presented above, we neglect the contribution of the crust to the strength of the lithosphere.

The thermal evolution of the lithosphere is described by

$$\frac{\partial T}{\partial t} + v\frac{\partial T}{\partial z} = \varkappa\frac{\partial^2 T}{\partial z^2} + \frac{H(z)}{\varrho C_p},\qquad(A2)$$

where T is temperature, v is the vertical velocity, $\varkappa$ is thermal diffusivity, H is radiogenic heat production, ϱ is density and C_p is specific heat. We assume that H is constant throughout the crust and is zero in the mantle; $\varkappa$ and C_p are constant everywhere.

The vertical velocity is related to the strain rate by

$$-\dot{\epsilon}_{xx} = \dot{\epsilon}_{zz} = \frac{\partial v}{\partial z}.\qquad(A3)$$

We define a measure of extensional strain, β, equal to the ratio of the thickness of crust immediately after compression to that of extended crust. The relationship between β and the horizontal strain rate is

$$\frac{1}{\beta}\frac{\partial \beta}{\partial t} = \dot{\epsilon}_{xx}.\qquad(A4)$$

Equations (A2) and (A4) are solved by finite-difference techniques; a Crank–Nicholson scheme is used for (A2) and a modified predictor–corrector scheme is used for (A4). At each time-step $\bar{\tau}_{xx}$ is calculated from the temperature profile and a guess for $\dot{\epsilon}_{xx}$. The value of $\dot{\epsilon}_{xx}$ which gives the correct $\bar{\tau}_{xx}$ (Equation (A1)) is found by iteration using Newton's method.

Boundary and initial conditions

Implicit in the derivation of Equation (A1) is the assumption that shear stresses on the upper and lower surface of the lithosphere are zero. In addition the normal stress σ_{zz} is zero on the upper surface (z_t). For the temperature equation (A2) we assume constant boundary conditions $T = T_0$ and $T = T_1$ on the top and bottom of the lithosphere, respectively.

The initial temperature condition represents the geotherm resulting from instantaneously and uniformly thickening continental lithosphere that is previously in thermal equilibrium with constant heat production, H_0, throughout crust of thickness, h, (see Fig. 3). We assume that all lithosphere below the isotherm T_{MBL} is gravitationally unstable and is replaced by asthenosphere of temperature T_1 at time zero (see text—Description of the Model). Hence the initial temperature condition is

$$T = T_0 + \frac{(T_1 - T_0)z}{fL} + \frac{H_0 L}{2K}\frac{z}{f}\times$$
$$\left(\frac{2h}{L} - \frac{h^2}{L^2} - \frac{z}{fL}\right)\qquad z \leq fh,$$

$$= T_0 + \frac{(T_1 - T_0)z}{fL} + \frac{H_0 h^2}{2K}\left(1 - \frac{z}{fL}\right)$$
$$fh < z \leq z_{BL},$$

$$= T_1\qquad\qquad z_{BL} < z,\qquad(A5)$$

where f is the factor by which the lithosphere is thickened, K is thermal conductivity, and z_{BL} is the depth at which the lower part of the lithosphere detaches.

Tectonomagmatic evolution of Cenozoic extension in the North American Cordillera

B.P. Wernicke, R.L. Christiansen, P.C. England & L.J. Sonder

SUMMARY: The spatial and temporal distributions of Cenozoic extension and magmatism in the Cordillera suggest that the onset of major crustal extension at a particular latitude was confined to a relatively narrow belt (<100 km, pre-extension) and followed the onset of intermediate and silicic magmatism by no more than a few million years. Extension began in early Eocene time in southern British Columbia, northern Washington, Idaho and Montana. Farther S, extension began at about the Eocene–Oligocene boundary in the Great Basin and slightly later in the Mojave–Sonora Desert region. The intervening area, at the latitude of Las Vegas, remained quiescent until mid-Miocene time. Compositional and isotopic characteristics of most pre-Miocene magmas are consistent with their containing major components of melted continental crust.

In mid-Miocene time, two major changes occurred: widening of the area of extension and the widespread appearance of basaltic magmas. The area affected by extension, from southwestern Montana to the Lake Mead region, widened to several hundred kilometres. By this time extension in southern British Columbia, northern Washington and northern Montana had ceased (probably before the end of the Eocene), and extension S of Lake Mead (except in the Gulf of California) had waned. Regions affected by the broader belt of extension during late Miocene, Pliocene, and Quaternary time experienced basaltic magmatism, which began along a central rift zone in the northern part of the region, and which had within a few million years spread to include most of the region; later basaltic activity has tended to concentrate in restricted zones, especially near the margins of the extended area.

We recognize a correlation between the amount of earlier crustal thickening and Cenozoic extension, and between the length of time after shortening but before extension and the degree to which a given region was intruded by Late Cretaceous plutons. The localization of extension in areas of previous crustal thickening and the dependence of the timing of extension on the thermal state of the overthickened crust is consistent with a simple thermal-mechanical model developed in a companion paper (Sonder et al.). This raises the possibility that stresses inherent in the North American Plate dominated over plate-interaction forces as controls of the Cenozoic tectonomagmatic evolution of the North American Cordillera, especially in its earlier stages.

We distinguish two classes of control for the middle Eocene and younger (<55 Ma) magmatism and tectonism in western North America. One class, purely kinematic, relates the deformation and igneous activity to the post-early Eocene relative motions between North America and the plates to its W (e.g. Atwater 1970; Lipman et al. 1972; Christiansen & Lipman 1972; Snyder et al. 1976; Coney 1978). These hypotheses are difficult to evaluate, first because of the inconsistency involved in relating the large-scale diffuse deformation of the continents to the relative motions of rigid plates, and secondly because these motions are themselves poorly constrained. The more recent attempts to relate the Cenozoic tectonics of western North America to plate motions have relied on the assumption of fixed hot-spots (Coney 1978; Engebretson 1982); even without this assumption, the quantitative analysis of uncertainties in plate reconstructions by Stock & Molnar (1983) shows that it may be unwise to interpret relative

or absolute motion vectors without considering their error bars.

A second class of hypotheses for the origin of the middle Eocene and younger extension and magmatism is related to the evolution of stresses arising within the North American lithosphere itself. This class recognizes that continental lithosphere containing overthick crust has a tendency to spread under its own weight (e.g. Tapponnier & Molnar 1977) and that the key to understanding the Cenozoic extensional tectonics of western North America may lie in its late Mesozoic compressional history (see Molnar & Chen 1983, p. 1184). We consider a simple physical model in which the Cenozoic extension results from the gravitationally driven thinning of lithosphere previously thickened in late Mesozoic and earliest Tertiary times. This paper represents a synthesis of observations concerning the timing and extent of deformation and magmatism in western North America; these data are compared with the results of calculations

From COWARD, M.P., DEWEY, J.F. & HANCOCK, P.L. (eds), 1987, Continental Extensional Tectonics, Geological Society Special Publication No. 28, pp. 203–221.

(Sonder *et al.*, this volume) in order to evaluate the physical model. This analysis serves as a first step towards understanding the relative importance of the two classes of controls on the extension and magmatism.

We consider in detail three major regions of Cenozoic magmatism and tectonism (Figs 1 & 2): the Pacific Northwest, the Great Basin region, and a southern Great Basin 'amagmatic corridor'. We briefly discuss a fourth domain to the S comprising the Mojave and Sonoran Desert portions of the Basin and Range Province, previously treated in greater detail by Glazner & Bartley (1984). All of the domains experienced crustal thickening during Late

Cretaceous and early Tertiary times before becoming regions of extension later in the Cenozoic.

The minimum amount of Late Cretaceous–early Tertiary shortening is well known in many areas, and locally exceeds 50% for supracrustal rocks in frontal parts of the thrust belt, implying substantial thickening of the crust in 'hinterland' areas to the W (e.g. Price 1981). Shortening reaches values locally as great as 30% in areas of Laramide-style foreland deformation (e.g. Smithson *et al.* 1978). Areas affected by this shortening event either had a non-cratonic hinterland thickened in mid-Jurassic to mid-Cretaceous time, or were

FIG. 1. Map showing geographical regions and localities mentioned in text. State, provincial and international boundaries (dashed lines) are also shown in Figs. 2, 3 and 4. Heavy lines delimit physiographic regions. BR = Belted Range; FV = Flathead Valley; GM = Grapevine Mountains; GR = Grant Range; GSL = Great Salt Lake; OV = Okanagan Valley; NE = Northern Egan Range; NT = Northern Toiyabe Range; PM = Pioneer Mountains; RR = Raft River Range area; SD = Sevier Desert; SR = Sonoma Range; VH = Valhalla area; YR = Yerington area.

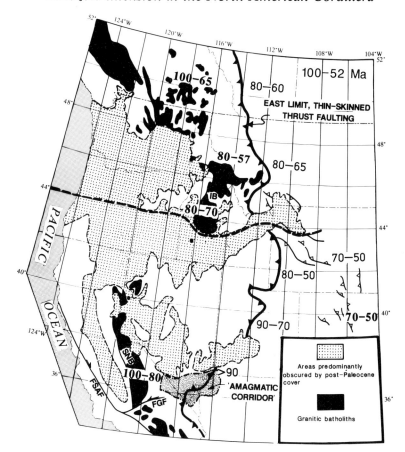

FIG. 2. Map showing key features discussed in text for Late Cretaceous and early Tertiary time. Bold numbers indicate times of emplacement of granitic batholiths; plain numbers—principal times of shortening in thrust belt and Laramide uplift regions; heavy dashed line—boundary between Pacific Northwest and Great Basin regions; thin lines with open barbs—major faults bounding Laramide uplifts. FGF = future trace of Garlock fault; FSAF = future trace of San Andreas Fault; IB = Idaho batholith; SNB = Sierra Nevada batholith.

developed within the craton itself. Thus, the Late Cretaceous–early Tertiary shortening represents a culminating event in which the entire Cordillera attained a crustal thickness greater than that of the craton, and in which cratonic areas well inboard from the continental margin became involved in Cordilleran orogenesis (e.g. Burchfiel & Davis 1975). Also during this time, extensive calc-alkalic magmatism intruded the continental margin in a virtually continuous belt from British Columbia to Mexico.

The approximate synchronism of magmatism and overthickening of the crust in the Late Cretaceous (Fig. 2) contrasts with pronounced differences in timing of the Cenozoic magmatism and extension between various sectors of the orogen. Despite this diachronism, there is a common pattern to the development of extension in any given part of the orogen. We identify a four-stage history for each part of the extensional terrain: (i) the formation of early intermontane basins; (ii) the eruption of predominantly intermediate to silicic volcanic rocks; (iii) areally restricted large-magnitude crustal extension, occurring during or immediately after second-stage magmatism; and (iv) basaltic or bimodal volcanism, accompanied regionally by varied amounts of extension.

There are marked variations on this theme, as well as variations in timing during the development of the extensional and magmatic terrains (Table 1), that permit us to test the simple model presented in Sonder *et al.* (this volume).

TABLE 1. *Constraints on timing of tectonic events in the Cordillera, My BP.*

	Limits on cessation of major compression	Limits on onset of major extension	Limits on interval between compression and extension
Pacific Northwest	58–55	55–49	0–9
Great Basin	75–53	38–20	15–55
Amagmatic Corridor	90–85	20–15	65–75
Mojave–Sonora	55–40(?)	40(?)–20	0–35

Pacific Northwest

Cretaceous tectonism and magmatism

Crustal thickening occurred in this region during the interval 80–55 Ma in the southern Canadian Rockies and the Montana sector of the thrust belt (Fig. 2). In the southern Canadian Rockies, shortening of cratonic strata and their overlying foreland basin deposits exceeded 100 km between the early Campanian, the age of the youngest conformable strata in the fore-deep, and latest Eocene time (Price 1981), the age of the post-tectonic Kishenehn Formation, deposited on the Lewis thrust sheet. Price (1981) has suggested that since fore-deep sedimentation had ceased by the end of the deposition of the Palaeocene Paskapoo Formation, the bulk of the shortening had been completed by this time. However, the Paskapoo, which is deposited conformably on underlying Late Cretaceous strata in the most external part of the thrust belt, is involved in the frontalmost fold of the thrust belt, as well as in the Williams Creek syncline, 35 km W of the thrust front. It is therefore possible that deformation continued into the Eocene. This event involved the stripping of cratonic Palaeozoic rocks and fore-deep deposits from their basement, and thus the shortening that the supracrustal rocks record must have involved substantial thickening of the crust much farther W, where Tertiary extensional deformation has since taken place (Price 1981).

Further S, in the Montana sector of the orogen, the Late Cretaceous–early Tertiary thrust belt changes character, where it involves sub-miogeoclinal, Proterozoic belt strata and, in some areas, cratonic crystalline basement (Ryder & Scholten 1973). S of the Lewis and Clark line (LCL, Fig. 3) the main period of shortening— as interpreted from the time of most rapid fore-deep sedimentation—seems to have been in Campanian and Maastrichtian times, based on recent palynological studies of the syntectonic Beaverhead Group (Nichols *et al.* 1985). Deformation could have continued into the Eocene in the belt of E-directed thrusts, but no post-Maastrichtian compressional orogenic deposits are known in the region. Farther E of the fold thrust belt at this latitude, Laramide-style uplifts were active into the Palaeocene. Since thrusting in the Montana sector of the thrust belt seems to be less 'thin-skinned' than in southern Canada, overthickening of the crust may have been more closely centred upon the area of supracrustal shortening, rather than having occurred to the W as it did in the Canadian sector.

Magmatism in the Pacific Northwest region was intense during Late Cretaceous and early Tertiary times, and, in contrast to regions farther S, occurred *within* the area of maximum overthickening of continental crust (Fig. 2). Plutonism was synchronous with the major pulse of crustal overthickening during Campanian, Maastrichtian, and Palaeocene (?) times, about 85–55 Ma (Fig. 2). Major plutonic centres include the Whatshan batholith at 80 to 70 Ma (R. Parrish, pers. comm.), protoliths of the Valhalla gneiss complex at around 65–55 Ma (Parrish 1984; Parrish *et al.* 1985), numerous bodies of probable Late Cretaceous to early Tertiary age in northeastern Washington (Fox *et al.* 1977), and the Idaho and Boulder batholiths, the bulk of which appear to have intruded between 80 and 57 Ma (Armstrong *et al.* 1977; Criss & Fleck 1983; Sutter *et al.* 1984; L. Garmezy, pers. comm.).

The pattern of Late Cretaceous evolution is thus that of (N of the Lewis and Clark line) thin-skinned thrusting associated with crustal thickening of areas W of the main part of the thrust belt, and (S of the line) a more thick-skinned style of thrusting, causing substantial thickening of the crust, closer to the locus of supracrustal shortening. In both areas, calc-alkaline plutonism and volcanism accompanied deformation within the zone of greatest over-thickening. As noted by Armstrong (1978), thrusting throughout this region appears to have

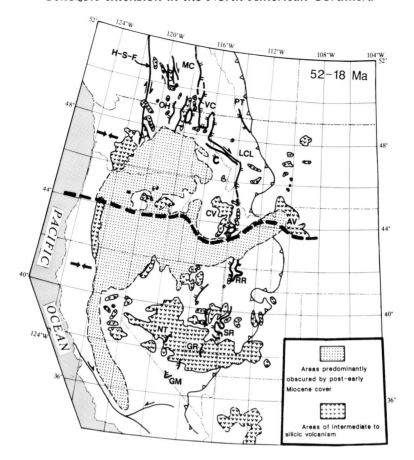

FIG. 3. Map showing key features discussed in text for middle Eocene through mid-Miocene time. Heavy dashed line—boundary between Pacific Northwest and Great Basin regions; heavy, double-hachured lines— principal detachments known to be active during this time interval N of latitude 35°N; opposing arrows depict crustal shortening during Tertiary time as discussed in text; AV = Absaroka volcanic region; CV = Challis volcanic region; GM = Grapevine Mountains; GR = Grant Range; H-S-F = Hope-Straight Creek–Fraser River fault system; LCL = Lewis and Clark line; MC = Monashee crystalline complex; NT = northern Toiyabe Range; OH = Okanagan Highlands; PT = Purcell Trench; RR = Raft River Range area; SR = Snake Range area; VC = Valhalla crystalline complex. Future traces of Garlock and San Andreas faults as in Fig. 2.

ended by 55 Ma and younger volcanism of the Challis belt.

Palaeogene extensional tectonics and associated magmatism

In the last few years, it has become apparent that the Pacific Northwest region experienced major crustal extension, principally during the Eocene (Fig. 3). Intermediate to silicic volcanism over-lapped closely in time with the extension.

In Canada, major Eocene extension occurred in S-central British Columbia (Fig. 3; Price 1979). The major structures identified as having

Eocene displacement include the Columbia River fault zone, which appears to have had several kilometres of down-to-the-E displacement, but whose major period of activity was during the middle Jurassic (Read & Brown 1981; Brown & Murphy 1982). Farther S, Parrish *et al.* (1985) and Carr (1985) have shown possible Eocene normal displacement on the Slocan Lake fault zone, which bounds the eastern side of the Valhalla gneiss complex (Fig. 3). To the W, near Kamloops, British Columbia, Ewing (1981a, b) reports a major episode of Eocene tectonism, recorded by a network of faults bounding exposures of the lower and middle Eocene

Kamloops Formation. The lowest units in this succession are predominantly non-volcanic, but grade upward into locally thick intermediate to silicic volcanic piles that yield K–Ar ages of 42–52 Ma.

In northern Washington, S of 49°N, the extensional terrane is apparently wider, as major detachments of Eocene age have been identified from the Okanogan Valley eastward to the Purcell trench (Fig. 3). From W to E, these include faults separating mylonitic gneisses from unmetamorphosed Tertiary strata in the Republic and Toroda Creek 'grabens' (Rhodes & Cheney 1981), the Kettle River fault on the E side of the Kettle River dome (Rhodes & Cheney 1981), the Jumpoff Joe and Newport faults N of Spokane (Cheney 1980; Harms & Price 1983; Rhodes & Hyndman 1984) and an inferred detachment in the Purcell trench forming the E margin of the Priest River crystalline complex (Rehrig et al. 1982).

The timing of extension in Washington is recorded by a sedimentary and volcanic succession present at high structural levels within the upper plates of these detachments and K–Ar mineral ages from deep structural levels. According to Pearson & Obradovich (1977) the stratified rocks comprise a lower, tuffaceous fluvio–lacustrine unit, a middle unit of predominantly intermediate to silicic volcanic rocks, and an upper unit of mixed volcanic and coarse-sedimentary detritus, including debris flows. The lower two units are conformable and appear to have been deposited over the entire region prior to severe structural disruption that preceded and accompanied the deposition of the youngest unit in restricted basins. The lower two units were deposited between about 53 and 52 Ma, and may thus be equivalent to the lower part of the Kamloops Formation. The uppermost unit contains Upper Eocene (Bridgerian) floras, and volcanics in the sequence yield ages between 49 and 41 Ma (Pearson & Obradovich 1977), suggesting that the major period of extension occurred between 50 and 41 Ma ago. However, since no deposits older than the mid-Miocene Columbia River basalts overlap the extensional terrane, extension could have persisted past 41 Ma. Corroborating evidence for dominantly Eocene extension comes from K–Ar mineral ages of lower-plate crystalline rocks (Miller & Engels 1975; Rehrig et al. 1982), which are highly varied in the region but at the deepest structural levels are no younger than 45–42 Ma. K–Ar ages in lower-plate crystalline rocks of the Valhalla and Monashee complexes farther N in Canada also give ages as young as 42 Ma (Read & Brown 1981).

The extensional terrain of southern British Columbia and northern Washington strikes southward beneath relatively undeformed mid-Miocene basalts of the Columbia Plateau without a noticeable decrease in intensity, and presumably continues for some distance beneath the plateau basalts (Figs 3 & 4). It cannot, however, continue as far S as the Blue Mountains region of NE Oregon since pre-Tertiary rocks there seem to have experienced only minor shortening of Oligocene and younger age (e.g. Brooks et al. 1976; Davis 1977).

To the SE, near Clarkia, Idaho, Seyfert (1984) reports the presence of the 'Clearwater core complex', which he infers to be genetically linked to Eocene strike-slip faulting on the Lewis and Clark line (Fig. 3). Rehrig & Reynolds (1981) suggested that the Lewis and Clark line was an intracontinental transform linking Eocene down-to-the-E normal faulting in the Purcell trench to that along the eastern side of the northern part of the Idaho batholith (Hyndman 1980). Garmezy & Sutter (1983), using the ^{40}Ar–^{39}Ar technique, have shown that top-to-the-E shear along the top of the northern part of the batholith occurred at 45–43 Ma.

Farther S preliminary fieldwork by K.V. Hodges (pers. comm.) suggests that much of the tectonic unroofing of the Pioneer Mountains crystalline core (Dover 1982), and the emplacement of low-grade metamorphic rocks on high-grade, post-dates eruption of the Challis volcanics. In that area, the volcanics range in age from about 50–46 Ma (Marvin et al. 1982). Lower-plate muscovite K–Ar ages range between 45 and 43 Ma (Dover 1982), similar to those in tectonically exhumed crystalline complexes to the N. The precise age of extensional deformation in the Pioneers remains an outstanding problem, especially because the next recognized extensional complex to the S, in the Raft River Range area, appears to have formed principally during Oligocene and Miocene times (Fig. 3). It is not known whether the Snake River Plain represents a boundary between Eocene extension to the N versus Oligocene and Miocene extension farther S, or whether extension is smoothly time-transgressive toward the S. It appears that Eocene extension ended N of the Snake River Plain and that Oligocene and Miocene extension overprinted that part of the Eocene extensional terrain S of the Lewis and Clark line.

The compositions of Challis-age (53–37 Ma) magmas in the Pacific Northwest are predominantly intermediate to silicic; there is some basalt in the western part of the region. The most extensive igneous activity occurred in areas

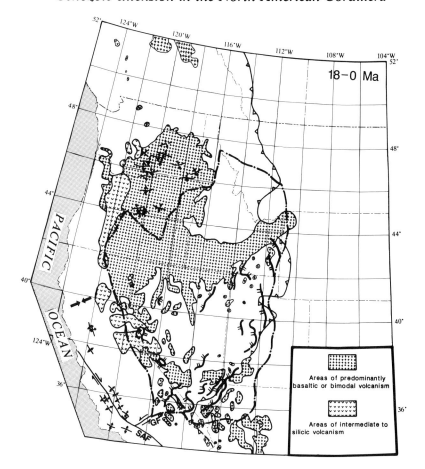

Fig. 4. Map showing key features discussed in text for mid-Miocene and younger time. Heavy dot–dashed line bounds region of significant extension during this time interval. Heavy double-ticked lines—detachments known to be active during this interval. Opposing arrows—region of crustal shortening discussed in text; traces of anticlines schematically depict regions of shortening in California and on the Colombia Plateau active during this interval. GF = Garlock fault; SAF = San Andreas Fault.

of previously overthickened crust, but minor activity also took place outside the areas of crustal thickening (see Armstrong 1978). The increasing prevalence of rhyolites in the central part of the Challis belt suggests a greater role for crustal (probably lower-crustal) melting in the magmatic systems there than in the more andesitic systems around its margins. This may be supported by the presence of two-mica granites, apparently of crustal origin, associated with parts of the Challis belt that produced extensive rhyolites (Miller & Bradfish 1980).

There is no discernible time-transgression of Challis-episode volcanism (Armstrong 1978); both the oldest and youngest K–Ar ages are virtually the same in all areas, principally be-

tween about 53 and 43 Ma, although minor volcanism continued until about 37 Ma. After this time, Palaeogene magmatism occurred only W of the extensional terrain. Although regional magmatism and extension are synchronous within this interval, there is no apparent relationship between the intensity of the magmatic event and the intensity of upper- and middle-crustal extensional strain. The main intrusive centres of both the Challis and Absaroka fields, the two most important parts of the volcanic belt, lie outside areas that are known to have undergone extension. Conversely, some areas of severe extension (e.g. the Kettle River and Toroda Creek areas in N-central Washington) are sites of relatively modest Eocene magmatism. Similar relations are apparent in some younger areas to the S (Fig. 3).

Palaeogene compression in western areas

In contrast to the Palaeogene extensional tectonism described above, areas to the W experienced transpressive shortening during this time. The southern part of the Hope-Straight Creek–Fraser River fault system (Fig. 3), a right-lateral strike-slip system, was probably active between deposition of the early to middle Eocene Swauk and Teanaway Formations next to its southern (Straight Creek) part, as suggested by a pre-Teanaway folding event (50–47 Ma; Tabor *et al.* 1984). Deformation may have continued through Eocene to perhaps late Oligocene times (Tabor *et al.* 1984). Farther N, the late Eocene(?)–Oligocene Chilliwack composite batholith truncates the fault (Misch 1966). Although the total displacement on the Straight Creek fault appears to be 100 km-or more (e.g. Davis *et al.* 1978), it is not certain whether the bulk of this displacement occurred during Eocene extension farther E or at an earlier time, as features believed to reflect large offset on the fault are no younger than Late Cretaceous. Thus, folding and deformation of Eocene volcanic and sedimentary rocks along the southern portion of the fault system may simply reflect dip-slip reactivation of the structure, perhaps during uplift of the North Cascades crystalline core to the E of the fault (Fig. 3).

Just E of the southernmost exposures of the Straight Creek fault system, middle Eocene strata in the Chiwaukum 'graben' were folded about NNW-trending axes. These strata are overlain with angular unconformity by the early-Oligocene Wenatchee Formation, which in turn is folded and thrust-faulted (Gresens 1980). Whether any of the Eocene or Oligocene Formations in this part of western Washington are related to crustal extension is unclear, as no clearly defined extensional faults have been identified. It is certain, however, that shortening in the region occurred during Eocene–Oligocene volcanism and sedimentation by folding along NW- to NNW-trending axes and local thrust faulting, which are here interpreted to represent transpressional yielding in association with minor (?) mid- to late-Eocene dextral motion on the Straight Creek fault. Major dextral translation on the Hope segment of the fault in southern British Columbia ended before intrusion of the 84-Ma Spuzzum pluton, yet the fault also locally offsets Eocene rocks (Okulitch *et al.* 1977).

It thus appears that the Eocene tectonics W of the Okanagon Highlands may have been entirely compressional or transpressional—an interesting observation in light of the large-scale, roughly E–W extensional tectonism that occurred at the same time further E.

Neogene extension and associated magmatism

A later period of extension, synchronous with regional extension farther S, overprints a part of the Pacific Northwest region (Figs 3 & 4). During Oligocene and Miocene times, the triangular area of thrust-belt and Laramide-style tectonism S of the Lewis and Clark line and N of the Snake River Plain was extended by normal faulting. The extension partly accompanied, but mainly followed, widespread deposition of a thin (<500 m) sequence of Oligocene and early-Miocene tuffaceous clastic rocks (Pardee 1950; Kuenzi & Fields 1971; Reynolds 1979). Angular unconformities between that sequence and late-Miocene strata indicate that the greatest extension was underway by that time and may have begun as early as mid-Miocene time. Fault scarps and active seismicity indicate that this event has continued into the Quaternary (Pardee 1950; Robinson 1963; Smith 1978; Reynolds 1979). Tertiary strata are characteristically tilted to the E and large range-front faults dip W. The northern boundary to this extensional terrane, the Lewis and Clark line, may have been a right-lateral intracontinental transform at this time (Reynolds 1979), as it may during the Eocene (cf. Figs 3 & 4). The trends of major range-front faults and the orientation of *T*-axes of fault-plane solutions (Freidline *et al.* 1976) indicate that the extension direction is NW–SE. This event appears to be a northward continuation of broadly distributed Neogene extension in the Great Basin region S of the Snake River Plain (Fig. 4).

N of the Lewis and Clark line, extension is recorded by the late Eocene (?) and early Oligocene deposition of the Kishenehn Formation in a half-graben that forms the modern-day Flathead Valley (Price 1981). The fault that bounds the half-graben has been interpreted by McMechan & Price (1984) as having reactivated the Lewis thrust fault. This faulting event, reflected also in 'back-slipped' thrusts farther W, is unusual in being younger than most of the extension further W in Washington but older than the down-to-the-W event that affected areas S of the Lewis and Clark line. The Lewis and Clark line thus represents the northern extremity of widely distributed Neogene extension that affected large areas to the S (Reynolds 1979).

Predominantly basaltic and bimodal volcanism did not begin in most of the Pacific Northwest region until approximately 17 Ma (Fig. 4), probably at least 20 Ma after the main crustal-thinning event. It is unclear whether extensive outpourings of the Columbia River Basalt Group (mainly 16.5–13.5 Ma) from vents W of the Idaho batholith intruded a crust that had experienced significant upper-crustal extension.

Although the Columbia River basalts represent the only major post-Eocene magmatic activity to have affected the Pacific Northwest region E of the Cascades, a relatively minor episode of bimodal volcanism (Chadwick 1978; Marvin *et al.* 1982) did accompany the Oligocene and younger extension that has affected the region S of the Lewis and Clark line. Except for these areas, and the distal edges of Miocene and Pliocene plateau basalts erupted N of the extended region in British Columbia, most of the area that experienced upper- and middle-crustal extension during the Eocene was amagmatic after the Oligocene.

Great Basin region and areas to the south

Late Cretaceous and early Tertiary tectonism and magmatism

Although the Great Basin region has a history of intermittent crustal shortening dating from the mid-Palaeozoic, involvement of cratonic North America in large-scale, E-directed thrust faulting (and therefore the earliest clear indication of overthickening of the continental crust) did not occur until Late Cretaceous and early Tertiary times. Thin-skinned thrust faulting apparently shows a northward-migrating time of cessation within the Great Basin region, but at these latitudes early-Tertiary Laramide-style shortening to the E was more pronounced than in much of the Pacific Northwest region (Burchfiel & Davis 1975).

Wiltschko & Dorr (1983) conclude that the movement on the Crawford–Meade, Absaroka, Darby, and Prospect thrust systems in the Idaho–Wyoming sector of the thrust belt (Fig. 2), occurred between Coniacian and earliest-Eocene times (≈ 88–58 Ma), accommodating at least 65 and perhaps as much as 90 km of shortening, all of which occurred within previously cratonic supracrustal rocks (Royse *et al.* 1975). As in the southern Canadian Rockies, the locus of upper-crustal shortening

does not represent the region of maximum crustal thickening, which must lie farther W (e.g. Coney & Harms 1984), beneath terrane also shortened during Jurassic–Early Cretaceous time. Like British Columbia (e.g. Read & Brown 1981; Klepacki *et al.* 1985), the 'hinterland' of the Sevier thrust belt was probably shortened during this time interval, and may have experienced periods of extension as well (Burchfiel *et al.* 1970; Chen & Moore 1982; Allmendinger & Jordan 1981; Allmendinger & Platt 1983; Miller 1983; Jordan & Allmendinger 1983). However, it may not have been until the Late Cretaceous that crustal thickness in the orogenic terrane exceeded that of cratonic North America.

Within the Idaho–Wyoming sector of the thrust belt, both thin-skinned thrusting (in the W) and Laramide-style uplifts (in the E) were active during the Palaeocene, but Laramide-style tectonism continued at least into latest early-Eocene time, and perhaps even later into the Eocene (Dorr *et al.* 1977). S of that sector, in the central Utah segment of the thrust belt, thrusting appears to have persisted no later than the deposition of the latest-Cretaceous Price River Formation (Burchfiel & Hickox 1972; Armstrong 1968). Analysis of foreland-basin deposits in central Utah (Lawton & Mayer 1982) indicates that thrust faulting occurred primarily between Cenomanian and Campanian time, between approximately 93 to 75 Ma. At about 70–75 Ma, shortening at the latitude of central Utah was restricted to Laramide-style tectonism of the the craton in Colorado, which occurred no earlier than the Campanian/Maastrichtian boundary (≈ 74 Ma), the last time at which marine strata blanketed the entire region (fig. 2; Tweto 1975). Laramide tectonism had begun in many areas by latest-Maastrichtian time (67 Ma), and, in the case of some of the uplifts (e.g. White River uplift in NW Colorado), continued into earliest middle-Eocene time (i.e. at least until ≈ 52 Ma; Tweto 1975), possibly overlapping in time with extensional tectonism in the Pacific Northwest (Fig. 2).

To the W, over 50% of the exposed area of plutonic rock in the central portion of the Sierra Nevada batholith was emplaced in the interval between 100 and 80 Ma (Chen & Moore 1982), coeval with the most intense period of shortening in the thrust belt to the E (Fig. 2). Within the region of Laramide uplifts, plutonism and volcanism began locally as early as 74 Ma, but generally no later than approximately 70 Ma (Obradovich *et al.* 1969). Most K–Ar ages of shallow-level plutons in the Laramide belt fall between about 70 and 60 Ma, at the same time as the early part of the Laramide Orogeny (Tweto 1975). It appears that the end of thrust-belt tectonism and Sierran plutonism (74–80 Ma) and the beginning of Laramide tectonism and plutonism (70–74 Ma) in Colorado were separated by no more than about 10 My and could have been simultaneous or partly overlapping. This swiftness of the shift in plutonism may argue against hypotheses which favour a flattening Benioff zone beneath North America at this time as an explanation for the eastward shift in tectonism and plutonism of latest-Cretaceous time (e.g. Coney 1978).

We emphasize that Late Cretaceous Sierran plutonism occurred well to the W both of early extensional activity (discussed below) and of Cretaceous orogenesis in the thrust belt—in contrast to areas farther N, where extensive Late Cretaceous plutonism took place adjacent to or within the loci of tectonism (Figs 2 & 3).

Pre-mid-Miocene extensional tectonics and associated magmatism

In contrast to the Eocene onset extensional tectonism and intermediate volcanism N of the Snake River Plain, Cenozoic extensional deformation to the S did not begin until latest-Eocene or early Oligocene time. The early phase of extension, here defined as pre-mid-Miocene (before 18–15 Ma), occurred in the eastern Great Basin in a relatively narrow belt that was less than 100 km wide at the surface before extension (Fig. 3). The onset of extension at a particular latitude was synchronous with a generally southward-migrating belt of intermediate to silicic volcanism. At any given time, this magmatic belt trended E–W, at a high angle to the continental margin and was of the order of several hundred kilometres long—much greater than the width of the coeval extensional belt (see e.g. Snyder *et al.* 1976).

The earliest documented extensional events in the Great Basin had begun by the early Oligocene, or perhaps as early as latest Eocene time. Solomon *et al.* (1979) and Smith & Ketner (1977) report both block faulting and folding of the late-Eocene-early-Oligocene tuffaceous clastics of the Elko Formation. An angular unconformity above the deformed Elko, which contains tuff beds as young as 37–38 Ma (latest Eocene), is overlapped by volcanics that give ages as old as 35 Ma, suggesting a latest Eocene–earliest Oligocene age for the onset of extension.

To the S of the Elko area in the Northern Egan Range, Nevada, Gans (1982) and Gans & Miller (1983) have shown that 36-Ma old dykes cut normal faults with up to 1 km of displacement. Eruptive units in the same area, also dated

as early Oligocene, were deposited prior to a major tilting of the Egan Range (Gans 1982) block indicating that extension and tilting took place over a brief period in the early Oligocene.

In the northern Toiyabe Range of central Nevada large normal faults pre-date the deposition of 28.5 Ma-old volcanic rocks that were subsequently extended by a younger set of faults (Smith 1984). The entire system is blanketed by relatively undeformed volcanics of late Oligocene–early Miocene age. Smith (1984) estimates extension in this area to be as great as 250%.

In the Raft River Range area, Compton *et al.* (1977) suggested that displacement on one of the larger detachments in the area occurred largely before the emplacement of 25 Ma-old stocks, since the metamorphic aureole around the plutons is only slightly offset by the fault. Jordan (1983) reported two younger-on-older faults in the same area that pre-date intrusion of the latest Eocene (38 Ma) Immigrant Pass pluton, although her interpretation that both faults were involved in an episode of recumbent folding may support a Mesozoic age for them.

Based on stratigraphic analysis of pre-volcanic Tertiary sequences throughout E-central Nevada, Fouch (1979) suggested that the pre-Oligocene Cenozoic palaeogeography consisted of a number of restricted lakes that shifted their depositional loci through time. Although Fouch (1979) suggested that the basins formed by tectonic disturbance during their Late Cretaceous to early-Oligocene period of deposition, the lack of thick sections of coarse detritus and angular unconformities within them indicates that major extension or shortening of the upper crust probably did not take place during pre-Oligocene, post-Cretaceous times. Here, as in the Pacific Northwest, the deposition of thin, conformable lacustrine sediments preceded volcanism and major extension, although for a much longer period of time in this case. These sequences, largely confined to the N of latitude 38°, are typically only a few tens of metres thick but locally may be several hundred metres thick. Their loci of deposition are centred about the narrow pre-mid-Miocene belt of extension (Fig. 3).

S of latitude 39°N, the onset of the early extension appears to have occurred during the late Oligocene (<30 Ma), as did the main period of intermediate to silicic volcanism. Early extensional tectonism included displacement on NE- and NW-trending faults that involve the 25 Ma-old Shingle Pass Tuff, which, in the Belted Range are cut by 14–17 Ma intrusive rhyolites (Ekren *et al.* 1968). Volcanic rocks younger than 17 Ma in the same region generally are cut only by a later set of N-trending faults. Immediately S of that region, in the northern Death Valley area, no normal faults of early-Miocene or Oligocene age are known, but the deposition of up to 1000 m of Oligocene and lower Miocene (?) Titus Canyon Formation in the Grapevine Mountains (Stock & Bode 1935; Reynolds 1969, 1976) may record the onset of extensional tectonism in this area. The basal Titus Canyon contains lenses of non-volcanic megabreccia, above which occur fossils of early-Oligocene age. The top of the formation is overlain by volcanic rocks between 22 and 20 Ma old. Whether the Titus Canyon represents a period of major extension, or is simply a younger analogy to the pre-volcanic sedimentary sequences farther N is not yet known.

Igneous activity that accompanied early extension in the northern Great Basin region resembles in several respects the Eocene magmatism of the Pacific Northwest. In particular, silicic volcanic rocks constitute a high proportion of the volcanic suite, especially in the region around the belt of major early extension (Stewart 1980). The importance of crustal melting in the genesis of this suite is emphasized by the aluminous character of many of the associated granitic rocks (Best *et al.* 1974; Miller & Bradfish 1980). Studies of Nd and Sr isotopes of the granitic rocks of this region suggest their origin principally by the melting of lower-crustal granulitic source materials (Farmer & De Paolo 1983).

Mid-Miocene and younger extensional tectonics and associated magmatism

Two major changes affected the Great Basin beginning between about 20 and 17 Ma, following the early phase of extension, the southward sweep of intermediate to silicic volcanism, and a brief lull in magmatism (McKee *et al.* 1970; Fig. 4). One is the predominantly basaltic to bimodal volcanism, which began in mid-Miocene time near the axis of the province in already-extended terrane, and within a few million years had spread widely across it (Christiansen & McKee 1978). The other major change is the widening of the extensional terrane. The region from the frontalmost part of the thrust belt to the area of extensive Late Cretaceous Sierran plutonism became involved in the extension. The widening of the affected area and the onset of basaltic and bimodal volcanism thus define a larger scale example of the pattern seen in the Pacific Northwest S of the Lewis and Clark line. This widening of the

extensional terrane involved neither the cessation of extension in the core of the province nor the cessation of large-magnitude extensional tectonics (Figs 3 & 4).

In mid- to late-Miocene times, the sequence of basin sedimentation, succeeded by intermediate to silicic volcanism, followed immediately by large-magnitude extension in turn followed by predominantly basaltic volcanism occurs in a corridor from the Yerington area of the western Great Basin (Proffett 1977; Hardyman *et al.* 1984; Gilbert & Reynolds 1973) down to the Death Valley region in the southern Great Basin (e.g. Wright *et al.* 1981, 1984; Burchfiel *et al.* 1983; Stewart 1983; Hodges *et al.* 1984, 1986; Ekren *et al.* 1968). N of the Yerington area, large-magnitude extension is perhaps indicated by the steep dips of mid-Miocene volcanics in the Sonoma Range near Winnemucca, (see e.g. Gilluly 1967), suggesting that this part of the Great Basin may have been extended a great deal more than has been generally suspected (see also Zoback *et al.* 1981). N of the latitude of Winnemucca, the High Lava Plains of southwestern Oregon are blanketed by mid-Miocene and younger volcanics that have been broken by normal and strike-slip faults (Donath 1962). Lawrence (1976) analysed WNW-striking, regionally persistent shear zones across which he inferred differential extension had occurred, with increasing amounts of extension to the S.

It is uncertain how much extension has occurred in the High Lava Plains (Lawrence 1976). Firstly, because most of the exposed rocks are less than 16-Ma old, it is unknown how much pre-mid-Miocene extension may have occurred. Secondly, although stratal tilts within the extended volcanic terrane are typically not large, such an observation is insufficient to rule out large-magnitude extension there. For example, strata in the hanging wall of the Sevier Desert detachment (McDonald 1976; Allmendinger *et al.* 1983) as a rule dip at less than about 20°, yet this structure has accommodated several tens of kilometres of crustal extension (Wernicke 1981).

In the Death Valley area, as in the Oregon High Lava Plains, late Miocene to Recent extension terminates to the S against a strike-slip boundary, the Garlock fault (Hamilton & Myers 1966; Davis & Burchfiel 1973; Burchfiel *et al.* 1983). It is noteworthy that the Death Valley area, which represents one of the youngest large-magnitude extensional terranes, experienced the same cycle, noted elsewhere in the Great Basin and Pacific Northwest regions, of local sedimentation, intermediate magmatism, large-magnitude extension and finally basaltic or bimodal volcanism, but entirely within mid-Miocene to Quaternary times (Wright & Troxel 1973; Wright *et al.* 1984). Similarly, the Eldorado Mountains–Black Mountains extensional terrain (Anderson 1971; Anderson *et al.* 1972) developed between about 15 and 11 Ma amid an intermediate-volcanic field. These examples emphasize that the sequence we propose as 'typical' for the development of an extended terrane is independent of its time of development.

Extension within the narrow, pre-mid-Miocene belt continued during mid-Miocene and younger time, and locally may be of large magnitude, not having waned significantly in the last 10–15 Ma. For example, Snoke & Howard (1984) report large stratal rotations of 13.5-My old rhyolitic flows in the Elko area, the locus of some of the earliest extension in the Great Basin. Similarly, Compton (1983) mapped a large-scale detachment complex in the Raft River Range area that involves 11.5-My old volcanic rocks. The opening of the adjacent Raft River basin along a shallowly inclined detachment (Covington 1983) occurred in the last 15 My, and may still be active. Covington's (1983) reconstructions suggest about 30 km of transport of upper-plate rocks. Farther S in the pre-mid-Miocene belt, Bartley *et al.* (1984) have shown that large-magnitude extension was responsible for the development of the Miocene and Pliocene Horse Camp basin (Moores *et al.* 1968) in the Grant Range area, E-central Nevada.

E of the early belt, post-15 Ma extension, some of large magnitude, disrupted the frontal part of the thrust belt, from just S of the Yellowstone Plateau volcanic field to southern Nevada (Fig. 4). Detachments and rotated normal-fault blocks typically are downthrown to the W, and some have been shown to have reactivated older Sevier thrust faults (Royse *et al.* 1975). The magnitude of extension accommodated on these faults is quite varied, ranging from 7–8 km of supracrustal extension across the entire Idaho–Wyoming thrust belt (Royse 1983) to many tens of kilometres of extension in the Great Salt Lake, Sevier Desert, and southern Nevada sectors of the orogen. Davis & Burchfiel (1973), Guth (1981) and Wernicke *et al.* (1982, 1984) have shown that much of the 140-km translation of crustal blocks on large strike-slip faults in southern Nevada is absorbed by crustal extension between blocks. Based on seismic reflection profiling in the Sevier Desert area, Allmendinger *et al.* (1983) and Anderson *et al.* (1983) have suggested offsets of 30–60 km on the Sevier Desert detachment. Given that most of the rotated basin-fill there is of Miocene–Pliocene age and

the fact that abundant Quaternary faulting occurs in the hanging wall of the detachment without offsetting it, the bulk of displacement on the detachment appears to be post-mid-Miocene, and it may still be active (Wernicke 1981; Anderson *et al.* 1983; Allmendinger *et al.* 1983; Smith & Bruhn 1984).

While most of the down-to-the-W extension within the thrust belt is post-mid-Miocene, there may be exceptions. Both Allmendinger *et al.* (1983) and Hopkins & Bruhn (1983) have suggested an Oligocene age of initiation for extension in the Sevier Desert and northern Wasatch Mountains areas, respectively. However, evidence for Oligocene extension of a magnitude comparable to that during Miocene and Pliocene times is lacking. Widespread Oligocene and lower-Miocene sheets of rhyolitic ash-flow tuff spanned areas much larger than the present ranges and basins without significant deflections caused by buried topography.

Las Vegas amagmatic corridor and the Mojave and Sonoran Desert regions

Considering the Great Basin as a whole, it is a reasonable generalization that one is never very far from a Tertiary volcanic–plutonic centre. Perhaps one of the most striking exceptions to this is a region W and N of Las Vegas, which experienced large-magnitude extension but shows no sign of igneous activity at any time during the Phanerozoic (Longwell *et al.* 1965; Anderson *et al.* 1972; Guth 1981; Wernicke *et al.* 1984). This 'amagmatic corridor' (Fig. 2; Anderson 1981) is the same area, as mentioned above, that was shortened mainly during the Jurassic (e.g. Carr 1980) with the latest phases occurring at about 90 Ma (Burchfiel & Davis 1971, 1981)—at least 20 My before the end of shortening in central Utah and about 40 My before thrusting ended in the Idaho–Wyoming sector of the thrust belt (Fig. 2). Despite the fact that this is one of the first areas to have thickened the craton, major extension did not begin until about 15 Ma—the latest time of initiation at any latitude along the belt. The southward cut-off in igneous activity is extremely abrupt (e.g. Eaton 1982), and some of the most extensive Tertiary intermediate and silicic volcanism in the Great Basin occurred just to the N of it, where volcanic accumulations are commonly 500–1000 m thick (Stewart 1980). Some of these large fields occur away from areas of major extensional tectonism. For example, the Marysvale field in southwestern Utah (Steven *et al.* 1984) contains a section up to 3 km thick near volcanic centres on the western edge of the Colorado Plateau. Other fields, however, such as the southern Nevada volcanic field (Christiansen *et al.* 1977), are in areas of major extension.

S of the 'amagmatic corridor', in the Mojave and Sonoran Desert regions, extension was of large magnitude and followed the pattern of early sedimentation, intermediate volcanism, extension, and then basaltic or bimodal magmatism. Like the Great Basin, this region experienced extension and intermediate magmatism between early-Oligocene and mid-Miocene times (≈ 35–15 Ma). The principal distinction between this part of the extending Cordillera and areas to the N is that extension waned immediately following the mid-Miocene onset of basaltic magmatism, while extension continued farther N. Other key distinctions include its position within; (i) pre-Mesozoic cratonic North America; (ii) a long-lived Mesozoic magmatic arc; and (iii) a zone of latest-Cretaceous and early-Tertiary compressional orogenesis and magmatism (Haxel *et al.* 1984; see also Coney & Harms 1984). The more detailed synthesis by Glazner & Bartley (1984) suggests that the most intense magmatism and extension in the region migrated generally northward from the Tucson area during the mid-Oligocene to the Las Vegas area by the mid-Miocene—an apparent "mirror-image" of events farther N, with an axis about the 'amagmatic corridor' (Anderson 1981).

Neogene compression in western areas

As in the Pacific Northwest, the continental margin W of the extended Great Basin region was characterized by either tectonic quiescence or crustal shortening during extensional deformation farther E. Notable events include post-latest-Eocene folding and accretion of Franciscan rocks in the northern California Coast Ranges (e.g. Blake & Jones 1981); movement on the Coast Range thrust during the Tertiary (Page 1981); and Neogene transpression of the southern Coast Ranges next to the San Andreas Fault (e.g. Page 1981; Figs 3 & 4). The presence of mid-Miocene fossils in deep-sea deposits of the Coastal Belt Franciscan (McLaughlin *et al.* 1982) suggests shortening after that time along the margin. While Neogene transtensional basins appeaɪ to have opened locally adjacent to the San Andreas (e.g. Crowell 1974; Hall 1981), the dominant tectonic regime along the margin appears to have been compressional or transpressional during much of post-Eocene time. There is little evidence of extensional events affecting the entire margin during the Cenozoic.

The history of the compressional or transpressional shortening of the edge of North America during much of the Cenozoic provides an important constraint for models of coeval extensional tectonics occurring further inland (Sonder *et al.* this volume).

Summary and conclusions

In the Pacific Northwest, extension began in the middle Eocene (≈ 53 Ma), possibly overlapping in time with the latest phases of foreland thrusting to the E. Its onset was more or less synchronous with intermediate to silicic magmatism. S of the Lewis and Clark line, extension continued in a broader belt after the mid-Miocene, simultaneously with local basaltic or bimodal volcanism.

In the Great Basin region, major extension did not begin until latest Eocene or early-Oligocene time (≈ 38 Ma) and was initially concentrated in a narrow zone; this extension was also accompanied by intermediate to silicic magmatism. Following the onset of predominantly basaltic or bimodal volcanism in mid-Miocene time, extension developed over a much broader area than in pre-mid-Miocene time. Magmatism has tended to concentrate outward with time since the mid-Miocene, and since the beginning of the Quaternary has occurred mainly near the margins of the region. Post-mid-Miocene extensional strain is not of lesser magnitude than in the early belt in the Great Basin, and extension seems to be as active today in some parts of the Great Basin as it has ever been.

In the southern Nevada 'amagmatic corridor', extension did not begin until the mid-Miocene (≈ 15 Ma), the latest onset time of any latitude in the Cordillera. This region also has the earliest time of cessation of Mesozoic thrust faulting.

We are impressed by what appears to be a consistent relationship between the timing of onset of extension and the intensity of the Cretaceous–early-Tertiary plutonic history of the various extended regions. Where extension began earliest N of the Snake River Plain at about 55–49 Ma, it took place astride a number of Late Cretaceous–early-Tertiary batholiths. Farther S in the Great Basin region, where only minor Late Cretaceous plutonism occurred within the overthickened crust, extension began 38–20 Ma. In the 'amagmatic corridor', where there are no Phanerozoic plutons, extension began at about 15 Ma, with the longest hiatus between compression and extension, an interval of at least 65 Ma. S of the 'amagmatic corridor,' where Late Cretaceous magmatism is prevalent (though apparently less extensive than in the Pacific Northwest), extension began at about the same time as in the northern Great Basin (e.g. Glazner & Bartley 1984).

We conclude that the locus of extension is controlled principally by crustal thickness, while its timing is governed by the thermal state of the lithosphere at the time of thickening. As we show in a companion paper (Sonder *et al.* this volume), the observations shown in Table 1 are consistent with calculations based on a simple thermal-mechanical model in which extension of the lithosphere results from gravitational spreading of a previously thickened crust. Because the onset of extension is, as a rule, accompanied by calc-alkaline magmatism, a lower crust at or near its minimum-melting temperature (≈ 650–$750°C$) is apparently a requirement for it to begin. However, since magmatism of this type also occurs well away from extended regions, it does not appear to be the driving mechanism of extension, as has been proposed in some models.

We also emphasize that the continental margin W of the extensional terrane was the locus of crustal shortening during the Cenozoic, coeval in several places with major phases of extension to the E. Such a kinematic boundary condition is inconsistent with hypotheses that relate inland extension to extensional deviatoric stresses along the adjacent margin, induced by e.g. changes in plate motion.

Recent speculation that a decrease in Farallon–Pacific convergence rates is the cause of extension (Coney 1978; Engebretson *et al.* 1984; Coney & Harms 1984) is not supported by the observation in active systems that tectonic regimes in overriding plates show no consistent relationship to convergence rates (Molnar & Atwater 1978). For example, the Tonga–Kermadec and Peru–Chile systems both have convergence rates of about 10 cm yr^{-1}, yet the tectonics of the overriding plates are strongly extensional and compressional, respectively. Engebretson *et al.* (1984) suggested that the progressive decrease in age of the subducting Farallon Plate may have brought about the

slowing of convergence because of a change from negative to positive buoyancy of the downgoing slab. By contrast, Molnar & Atwater (1978) demonstrated a strong correlation between extensional tectonics and old subducting lithosphere, and between compressional tectonics and young subducting lithosphere. Thus, the reconstruction of Engebretson *et al.* (1984) would predict behind-the-arc extensional tectonics during the Cretaceous and early Tertiary, changing to compressional later in the Tertiary.

We also view the timing of the calculated major transition in plate motions at 40 Ma (Coney 1978) as being too young to explain the earliest-middle-Eocene (55–53 Ma) transition in tectonic style N of the Snake River Plain, where its timing is most tightly bracketed. While Coney (1972) has argued for a fundamental transition in Cordilleran tectonics at 40 Ma, this figure represents only the upper age limit for Laramide tectonism throughout much of the Cordillera. We could not find any examples of post-early-middle-Eocene (≈ 52–50 Ma) strata deformed by Laramide compression. Based on this evidence, we feel a more likely time for a synchronous, Cordillera-wide transition, *if any*, is 55–50 Ma, centred in time on the peak in convergence rates calculated by Engebretson *et al.* (1984).

While we agree with these authors that some relaxation of horizontal boundary stresses is necessary for extension to begin, it is not clear that the calculated plate motions would predict such a relaxation. It would of course be incorrect to rule out plate-interaction forces as a major factor in Cenozoic Cordilleran tectonics. For example, reorientation of the horizontal stress axes during the past 17 My is likely best explained by variations in plate-interaction forces (Zoback & Thompson 1978; Zoback *et al.* 1981).

ACKNOWLEDGMENTS: Research leading to this report was funded by NSF grants EAR84-08352 and EAR83-19767 awarded to P.C.E. and B.P.W. respectively. B.P.W. also acknowledges support from the Clifford P. Hickok Junior Faculty Development Fund of Harvard University. L.J.S. acknowledges support from an Exxon Teaching Fellowship.

References

ALLMENDINGER, R.W. & JORDAN, T.E. 1981. Mesozoic evolution, hinterland of the Sevier orogenic belt. *Geology*, **9**, 308–13.
—— & PLATT, L.B. 1983. Stratigraphic variation and low-angle faulting in the North Hansel Mountains and Samaria Mountain, southern Idaho. *Mem. geol. Soc. Am.* **157**, 149–64.

——, SHARP, J.W., VON TISH, D., SERPA, L., BROWN, L., KAUFMAN, S., OLIVER, J. & SMITH, R.B. 1983. Cenozoic and Mesozoic structure of the eastern Basin and Range province, Utah, from COCORP seismic-reflection data. *Geology*, **11**, 532–6.
ANDERSON, R.E. 1971. Thin skin distension in Tertiary

rocks of southeastern Nevada. *Bull. geol. Soc. Am.* **82**, 43–58.

—— 1981. Structural ties between the Great Basin and Sonoran Desert sections of the Basin and Range Province. *US. geol. Surv. Open-file Rep.* **81-503**, 4–6.

——, ZOBACK, M.L. & THOMPSON, G.A. 1983. Implications of selected subsurface data on the structural form of some basins in the northern Basin and Range province, Nevada and Utah. *Bull. geol. Soc. Am.* **94**, 1055–72.

——, LONGWELL, C.R., ARMSTRONG, R.L. & MARVIN, R.F. 1972. Significance of K–Ar ages of Tertiary rocks from the Lake Mead region, Nevada-Arizona. *Bull. geol. Soc. Am.* **83**, 273–87.

ARMSTRONG, R.L. 1968. The Sevier orogenic belt in Nevada and Utah. *Bull. geol. Soc. Am.* **79**, 429–58.

—— 1978. Cenozoic igneous history of the U.S. Cordillera from lat. 42° to 49°N. *Mem. geol. Soc. Am.* **152**, 265–282.

——, TAUBENECK, W.H. & HALES, P.O. 1977. Rb–Sr and K–Ar geochronometry of Mesozoic granitic rocks and their Sr isotopic composition, Oregon, Washington, and Idaho. *Bull. geol. Soc. Am.* **88**, 397–411.

ATWATER, T. 1970. Implications of plate tectonics for the Cenozoic tectonic evolution of western North America. *Bull. geol. Soc. Am.* **81** 3513–35.

BARTLEY, J.M., FRYXELL, J.E., MURRAY, M.E. & WRIGHT, S.D. 1984. Patterns of Tertiary extension in the Great Basin exemplified in the Grant/Quinn Canyon Range, Nevada. *Abstr. with Programs geol. Soc. Am.* **16(6)**, 438.

BLAKE, M.C. JR & JONES, D.L. 1981. The Franciscan assemblage and related rocks in northern California: A reinterpretation. *In*: ERNST, W.G. (ed.) *The Geotectonic Development of California*, pp. 306–28.

BEST, M.G., ARMSTRONG, R.L., GRANSTEIN, W.C., EMBREE, G.F. & AHLBORN, R.C. 1974. Mica granites of the Kern Mountain pluton, eastern White Pine County, Nevada: Remobilized basement of the Cordilleran miogeosyncline?. *Bull. geol. Soc. Am.* **85**, 1277–86.

BROOKS, H.C., MCINTYRE, H. & WALKER, G. 1976. Geology of the Baker quadrangle. *Oregon Dept. Geol. Min. Ind. Map. GMS-7.*

BROWN, R.L. & MURPHY, D.C. 1982. Kinematic interpretation of mylonitic rocks in part of the Columbia River fault zone, Shuswap terrane, British Columbia. *Can. J. Earth Sci.* **19**, 456–65.

BURCHFIEL, B.C. & DAVIS, G.A. 1971. Clark Mountain thrust complex in the Cordillera of southeastern California, Geologic Summary and Field Trip Guide. *Univ. California Riverside Museum contrib.* **1**, 1–28.

—— & —— 1975. Nature and controls of Cordilleran orogenesis, western United States: extensions of an earlier synthesis. *Am. J. Sci.* **275-A**, 363–96.

—— & —— 1981. Mojave desert and environs. *In*: ERNST, W.G. (ed.) *The Geotectonic Development of California*, pp. 217–52. Prentice-Hall, Englewood Cliffs.

—— & HICKOX, C.W. 1972. Structural development of central Utah. *Utah geol. Assoc. Publ.* **2**, 55–66.

——, HAMILL, G.S., IV & WILHELMS, D.E. 1983. Structural geology of the Montgomery Mountains and the northern half of the Nopah and Resting Springs Ranges, Nevada and California. *Bull. geol. Soc. Am.* **94**, 1359–76.

——, PELTON, P.J. & SUTTER, J.F. 1970. An early Mesozoic deformation belt in south-central Nevada —southeastern California. *Bull. geol. Soc. Am.* **81**, 211–6.

——, WALKER, D., DAVIS, G.A. & WERNICKE, B. 1983. Kingston Range and related detachment faults—a major 'breakaway' zone in the southern Great Basin. *Abstr. with Progams geol. Soc. Am.* **15(6)**, 536.

CARR, M.D. 1980. Upper Jurassic to Lower Cretaceous (?) synorogenic sedimentary rocks in the southern Spring Mountains, Nevada. *Geology*, **8**, 385–9.

CARR, S.D. 1985. Ductile shearing and brittle faulting in Valhalla gneiss complex, southeastern British Columbia. *U.S. geol. Surv. Contr. Paper*, **85-1A**, 89–96.

CHADWICK, R.A. 1978. Geochronology of post-Eocene rhyolitic and basaltic volcanism in southwestern Montana. *Isochron/West*, **22**, 25–8.

CHEN, J.H. & MOORE, J.G. 1982. Uranium-Lead isotopic ages from the Sierra Nevada batholith, California. *J. geophys. Res.* **87**, 4761–84.

CHENEY, E.S. 1980. Kettle dome and related structures of northeastern Washington. *Mem. geol. Soc. Am.* **153**, 463–84.

——, OLIVER, L.A., ORR, K.E. & RHODES, B.P. 1982. Kettle and Okanogan domes and associated structural lows of north-central Washington. *Abstr. with Programs. geol. Soc. Am.* **14(4)**, 155.

CHRISTIANSEN, R.L. & LIPMAN, P.W. 1972. Cenozoic volcanism and plate tectonic evolution of the western United States. II, Late Cenozoic. *Phil. Trans. R. Soc. London*, **271**, 249–84.

—— & MCKEE, E.D. 1978. Late Cenozoic volcanic and tectonic evolution of the Great Basin and Columbia intermontane regions. *Mem. geol. Soc. Am.* **152**, 283–312.

——, LIPMAN, P.W., CARR, W.J., BYERS, F.M., JR, ORKILD, P.P. & SARGENT, K.A. 1977. Timber Mountain-Oasis Valley caldera complex of southern Nevada. *Bull. geol. Soc. Am.* **88**, 943–59.

COMPTON, R.R. 1983. Displaced Miocene rocks on the west flank of the Raft River—Grouse Creek core complex. *In*: MILLER, D.M. (ed.) *Tectonic and Stratigraphic Studies in the Eastern Great Basin*, *Mem. geol. Soc. Am.* **157**, 271–328.

——, TODD, V.R., ZARTMAN, R.E. & NAESER, C.W. 1977. Oligocene and Miocene metamorphism, folding, and low-angle faulting in northwestern Utah. *Bull. geol. Soc. Am.* **88**, 1237–50.

CONEY, P.J. 1972. Cordilleran tectonics and North American plate motion. *Am. J. Sci.* **272**, 603–28.

—— 1978. Mesozoic–Cenozoic Cordilleran plate tectonics. *Mem. geol. Soc. Am.* **152**, 33–50.

—— & HARMS, T.A. 1984. Cordilleran metamorphic core complexes: Cenozoic extensional relics of Mesozoic compression. *Geology*, **12**, 550–4.

COVINGTON, H.R. 1983. Structural evolution of the Raft River Basin, Idaho. *In*: MILLER, D.M. *et al.* (eds) *Tectonic and Stratigraphic Studies of the Eastern Great Basin, Mem. geol. Soc. Am.* **157**, 229–38.

CRISS, R.E. & FLECK, R.J. 1983. Isotopic characteristics of granitic rocks from the north half of the Idaho batholith. *Abstr. with Programs geol. Soc. Am.* **15**, 550.

CROWELL, J.C. 1974. Sedimentation along the San Andreas fault, California. *In*: DOTT, R.H. & SHAVER, R.H. (eds) *Modern and Ancient Geosynclinal Sedimentation, Soc. econ. Paleontol. and Mineral. Spec. Publ.* **19**, 292–303.

DAVIS, G.A. 1977. Tectonic evolution of the Pacific Northwest: Precambrian to present. *Wash. Pub. Power Supply System, Nuclear Proj. No. 1, Subappendix 2RC, PSAR, Amendment 23, i-2R-c-46.*

—— & BURCHFIEL, B.C. 1973. Garlock fault: an intracontinental transform structure, southern California. *Bull. geol. Soc. Am.* **84**, 1407–22.

——, MONGER, J.W.H. & BURCHFIEL, B.C. 1978. Mesozoic construction of the Cordilleran 'collage', central British Columbia to central California. *In*: HOWELL, D.G. & McDOUGALL, K.A. (eds) *Mesozoic Paleogeography of the Western United States.* pp. 1–32. Soc. econ. Paleontol. and Mineral., Pac. sect. Los Angeles.

DONATH, R. 1962. Analysis of basin-range structure, south-central Oregon. *Bull. geol. Soc. Am.* **73**, 1407–22.

DORR, J.A., SPEARING, D.R. & STEIDTMANN, J.R. 1977. Deformation and deposition between a foreland uplift and impinging thrust belt, Hoback basin, Wyoming. *Geol. Soc. Am. Spec. Pap. 177*, 82 pp.

DOVER, J.H. 1982. Geology of the Boulder-Pioneer Wilderness Study Area, Blaine and Custer Counties, Idaho. *U.S. geol. Surv. Bull. 1497*, 15–75.

EATON, G.P. 1982. The Basin and Range province: origin and tectonic significance. *Ann. Rev. Earth planet. Sci.* **8**, 409–40.

EKREN, E.B., ROGERS, C.L., ANDERSON, R.E. & ORKILD, P.P. 1968. Age of basin and range normal faults in Nevada Test Site and Nellis Air Force Range, Nevada. *Mem. geol. Soc. Am.* **110**, 247–50.

ENGEBRETSON, D.C. 1982. Relative motions between oceanic and continental plates in the Pacific basin. Ph.D. thesis, Stanford Univ. Stanford, California, 211 pp.

——, COX, A. & THOMPSON, G.A. 1984. Correlation of plate motion with continental tectonics: Laramide to Basin-Range. *Tectonics*, **3**, 115–20.

EWING, T.E. 1981a. Regional stratigraphy and structural setting of the Kamloops Group, south-central British Columbia. *Can. J. Earth Sci.* **18**, 1464–77.

—— 1981b. Petrology and geochemistry of the Kamloops Group volcanics. British Columbia. *Can. J. Earth Sci.* **18**, 1478–691.

FARMER, G.L. & DE PAOLO, D. 1983. Origin of Mesozoic and Tertiary granite in the western United States and implications for pre-Mesozoic crustal structure. 1. Nd and Sr isotopic studies

in the geocline of the Northern Great Basin. *J. geophys. Res.* **88**, 3379–401.

FOUCH, T.D. 1979. Character and palaeogeographic distribution of upper Cretaceous (?) and Paleogene nonmarine sedimentary rocks in east-central Nevada. *In*: ARMENTROUT, J.M. *et al.* (eds) *Cenozoic Paleogeography of the Western United States.* pp. 97–112. Soc. econ. Paleontol. and Mineral., Pac. sect. Los Angeles.

FOX, K.F., JR, RINEHART, C.D. & ENGELS J.C. 1977. Plutonism and orogeny in north-central Washington —timing and regional context. *U.S. geol. Surv. Prof. Pap.* **989**, 27 pp.

FREIDLINE, R.A., SMITH, R.B. & BLACKWELL, D.D. 1976. Seismicity and contemporary tectonics of the Helena, Montana area. *Bull. seism. Soc. Am.* **66**, 81–95.

GANS, P.B. 1982. Geometry of Tertiary extensional faulting, Northern Egan Range, east-central Nevada. *Abstr. with Programs geol. Soc. Am.* **14**, 165.

—— & MILLER, E.L. 1983. Style of mid-Tertiary extension in east-central Nevada. *In*: GURGEL, K.D. (ed.) *Geologic Excursions in the Overthrust Belt and Metamorphic Core Complexes of the Intermountain Region*, pp. 107–39. Utah geol. Min. Surv., Salt Lake City, Utah.

GARMEZY, L. & SUTTER, J.F. 1983. Mylonitization coincident with uplift in an extensional setting, Bitterroot Range, Montana-Idaho. *Abstr. with Programs geol. Soc. Am.* **15**(6), 578.

GILBERT, C.M. & REYNOLDS, M.W. 1973. Character and chronology of basin development, western margin of the Basin and Range province. *Bull. geol. Soc. Am.* **84**, 2489–509.

GILLULY, J. 1967. Geologic map of the Winnemucca quadrangle, Pershing and Humboldt Counties, Nevada. *Geol. Surv. Map, GQ-656.*

GLAZNER, A.F. & BARTLEY, J.M. 1984. Timing and tectonic setting of Tertiary low-angle normal faulting and associated magmatism in the southwestern United States. *Tectonics*, **3**, 385–96.

GRESENS, R.L. 1980. Deformation of the Wenatchee Formation and its bearing on the tectonic history of the Chiwaukum graben, Washington, during Cenozoic time. *Bull. geol. Soc. Am.* **91**, 4–7.

GUTH, P.L. 1981. Tertiary extension north of the Las Vegas Valley shear zone, Sheep and Desert Ranges, Clark County, Nevada. *Bull. geol. Soc. Am.* **92**, 763–71.

HALL, C.A., JR 1981. Evolution of the western Transverse Ranges microplate: late Cenozoic faulting and basinal development. *In*: ERNST, W.G. (ed.) *The Geotectonic Development of California*, pp. 559–82. Prentice-Hall, Englewood Cliffs.

HAMILTON, W. & MYERS, W.B. 1966. Cenozoic tectonics of the western United States. *Rev. Geophys.* **4**, 509–49.

HARDYMAN, R.F., EKREN, E.B., PROFFETT, J.M. & DILLES, J.H. 1984. Tertiary tectonics of west-central Nevada: Yerington to Gabbs Valley (Field Trip 8). *In*: LINTZ, J.P. (ed.) *Western Geological Excursions 4*, pp. 160–231. Mackay School of Mines, Reno.

HARMS, T.A. & PRICE, R.A. 1983. The Newport fault, Eocene crustal stretching, necking and listric normal faulting in NE Washington and NW Idaho. *Abstr. with Programs Geol. Soc. Am.* **15**, 309.

HAXEL, G.B., TOSDAL, R.M., MAY, D.J. & WRIGHT, J.E. 1984. Latest Cretaceous and early Tertiary orogenesis in south-central Arizona: thrust faulting, regional metamorphism and granitic plutonism. *Bull. geol. Soc. Am.* **95**, 631–53.

HODGES, K.V. This Volume. Footwall structural evolution of the Tucki Mountain detachment system, Death Valley region, southeastern California.

——, WALKER, J.D. & WERNICKE, B.P. 1984. Tertiary folding and extension, Tucki Mountain area, Death Valley region, CA. *Abstr. with Programs geol. Soc. Am.* **16(6)**, 540.

HOPKINS, D.L. & BRUHN, R.L. 1983. Extensional faulting in the Wasatch Mountains, Utah. *Abstr. with Programs geol. Soc. Am.* **15(5)**, 402.

HYNDMAN, D.W. 1980. Bitterroot Dome-Sapphire tectonic block, an example of a plutonic-core gneiss-dome complex with its detached suprastructure. *Mem. geol. Soc. Am.* **153**, 427–44.

JORDAN, T.E. 1983. Structural geometry and sequence, Bovine Mountain, northwestern Utah. *Mem. geol. Soc. Am.* **157**, 215–28.

—— & ALLMENDINGER, R.W. 1983. Known and inferred Mesozoic deformation, hinterland of the Sevier belt, northwestern Utah. *Abstr. with Programs geol. Soc. Am.* **15(5)**, 319.

KLEPACKI, D.W., READ, P.B. & WHEELER, J.O. 1985. Geology of the headwaters of Wilson Creek, Lardeau map area, southeastern British Columbia. *Geol. Surv. Can. Pap.* **85-1A**, 273–6.

KUENZI, W.D. & FIELDS, R.W. 1971. Tertiary stratigraphy, structure and geologic history, Jefferson basin, Montana. *Bull. geol. Soc. Am.* **82**, 3373–94.

LAWRENCE, R.D. 1976. Strike-slip faulting terminates the Basin and Range province in Oregon. *Bull. geol. Soc. Am.* **87**, 846–50.

LAWTON, T.F. & MAYER, L. 1982. Thrust load-induced basin subsidence and sedimentation in the Utah foreland: temporal constraints on the upper Cretaceous Sevier orogeny. *Abstr. with Programs geol. Soc. Am.* **14(7)**, 542.

LIPMAN, P.W., PROSTKA, H.J. & CHRISTIANSEN, R.L. 1972. Cenozoic volcanism and plate-tectonic evolution of the western United States, I. Early and middle Cenozoic. *Phil. Trans. R. Soc. London,* **A-271**, 217–48.

LONGWELL, C.R., PAMPEYAN, E.H., BOWYER, B. & ROBERTS, R.J. 1965. Geology and mineral deposits of Clark County, Nevada. *Nevada Bur. Min. Geol. Bull.* **62**, 218 pp.

McDONALD, R.W. 1976. Tertiary tectonics and sedimentary rocks along the transition, Basin and Range province to plateau and thrust belt province. *In*: HILL, V.G. (ed.) *Symposium on Geology of the Cordilleran Hingeline*, pp. 281–318. Rocky M. Assoc. Geol. Denver.

McKEE, E.H., NOBLE, D.C. & SILBERMAN, M.L. 1970. Middle Miocene hiatus in volcanic activity in the Great Basin area of the western United States. *Earth planet. Sci. Lett.* **8**, 93–6.

McLAUGHLIN, R.J., KLING, S.A., POORE, R.Z., McDOUGALL, K. & BEUTNER, E.C. 1982. Post-middle Miocene accretion of Franciscan rocks, northwestern California. *Bull. geol. Soc. Am.* **93**, 595–605.

McMECHAN, R.D. & PRICE, R.A. 1984. Crustal extension and thinning in a foreland thrust and fold belt, southern Canadian Rockies. *Abstr. with Programs geol. Soc. Am.* **16(6)**, 591.

MARVIN, R.F., ZEN, E. & MEHNERT, H.H. 1982. Tertiary volcanoes along the eastern flank of the Pioneer Mountains, southwestern Montana. Montana. *Isochron West*, **33**, 11–3.

MILLER, C.F. & BRADFISH, L.J. 1980. An inner Cordilleran belt of muscovite-bearing plutons. *Geology*, **8**, 412–6.

MILLER, D.M. 1983. Mesozoic metamorphism and low-angle faults in the hinterland of Nevada linked to Sevier-belt thrusts. *Abstr. with Programs geol. Soc. Am.* **15**, 644.

MILLER, F.K. & ENGELS, J.C. 1975. Distribution and trends of discordant ages of the plutonic rocks of northeastern Washington and northern Idaho. *Bull. geol. Soc. Am.* **86**, 517–28.

MISCH, P. 1966. Tectonic evolution of the Northern Cascades of Washington State. *Can. Inst. Min. Met. Spec. Vol.* **8**, 101–48.

MOLNAR, P. & ATWATER, T. 1978. Interarc spreading and Cordilleran tectonics as alternates related to the age of subducted oceanic lithosphere. *Earth planet. Sci. Lett.* **41**. 330–40.

MOLNAR, P. & CHEN, W.-P. 1983. Focal depths and fault plane solutions of earthquakes under the Tibetan plateau. *J. geophys. Res.* **88**, 1180–96.

MOORES, E.M., SCOTT, R.B. & LUNSDEN, W.W. 1968. Tertiary tectonics of the White Pine-Grant Range region, east-central Nevada, and some regional implications. *Bull. geol. Soc. Am.* **79**, 1703–26.

NICHOLS, D.J., PERRY, W.J. & HALEY, J.C. 1985. Reinterpretation of the palynology and age of Laramide syntectonic deposits, southwestern Montana, and revision of the Beaverhead Group. *Geology*, **13**, 149–59.

OBRADOVICH, J.D., MUTSCHLER, F.E. & BRYANT, B. 1969. Potassium–argon ages bearing on the igneous and tectonic history of the Elk Mountains and vicinity, Colorado—a preliminary report. *Bull. geol. Soc. Am.* **80**, 1749–56.

OKULITCH, A.V., PRICE, R.A. & RICHARDS, T.A. 1977. A guide to the geology of the southern Canadian Cordillera. *GAC/MAC/SEG Fieldtrip Guidebook 8*, 135 pp.

PAGE, B.M. 1981. The Southern Coast Ranges. *In*: ERNST, W.G. (ed.) *The Geotectonic Development of California*, pp. 329–417. Prentice-Hall, Englewood Cliffs.

PARDEE, J.T. 1950. Late Cenozoic block faulting in western Montana. *Bull. geol. Soc. Am.* **61**, 359–406.

PARRISH, R. 1984. Slocan Lake fault: a low-angle fault zone bounding the Valhalla gneiss complex, Nelson Map Area, southern British Columbia. *Geol. Surv. Can. Pap.* **84-1A**, 323–30.

—— , CARR, S.D. & BROWN, R.L. 1985. Valhalla gneiss complex, southeast British Columbia: 1984 field work. *Geol. Surv. Can. Pap.* **85-1A**, 81–7.

PEARSON, R.C. & OBRADOVICH, J.D. 1977. Eocene rocks in northeast Washington—radiometric ages and correlation. *U.S. geol. Surv. Bull. 1433*, 41 pp.

PRICE, R.A. 1979. Intracontinental ductile crustal spreading linking the Fraser River and northern Rocky Mountain trench transform fault zones, south-central British Columbia and northeastern Washington. *Abstr. with Programs geol. Soc. Am.* **11**, 499.

—— 1981. The Cordilleran foreland thrust and fold belt in the southern Canadian Rocky Mountains. *In*: MCCLAY, K.R. & PRICE, N.J. (eds) *Thrust and Nappe Tectonics, Spec. Pub. geol. Soc. London*, **9**, 427–47.

PROFFETT, J.M., JR 1977. Cenozoic geology of the Yerington district, Nevada, and implications for the nature and origin of Basin and Range faulting. *Bull. geol. Soc. Am.* **88**, 247–66.

READ, P.B. & BROWN, R.L. 1981. Columbia River fault zone: southeastern margin of the Shuswap and Monashee complexes, southern British Columbia. *Can. J. Earth Sci.* **18**, 1127–45.

REHRIG, W.A. & REYNOLDS, S.J. 1981. Eocene metamorphic core complex tectonics near the Lewis and Clark zone, western Montana and northern Idaho. *Abstr. with Programs geol. Soc. Am.* **13**, 102.

—— , —— & ARMSTRONG, R.L. 1982. Geochronology and tectonic evolution of the Priest River crystalline/metamorphic complex of northeastern Washington and northern Idaho. *Abstr. with Programs geol. Soc. Am.* **14(4)**, 277.

REYNOLDS, M.W. 1969. Stratigraphy and structural geology of the Titus and Titanothere Canyons area, Death Valley, California. *Ph.D. Thesis*, Univ. California, Berkeley, 310 pp.

—— 1976. Geology of the Grapevine Mountains, Death Valley, California: a summary. *Calif. Div. Min. Geol. Spec. Rep.* **106**, 19–26.

—— 1979. Character and extent of Basin–Range faulting, western Montana and east-central Idaho. *In*: NEWMAN, G.W. & GOODE, H.D. (eds) *Basin and Range Symp.* pp. 185–93. Rocky Mt. Assoc. Geol. Denver.

RHODES, B.P. & CHENEY, E.S. 1981. Low-angle faulting and origin of Kettle Dome, a metamorphic core complex in northeastern Washington. *Geology*, **9**, 366–69.

—— & HYNDMAN, D.W. 1984. Kinematics of mylonites in the Priest River 'metamorphic core complex', northern Idaho and northeastern Washington. *Can. J. Earth Sci.* **21**, 1161–70.

ROBINSON, G.D. 1963. Geology of the Three Forks quadrangle, Montana. *U.S. geol. Surv. Prof. Pap. 370*, 143 pp.

ROYSE, F., JR. 1983. Extensional faults and folds in the foreland thrust belt, Utah, Wyoming, Idaho. *Abstr. with programs geol. Soc. Am.* **15(5)**, 295.

—— , WARNER, M.A. & REESE, D.L. 1975. Thrust belt structural geometry and related stratigraphic problems, Wyoming-Idaho-northern Utah, *In*: *Deep Drilling Frontiers in the Central Rocky Mountains.* pp. 41–54. Rocky Mt. Assoc. Geol. Denver.

RYDER, R.T. & SCHOLTEN, R. 1973. Syntectonic conglomerates in southwest Montana; their nature, origin and tectonic significance. *Bull. geol. Soc. Am.* **84**, 773–96.

SEYFERT, C.K. 1984. The Clearwater core complex, a new Cordilleran metamorphic core complex, and its relation to a major continental transform fault. *Abstr. with Programs geol. Soc. Am.* **16(6)**, 651.

SMITH, D.L. 1984. Effects of unrecognized Oligocene extension in central Nevada on the interpretation of older structures. *Abstr. with Programs geol. Soc. Am.* **16(6)**, 660.

SMITH, J.F., JR & KETNER, K.B. 1977. Tectonic events since early Paleozoic in the Carlin-Pinon Range area, Nevada. *U.S. geol. Surv. Prof. Pap. 867-C*, 18 pp.

SMITH, R.B. 1978. Seismicity, crustal structure, and intraplate tectonics of the interior of the western Cordillera. *Mem. geol. Soc. Am.* **152**, 111–44.

—— & BRUHN, R.L. 1984. Intraplate extensional tectonics of the eastern Basin and Range: Inferences on structural style from seismic reflection data, regional tectonics, and thermal-mechanical models of brittle-ductile deformation. *J. geophys. Res.* **89**, 5733–62.

SMITHSON, S.B., BREWER, J.A., KAUFMAN, S., OLIVER, J., HURICH, C. 1978. Nature of the Wind River thrust, Wyoming, from COCORP deep-reflection data and from gravity data. *Geology*, **6**, 648–52.

SNOKE, A.W. & HOWARD, K.A. 1984. Geology of the Ruby Mountains-East Humboldt Range: A Cordilleran metamorphic core complex (Field Trip 9). *In*: LINTZ, J.P. (ed.) *Western Geological Excursions 4*, pp. 232–303. Mackay School of Mines, Reno.

SNYDER, W.S., DICKINSON, W.R. & SILBERMAN, M.L. 1976. Tectonic implications of space–time patterns of Cenozoic magmatism in the western United States. *Earth planet. Sci. Lett.* **32**, 91–106.

SOLOMON, B.J., MCKEE, E.H. & ANDERSON, D.W. 1979. Stratigraphy and depositional environments of Paleogene rocks near Elko, Nevada. *In*: ARMENTROUT, J.M. *et al.* (eds). *Cenozoic Palaeogeography the Western United States*, pp. 75–88. Soc econ. Paleontol. and Mineral., Pac. sect. Los Angeles.

SONDER, L.J., ENGLAND, P.C., WERNICKE, B.P. & CHRISTIANSEN, R.L. This Volume. A physical model for extension of western North America.

STEVEN, T.A., ROWLEY, P.D. & CUNNINGHAM, C.G. 1984. Calderas of the Marysvale volcanic field, west central Utah. *J. geophys. Res.* **89**, 8751–64.

STEWART, J.H. 1980. Geology of Nevada. *Nev. Bur. Min. Geol. Spec. Publ. 4*, 136 pp.

—— 1983. Spatial variation, style, and age of Cenozoic extensional tectonics in the Great Basin. *Abstr. with Programs geol. Soc. Am.* **15(5)**, 286.

STOCK, C. & BODE, F.D. 1935. Occurrence of lower Oligocene mammal-bearing beds near Death Valley, Calif. *Nat. Acad. Sci. Proc.* **21**, 571–9.

STOCK, J.M. & MOLNAR, P. 1983. Some geometrical aspects of uncertainties in combined plate reconstructions. *Geology*, **11**, 697–701.

SUTTER, J.F., SNEE, L.W. & LUND, K. 1984. Metamorphic, plutonic and uplift history of a continent–island arc suture zone, west-central Idaho. *Abstr. with Programs Geol. Soc. Am.* **16(6)**, 670.

TABOR, R.W., FRIZZELL, V.A., JR, VANCE, J.A. & NAESER, C.W. 1984. Ages and stratigraphy of lower and middle Tertiary sedimentary and volcanic rocks of the central Cascades, Washington. *Bull. geol. Soc. Am.* **95**, 26–44.

TAPPONNIER, P. & MOLNAR, P. 1977. Active faulting and Cenozoic tectonics of China. *J. geophys. Res.* **82**, 2905–30.

TWETO, O. 1975. Laramide (Late Cretaceous–early Tertiary) orogeny in the southern Rocky Mountains. *Mem. geol. Soc. Am.* **144**, 1–44.

WERNICKE, B.P. 1981. Low-angle normal faults in the Basin and Range province: nappe tectonics in an extending orogen. *Nature*, **291**, 645–8.

WERNICKE, B.P., GUTH, P.L. & AXEN, G.J. 1984. Tertiary extensional tectonics in the Sevier thrust belt of southern Nevada (Field Trip 19). *In*: LINTZ, J.P. (ed.) *Western Geological Excursions 4*, pp. 473–510. Mackay School of Mines, Reno.

WERNICKE, B.P., SPENCER, J.E., BURCHFIEL, B.C. & GUTH, P.L. 1982. Magnitude of crustal extension in the southern Great Basin. *Geology*, **10**, 499–502.

WILTSCHKO, D.V. & DORR, J.A. 1983. Timing of deformation in overthrust belt and foreland of Idaho, Wyoming, and Utah. *Am. Assoc. Pet. Geol.* **67**, 1304–12.

WRIGHT, L.A. & TROXEL, B.W. 1973. Shallow-fault interpretation of Basin and Range structure, southwestern Great Basin. *In*: DE JONG, K.A. & SCHOLTEN, R. (eds) *Gravity and Tectonics*, pp. 397–407. John Wiley and Sons, Chichester.

——, DRAKE, R.E. & TROXEL, B.W. 1984. Evidence for westward migration of severe Cenozoic extension, southwestern Great Basin, California. *Abstr. with Programs geol. Soc. Am.* **16(6)**, 701.

——, TROXEL, B.W., BURCHFIEL, B.C., CHAPMAN, R.H. & LABOTKA, T.C. 1981. Geologic cross-section from the Sierra Nevada to the Las Vegas Valley, eastern California to southern Nevada. *Geol. Soc. Am. Map and Chart Ser. MC-28M.*

ZOBACK, M.L. & THOMPSON, G.A. 1978. Basin and Range rifting in northern Nevada: Clues from a mid-Miocene rift and its subsequent offsets. *Geology*, **6**, 111–16.

——, ANDERSON, R.E. & THOMPSON, G.A. 1981. Cainozoic evolution of the state of stress and style of tectonism of the Basin and Range province of the western United States. *Phil. Trans. R. Soc. London,* **A300**, 407–34.

BRIAN P. WERNICKE, PHILIP C. ENGLAND & LESLIE J. SONDER, Department of Earth and Planetary Sciences, Harvard University, Cambridge, MA 02138, USA.

ROBERT L. CHRISTIANSEN, US Geological Survey, 345 Middlefield Road, Menlo Park, CA 94025, USA.

Tectonic heredity and the layered lower crust in the Basin and Range Province, western United States

R.W. Allmendinger, T.A. Hauge, E.C. Hauser, C.J. Potter & J. Oliver

SUMMARY: COCORP deep seismic reflection data were collected in a transect at 40°N latitude across the entire Basin and Range extensional province and its boundaries, the Sierra Nevada Mountains and the Colorado Plateau. In general, the data display little of the province-wide symmetry of the modern Basin and Range, and instead can be more directly related to the pre-17 Ma asymmetric orogens of the western United States, particularly in the eastern part (112–115°W) of the region. No one model of intracontinental extension is applicable to the entire province: it may be that pre-existing structure of the continental crust predisposes it to a particular mode of extension unless thermally activated processes render the crust mechanically isotropic. Such processes (e.g. enhanced ductility, magmatism, etc.) may be responsible for the development of a highly layered lower crust and pronounced reflection Moho; features not commonly seen in reflection profiles from cratonic regions.

Concepts of extensional structures have changed drastically in recent years; the long-held model of symmetrical rift graben bounded on both sides by steeply dipping normal faults has been shown to occur only in rather specialized instances. Instead, listric faults and low-angle normal faults constitute the structural components of crustal-scale models of extension (Fig. 1). This change can be attributed to two factors: first, the availability of high-quality seismic reflection data from rift provinces around the world and second, field work during the last 20 years in the Basin and Range Province of the western United States, the widest intracontinental rift province in the world. From 1982 to 1984, the Consortium for Continental Reflection Profiling (COCORP) collected more than 1000 km of deep seismic reflection data in a transect at approximately 40°N Latitude, crossing the entire Basin and Range Province and its eastern and western margins, the Sierra Nevada Mountains and the Colorado Plateau (Fig. 2). Although the transect provides some excellent images of individual extensional structures, its broader significance lies in the province-wide, crustal-scale perspective it provides of extensional processes and their relationship to the pre-existing fabric of the continental crust.

Rather than describe and document individual extensional structures, this paper takes a broader view of the entire data set of the COCORP transect. The approach taken here is to identify regionally consistent domains of generally similar seismic data in the transect; the dominant orientations of reflectors in these domains are referred to as 'seismic fabrics', a term

that is analogous to its metamorphic or structural counterpart. Viewed in this way, the reflection data from the Basin and Range and its

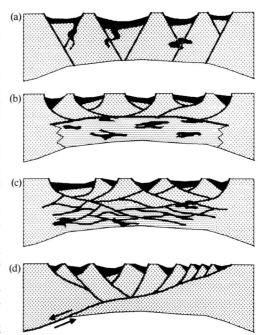

FIG. 1. Models of intracontinental extension; (a) symmetrical rift graben, (b) sub-horizontal, midcrustal decoupling horizon (Eaton 1979; Miller et al. 1983; Smith & Bruhn 1984), (c) lens or anastomosing shear zones (Hamilton 1982; Kligfield et al. 1984), (d) crustal-penetrating shear zone (Wernicke 1981).

From COWARD, M.P., DEWEY, J.F. & HANCOCK, P.L. (eds), 1987, *Continental Extensional Tectonics*, Geological Society Special Publication No. 28, pp. 223–246.

223

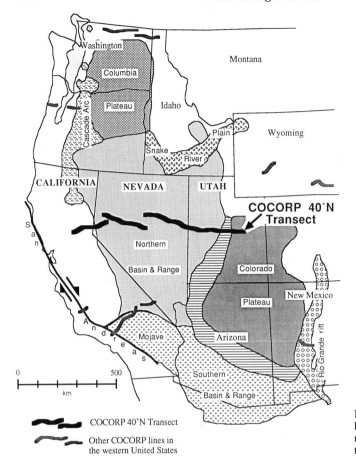

FIG. 2. Location of the COCORP lines in the western United States; map shows major Cenozoic tectonic provinces.

margins can be described in terms of five major, overlapping domains: (i) crossing fabric of the Colorado Plateau; (ii) W-dipping features of the eastern Basin and Range; (iii) sub-horizontal, lower-crustal reflections of the central and western Basin and Range; (iv) E- and W-dipping reflections of the Sierra Nevada; and (v) the reflection Moho. The relationships between these features and with Cenozoic and pre-Cenozoic tectonic features recognized from surface geology show that the seismic fabric of the province is markedly asymmetrical and is probably in part inherited from the pre-Basin and Range (pre-17 Ma) asymmetric orogens of the western United States. The symmetry of the modern Basin and Range extensional province, so clearly displayed in patterns of regional topography and gravity (Eaton *et al.* 1978), is not apparent in the COCORP data. In this paper, we discuss the implications of these data for existing models of extensional tectonism, for the relationships of pre-existing features in the

crust to younger structures, and for the age and significance of the reflection Moho in orogenic belts. More detailed accounts of individual aspects of the data can be found in Von Tish *et al.* (1985), Klemperer *et al.* (in press), Hauge *et al.* (1986), Hauser *et al.* (1986), and Potter *et al.* (1986).

Regional tectonics of the western US at 40°N

The tectonic history of the western margin of North America spans at least 600 Ma; the middle-and late-Cenozoic extension comprise only about 5% of that history. Because the Basin and Range Province so dominates the present-day regional morphology of the western United States, there has been a tendency to consider extensional processes separately from the previous history of the region. However, those extensional processes are acting on continental crust with a large number of heterogeneities related to previous deformations; thus extension must be considered in that context.

Proterozoic to Devonian—continental breakup and passive margin

The Phanerozoic tectonic history of western North America began with continental rifting and the breakup of a supercontinent (Stewart 1972); this event was originally considered to be as old as 850 Ma based on the radiometric ages of lavas intercalated with Proterozoic clastic strata. The application of back-stripping techniques to the subsequent passive-margin deposits, however, has indicated that rifting was considerably younger, perhaps between 625 and 550 Ma (Armin & Mayer 1983; Bond & Kominz 1984; Bond et al 1984). Faults related to this rifting are rarely preserved due to the superposition of numerous subsequent phases of deformation, but have been inferred in the eastern part of the COCORP transect on the basis of marked thickness changes of upper Proterozoic and Cambrian clastic strata in palinspastically restored sections (Sharp 1984; Allmendinger et al. 1985). At least 6 km of upper Proterozoic and Cambrian clastic strata have been recognized in southern Idaho and almost 5 km have been measured in W-central Utah (Stewart 1972; Hintze 1973; Stewart & Poole 1974).

Following the rifting event, the sedimentary rocks of the Cordilleran miogeocline were deposited on a passive margin. Carbonates with minor shales and sandstone of middle Cambrian to Devonian age reach a maximum thickness of 4–5 km in E-central Nevada (Stewart & Poole 1974). This passive margin was comparatively long-lived; it persisted uninterrupted for at least 200 Ma. Lateral thickness changes in the Proterozoic to Devonian strata indicate that the hinge-line of the passive margin in central Utah was located at about 112°30′W (Fig. 3; Hintze 1973; Stewart & Poole 1974; Stokes 1976; Allmendinger et al. 1985). The present position of the western edge of the Precambrian North American craton along the COCORP transect is somewhat problematical because crystalline basement is nowhere exposed. The location of the western edge has been inferred on the basis of the westernmost miogeoclinal deposits and the initial $^{87}Sr/^{86}Sr = 0.706$ isopleth being located in central Nevada at approximately 117°W (Fig. 3; Stewart & Poole 1974; Kistler 1974; Stewart 1980; Speed 1982; Farmer & DePaolo 1983).

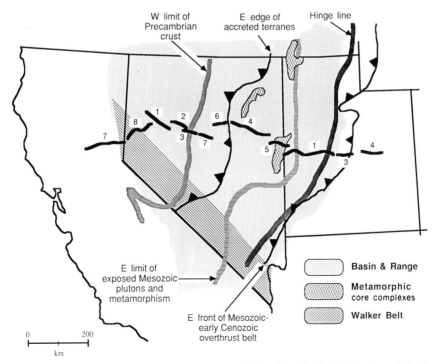

FIG. 3. Main Phanerozoic tectonic features of the western US Cordillera in Utah, Nevada, and California, See discussion in text.

Mississippian to Jurassic—terrane accretion

The simple passive margin was disrupted at the end of the Devonian by the first episode of intermittent terrane accretion that dominated the western margin of the continent for about the next 200 Ma. During the Antler Orogeny, lower-Palaeozoic oceanic rocks were thrust eastward across the edge of the continent (Roberts *et al.* 1958; Dickinson 1977; Speed 1982). The exact magnitude of thrusting is not known due to the possible superposition of Mesozoic thrusting (Ketner & Smith 1982) but has been suggested to be more than 100 km based on the present overlap of oceanic rocks across the miogeoclinal sequence. The polarity of subduction during the emplacement of this terrane is uncertain because the coeval magmatic arc has not been found either to the E or W of the frontal thrust (the Roberts Mountain thrust). Most authors consider it likely that the subduction zone dipped to the W away from the continent and that the arc was either rifted away or buried beneath younger accreted terranes (Dickinson 1977; Speed 1982).

Following a period of relative quiescence during the Pennsylvanian and part of the Permian, the margin of the continent was again overridden by an allocthonous terrane. During the late-Permian and early-Triassic Sonoma Orogeny (Silberling & Roberts 1962) an accretionary prism and upper-Palaeozoic island arc were emplaced by eastward thrusting along a W-dipping subduction zone (Schweikert & Snyder 1981; Speed 1982). The 'Sonomia' terrane is presently exposed locally in northwestern Nevada and possibly in northern California Speed 1979).

The Triassic to early Jurassic period was characterized by complex thrusting and transpression due to oblique subduction beneath the continent (Saleeby 1981; Speed 1979). The episode of major terrane accretion in the region crossed by the COCORP transect culminated in the middle and late Jurassic with the Nevadan Orogeny, when island-arc and oceanic rocks were sutured to the edge of the continent (Schweikert & Cowan 1975; Schweikert 1981; cf. Burchfiel & Davis 1981). Although there is general agreement as to the polarity of subduction during this time, considerable debate exists over whether the terranes were obducted along W-dipping thrusts (Moores & Day 1984) or were accreted along E-dipping thrust faults with the same vergence as the subduction zone. Although the previous episodes of accretion had limited structural effect on the continent E of the emplaced terrane, magmatism, metamorphism

and thrusting coeval with the Nevadan Orogeny have been recognized as far E as northwestern Utah (Fig. 3; Allmendinger *et al.* 1984).

In summary, terrane accretion from the Mississippian to the Jurassic produced dominantly W-dipping structures from westernmost Utah to California and built out the edge of the continent by 200–400 km (depending on the amount of subsequent shortening and extension). All of western Nevada and much of northern and central California are exotic with respect to Early Palaeozoic North America (Fig. 3; Coney *et al.* 1980).

Cretaceous to Eocene—Andean-type margin

Several authors have noted the similarity between the Cretaceous and early Tertiary of the western United States and the modern Andean continental margin (Hamilton 1969, 1978; Burchfiel & Davis 1975; Coney 1978; Dickinson & Snyder 1978; Jordan *et al.* 1983). During this time, subduction was eastward beneath the continent and accretion was limited to small exotic fragments rather than major terranes. During the Cretaceous (~125–75 Ma) the Sierra Nevada batholith was emplaced (Bateman 1981; Chen & Moore 1982); at the latitude of the COCORP profile the batholith crops out within the northwestern Basin and Range Province, rather than in the Sierra Nevada Mountains to the W. Cretaceous plutons are present E of the main magmatic arc across much of Nevada (Stewart 1980). Coeval retroarc foreland thrusting is well known in central and northern Utah (Armstrong 1968), but is not well documented in the hinterland of Nevada and Utah. Locally in the hinterland, Mesozoic normal faults have been recognized (Allmendinger & Jordan 1984a; Allmendinger *et al.* 1984). Foreland shortening on W-dipping, thin-skinned thrust faults was a minimum 150 km or about 50% during the Cretaceous and early Tertiary in southern Idaho and western Wyoming (Royse *et al.* 1975) and about 105 km in western and central Utah along the COCORP line (Fig. 3; Sharp 1984). Thrust faulting throughout this time constituted the major deformation of Armstrong's (1968) Sevier Orogeny.

Between the latest Cretaceous and the end of the Eocene, magmatism was largely absent in the central part of the western US Cordillera, and Dickinson & Snyder (1978) have interpreted this as a period of flat subduction eastward beneath the continent. During this time the basement uplifts of the Laramide Province of Wyoming, Colorado, and eastern Utah were formed; the easternmost line in the COCORP transect crosses the Laramide San Rafael Swell. COCORP and commercial seismic reflection data show that the basement uplifts are in general bounded by moderately dipping thrust faults that cut deeply into the crust, forming a province of thick-skinned deformation (Smithson *et al.* 1978; Gries 1983).

Oligocene to Present—continental extension

Zoback *et al.* (1981) pointed out that extension in the western US has occurred during two fundamentally different types of plate inter-action at the continental margin. Eastward sub-duction beneath the region of the Basin and Range Province continued until the transgressive development of the San Andreas transform boundary between 24 Ma and the present (Atwater 1970). Extension began during the Oligocene (locally at least 30 Ma) in an intra-arc and back-arc setting, and coincided with the renewal of volcanism following the Laramide flat subduction (Zoback *et al.* 1981). The Cor-dilleran metamorphic core complexes S of the Snake River Plain and their characteristic suite of low-angle normal faults were formed during this early phase of extension (Fig. 3; Davis & Coney 1979; articles in Crittenden *et al.* 1980; articles in Frost & Martin 1982). Coney & Harms (1984) proposed that this phase of extension was initiated by the gravitational collapse of the orogenic belt thickened by Mesozoic shortening. A major gap in our knowledge is the regional distribution of Oligocene and early Miocene ex-tension in the western United States. Such defor-mation has been recognized along the COCORP transect in the eastern part of the province (112–116°W) but has not been described farther W (although 100 km S of the COCORP transect in western Nevada, Profett (1977) documented a complex history of middle- and late-Cenozoic normal faulting in the Yerrington district).

The characteristic morphology recognized to-day as the Basin and Range began to form in central Nevada (the northern Nevada rift) be-tween 17–15 Ma (Zoback & Thompson 1978; Zoback *et al.* 1981). Ranges are spaced 20–50 km apart and are bounded on one or, less com-monly, both sides by normal faults which dip relatively steeply at the surface. Although many of the low-angle normal faults now exposed in the metamorphic core complexes ceased being active around this time (e.g. the Snake Range decollement, Lee *et al.* 1970; Miller *et al.* 1983), others have continued to be active until nearly the Present (e.g. the Sevier Desert detachment, Allmendinger *et al.* 1983, Von Tish *et al.* 1985). A characteristic feature of this later phase of ex-

tension is the development of regional 'tilt do-mains' in which normal-fault-bounded blocks all have the same sense of structural rotation (Stewart 1980).

At present, the regional topography and Bouguer gravity field of the Basin and Range Province display a remarkable symmetry (Eaton *et al.* 1978). High topography marks the flanks of the province in the Sierra Nevada Mountains and the Colorado Plateau and also the central part of the province in E-central Nevada. Be-tween these highs are two regional topographic lows in western Nevada and western Utah. As expected, the Bouguer gravity shows an inverse relationship to the topography, with gravity highs in western Utah and western Nevada and a broad regional low in the central part of the province. Earthquake seismicity tends to be con-centrated along the margins of the province (Smith 1978) but patterns of Holocene and late Quaternary faulting as deduced from field studies suggest a more complicated distribution of recent faulting (Wallace 1984). Refraction data have been interpreted as showing crustal thicknesses varying from <25 to >30 km, with thinner crust beneath regions of lower topography (Smith 1978; Prodehl 1979). Such data have a relatively large uncertainty associated with them; the COCORP data indicate smaller variations in Moho depths than some interpreta-tions of the refraction data (Klemperer *et al.* 1986.

The COCORP deep seismic reflec-tion data and related commercial data

The COCORP 40°N Transect consists of 15 in-dividual seismic lines totalling 1254 line km (Fig. 4). The field data were collected by Petty Ray, Division of Geosource, Inc., using a Vibroseis (trademark of Conoco) source and a 96 channel, MDS-10 recording system. Shooting in an off-end configuration with a 100 m station spacing and a near offset of 0.3–0.4 km produced a max-imum offset of 9.8–9.9 km. Four or five vibrators generally vibrated eight sweeps at every station (commonly an 8–32 Hz upsweep; some data were collected at 4 or 16 sweeps/ station) so as to produce nominal 48-fold (4800%) common depth-point (CDP) stacked data. Vibrating and recording times were ad-justed to produce correlated record lengths be-tween 14 and 20 sec (~42–60 km; all times cited are two-way travel times). Selected parts of the data were reprocessed by correlation with the lower-frequency part of the Vibroseis sweep to produce correlated records, longer in time than

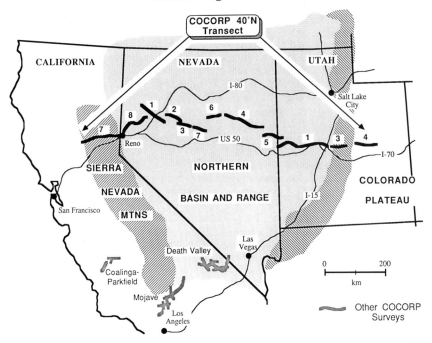

Fig. 4. Geographical map of Utah Nevada, and California showing locations of individual COCORP lines, and some of the features labelled in Fig. 5 and discussed in the text.

originally anticipated, to check for the presence of very deep reflections. These recording parameters, particularly the frequencies, station spacing, and offsets, differ from those commonly used in industry. Some shallow resolution is sacrificed to 'tune' the field arrays for energy returning from deeper crustal levels, beyond the general realm of commercial industrial exploration.

The entire COCORP 40°N Transect was processed at Cornell University using a MEGASEIS system (trademark Seiscom Delta, Inc.). The processing sequences for different lines varied somewhat depending on local noise conditions, but generally were as follows: (i) demultiplex and Vibroseis correlation; (ii) trace editing; (iii) F–K filtering; (iv) elevation and refraction statics corrections; (v) deconvolution; (vi) CDP gathering using crooked-line geometries; (vii) mute and velocity analyses; (viii) normal moveout (NMO) corrections; and (ix) stacking. Velocity analyses, using velocity spectra and constant-velocity stacks at 200 to 500 m sec^{-1} increments, were carried out about every 5 to 50 stations, depending on lateral complexities in velocity structure. The long COCORP offsets give significant stacking velocity resolution to 5–7 sec (~15–20 km). Stacking velocities, however, are simply those velocities which produce the best coherence for

the reflectors chosen and may bear little relation to the actual rock velocities. Interval velocities, which relate more directly to the physical properties of the rocks, can be calculated from stacking velocities, but only by making a number of simplifying assumptions (see Dobrin 1976). In addition to this standard processing sequence, synthetic seismic modelling has been used on parts of the lines to evaluate the lateral and vertical effects of the slow-velocity material in the Cenozoic basins (e.g. Peddy *et al.* 1986), and migration of the stacked data or line drawings has also been selectively applied.

The COCORP 40°N Transect represents an enormous amount of data: approximately 7.5×10^9 individual items of information [(12540 vibration points × 96 channels × 50 sec recording time)/0.008 sec sampling rate]. Because of the length of the transect and the amount of data (constituting a cross-section of the earth's crust 1254 km long and ~30–50 km deep), it is virtually impossible to display all the data here at a practical scale. Thus, we use line drawings abstracted from the original sections at large scales, combined with reproductions of small parts of the actual data, to represent the transect. Despite this compromise in publication, the reader should note that all COCORP lines may be obtained for the cost of reproduction by writing to the Executive Director of COCORP, Snee Hall, Cornell University, Ithaca, New York, 14853, USA.

In addition to the COCORP transect, the Basin and Range has been the site of considerable commercial exploration during the last 10 years. Although many of these seismic lines remain proprietary, some commercial data have been described and published by McDonald (1976), Hastings (1979), Vreeland & Berrong (1979), Effimoff & Pinezich (1981), Robison (1983), Anderson *et al.* (1983), Zoback (1983), Smith & Bruhn (1984), Okaya & Thompson (1985), and Gans *et al.* (1985). Most of the published commercial data have correlated record lengths between 3 and 5 sec and show good to excellent structural and stratigraphic detail in the Cenozoic basins; Okaya (1984), however, reprocessed commercial data by correlation with the low end of the Vibroseis sweep to produce a narrow, crustal-scale profile.

First-order domains in the COCORP deep seismic reflection data

In a survey of this magnitude, it is difficult to describe the geometry and significance of each individual reflector; in fact, as most of the reflectors do not project to the surface their nature cannot be uniquely identified. However, the character of the data in the COCORP 40°N Transect varies in a relatively systematic way across the transect such that it is possible to identify large areas within the crust which have generally similar patterns of reflectors. We refer to these regions as 'domains' and the nature and orientations of reflectors within the domains are called 'seismic fabrics'. Though the geological nature of individual reflectors cannot often be uniquely identified, domains of reflectors do exhibit relatively simple spatial relations to each other and to the major tectonic features described above, and thus may be understood in their entirety even if the individual parts remain enigmatic. A potential criticism of this approach is that such fabrics may be largely an artefact of processing (e.g. spatial aliasing). In the COCORP 40°N Transect, however, changes in the geometry of the field survey (e.g. pushing or pulling a line in an E or W direction, a change in station spacing, or change in processing stream) do not coincide with the fabric domains described below. Thus, the fabrics are considered to have real geological significance. Although referred to below using geographical names, the domains overlap both laterally and vertically within the crust.

A special caveat with respect to the identification of Moho on the COCORP 40°N Transect is necessary prior to the following description. The Moho as defined on these reflection data is the generally high-amplitude, sub-horizontal boundary or zone that separates the reflective crust from the almost completely unreflective upper mantle (for a discussion, see Klemperer *et al.* 1986). Because of the lack of velocity resolution of the near-vertical incidence reflection data at depths corresponding to the base of the crust, our definition of Moho necessarily differs from the refraction-based definition, although observations suggest that the two commonly coincide (e.g Barton *et al.* 1984). The lack of apparent velocity precision in seismic reflection data, however, is more than made up for by the spatial resolution of the reflection data.

Colorado Plateau crust—crossing fabric

The crust of the Colorado Plateau at the E end of the 40°N Transect was deformed by minor shortening during the Laramide deformation and has been regionally uplifted during the late Cenozoic, but in general it escaped most of the tectonism and magmatism experienced by the rest of the orogen to the W. Four major features describe the seismic data from this part of the Colorado Plateau: (i) a broad, gentle arch defined by Palaeozoic and Mesozoic strata and known as the San Rafael Swell; (ii) a fabric of dipping and crossing events distributed discontinuously within the crust beneath the sedimentary section; (iii) a relatively persistent mid-crustal horizon at about 28 km depth; and (iv) the reflection Moho. The San Rafael Swell, a Laramide structure (Davis 1978), will not be described except to point out that unlike other Laramide structures profiled by COCORP and commercial organizations (Smithson *et al.* 1978; Gries 1983) no basement thrust or reverse fault associated with the swell is observed on the seismic data. This, however, could be due to a number of possibilities, only one of which is that the fault does not exist.

Most of the crust beneath COCORP Utah line 4 is characterized by numerous dipping and crossing events and by irregular transparent zones with few reflections (Fig. 6). Many of the dipping events exhibit curvature characteristic of diffractions, and can be modelled as such. Others, however, do not collapse to a point on migration and are probably due to dipping reflectors in the crust, either in the plane of the section or off to the side. The large irregular blank zone in the upper crust on the eastern part of the line (Fig. 5), is truly transparent (as can be seen from the excellent reflections obtained from beneath it) and may represent a rather homogeneous crust. Most importantly, there is no obvious preferred orientation to the dipping events or the distribution and shape of the blank zone. Reflection events dip in both directions, giving the section a crossing fabric.

Cutting across this fabric is a nearly flat crustal horizon at 8.5–9.0 sec (Fig. 6). This horizon, which has a complex internal structure, coincides with a boundary or steep velocity gradient between 6.5 and 6.7 km sec^{-1} at 25–29 km observed on a refraction line located to the S of the COCORP transect (Prodehl 1979). This horizon is also at about the same depth as the reflection Moho observed in the Basin and Range Province to the W, but cannot be traced from one province to the other.

The reflection Moho on the E end of the COCORP 40°N Transect consists of a prominent band of flat reflections that extend across the easternmost 15 km of Line 4. It is con-

siderably deeper (15 sec or ~48 km) than the refraction Moho on the Hanksville refraction survey, the midpoint of which was ~200 km S of the COCORP line (42 km; Prodehl 1979). This difference in depth could be due to the lateral variability of the Moho, interpretation of the refraction data, a variable crustal velocity structure, or the possibility that the reflection and refraction Mohos are not the same here. Farther to the W in the Colorado Plateau, reflections were obtained to at least 15 sec but they are dipping and migrate to somewhat higher levels in the crust.

The seismic reflection data from the westernmost part of the Colorado Plateau and the transition zone between the Plateau and the Basin and Range (W end of line 4 and all of line 3; Figs 4 & 5) show few deep events and thus provide little information about the important transition between the rift province and the craton to the E (Fig. 5). The poor data quality is a common problem for commercial organizations surveying

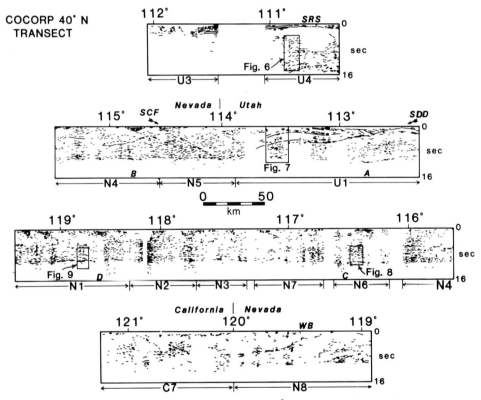

FIG. 5 Line drawing of the entire COCORP 40°N transect. Individual seismic lines labelled at the bottom of each panel. The locations of the data shown in Figs 6–9 are indicated in this figure. Cenozoic and Mesozoic structures ETB = eastern edge of Mesozoic–early Cenozoic thrust belt; SRS = San Rafael Swell; SDD = Sevier Desert detachment; SCF = Schell Creek fault; NNR = northern Nevada rift; WB = Walker Belt. Cenozoic basins producing significant velocity pull-down: A = Sevier Desert basin; B = Steptoe Valley; C = Grass Valley; D = Humboldt River Valley.

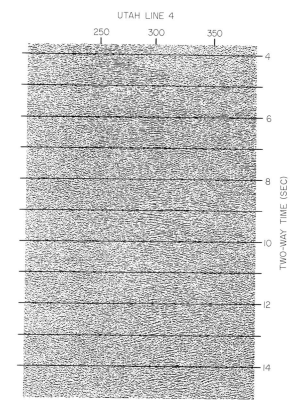

FIG. 6. Reflection data from E end of Utah line 4 (Colorado Plateau). Illustrates dipping and crossing seismic fabric characteristic of the Colorado Plateau. 4–14 sec two-way time shown. There is a 100 m station spacing; thus, stations 250–350 ≈ 10 km.

in the same region (Standlee 1982) and work by J. Mayer (pers comm.) suggests that the problem is due to both lack of signal penetration and cultural noise. The data do show that the easternmost position of the Mesozoic–early-Cenozoic thin-skinned thrust belt (Fig. 5) coincides with the Wasatch Plateau (Standlee 1982; Allmendinger *et al.* 1985).

Eastern Basin and Range (112–115°W)— W-dipping fabric

The COCORP 40°N Transect between 112 and 115°W (western Utah and easternmost Nevada; Figs 4 & 5) provides some of the most spectacular seismic reflection data in the survey. Reflection data from that segment can be directly related to the surface geology, and thus individual reflectors can be identified. Both COCORP and commercial seismic data in western Utah show the presence of dominantly W-dipping, low-angle detachment faults, including the Sevier Desert detachment, which have moved most recently in the late Cenozoic (McDonald 1976; Allmendinger *et al.* 1983; Zoback 1983; Smith & Bruhn 1984). In addition to reflectors identified as low-angle faults, most of the crust in the region has a W-dipping fabric

(Figs 5 & 7); this fabric is probably associated with the well-known Mesozoic and Cenozoic W-dipping thrust faults and normal faults present in the region.

There is a reversal in vergence of shallow Cenozoic structures, coincident with the axis of the Confusion Range synclinorium, at 113°45′W. The W-dipping fabric continues W of this point to at least 115°W although both E-dipping and especially sub-horizontal reflectors become more numerous. The western boundary of this domain is not sharp but grades laterally and vertically into a more horizontal fabric in eastern Nevada between 114 and 115°W (Fig. 5). This gradation occurs in part across a prominent E-dipping feature against which horizontal reflectors to the W are terminated (labelled 'SCF' on Fig. 5); the W-dipping fabric is present on both sides. At the surface, this E-dipping feature correlates with a young range-bounding normal fault (the 'Schell Creek fault'; Gans *et al.* 1985).

The deepest reflectors in western Utah are prominent but discontinuous horizontal events at 11.5 sec (~32 km) localized immediately beneath the Sevier Desert basin. Based on the criteria established above, these are interpreted

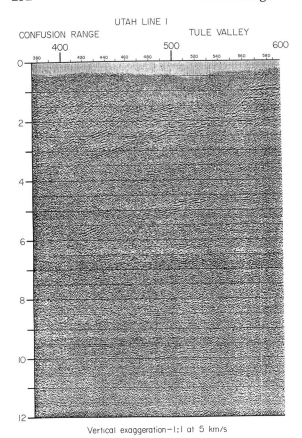

UTAH LINE 1

CONFUSION RANGE TULE VALLEY

Vertical exaggeration—1:1 at 5 km/s

FIG. 7. Reflection data from Utah line 1 showing W-dipping fabric beneath the eastern Confusion Range and Tule Valley of the eastern Basin and Range. Reflection Moho is at ~9.5 sec two-way time. Stations 400–500 ≈ 10 km.

as the reflection Moho. The Moho here, though, is less continuous and has a different character than the Moho to the W in Nevada (see below).

Central and western Basin and Range (116–119°W)—lower-crustal sub-horizontal fabric

The seismic reflection data from the central and western Basin and Range in Nevada show little detail in the upper crust except for the regularly spaced Cenozoic basins of the region. Locally, dipping reflectors that may represent Cenozoic or pre-Cenozoic faults were imaged, but in general the upper crust beneath the basins is relatively blank. This is in marked contrast to data from the eastern Basin and Range (Fig. 5). For this reason, few reflections can be directly linked to surface features and the interpretation of this western region is somewhat more speculative.

In contrast to the upper crust of this region, the middle and lower crust has numerous reflections which define a sub-horizontal fabric (Figs 5 & 8). The seismic data display 'paneling' produced by zones of higher and lower data quality

having little to do with crustal-scale geological variation, and are also distorted by velocity pull-down from the overlying low-velocity sediments in the Cenozoic basins. Many of the events with apparent dips in the time section can be related to this velocity effect. Within the dominantly sub-horizontal fabric there are some dipping events which cannot be dismissed as velocity effects. They are, however, much less common than farther E.

The two-way time to the top of the well-developed zone of sub-horizontal fabric varies across the area but in general is between 3.5 and 6 sec (~10–18 km). The top of the zone is locally gradational in nature; elsewhere it is more abrupt. The base of the domain is the reflection Moho, described below.

The base of the crust (114–119°)—the highly layered Moho

The most striking features of the COCORP 40°N Transect in Nevada are the high-amplitude, layered Moho and the sparsity of reflectors beneath it (Figs 5, 8 & 9). In

NEVADA LINE 6

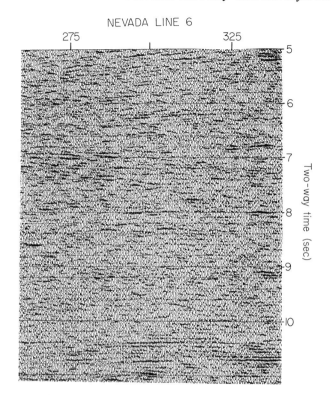

FIG. 8. Reflection data from Nevada line 6, crossing Grass Valley in the vicinity of the northern Nevada rift (NNR in Fig. 5) showing flat reflections of the middle and lower crust in central Nevada. The prominent events below 10 sec are part of the reflection Moho. Stations 275–325 ≈ 5 km; note that only 5–10 sec two-way time is shown.

general, the base of the crust on stacked sections is defined by a band of internally complex reflections that is commonly 1–1.5 sec thick (3–5 km) and is composed of numerous relatively short reflection segments (Figs 8 & 9). Work by Klemperer *et al.* (1986) using single-trace displays rather than stacked data has shown that this band of reflection is defined by two distinct events at the top and bottom of the zone; interpret the bottom of the two to be Moho. On the stacked sections, the Moho reflections vary in time between 9.0 and 12.0 sec; some of that variation is due to velocity pull-down caused by the Cenozoic basins, as is particularly obvious beneath the Sevier Desert basin, Schell Creek Valley, Grass Valley, and the Humboldt River Valley (A–D, Fig. 5). However, there is also a systematic, long-wavelength variation in depth (~30±3 km) to the Moho (Klemperer *et al.* 1986).

The pronounced layered-reflection Moho can be traced westwards on Nevada line 8 (Fig. 5) where it appears to gradually deepen and become less pronounced. In the Sierra Nevada (California line 7) the deepest reflections are sparse events at about 13 sec (~40 km). These events are much weaker and less continuous than those observed in Nevada (Fig. 5). To the E, the highly layered Moho ends relatively

abruptly at the Nevada–Utah border (114°W), although weaker reflections continue farther E shallowing slightly to 9.5 sec. On the stacked sections, there is little continuity or similarity in character between the prominent Sevier Desert Moho and the Nevada Moho.

There is a possibility that the lateral change in Moho character on the COCORP 40°N Transect is primarily related to surface or shallow-crustal effects (noise variations, coupling, variations in shallow-crustal rock types, etc.) rather than to any real variation in the nature of the base of the crust. Shallow-crustal variations can be ruled out for two reasons: (i) basins and ranges type of structure and accompanying lateral variations in velocities exist across the entire transect yet the Moho beneath is variable; and (ii) the Moho is continuous beneath significant near-surface lithological variations such as the transition from miogeocline to accreted terranes.

The question of noise and coupling variations during the field survey is more difficult to evaluate. Clearly, such variations exist in any seismic reflection survey and are present in the COCORP 40°N Transect, as well (Klemperer *et al.* 1986). However, there are two observations that suggest that the transition in Moho character at the Nevada–Utah border may be in

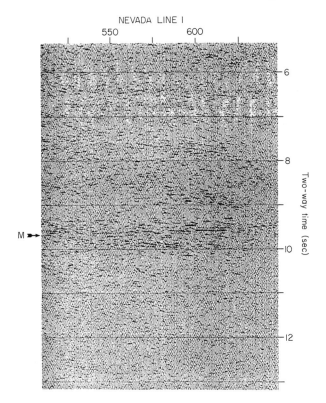

NEVADA LINE I

FIG. 9. Reflection data from Nevada line 1 showing the reflection Moho ('*M* ') of western Nevada. Note the contrast between the reflective crust and Moho and the much less reflective upper mantle. Stations 550–600 ≈ 5 km; note that only 6–13 sec two-way time is shown.

part real. (i) It coincides directly with the lower-crustal position of the Schell Creek fault on Nevada line 5 (described above). This E-dipping zone coincides with changes in seismic fabric throughout the crust and thus appears to have considerable geological significance; changes in Moho character across it might also be expected. (ii) As noted above, the base of the crust beneath the Sevier Desert detachment is different in character from that in Nevada. The former is comprised of three or four distinct, regularly spaced cycles spanning just 300 msec two-way time; it lacks the two distinct events identified by Klempcrer *et al.* (1986).

The crust of the northern Sierra Nevada Mountains

The data from the northern Sierra Nevada Mountains (California line 7) are of relatively poor quality, due at least in part to the low vibrator power (commonly 30%) required to prevent damage to local roads in poor condition (Nelson *et al.* in press). The data show a number of steeply dipping events and an overall seismic fabric with an E-dipping grain. Superimposed upon those are some prominent, W-dipping reflections, forming a prominent 'X'-shaped feature on the unmigrated, stacked section (at

120°30′W in Fig. 5). Nelson *et al.* (in press) have interpreted most of these features as Mesozoic and Cenozoic faults.

The change in Moho character from Nevada to California could either be due to conditions at the time of the survey or to real changes at the base of the crust. Regardless of that question, however, the deepest events on the Northern Sierras data are deeper than those in the Basin and Range Province (Fig. 5).

Summary—a simplified cross-section of the COCORP 40°N Transect

The above descriptions are summarized in a simplified cross-section which presents a vertical 'map' of the seismic fabric domains along the COCORP transect (Fig. 10). The cross-section has been converted to depth and has considerable vertical exaggeration; thus, we do not show individual structures on it. The most interesting aspect of the seismic domains viewed together is the marked asymmetry displayed by the reflection data. The asymmetry suggests dominant eastward vergence of the crustal fabric in the Basin and Range Province that is not consistent with its morphological symmetry. In the next section, we relate the seismic domains and

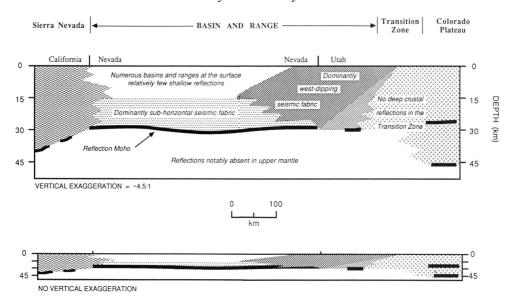

FIG. 10. Schematic cross-section summarizing reflection data from COCORP 40°N Transect. The upper section has 4.5× vertical exaggeration; lower section is true scale.

their mutual boundaries to tectonic features of the orogenic belt of the western US.

Asymmetry of seismic domains in relation to regional tectonic features

The W-dipping fabric of the eastern Basin and Range correlates with a number of different tectonic features of different ages. The oldest is the latest Proterozoic and Palaeozoic hinge-line of the Cordilleran miogeocline which coincides closely with the eastern edge of the W-dipping fabric domain (Fig. 11a). The position of the hinge-line is defined both by field data (Kay 1951; Stewart & Poole 1974; Stokes 1976) and by palinspastically restored sections constructed using the COCORP and related sub-surface data (Sharp 1984; Allmendinger *et al.* 1985). West of the hinge-line, the Precambrian North American craton was significantly thinned by latest Proterozoic rifting; to the E it was little disturbed. The restored sections of Sharp (1984) and Allmendinger *et al.* (1985) based on COCORP data, commercial drilling, and surface geology show abrupt westward-thickening of upper Proterozoic and lower Cambrian clastic strata that was probably normal-fault controlled.

This abrupt change in thickness has subsequently controlled the trajectories of Mesozoic thrust faults and Cenozoic low-angle normal faults (including the Sevier Desert detachment).

The Mesozoic and Cenozoic low-angle faults cut significantly into basement only W of the hinge-line even though the front of Mesozoic thrusting is located farther E (Fig. 11c). Part of the W-dipping fabric is related to a major Mesozoic thrust ramp (at approximately 113°30′W) that probably involved basement and had ~10 km of structural relief (Armstrong 1982; Allmendinger *et al.* 1983). The W-dipping fabric then, partly represents the involvement of thicker sections of Precambrian basement in Mesozoic compression. As discussed below, lower-crustal structural thickening during the Mesozoic would have occurred primarily within and W of the W-dipping fabric.

In the scope of this discussion, the question as to whether individual Cenozoic low-angle normal faults are reactivated thrust faults is not significant; both new and reactivated faults probably exist. However, it seems clear that early rifting controlled the general location and geometry of many subsequent compressional and extensional structures in the eastern Basin and Range; discussions limited to the reactivation of Mesozoic thrusts by Cenozoic normal faults are thus incomplete. Therefore, we consider the W-dipping fabric to be related to structural features produced during latest Proterozoic rifting and subsequent Mesozoic and Cenozoic low-angle faulting.

The gradational transition from the W-dipping fabric domain to the more horizontally layered middle- and lower-crustal fabric also correlates with a variety of features of different ages. Most prominently, it coincides with the broad region of Tertiary metamorphic core complexes (Fig. 11d) and the E-dipping Schell Creek fault (with a regional dip of about 30°), a late-Cenozoic normal fault. Correlation of this transition with Mesozoic features is somewhat more speculative because such features owe their present exposure to Cenozoic deformation and because they are allochthonous due to both Mesozoic and Cenozoic faulting. In general, however, the eastern edge of exposed Mesozoic plutons and metamorphism does coincide with the transition from W-dipping to horizontal fabric, particularly if one takes into account the fact that the easternmost of the plutons (e.g. the House Range stock at 113°20′W) have undoubtedly been translated eastward relative to

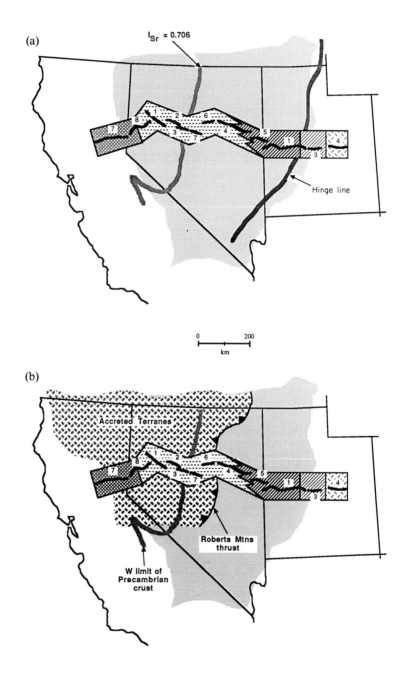

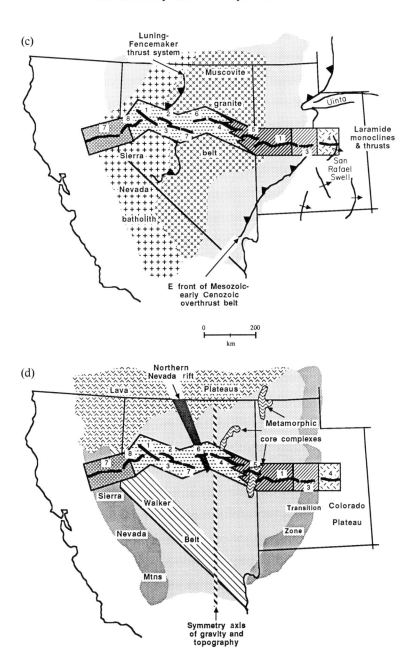

FIG. 11. Maps showing seismic domains of the COCORP 40°N transect in relation to regional Phanerozoic tectonic features. Patterns in the bands enclosing the COCORP lines are the same as those shown on the cross-section in Fig. 10. Maps are *not* on a palinspastic base. Broad stippled region on all maps is the northern Basin and Range. Wide, lighter gray lines show boundaries of features not active during the age range shown. (a) Map of Precambrian–Palaeozoic tectonic features; (b) map of accreted terranes; (c) map of Mesozoic tectonic features; (d) map of Cenozoic tectonic features.

the middle and lower crust on shallow thrust faults (Allmendinger *et al.* 1983; Bartley & Wernicke 1984). Interestingly, the western transition of horizontal fabric to Sierra Nevada crust also correlates with the western edge of Mesozoic plutonism, the Sierra Nevada batholith (Fig. 11c).

The western end of the W-dipping fabric coincides with and overlaps the eastern end of the highly layered Moho and the beginning of the sub-horizontal lower-crustal fabric in Nevada (Fig. 10). Because the W-dipping fabric seems most reasonably interpreted as a structural fabric, and as the Moho changes character but does not change depth significantly at this junction, it is possible that the pronounced reflection Moho is at least in part a zone of structural decoupling, as elaborated in the next section.

The sub-horizontal fabric is traceable across the whole of Nevada and coincides spatially with the region of Mesozoic magmatism and metamorphism and also with regions of extensive Cenozoic magmatism. It is, for example, very prominent beneath the mid-Miocene northern Nevada rift (Figs 5 & 8), and the whole of Nevada has exposed Mesozoic plutons. Furthermore, major pre-Cenozoic structural features in Nevada (e.g. the eastern edge of the accreted terranes and the western edge of Precambrian basement) have little or no expression on the seismic data (Fig. 11a, b). Thus, the sub-horizontal fabric is most clearly related to thermally activated processes; these might include magmatism and enhanced ductility of the lower crust due to increased temperatures. A rise in temperature in the lower crust could be produced either by crustal thickening forcing the lower crust deeper, by influx of molten material, or by lithospheric thinning. Penetrative ductile flow during deformation in a thermally weakened lower crust, accompanied by igneous intrusion, could produce the observed sub-horizontal seismic fabric. Magma bodies have been mapped by COCORP at mid–lower-crustal depths in extensional terranes elsewhere in the western US (Brown *et al.* 1979; Serpa *et al.* 1984b; de Voogd *et al.* 1986). Although the sub-horizontal fabric is probably younger than Palaeozoic in age, it is more difficult to determine whether it is Mesozoic, Cenozoic, or some combination of the two.

The most striking 'non-correlation' exhibited by the data is that no one fabric domain characterizes the entire morphological Basin and Range Province (i.e. the extensional deformation and morphology younger than ~17 Ma; Zoback *et al.* 1981). The late-Cenozoic basins filled with low-velocity clastic debris are clearly displayed and in general, the data show that the crust of the Basin and Range is thinner than the crust of either the Colorado Plateau or the Sierra Nevada. However, the symmetry of the modern province contrasts sharply with the asymmetry of the seismic data (Figs 10 & 11d).

The COCORP 40°N Transect and models of crustal extension

Previous models

In recent years, the recognition of low-angle normal faults in the Basin and Range Province has led to a number of new models of extension (Fig. 1). The COCORP transect allows one to evaluate these models on a province-wide, crustal scale with a single uniform data base, the deep reflection data. In evaluating these models, one must keep in mind the inherent strengths and limitations of the seismic reflection method, particularly the inability to directly image steep to near-vertical interfaces and the fact that boundaries lacking sufficient acoustic impedance will not produce reflections no matter how important they may be. The newer models of crustal extension in the Basin and Range Province fall into three basic, somewhat overlapping categories:

Sub-horizontal, mid-crustal decoupling horizon

This model (Fig. 1b) has been proposed by numerous investigators (Eaton *et al.* 1978; Eaton 1979; Stewart 1971; Smith 1978; Smith & Bruhn 1984; Miller *et al.* 1983) and is based on the observations that: (i) faults commonly are inferred to have a listric geometry and thus flatten at depth; (ii) magmatism commonly accompanies crustal extension; (iii) earthquakes in the province generally do not occur below 8–15 km and in the shallow crust have high-angle nodal planes; and (iv) refraction data have been interpreted to show a crustal low-velocity zone near the depths where earthquakes cease. In this model, the brittle–ductile transition is interpreted as occurring at or near the base of the seismogenic part of the crust; above this transition extension is accommodated by brittle normal faulting and beneath it occurs by pervasive ductile flow and magmatic intrusion. The brittle–ductile transition itself is interpreted as a sub-horizontal decoupling horizon which may have little or no relative displacement across it.

The COCORP reflection data suggest that this model does not apply to the eastern part of the Basin and Range Province in the region of the dominantly W-dipping fabric (western Utah and eastern Nevada). Pervasive middle- and lower-crustal ductile flow in a horizontally extending orogen should produce a dominantly horizontal fabric and it seems unlikely that the observed W-dipping fabric of the middle and lower crust would be preserved. This model could be applied, however, to the seismic data from the central and western part of the Basin and Range Province in Nevada (W of 115°W), where the crust below about 5 sec (~15 km) does have a sub-horizontal fabric.

Extending 'lenses' model

This model has been proposed by Hamilton (1982) and Kligfield *et al.* (1984), and is in some ways a modification of the crustal boudinage model of Davis & Coney (1979). It relies on the observation that in many core complexes, deformation decreases downward away from ductile decollements, thus suggesting lenses of relatively little deformed material surrounded by narrow zones of high strain. Commercial seismic reflection data in Arizona and elsewhere have been cited in support of this model (Hamilton 1982).

It is difficult to know how to evaluate this hypothesis in light of the COCORP reflection data. Certainly, large parts of the data from the middle and lower crust on the seismic lines could be interpreted as extending lenses, and it may well be that this is an important mechanism across almost the entire province. However, the seismic data and the model are completely non-unique in this regard and thus the main problem is one of testability. Thus, while the COCORP data are consistent with this model, they do not necessarily prove it.

Crustal-penetrating shear-zone model

This model was proposed by Wernicke (1981) and Wernicke & Burchfiel (1982) based primarily on field data from the Colorado River region of the southern Basin and Range (Davis *et al.* 1980, 1982; Anderson 1971), with some additional support from the region of the metamorphic core complexes and the Sevier Desert farther N (McDonald 1976; Allmendinger *et al.* 1983). The model, based in part on balanced cross-section arguments, suggests a way of thinning the lower crust at a point displaced laterally from the observed upper-crustal extension.

The Wernicke model may well apply to parts of the eastern Basin and Range. The Sevier Desert detachment fits the model in the upper

and middle crust, but cannot be traced to lower-crustal depths as a single coherent reflector. In fact, most dipping reflections in the eastern part of the province are not traceable throughout the crust, although that does not in itself mean that there are no crustal-penetrating structures. The one exception is the E-dipping Schell Creek fault beneath the Snake Range on Nevada line 5 ('SCF,' Fig. 5). It can be traced from a normal fault at the surface (Gans *et al.* 1985) nearly to the Moho, 30 km below and 55 km to the E (a regional dip of about 30° east). However, this fault does not appear to offset the Moho. Although the Moho reflection does change its character at the projected point of intersection, large offsets are lacking; in fact the Moho in the footwall is slightly deeper than the hanging wall Moho (Fig. 5).

On a more regional scale, however, the COCORP 40°N Transect does not support the Wernicke model, particularly in the central and western Basin and Range. The Sevier Desert detachment and the Schell Creek fault are in some ways remarkably atypical features of the data set. With the possible exception of a feature on the recently profiled Nevada line 8 (119°–120°W, Fig. 5), the seismic sections are mostly devoid of low-angle reflections that demonstrably correspond to low-angle normal faults. More importantly, however, evidence for significant offset of the Moho anywhere on the survey is lacking (Fig. 5) and there are no data to suggest that low-angle normal faults cut the entire lithosphere. Thus, either the Moho 'heals' itself on very short time-scales or is itself a decoupling horizon.

Summary

The data from the COCORP 40°N Transect do not uniquely support any one model of crustal extension in the Basin and Range; conversely, elements of all models are represented in the data. Given the apparently strong control exerted by palaeotectonic features described above, it seems likely that a particular mode of extension may be determined by pre-existing crustal heterogeneities. Thinned Precambrian continental crust deformed by Mesozoic thrust faults that cut basement may be predisposed to extend by slip along low-angle fault planes that may anastomose in the deep crust or may cut entirely through the crust. More uniform modes of extension may be favoured where (i) pre-existing dipping fabric was not present (ii) a relatively thick Precambrian crust was not present, or (iii) heat flow rendered inherited fabrics mechanically isotropic.

Mechanisms of extension in the Basin and Range

The driving mechanisms of extension in the Basin and Range and their relations to the plate interactions have been the subject of numerous studies (Atwater 1970; Dickinson & Snyder 1979; Fletcher & Hallet 1983). The COCORP data do not uniquely constrain mechanisms of extensional deformation but combined with regional tectonic information suggest some likely possibilities. One mechanism to drive extension is the equilibration of a structurally thickened crust following the removal of the horizontal compression responsible for the thickening (Coney & Harms 1984; Glazner & Bartley 1985). The magnitude of crustal thickening by thrusting is related to the sum of the heights of individual thrust ramps, with the greatest thickening over the highest ramps. If the W-dipping fabric observed on the COCORP 40°N Transect is in part related to Mesozoic thrust faults cutting deeply into the basement, then crustal thickening and uplift during that event must have occurred primarily to the W of the Sevier Desert (113°W). As pointed out by Coney & Harms (1984), this is also the region of greatest development of low-angle normal faults, and early extension in the region could well have been driven by local thickening of the crust. Furthermore, thickening of the lower crust would have occurred in the region now characterized by subhorizontal fabric, suggesting that the fabric could be produced by extension of a thickened crust. Similar processes at an earlier stage of development have been described in the Himalayas (Burchfiel & Royden 1985) and in the Andes (Dalmayrac & Molnar 1981; Allmendinger & Jordan 1984b; Froidvaux & Isacks 1984). Furthermore, Mesozoic normal faults have locally been recognized in the hinterland of the Sevier thrust belt (Allmendinger *et al.* 1984). An implication of this model, however, is that an extending mantle is not required.

There are two potential problems with this hypothesis. First, if the mantle does not extend, then spreading of a thickened crustal welt should produce thrusting on the margins of the welt. At the eastern margin of the Basin and Range Province, there is no documented thrusting during extension. However, thrusting would not have occurred if the entire region of early spreading moved laterally away from the Colorado Plateau. The asymmetry of the COCORP 40°N Transect is not inconsistent with this asymmetrical spreading model. A second problem is the lack of evidence for marked uplift in the hinterland region W of the Sevier Desert during the Mesozoic and early Cenozoic thrusting. Although the region was generally a positive area throughout that time, mid-Oligocene strata were deposited on gently deformed upper Palaeozoic and lower Mesozoic rocks over a wide region in the hinterland, implying only modest relief and erosion of at most a few kilometres (Armstrong 1972; Miller *et al.* 1983). Furthermore, most foreland-basin deposits during that time were derived from the foreland thrust sheets rather than from an uplifted hinterland (Royse *et al.* 1975; Armstrong & Oriel 1965). These arguments are based on the assumptions that erosion equates with relief and relief with crustal thickening; if those assumptions are invalid, then the existence of an uplifted hinterland during the Mesozoic is possible.

Although Cenozoic extension may have been initiated by spreading of a thickened crustal welt, the present-day extension (and probably the extension for the last 17 Ma) is most likely being driven by a different mechanism. Otherwise, extension would have ceased when the previously thickened crust returned to equilibrium with respect to the crustal thickness in the Sierra Nevada and Colorado Plateau. The fact that both refraction data and the COCORP reflection data show markedly thinner crust in the Basin and Range Province and the inference from refraction and earthquake data that the mantle beneath the province has anomalously low P_n velocities to 60 km depth (Archambeau *et al.* 1969; Thompson & Zoback 1979; Thompson 1983) indicates that the present extension is driven by flow in the asthenosphere, perhaps due to the presence of the 'no-slab window' related to the formation and migration of the Mendecino triple junction (Dickinson & Snyder 1979).

Age and origin of the reflection Moho in the Basin and Range

In discussing the age of the Moho, it is important to distinguish the age of those tectonic features or events causing the reflections from those which produced the compositional variations and depths to the Moho. For example, the Moho is shallower throughout the entire Basin and Range Province than in the bounding provinces and this correlation indicates that the *depth* to Moho is a function of the youngest extensional tectonics. In contrast, the character of the Moho *reflections* varies across the Basin and Range and may be related to mid-Cenozoic or Mesozoic tectonics. Finally, it is conceivable that Mesozoic or Cenozoic structural processes acted on an older *compositional* boundary to produce the reflections seen today.

The key observations regarding the prominent, highly layered Moho of Nevada are: (i) the lack of correlation of the Moho with the inferred edge of the Precambrian craton and the Palaeozoic accreted terranes; (ii) its spatial association with a broad region of Cenozoic and Mesozoic magmatism and metamorphism; and (iii) the coincidence and overlap of the W-dipping structural fabric with the Nevada Moho. The first observation suggests that the reflection Moho post-dates the Palaeozoic accretion. The second indicates that well-developed layering may be enhanced or produced by high heat flow during the Cenozoic and/or Mesozoic. The high heat flow could either result from elevated crustal geotherms or the deepening of the base of the crust due to crustal thickening. The third observation is the most ambiguous, but might suggest that the reflection Moho may also be a zone of structural decoupling. Smith & Bruhn (1984) have shown that a strong ductility contrast probably exists across the Moho in the Basin and Range. The coincidence of dipping structures with Moho reflections and the lack of offset of the Moho indicate that the highly layered character may result from large-scale ductile flow at the base of the crust.

Though the features producing reflections at the Moho may be of Mesozoic and/or Cenozoic age, we suggest that they are more likely primarily Cenozoic in age. In eastern Nevada over the well-developed Moho, rocks now exposed at the surface in the Snake and Schell Creek Ranges (114–114°30′W) were at least 10 km deeper in the crust during the Oligocene than rocks now exposed in the neighbouring Butte Mountains (115°W) and Confusion Range (113°45′W.) (Miller *et al.* 1983). Yet, the reflection Moho throughout this region is at a remarkably uniform level. Other scenarios are possible, but the simplest explanation of these relationships is that the formation of the presently observed Moho was synchronous with or younger than the development of that vertical uplift.

Seismic fabric of the crust in orogenic belts

The strong preferred orientation of seismic fabrics in the Basin and Range Province raises the question—do orogenic belts, and in particular rift provinces, have a fundamentally different seismic character from the crust of cratonic regions; and, if so, what are the processes which produce those differences? It is beyond the scope of this paper to review all available deep seismic reflection data, and in fact the world data base is probably not yet large enough to provide a definitive answer to this question. As pointed out by Meissner (1984) based on a comparison of European and North American seismic reflection data, the lower crust is generally most reflective where it has experienced a strong thermal event. A comparison of COCORP data from various sites suggests that not only reflectivity, but strong preferred orientation and a layered, high-amplitude Moho zone are characteristic of young orogenic belts.

COCORP sites in Kansas, Minnesota, and Michigan are located in parts of the North American craton that have not been disturbed by tectonism for at least a billion years (Brown *et al.* 1983; Serpa *et al.* 1984a; Gibbs *et al.* 1984). The Kansas site provides a particularly good example because of the high quality of data collected there (Fig. 12), but similar observations can be made from the other sites in the craton. The crust there has the following seismic characteristics: (i) a shallow zone of layered reflections corresponding to the Palaeozoic strata; (ii) a relatively blank zone in the upper crust between .5 and 3.0 sec; (iii) a middle and lower crust with numerous dipping, curved, and crossing events (many interpreted as diffractions) but lacking in a preferred orientation to the seismic fabric; and (iv) a rapid decrease in the number of reflections and diffractions at Moho depths (although with some events beneath Moho) but no pronounced Moho reflection or zone of reflections.

These characteristics are similar to those of the Colorado Plateau crust (cf. Figs 6 & 12), but are very different to those observed in the Basin and Range (described above) and those observed in the Rio Grande rift (Brown *et al.* 1979) with their distinct Moho reflections and layering in the middle and lower crust. The Basin and Range and Rio Grande rift are relatively young, hot-rift provinces suggesting that extension and thermal events (including magmatism) are responsible for the layered seismic fabrics. However, part of the data in Kansas were collected over a Proterozoic rift, and futhermore, comparable deep seismic reflection data from compressional orogens as young as the Basin and Range are lacking.

It may be that the key to producing a highly layered lower crust is some combination of elevated crustal temperatures and/or dominantly horizontal displacements (resulting from either extensional or contractional regimes). The fact that both compressional and extensional

KANSAS LINE 1

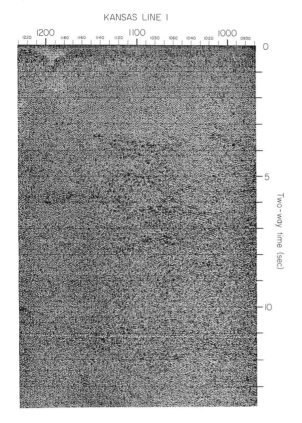

FIG. 12. Reflection data from COCORP Kansas line 1 (Brown *et al.* 1983). Note the prominent dipping, curved and crossing events indicating numerous diffractions, and the upper-crustal blank zone.

terranes profiled to date in Precambrian cratons (Serpa *et al.* 1984; Gibbs *et al.* 1984) do not display equally strong preferential layering as that observed in the Basin and Range might suggest that such layering is a relatively transient phenomenon with time constants on the order of several tens, or more likely, several hundreds of millions of years. Clearly, more deep seismic reflection profiling is needed to either document or disprove these observations.

ACKNOWLEDGMENTS: The COCORP 40°N Transect is the result of efforts by a large number of people. We would like to thank S. Burch, S. Burgess, C. Caruso, H. Farmer, S. Klemperer, P. Lemiszki, C-S. Liu, J. Mayer, D. Nelson, S. Opdyke, C. Peddy, W. Sanford, L. Serpa, J. Sharp, D. Von Tish, and T-F. Zhu for help with processing the data and for discussions of its significance. The transect was first proposed by G. Thompson, M.L. Zoback, and J. Stewart, and we thank them and R.B. Smith, R.C. Speed, W. Arabasz, B. Wernicke, J. Bartley, F. Royse as well as many others for enlightening discussions of these data. The field data were collected by Crew 6832 of Petty Ray, Division of Geosource, Inc. The data were processed at Cornell University on a Megaseis data processing system. We thank the COCORP Site Selection and Technical Advisory Committees, and the National Science Foundation for their support of this project under grants (EAR-8212445 and EAR-8418157).

References

ALLMENDINGER, R.W. & JORDAN, T.E. 1984a. Mesozoic structure of the Newfoundland Mountains, Utah: Horizontal shortening and subsequent extension in the hinterland of the Sevier Belt. *Bull. geol. Soc. Am*, **95**, 1280–92.

—— & —— 1984b. Hinterland tectonics of the Andes and the Cordillera. *Abstr. with Programs geol. Soc. Am.* **16**, 1.

——, MILLER, D.M. & JORDAN, T.E. 1984. Known and inferred Mesozoic deformation in the hinterland of the Sevier Belt, northwest Utah. *Utah geol. Assoc. Publ.* **13**, 21–34.

——, SHARP, J.W., VON TISH, D., SERPA, L., KAUFMAN, S., OLIVER J. & SMITH, R.B. 1983. Cenozoic and Mesozoic structure of the eastern Basin and Range Province, Utah, from COCORP seismic reflection data. *Geology*, **11**, 532–6.

——, FARMER, H., HAUSER, E., SHARP, J., VON TISH, D., OLIVER, J. & KAUFMAN, S. 1985. Phanerozoic tectonics of the Basin and Range–Colorado Plateau transition from COCORP data and geologic data: A Review. *In*: BARAZANGI, M. & BROWN, L. (eds) *Reflection seismology: The continental crust; Am. geophys. Union Geodyn. Ser.* **14**, 257–67.

ANDERSON, R.E. 1971. Thin skin distension in Tertiary rocks of southeastern Nevada. *Bull. geol. Soc. Am.* **82**, 43–58.

——, ZOBACK, M.L. & THOMPSON, G.A. 1983. Implications of selected subsurface data on the structural form and evolution of some basins in the northern Basin and Range province, Nevada and Utah. *Bull. geol. Soc. Am.* **94**, 1055–72.

ARCHAMBEAU, C.B., FLINN, E.A. & LAMBERT, O.G. 1969. Fine structure of the upper mantle. *J. geophys. Res.* **74**, 5825–65.

ARMIN, R. & MAYER, L. 1983. Subsidence analysis of the Cordilleran miogeocline: implications for timing of late Proterozoic rifting and amount of extension. *Geology*, **11**, 702–5.

ARMSTRONG, R.L. 1968. Sevier orogenic belt in Nevada and Utah. *Bull. geol. Soc. Am.* **79**, 429–58.

—— 1972. Low-angle (denudation) faults, hinterland of the Sevier orogenic belt, eastern Nevada and western Utah. *Bull. geol. Soc. Am.* **83**, 1729–54.

—— 1982. Cordilleran metamorphic core complexes—From Arizona to southern Canada. *Ann. Rev. Earth planet Sci.* **10**, 129–54.

—— & ORIEL, S.S. 1965. Tectonic development of Idaho–Wyoming thrust belt. *Bull. Am. Assoc. Pet. Geol.* **49**, 1847–66.

ATWATER, T. 1970. Implications of plate tectonics for the Cenozoic tectonic evolution of western North America. *Bull. geol. Soc. Am.* **81**, 3513–36.

BARTLEY, J. & WERNICKE, B. 1984. The Snake Range décollement interpreted as a major extensional shear zone. *Tectonics*, **3**, 647–57.

BARTON, P., MATTHEWS, D., HALL, J. & WARNER, M. 1984. Moho beneath the North Sea compared on normal-incidence and wide angle seismic records. *Nature*, **308**, 55–6.

BATEMAN, P. 1981. Geologic and geophysical constraints on models for the origin of the Sierra Nevada batholith, California. *In*: ERNST, W.G. (ed.) *The Geotectonic Development of California*, pp. 71–86. Prentice-Hall, Inc., New Jersey.

BOND, G.C. & KOMINZ, M.A. 1984. Construction of tectonic subsidence curves for the early Paleozoic miogeocline: implications for subsidence mechanisms, age of breakup, and crustal thinning. *Bull. geol. Soc. Am.* **95**, 155–73.

——, NICKESON, P.A. & KOMINZ, M.A. 1984. Breakup of supercontinent between 625 Ma and 555 Ma: new evidence and implications for continental histories. *Earth planet. Sci. Lett.* **70**, 325–45.

BROWN, L.D., KRUMHANSL, P.A., CHAPIN, C.E., SANFORD, A.R., COOK, F.A., KAUFMAN, S., OLIVER, J.E. & SCHILT, F.S. 1979. COCORP seismic reflection studies of the Rio Grande rift. *In*: RIEKER, R.E. (ed.) *Rio Grande Rift: Tectonics and Magmatism. Am. geophys. Union, Spec. Publ.* **23**, 169–84.

——, SERPA, L. SETZER, T., OLIVER, J., KAUFMAN, S., LILLIE, R., STEINER, D. & STEEPLES, D. 1983. Intracrustal complexity in the U.S. Mid-continent: Preliminary results from COCORP surveys in N.E. Kansas. *Geology*, **11**, 25–30.

BURCHFIEL, B.C. & DAVIS, G.A. 1975. Nature and controls of Cordilleran orogenesis, extensions of an earlier synthesis. *Am. J. Sci.* **275-a**, 363–96.

—— & —— 1981. Triassic and Jurassic tectonic evolution of the Klamath Mountains-Sierra Nevada geologic terrane. *In*: ERNST, W.G. (ed.) *The Geotectonic Development of California*, pp. 50–70. Prentice-Hall, Inc., New Jersey.

—— & ROYDEN, L.H. 1985. North–south extension within the convergent Himalayan region. *Geology*, **13**, 679–82.

CHEN, J.H. & MOORE, J.G. 1982. Uranium–lead isotopic ages from the Sierra Nevada batholith, California. *J. geophys. Res.* **87**, 4761–84.

CONEY, P.J. 1978. Mesozoic-Cenozoic Cordilleran plate tectonics. *In*: SMITH, R.B. & EATON, G.P. (eds) *Cenozoic tectonics and regional geophysics of the western Cordillera, Mem. geol. Soc. Am.* **152**, 33–50.

—— & HARMS, T. 1984. Cordilleran metamorphic core complexes: Cenozoic extensional relics of Mesozoic compression. *Geology*, **12**, 550–4.

——, JONES, D.L. & MONGER, J.W.H. 1980. Cordilleran suspect terranes. *Nature*, **288**, 329–33.

CRITTENDEN, M.D. JR, CONEY, P.G. & DAVIS, G.H. (eds) 1980. *Cordilleran metamorphic core complexes, Mem. geol. Soc. Am.* **153**, 490 pp.

DALMAYRAC, B. & MOLNAR, P. 1981. Parallel thrust and normal faulting in Peru and constraints on the state of stress. *Earth planet. Sci. Lett.* **55**, 473–81.

DAVIS, G.A., ANDERSON, J.L., FROST, E.G. & SHACKELFORD, T.J. 1980. Mylonitization and detachment faulting in the Whipple-Buckskin-Rawhide Mountains terrane, southeastern California and western Arizona. *In*: CRITTENDEN, M.D. JR., CONEY, P.J. & DAVIS, G.H. (eds) *Cordilleran metamorphic core complexes, Mem. geol. Soc. Am.* **153**, 79–129.

——, ——, MARTIN, D.L., KRUMMENACHER, D., FROST, E.G. & ARMSTRONG, R.L. 1982. Geologic and geochronologic relations in the lower plate of the Whipple detachment fault, Whipple Mountains, souteastern California: a progress report. *In*: FROST, E.G. & MARTIN, D.L. (eds) *Mesozoic-Cenozoic tectonic evolution of the Colorado River Region, California, Arizona and Nevada*, pp. 408–32. Cordilleran Publishers, San Diego.

DAVIS, G.H. 1978. The monocline fold pattern of the Colorado Plateau. *In*: MATTHEWS, V., III, (ed.) *Laramide folding associated with basement block faulting in the western United States, Mem. geol. Soc. Am.* **151**, 215–33.

—— & CONEY, P.J. 1979. Geologic development of the Cordilleran metamorphic core complexes. *Geology*, **7**, 120–4.

DE VOOGD, B., SERPA, L., BROWN, L., HAUSER, E., KAUFMAN, S., OLIVER, J., TROXEL, B., WILLEMIN, J. & WRIGHT, L.A. 1986. Death Valley bright spot: A mid-crustal magma body in the Southern Great Basin, California? *Geology*, **14**, 64–7.

DICKINSON, W.R. 1977. Paleozoic plate tectonics and the evolution of the Cordilleran continental margin. *In*: STEWART, J.H., STEVENS, C.H. & FRITSCHE, E.A. (eds) *Paleozoic paleogeography of the western United States, Pacif. Coast Paleogeog. Symp. 1, Soc. econ. Paleontol. and Mineral.*, Pac. sect. 137–56.

—— & SNYDER, W.S. 1978. Plate tectonics of the Laramde orogeny. *In*: MATHEWS, V. (ed.) *Laramide folding associated with basement block faulting in the western United States. Mem. geol. Soc. Am.* **151**, 355–66.

—— & SNYDER, W.S. 1979. Geometry of triple junctions related to San Andreas transform. *J. geophys. Res.* **84**, 561–72.

DOBRIN, M.B. 1976. *Introduction to Geophysical Prospecting*, 930pp. McGraw-Hill, New York.

EATON, G.P. 1979. Regional geophysics, Cenozoic tectonics, and geologic resources of the Basin and Range Province and adjoining regions. *In*: NEWMAN, G.W. & GOODE, H.D. (eds) *Basin and Range Symp.*, pp. 11–39. Rocky Mtn. Assoc. Geol.

——, WAHL, R.R., PROSTKA, H.J., MABEY, D.R. & KLEINKOPF, M.D. 1978. Regional gravity and tectonic patterns: Their relation to late Cenozoic epeirogeny and lateral spreading in the western Cordillera. *In*: SMITH, R.B. & EATON, G.P. (eds) *Cenozoic tectonics and regional geophysics of the western Cordillera, Mem. geol. Soc. Am.* **152**, 93–106.

EFFIMOFF, I. & PINEZICH, A.R. 1981. Tertiary structural development of selected valleys based on seismic data, Basin and Range Province, northeastern Nevada. *Phil. Trans. R. Soc. London*, **A300**, 435–43.

FARMER, G.L. & DePAOLO, D.J. 1983. Origin of Mesozoic and Tertiary granite in the western United States and implications for pre-Mesozoic crustal structure, 1. Nd and Sr isotopic studies in the geocline of the northern Great Basin. *J. geophys. Res.* **88**, 3379–401.

FLETCHER, R.C. & HALLET, B. 1983. Unstable extension of the lithosphere: A mechanical model for Basin-and-Range structure. *J. geophys. Res.* **88**, 7457–66.

FROIDEVAUX, C. & ISACKS, B.L. 1984. The mechanical state of the lithosphere in the Altiplano–Puna segment of the Andes. *Earth planet. Sci. Lett.* **71**, 305–14.

FROST, E.G. & MARTIN, D.L. (eds) 1982. *Mesozoic-Cenozoic tectonic evolution of the Colorado River Region, California, Arizona, and Nevada, pp. 608.* Cordilleran Publishers, San Diego.

GANS, P.B., MILLER, E.L., McCARTHY, J. & OULDCOTT, M.L. 1985. Tertiary extensional faulting and evolving ductile–brittle transition zones in the northern Snake Range and vicinity: New insights from seismic data. *Geology*, **13**, 189–93.

GIBBS, A.K., PAYNE, B., SETZER, T., BROWN, L.D., OLIVER, J.E. & KAUFMAN, S. 1984. Seismic reflection study of the Precambrian crust of central Minnesota. *Bull. geol. Soc. Am.* **95**, 280–94.

GLAZNER, A.F. & BARTLEY, J.M. 1985. Evolution of lithospheric strength after thrusting. *Geology*, **13**, 42–5.

GRIES, R. 1983. Oil and Gas prospecting beneath Precambrian of foreland thrust plates in Rocky Mountains. *Bull. Am. Assoc. Pet. Geol.* **67**, 1–28.

HAMILTON, W. 1969. The volcanic central Andes—A modern model for the Cretaceous batholiths and tectonics of western North America. *Oregon Dept. Geol. Min. Ind. Bull.* **65**, 175–84.

—— 1978. Mesozoic tectonics of the western United States. *In*: HOWELL, D.G. & McDOUGALL, K.A. (eds) *Mesozoic paleogeography of the western United States, Pacif. coast Paleogeog. Symp. 2, Soc. econ. Paleontol. and Mineral.*, Pac. sect. 33–70.

—— 1982. Structual evolution of the Big Maria Mountains, northeastern Riverside County, southeastern California. *In*: FROST, E.G. & MARTIN, D.L. (eds) *Mesozoic–Cenozoic tectonic evolution of the Colorado River Region, California, Arizona, and Nevada*, pp. 1–28. Cordilleran Publishers, San Diego.

HASTINGS, D.D. 1979. Results of exploratory drilling northern Fallon Basin, western Nevada. *In*: NEWMAN, G.W. & GOODE, H.D. (eds) *Basin and Range Symp.*, pp. 515–22. Rocky Mtn Assoc. Geol.

HAUGE, T.A., ALLMENDINGER, R.W., CARUSO, C., HAUSER, E.C., KLEMPERER, S.L. OPDYKE, S., POTTER, C.J., SANFORD, W., BROWN, L., KAUFMAN, S. & OLIVER, J. 1986. Crustal structure of eastern Nevada from COCORP deep seismic reflection data. *Bull. geol. Soc. Am.* Submitted.

HAUSER, E., BURGESS, S., BURTCH, S., MUTSCHLER, J., POTTER, C., HAUGE, T.A., ALLMENDINGER, R.W., BROWN, L., KAUFMAN, S. & OLIVER, 1986. Crustal structure of eastern Nevada from COCORP deep seismic reflection data. *Bull. geol. Soc. Am.* Submitted.

HINTZE, L.F. 1973. Geologic history of Utah. *Brigham Young Univ. geol. Stud.* **25**, 1–181.

JORDAN, T.E., ISACKS, B.L., ALLMENDINGER, R.W., BREWER, J.A., RAMOS, V.A. & ANDO, C.J. 1983. Andean tectonics related to geometry of subducted Nazca plate. *Bull. geol. Soc. Am.* **94**, 341–61.

KAY, M. 1951. North American geosynclines. *Mem. geol. Soc. Am.* **48**, 1–143.

KETNER, K.B. & SMITH, J.F. JR 1982. Mid-Paleozoic age of the Roberts thrust unsettled by new data from northern Nevada. *Geology*, **10**, 298–303.

KISTLER, R.W. 1974. Phanerozoic batholiths in western North America: A summary of some recent work on variations in time, space, chemistry, and isotopic composition: *Ann. Rev. Earth planet. Sci.* **2**, 403–18.

KLEMPERER, S.L., HAUGE, T.A., HAUSER, E.C., OLIVER, J.E. & POTTER, C.J. 1986. The Moho in the northern Basin and Range, Nevada, along the COCORP 40°N seismic reflecting transect. *Bull. geol. Soc. Am.* **97**, 603–18.

KLIGFIELD, R. CRESPI, J., NARUK, S. & DAVIS, G.H. 1984. Displacement and strain patterns of extensional orogens. *Tectonics*, 3, 557–609.

LEE, D.E., MARVIN, R.F., STERN, T.W. & PETERMAN, Z.E. 1970. Modification of K–Ar ages by Tertiary thrusting in the Snake Range, White Pine County, Nevada. *U.S. geol. Surv. Prof. Pap.* **700D**, D93–D102.

MCDONALD, R.E. 1976. Tertiary tectonics and sedimentary rocks along the transition, Basin and Range Province to Plateau and thrust belt province, Utah. *In*: HILL, J. (ed.) *Geology of the Cordilleran hingeline*, pp. 281–317. Rocky Mtn. Assoc. Geol.

MEISSNER, R. 1984. The continental crust in central Europe as based on data from reflection seismology. *Int. Symp. Deep Structure of the Continental Crust*, pp. 57–8. Cornell University.

MILLER, E.L., GANS, P.B. & GARING, J. 1983. The Snake Range décollement: An exhumed mid-Tertiary ductile–brittle transition. *Tectonics*, 2, 239–63.

MOORES, E.M. & DAY, H.W. 1984. Overthrust model for the Sierra Nevada. *Geology*, 12, 416–9.

NELSON, D.K., ZHU, T.F., GIBBS, A., HARRIS, R., OLIVER, J.E., KAUFMAN, S., BROWN, L.D. & SCHWEIKERT, R.A. In press. COCORP deep seismic reflection profiling in the northern Sierra Nevada Mountains. *Tectonics*.

OKAYA, D.A. 1984. Reflection profiling of the lower crust in the Basin and Range: Dixie Valley, Nevada. *Int. Symp. Deep Structure of the Continental Crust*, pp. 65–6. Cornell University.

—— & THOMPSON, G.A. 1985. Geometry of Cenozoic extensional faulting: Dixie Valley, Nevada. *Tectonics*, 4, 107–26.

PEDDY, C.P., BROWN, L.D. & KLEMPERER, S.L. 1986. Interpreting the deep structure of rifts with synthetic seismic sections. *In*: BARAZANGI, M. & BROWN, L.D. (eds) *Am. Geophys. Union Geodyn. Ser.* 13, 301–11.

POTTER, C.J., LIU, C-S., HUANG, J., ZHENG, L., HAUGE, T.A., HAUSER, E.C., ALLMENDINGER, R.W., OLIVER, J.E., KAUFMAN, S. & BROWN, L. 1986. Crustal structure of north-central Nevada: Results from COCORP deep seismic profiling. *Bull. geol. Soc. Am.* Submitted.

PRODEHL, C. 1979, Crustal structure of the western United States. *U.S. geol. Surv. Prof. Pap.*, **1034**, 74 pp.

PROFFETT, J.M. JR 1977. Cenozoic geology of the Yerrington district, Nevada, and implications for the nature and origin of Basin and Range faulting. *Bull. geol. Soc. Am.* 88, 247–66.

ROBERTS, R.J., HOTZ, P.E., GILLULY, J. & FERGUSON, H.G. 1958. Paleozoic rocks of north central Nevada. *Bull. Am. Assoc. Pet. Geol.* 42, 2813–57.

ROBISON, B.A. 1983. Low-angle normal faulting, Marys River Valley, Nevada. *In*: BALLY, A.W. (ed.) *Seismic expressions of structural styles, Volume Two. Am. Assoc. Pet. Geol. Studies in Geology*, 15, 2.2.2-12–16.

ROYSE, F., WARNER, M.A. & REESE, D.L. 1975. Thrust belt structural geometry and related stratigraphic problems, Wyoming–Idaho-northern Utah. *In*:

BOLYARD, D.W. (ed.) *Deep drilling frontiers of the central Rocky Mountains*, pp. 41–54. Rocky Mtn Assoc. Geol.

SALEEBY, J. 1981. Ocean floor accretion and volcano-plutonic arc evolution of the Mesozoic Sierra Nevada. *In*: ERNST, W.G. (ed.) *The Geotectonic Development of California*, pp. 132–81. Prentice-Hall Inc., New Jersey.

SCHWEIKERT, R.A. 1981. Tectonic evolution of the Sierra Nevada Range. *In*: ERNST, W.G. (ed.) *The Geotectonic Development of California*, pp. 87–131. Prentice-Hall Inc., New Jersey.

—— & COWAN, D.S. 1975. Early Mesozoic tectonic evolution of the western Sierra Nevada, California. *Bull. geol. Soc. Am.* **86**, 1329–36.

—— & SYNDER, W.S. 1981. Paleozoic plate tectonics of the Sierra Nevada and adjacent regions. *In*: ERNST, W.G. (ed.) *The Geotectonic Development of California*, pp. 182–202. Prentice-Hall Inc., New Jersey.

SERPA, L., SETZER, T., FARMER, H., BROWN, L., OLIVER, J., KAUFMAN, S. & SHARP, J. 1984a. Structure of the southern Keweenawan rift from COCORP surveys across the Midcontinent geophysical anomaly in northeastern Kansas. *Tectonics*, 3, 367–84.

——, DE VOOGD, B., WILLEMIN, J., OLIVER, J., KAUFMAN, S., BROWN, L., HAUSER, E., WRIGHT, L.A. & TROXEL, B.W. 1984b. Late Cenozoic fault patterns and magma migration in Death Valley from COCORP seismic profiles. *Eos.* 65, 985.

SHARP, J. 1984. West-central Utah: *Palinspastically restored sections constrained by COCORP seismic reflection data*. M.Sc. Thesis, Cornell Univ. 60 pp.

SILBERLING, N.J. & ROBERTS, R.J. 1962. Pre-Tertiary stratigraphy and structure of northwestern Nevada. *Geol. Soc. Am. Spec. Pap.* 72, 1–50.

SMITH, R.B. 1978. Seismicity, crustal structure, and intraplate tectonics of the interior of the western Cordillera. *In*: SMITH, R.B. & EATON, G.P. (eds) *Cenozoic tectonics and regional geophysics of the western Cordillera, Mem. geol. Soc. Am.* 152, 111–44.

—— & BRUHN, R.L. 1984. Intraplate extensional tectonics of the eastern Basin–Range: Inferences on structural style from seismic reflection data, regional tectonics, and thermal mechanical models of brittle–ductile deformation. *J. geophys. Res.* 89, 5733–62.

SMITHSON, S.B., BREWER, J.A., KAUFMAN, S., OLIVER, J. & HURICH, C. 1978. Nature of the Wind River thrust, Wyoming, from COCORP deep reflection data and from gravity data. *Geology*, 6, 648–52.

SPEED, R.C. 1979. Collided Paleozoic microplate in the western United States. *J. Geol.* 87, 279–90.

—— 1982. Evolution of the sialic margin in the central western United States. *In*: WATKINS, J. & DRAKE, C. (eds) *Geology of Continental margins, Mem. Am. Assoc. Pet. Geol.* 34, 457–68.

STANDLEE, L.A. 1982. Structure and stratigraphy of Jurassic rocks in central Utah: Their influence on tectonic development of the Cordilleran fold and thrust belt. *In*: POWERS, R.B. (ed.) *Geologic studies of the Cordilleran thrust belt, Volume 1*, pp. 357–82. Rocky Mtn Assoc. Geol.

STEWART, J.H. 1971. Basin and Range structure—a system of horsts and grabens produced by deep-seated extension. *Bull. geol. Soc. Am.* **82**, 1019–44.

—— 1972. Initial deposits in the Cordilleran geosyncline: Evidence of a late Precambrian (<850 m.y.) continental separation. *Bull. geol. Soc. Am.* **83**, 1345–60.

—— 1980. Geology of Nevada. *Nevada Bur. Mines geol. Spec. Publ.* **4**, 1–136.

—— & POOLE, F.G. 1974. Lower Paleozoic and uppermost Precambrian Cordilleran miogeocline, Great Basin, western United States. *In*: DICKINSON, W.R. (ed.) *Tectonics and sedimentation, Soc. econ. Paleontol. and Mineral., Spec. Publ.* **22**, 28–57.

STOKES, W. 1976. What is the Wasatch Line? *In*: HILL, J. (ed.) *Geology of the Cordilleran hingeline*, pp. 11–25. Rocky Mtn Assoc. Geol.

THOMPSON, G.A. 1983. Anomalous upper mantle: Its role in continental rifts and plateaus. *Abstr. with Programs geol. Soc. Am.* **15**, 706.

—— & ZOBACK, M. L. 1979. Regional geophysics of the Colorado Plateau. *Tectonophysics*, **61**, 149–81.

VON TISH, D., ALLMENDINGER, R.W. & SHARP, J. 1985. History of Cenozoic extension in the central Sevier Desert, west-central Utah, from COCORP seismic reflection data. *Bull. Am. Assoc. Pet. Geol.* **69**, 1077–87.

VREELAND, J. H. & BERRONG, B. H. 1979. Seismic exploration in Railroad Valley, Nevada. *In*: NEWMAN, G. W. & GOODE, H. D. (eds) *Basin and Range Symp.* pp. 557–69. Rocky Mtn Assoc. Geol.

WALLACE, R. E. 1984. Patterns and timing of Late Quaternary faulting in the Great Basin Province and relations to some regional tectonic features. *J. geophys. Res.* **89**, 5763–69.

WERNICKE, B. 1981. Low-angle normal faults in the Basin and Range Province: Nappe tectonics in an extending orogen. *Nature*, **291**, 645–8.

—— & BURCHFIEL, B.C. 1982. Modes of extensional tectonics. *J. struct. Geol.* **4**, 105–15.

ZOBACK, M.L. 1983. Shallow structure of the Sevier Desert detachment. *Abstr. with Programs geol. Soc. Am.* **15**, 287.

—— , ANDERSON, R.E. & THOMPSON, G.A. 1981. Cainozoic evolution of the state of stress and style of tectonism of the Basin and Range province of the western United States. *Phil. Trans. R. Soc. London* **A300**, 407–34.

—— & THOMPSON, G.A. 1978. Basin and Range rifting in northern Nevada: Clues from a mid-Miocene rift and its subsequent offsets. *Geology*, **6**, 111–6.

RICHARD W. ALLMENDINGER & JACK OLIVER, Institute for the Study of the Continents and Department of Geological Sciences, Cornell University, Ithaca, New York 14853, USA.
THOMAS A. HAUGE, ERNEST C. HAUSER & CHRISTOPHER J. POTTER, Institute for the study of the Continents, Cornell University, Ithaca, New York 14853, USA.

A shear-zone model for the structural evolution of metamorphic core complexes in southeastern Arizona

G.H. Davis

SUMMARY: Some of the world's best exposed and most thickly developed mylonites, ultramylonites, and cataclasites are found in parts of a number of mountain ranges in southeastern Arizona. These fault rocks and associated structures occupy metamorphic core complexes, which I view as mountain-size geological exposures of regional, upward-tapering ductile–brittle shear zones. The fundamental characteristics of the core complexes were fashioned by regional crustal extension in the Tertiary. Normal-slip shearing served to 'telescope' fault rocks and structures which had formed originally at different depth levels in the crust. The result of normal-slip simple shear within the shear zones was the translation of hanging wall crust by tens of kilometres. The shear zones and linked fault zones are interpreted to have dipped at 45° or more initially, rotating progressively to more gentle inclinations and shallower depths as the crust thinned and stretched. Progressive simple-shear under conditions of a steadily decreasing confining pressure and temperature is dramatically recorded in suites of structures and fabrics: for example mylonite gneiss is converted to microbrecciated mylonite gneiss, which in turn is transformed to cataclasite and ultracataclasite. The physical nature of this progressive deformation is beautifully exposed in the gently dipping Catalina–Rincon shear zone, whose once-deep and once-shallow parts are now exposed to view over broad expanses E and NE of Tucson, Arizona.

The expression 'metamorphic core complex' in part denotes a very distinctive structural association (Davis & Coney 1979; Davis 1977, 1980b) marked by the presence of a thick, extensive, low-angle tabular zone of mylonites that gives way upward to microbrecciated mylonites (cataclasites), which in turn are capped by a sub-regional to regional low-angle detachment fault. Most workers agree that the detachment faults and associated cataclasites in core complexes of the southern part of the Basin and Range are products of Tertiary extensional deformation. Miocene movement along such faults and within the associated, immediately underlying zones of cataclasis is often self-evident, given the presence of tilted mid-Miocene sedimentary and volcanic rocks in the hanging wall, upper-plate position (Davis & Coney 1979; Davis et al. 1980; Davis & Hardy 1981). However, the mylonites themselves are controversial both with respect to their age and origin. Some workers have emphasized that the mylonites are the products of regional thrusting during the Laramide (Thorman 1977; Davis et al. 1980; DeWitt 1980; Drewes 1981). Others have emphasized that the mylonites were fashioned by crustal extension during the Tertiary (Davis 1977, 1980b; Reynolds 1982, 1985; Reynolds & Rehrig 1980). Still others place the emphasis on a hybrid origin of the mylonites, in which mylonites that formed during Laramide crustal shortening are overprinted by mylonites formed during the mid-Tertiary (Bykerk-Kauffman & Janecke 1986).

My interpretation is that core-complex mylonites in southern Arizona are largely 50 My and younger in age and formed within shear zones which accommodated extension of the crust through normal-slip shearing (Davis 1980a, 1981a, 1983). Moreover, I regard the formation of mylonites by shearing at depth to be genetically linked, and kinematically coordinated with, the development of cataclasites, detachment faults, and associated normal faults at shallower levels. The purpose of this paper is to describe the general nature of the linkage in geometric and kinematic terms.

Shear-zone origin of core-complex mylonites and cataclasites

The physical and geometric properties of the structures, fault rocks, and contact relationships that developed in metamorphic core complexes are especially well displayed in southeastern Arizona (Davis 1980b; Reynolds & Rehrig 1980). Core-complex mylonites and cataclasites, as a system, appear to reflect a ductile–brittle continuum of deformation. Careful mapping and analysis of the structural system has led to the realization that strain and displacement were partitioned across a host of structures, through a spectrum of scales, in rocks of progressively changing rheology. By integrating observations made in different parts of the extensional system, especially at different inferred depth

From COWARD, M.P., DEWEY, J.F. & HANCOCK, P.L. (eds), 1987, Continental Extensional Tectonics, Geological Society Special Publication No. 28, pp. 247–266.

levels, it has been possible to construct a descriptive/kinematic model of the progressive deformation that achieved continental crustal extension in general and the development of metamorphic core complexes in particular.

The physical and geometric nature of the mylonites and cataclasites in metamorphic core complexes of southeastern Arizona can be understood in the context of shear-zone deformation. When so viewed, the mylonites of metamorphic core complexes emerge as mountain-size geological exposures of deep reaches of regional brittle–ductile shear zones (Davis 1980a, 1981a; Davis et al. 1981; Davis 1983; Naruk, in press). The zones vary in thickness from approximately 0.3 to 3 km.

Normal-slip simple-shear within individual shear zones resulted in kilometres of differential translation. Mylonites formed within the shear zones at depth levels of 10 km and more. The denudation which accompanied progressive simple-shear raised early-formed, deep-level mylonites through higher and higher structural levels. The mylonites thus experienced a progressive deformation (mylonitization through cataclasis to faulting along discrete surfaces) carried

out under conditions of steadily decreasing temperature and confining pressure (Davis 1983). The record of fault rocks and fabrics displays this history strikingly: mylonite gneiss comprising the interior of shear zones is transformed upward into microbrecciated mylonite gneiss, which in turn is converted to cataclasite (and even ultracataclasite) derived from microbrecciated mylonite gneiss (Fig. 1).

In outcrop the cataclasites typically form a resistant tabular ledge (Fig. 2), the upper surface of which is a gently dipping detachment fault, or decollement (Davis 1977, 1980b; Davis et al. 1980). This surface of profound structural discontinuity, dipping 10–30°, sharply separates mylonitic and cataclastic fault rocks below from a diverse suite of deformed and/or tilted cover rocks above. The cover rocks range in age from Precambrian to mid-Miocene.

We do not know the original shapes and inclinations of the ductile–brittle shear zones at the time of their initial development. They may have been smoothly listric in profile view, or they may have been planar. They may have had spoon-shaped and/or mullion-like curviplanar forms, or have been straight in plan-view trace

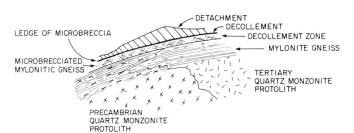

FIG. 1. Schematic diagrams showing components and characteristics of metamorphic core complexes. The mylonites in this example are derived from igneous protolith.

FIG. 2. Photograph showing the expression of cataclasite ledge (cliff), the upper surface of which is the Santa Catalina detachment fault or decollement. Rincon Mountains near Colossal Cave.

expression. They may have initiated at shallow angles of inclination, or have been steep initially and then rotated to shallower inclinations.

I would emphasize that the shear-zone principles presented in this paper will have a bearing on kinematic interpretation, regardless of what the original shear-zone forms and inclinations prove to be. Possibilities are almost without limit, as noted by Kligfield et al. (1984). Kligfield et al. (1984) also stressed that the interpretations of specific distributions of strains and translations will ultimately depend upon knowledge and assumptions regarding initial geometries.

My present bias is this: when the brittle–ductile shear zones formed initially, as a response to continental crustal extension, they probably dipped at angles averaging 45° or more, and not at their presently observed inclinations of 30°.

At the time of formation of the brittle–ductile shear zones, only the uppermost brittle surficial expression(s) of the zones would have been exposed to view. As crustal extension progressed, the brittle–ductile shear zones rotated incrementally to lower angles of inclination. Proffett's (1977) model for the kinematics of extensional faulting in the Yerington district of Nevada is an example of this kinematic behaviour. While actively accommodating simple-shear deformation and displacement, the shear zones were simultaneously required to rotate to shallower inclinations as the crust was distorted into a stretched, thinned counterpart of its original shape and size. Following this early- to mid-Tertiary deformation, the rotated shallow-dipping, brittle–ductile shear zones were cut and differentially displaced along younger high-angle normal faults, which are fundamentally responsible for blocking-out the basins and ranges of southeastern Arizona today. Because of the combination of these structural circumstances, broad expanses of sub-regional brittle–ductile shear zones can be examined in single and/or adjacent mountain ranges. By traversing range to range, parallel to the direction of shear, the once-shallow and once-deep parts of a common shear zone may be examined at the surface of the Earth.

Work is underway to test the concept of progressive rotation of the shear zones in southeastern Arizona. There are no hard data to document the reality of the rotation at present, but the probability of rotation would seem inescapable bearing in mind both strain theory and the ubiquitous mid-Tertiary rotational faulting in the southern Basin and Range.

Computer-card simulation of the shear-zone model

Non-rotational aspects of the shear-zone model for the origin of metamorphic core complexes can be illustrated through shearing of a suitably embossed deck of computer cards. Drawn on the face of the deck shown in Fig. 3a is a simplified portrayal of the geological column of southeastern Arizona. The basement of the column consists of Precambrian quartz monzonite, 1.4 By old, intruded by Laramide quartz monzonitic plutons approximately 55 My old, some of which are shown to invade overlying sedimentary cover. Unconformably overlying basement are younger Precambrian sedimentary rocks of the Apache Group, which in turn are disconformably overlain by strata of the Palaeozoic sedimentary rock column. The Apache Group

sedimentary rocks, approximately 1.2 By old, are only 150 m thick in southeastern Arizona, and the entire Palaeozoic shelf/platform sedimentary sequence attains only 1200 m. The Mesozoic component of the geological column of southeastern Arizona consists of interbedded volcanics and clastic sedimentary rocks of Jurassic age, and clastic sedimentary strata of Cretaceous age. Thicknesses of Mesozoic strata in southeastern Arizona range up to 6000 m and more, but vary significantly from place to place.

Following Ramsay & Huber (1983), I designed a deformation box that could be used to simulate shear-zone deformation of the geological column of southeastern Arizona. The box was made to hold a single, suitably embossed computer-card deck, and to guide the insertion of a wooden template. The wooden template was cut in such a way that its insertion into the side of the deck created a discrete normal-slip shear zone.

The shear-zone geometries which emerged in the card-deck experiments provide a visual basis for understanding the basic configuration of rocks, contacts and structures in metamorphic core complexes (Fig. 3a–d). Hanging wall strata of sub-regional proportions were translated down-dip with respect to footwall rocks. The hanging wall and footwall blocks translated with respect to each other without enduring penetrative shear. In contrast, that part of the rock column situated *within* the developing shear zone was subjected to wholesale distortion. Bedding, unconformities, and contacts intercepted by the shear zone became distorted and underwent radical changes in length and orientation. Layered sequences were thinned dramatically, but they retained the stratigraphic ordering which they possessed before shearing. Thinned sheared rocks derived from originally undistorted strata were smeared above footwall basement, *but at a much deeper level than that at which they originally resided.* Tongues and dykes of intrusive rocks became distorted, flattened, and progressively aligned with the shear zone. The edges of plutons caught-up in shear-zone deformation were sheared into huge tails which disclosed sense-of-shear.

In nature, all rocks affected by shear-zone deformation are transformed into tectonites marked by the penetrative development of foliation and lineation. Primary objects like fossils, pebbles, and xenoliths are markedly distorted within the zones of shear.

Viewing the computer-card models as if they corresponded to sub-regional or regional structural systems (Fig. 4), it is possible to imagine the mapping and interpretive challenges. The

(a)

(b)

(c)

(d)

shear zones in the computer-card model are manifest in southeastern Arizona as sub-regional, crudely tabular zones of mylonite derived from Precambrian basement (and plutons intruding basement) and younger Precambrian, Palaeozoic, and Mesozoic strata. Undistorted footwall basement rocks beneath the shear zone in the computer-card model correspond in the field to exposures of original protolith from which overlying mylonites were derived. Hanging wall strata are the so-called upper-plate or cover rocks, which translate down-dip into a younger-on-older contact relationship with underlying sheared-out footwall. Hanging wall cover rocks would include growth-fault sediments deposited as a result of basin formation accompanying displacement(s) along the shear zones (Davis & Coney 1979; Coney 1980; Davis 1980b). Such basin-fill deposits are themselves translated down-dip on to shear-zone rocks derived from older parts of the rock column. In southeastern Arizona the basin-fill deposits are mid-Tertiary in age and thousands of metres thick.

Kinematic implications of the shear-zone model

Figure 5a & b taken from a sequence of illustrations presented elsewhere (Davis 1981c, 1983), depicts in a *schematic* fashion the stretching of southeastern Arizona continental crust, a stretching achieved through displacements along spaced normal-slip faults and normal-slip shear zones. Figure 5a shows simple domino-like faulting of the rock column along spaced normal-slip faults. Block tilt, fault dip, and fault displacement are compatible with an overall crustal stretching of 67%, assuming an original fault dip of 45° and an original spacing of fault traces of 6 km. Calculations assuring internal

Fig. 3. Computer-card simulation of progressive simple shearing. (a) Geological column viewed in cross-section painted on side of a computer-card deck. Total vertical thickness simulated is approximately 10 km. The white horizontal layer represents younger Precambrian sedimentary strata, which rests unconformably upon 1.4 By granite basement (v-pattern). The younger Precambrian strata are overlain unconformably by Palaeozoic sedimentary rocks (medium grey), and Mesozoic strata (dark grey). Tertiary plutonic rocks (stippled) intrude basement and cover. (b–d) Progressive normal-slip shearing of the deck, creating a distortion of the rocks of the column within a zone whose scaled thickness is approximately 1 or 2 km.

FIG. 4. The model, viewed from a distance.

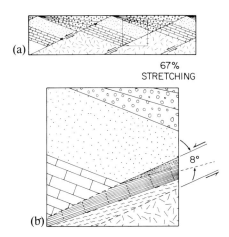

FIG. 5. (a) Stretching accommodated by normal-slip displacements on spaced faults. (b) Stretching accommodated by normal-slip shear displacements on spaced shear zones. Note orientation of the plane of flatening within the shear zone.

geometric consistency are based on equational relationships prescribed by Le Pichon & Sibuet (1981), and on strain equations published by Ramsay (1967). The sequence of diagrams from which Fig. 5a was extracted (Davis 1983, fig 3a–g) shows the natural evolution of younger-on-older contact relationships, the progressive decrease in fault inclination, the steady increase in block tilt, and the accumulation of growth-fault basin deposits. As a geometric/mathematical convenience in the construction of the diagrams, the faults, like those in Fig. 5a, are shown to be planar. In reality, the faults may well be curved.

In Fig. 5b, one of the single discrete normal-slip faults of Fig. 5a is replaced by a zone of distributed simple-shear. Based on knowledge of shear-zone thickness and shear-zone displacement, assuming that the walls of the shear zone are parallel, and assuming that shear strain is constant across the zone, equations of strain (Ramsay 1967; Ramsay & Huber 1983) were used to calculate the orientation of the plane of flattening (XY) within the shear zone. For 67% stretching under the conditions specified, the plane of flattening dips 8° more gently than the shear-zone walls. In nature the plane of flattening would be expressed as foliation within the interior of the shear zone. As the shear zone accommodates more and more displacement, the plane of flattening (and thus the foliation within the shear zone) would move closer and closer into parallelism with the shear-zone walls. After substantial crustal stretching, and assum-

ing that the shear zone itself progressively
rotates to shallower and shallower inclinations,
both the shear-zone boundaries and foliation
within the shear zone would dip gently by about
the same amount in the same direction. *The
characteristically gentle inclination of foliation
and lithological layering in metamorphic core
complexes, in my view, reflects such a kinematic
evolution.* The sequence of diagrams in Davis
(1983, fig. 5a–g), from which Fig. 5b was
extracted, show that with each increment of
crustal stretching, shear-zone tectonites acquire
increasing shear strain and at the same time are
passively elevated into shallower reaches of the
crust. Fault rocks which were created by plastic
deformation in ductile regimes are steadily introduced to shear and slip under progressively
less ductile, more brittle conditions. The quantitative implications of this and other sequential
progressions are presented in Kligfield *et al.*
(1984).

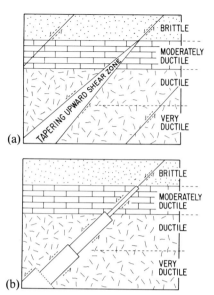

FIG. 6. (a) Schematic rendering of upward-tapering
shear zone, cutting through Precambrian,
Palaeozoic, and Mesozoic rocks. (b) Representation
of tapered shear zones through array of aligned
rectangular elements.

Kinematics of a tapering-upward brittle–ductile shear zone

Computer-card models and geometric constructions based on images of tabular shear zones
with parallel walls do not lend themselves to
exploring the kinematic implications of shear
within, and displacement(s) along, brittle–
ductile shear zones that taper upward. Yet the
decrease in thickness of the zone of mylonites
northeastward across the Rincon Mountains
and the western part of the San Pedro Valley
in southeastern Arizona suggests that shear
zones integral to metamorphic core complexes
do indeed taper upward and connect upward
into faults and fault zones. Such a shear-zone/
fault zone linkage is shown in Fig. 6a, set in the
context of rather arbitrary, illustrative, depth-
dependent regimes of brittle, moderately ductile,
ductile, and very ductile deformation. The
brittle regime is visualized as a domain within
which rocks respond to simple shear by discrete
faulting, fracturing, and microbrecciation. In
the ductile regimes, rocks within the shear zones
are pictured as responding to distributed simple
shear by non-rigid-body deformation and the
formation of tectonites, especially mylonites.
Each rheological domain fosters its own
characteristic fault rocks and accompanying
structures.

To model such an upward-tapering brittle–
ductile shear zone, I chose to represent the zone
by a series of aligned rectangular elements
(Fig. 6b). The lengths of the elements, and the

length of the discrete fault zone to which the
elements are linked upward, reflect inclined
distances through each of the rheological
domains—brittle, moderately ductile, ductile,
and very ductile. To a first approximation, these
elements, taken together, constitute a tapered
zone about to undergo shear. In trying to
diminish structural incompatibility among the
elements comprising the shear zone, I employed
the principles and guidelines presented by
Cobbold & Percevault (1983) for palinspastic
restoration.

I first modelled the tapered shear zone for
conditions of 23% stretching of the southeastern
Arizona rock column, once again assuming that
shear-zone/fault-zone dip was initially 45°, and
that shear-zone/fault-zone spacing (measured in
map view) was 6 km. Given these constraints,
each part of the shear zone would accommodate
1650 m of normal-slip displacement. Displacement would be accommodated by and distributed within the elements of the model in the
manner shown in Fig. 7. Shearing of thinner
elements would result in higher levels of shear
strain. Foliation orientation would vary as a
function of shear strain sustained by each
element (Fig. 7). Where shear strain is highest,
foliation is more closely aligned with the (shear-
zone) walls of the elements.

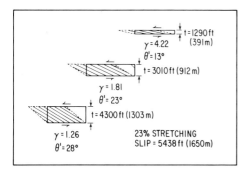

FIG. 7. Calculations of shear-strain distortion of the rectangular elements, based on requirements for 23% stretching.

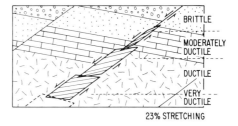

FIG. 8. Best-fit approximation of the nature and form of the tapered shear zone after 23% stretching.

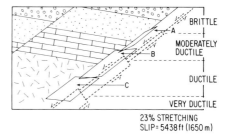

FIG. 9. Preparation for superimposing additional shear strain on a pre-existing upward-tapering shear zone. At point A, brittle deformation will be superimposed on earlier developed moderately ductile fabrics and structures. At point B, moderately ductile deformation will be superimposed on earlier formed ductile fabrics and structures. At point C, ductile deformation will be imposed on earlier developed very ductile fabrics and structures.

The sheared elements are fitted together in Fig. 8 in a way that tends to minimize structural incompatibility (Cobbold & Percevault 1983). Note that the mid-points of the boundary lines of adjacent elements are superposed to create best fits. Viewed overall, the shear zone displays a smoother upward taper than that inherent at the start of the construction in Fig. 6b. Now dipping at 35°, the tapered shear zone reveals the effect of passive rotation within thinning, extending crust. The absolute inclination of foliation decreases with depth in the shear zone, reflecting the fact that thicker zones are marked by lesser shear strain, given the constancy of required displacement.

What if progressive simple shear continued, and crustal stretching increased from 23 to 106%? How would the structural nature of the shear zone change? And what would happen to the earlier-formed tectonites that developed during the 23% stretching? To seek answers to these questions I superimposed new, undistorted rectangular elements on the earlier deformed elements, as shown in Fig. 9. Lengths of the new shear-zone elements were found to be greater than originally, corresponding to increased inclined distances through the respective rheological domains, which I held fixed in thickness and depth. The length of the discrete brittle fault zone into which the uppermost shear-zone element connected had become longer than at the start. The impact of these differences is such that at location A (Fig. 9), brittle fabrics and structures (produced by faulting, fracturing, and cataclasis) will be superimposed on moderately ductile fabrics (like highly strained mylonites). At locations B and C (Fig. 9), more highly strained mylonitic tectonites will be superimposed on less highly strained mylonitic tectonites. When the new undistorted elements and the original, now-distorted elements are actually superimposed, as in Fig. 10, it becomes apparent that the new elements effectively insert themselves into the interior of the original zone. At the level of observation, the active zone of shear (steadily) decreased in thickness. Thus some earlier-formed mylonitic tectonites become excluded from the zone of active shear, and as a consequence are translated passively along with hanging wall and footwall rocks of the normal southeastern Arizona geological column.

The superposition of shear strain and displacement for conditions of 106% crustal stretching is constructed in Fig. 11. The earlier-formed, now passive, tectonites are translated 5088 m, or approximately 5 km. Total displacement along the shear-zone/fault-zone network, including displacement accommodated during the 23% stretching, is 6736 m. Strains within the active part of the shear zone were calculated, taking into consideration the state of strain in the earlier-deformed elements and the requirements for shear strain in the new, superposed elements (see Fig. 11). The overall tapered shear-zone form which emerges from this construction is sleek (Fig. 12).

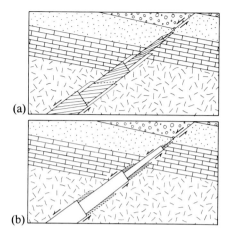

(a)

(b)

FIG. 10. The next increment of shearing (see Fig. 9) will be imposed on earlier formed tectonites within the medial part of the upward-tapering shear zone. (a) Note the orientation of pre-existing foliation within the zones about to be subjected to shearing. (b) Note the fact that some earlier formed tectonite lies outside the region about to become the active zone of shear.

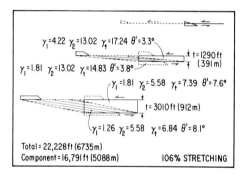

FIG. 11. Calculations of shear-zone distortion of the new rectangular elements for conditions of 106% stretching.

Geological implications of brittle–ductile shear-zone model

Figure 13 shows the integrated results of the construction of an upward-tapering brittle–ductile shear zone, one that has participated in accommodating 106% stretching of continental crust. Near the upper reaches of the shear zone, tilted hanging wall cover rocks of Tertiary age rest in low-angle (decollement) fault contact with early-formed, brittlely overprinted shear-zone tectonites. These overprinted tectonites in turn overlie tectonites fashioned wholly under moderately ductile or ductile conditions. Within

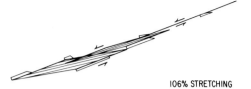

106% STRETCHING

FIG. 12. Geometry of the shear zone which emerges from minimizing structural incompatibility.

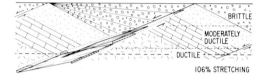

106% STRETCHING

FIG.13. Integrated view of the upward-tapering shear zone as it cuts and displaces the geological column of southeastern Arizona.

the interior of the shear zone, contacts between the pervasively sheared members of the southeastern Arizona geological column can be traced. Structural relations are such that the Tertiary cover rocks are in brittle–ductile shear-zone contact with an extravagantly thinned fault-rock column of Mesozoic, Palaeozoic, younger Precambrian, and Precambrian rock, in descending order through the shear zone.

From this model, 'metamorphic core complexes' can be seen to be exposures of regional to sub-regional (upward-tapering) shear zones with or without exposure(s) of hanging wall cover and/or footwall protolith. Ideal 'metamorphic core complexes,' with all of the characteristic structural geological components (Davis 1977, 1980b; Coney 1980; Davis & Coney 1979; Reynolds & Rehrig 1980), are parts of large brittle–ductile shear zones *exposed at a depth where brittle-shearing movements have been conspicuously superimposed on ductile/plastic-shearing movements.* Where simple shear has taken place above the brittle–ductile transition, the fault and tilt-block relationships comprise detachment terrains devoid of exposed mylonite gneiss (Wernicke 1981). Where simple shear has taken place exclusively in a ductile regime, the structural relationships would not be identified as constituting a metamorphic core complex, for the decollement and microbreccia zone, so characteristic of core complexes, would be absent. Instead, the structural relationships would conform to properties of an ideal ductile shear zone (Ramsay 1980), albeit one on a grand scale.

The kinematic and mechanical implications of the model are illuminating and go well beyond the scope of this paper. As simple shear proceeds along a tapering-upward brittle–ductile shear zone, and as rotation of the shear zone commences, the spatial domains of formation of mylonite, microbreccia, ultracataclasite, and discrete faults migrate systematically. They migrate in such a way that early-formed mylonites are overprinted first by microbreccia and cataclasite, and then by discrete faulting. Furthermore, they migrate such that brittle overprinting may become concentrated preferentially along the hanging wall margin of the brittle–ductile shear zone. If this is true, the position of the decollement/detachment in any core complex may be predetermined by the peculiar way in which an evolving tapered shear zone rotates through the ductile to brittle transition.

It is apparent that highest shear strains characterize the thinnest zones of fault-rock development. The constraints of the model presume that the more brittle the conditions, the thinner the zone affected by rock response to simple-shear translation. Where the rocks can respond in a ductile manner, the zones of accommodation to a given simple-shear displacement are presumed to be relatively thick, thus minimizing and distributing shear strain.

The tendency for the normal-slip shear zone to decrease in thickness through time, as observed at a given level of observation, has other interesting geological implications. Steady progressive simple shear within a regional shear zone of ever-decreasing thickness naturally generates a macroscopic sigmoidal foliation pattern (Fig. 13). The geometry and asymmetry of such a pattern explicitly discloses sense-of-shear and variation in strain intensity for the zone as a whole (Davis 1983).

Steady decrease in shear-zone thickness through time also permits early-formed shear-zone tectonites, on the hanging wall side of the shear zone, to be intercepted and carried by the main discrete fault zone (see Figs 11, 12 & 13). Tectonite faulted in this manner is translated to an 'upper-plate' position, above the detachment fault (Fig. 13). Small outcrop areas of micro-brecciated tectonite in upper-plate positions do indeed occur. To date they have been difficult to understand in the context of conventional models.

The Catalina–Rincon brittle–ductile shear zone

Location

To illustrate what I believe are the products of a progressive normal-slip shearing and faulting of continental crust in southeastern Arizona, I will discuss examples from the Santa Catalina and Rincon Mountains N and E of Tuscon, including the San Pedro Valley which borders these mountains to the E and NE. In my view the rocks and structures of the Catalina and Rincon Mountains comprise a sub-regional brittle–ductile shear zone, which I name here the Catalina–Rincon brittle–ductile shear zone. The physiography and geography of the setting of this shear zone is illustrated in Fig. 14, a U2 oblique aerial photo of Tucson, Arizona and its surroundings to the NE. Localities and structures germane to the discussion that follows are identified in this photo.

General structural relationships

The Catalina–Rincon shear zone is gently SW dipping, and kinematic indicators such as folds and *S*–*C* relationships indicate a dominant normal-slip sense of shear directed along a line N60E/S60W (Davis 1981a, 1983; Davis *et al*. 1981; Davis & Hardy 1981; Martins 1984). Exceptions to SW-directed shear have been discovered by Bykerk-Kauffman (1983, 1986) in parts of the southeastern Catalinas and Redington Pass (Fig. 14), and by Naruk in a part of the central Catalinas (work in progress). Although it cannot yet be proved with certainty, it is probable that the Catalina–Rincon shear zone originally dipped more steeply southwestward than it does today. Large tilted step-blocks in the San Pedro Valley (Fig. 14) display a consistent sense of tilt, toward the NE. Although these are hanging wall rotations, it seems possible that the Catalina–Rincon Mountains themselves occupy a tilted step-block characterized by the same sense of rotation. Magnitude of rotation could easily be 30° or more, in which case the Catalina–Rincon shear zone would have dipped at least 55° at its inception.

Southwesternmost exposures of the shear zone consist of the mylonite gneisses that make up the Santa Catalina and Rincon Mountains (Fig. 14). These gneisses are interpreted here as representing the deepest reaches of the Catalina–Rincon shear zone that are exposed to view. The mylonite gneisses appear to be derived mainly from 1.42 By quartz monzonite (Shakel *et al*. 1977), and Eocene two-mica garnet-bearing granites (Shakel *et al*. 1977; Keith *et al*. 1980). The Catalina–Rincon shear zone climbs up-section to the NE such that along the crest of the Santa Catalina Mountains, within the Redington Pass area, and in Happy Valley E of the Rincon Mountains (Fig. 14), the mylonitic tectonites comprising the shear zone are derived mainly from Apache Group and Palaeozoic sedimentary

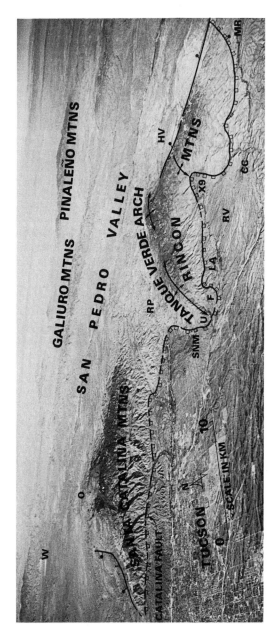

FIG. 14. U2 aerial view of Tucson and the Catalina–Rincon shear zone. W = Winkleman. O = Oracle. RP = Redington Pass. SNM = Saguaro National Monument. U = ultracataclasite locality. F = Flatrocks. LA = Loma Alta. RV = Rincon Valley. X9 = X9 Ranch. CC = Colossal Cave. HV = Happy Valley. MR = Martinez Ranch.

rocks. Still further up-section and north-eastward, mainly in the San Pedro Valley (Fig. 14), the uppermost exposed reaches of the brittle–ductile shear zone have created a detachment terrain in which thick sequences of mid-Tertiary basin deposits are faulted and tilted along low-dipping normal-slip faults.

The Catalina–Rincon brittle–ductile shear zone displays outstanding examples of migration of rocks and structures through the brittle–ductile transition. The entire western/south-western margin of the mylonitic gneisses in the Santa Catalina and Rincon Mountains is marked by a major detachment fault, or decollement, known as the Santa Catalina fault (Fig. 14). Directly beneath it lies cataclastic and/or microbrecciated mylonitic gneiss, while above it lies upper-plate, mainly brittly deformed rocks ranging from Precambrian granite to mid-Tertiary basin-fill sediments. The upper-plate rocks are non-mylonitic except in some rare cases where shear-zone tectonites derived from Palaeozoic rocks have been picked-off and translated along the main detachment, thus creating some hanging wall exposures of highly fractured and/or brecciated mylonitic marbles, quartzites, and calc-silicate rocks.

The original continuity of the Catalina–Rincon brittle–ductile shear zone must be pieced together from the composite exposures and relationships. It is by no means laid out as it appeared originally. Exposures of the shear zone in the Happy Valley/San Pedro Valley region (Fig. 14) are due to the preserving effects of Basin and Range faulting, which down-dropped the upper reaches of the shear zone from a structural elevation at or above the crests of the Santa Catalina and Rincon Mountains. Late arching and/or tilting of the region in which the shear zone resides has modified the original orientation and form of the shear zone even further. Locally, for example in Happy Valley, the mylonites dip northeastward, although it can be shown that at the time of their formation the mylonites dipped southwestward (Lingrey 1982). Upright arches of mylonite gneiss, like that comprising Tanque Verde Mountain (Fig. 15, might represent late-stage arching of an originally planar shear-zone (and/or fault zone) geometry (Spencer 1984). Alternatively, the upright arch-like structures might reflect original structural form, akin to large fault-mullion structure.

Mylonite gneisses

Mylonitic gneisses that make up the heart of the Catalina–Rincon shear zone are beautifully expressed in the physiography of the Santa Catalina and Rincon Mountains. In the fore-range of the Santa Catalina Mountains, the mylonite gneisses are so strongly layered that they look like a thick stack of gently dipping, massively bedded sedimentary and/or volcanic rocks. However, in outcrop view (Fig. 15) the rocks are seen to be mylonitic quartz-feldspathic gneisses, and the layering proves to be just one expression of the penetrative foliation within the gneisses.

Identification of the protolith for the mylonitic gneisses was the outgrowth of geological mapping and geochronological analysis by a number of workers, notably Creasey & Theodore (1975), Shakel *et al.* (1977), Drewes (1978), Banks (1976), Banks *et al.* (1977), and Keith *et al.* (1980). The mylonitic gneisses derived from 1.42 By quartz monzonite are coarse-grained augen gneisses, with abundant large feldspar porphyroclasts (0.5–6 cm) (Fig. 15). Ribbon-like layers and laminae of quartz wrap around the feldspars in a gently undulating habit, creating the most conspicuous expression of the foliation which pervades these gneisses. Alignment of unequidimensional feldspar porphyroclasts contributes to foliation expression as well. The foliation dips gently, typically less than 30°. The strike of foliation is systematically variable, defining a number of macroscopic antiforms and synforms trending E-NE (Pashley 1966).

Mineral lineation in the coarse-grained gneisses, derived from Precambrian quartz monzonite, is exquisitely developed (Davis 1980b) (Fig. 16). It lies within the plane of foliation and thus is everywhere gently plunging. Defined mainly by the structural response of quartz and quartz laminae to flattening and stretching, the streaky mineral lineation is ubiquitous throughout the entire 1000 + m thick sequence of mylonitic gneisses. Furthermore, the lineation shows extraordinary preferred orientation, at

FIG. 15. Outcrop expression of mylonite gneiss derived from Precambrian quartz monzonite.

FIG. 16. Outcrop expression of penetrative mineral lineation in mylonite gneiss derived from Precambrian quartz monzonite.

N60E (Davis 1980b), although departures from this trend do occur.

Mylonitic gneisses derived from the penetrative deformation of Tertiary quartz monzonite are also very well exposed in the Santa Catalina and Rincon Mountains. Physiographic expression of the very gently dipping foliation in these gneisses is especially well displayed in the high country of the Santa Catalina and Rincon Mountains. The gneisses appear almost bedded. Lighter coloured than the gneisses derived from Precambrian quartz monzonite, the gneisses derived from Tertiary granites(s) form thick sill-like bodies boldly exposed on the mountain flanks. As in the computer-card models, the layered, sill-like form are likely to be an expression of extreme shearing and thinning of original non-tabular igneous bodies.

Seen in outcrop, the gneisses derived from Tertiary protolith are light-coloured medium-grained rocks with abundant small augen of feldspar. Martins (1984) studied the structural characteristics of these rocks at the Flatrocks area on the SE margin of Tanque Verde Mountain in the Rincons (Fig. 14). Flatrocks is an area of distinctively smooth, low, rounded hills whose physiographic expression is controlled by gently SW-dipping penetrative foliation in mylonitic gneiss. Lineation pervades Flatrocks, trending consistently N60E and plunging 14° SW (Martins 1984). Close-spaced extensional fractures are abundantly exposed within the outcrop area as well, with orientations strictly perpendicular to lineation.

Mylonitic gneisses at Flatrock are pervaded by S–C fabrics of exceptional quality and expression (Fig. 17). Martins (1984) concluded, on the basis of 70 determinations, that the angle between S and C ranges from 19 to 23°. Furthermore, she emphasized that the configuration of S and C consistently indicates normal-slip simple shear. Although the C surfaces are more obvious in some ways than S surfaces in the thin-section view, it is S that is expressed so dominantly in outcrop.

Foliation in the quartzo-feldspathic mylonitic gneisses of the Santa Catalina and Rincon Mountains is interpreted to represent the XY finite plane of flattening within the Catalina–Rincon shear zone (Davis 1980b, 1983). There is little doubt that foliation parallels the flattening plane, for axial surfaces of folds are consistently parallel to foliation attitude. It is S that is expressed in outcrop and topography; C-surfaces are more steeply dipping than S and may well parallel the lower shear-zone boundary. Naruk (1983, 1985) demonstrated this to be the case within the Pinaleno shear zone near Safford, Arizona.

The lineation is interpreted to represent the X-direction of greatest finite elongation (Davis 1980b). Fold hinges in the gneisses show great variability in trend within the plane of foliation, but in the most highly strained rocks the fold hinges parallel L. The direction of lineation corresponds to the direction of elongation of stretched pebbles in those parts of the Catalina–Rincon

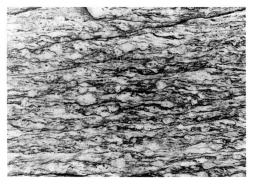

FIG. 17. Photograph of sawed slab of S–C relations in mylonite gneiss from the Flatrocks locality.

shear zone that intercept Apache Group sedimentary rocks (Davis *et al.* 1975). This fact underscores the stretch significance of *L*.

It seems clear that fabrics and structures within the quartzo-feldspathic gneisses originated during a normal-slip simple shear which served to simultaneously flatten and stretch the rocks intercepted by the shear zone. Exposures of the mylonitic gneisses in the Santa Catalina and Rincon Mountains reflect a depth of shearing well beneath the great unconformity separating basement and cover. Depth estimates of 12 km are not unreasonable, as based on geological reconstructions, which suggests that we see in the mylonites the products of shearing of upper-middle crust.

Microbreccias and cataclasites

Progressive brittle overprint of the mylonitic gneisses in the Santa Catalina and Rincon Mountains is well recorded in rocks directly beneath the Santa Catalina fault. The physical and structural distinctiveness of microbrecciated, cataclastically deformed mylonitic rocks provided the basis for identifying the 'decollement zone' as an integral and distinctive component of metamorphic core complexes (Davis 1977, 1980b). A show-piece locality for examining ductile-to-brittle progressive deformation is to be found in Saguaro National Monument at the eastern edge of Tuscon (Fig. 14). There, a fault-rock stratigraphy is laid out within a zone tens of metres thick, in which mylonite gneisses derived both from Precambrian and Tertiary protolith are transformed to microbrecciated mylonitic gneiss, which in turn is rendered into a very fine-grained, cataclastically reduced version of the microbrecciated mylonitic gneiss (Davis 1980b; Davis *et al.* 1981). The top surface of the ledge of cataclastic and ultracataclastic rock is the decollement, or detachment fault, proper.

Mapping and structural analysis reveal that the microbrecciated mylonitic gneisses at Saguaro National Monument represent a zone of coalescing normal-slip faults (Davis *et al.* 1981; DeTullio 1983). The contact between this zone and the underlying mylonitic gneisses is very sharp and appears to be a discrete fault. The faulting accompanying microbrecciation had the effect of rigid-body rotation of fault-bounded domains of mylonite gneiss. As a result, orientations of recognizable foliation and lineation within the microbrecciated mylonitic gneisses are disorderly, in striking contrast with the exceedingly systematic nature of orientations that typify the *L* and *S* fabrics of non-microbrecciated mylonitic gneiss.

At Saguaro National Monument it can be shown that some of the gneisses were rotated from 30° inclinations to vertical and overturned attitudes (Davis 1981a; Davis, *et al.* 1981; DiTullio 1983). Lineations can be shown to depart from the N60E norm by more than 40°. Stereographic analysis of *L–S* fabrics within and outside the zone of microbrecciation reveals that the rotation has been about a NNW subhorizontal axis (Davis 1981a; Davis *et al.* 1981; DiTullio 1983). This suggests that fault movements accompanying the brittle overprint were kinematically coordinated with the SSW-sense of simple shear that fashioned the mylonitic gneisses beneath.

Whether viewed in outcrop, hand-specimen, or thin section, the microbrecciated mylonitic gneisses are seen to be very strongly brecciated, fractured, and altered, yet overall the rock is coherent and well indurated (Fig. 18). Microbrecciation of the original mylonite gneiss resulted in comminution and grain-size reduction. Where microbrecciation is slight, original mylonitic fabrics and textures are readily identified as such at outcrop and in hand-specimen. Where mircobrecciation is severe, the nature of the original texture and fabric is entirely masked. But by examining the various degrees of microbrecciation of the original mylonitic gneiss, it can be demonstrated that even the finest grained microbreccias have been derived from pervasive microbrecciation of the mylonite gneiss. Hand-samples and thin sections reveal identical textures: angular to sub-angular mineral grains and rock fragments set in a very fine-grained matrix of crushed material. Breccia fragments are themselves seen to be composed of breccia, and this suggests that microbrecciation was carried out by progressive deformation through time.

The microbrecciated mylonitic gneiss is blue or blue/green on fresh surfaces, reflecting the

FIG. 18. Outcrop expression of microbrecciated mylonite gneiss in Saguaro National Monument.

presence of abundant chlorite and epidote in the rock (Davis 1980b; Reynolds & Rehrig 1980; Reynolds 1982). This colour hue is so characteristic and diagnostic that it has been useful to describe the microbrecciated mylonitic gneiss as 'chlorite breccia'. Where weathered, the microbreccias are light to medium brown. The pervasiveness of fracturing is more evident in the weathered outcrops of microbreccia. The fractures occur at every scale, down to the microscopic, in spacing. Fracture orientations appear to be non-systematic, although there may well be order within the apparent disorder. Some of the fracture surfaces bear striations, as distinct from the streaky mineral lineation that pervades the non-microbrecciated mylonite gneiss. Although the dominant striation orientation is ENE, the overall trends of striations are quite variable.

One of the diagnostic structural characteristics of large areas of microbrecciated mylonitic gneiss outcrops is the presence of very gently dipping, planar continuous fracture partings whose traces are metres or tens of metres in length. Striations are recognizable on some of these fracture surfaces, but for the most part fault striae cannot be seen. These fracture partings may be expressions of faults that have accommodated metres or tens of metres of fault.

The ledge of cataclasite and ultracataclasite which typically caps the zone of microbrecciated mylonitic gneiss may contain a variety of cataclastic fault rocks. The most common rock found in this structural position is very fine-grained, apparently homogeneous cataclasite with few mesoscopically recognizable mineral grains and rock fragments. However, some of the cataclasites appear similar to fine-grained volcanic breccias, characterized by fragments as large as 0.25 cm set in a very fine-grained matrix of ultracataclasite.

The very top of the ledge of cataclasite is the decollement, or detachment fault, proper (see Fig. 2). Although cylindrically curviplanar at the scale of the entire Santa Catalina–Rincon mountain front, the fault in outcrop view is typically planar and gently dipping. Striations can be seen and measured from place to place along the surface, with dominant trends measuring ENE and NNW. Locally, polished fault grooves adorn the detachment-fault surface, identical in appearance to glacial grooves. Where well exposed, near Colossal Cave (Fig. 14), fault grooves measuring metres in wavelength trend N60E, perfectly parallel to the mineral lineation in nearby mylonite gneiss (Drewes 1978; Krantz 1983).

The relationship between mylonite gneiss, microbrecciated mylonite gneiss, cataclasite ledge, and decollement is akin to a stack of fault-rock units within a structural stratigraphy (Davis 1980a, 1981c). Although these structural units appear to be generally sub-parallel and concordant, striking disharmonies exist (see Fig. 1). For example, the orientation of rotated, relict foliation within the zone of microbrecciated mylonitic gneiss is often more steeply dipping than the foliation in underlying non-microbrecciated mylonite gneiss. Furthermore, the base of the ledge zone of cataclasite and ultracataclasite typically truncates more steeply tilted foliation in the underlying zone of microbrecciated mylonitic gneiss. The overall disharmony reflects a progressive ductile-to-brittle deformation during which mylonite gneiss formed, followed by microbrecciated mylonite gneiss, cataclasite and decollement, in that order. Each successive fault-rock/structural unit is many times thinner than the more ductile fault-rock/structural unit immediately beneath. Using Saguaro National Monument in the Rincon Mountains as an example, the mylonite gneiss is approximately 1000 m thick; the microbrecciated mylonite gneiss is approximately 60 m thick; the cataclasite ledge is 6 m thick; and the detachment fault zone proper is 1 m or less.

The most extraordinary example of ultracataclastic fault rock associated with the Catalina–Rincon shear zone is found along the southwesternmost part of Tanque Verde Mountain, at a location which corresponds to the structural crest of Tanque Verde arch (Fig. 14). Just beneath the projected position of the Santa Catalina fault is a 1–5-m thick fault-rock unit of black ultracataclasite. Weathered surfaces are coated with desert varnish marked by abundant petroglyphs. The hard fine-grained rock characteristically spalls along conchoidal fractures, both large and small, and the jet-black fresh rock exposed by the spalling has a similar appearance to basalt or obsidian. Close examination of outcrops, hand-samples, and thin sections reveals that this well-indurated rock is not volcanic, but instead is a very fine-grained ultracataclasite. Hues of brecciated aggregates within the fault rock are light grey, dark grey, and black (DiTullio 1983). The contrasts in shade of grey permit microfaults and distinct brecciated aggregates to be distinguished (Fig. 19). Discrete faults can be recognized from place to place, in the form of black continuous to discontinuous seams up to 5 mm thick along which truncation and offset is apparent. The black seams resemble pseudotachylite, but are probably composed of ultramylonite or ultracataclasite. Thin-section examination reveals patchwork mosaics of extremely fine-grained breccia.

FIG. 19. Photography of outcrop of ultracataclasite on Tanque Verde ridge. Note black seam of crush rock along discrete fault.

Geological mapping reveals that this black ultracataclasite rests structurally on top of microbrecciated mylonite gneiss (Di Tullio 1983). The contact between the two fault rocks is very sharp, with hardly any gradation. In a few locations the ultracataclasite and microbreccia are juxtaposed along moderately high-angle normal-slip faults. Beneath the microbrecciated mylonite gneiss is the non-microbrecciated mylonite gneiss which makes up the Rincon Mountains as a whole.

The location of this black ultracataclasite fault rock is strategic. It would appear that mylonite gneisses along the structural crest of the Tanque Verde antiform were subjected to the very highest stresses as overlying, upper-plate rock, kilometres thick, was sheared past, southwestward. The immediate crest of the arch of mylonites became truncated by the crushing and grinding associated with the frictional sliding. The truncated crest is now occupied by the black ultracataclasite, the most intensely cataclastically deformed fault rock exposed within the Catalina–Rincon shear zone.

Marble quartzite and calc-silicate tectonites

To the NE of the Tucson basin the Catalina–Rincon shear zone cuts up-section and involves younger Precambrian and Palaeozoic sedimentary rocks. The best examples of this deformed rock are found along the crest of the Santa Catalina Mountains in the vicinity of Mt Bigelow and Mt Lemmon (Waag 1968), Redington Pass (Benson 1981; Bykerk-Kauffman 1983), and Happy Valley (Davis 1975; Frost 1977; Lingrey 1982; Trever 1983) (Fig. 14). Strata that were caught up in the shearing are tectonites, which like the mylonite gneisses are characterized by gently dipping foliation and lineation. The

dominant lithologies are marble, quartzite, and calc-silicate rocks. Simple-shear deformation of the sedimentary cover strata had the geometric effect of strongly flattening and attenuating the rock, creating a carapace-like form atop mylonite gneisses derived from Precambrian and Tertiary quartz monzonites at a deeper level (Davis 1977, 1980b, 1983). This systematic simple shearing preserved the fundamental stratigraphic ordering of the various, now-distorted, formations. However, the primary physical nature of the original sedimentary rocks was radically transformed.

The effects of the simple shear are clearly displayed in the form of spectacular outcrop-scale structures, notably isoclinal intrafolial folds, brittle–ductile normal faults (Fig. 20), boudinage, and stretched-pebble conglomerates (Davis 1980b). Stretched pebbles typically trend parallel to the dominant direction of streaky mineral lineation in the closest mylonite gneiss derived from Precambrian and Tertiary quartz monzonites. Asymmetrical fold structures in the carapace tectonites for the most part disclose a SW vergence, which together with the overall attitude of the Catalina–Rincon shear zone indicates a normal-slip simple shear along a S60W line. However, as mentioned, a significant exception to this slip-line determination has been identified by Bykerk-Kauffman (1983, 1986). Like mylonitic gneiss derived from basement, the mylonitic tectonites, derived from sedimentary strata at higher levels within the shear zone, locally record progressive overprinting by brittle structures and textures. For example, in Happy Valley marble, quartzite, and calc-silicate rocks of the carapace directly

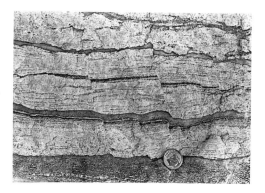

FIG. 20. Brittle–ductile normal-slip faults in interlayered marble and calc-silicate rock. Stiff layers are sharply truncated and displaced by faulting. Soft layers accommodate the displacement by non-rigid-body distortion.

beneath the decollement are strongly brecciated (Trever 1983). The brecciated rocks are true microbreccias, equivalent in tectonic significance to the microbrecciated mylonite gneisses (Fig. 1).

'Cover rocks' above the Santa Catalina fault

A wide variety of rocks lie above the Santa Catalina detachment or decollement, in fault contact with underlying cataclasites and mylonites. The so-called cover rocks are not exotic to the region, but rather are conventional stratigraphic elements of the geological column of southeastern Arizona. Along the front of the Santa Catalina Mountains (Fig. 14), the exposed cover rocks are almost exclusively Tertiary sedimentary rocks of Oligocene–Miocene age (Pashley 1966; Creasey & Theodore 1975; Banks 1976). However, exposures flanking the base of the Rincon Mountains reveal that a great thickness of older rocks as well were translated along the Santa Catalina fault (or decollement) during the progressive deformation by brittle–ductile shearing. The dominant units are Precambrian granite and schist, Palaeozoic and Mesozoic sedimentary strata, and the Oligocene–Miocene sedimentary rocks (Drewes 1978). The cover rocks attain observed thicknesses of up to hundreds of metres.

Structures in the cover rocks are either exclusively brittle or are a superposition of brittle structure on ductile structure. The Oligocene–Miocene sandstones and conglomerates, for example, are typically tilted homoclinally and marked by internal fracturing and faulting. Faults in the sediments are normal faults that have accommodated an overall layer-parallel stretching. Precambrian Rincon Valley granite, which is abundantly exposed around the Rincon Mountains, especially in Rincon Valley (Fig. 14) (Drewes 1978), occupies the faulted cover and is characterized by fracturing and faulting that is pervasive at outcrop scale. Wherever seen it is a completely shattered rock, without any sign of mylonitic fabrics. The intense fracturing and shattering of the granite is due to kilometres of southwestward translation under brittle conditions of deformation (Krantz 1983).

Palaeozoic and Mesozoic sedimentary strata are the most spectacularly deformed cover rocks residing above the Catalina–Rincon brittle–ductile shear zone. Sequences of Palaeozoic and/or Mesozoic strata are marked by abundant overturned to recumbent fold structures (Fig. 21). The folds are dominantly flexural-slip folds whose layer shapes conform to Ramsay-class 1C fold profiles (Davis 1975). As a system, the folds conform to overall southwestward normal-slip shearing. As I pointed out in earlier work (Davis 1981a, 1983), poles to axial surfaces of hundreds of measured folds statistically coincide with the trend of mineral lineation of the gneisses which lie beneath the Santa Catalina fault. Furthermore, the sense of overturning of the folds is southwestward, based on slip-line diagrams of fold hinges plotted according to fold asymmetry. Such geometric/kinematic coordination of structures in cover with structures in underlying mylonitic gneiss suggests that the folds in strata that now occupy cover were generated during ductile–brittle normal-slip shearing. Where the folded strata now lie close to the Santa Catalina fault, the rocks are overprinted by fractures and faults.

Some Laramide thrust and/or reverse-fault relations have been identified in cover rocks (Krantz 1983; Lingrey 1982; Bykerk-Kauffman 1986). Krantz (1983), for example, mapped an older-over-younger low-angle fault relationship between Palaeozoic and Cretaceous strata near Colossal Cave (Fig. 14). He interpreted the relationship as a Laramide thrust that was translated to its present site by kilometres of movement related to normal slip on the Santa Catalina fault. This interpretation is consistent with Drewes' (1978, 1981) emphasis on the role

FIG. 21. Folds in cover above the Catalina detachment fault (dark cliff at left) in the Colossal Cave area.

of Laramide thrusting in the geological evolution of the Rincon Mountains.

Detachments in the San Pedro Valley

To the E and N of the Santa Catalina and Rincon Mountains there are spectacular and illuminating exposures of faulted and tilted Oligocene–Miocene strata. These rocks and structures comprise a detachment terrain whose stratigraphic and structural relations record the history of movements along the upper reaches of the Catalina–Rincon brittle–ductile shear zone. Especially good exposures of the fundamental relations are found in the area between Oracle and Winkleman along the western side of the San Pedro Valley (Fig. 14) (Creasey 1967; Krieger 1974; Dickinson 1984).

The consistent structural relation in this detachment terrain is moderately to steeply tilted Oligocene–Miocene strata in low-angle fault contact with underlying, fractured Precambrian granite. The sediments occupying the faulted detachments are hundreds to thousands of metres thick. Tilting within the sequence(s) steadily decreases upward, indicating that sedimentation and progressive tilting during faulting were contemporaneous. Although microbrecciated rocks sometimes mark the uppermost footwall rocks of granite, no mylonites are ever observed. The fault contacts themselves are commonly marked by gouge.

Sense of movement along the detachment faults is clear from a number of lines of evidence. Normal offsets can be directly observed on subsidiary faults, and this information combined with dip-slip striae affirm normal-slip translation. Gouge along parts of some fault zones displays cleavage whose orientation is consistent with normal-slip translation. Block tilt throughout the San Pedro Valley is consistently northeastward, suggesting southwestward-directed movement of the hanging-wall blocks (Davis & Hardy 1981). The strike of the Tertiary strata is N30W, perfectly orthogonal to the trend of mineral lineation in the mylonite gneisses of the nearby Santa Catalina and Rincon Mountains. Finally, Lowell (1968) demonstrated normal-slip offset of a laramide copper-bearing stock near Oracle (Fig. 14). He cleverly deduced that the San Manuel ore body had been beheaded in the Tertiary by the San Manuel (detachment) fault, and proceeded to discover what is now called the Kalamazoo ore body at a location 4 km away along a S50–60W line of bearing. It is significant to note that Lowell demonstrated that the San Manuel stock, which resides in Precambrian basement, has suffered nearly 70° of tilt since its Laramide emplacement. This fact demonstrates that certain major detachment faults, now low angle, formed originally at much steeper angles of inclination.

In my view the geology and geometry of structures in the San Pedro Valley detachment terrain support the concept that the Tertiary sediments formed as a response to normal-slip movements and offsets along the Catalina–Rincon shear zone; that the history of progressive movement on the shear zone is partly if not nearly fully recorded in the history and duration of Tertiary sedimentation in the San Pedro Valley region; and that structures and fault rocks of the detachment terrain, the cover rocks, the Catalina fault, and the mylonite gneisses formed as a common response to tectonic movements driving the extension of the continental crust of southeastern Arizona. Differences simply reflect different depths of formation, and different locations with respect to the boundaries of the brittle–ductile shear zone as it evolved through time.

Complications and opportunities

The overall structural geometry of a southeastern Arizona metamorphic core complex will record two dominant influences: (i) structural relationships that were fashioned in the Precambrian to the Laramide; and (ii) structural relationships that evolved during Tertiary normal-slip brittle–ductile shearing. The deformational history of southeastern Arizona is known to be one of superposed events (Davis 1981b). For example Jurassic faulting locally resulted in such differential uplift that the entire Palaeozoic section was removed locally by erosion before the deposition of Cretaceous strata (Fig. 22a). Furthermore, Laramide thrusting and reverse faulting created older-on-younger fault relations which effectively shortened the crust (Fig. 22a). Some of this early deformation surely affected the Catalina–Rincon region!

Amazing structural complications arise when brittle–ductile normal-slip shearing is imposed on a framework that is already marked by structural disharmony. This becomes clear upon examining the card-deck model shown in Fig. 22(a–d). Contact relationships of a geologically conventional nature become drawn-out and distorted into seemingly unmanageable, seemingly uninterpretable geometries. The patterns capture the kinds of thin, tabular repetitions of Precambrian and Phanerozoic strata that occur in metamorphic core complex terrains in regions

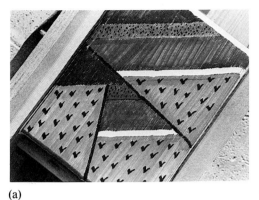

(a)

(b)

(c)

Fig. 22. Shear-zone deformation of computer-card deck. (a) Cross-section showing Precambrian basement (v's) overlain by younger Precambrian sedimentary rock (white), Palaeozoic strata (medium grey), Jurassic rocks (stippled), and Cretaceous rocks (darkest grey). High-angle faulting of Jurassic age resulted in erosional removal of Palaeozoic strata in the left block, where Cretaceous strata lie unconformably on basement. A thrust fault dipping to the right achieves Laramide crustal shortening. (b–d). Progressive shearing of the geological column, resulting in geological relationships that appear to be more complicated than they really are.

(d)

like western Arizona, where Mesozoic and early-Tertiary deformation was marked by profound thrusting and thrust-induced repetitions. Shear-zone theory, in regions of even the most complicated pre-extension history, provides the guide to deciphering the structural significance of such structure. Palinspastic reconstruction becomes possible by constructing detailed longitudinal sections of the contact relations and then removing angular shear until the thinned, stretched tabular forms begin to retrodeform into shapes that have some geological meaning.

ACKNOWLEDGMENTS: Support for field work and structural analysis has been supported over the years by NSF (grant No. EAR 76-84167 with Thomas H. Anderson; grant No. EAR 7823404; No. EAR 8018231 with William R. Dickinson; and grant No. EAR 8206040, with Roy Kligfield) and by The University of Arizona. I am indebted to colleagues with whom I have worked, and to my students who have themselves contributed so much to unravelling the structural systems addressed in this paper.

References

BANKS, N.G. 1976. Reconnaissance geologic map of the Mount Lemmon quadrangle, Arizona. *U.S. geol. Surv. Misc, Field Studies Map MF-747*, scale 1:62,500.

—— et al. 1977. Reconnaissance geologic map of the Tortolita Mountains quadrangle, Arizona. *U.S. geol. Surv. Misc. Field Studies Map MF-864*, with text.

BENSON, G.S. 1981. *Geology and kinematic analysis of the Italian Trap Allochthon, Redington Pass area of Pima County, Arizona*. MSc. Thesis, Univ. Arizona. 85 pp.

BYKERK-KAUFFMAN, A. 1983. *Structural investigation of a transition zone between metamorphic tectonites and their unmetamorphosed equivalents, Buehman Canyon, Arizona*. MSc. Thesis, Univ. Arizona. 79 pp.

—— 1986. Multiple episodes of ductile deformation within the lower plate of the Santa Catalina metamorphic core complex. *Az. geol. Soc. Dig.* 16, 460–3.

—— & JANECKE, S.V. 1986. Laramide-age ductile deformation within the lower plate of the Santa Catalina metamorphic core complex, Arizona. *Abstr. with Programs geol. Soc. Am.* 18, 92.

COBBOLD, P.R. & PERCEVAULT, M.N. 1983. Spatial integration of strains using finite elements. *J. struct. Geol.* 5, 299–306.

CONEY, P.J. 1980. Cordilleran metamorphic core complexes: an overview. *In*: CRITTENDEN, M.D., JR, CONEY, P.J. & DAVIS, G.H. (eds) *Cordilleran Metamorphic Core Complexes, Mem. geol. Soc. Am.* 153, 7–31.

CREASEY, S.C. 1967. General geology of the Mammoth Quadrangle, Pinal County, Arizona. *Bull. U.S. geol. Surv.* 1218.

—— & THEODORE, T.G. 1975. Preliminary reconnaissance geologic map of the Bellota Ranch 15-minutes quadrangle, Pima County, Arizona. *U.S. geol. Surv. Open-File. Rep. 75–295*, scale 1:31,680.

DAVIS, G.A., ANDERSON, J.L., FROST, E.G. & SHACKELFORD, T.H. 1980. Geologic and tectonic history of the Whipple–Buckskin–Rawhide Mountain dislocational terrane, California–Arizona. *In*: CRITTENDEN, M.D., JR, CONEY, P.J. & DAVIS, G.H. (eds) *Cordilleran Metamorphic Core Complexes, Mem. geol. Soc. Am.* 153, 79–129.

DAVIS, G.H. 1975. Gravity-induced folding off a gneiss dome complex, Rincon Mountains, Arizona. *Bull. geol. Soc. Am.* 86, 979–90.

—— 1977. Characteristics of metamorphic core complexes, southern Arizona. *Abstr. with Programs geol. Soc. Am.* 9(7), 944.

—— 1980a. Metamorphic core complexes—structural characteristics, kinematic expression and relation to mid-Miocene listric faulting. *In*: CONEY, P.J. & REYNOLDS, S.J. (eds) *Cordilleran Metamorphic Core Complexes and their Uranium Favorability, U.S. Dept. Energy Open-File Rep. GJBX-258(80)*.

—— 1980b. Structural characteristics of metamorphic core complexes, southern Arizona. *In*: CRITTENDEN, M.D., JR, CONEY, P.J. & DAVIS, G.H. (eds) *Cordilleran Metamorphic Core Complexes, Mem. geol. Soc. Am.* 153, 35–77.

—— 1981a. Metamorphic core complexes—expressions of regional ductile stretching and rotational, listric (?) faulting. *Abstr. with Programs geol. Soc. Am.* 13(2), 51.

—— 1981b. Regional strain of the superposed deformations in southeastern Arizona and the eastern Great Basin. *In*: DICKINSON, W.R. & PAYNE, W.D. (eds) *Relation of tectonics to ore deposits in the Southern Cordillera*.

—— 1981c. The structural frontier of metamorphic core complexes and listric normal fault systems in the Basin and Range of the Western Cordillera. *Abstr. with Programs geol. Soc. Am.* 13(7), 436.

—— 1983. Shear-zone model for the origin of metamorphic core complexes. *Geology*, 11(6), 342–7.

—— & CONEY, P.J. 1979. Geological development of metamorphic core complexes. *Geology*, 7(3), 120–4.

—— & HARDY, J.J., JR 1981. The Eagle Pass detachment, southeastern Arizona—product of mid-Miocene normal faulting in the southern Basin and Range. *Bull. geol. Soc. Am.* 92, 749–62.

——, GARDULSKI, A.F. & ANDERSON, T.H. 1981. Structural and structural-petrological characteristics of some metamorphic core complex terranes in southern Arizona and northern Sonora. *In*: ORTLIEB, L. & ROLDAN, J.Q. (eds) *Geology of Northwestern Mexico and Southern Arizona*, pp. 323–65. Instituto de Geologia, U.N.A.M., Hermosillo, Sonora.

——, ANDERSON, P., BUDDEN, R.T., KEITH, S.B. & KIVEN, C.W. 1975. Origin of lineation in the Catalina–Rincon–Tortolita gneiss complex, Arizona. *Abstr. with Programs geol. Soc. Am.* **7(5)**, 602.

DICKINSON, W.R., 1984. Stratigraphic record of Mid Tertiary crustal extension in the San Pedro region of Southern Arizona. *Abstr. with Programs geol. Soc. Am.* **16**, 488.

DEWITT, E. 1980. Geologic development of the Cordilleran metamorphic core complexes: Discussion. *Geology*, **8(1)**, 6–7.

DITULLIO, L.D. 1983. *Fault rocks of the Tanque Verde Mountain decollement zone, Santa Catalina metamorphic core complex, Tucson, Arizona.* MSc. Thesis, Univ. Arizona. 90 pp.

DREWES, H. 1978. Geologic map and sections of the Rincon Valley quadrangle, Pima County, Arizona. *U.S. geol. Surv. Misc. Investigations Map.*

DREWES, H. 1981. Tectonics of southeastern Arizona. *U.S. geol. Surv. Prof. Pap. 1144.* 96 pp.

FROST, E.G. 1977. *Mid-Tertiary, gravity-induced deformation in Happy Valley, Pima and Cochise Counties, Arizona.* MSc Thesis, Univ. Arizona, 86 pp.

KEITH, S.B., REYNOLDS, S.J., DAMON, P.E., SHAFIQULLAH, M., LIVINGSTON, D.E. & PUSHKAR, P.D. 1980. Evidence for multiple intrusion and deformation within the Santa Catalina–Rincon–Tortolita crystalline complex, southeastern Arizona. *In*: CRITTENDEN, M.D., JR, CONEY, P.J. & DAVIS, G.H. (eds) *Cordilleran Metamorphic Core Complexes*, Mem. geol. Soc. Am. **153**, 217–67.

KLIGFIELD, R., CRESPI, J., NARUK, S.J. & DAVIS, G.H. 1984. Displacement and strain patterns of extensional orogens, *Tectonics*, **3**, 577–609.

KRANTZ, R.W. 1983. *Detailed structural analysis of detachment faulting near Colossal Cave, southern Rincon Mountains, Pima County, Arizona.* MSc Thesis, Univ. Arizona. 58 pp.

KREIGER, M.H. 1974. Geologic map of the Putnam Wash Quadrangle, Pinal County, Arizona. *U.S. geol. Surv. Quadrangle Map. GQ 1109.*

LEPICHON, X. & SIBUET, J. 1981. Passive margins: a model of formation. *J. geophys. Res.* **86**, 3708–20.

LINGREY, S.H. 1982. *Structural geology and tectonic evolution of the northeastern Rincon Mountains, Cochise and Pima Counties, Arizona.* Ph.D. Thesis, Univ. Arizona. 202 pp.

LOWELL, J.D. 1968. Geology of the Kalamazoo ore body, San Manuel district, Arizona. *Econ. Geol.* **63**, 645–54.

MARTINS, V.E. 1984. *A Microstructural study of the S–C mylonites of part of the Tanque Verde*

Mountains, Tucson, Arizona. MSc Thesis, Univ. Arizona, 52 pp.

NARUK, S.J. 1983. *Determination of strain values from mylonites in the Pinaleño Mountains, Arizona.* MSc Thesis, Univ. Arizona. 79 pp.

——. Strain and displacement across the Pinaleño Mountains shear zone, Arizona, U.S.A. *J. struct. Geol.* **8**, 35–46.

PASHLEY, E.F. 1966. *Structure and stratigraphy of the central, northern, and eastern parts of the Tuscon basin, Pima County, Arizona.* Ph.D. Thesis, Univ. Arizona, 273 pp.

PROFFETT, J.M., JR 1977. Cenozoic geology of the Yerington district, Nevada, and its implications for the nature and origin of Basin and Range faulting. *Bull. geol. Soc. Am.* **88**, 247–66.

RAMSAY, J.G. 1967. *Folding and Fracturing of Rocks*, 560 pp. McGraw-Hill, New York.

—— 1980. Shear zone geometry: a review. *J. struct. Geol.* **2**, 83–99.

—— & HUBER, M.I. 1983. *The Techniques of Modern Structural Geology. Volume 1: Strain Analysis*, 307 pp. Academic press, New York.

REYNOLDS, S.J. 1982. *Geology and geochronology of the South Mountains, central Arizona.* Ph.D. Thesis, Univ. Arizona, 220 pp.

—— 1985. Geology of the South Mountains, central Arizona. *Az. Bur. Geol. Min. Tech. Bull. 195.*

—— & REHRIG, W.A. 1980. Mid-Tertiary plutonism and mylonitization, South Mountains, central Arizona. *In*: CRITTENDEN, M.D., JR, CONEY, P.J. & DAVIS, G.H. (eds) *Cordilleran Metamorphic Core Complexes*, Mem. geol. Soc. Am. **153**, 159–76.

SHAKEL, D.W., SILVER, L.T. & DAMON, P.E. 1977. Observations on the history of the gneiss core complex, Santa Catalina Mountains, southern Arizona. *Abstr. with Programs geol. Soc. Am.* **9**, 1169.

SPENCER, J.E. 1984, The role of tectonic denudation in the warping and uplift of low-angle normal faults. *Geology*, **12**, 95–8.

THORMAN, C.H. 1977. Gravity-induced folding off a gneiss dome complex, Rincon Mountains, Arizona: Discussion. *Bull. geol. Soc. Am.* **88**, 1211–2.

TREVER, P.F. 1983. *Geology of the Gardner Mountain area, Happy Valley Quadrangle, Cochise County, Arizona.* MSc Thesis, Univ. Arizona, 130 pp.

WAAG, C.J. 1968. *Structural geology of the Mount Bigelow–Bear Wallow–Mount Lemmon area, Santa Catalina Mountains, Arizona.* Ph.D. Thesis, Univ. Arizona, 133 pp.

WERNICKE, B. 1981. Low-angle normal faults in the Basin and Range Province: nappe tectonics in an extending orogen. *Nature*, **291**, 645–8.

GEORGE H. DAVIS, Department of Geosciences, The University of Arizona, Tucson, AZ 85721, USA.

Ductile strain and metamorphism in an extensional tectonic setting: a case study from the northern Snake Range, Nevada, USA

J. Lee, E.L. Miller & J.F. Sutter

SUMMARY: In recent years considerable attention has focused on metamorphic core complexes of the Basin and Range Province of the western US Cordillera. These highly extended areas are characterized by an upper plate that has been brittlely attenuated by normal faults separated by a sub-horizontal detachment surface from a lower plate that has been ductilely thinned and stretched. A study of mesoscopic structures, finite strain, microstructures, quartz c-axis fabrics and $^{40}Ar/^{39}Ar$ geochronology was undertaken in order to characterize the nature, geometry, kinematic history and timing of ductile extension in the lower plate of the northern Snake Range metamorphic core complex in E-central Nevada. These data provide new insights into the processes of deep-seated ductile strain beneath supracrustal normal fault mosaics in highly extended regions. Mesoscopic structures and finite strain analyses indicate that the lower plate underwent plane strain with a sub-vertical Z-axis and a sub-horizontal WNW–ESE X-axis. The magnitude of strain increases dramatically from W-to-E, and is constant vertically. Bedding and foliation are everywhere parallel and bedding is thinned 30-90%. The nature and geometry of microstructures and c-axis fabrics changes progressively from W-to-E. Lower strain rocks on the W flank of the range are characterized by a single bedding-parallel foliation, defined by flattened detrital grains, globular grains which have their c-axes parallel to the Z-axis and symmetrical cross-girdle c-axis fabrics. Further E to slightly higher strains, the rocks are characterized by asymmetrical cross-girdle c-axis fabrics, although globular grains with their c-axes parallel to Z are still present. The high-strain rocks on the E flank of the range are characterized by C-planes, asymmetrical mica 'fish' and oblique quartz foliations, and asymmetrical single-girdle c-axis fabrics. These data suggest that the lower plate has not deformed entirely by either coaxial or non-coaxial strain, and we propose an evolutionary model whereby the lower plate deformed during an early period of coaxial strain followed by a later component of non-coaxial strain accompanied by coaxial strain on the E flank of the range. $^{40}Ar/^{39}Ar$ geochronology on lower-plate hornblendes and micas indicates that temperatures of deformation were >280°C, but <530°C, and increased with depth. Geochronological data suggest that lower-plate ductile strain is post-latest Cretaceous, and biotite and muscovite data indicate that ductile deformation was probably ongoing 22–26 Ma. Our data and regional geological relations suggest that ductile extensional deformation in the northern Snake Range occurred because of localized heat input to shallow levels of the crust, and together with seismic reflection data, indicate that lower-plate rocks probably represent the top of a regional metamorphic terrane of Tertiary age.

In recent years considerable attention has focused on metamorphic core complexes of the Basin and Range Province of the western US Cordillera (see Crittenden *et al.* 1980). These highly extended areas are characterized by an upper plate of generally unmetamorphosed to slightly metamorphosed rocks that have been brittlely attenuated by normal faults, and a lower plate of metamorphic and plutonic rocks that have been ductilely thinned and stretched. Separating these two dramatically different structural styles are sub-horizontal detachment surfaces. Due to the lack of suitable offset markers across these detachment surfaces, their origin, kinematic evolution and amount of displacement are the subjects of much controversy. At present, many workers feel that an areally ex-

tensive low-angle rooted normal fault or a rotating shear-zone model, such as that proposed by Wernicke (1981) and Davis (1983), respectively, best explains the juxtaposition of the different structural styles across detachment faults. These models postulate that the loci of brittle attenuation at supracrustal depths are far removed from ductile attenuation at mid-crustal depths, and that the juxtaposition of these two structural styles occurs by tens of kilometres of translation or simple shear along the low-angle normal fault or shear zone. Others feel that the ductile–brittle transition models of Proffett (1977), Rehrig & Reynolds (1980), Eaton (1982), Miller *et al.* (1983), Gans *et al.* (1985b) and Jackson (this volume) best explains the juxtaposition of the different structural styles

From COWARD, M.P., DEWEY, J.F. & HANCOCK, P.L. (eds), 1987, *Continental Extensional Tectonics*, Geological Society Special Publication No. 28, pp. 267–298.

across detachment surfaces. In these models, supracrustal normal faulting is accommodated at mid-crustal depths by penetrative stretching and/or by dilation due to intrusion of plutons. Thus, detachment surfaces in core complexes may, in part, represent transition zones between brittle and ductile deformation, and hence, may have undergone only minor translation.

One way to address the significance of meta-morphic core complex detachment faults is to establish the deformational history or the strain path of ductilely deformed lower-plate rocks. Early studies suggested a largely pure-shear deformational history. For example, Davis *et al.* (1982) and Reynolds & Rehrig (1980) studied mylonitized dykes in the Whipple Mountains, southeastern California and the South Mountains, southern Arizona, respectively, and concluded that the strain was largely coaxial. Similarly, Compton (1980) and Snoke (1980) argued for a pure-shear deformational path based on orthorhombic quartz *c*-axis fabric patterns from the Raft River Mountains, north-western Utah and Ruby Mountains, northeastern Nevada, respectively. Recently, however, the recognition of microstructures such as *C*-planes, asymmetric mica 'fish' and oblique quartz foli-

ations in *S–C* mylonites in lower-plate rocks (Davis *et al.* 1983; Lister & Snoke 1984) and the documentation of a shear-zone boundary oblique to the mylonitic foliation in the Pinaleno Mountains, eastern Arizona (Naruk 1986) has been used to argue for simple shear deformation.

The northern Snake Range metamorphic core complex, described by Gans & Miller (1983), Miller *et al.* (1983) and Gans *et al.* (1985b) (Fig. 1), has several unique characteristics that make it an excellent area for testing models of lower-plate strain. In the northern Snake Range the lower plate consists of attenuated quartzite and schist units that represent an easily recognizable and well-known stratigraphy. Based on the study of non-attenuated counterparts in adjacent ranges, it can be argued that the lower-plate quartzite units in the northern Snake Range have undergone little pre-mylonitic defor-mation. In addition, the northern Snake Range offers excellent three-dimensional exposure of the lower-plate rocks allowing lateral and verti-cal studies of structures in the lower plate. In this paper we discuss the results of new finite strain, microstructure and petrofabric studies together with $^{40}Ar/^{39}Ar$ geochronological data

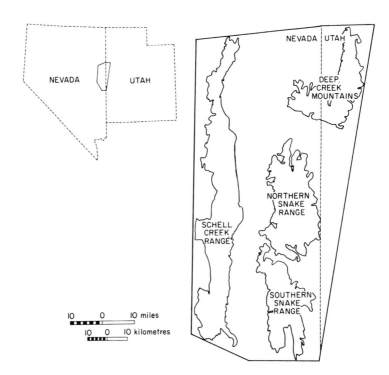

Fɪɢ. 1. Index map of E-central Nevada showing the location of the Deep Creek Mountains, the northern Snake Range, the southern Snake Range and the Schell Creek Range.

from the lower plate of the northern Snake Range and their bearing on the kinematic history of ductile deformation in an extensional tectonic setting.

Geological setting

The northern Snake Range is located in E-central Nevada (Fig. 1), which prior to Mesozoic and Cenozoic deformation was underlain by a 12–13-km thick stratigraphic sequence of continental shelf sediments. This section is composed of a 4–6-km thick sequence of upper Precambrian to lower Cambrian clastic rocks overlain by a 5–7-km thick sequence of Palaeozoic carbonate rocks (Stewart & Poole 1974; Hose & Blake 1976). During the Mesozoic the upper part of the sequence was gently folded, whereas at deeper levels the strata were variably metamorphosed, penetratively deformed and intruded by plutons (Misch 1960; Misch & Hazzard 1962; Gans & Miller 1983; Miller *et al.* 1983). Studies by Miller *et al.*, in press and D. W. Rodgers (in prep.) in the surrounding Schell Creek, southern Snake and Deep Creek Ranges (Fig. 1) indicate that the schist units in the lower part of the section accommodated most of the strain during the Mesozoic, whereas the interbedded quartzites underwent little or no penetrative deformation. In the northern Snake Range proper, mineral isograds related to Mesozoic metamorphism have been mapped in the Precambrian schist units on the E side of the range and indicate an increase in metamorphic grade from biotite grade S of Hendry's Creek to staurolite grade in Hampton Creek (Geving 1986; J. Lee, work in progress) where metamorphism has been dated as Late Cretaceous (Fig. 2) (Lee & Fischer 1985). Contact metamorphic mineral assemblages around Mesozoic plutons that intrude these rocks along the southern flank of the range indicate pressures of metamorphism less than 3.7 kb (andalusite stable) (Gans & Miller 1985; Miller *et al.*, in press). The data support the inference of Gans & Miller (1983) and Miller *et al.* (1983) that the structural depth of the sedimentary sequence in the lower plate can be estimated from its stratigraphic depth as 9–12 km during Mesozoic amphibolite facies metamorphism and as 7–10 km at the onset of Tertiary ductile deformation (Gans & Miller 1985).

Following Mesozoic compressional deformation, E-central Nevada was extended about 250% in a WNW–ESE direction during the Tertiary (Gans & Miller 1983). During extension, Palaeozoic carbonates in the northern Snake Range were attenuated by two generations of normal faults that soled into a detachment, the Northern Snake Range Decollement (NSRD), at a stratigraphically determined depth of ~7 km. In the lower plate the upper Precambrian to lower Cambrian clastic rocks were penetratively stretched and thinned forming *L–S* tectonites. Strain in the lower plate increases dramatically from W-to-E and has transposed earlier structural fabrics on the E flank of the range. Synkinematic greenschist facies metamorphism, as documented by chlorite, white mica and biotite pressure shadows that parallel lineation, increases with depth as evidenced by the growth of new chlorite at the highest levels in the lower plate and new biotite at the deepest structural levels. Differential uplift and bending due to younger normal faulting domed the NSRD to its present disposition (Gans *et al.* 1985b).

The age of extensional deformation is best constrained at supracrustal levels by the syntectonic relationship between faulting and volcanism (Gans & Miller 1983; Gans *et al.* 1985a). Normal faults in the northern Snake Range cut 35 Ma volcanics in the Sacramento Pass region (Fig. 2) and were moving in this same area at about 32 Ma (Grier 1983). A 24 Ma vitric tuff, at the northern end of the range, is moderately tilted by the youngest set of normal faults in this region (Gans *et al.* 1985a). As yet, no stratigraphic relations have been found that place a younger age limit on upper-plate faulting. Widespread resetting of K–Ar mica ages to Tertiary ages has been documented in the lower-plate rocks in the northern Snake Range (Armstrong & Hansen 1966; Lee *et al.* 1970, 1980) (Fig. 2). Miller *et al.* (1983) interpreted the formation of the NSRD and the lower-plate *L–S* tectonites as synchronous with upper-plate faulting based on the lack of stratigraphic omission across the NSRD, the similar orientation and magnitude of upper- and lower-plate strain and the fact that lower-plate rocks yield Tertiary K–Ar ages compared to Mesozoic ages in equivalent units from adjacent ranges.

Our study of lower-plate strain was carried out in the southern part of the northern Snake Range where excellent exposure of the lower-plate quartzites occurs in the Hendry's, Hampton and Negro Creek areas (Fig. 2). The exposures in the central portion of Hendry's Creek afford the deepest view into the lower plate where 670 m of structural relief are exposed; progressively shallower levels are exposed eastward towards the E flank of the range and westward into Negro Creek.

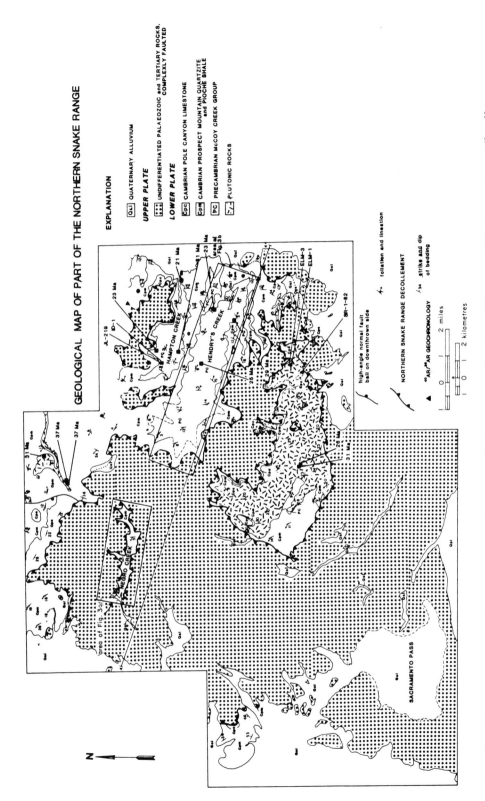

FIG. 2. Simplified geological map of the southern part of the northern Snake Range (modified from Miller *et al.* 1983). The locations of $^{40}Ar/^{39}Ar$ geochronology samples from the Hampton Creek area and the southern flank of the range and K–Ar mica ages (solid squares) from Armstrong & Hansen (1966) and Lee *et al.* (1970, 1980) are shown.

Orientation and magnitude of finite strain

The lower-plate rocks of the northern Snake Range possess a strong sub-horizontal foliation and N60W mineral elongation lineation. The mesoscopic foliation measured in the field corresponds to compositional layering or bedding (i.e. the interface between quartzite and schist layers, the *average* mesoscopic orientation of metamorphic micas, and banding defined by impurities within quartzite beds). This foliation is domed across the range dipping 15–20° to the W on the W flank of the range and 15–20° to the E on the E flank of the range. A carefully documented observation that has important implications for the interpretation of lower-plate strain is that, throughout the study area, the flattening or XY plane of the finite-strain ellipsoid, represented by the orientation of flattened detrital grains and quartz-ribbon grains (measured in oriented thin sections) and pebbles (as measured in outcrop and in oriented specimens) is parallel to lower-plate compositional layering or bedding, and, thus to the mesoscopically measured foliation, as well as to the overlying NSRD. This parallelism occurs in both the low-strain rocks of Negro Creek and the high-strain rocks of Hendry's Creek.

Finite-strain measurements in quartzite units were undertaken in order to characterize the nature and amount of lower-plate strain. Samples were collected along a transect roughly parallel to the direction of extension, as determined by the mineral elongation lineation in lower-plate rocks and the direction of movement of upper-plate normal faults (Fig. 3). Measurements were made on stretched detrital quartz grains in Negro Creek on the W side of the range and on stretched pebbles in Hendry's Creek on the E side of the range. Unfortunately, no pebble-bearing units are exposed in Negro Creek and syntectonic recrystallization in the quartzite units has precluded the use of detrital quartz grain aspect ratios as strain markers in Hendry's Creek. In Negro Creek, aspect ratios of stretched detrital grains from eight samples were measured using the technique of Shimamoto & Ikeda (1976) on both the XY and XZ principal sections to calculate the X:Y:Z axes of the finite-strain ellipsoid (Fig. 3a). In Hendry's Creek, the long and short axes of stretched pebbles were measured from each of the three principal sections for three samples (Fig. 3b). The harmonic mean was then calculated to obtain the ratio X:Y:Z. The results of these analyses,

shown in Table 1, indicate that strain increases W-to-E across the range, as measured parallel to the extension direction, from a low in the W of 5.8:1 (X:Z) to a high in the E of 31:1 (X:Z). Analyses have been plotted on a Flinn diagram (Fig. 4) which shows that these rocks have undergone approximately plane strain, although most analyses plot slightly in the constrictional field.

Samples JL1-148, JL1-149, JL1-150, JL1-151 and JL1-152, in the Negro Creek area (Fig. 3a; Table 1), cover a vertical distance of 110 m in the lower plate and allow us to evaluate the vertical strain gradient in the lower plate. They show a slight increase in strain up towards the NSRD and down toward deeper structural levels. We believe that these measured differences are not significant because a certain amount of strain heterogeneity, even in these comparatively monotonous quartzites, is commonly observed. Calculated finite strain from the measurement of ubiquitously flattened foreset beds in Negro Creek is also consistent with the heterogeneity and magnitude of the finite strain (Larue *et al.* 1986). The amount of thinning of the Precambrian McCoy Creek Group quartzites in Hendry's Creek, as determined from finite strain (see Table 1) and the amount of thinning of the overlying Cambrian Prospect Mountain Quartzite, as determined from its present thickness and its original, pre-strain sedimentary thickness of 1.2 km (Hose & Blake 1976), are comparable. Both the McCoy Creek Group quartzites and the Prospect Mountain Quartzite have undergone similar thinning both at the headwaters (65–70%) and at the mouth (80%) of Hendry's Creek. Thus, based on the limited data presently available, a pronounced vertical strain gradient has not been documented anywhere in the study area. In addition, nowhere in the study area is there a pronounced lateral strain break or 'boundary' between deformed and undeformed lower-plate rocks. However, N of Negro Creek towards the N flank of the range, ductile strain decreases and dies out (J. Lee unpub. data; Gans *et al.* 1985b).

Reconstruction of the Prospect Mountain Quartzite from its present lateral extent to its original (pre-strain) sedimentary thickness of 1.2 km (Hose & Blake 1976), based on the percent extension and shortening as determined from the finite-strain data, together with the presently observed thickness of the Prospect Mountain Quartzite in Hendry's Creek, indicates an average of 250% extension. This is a close, but we believe more accurate estimate than the 330% determined by Miller *et al.* (1983).

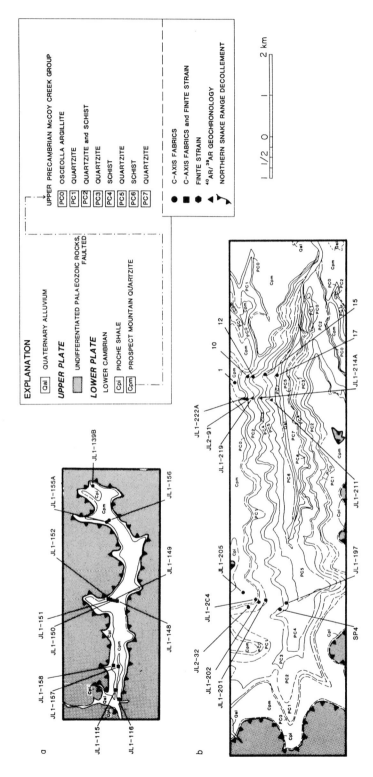

FIG. 3. Location of finite-strain, quartz petrofabric and $^{40}Ar/^{39}Ar$ geochronology samples. (a) Negro Creek. (b) Hendry's Creek. See Fig. 2 for location of (a) and (b).

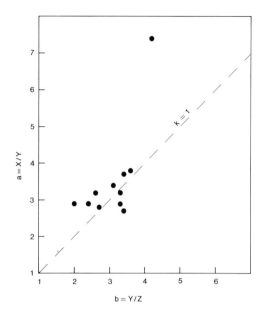

FIG. 4. Flinn plot of calculated *X:Y:Z* axes of the finite-strain ellipsoid. Most samples plot within the constrictional field, but close to *k*=1, suggesting approximately plane-strain deformation.

Kinematic interpretation of the orientation and magnitude of finite strain

In summary, lower-plate strain was characterized by approximate plane strain with a presently sub-vertical *Z*-axis and a sub-horizontal WNW–ESE *X*-axis. The magnitude of strain increases dramatically from W-to-E but is apparently constant vertically. Compositional layering, or bedding, and mesoscopic foliation are everywhere parallel and bedding is thinned from 30–90%.

The map-scale strain data are compatible with pure-shear deformation caused by necking during sub-horizontal extension and flattening perpendicular to bedding. The data can also be explained by progressive simple shear, but this interpretation places some important constraints on the initial orientation of the inferred shear zone as shown in Fig. 5. If the initial orientation of the shear-zone boundary is assumed to be parallel or at very low angles to bedding, there would be little or no thinning of beds in the lower plate, the *XY* plane would be at measurable angles to bedding in the low-strain rocks on the W flank of the range, and the strong observed W-to-E strain gradient would not have developed (Fig. 5a & b). We have used the following two equations of Ramsay & Huber (1983):

$$\tan 2\theta' = \frac{2}{\gamma}$$

where γ = shear strain and θ' = the angle between the principal extension axis of the strain ellipsoid and the shear zone boundary, and

$$\cot \alpha' = \cot \alpha + \gamma$$

where α and α' are the angles between bedding and the shear-zone boundary before and after simple shear, respectively, to calculate the attitude of the finite-strain axes and bedding for different initial shear-zone orientations. Only if the shear zone initiates at moderate to high angles ($\geq 40°$) to bedding would the parallelism between the *XY* plane and bedding be observed (Figs 6 & 5b). Synkinematic and/or post-kinematic rotation of this inferred shear zone would result in the presently observed lower-plate geometry (Fig. 5a). However, if lower-plate strain is related to a zone of simple shear that initiated at $\geq 40°$ to bedding, then the observed NSRD would be younger and unrelated to this

TABLE 1. *Table of* X:Y:Z *ratios of the finite-strain ellipsoid and calculated* k *value. Finite-strain values show that strain increases dramatically across the range from a low on the W of 5.8:1 (X:Z; sample JL1-115) to a high on the E of 31:1 (X:Z; sample JL2-91).*

Area	Sample	Unit	Strain Marker	X:Y:Z	k
Negro	JL1-115	Cpm	Qtz grains	5.8:2.0:1.0	1.9
Creek	JL1-116	Cpm	Qtz grains	6.9:2.4:1.0	1.3
	JL1-157	Cpm	Qtz grains	10.4:3.1:1.0	1.1
	JL1-148	Cpm	Qtz grains	10.7:3.3:1.0	0.98
	JL1-149	Cpm	Qtz grains	9.6:3.3:1.0	0.83
	JL1-150	Cpm	Qtz grains	8.3:2.6:1.0	1.4
	JL1-151	Cpm	Qtz grains	7.5:2.7:1.0	1.0
	JL1-152	Cpm	Qtz grains	9.1:3.4:1.0	0.70
Hendry's	JL2-32	PC1	Pebbles	13.8:3.6:1.0	1.1
Creek	SP 4	PC3	Pebbles	12.7:3.4:1.0	1.1
	JL2-91	PC1	Pebbles	31.1:4.2:1.0	2.0

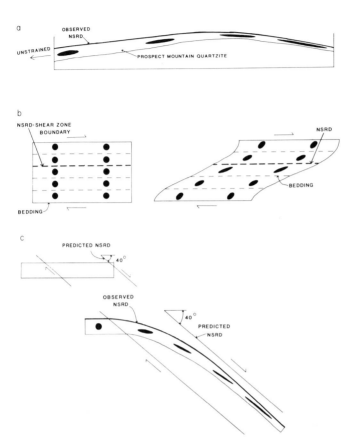

FIG. 5. Geometry of lower-plate strain. (a) A to-scale WNW–ESE cross-section (thickness of the Prospect Mountain Quartzite is exaggerated) showing the presently observed geometry and the relationship of lower-plate finite strain to bedding and the NSRD. This cross-section is simplified from the more detailed one shown in Fig. 8. (b) Schematic diagram showing that simple-shear parallel to the NSRD would not produce the observed thinning of units, the parallelism between the finite-strain ellipsoid, bedding and the NSRD, and the W-to-E strain gradient (modified from fig. 3.2 of Ramsay & Huber 1983). (c) Schematic diagram showing a shear zone initiating at 40° to bedding. This would result in a close match of the observed parallelism between the finite-strain ellipsoid and bedding, but is not compatible with other geological relationships in the northern Snake Range (see text for details). Synkinematic and/or post-kinematic rotation of this inferred shear zone would result in the presently observed geometry illustrated in (a). Diagrams are drawn perpendicular to the Y-axis and parallel to the XZ plane of the finite-strain ellipsoid.

inferred shear zone and would not parallel the shear-zone boundary (Fig. 5c). Several geological relationships do not support this alternative:

1 The quartz c-axis fabrics and microstructures discussed below suggest that a large component of the lower-plate strain is coaxial. In particular, moderately strained rocks on the W side of the range appear to have deformed primarily by pure shear and are thus, kinematically incompatible with deformation resulting entirely from simple shear.

2 If the NSRD were strictly a younger and genetically unrelated detachment fault, then the age of upper-plate normal faulting should be consistently younger than the age of lower-plate ductile deformation. Geochronological constraints reviewed below suggest that the earliest upper-plate normal faults are Oligocene, whereas lower-plate ductile strain continued at least until the early Miocene.

3 Finally, it does not seem mechanically reasonable to us that a *steeply dipping* ductile shear zone would be cut by a much more *gently dipping, convex-upward*, brittle fault (Fig. 5c). In strictly brittle regimes it is well documented that steeper, younger faults consistently cut older, gently dipping, rotated normal faults (e.g. Proffett 1977; Gans & Miller 1983; Chamberlin 1983) and sparse data suggests that extensional ductile shear zones tend to initiate at greater angles to the principal shortening direction than do brittle normal faults (Ramsay 1980).

In light of these geological relationships, it seems most reasonable to interpret the finite-strain data as indicating primarily pure-shear deformation.

Microstructures and c-axis fabrics

Many workers have used quartz microstructures and quartz c-axis fabric studies to describe the

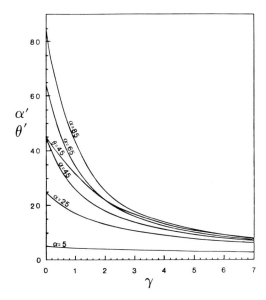

FIG. 6. Plot of the angle between a shear-zone boundary and bedding (α'), and foliation (θ'), as a function of shear strain (γ) for several initial bedding (α) orientations (modified from fig. 2.12 of Ramsay & Huber 1983). If all the accumulated finite strain is the result of simple shear, then the graph shows that for a shear zone initiating at $\leq 35°$ to bedding the XY plane and bedding are not everywhere parallel over the range of finite strain measured. Only for a shear zone initiating at $\geq 40°$ to bedding will bedding and foliation be parallel for the strain gradient measured across the northern Snake Range. See text for full discussion.

kinematic history of ductilely deformed rocks (e.g. Burg & Laurent 1978; Compton 1980; Behrmann & Platt 1982; Law *et al.* 1984; Lister & Snoke 1984). Experimental (Tullis *et al.* 1973; Tullis 1977) and theoretical studies (Etchecopar 1977; Lister *et al.* 1978; Lister & Hobbs 1980) of quartz *c*-fabrics show a relationship between quartz *c*-axis preferred orientations and the kinematic history of deformation that produces them. Although the limitations and assumptions of these latter studies raise questions about their applicability to naturally deformed rocks (see, for instance, discussion in Lister & Williams 1979) they none the less provide a comparison for interpreting the kinematics of naturally deformed rocks.

We have undertaken microstructural and petrofabric analyses of the quartzites in the lower plate of the northern Snake Range in order to further describe the development of

ductile extensional fabrics in the lower plate. These studies show a systematic variation in, and evolution of, quartz *c*-axis fabrics with increasing strain across the range that are accompanied by changes in the type and nature of microstructures developed.

The samples described below were collected from the lower Cambrian Prospect Mountain Quartzite exposed in Negro Creek, and from this same quartzite and underlying quartzites of the upper Precambrian McCoy Creek Group exposed in Hendry's Creek (Figs 2 & 3). Microstructure descriptions and petrofabric analyses were made on thin sections cut parallel to the mesoscopic elongation lineation and perpendicular to the mesoscopic foliation. Note that finite strain analyses have been completed for many of these samples. Quartz *c*-axis measurements for samples from Hendry's Creek were collected by A.M.B. Marks as part of her M.Sc thesis at the University of Utrecht, The Netherlands (1984) and have been published with her permission. These *c*-axis measurements were collected on a digitized universal stage designed by G.S. Lister and P.F. Williams using the calcite method. Orientation information was sent to an LSI 11/23+ based microcomputer and contoured using a contouring program developed by Lister. Quartz *c*-axis measurements for samples from Negro Creek (completed by Lee) were performed on a conventional universal stage and the data contoured using a Kalsbeek counting net.

Microstructures and c-axis fabrics from Negro Creek

In the far W end of the study area, in Negro Creek, moderately strained quartzites are characterized by a single sub-horizontal foliation and a conspicuous mineral elongation lineation in hand specimen. In thin section (samples JL1-115, JL1-116, JL1-157 and JL1-158), detrital grains are seen to have been stretched and flattened and exhibit undulatory extinction, deformation lamellae and variable, but small amounts of recrystallization into smaller grains along grain boundaries (Fig. 7a). Surrounding the elongate grains are recrystallized, equant polygonal grains (Fig. 7a). Also present are globular quartz grains around which elongate detrital grains anastomose and flatten (Fig. 7b). Feldspars form up to 3% of the rock and are commonly blocky to rounded. They are occasionally fractured perpendicular to the long axis of the detrital grains and pulled apart parallel to the long axis. Micas constitute 1–3% of the

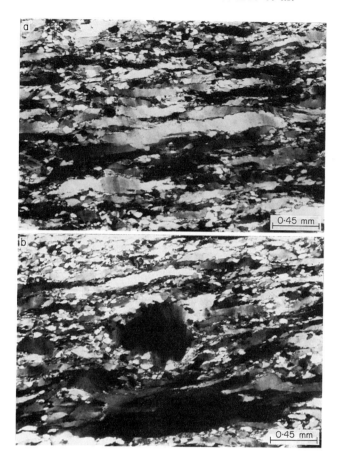

FIG. 7. Deformed quartzites from Negro Creek. (a) This is the least deformed quarzite sample (sample JL1-115). Foliation (S_1) is defined by the alignment of elongate grains and parallels bedding. Note recrystallization to small new grains at detrital grain boundaries. (b) Globular quartz grain (centre of photomicrograph) from sample JL1-115. Note that elongate grains flatten and anastomose around the globular grain. Photomicrographs are from thin sections cut parallel to the elongation lineation and perpendicular to the foliation and with crossed nicols.

rock and are strung-out and flattened parallel to the long axis of the deformed detrital grains. The elongate quartz grains define the mineral lineation, and the flattened detrital quartz grains and strung-out, flattened micas define the single foliation (S_1) that is parallel to the hand-specimen foliation and to compositional layering or bedding.

Further E in Negro Creek (samples JL1-152, JL1-151, JL1-150, JL1-149 and JL1-148) the detrital grains are slightly more elongate and show increased amounts of recrystallization to small new grains and sub-grains at their grain boundaries. The elongate grains exhibit undulatory extinction and deformation bands. The matrix surrounding the elongate detrital grains is composed of small equant to slightly elongate (aspect ratios of 1.5–2:1) recrystallized quartz grains. The long axis of these recrystallized

grains parallels the long axis of the elongate detrital grains. Globular grains are still present, although now they are commonly recrystallized to new small grains and sub-grains. The feldspar content varies reaching as much as 5% of the rock. The feldspars are rounded to blocky and are commonly fractured perpendicular to the length of the elongate detrital grains. Micas form 1–3% of the rock and are strung-out and flattened parallel to the length of the detrital grains. The elongate detrital grains define the mineral lineation, and the flattened detrital grains, recrystallized quartz grains and the strung-out, flattened micas define a single foliation (S_1) that is parallel to compositional layering or bedding.

Microstructural evidence for late-stage brittle deformation is common. Small fractures generally cut elongate detrital quartz grains perpendicular to their length, although fractures also occur at low angles to the length of these grains. Larger fractures cross-cut the foliation at high angles. No slip is observed along these fractures.

Quartz c-axis fabric patterns from the western portion of Negro Creek are shown in Figs 8, 9 & 10. Most of the samples have fabric patterns similar to type I cross-girdle patterns (Lister & Williams 1979) with a 20–37° small-circle girdle opening angle about Z and two cross-girdles that intersect at Y. Note that the skeletal outline and density distribution of the fabric patterns from samples JL1-115, JL1-116, JL1-150 and possibly JL1-158 are symmetrical about the finite-strain axes: a small-circle girdle about Z, girdles intersecting at Y and a pole-free area at X. Samples JL1-151, JL1-149 and JL1-148 have skeletal outlines that are symmetrical, but the density distribution is asymmetrical; the NW-dipping girdle shows a stronger concentration of c-axes. Samples JL1-157 and JL1-152 show very weak cross-girdle patterns which more closely approximate asymmetrical single girdle patterns. C-axes measured from globular quartz grains in all of these samples are at small angles to Z.

Microstructures and quartz c-axis fabrics from Hendry's Creek

Quartzites in the headwaters of Negro Creek (samples JL1-155A, JL1-156 and JL1-139B) and throughout Hendry's Creek are well developed L–S tectonites exhibiting intense recrystallization. At high structural levels in Hendry's Creek (samples JL1-205, JL1-204, JL1-202, 1 and 10) detrital grains are ribbon-like showing recrystallization into new grains with $X{:}Z$ ratios of up to 30:1 (Fig. 11a). These new ribbon-like quartz grains have also been variably recrystallized to smaller grains and sub-grains at their grain boundaries. In some areas where recrystallization is more extensive the outline of these elongate 'ghost' grains is still preserved. At deeper structural levels in Hendry's Creek and within those samples from Negro Creek, recrystallization is even more intense and all ribbon-like quartz grains and 'ghost' grains have been completely recrystallized to smaller grains. These smaller recrystallized quartz grains are equant and polygonal to elongate with aspect ratios of up to 3:1 (Fig. 11b). No globular grains are present. Feldspars constitute as much as 10% of the rock and are commonly fractured and involved in cataclastic deformation. Fracturing may be perpendicular to the elongation lineation with fractured pieces pulled

apart parallel to the lineation, or fractures may dip to the SE at high angles to the lineation with slip in the down-dip direction of the fracture. New quartz commonly fills these fractures. Micas form as much as 5–7% of the rock and are commonly lozenge-shaped with tails of small, recrystallized micas and are similar in appearance to the asymmetrical mica 'fish' of Lister & Snoke (1984) (Fig. 11b). Commonly, the tails of several lozenge-shaped micas are linked forming a 'stair-step' pattern (Fig. 12). The lozenge-shaped micas and the 'stair-step' pattern show the same sense of asymmetry in all the samples studied.

The mesoscopic mineral lineation in this area is defined by elongate quartz grains and stretched and strung-out staurolite and biotite porphyroblasts. There is only a single mesoscopic foliation; however, in thin section four different foliations, not all of which are present in the same sample, have been recognized in these high-strain quartzites. Generally, the most obvious foliation (C) is a discrete, spaced (0.1–0.5 mm) foliation defined by the strung-out and recrystallized mica tails of the lozenge-shaped micas (Figs 11b & 12). At deep structural levels the C foliation parallels bedding and the mesoscopic foliation with the lozenge-shaped micas dipping more steeply to the NW. At higher structural levels the C foliation dips 5–9° more steeply to the SE than bedding and the mesoscopic foliation, and the lozenge-shaped micas are sub-parallel to bedding.

Between this spaced foliation (C) is a well-developed penetrative foliation that at high structural levels is defined by ribbon-like detrital grains (S_1) that lie within the mesoscopic foliation and dip 5–9° shallower than C (Fig. 11a). With increasing depth these ribbon grains are recrystallized to smaller grains that are equant to slightly elongate with aspect ratios of up to 3:1 and that define the third foliation (S_2). This foliation (S_2) is oblique to bedding and dips 18–31° more steeply to the NW (Fig. 11b). In rocks where the S_2 foliation is observed, the C foliation parallels bedding and the mesoscopic foliation.

The fourth foliation is poorly developed, quite rare and is at a high angle to C and S_2, dipping more steeply to the SE (Fig. 13a). The C and S_2 foliations adjacent to the fourth foliation are dragged slightly into parallelism with this foliation, suggesting a down-to-the-SE sense of shear. Recrystallization of quartz grains occurs along this foliation resulting in a reduction in grain size. A morphologically similar foliation is pervasively developed in the interbedded schist units (Fig. 13b). It is a spaced foliation that

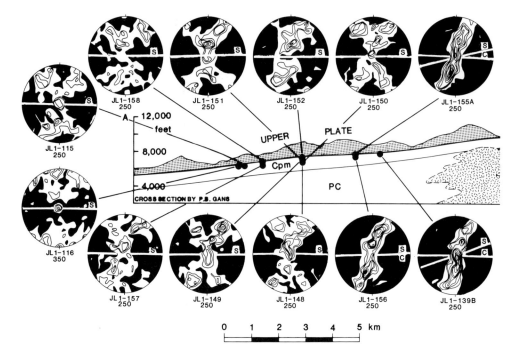

Fig. 8. Geological cross-section of the northern Snake Range showing locations of *c*-axis fabric samples. All fabric patterns were measured from thin sections cut parallel to the WNW–ESE elongation lineation and perpendicular to the mesoscopic foliation. The first number below each fabric pattern is the sample number, the second number is the number of *c*-axes measured. Contour intervals are given in Figs 9, 10 & 14, and Table 2. See Fig. 2 for location of the cross-section. *C*-axis fabric patterns from Hendry's Creek (see Fig. 3b) are from Marks (1984).

generally dips ~30° SE relative to the bedding and flattened micas, but conjugate NW-dipping foliations are also present. Offset along these planes is in a normal sense. These foliations are similar in character and geometry to the shear bands of White *et al.* (1980) and to the extensional crenulation cleavage of Platt & Vissers (1980). This foliation shallows abruptly into, but is not present in the interbedded, ductilely deformed quartzites. It is apparently a synchronous, but more brittle response to the extension accomplished by ductile flow in the surrounding quartzites.

Quartz *c*-axis fabric diagrams from samples in the headwaters of Negro Creek and throughout Hendry's Creek (Marks 1984) are illustrated in Figs 8, 14 & 15. All the fabric patterns show a single girdle that is 'dog-leg' shaped, that is asymmetrical with respect to the mesoscopic

foliation and bedding, and that dips steeply to the NW. In the lower-strain samples the fabric patterns exhibit a continuous single girdle with maxima at *Y* and at 30–50° from the mesoscopic foliation. The more highly strained samples have fabric patterns that exhibit a fragmented single girdle and also exhibit a strong maximum at *Y* and at 30–50° from the mesoscopic foliation.

Kinematic interpretation of microstructures and quartz c-axis fabrics

Several microstructural observations are important to the kinematic interpretation of the quartz *c*-axis fabric diagrams discussed above. More importantly, the progressive change in the nature and geometry of microstructures developed in the rocks from W-to-E is accompanied by a change in *c*-axis fabric patterns. In the lower-

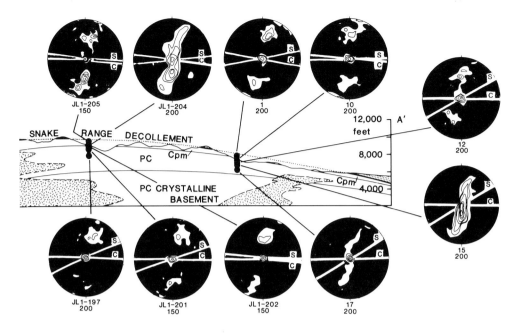

FIG. 8 (*cont.*)

strain quartzites of Negro Creek the single foliation, defined by flattened elongate detrital grains and strung-out, flattened micas, parallels bedding. Globular grains are rare, but present and their *c*-axes are sub-perpendicular to foliation and bedding and sub-parallel to Z. These relationships among microstructure, crystallographic orientation and finite-strain axes have been described in coaxially deformed quartzites from experiments (Tullis *et al*. 1973) and from nature (Compton 1980; Law *et al*. 1984).

C-axis fabrics measured from these elongate detrital and recrystallized quartz grains (samples JL1-115, JL1-116, JL1-158 and JL1-150), from Negro Creek, comprise symmetrical skeletal cross-girdles with a symmetrical density distribution about the finite-strain axes. Similar *c*-axis fabrics have been produced experimentally (Tullis *et al*. 1973) and with computer simulations (Lister & Hobbs 1980) under coaxial deformation conditions. These symmetrical cross-girdle patterns are unique for coaxial

deformation if shortening exceeds ~ 30% (Lister & Hobbs 1980), a condition clearly satisfied in Negro Creek where symmetrical cross-girdle fabrics were obtained from quartzites characterized by at least 55% shortening. Thus, we interpret these quartz fabric patterns from Negro Creek as indicating coaxial deformation.

C-axis fabrics measured from recrystallized grains (samples JL1-151, JL1-149 and JL1-148), from Negro Creek, are symmetrical in skeletal outline but asymmetrical in density distribution. Similar *c*-axis fabrics have been produced by computer simulation of non-coaxial deformation (Lister & Hobbs 1980) and have also been reported in naturally deformed rocks by Law *et al*. (1984) who interpret these *c*-axis fabric patterns as indicating non-coaxial deformation overprinting coaxial deformation. In light of the presence of globular grains in these samples, we interpret these fabrics in the same way. This superimposed non-coaxial deformation has to be of low enough magnitude so as not to rotate

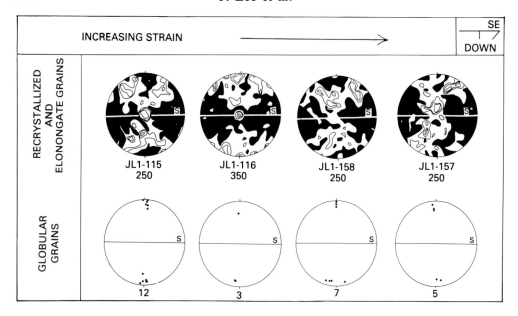

FIG. 9. Quartz c-axis fabrics and globular quartz-grain c-axis measurements from the western end of Negro Creek. Foliation ($S = S_1$) is vertical and lineation on S_1 is horizontal. Geographical orientation of stereo nets is indicated. For sample locations see Figs 3a & 8. Labelling as in Fig. 8. Numbers below globular grain c-axes stereo nets are the number of c-axes measured. Contour intervals are 0.8, 2.0, 2.8, 4.0%.

and, thus, deform and obliterate the globular grains.

In the higher-strain rocks from the headwaters of Negro Creek and throughout Hendry's Creek, distinct microstructural changes occur in the rocks. These changes are associated with a change in the c-axis fabric pattern from symmetrical cross-girdles to an asymmetrical single girdle. In particular, step-like microscopic discontinuities, C foliations, develop in the rocks that bound lozenge-shaped micas or asymmetrical mica 'fish'. The development of these microstructures is accompanied by variable to complete syntectonic recrystallization of quartz and the development of a NW-dipping quartz grain shape foliation.

The step-like discontinuities (C foliations) were first described by Berthe et al. (1979) in deformed granites. They labelled these foliations as C-planes (shear surfaces) and interpreted them as indicators of a non-coaxial or simple-shear strain history. Lister & Snoke (1984) follow Berthe et al (1979) and interpret C-planes in quartz mylonites as forming sub-parallel to

the bulk flow plane or shear-zone boundary. The angular relationship between C-planes and the oblique quartz foliation and the asymmetry of the lozenge-shaped micas indicates the sense of shear. Throughout the study area in the northern Snake Range the asymmetry of these microstructures is consistent, and according to Lister & Snoke's (1984) interpretation, indicates top-to-the-SE-shear sub-parallel or at very low angles to lower-plate bedding and the NSRD.

C-axis fabrics measured from samples JL1-157 and JL1-152 (Negro Creek) and the more highly strained, dynamically recrystallized quartzites in the headwaters of Negro Creek and throughout Hendry's Creek are asymmetrical, both in density distribution and with respect to their skeletal outline, and all the fabric patterns show the same sense of asymmetry. Following Bouchez (1977), Burg & Laurent (1978), Behrmann & Platt (1982), Law et al. (1984), Lister & Snoke (1984) and many others, the single-girdle asymmetrical fabric patterns can be interpreted as indicating top-to-the-SE simple shear. If the single-girdle

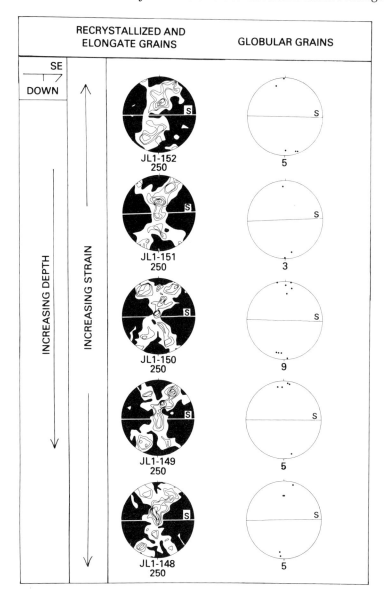

FIG. 10. Quartz *c*-axis fabrics and globular quartz grain *c*-axis measurements from the middle of Negro Creek. Foliation ($S = S_1$) is vertical and lineation on S_1 is horizontal. Geographical orientation of stereo nets is indicated. For sample locations see Figs 3a & 8. Labelling as in Fig. 8. Contour intervals are 0.8, 2.0, 2.8, 4.0, 5.2, 6.0, 6.8%.

asymmetrical fabric diagrams are interpreted as indicating top-to-the-SE-shear, and the single girdle is orientated orthogonal to the flow plane or shear-zone boundary (Lister & Hobbs 1980), then the present orientation of the shear zone is predicted, (i) to dip ~27° more steeply to the SE than bedding in the vicinity of samples JL1-157

and JL1-152, and (ii) to be sub-parallel to bedding, to the macroscopic foliation and to the NSRD in the headwaters of Negro Creek and throughout Hendry's Creek.

The quartzite samples from Hendry's Creek are dynamically recrystallized and, therefore, record only the last increment of strain. Although

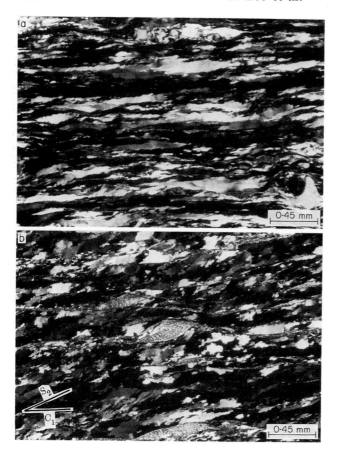

FIG. 11. Deformed quartzites from high structural levels (a), and deep structural levels (b) in Hendry's Creek. (a) Recrystallization of elongate detrital grains into elongate ribbon-like grains, with $X{:}Z$ ratios of up to 30:1, defines the bedding-parallel foliation (S_1; sample JL1-202). (b) Lozenge-shaped micas (or mica 'fish') with recrystallized mica tails defines the C foliation that parallels bedding. Recrystallized, slightly elongate quartz grains define S_2 that is oblique to C (sample JL1-201). Photomicrographs are from thin sections cut parallel to the elongation lineation and perpendicular to the foliations and with crossed nicols.

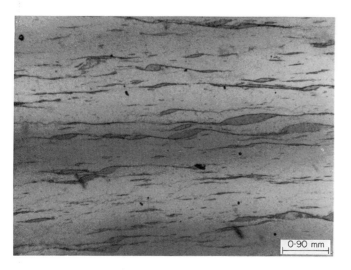

FIG. 12. Deformed quartzite from Hendry's Creek. Step-like pattern defined by lozenge-shaped micas and recrystallized mica tails. Mica tails define the C foliation. The photomicrograph is from a thin section cut parallel to the elongation lineation and perpendicular to C and in plane polarized light.

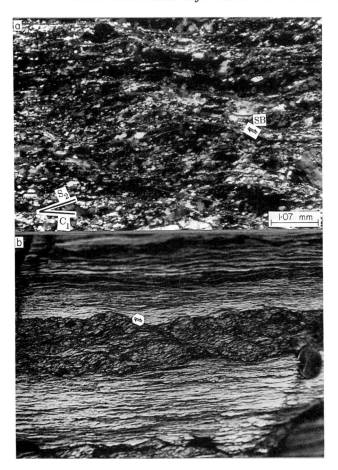

FIG. 13. Deformed quartzites and interbedded schists from Hendry's Creek. (a) Shear bands from sample JL1-197. Both S_2 and C foliations are dragged slightly into parallelism with the shear band indicating down-to-the-SE shear. The photomicrograph is from a thin section cut parallel to the elongation lineation and perpendicular to C and with crossed nicols. (b) Photograph of mesoscopic foliations in interbedded quartzites and schists. Schist layers are cut, dragged into parallelism with and tilted towards the NW by moderately steep, SE-dipping shear bands suggesting down-to-the-SE shear. Note that the shear bands abruptly flatten into the underlying quartzite.

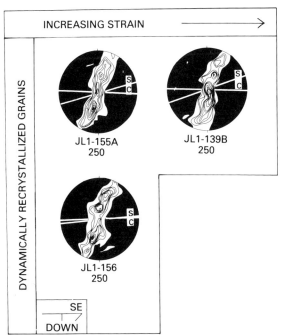

FIG. 14. Quartz c-axis fabrics from the headwaters of Negro Creek. Foliations ($S = S_2$; C) are vertical and lineation on C is horizontal. The angular relationship between foliations and the geographical orientation of stereo nets is indicated. For sample locations see Figs 3a & 8. Labelling as in Fig. 8. Contour intervals are 0.8, 2.0, 2.8, 4.0, 5.2, 6.0, 6.8, 8.0, 8.8, 9.6%.

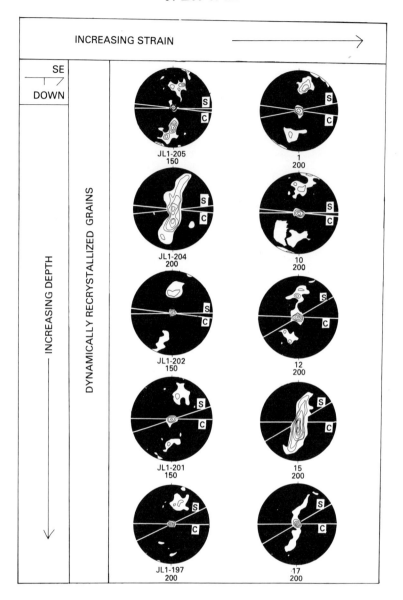

FIG. 15. Quartz c-axis fabrics from Hendry's Creek (from Marks 1984). Foliations ($S = S_1$ for samples JL1-205, JL1-204, JL1-202, 1 and 10; $S = S_2$ for samples JL1-201, JL1-197, 12, 15 and 17; C) are vertical and lineation on either S_1 (samples JL1-205, JL1-204, JL1-202, 1 and 10) or on C (samples JL1-201, JL1-197, 12, 15 and 17) is horizontal. The angular relationship between foliations and the geographical orientation of stereo nets is indicated. For sample locations see Figs 3b & 8. Labelling as in Fig. 8. Contour intervals are listed in Table 2.

the microstructural and quartz petrofabric data discussed above are indicative of non-coaxial flow, they cannot be used alone to argue for a deformational history resulting entirely from simple shear. This is particularly true in light of the evidence for progressive overprinting of coaxial fabrics by non-coaxial fabrics in Negro Creek and the arguments presented above that suggest that mesoscopic strain data and map-scale geological relationships in the northern Snake Range are more compatible with a large component of coaxial strain. Thus, the exact

TABLE 2. *Contour intervals for quartz* c-*axis fabric diagrams from Hendry's Creek (see Figs 8 & 15).*

Sample	Contour Interval (%)
JL1-205	0.9, 1.9, 2.9, 3.8, 8.6
JL1-204	1.0, 2.5. 5.0, 10.0, 15.0
JL1-202	1.5, 3.1, 7.7, 13.9
JL1-201	1.3, 2.5, 5.1, 11.4
JL1-197	1.4, 2.7, 6.8, 12.2
1	1.1, 2.2, 3.3, 8.7
10	1.0, 2.0, 3.9, 7.8
12	1.1, 2.1, 3.2, 6.4, 9.6
15	1.0, 3.0, 5.0, 7.0, 9.0, 11.0, 13.0, 15.0
17	1.5, 3.0, 6.0, 10.5, 13.5

partitioning of strain between coaxial and non-coaxial strain cannot be determined without significant further work on these rocks. Furthermore, we are concerned about the development of C-planes, their kinematic history and their effect on the development of quartz c-axis fabrics in these rocks.

Figure 16 illustrates an alternative interpretation to that of Lister & Snoke (1984) for the kinematic history of C-planes. This alternative

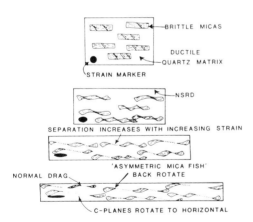

FIG. 16. Alternative interpretation to the development of C-planes. 'C-planes' may represent discontinuous microfaults in brittle micas surrounded by a plastically deforming quartz matrix. With increasing strain the apparent separation along 'C-planes' increases and they rotate into parallelism with bedding. Back-rotation of micas, as well as normal shear between and along 'C-planes' may have some effect on the developing quartz c-axis fabric pattern. Thus, the development of asymmetrical quartz fabrics may be related to shear along C-planes and not necessarily to the bulk strain history of the rocks on a larger scale.

interpretation suggests that C-planes may not form parallel to the bulk flow plane, and thus their use in defining the bulk flow plane should be carefully considered. In this interpretation 'C-planes' may originate as slip surfaces or microfaults within brittle micas that are surrounded by a plastically deforming and recrystallizing quartz matrix. At the onset of deformation, 'C-planes', like normal faults, initiate at moderate to high angles. As strain increases, the 'C-planes' may rotate to a lower angle and the apparent 'separation' between micas along the 'C-planes' increases. Indicative of this rotation are the canted or back-rotated lozenge-shaped micas, which are difficult to explain if 'C-planes' are surfaces that form and remain fixed in space. The lack of continuity of 'C-planes' beyond the ends of separated micas also suggests that they are not through-going slip surfaces as originally described by Berthe *et al.* (1979). Although the 'C-planes' may represent narrow zones of concentrated shear, they may not necessarily form or move parallel to the bulk flow plane on a macroscopic scale. Thus, 'C-planes' in quartz mylonites may not have the same kinematic significance as those originally described by Berthe *et al.* (1979) and may not be an independent means of determining the orientation of the bulk flow plane or shear-zone boundary. More work is clearly required before these structures are well understood, but in either interpretation, the possible rotational components of strain due to normal drag and/or tilting and back-rotation induced by shear along these discontinuities must be taken into account in terms of their effects on the development of quartz c-axis fabrics in the same rocks.

^{40}Ar/^{39}Ar geochronology

Published K–Ar ages for biotite and muscovite from the ductilely deformed metamorphic and plutonic rocks in the northern Snake Range obtained by Armstrong & Hansen (1966) and Lee *et al.* (1970, 1980) show an apparent eastward-younging trend from 57 Ma N of Negro Creek on the N flank of the range, where ductile strain decreases and dies out, to 21 Ma on the eastern flank of the range. These anomalously young K–Ar ages lead Miller *et al.* (1983) to conclude that the high-strain ductile fabrics in the lower plate of the northern Snake Range were localized by high thermal gradients during the Tertiary. A similar eastward-younging of K–Ar ages in the southern Snake Range has been interpreted as resulting from shear heating with proximity to the southern Snake Range decollement

(Lee *et al.* 1970). In light of the complex structural and metamorphic history of lower-plate rocks of the northern Snake Range, it was unclear what these K–Ar ages meant in terms of the absolute timing of events. Therefore, we have carried out ^{40}Ar/^{39}Ar geochronology on a variety of minerals from lower-plate igneous and metamorphic rocks with three goals in mind:

1 To date pre-mylonitic metamorphic rocks and plutons in order to place an older age limit on mylonitization.

2 To determine the age of mylonitization by dating minerals that were retrograded and which grew during this younger event.

3 To study the spatial variation of cooling ages in the lower plate to establish if ages were reset because of proximity to the NSRD and to better establish the temperature conditions of ductile flow.

Together, this information is needed in order to understand more about the timing of, conditions of and driving mechanisms for lower-plate extensional deformation and metamorphism.

The use of the ^{40}Ar/^{39}Ar geochronology technique on hornblende, biotite and muscovite has been well documented (see, for instance, Dallmeyer & Sutter 1976) and is a technique suited to deciphering the thermal history of a region that has suffered multiple heating events (see Sutter *et al.* 1985). In our discussion of the data we use the term weight-average plateau (WAP) age if 50% or more of the total released argon from two or more adjacent heating steps shows the same age (Fleck *et al.* 1977). The plateau age is interpreted as the time when the mineral became closed to the diffusion of argon. The argon closure temperatures for hornblende, muscovite and biotite are considered to be about $530 \pm 40°C$, $320 \pm 40°C$ and $280 \pm 40°C$, respectively (Harrison & McDougall 1980). If no age plateau exists, then the age spectrum is said to be disturbed, and may or may not be interpretable depending on its complexity. The interpretation of the data we present below should be viewed as preliminary because more ^{40}Ar/^{39}Ar dating, complemented by U–Pb dating, is presently in progress. Sample localities are shown in Figs 2 & 3b, and age spectra of dated minerals are shown in Figs 17 & 18. Analytical techniques and isotopic analyses are listed in Appendix 1.

Hornblende and biotite ^{40}Ar/^{39}Ar data

Two hornblende–biotite pairs from a premylonitic pluton exposed on the southern flank of the range and two metamorphic hornblendes from pre-mylonitic rocks in the Hampton Creek area were dated in order to help constrain the conditions of, and place an older age limit on, mylonitization. The two hornblende–biotite pairs, ELM-1 and ELM-3, are from a hornblende diorite, the border phase of a large tonalitic to granitic pluton (Fig. 2). Mylonitic strain is heterogeneous within this plutonic complex and is largely a function of the percentage of quartz present. Samples ELM-1 and ELM-3 have identical compositions; ELM-1 exhibits a weak mylonitic fabric and biotite retrograding to chlorite while ELM-3 exhibits no deformational fabric with little or no growth of retrograde minerals. Both hornblendes show complicated, disturbed age spectra (Fig. 17). The first few fractions of gas released from each sample show incorporation of excess argon and argon loss at times younger than 90 Ma (ELM-1) and 117 Ma (ELM-3). Subsequent heating steps result in disturbed age spectra that do not exhibit an age plateau or a simple diffusion pattern. The complexity of the spectra indicates that the oldest ages of 127 Ma (ELM-1) and 145 Ma (ELM-3) cannot be strictly interpreted as minimum ages of crystallization. Because the hornblendes have both lost and gained argon subsequent to their crystallization, the total gas (TG) ages of these samples, 129 Ma and 152 Ma, analogous to standard K–Ar ages, are not geologically significant. U–Pb data from this pluton indicate it is Jurassic in age (Wright & Miller, in prep.); thus the ^{40}Ar/^{39}Ar data are compatible with a Jurassic age for the crystallization of the hornblende and at least one episode of argon loss concomitant with incorporation of excess argon at some time younger than 90–117 Ma.

Biotites from the same samples yield WAP ages of 23.5–24.5 Ma indicating that they last cooled below ~280°C in the early Miocene (Fig. 17). These data suggest that the complex age spectra for the hornblendes are the result of at least one reheating event to temperatures in excess of 280°C, but less than 530°C, since their crystallization in the Jurassic.

Recent U–Pb work by Lee & Fischer (1985) on metamorphic monazite and metamorphosed detrital zircons from Hampton Creek indicate a Late Cretaceous (78 ±9 Ma) age for the amphibolite-facies metamorphism. We have, in addition, dated two samples of metamorphic hornblende from the Hampton Creek area (Fig. 2). Samples ID-1, from a hornblende-bearing quartzite, and JL-219, from a metamorphosed mafic dyke, both exhibit a strong sub-horizontal mylonitic fabric. The hornblende from both samples pre-dates the mylonitization which occured at lower metamorphic grade. The initial heating steps for sample ID-1 show the incorporation of excess argon and loss of argon at some

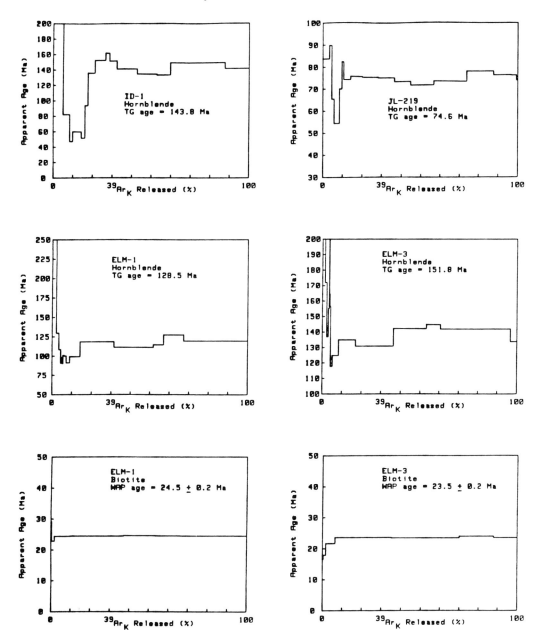

FIG. 17. ^{40}Ar/^{39}Ar age spectra from the lower plate of the northern Snake Range. Sample ID-1 is from a deformed hornblende-bearing quartzite and sample JL-219 is from a deformed and metamorphosed mafic dyke. Both samples are from the Hampton Creek area (see Fig. 2). Samples ELM-1 and ELM-3 are hornblende–biotite pairs from the hornblende diorite border phase of the tonalitic-to-granitic pluton on the S flank of the range (see Fig. 2). ELM-1 is undeformed and ELM-3 is moderately deformed. TG = total gas; WAP = weight-average plateau.

time younger than 47 Ma (Fig. 17). The subsequent higher heating steps result in a disturbed spectrum that exhibits neither an age plateau nor a pattern typical of single-stage diffusive argon loss. Several other hornblendes of similar composition from the same lithology in other parts of E-central Nevada have recently been analysed and in all cases they contain variable, but large, amounts of excess argon, and in one case the lowest apparent age is significantly older than the known age of the crystallization of the hornblende (P.B. Gans, pers. comm.). With this in mind, we view the data from ID-1 as uninterpretable.

Hornblende from sample JL-219 shows the incorporation of small amounts of excess argon and a loss of argon at some time younger than 54 Ma (Fig. 17). The age spectrum then climbs and levels out at ~75 Ma, although it does not strictly plateau. This less complicated age spectrum suggests that the TG age of 74.6 Ma may be reasonably close to the age of cooling of the hornblende and thus may be a minimum age for the amphibolite-facies metamorphism. These data are compatible with a Late Cretaceous age for the amphibolite-facies metamorphism as determined by Lee & Fischer (1985).

Muscovite ^{40}Ar/^{39}Ar data

Metamorphic muscovites from Hendry's Creek and the southern flank of the range were dated to determine whether mica ages were reset with proximity to the NSRD and to determine the age of mylonitization. Four muscovite samples were collected in a vertical transect in lower Hendry's Creek (Fig. 3b). Samples JL1-211 and JL1-214A, units 6 and 4 respectively of the McCoy Creek Group, are from a coarse-grained staurolite + garnet + biotite + muscovite + quartz schist in the deepest exposed levels of the lower plate of the range. Sample JL1-219, from unit 2, is a coarse-to-medium-grained garnet + biotite + muscovite + quartz schist and JL1-222A, from the Osceolla Argillite, is a medium-grained muscovite + quartz schist. All coarse-grained micas in these rocks grew during the amphibolite-facies metamorphism that pre-dated mylonitization. Fine-grained, new white mica, chlorite and biotite are variably present in much smaller amounts and grew synkinematically with mylonitization. The deepest sample, JL1-211, does not strictly yield a WAP age (Fig. 18). However, the TG age of 23.5 Ma and the most concordant portion of the age spectrum give indistinguishable ages suggesting that the TG age approximates the age at which the muscovite

was finally closed to argon. Samples JL1-214A and JL1-219 show disturbed, but relatively uncomplicated, age spectra that nearly achieve age plateaus (Fig. 18). This indicates that their TG ages are probably geologically meaningful. These three samples show an increase in age upwards from 23.5 Ma (JL1-211) to 25.6 Ma (JL1-214A) and 26.2 Ma (JL1-219). Sample JL1-222A, the structurally highest sample and the nearest to the NSRD shows a more complicated, disturbed age spectrum (Fig. 18). The initial heating steps indicate argon loss at some time younger than 20.3 Ma; the pattern then climbs to higher ages with each additional heating step until ~24 Ma, where it releases most of its gas, and then continues to climb until it reaches a high of 27.6 Ma. This complicated pattern is difficult to interpret but suggests that the timing of the latest event (heating or uplift) to affect this muscovite is approximated by the low-temperature portion of the age spectrum, at ~20.3 Ma.

All four samples show minor, marginal argon loss since the approximate time of closure of these minerals. If the loss occurs by simple diffusion, then the age of the first few gas fractions released should approximate the time of argon loss or the time of final closure with respect to argon retention (Turner 1968; Harrison & McDougall 1980). This marginal loss could be related to either a younger heating event or to later uplift. The apparent ages of the first heating step from samples JL1-211, JL1-214A, JL1-219 and JL1-222A are 20.0, 20.8, 17.6 and 20.3 Ma, respectively.

Muscovite from sample SR-82-1, from the lower Cambrian Prospect Mountain Quartzite along the S flank of the range (Fig. 2) yields a disturbed but relatively uncomplicated spectrum, thus indicating that the TG age of 21.6 Ma is geologically interpretable (Fig. 18). Like the muscovites from Hendry's Creek, this sample shows minor, marginal argon loss since the approximate time at which muscovite was closed to argon.

We interpret the muscovite and biotite data as indicating that older metamorphic and plutonic rocks in the lower plate of the northern Snake Range were above the biotite closure temperature for argon (~280°C) to times as young as the early Miocene. Flow laws of 'wet' quartzite suggest that quartz may deform ductilely at temperatures as low as 280–320°C (Koch 1983). We can, therefore, conclude that deformation of the quartzites and schists is likely to have been ongoing in the late Oligocene to early Miocene and probably ceased shortly thereafter as the micas cooled through their argon closure temperature.

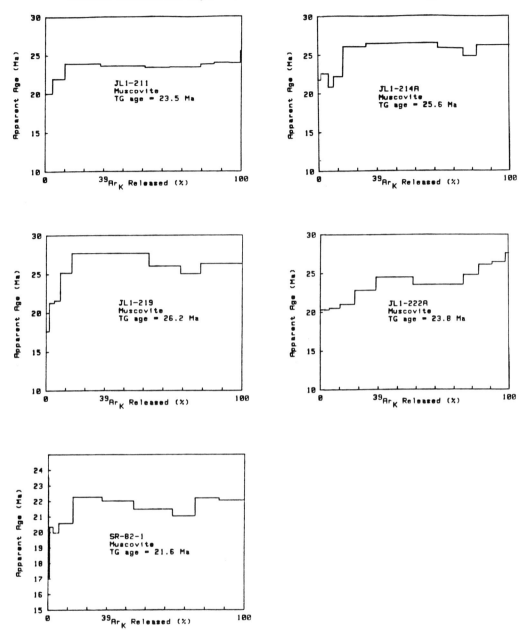

FIG. 18. $^{40}Ar/^{39}Ar$ age spectra from the lower plate of the northern Snake Range. Samples JL1-211, JL1-214A, JL1-219 and JL1-222A are deformed coarse- to medium-grained schists from the Precambrian McCoy Creek Group in Hendry's Creek (see Fig. 3b). SR-82-1 is from the highly deformed Cambrian Prospect Mountain Quartzite from the S flank of the range (see Fig. 2). TG = total gas.

In brief we would infer the following chronology for events in the northern Snake Range:

1 Work in progress by Wright & Miller and unpublished U–Pb data suggest that the large plutonic complex on the southern flank of the northern Snake Range was emplaced during the Jurassic. Hornblende $^{40}Ar/^{39}Ar$ from these plutons indicate a complex, and possibly multi-stage younger history of argon loss as well as incorporation of excess argon.

2 U–Pb age data suggest a Late Cretaceous age (78 Ma; Lee & Fischer 1985) for the amphi-

bolite-facies metamorphism in the Hampton Creek area. This is supported by the $^{40}Ar/^{39}Ar$ data on hornblende from this area. The mapping of mineral isograds indicates that temperatures decrease southward, thus the Jurassic hornblendes in plutonic rocks on the S flank of the range may have been disturbed, but not entirely reset, during this younger metamorphic event.

3 A post-Late Cretaceous metamorphic event accompanied by high-strain ductile deformation occurred during regional extension that was probably ongoing during the late Oligocene to early Miocene (21.6–26.2 Ma) and which ceased shortly thereafter. Metamorphic petrology and $^{40}Ar/^{39}Ar$ geochronology show that this event occurred at greenschist-facies conditions in excess of 280°C but less than 530°C. The temperatures attained during this metamorphism increase with depth as documented by the new growth of chlorite at the highest structural levels and by new biotite growth at the deepest structural levels, as well as by the increase in syntectonic recrystallization of quartz with depth. The $^{40}Ar/^{39}Ar$ data from micas show that deeper levels cooled at slightly younger ages than higher levels. These data *do not* support shear heating with proximity to the decollement, but they do support pervasive heating of the lower plate with temperatures increasing with depth. This suggests that lower-plate metamorphism and deformation is related to a regional heating event of Tertiary age.

4 A slow uplift or cooling of the eastern flank of the range at ~20 Ma to temperatures below which argon is no longer lost from muscovite (~250°C).

Discussion of lower-plate strain models

Any model that attempts to chart the evolution and deformational history of the lower plate of the northern Snake Range must account for the following observations:

1 Upper-plate normal faults rotated as they moved, suggesting that they must have soled into a sub-horizontal detachment, the NSRD. Palinspastic reconstruction of the upper plate indicates that the NSRD originated at a depth of ~7 km. Flat-lying sedimentary units beneath the NSRD and the lack of stratigraphic omission across the NSRD rules out large translations on a surface that originally cut down-section to the E but does not pre-clude bedding-parallel movement (Miller *et al.* 1983; Gans *et al.* 1985b).

2 Across the entire Snake Range, from the low-strain rocks on the W flank of the range to the high-strain rocks on the E flank, the *XY* flattening plane of the finite-strain ellipsoid is parallel to the lower-plate bedding and the NSRD. This, along with (1) above, argues for a genetic relationship between the lower-plate strain and the development of the NSRD. The overall geometry of lower-plate strain and the observed thinning of units is compatible with coaxial deformation with a sub-vertical *Z*-axis perpendicular to the NSRD and bedding and a sub-horizontal *X*-axis parallel to the WNW–ESE-trending mineral elongation lineations. These data preclude relating lower-plate strain entirely to a history of simple shear parallel or at low angles to bedding and the NSRD. Alternatively, the geometry of lower-plate strain could be related to a zone of simple shear that initiated at ≥40° to bedding. However, several geological relationships do not support this alternative: (i) Quartz *c*-axis fabrics from the W side of the range indicate that deformation was primarily by pure shear. (ii) If the NSRD was strictly a younger and genetically unrelated detachment fault, then the age of upper-plate normal faulting should be younger than lower-plate ductile deformation. Geochronological constraints suggest that the earliest normal faults are Oligocene (35 Ma), but ductile deformation was still ongoing at times as young as Miocene (22–26 Ma). (iii) It does not seem mechanically reasonable that a steeply dipping ductile shear zone should be cut by a much more gently dipping, convex-upward, brittle detachment fault.

3 Based on presently available data we have not been able to document a significant vertical strain gradient perpendicular to the NSRD in the lower plate. Discontinuous, sub-horizontal reflections in the middle and lower crust imaged on seismic data from the northern Snake Range have been interpreted as indicating that ductile extension is distributed throughout the entire crustal column (McCarthy 1986) which supports the interpretation that strain may not die out at depth.

4 Within the lower-strain region of the lower plate in Negro Creek, symmetrical cross-girdle *c*-axis fabrics and globular grains with their *c*-axes parallel to *Z* suggest a pure-shear deformational history. Asymmetrical cross-girdle and asymmetrical single-girdle *c*-axis fabrics, along with globular grains with their *c*-axes

still parallel to Z, suggest a change through time from early pure-shear deformation to younger, superimposed simple-shear deformation. The skeletal outline of the asymmetrical single-girdle fabrics indicates that the present orientation of the flow-plane dips 27° E relative to sub-horizontal bedding. Asymmetrical single-girdle c-axis fabrics and microstructures characterize the higher-strain rocks to the E in Hendry's Creek. The strong asymmetry of microstructures and fabrics suggests non-coaxial deformation; the skeletal outline of the c-axis fabrics indicates that the present orientation of the flow plane is sub-parallel to bedding. The development of these asymmetrical single-girdle quartz c-axis fabrics is accompanied by the development of C-planes, back-rotated asymmetrical mica 'fish' and oblique quartz foliations. The complete syntectonic recrystallization characterizing the high-strain quartzites in the northern Snake Range, makes it difficult to interpret the entire kinematic history of lower-plate fabrics in the more highly strained rocks. In particular the partitioning of strain between pure and simple shear cannot be

determined based on the available micro-structural and quartz petrofabric data alone.

We have utilized all available data to construct a series of highly simplified and speculative E–W cross-sections that chart the kinematic evolution of the lower-plate rocks of the northern Snake Range metamorphic core complex (Fig. 19). Based on relationships in Sacramento Pass and in surrounding areas, the onset of extensional faulting in the upper plate of the northern Snake Range appears to have occurred in the early Oligocene (Gans & Miller 1983; Grier 1983; Gans et al. 1985a, b). These normal faults cut sub-horizontal Palaeozoic strata to a depth of ~7 km where they shallowed into a sub-horizontal zone of decoupling, the NSRD. Ductile deformation below this zone occurred because of locally elevated isotherms, the result of active intrusion in this region (Gans & Miller 1983; Miller et al. 1983; Gans et al. 1985b). The thermally weakened lower-plate rocks deformed primarily by pure shear necking with sub-horizontal extension and sub-vertical shortening perpendicular to bedding. This proposed deformation is consistent with the observed

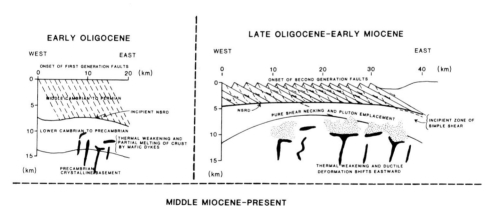

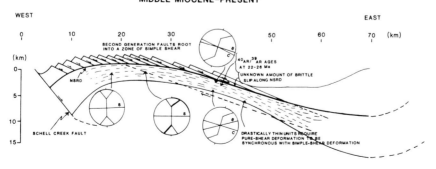

FIG. 19. Highly generalized E–W cross-sections charting the kinematic evolution of the northern Snake Range from the early Oligocene to Miocene (modified from Gans et al. 1985b).

thinning of units, the elongation and flattening of detrital grains and micas to define the bedding-parallel foliation (S_1), the W-to-E strain gradient and the development of cross-girdle *c*-axis fabrics. Although we cannot rule out a component of non-coaxial shear sub-parallel to the NSRD during this stage of the deformation, it must be of low enough magnitude for globular quartz grains and symmetrical cross-girdle fabrics to be preserved on the W flank of the range. Based on the minimum amount of finite strain measured at the mouth of Negro Creek (i.e. *X:Z* of 5.8:1), at least 140% extension of lower-plate units may have been accommodated by pure-shear necking alone.

Supracrustal faulting in the northern Snake Range either was continuous or episodic until the late Oligocene to early Miocene as documented by the youngest faults at the N end of the range that moderately tilt 24 Ma volcanic rocks (Gans *et al.* 1985a). In the lower plate, the locus of thermal weakening appears to have shifted eastward resulting in the 'freezing in' of pure-shear ductile fabrics in Negro Creek. In order to explain the asymmetrical fabrics developed in lower-plate rocks, we suggest that younger upper-plate faults root into a diffuse zone of down-to-the-SE ductile shear. At the shear zone's western edge shear strains are presumably small, and pure-shear microstructures (i.e. bedding-parallel S_1 and globular grains) are preserved. However, *c*-axis fabrics are altered to asymmetrical cross-girdle and asymmetrical single-girdle patterns. Further E, shear strains are higher and earlier formed pure-shear fabrics have been obliterated due to superimposed strain as well as dynamic recrystallization. *C*-planes, and asymmetrical mica 'fish', oblique quartz foliations and single-girdle *c*-axis fabrics from dynamically recrystallized quartz grains develop and indicate SE-directed bedding-parallel shear. Unfortunately, the absence of strain markers that indicate the partitioning of strain between pure and simple shear precludes an estimate of the contribution of coaxial versus non-coaxial strain to the total accumulated finite strain. Thus, the amount of translation due to ductile simple shear cannot be determined. Finally, in order to thin units to the extreme seen on the E flank of the range penetrative shortening perpendicular to bedding must have occurred simultaneously with the proposed bedding-parallel shear.

Conclusions

We have proposed an evolutionary model for the northern Snake Range whereby the lower plate deformed by coaxial flattening and stretching (necking) overprinted by non-coaxial shear accompanied by an unknown amount of pure-shear stretching on the E flank of the range. This interpretation is compatible with the temporal sequence of events as recorded by microstructures and *c*-axis fabrics. More studies are needed in order to characterize the amount of partitioning of strain between pure and simple shear.

Metamorphic petrology and $^{40}Ar/^{39}Ar$ geochronology have provided new data to help constrain the conditions and timing of lower-plate strain. Low greenschist-facies metamorphism, syntectonic with ductile extensional deformation increases with depth and younger $^{40}Ar/^{39}Ar$ TG muscovite ages with depth indicate higher temperatures and/or slower cooling vertically in the lower plate. These data do not support shear heating with proximity to the NSRD, but do support pervasive heating with temperature increasing with depth. Based on $^{40}Ar/^{39}Ar$ geochronology of hornblendes, muscovites and biotites, temperatures during this deformation were above 280°C but below 530°C. Palinspastic reconstruction of a well-known stratigraphy in the upper plate indicates that lower-plate rocks were at a depth of about 7–10 km during the early Tertiary suggesting an average thermal gradient in the northern Snake Range of about 40°C km^{-1} at this time. Equivalent units in adjacent ranges exhibit no Tertiary metamorphic fabrics and yield mostly Mesozoic K–Ar ages, suggesting that they were cooler in the Tertiary than the northern Snake Range. This implies that ductile extension was related to a specific and localized heating event in the Tertiary.

Constraints on the timing of extension in the northern Snake Range come from ages of syntectonic volcanic rocks in the upper plate and from biotite and muscovite ages in the lower plate. Upper-plate normal faulting began about 35 Ma and apparently continued, or began again after the extrusion of younger volcanic rocks at 24 Ma (Grier 1983; Gans *et al.* 1985a). The $^{40}Ar/^{39}Ar$ geochronology of lower-plate biotites and muscovites from the E flank of the northern Snake Range yields plateau ages or slightly disturbed spectra of 22–26 Ma. Textures indicate that the ductile deformation of quartz outpaced metamorphism and based on flow laws of 'wet' quartzite, ductile deformation of quartz is possible at the argon closure temperatures of micas (~ 300°C) (Koch 1983), suggesting that the lower plate was probably still deforming at this time.

In brief, our structural data indicate that ductile extension at depth beneath normal-fault mosaics can occur largely by coaxial strain, in conjunction with, or overprinted by, non-coaxial deformation. We emphasize that pure shear does not necessarily represent a strain incompatibility problem provided that stretching of higher-level rocks continues at depth and/or is compensated by either the intrusion of plutons and/or upwelling of deeper rocks. As regionally thinned and metamorphosed rocks are uplifted, zones of simple shear can overprint older, sub-horizontal stretching fabrics. Our petrographic observations coupled with $^{40}Ar/^{39}Ar$ data indicate that the lower plate of the northern Snake Range metamorphic core complex may represent only the uppermost exposures or levels of a Tertiary age extensional metamorphic terrane of much greater regional extent. Seismic reflection data from the northern Snake Range supports this interpretation in that crustal-stretching fabrics appear to continue into the middle and lower crust as evidenced by the presence of discontinuous, sub-horizontal reflections at depth (McCarthy 1986). The localization of regional metamorphism and deformation must be due to the input of heat by the intrusion of batholiths at depth.

ACKNOWLEDGMENTS: We thank P.B. Gans, D.W. Rodgers and P.S. Koch for critically reviewing an earlier version of this manuscript and for helpful discussions. We also wish to thank G.S. Lister for many heated discussions of the microstructural and petrofabric data. We are grateful to A.M.B. Marks for allowing us to publish the *c*-axis fabric patterns from Hendry's Creek. The drafting by W. Bohrson and mineral separations by D.A. Lee are greatly appreciated. We thank O. Tobisch and his students for use of their computerized finite-strain analysis laboratory at U.C. Santa Cruz. Mick Kunk's help with the $^{40}Ar/^{39}Ar$ analyses was invaluable. We also thank the staff at the USGS TRIGA reactor for the neutron irradiations. Helpful technical reviews were provided by referees R.J. Knipe and P.J. Coney, who do not necessarily agree with all the conclusions presented in this paper. Financial support was supplied by NSF grants EAR 8206399 awarded to E.L.M. and G.M. and EAR 8418678 awarded to E.L.M., and by SOHIO Petroleum. J.L., in addition, acknowledges field support from the Stanford Shell Foundation Fund, Tenneco Oil, Chevron, USA, Inc., and a GSA Penrose Grant.

References

ARMSTRONG, R.L. & HANSEN, E. 1966. Cordilleran infrastructure in the eastern Great Basin. *Am. J. Sci.* **254**, 112–27.

BEHRMANN, J.R. & PLATT, J.P. 1982. Sense of nappe emplacement from quartz c-axis fabrics: An example from the Betic Cordilleras (Spain). *Earth planet. Sci. Lett.* **59**, 208–15.

BERTHE, D., CHOUKROUNE, P. & JEGONZO, P., 1979. Orthogneiss, mylonite and non-coaxial deformation of granites: The example of the South Amorican shear zone. *J. struct. Geol.* **1**, 31–42.

BOUCHEZ, J-L. 1977. Plastic deformation of quartzites at low temperature in an area of natural strain gradient. *Tectonophysics*, **39**, 25–50.

BURG, J.P. & LAURENT, P. 1978. Strain analysis of a shear zone in a granodiorite. *Tectonophysics*, **47**, 15–42.

CHAMBERLAIN, R.M. 1983. Cenozoic domino-style crustal extension in the Lemitar Mountains, New Mexico: (a summary). *In*: CHAPIN, C.R. & CALLENDER, J.F. (eds) *Socorro Region II, New Mex. geol. Soc. Guidebook*, 34th Field Conf. pp. 111–8.

COMPTON, R.R. 1980. Fabrics and strains in quartzites of a metamorphic core complex, Raft River Mountains, Utah. *In*: CRITTENDEN, M.D., JR, CONEY, P.J. & DAVIS, G.H. (eds) *Cordilleran Metamorphic Core Complexes, Mem. geol. Soc. Am.* **153**, 385–98.

CRITTENDEN, M.D. JR, CONEY, P.J. & DAVIS, G.H. (eds) 1980. *Cordilleran metamorphic core complexes, Mem. geol. Soc. Am.* **153**, pp. 490.

DALLMEYER, R.D. & SUTTER, J.F. 1976. $^{40}Ar/^{39}Ar$ incremental release ages of biotite and hornblende from variably retrograded basement gneisses of the northeasternmost Reading Prong, New York: Their bearing on early Paleozoic metamorphic history. *Am. J. Sci.* **276**, 731–47.

DALRYMPLE, G.B. ALEXANDER, E.C., JR, LANPHERE, M.A. & KRAKER, G.P. 1981. Irradiation of samples for $^{40}Ar/^{39}Ar$ dating using the Geological Survey TRIGA reactor. *U.S. geol. Surv. Prof. Pap. 1176*, pp. 55.

DAVIS, G.A., LISTER, G.S. & REYNOLDS, S.J. 1983. Interpretation of Cordilleran core complexes as evolving crustal shear zones in an extending orogen. *Abstr. with Programs geol. Soc. Am.*, **15**, pp. 311.

——, ANDERSON, J.L., MARTIN, D.L., KRUMMACHER, D., FROST, E.G. & ARMSTRONG, R.L., 1982. Geologic and geochronologic relations in the lower plate of the Whipple detachment fault, Whipple Mountains, southeastern California: A progress report. *In*: FROST, E.G. & MARTIN, D.L. (eds) *Mesozoic-Cenozoic tectonic evolution of the Colorado River Region, California, Arizona and Nevada*, pp. 408–32. Cordilleran Publishers, San Diego.

DAVIS, G.H. 1983. Shear-zone model for the origin of metamorphic core complexes. *Geology*, **11**, 342–7.

EATON, G.P. 1982. The Basin and Range province — Origin and tectonic significance. *Ann. Rev. Earth planet. Sci.* **10**, 409–40.

ETCHECOPAR, A. 1977. A plane kinematic model of progressive deformation in a polycrystalline aggregate. *Tectonophysics*, **39**, 121–39.

FLECK, R.J., SUTTER, J.F. & ELLIOT, D.H. 1977. Interpretation of discordant ^{40}Ar/^{39}Ar age-spectra of Mesozoic tholeiites from Antarctica. *Geochim. cosmochim. Acta.* **41**. 15–32.

GANS, P.B. & MILLER, E.L. 1983. Style of mid-Tertiary extension in east-central Nevada. *Guide-book Part 1, Geol. Soc. Am. Rocky Mtn. and Cordilleran Sections Meeting, Volume 59*, pp. 107–60 Utah Geol. and Mining Surv. Spec. Studies.

—— & MILLER, E.L. 1985. Comment on 'The Snake Range decollement interpreted as a major extensional shear zone' by John M. Bartley and Brian P. Wernicke. *Tectonics*,**4**, 411–5.

——, MAHOOD, G. & SCHERMER, E. 1985a. Syn-extensional intermediate to silicic volcanism in the eastern Great Basin: The role of magmatism during crustal stretching. *In*: Continental Extensional Tectonics, Spec. Meeting, geol. Soc. London.

——, MILLER, E.L., McCARTHY, J. & OULDCOTT, M.L. 1985b. Tertiary extensional faulting and evolving ductile–brittle transition zones in the northern Snake Range and vicinity: New insights from seismic data. *Geology*, **13**, 189–93.

GEVING, R. 1986. A study of the metamorphic petrology of the northern Snake Range, east–central Nevada. MSc. Thesis, pp. 85, Southern Methodist Univ.

GRIER, S. 1983. Tertiary stratigraphy and geologic history of the Sacramento Pass area. Nevada. *Guidebook Part 1, Geol. Soc. Am. Rocky Mtn. and Cordilleran Sections Meeting, Volume 59*, pp. 139–44. Utah Geol. and Mining Surv. Spec. Studies.

HARRISON, T.M. & McDOUGALL, I. 1980. Investigations of an intrusive contact, northwest Nelson, New Zealand — II Diffusion of radiogenic and excess ^{40}Ar in hornblende revealed by ^{40}Ar/^{39}Ar age spectrum analysis. *Geochim. cosmochim. Acta*, **44**, 2005–2θ.

HOSE, R.K. & BLAKE, M.C., JR 1976. Geology and mineral resources of White Pine County, Nevada, 1, Geology. *Bull. Nev. Bur. Mines Geol.* **85**, pp. 105.

JACKSON, J. This volume. Active normal faulting and crustal extension.

KOCH, P.S. 1983. *Rheology and microstructures of experimentally deformed quartz aggregates.* Ph.D. Thesis, Univ. California, Los Angeles. pp. 464.

LARUE, D.K., LEE, J. & LAYER, P. 1986. On the straining of cross bed populations. *J. Geol.*

LAW, R.D., KNIPE, R.J. & DAYAN, H. 1984. Strain path partitioning within thrust sheets: Micro-structural and petrofabric evidence from the Moine Thrust zone at Loch Eriboll, northwest Scotland. *J. struct. Geol.* **6**, 477–97.

LEE, D.E. & FISCHER, L.B. 1985. Cretaceous metamorphism in the northern Snake Range, Nevada, a metamorphic core complex. *Isochron/West*, **42**, 3–7.

——, MARVIN, R.F. & MEHNERT, H.H. 1980. A radiometric age study of Mesozoic–Cenozoic metamorphism in eastern White Pine County, Nevada, and nearby Utah. *U.S. geol. Surv. Prof. Pap. 1158-C*, 17–28.

——, MARVIN, R.F., STERN, T.W. & PETERMAN, Z.E. 1970. Modification of potassium–argon ages by Tertiary thrusting in the Snake Range, White Pine County, Nevada. *U.S. geol. Surv. Prof. Pap. 700-D*, D92–D102.

LISTER, G.S. & HOBBS, B.E. 1980. The simulation of fabric development during plastic deformation and its application to quartzite: The influence of deformation history. *J. struct. Geol.* **2**, 355–70.

—— & SNOKE, A.W. 1984. S-C mylonites. *J. struct. Geol.* **6**, 617–38.

—— & WILLIAMS, P.F. 1979. Fabric development in shear zones: Theoretical controls and observed phenomena. *J. struct. Geol.* **1**, 283–97.

——, PATERSON, M.S. & HOBBS, B.E. 1978. The simulation of fabric development during plastic deformation and its application to quartzite: The model. *Tectonophysics*, **45**, 107–58.

McCARTHY, J. 1986. Reflection profiles from the Snake Range metamorphic core complex: A window into the mid-crust: Reflection Seismology. *The Continental Crust, Geodyn. Ser.* **14**, 281–92.

MARKS, A.M.B. 1984. *A fabric and microstructural study of the tectonites beneath the Snake Range decollement.* MSc. Thesis, Univ. Utrecht, pp. 43.

MILLER, E.L., GANS, P.B. & GARING, J.D. 1983. The Snake Range decollement: An exhumed mid-Tertiary ductile–brittle transition. *Tectonics*, **2**, 239–63.

——, ——; WRIGHT, J.E. & SUTTER, J.F. In press. Metamorphic history of the east–central Basin and Range Province: Tectonic setting and relationships to magmatism. *In*: ERNST, W.G. (ed.) *Rubey Vol. VII, Metamorphism and Crustal evolution, Western Coterminous United States.*

MISCH, P. 1960. Regional structural reconnaissance in central-northeast Nevada and some adjacent areas: Observations and interpretations. *Intermountain Assoc. Pet. Geol. 11th Annual Conference Guidebook*, pp. 17–42.

—— & HAZZARD, J.C. 1962. Stratigraphy and metamorphism of late Precambrian rocks of central-northeast Nevada and adjacent Utah. *Bull. Am. Assoc. Pet. Geol.* **46**, 289–343.

NARUK, S.J. 1986. Strain and displacement across the Pinaleno Mountains shear zone, Arizona, U.S.A. *J. struct. Geol.* **8**, 35–46.

PLATT, J.P. & VISSERS, R.L.M. 1980. Extensional structures in anisotropic rocks. *J. struct. Geol.* **2**, 397–410.

PROFFETT, J.M. 1977. Cenozoic geology of the Yerington district, Nevada, and implications for the nature and origin of basin and range faulting. *Bull. geol. Soc. Am.* **88**, 247–66.

RAMSAY, J.G. 1980. Shear zone geometry: a review. *J. struct. Geol.* **2**, 83–99.

—— & HUBER, M.I. 1983. *The techniques of modern structural geology, volume 1: Strain analysis.* Academic Press, New York. pp. 307.

REHRIG, W.A. & REYNOLDS, S.J. 1980. Geologic and geochronologic reconnaissance of a northwest trending zone of metamorphic core complexes in southern and western Arizona. *In*: CRITTENDEN, M.D., JR, CONEY, P.J. & DAVIS, G.H. (eds) *Cordilleran Metamorphic Core Complexes, Mem. geol. Soc. Am.* **153**, 131–57.

REYNOLDS, S.J. & REHRIG, W.A. 1980. Mid-Tertiary plutonism and mylonitization, South Mountains central Arizona. *In*: CRITTENDEN, M.D. JR, CONEY, P.J. & DAVIS, G.H. (eds) *Cordilleran Metamorphic Core Complexes, Mem. geol. Soc. Am.* **153**, 159–76.

ROWLES, L.D. 1982. *Deformation history of the Hampton Creek Canyon area, northern Snake Range, Nevada*. MSc. Thesis, Stanford Univ. pp. 80.

SHIMAMOTO, T. & IKEDA, Y. 1976. A simple algebraic method for strain estimation from deformed ellipsoidal objects. *Tectonophysics*, **36**, 315–37.

SNOKE, A.W. 1980. Transition from infrastructure to suprastructure in the northern Ruby Mountains, Nevada. *In*: CRITTENDEN, M.D., JR, CONEY, P.J. & DAVIS, G.H. (eds) *Cordilleran Metamorphic Core Complexes, Mem. geol. Soc. Am.* **153**, 287–334.

STEIGER, R.H. & JAGER, E. 1977. Subcommission on geochronology: Convention on the use of decay constants in geo- and cosmochronology.

Earth planet. Sci. Lett. **36**, 359–62.

STEWART, J.H. & POOLE, F.G. 1974. Lower Paleozoic and uppermost Precambrian of the Cordilleran miogeocline, Great Basin, western United States. *In*: DICKENSON, W.R. (ed.) *Tectonics and Sedimentation, SEPM Spec. Publ.* pp. 28–57.

SUTTER, J.F., RATCLIFFE, N.M. & MUKASA, S.B. 1985. ^{40}Ar/^{39}Ar and K–Ar data bearing on the metamorphic and tectonic history of western New England. *Bull. geol. Soc. Am.* **96**, 123–36.

TULLIS, J.A. 1977. Preferred orientation of quartz produced by slip during plane strain. *Tectonophysics*, **39**, 87–102.

——, CHRISTIE, J.M. & GRIGGS, D.T. 1973. Microstructures and preferred orientations of experimentally deformed quarzites. *Bull. geol. Soc. Am.* **84**, 297–314.

TURNER, G. 1968. The distribution of potassium and argon in chondrites. *In*: AHRENS, L.H. (ed.) *Origin and Distribution of the Elements*, pp. 387–98. Pergamon Press, Oxford.

WERNICKE, B. 1981. Low angle normal faults in the Basin and Range province: Nappe tectonics in an extending orogen. *Nature*, **291**, 645–8.

WHITE, S.H., BURROWS, S.E., CARRERAS, J., SHAW, N.D. & HUMPHREYS, F.J. 1980. On mylonites in ductile shear zones. *J. struct. Geol.* **2**, 175–87.

JEFFREY LEE & ELIZABETH L. MILLER, Department of Geology, Stanford University, Stanford, CA 94305, USA.

JOHN F. SUTTER, US Geological Survey, Reston, Virginia 22092, USA.

Appendix: Analytical Techniques

Hornblende (hand picked to >99.9% purity) and biotite and muscovite (hand picked to >99.0% purity) mineral separates were irradiated in the Central Thimble facility at the TRIGA reactor at the U.S. Geological Survey, Denver, Colorado. The isotopic composition of argon was measured with a VG Isotopes, Ltd Model 1200B mass spectrometer at the U.S. Geological Survey, Reston, Virginia. The monitor mineral used in this study was MMhb-1 hornblende described by Dalrymple *et al.* (1981). Corrections for irradiation-produced argon isotopes are those reported by Dalrymple *et al.* (1981).

^{37}Ar corrected values were calculated using a decay constant of 8.25×10^{-4} disintegrations/hr for ^{37}Ar. Apparent K/Ca ratios were calculated using the equation given in Fleck *et al.* (1977). ^{39}Ar$_K$ concentrations were calculated using the measured sensitivity of the mass spectrometer, and, thus have a precision of only about 10%. Estimated uncertainties in the ^{40}Ar/^{39}Ar ages were calculated using the equation given by Dalrymple *et al.* (1981). The use of trade names in this paper is for identification purposes only and does not constitute an endorsement by the U.S. Geological Survey.

TABLE A1. *Isotopic analyses for dated samples.*

Temp. (°C)	$^{40}Ar/^{39}Ar$	$^{37}Ar/^{39}Ar$	$^{36}Ar/^{39}Ar$	^{39}Ar (% of total)	^{40}Ar (%)	^{39}Ar ($\times 10^{-13}$ mole)	Apparent K/Ca (mole/mole)	Apparent age (My)
ELM-1 (hornblende), J = 0.006513: hornblende diorite								
700	76.44	1.132	0.0401	2.1	84.6	6.33	0.459	634.2±2.7
850	18.04	0.6547	0.0225	1.3	63.4	3.97	0.794	129.6±0.7
925	23.37	2.191	0.0475	1.0	40.7	2.84	0.237	108.3±0.7
975	27.73	3.088	0.0680	0.6	28.4	1.65	0.168	90.3±0.8
1000	31.94	2.720	0.0798	0.4	26.8	1.04	0. 191	97.9±1.4
1025	46.46	2.899	0.1315	0.3	16.9	0.84	0.179	89.7±2.3
1050	37.82	3.987	0.0991	0.6	23.3	1.72	0.130	100.8±0.7
1075	29.37	6.008	0.0713	1.0	29.8	3.01	0.086	100.0±0.7
1100	20.97	6.809	0.0459	1.7	37.8	5.19	0.076	90.8±0.6
1125	15.60	8.125	0.0256	5.3	55.6	15.6	0.064	99.1±0.5
1150	15.21	8.506	0.0185	17.2	68.4	51.1	0.061	118.2±0.6
1175	13.40	8.133	0.0145	20.3	72.8	60.3	0.064	111.1±0.5
1200	15.65	8.489	0.0211	5.2	64.3	15.5	0.061	114.5±0.6
1225	14.41	8.613	0.0131	10.2	77.8	30.4	0.060	127.1±0.6
FUSE	13.27	8.522	0.0116	32.8	79.1	97.2	0.061	119.3±0.6
							Total gas age = 128.5 NO PLATEAU	
ELM-3 (hornblende), J = 0.006426: deformed hornblende diorite								
700	113.33	2.497	0.0502	1.4	87.1	4.03	0.208	886.0±4.3
850	22.22	1.624	0.0229	0.9	70.1	2.63	0.320	172.0±0.9
925	25.32	4.393	0.0453	0.8	48.5	2.28	0.118	136.9±0.8
975	38.61	6.798	0.0851	0.5	36.2	1.30	0.076	155.1±1.5
1000	59.54	5.890	0.1412	0.1	30.7	0.43	0.088	200.3±6.1
1025	59.55	8.040	0.1534	0.2	24.9	0.63	0.064	164.3±2.2
1050	49.25	10.25	0.1216	0.4	28.6	1.09	0.050	156.3±2.9
1075	32.10	10.69	0.0759	1.0	32.7	2.73	0.048	117.7±1.0
1100	21.44	9.862	0.0374	3.1	52.0	8.91	0.052	124.8±0.7
1125	17.26	9.275	0.0199	8.6	70.0	24.6	0.056	134.9±0.7
1150	15.54	8.948	0.0513	19.4	75.4	55.5	0.058	130.9±0.7
1175	15.71	9.142	0.0123	16.9	81.3	48.4	0.057	142.2±0.7
1200	16.11	9.120	0.0129	7.3	80.8	20.8	0.057	144.8±0.7
1225	14.27	8.762	0.0074	36.1	89.4	103	0.059	142.0±0.7
FUSE	34.20	8.931	0.0775	3.3	35.1	9.40	0.058	133.9±0.8
							Total gas age = 151.8 NO PLATEAU	
ID-1 (hornblende), J = 0.006386: deformed hornblende-bearing quartzite								
550	47.18	2.149	0.0587	5.1	63.6	4.73	0.242	316.2±1.6
700	13.94	1.093	0.0228	3.4	52.2	3.14	0.475	82.0±0.5
800	10.13	1.346	0.0206	1.5	40.8	1.45	0.386	47.0±0.9
950	15.85	3.693	0.0368	4.4	33.2	4.07	0.140	59.7±0.5
1000	28.73	8.842	0.0842	1.8	15.8	1.71	0.059	51.5±0.6
1025	39.34	14.07	0.1086	1.5	21.2	1.38	0.037	93.6±1.6
1050	29.27	18.37	0.0623	3.5	42.0	3.23	0.028	136.1±1.4
1075	30.25	19.18	0.0606	5.3	45.8	4.94	0.027	152.7±0.8
1100	92.93	19.23	0.2698	2.0	15.8	1.84	0.027	161.9±2.8
1125	36.47	19.47	0.0820	3.8	37.7	3.49	0.026	151.8±2.1
1150	28.84	19.61	0.0595	10.4	44.3	9.59	0.026	141.4±1.0
1175	27.40	19.57	0.0567	10.2	44.4	9.39	0.026	134.8±0.7
1200	30.14	19.90	0.0664	6.9	40.0	6.34	0.026	133.6±1.7
1250	20.30	20.00	0.0282	27.9	66.6	2.57	0.026	149.3±0.8
FUSE	38.57	19.73	0.0924	12.4	33.2	11.4	0.026	141.7±1.2
							Total gas age = 143.8 NO PLATEAU	

TABLE A1 (cont.). *Isotopic analyses for dated samples.*

Temp. (°C)	$^{40}Ar/^{39}Ar$	$^{37}Ar/^{39}Ar$	$^{36}Ar/^{39}Ar$	^{39}Ar (% of total)	^{40}Ar (%)	^{39}Ar ($\times 10^{-13}$ mole)	Apparent K/Ca (mole/mole)	Apparent age (My)
JL-219 (hornblende), J = 0.005836: deformed, metamorphosed mafic dyke								
650	60.74	3.524	0.1789	3.4	13.4	1.61	0.147	83.7±1.3
750	36.06	5.182	0.0938	1.2	24.3	0.56	0.100	89.8±1.5
850	29.87	6.035	0.0812	1.2	21.2	0.57	0.086	65.4±1.0
950	28.47	7.392	0.0636	2.7	22.4	1.27	0.070	54.4±0.5
1000	27.89	9.147	0.0738	1.3	24.3	0.59	0.057	70.0±0.6
1050	30.10	9.439	0.0772	0.9	26.6	0.43	0.055	82.4±1.3
1100	16.95	12.97	0.0363	3.5	42.6	1.66	0.040	74.3±0.4
1150	15.46	14.05	0.0311	6.0	47.6	2.84	0.037	75.8±0.4
1200	14.63	14.66	0.0285	8.2	50.1	3.87	0.035	75.5±0.4
1250	14.05	15.14	0.0268	8.1	51.9	3.79	0.034	75.1±0.4
1300	12.15	15.53	0.0211	8.1	58.5	3.81	0.033	73.3±0.4
1350	9.70	15.87	0.0135	12.2	71.6	5.74	0.032	71.6±0.4
1400	8.68	15.92	0.0094	16.9	82.1	7.94	0.032	73.4±0.4
1450	9.17	15.83	0.0095	14.0	82.8	6.58	0.033	78.1±0.4
1500	9.58	15.57	0.0114	8.9	77.5	4.18	0.033	76.4±0.3
1650	18.39	15.68	0.0244	2.7	55.3	1.26	0.033	76.2±0.5
FUSE	22.42	15.77	0.0557	0.7	32.0	0.33	0.033	73.8±0.6

Total gas age = 74.6
NO PLATEAU

Temp. (°C)	$^{40}Ar/^{39}Ar$	$^{37}Ar/^{39}Ar$	$^{36}Ar/^{39}Ar$	^{39}Ar (% of total)	^{40}Ar (%)	^{39}Ar ($\times 10^{-13}$ mole)	Apparent K/Ca (mole/mole)	Apparent age (My)
ELM-1 (biotite), J = 0.006446: hornblende diorite								
550	10.02	0.0163	0.0253	0.4	25.3	1.57	31.8	29.3±0.5
750	4.00	0.0096	0.0068	1.5	49.3	6.37	54.0	22.8±0.2
850	2.66	0.0031	0.0018	8.1	79.4	35.5	168	24.4±0.1
950	2.38	0.0028	0.0009	27.1	88.8	119	187	24.5±0.1
1000	2.54	0.0074	0.0014	16.3	83.8	71.6	70.6	24.6±0.1
1050	2.72	0.0083	0.0020	12.8	78.1	56.1	62.5	24.6±0.1
FUSE	2.61	0.0139	0.0016	33.9	81.2	149	37.4	24.5±0.1

Total gas age = 24.5
PLATEAU AGE = 24.5±0.2

Temp. (°C)	$^{40}Ar/^{39}Ar$	$^{37}Ar/^{39}Ar$	$^{36}Ar/^{39}Ar$	^{39}Ar (% of total)	^{40}Ar (%)	^{39}Ar ($\times 10^{-13}$ mole)	Apparent K/Ca (mole/mole)	Apparent age (My)
ELM-3 (biotite), J = 0.006231: deformed hornblende diorite								
550	31.63	0.0555	0.1021	0.5	4.7	0.94	9.36	16.5±0.7
750	6.92	0.0979	0.0180	1.3	23.1	2.57	5.31	17.9±0.3
850	3.57	0.0280	0.0055	4.7	54.2	9.50	18.6	21.6±0.1
950	2.60	0.0031	0.0016	28.8	81.1	58.0	170	23.6±0.1
1000	2.61	0.0032	0.0017	34.8	80.5	70.0	163	23.4±0.1
1050	3.29	0.0053	0.0038	18.0	65.3	36.2	97.8	24.0±0.2
FUSE	4.09	0.0131	0.0067	12.0	51.5	24.1	39.7	23.5±0.1

Total gas age = 23.4
PLATEAU AGE = 23.5±0.2

Temp. (°C)	$^{40}Ar/^{39}Ar$	$^{37}Ar/^{39}Ar$	$^{36}Ar/^{39}Ar$	^{39}Ar (% of total)	^{40}Ar (%)	^{39}Ar ($\times 10^{-13}$ mole)	Apparent K/Ca (mole/mole)	Apparent age (My)
JL1-211 (muscovite), J = 0.005754: deformed st + gnt + biot + musc schist								
450	5.12	0.0029	0.0108	3.8	37.8	5.77	182	20.0±0.1
550	3.86	0.0011	0.0058	6.3	55.1	9.66	455	21.9±0.1
650	3.98	0.0001	0.0056	18.3	58.3	28.0	4230	23.9±0.1
750	3.11	0.0004	0.0027	22.8	73.7	35.0	1390	23.6±0.1
850	3.21	0.0038	0.0032	12.6	70.8	19.4	136	23.4±0.1
950	3.76	0.0025	0.0050	10.0	60.6	15.3	209	23.5±0.1
1000	3.88	0.0009	0.0054	5.6	58.8	8.57	588	23.5±0.1
1050	3.67	0.0009	0.0046	6.8	63.1	10.4	578	23.9±0.1
1150	3.37	0.0017	0.0035	7.6	69.1	11.7	300	24.0±0.1
1300	3.10	0.0084	0.0026	5.7	75.1	8.76	61.7	24.0±0.1
FUSE	7.02	0.1525	0.0154	0.5	35.3	0.79	3.41	25.5±0.2

Total gas age = 23.5
NO PLATEAU

TABLE A1 (cont.). *Isotopic analyses for dated samples.*

Temp. (°C)	$^{40}Ar/^{39}Ar$	$^{37}Ar/^{39}Ar$	$^{36}Ar/^{39}Ar$	^{39}Ar (% of total)	^{40}Ar (%)	^{39}Ar ($\times 10^{-13}$ mole)	Apparent K/Ca (mole/mole)	Apparent age (My)
JL1-214A (muscovite), J = 0.005643: deformed st + gnt + biot + musc schist								
450	6.89	0.3149	0.0161	1.7	31.2	2.40	1.65	21.8±0.2
550	7.63	0.2418	0.0183	2.6	29.2	3.62	2.15	22.6±0.2
650	5.27	0.0196	0.0109	2.7	39.0	3.76	26.5	20.8±0.1
750	4.11	0.0030	0.0065	4.8	53.4	6.74	171	22.2±0.1
850	4.08	0.0027	0.0051	11.7	63.3	16.6	191	26.1±0.1
950	3.61	0.0091	0.0033	37.1	72.6	52.3	56.8	26.5±0.1
1000	3.69	0.0177	0.0038	13.7	69.3	19.3	29.4	25.9±0.1
1050	4.06	0.0106	0.0054	7.1	60.6	10.1	49.1	24.9±0.1
FUSE	3.67	0.0117	0.0036	18.6	70.8	26.3	44.3	26.3±0.1

Total gas age = 25.6
NO PLATEAU

JL1-219 (muscovite), J = 0.005815: deformed gnt + biot + ms schist								
550	5.76	0.0115	0.0138	1.6	29.3	2.22	45.3	17.6±0.2
650	5.57	0.0078	0.0119	2.6	36.6	3.51	66.8	21.3±0.2
750	5.60	0.0058	0.0119	3.0	37.0	4.10	89.1	21.6±0.2
850	4.77	0.0069	0.0080	5.9	50.6	7.97	75.7	25.2±0.1
950	3.78	0.0027	0.0038	39.6	70.3	53.7	195	27.7±0.1
1000	3.56	0.0036	0.0036	16.1	70.3	21.9	143	26.0±0.1
1100	3.85	0.0046	0.0049	10.1	62.4	13.7	112	25.0±0.1
FUSE	3.50	0.0051	0.0033	21.1	72.3	28.7	102	26.3±0.1

Total gas age = 26.2
NO PLATEAU

JL1-222A (muscovite), J = 0.005618: deformed bt + musc schist								
450	4.38	0.0106	0.0080	4.1	46.0	5.05	49.0	20.3±0.1
550	3.87	0.0050	0.0062	5.6	52.6	7.03	104	20.5±0.1
650	2.81	0.0043	0.0024	7.6	74.1	9.47	122	21.0±0.1
750	3.01	0.0025	0.0025	10.8	75.2	13.5	211	22.8±0.1
850	3.01	0.0017	0.0019	19.3	80.8	24.0	309	24.5±0.1
950	2.88	0.0107	0.0018	26.6	81.2	33.2	48.7	23.6±0.1
1000	3.34	0.0156	0.0030	8.3	73.7	10.3	33.4	24.8±0.1
1050	3.48	0.0109	0.0030	7.1	74.6	8.86	47.6	26.1±0.1
1150	3.36	0.0091	0.0025	6.8	78.2	8.48	56.9	26.5±0.1
FUSE	3.66	0.0538	0.0031	3.7	75.0	4.66	9.66	27.6±0.1

Total gas age = 23.8
NO PLATEAU

SR-82-1 (muscovite), J = 0.006253: deformed quartzite								
550	21.49	0.2808	0.0657	0.2	9.8	0.49	1.85	23.5±2.6
650	9.84	0.0675	0.0282	0.6	15.5	1.13	7.70	17.1±0.4
750	5.34	0.0136	0.0119	1.7	34.0	3.45	38.3	20.3±0.3
850	5.36	0.0058	0.0121	2.9	33.2	5.78	89.6	20.0±0.2
900	4.50	0.0041	0.0090	7.3	40.7	14.5	126	20.6±0.1
950	3.55	0.0022	0.0053	14.9	55.9	29.6	240	22.3±0.2
975	3.41	-	0.0049	16.3	57.6	32.4	-	22.0±0.1
1025	3.93	0.0019	0.0068	19.8	48.7	39.9	278	21.5±0.1
1075	7.25	-	0.0182	11.4	25.9	2.28	-	21.0±0.2
1150	6.89	-	0.0166	12.1	28.7	24.0	-	22.2±0.2
FUSE	14.24	-	0.0415	12.8	13.8	25.5	-	22.1±0.2

Total gas age = 21.6
NO PLATEAU

Crustal extension along a rooted system of imbricate low-angle faults: Colorado River extensional corridor, California and Arizona

K. A. Howard & B. E. John

SUMMARY: The upper 10 to 15 km of crystalline crust in the 100-km-wide Colorado River extensional corridor of mid-Tertiary age underwent extension along an imbricate system of gently dipping normal faults. Detachment faults cut gently down-section eastward in the direction of tectonic transport from a headwall breakaway, best expressed in the Old Woman Mountains, California. Successively higher and more distal allochthons are displaced farther from the headwall, some as much as tens of kilometres. The basal fault(s) cut initially to depths of 10 to 15 km, the palaeothickness of a tilted allochthonous slab of basement rocks above the Chemehuevi–Whipple Mountains detachment fault(s). Hanging wall blocks tilt consistently toward the headwall as shown by dips of capping Tertiary strata and of originally horizontal Proterozoic diabase dykes. Block tilts and the degree of extension increase northeastward across much of the corridor. The faults are interpreted as rooting under the unbroken Hualapai Mountains and Colorado Plateau on the down-dip side of the corridor in Arizona. Slip on faults at all exposed levels of the crust was unidirectional, and totals an estimated 50 km. These data and inferences support the concept that the crust in California moved out from under Arizona along a rooted, normal-slip shear system. Brittle thinning above the sole faults affected the entire upper crust, and in places wholly removed it along the central part of the corridor. Upwarp exposed metamorphic core complexes in footwall domes.

Studies of continental extension have increasingly focused on low-angle faulting as a major tectonic process. Extensional faults that dip at low angles in western North America are documented around metamorphic core complexes (Crittenden *et al.* 1980) and in seismic reflection profiles of the Basin and Range Province (Allmendinger *et al.* 1983; Smith & Bruhn 1984). Several possible models of structural geometry have been proposed for extensional fault systems (Fig. 1). These models include distension over ductilely thinned crust (Fig. 1a, Eaton 1982; Gans & Miller 1983), or over magmatic intrusions (Fig. 1b, cf. Thompson & Burke 1974), crustal-scale lenses or boudins (Fig. 1c, Davis 1980; Hamilton 1982), and crustal shear zones (Fig. 1d, Wernicke 1981, 1985). In this paper we summarize geometrical aspects of the 100-km-wide Colorado River extensional corridor that indicate uniform-sense extension on rooted detachment faults to palaeodepths of at least 10–15 km in the crust. We infer from these data that crustal shear zones are an important mode of extension.

Setting and framework

The Basin and Range Province contains numerous tilt domains, with dimensions of the order of 100 km, in which fault blocks all tilt in one direction as shown by stratal dips of Tertiary rocks (Stewart 1980). We define the Colorado River extensional corridor as the tilt domain in the southern Basin and Range Province along the Colorado River as shown in Fig. 2. In this corridor, almost all fault blocks produced during mid-Tertiary crustal extension tilt to the W or S. This tilt is shown by steep to gentle dips of Tertiary strata (Fig. 3) and originally horizontal Proterozoic diabase dykes. The corridor is 50–100 km wide. Partial transects of the northern, central, and southeastern parts of the corridor, as shown in Fig. 2, have been described, respectively, by Spencer (1985), Davis *et al.* (1980), G. A. Davis & G. S. Lister (unpublished work), and Reynolds & Spencer (1985). We have mapped in many of the ranges shown in Fig. 2, including the Calumet, Ship, Clipper, Granite, Iron, Arica, Old Woman, Piute, Little Piute, Stepladder, Turtle, Chemehuevi, Mohave, Bill Williams, Buck, and Hualapai Mountains. Other tilt domains lie to the NW, SW, and SE of the area shown in Fig. 2 (Stewart 1980).

The rocks involved in the extension are syn-tectonic volcanic and sedimentary rocks of latest Oligocene(?) and early Miocene age, about 1–3 km thick, and a thick metamorphic and plutonic basement of Proterozoic, Mesozoic and locally Palaeozoic rocks (Figs 4 & 5a). Tertiary and older dykes are abundant in places. Dating by the K–Ar method places most of the faulted

From COWARD, M.P., DEWEY, J.F. & HANCOCK, P.L. (eds), 1987, *Continental Extensional Tectonics*, Geological Society Special Publication No. 28, pp. 299–311.

(a)

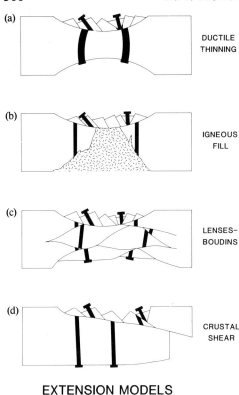

DUCTILE
THINNING

(b)

IGNEOUS
FILL

(c)

LENSES-
BOUDINS

(d)

CRUSTAL
SHEAR

EXTENSION MODELS

FIG. 1. Four major models for tectonic extension of continental crust. The fate of two initially vertical markers (black) illustrates different predictions of each model. The evidence presented in this paper favours model d, in which an inclined shear zone traverses much of the crust.

syntectonic rocks at between 17 and 22 Ma. Post-extensional fanglomerates and basalts dated at 10–15 Ma lap across the highly faulted rocks of the extensional corridor and cap the extensional episode (Dickey et al. 1980; Davis et al. 1980; Spencer 1985).

The extensional faults juxtapose shallow crustal rocks on rocks from deeper levels, forming a distinctive tectonic layering. Regional study both of this relationship and of tilted, obliquely eroded sections suggests a reconstructed crustal section that applies to much of the extensional corridor. This reconstruction is shown in Fig. 4.

Low-angle normal (detachment) faults are prominently exposed around the domal metamorphic core complexes in the central part of the corridor, including the Whipple and Rawhide Mountains (Davis et al. 1980; Frost & Martin 1982a), Chemehuevi Mountains (John

1982, this volume), Sacramento Mountains (McClelland 1982; Spencer & Turner 1982; Spencer 1985), and the Dead and Newberry Mountains (Mathis 1982; Spencer 1985). Numerous tilted blocks overlie the major low-angle faults and show NE upper-plate transport away from the tilt direction (Davis et al. 1980). Faults that we consider to be the sole faults of the extensional corridor (Fig. 5b, bottom) shoal along the W side of the corridor and cut down-section northeastward in the direction of tectonic transport, as indicated by evidence presented below. Higher and more distal allochthons are each displaced farther from the headwall break-away. The major detachment faults root at a shallow angle in the NE transport direction under relatively unbroken rocks that merge with the undeformed Colorado Plateau (Lucchitta & Suneson 1981). Progressive normal faulting and subsequent doming of the sole faults from palaeodepths of 10–15 km have exposed them in the metamorphic core complexes along the central part of the Colorado River corridor (Howard et al. 1982a, b; Spencer 1984).

The extensional strain, as deduced from exposures in the ranges we have mapped in, was primarily by brittle slip with a uniform shear sense, even at the deepest exposed levels which represent mid-crustal palaeodepths in the fault system. Igneous dykes in rocks exposed from deep levels can account for a few percent of the extension. Small Tertiary ductile shear zones and local protomylonites, thinner than 1 m, demonstrate a small amount of syntectonic ductile deformation at the deepest exposed levels (John, this volume). Thick sections of pre-Tertiary mylonitic gneiss in the core complexes here appear to be unrelated to the Tertiary extension; their pre-Tertiary age is well documented where cut by granite with a minimum age of 64 Ma in the Chemehuevi Mountains (John 1982, this volume). Mylonitization in the Whipple Mountains, where we have not mapped, has been variously interpreted as pre-Tertiary (Davis et al. 1980; Anderson & Rowley 1981) or partly Tertiary (G. A. Davis pers. comm. 1985). In the Chemehuevi Mountains and other areas that we have mapped, we conclude that the mid-Tertiary crustal extension was not accommodated in a major way by either igneous intrusion or ductile distension at any crustal levels now exposed.

Detachment faults

Detachment fault, as used in this paper, applies to major low-angle normal faults that attenuate

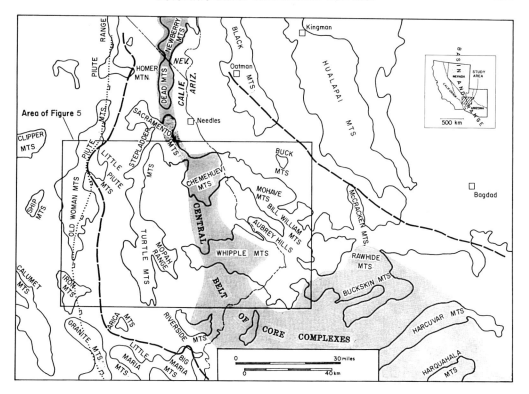

FIG. 2. Map of the Colorado River extensional corridor (between heavy dashed lines) in California, Arizona, and Nevada. Tertiary fault blocks within this corridor tilt to the W or SW. A central belt of metamorphic core complexes is shaded. Alluviated basins intervene between the named mountain ranges. The western dashed line indicates the position of westward-shoaling faults. The dotted line with teeth indicates the inferred breakaway line before erosion.

crustal section. The term detachment fault was coined to avoid the connotation of compressional thrusting on a low-angle fault along which strata were detached and moved (Pierce 1963; Campbell *et al.* 1966). Carr & Dickey (1976) broadened the term when they applied it to the Whipple Mountains fault in non-stratified crystalline rocks. Later authors have since widely used the term detachment fault for low-angle normal faults in the Colorado River region and elsewhere, whether in stratified rocks or not (e.g. Davis *et al.* 1980; papers in Frost & Martin 1982b; Davis 1984; Wernicke *et al.* 1985a). Such faults have also been called denudational faults (Armstrong 1972), decollements (Coney 1974, 1979), lag faults (Dennis *et al.* 1983) or by the acronym LANF (Brun & Choukroune 1983) for low-angle normal faults. The current widespread use of detachment fault deviates from the original meaning in that commonly no stratified rocks are involved. Furthermore, some low-angle faults may have rotated from initially much steeper dips during progressive extension (Proffett 1977); Gans & Miller 1983; Colletta & Angelier 1982), and yet closely resemble others (e.g. Wernicke *et al.* 1985a, b) that were low-angle initially. The primary dip of low-angle normal faults is commonly difficult to establish, and we suspect that faults labelled detachments in the literature embrace a wide variety of primary dips. Further, slip at low dips undoubtedly continues on some faults that have rotated from initially steep dips. Considering these difficulties, we here use the term detachment fault in its broadest sense, in order both to conform to popular use and to avoid genetic interpretations of primary dip where evidence for possible rotation is inconclusive. We emphasize that most of the faults termed detachments truncate discordantly the rock fabrics of both hanging walls and footwalls. In that sense, they cut across, rather than detach. In addition, some faults termed detachments were possibly initially steep faults now rotated to sub-horizontal.

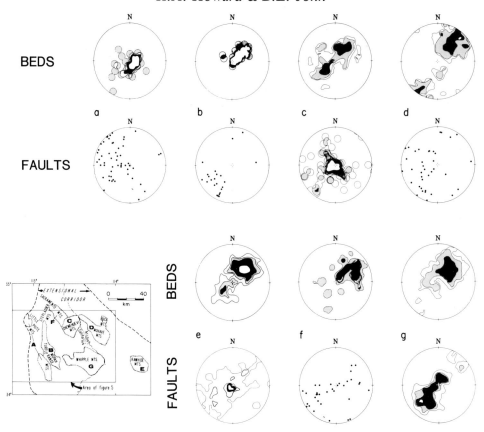

FIG. 3. Orientation of faults and of lower-Miocene and Oligocene(?) strata. Diagrams are lower-hemisphere, equal-area projection. Average stratal dips increase W to E through areas a, b, c, and d, then decrease in eastern area e. Areas f and g are similar to c in the central belt of metamorphic core complexes. Diagrams e are from Shackelford (1976); others are compiled from published and unpublished sources. Number of bedding measurements: (a) 49, (b) 34, (c) 148, (d) 149, (e) 328, (f) 88, (g) 219. Number of fault measurements: (a) 55, (b) 23, (c) 79, (d) 38, (e) 170, (f) 35, (g) 176. Contoured maxima are 6 to 9% per 1% area.

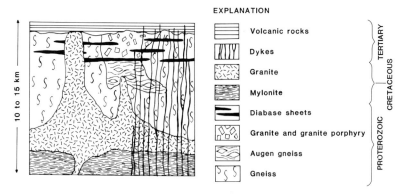

FIG. 4. A reconstructed generalized crustal section before extension schematically shows Proterozoic batholiths and sub-horizontal dykes near the surface, Cretaceous batholiths at depth, and mylonites beneath (modified slightly from Howard et al. 1982a). The mid-Tertiary extensional fault system transected this heterogeneous crystalline crust and exposed dismembered parts of it.

Shoaling faults on the west side of the corridor

The western margin of the extensional corridor traces Tertiary faults that dip E at low angles into the corridor, above footwalls of crystalline basement rocks (Fig. 5b). In contrast to the extensional corridor, areas 10–40 km W of these faults are relatively unbroken, contain no recognized large detachment faults and Tertiary tilting is either inconspicuous or variable in direction. The western dashed line in Fig. 2 outlines the inferred trace of westward-shoaling faults. The shoaling fault system where exposed in the Old Woman and Piute Mountains was initially shallow, barely into basement rocks; it juxtaposes two plates, each consisting of pre-Tertiary rocks and overlying lower Miocene strata and including an ignimbrite 18–19 My old that we consider to be the distinctive Peach Springs Tuff of Young (1966). The low-angle fault in the Old Woman and Piute Mountains was originally mapped by Cooksley (1960a) (BR in Fig. 5b). The fault dips 5 to 35° SE in the Piute Mountains and truncates Miocene fanglomerates that dip 20 to 30° into a footwall of crystalline rocks. Along part of its trace in the Old Woman Mountains the fault is steep, locally vertical. The hanging wall block contains a N-trending asymmetric syncline with a narrow W limb due to drag and a broad E limb resulting from block tilt, or 'reverse drag' in the sense of Hamblin (1965). Structural and stratigraphic markers in the pre-Tertiary crystalline basement of the hanging wall block (the Little Piute Mountains) demonstrate, when compared to the footwall block, that down-to-the-E displacement on the shoaling fault was no more than two or three kilometres either vertically or horizontally. The markers are narrow belts of attenuated and metamorphosed Palaeozoic strata along a system of Mesozoic thrust faults (Miller *et al.* 1982).

During extensional faulting, coarse detritus and landslides were shed eastward from the Old Woman and Iron Mountains breakaway area, as shown by distinctive clasts in lower Miocene deposits in the Turtle Mountains area. We therefore view the breakaway as a headwall scarp having substantial topographic relief. A young analog may be the Turtleback area in Death Valley (Wright *et al.* 1974).

In the Big Maria Mountains and Homer Mountain (Fig. 2) the exposed shoaling faults juxtapose contrasting suites of crystalline rocks that imply substantial excision of crustal section (Fig. 4) and suggest horizontal separation of many kilometres. Spencer & Turner (1982) and Spencer (1985) infer that the exposed detachment faults at Homer Mountain represent an eroded breakaway along which at least several kilometres of top-to-the E horizontal separation occurred. We interpret the faults of the northern Big Maria Mountains (Hamilton 1982; Martin *et al.* 1982), as analogous.

Crystalline rocks in the lower plate of the Big Maria Mountains contrast with those in the upper plate both in rock type and thermal history and no detachment faults are known throughout 30 to 40 km of virtually continuous exposure to the W. The Big Maria area then, like the Homer Mountain area, can be interpreted as deeply eroded footwall exposures, located many kilometres E of the original headwall region, where the faults surfaced. Displacement is larger on the faults in the Big Maria Mountains and at Homer Mountain than for the shoaling fault in the Old Woman–Piute range probably because cumulative displacement on the basal fault(s) increases eastward in the transport direction from the breakaway. This increase in fault displacement results from numerous upper-plate faults that each contribute displacement to the basal fault(s) (Fig. 5b, bottom). This type of geometry is described on the Crossman Peak fault in the Mohave Mountains (Fig. 5b, Howard *et al.* 1982a) as well as in other extensional terranes (Gans & Miller 1983).

The regional trace of gently dipping basal faults, which shoal to the W over a footwall of denuded crystalline rocks, forms the western margin of the detached and tilted terrane. We consider that the original position of the headwall breakaway is approximated by the exposure in the Old Woman Mountains, and that exposures in the Big Maria Mountains, as at Homer Mountain, are eroded remnants that lie many kilometres E of where the fault system initially surfaced (Fig. 2). Seismic reflection data (Frost & Okaya 1985) and regional map patterns of crystalline rock units (Howard *et al.* 1982b, unpub. data) both suggest that the breakaway fault system in the Old Woman Mountains connects at depth beneath the Turtle Mountains with the now-updomed detachment faults in the Chemehuevi Mountains.

Eastward from the headwall across much of the extensional corridor (as far as the Buck Mountains, Figs 2 & 5), block tilts generally steepen (Fig. 3). Many sub-vertical to overturned Tertiary stratal dips are measured in the Mohave and Buck Mountains, indicative of a high degree of upper-plate extension there (cf. Wernicke & Burchfiel 1982; Gans & Miller 1983).

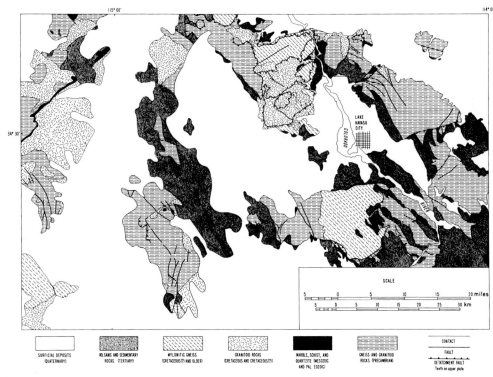

FIG. 5. (a) Generalized geological map of part of the Colorado River extensional corridor showing major Tertiary faults. The location of this map is shown in Fig. 2. Compiled from Cooksley (1960a, b), Collier (1960a, b), Miller *et al.* (1982), Howard *et al.* (1982a, b), John (this volume), Stone *et al.* (1983), Light *et al.* (1983), Miller & Howard (1985), W.J. Carr's mapping as compiled by Stone & Howard (1979), and unpublished mapping by the authors and P. Stone, J.E. Nielson, J.W. Goodge, and V.L. Hansen. (b) Top: Tectonic map of the area shown in Fig. 5(a). Low-angle faults are designated as follows: BR = breakaway fault in Old Woman–Piute range; CH = Chemehuevi fault; MW = Mohave Wash fault; DE = Devils Elbow fault; WM = Whipple Mountains fault; CP = Crossman Peak fault. Unpatterned areas show post-extension deposits (mid-Miocene and younger). The patterns show structural zones of rocks involved in the extension (see Fig. 4). Zone I (grey) is headwall and footwall terranes below the deepest known faults. IA (dark grey) is allochthons in the Chemehuevi Mountains above the Mohave Wash and another small-displacement fault. IIA (stipple) is gently tilted large blocks near the headwall breakaway. IIB (dots) is smaller, moderately tilted blocks. III is numerous mostly small blocks allochthonous over the central belt of metamorphic core complexes. IV is a large allochthon in the Mohave Mountains area, representing a thick upended crustal section. V is higher allochthons above the Crossman Peak fault. Bottom: Conceptual section across the width of the map at about 34° 30′ latitude. Patterns match the map patterns. Capping strata on tilt blocks diagrammatically indicate a Tertiary layer. The section is greatly simplified and does not indicate exact scale or angular relations.

Lithological match in allochthons

Normal faults, commonly spaced 1 to 3 km apart, separate allochthonous tilted blocks above the detachment faults (Fig. 5, Dickey *et al.* 1980; Carr *et al.* 1980). Tertiary volcanic and sedimentary strata and plutonic and metamorphic rock units of Proterozoic and Mesozoic age can be correlated in a general way from one allochthonous block to the next (Davis *et al.* 1980; Howard *et al.* (1982a, b), and to the rela-

tively undeformed terrane NE of the extensional corridor (Lucchitta & Suneson 1981). This match supports the concept that allochthons were initially contiguous. Lower plates below the detachment faults generally expose different crystalline rocks than those of the allochthons. Davis *et al.* (1982) point out that Proterozoic diabase and coarse-grained granite, typically present in the allochthons, crop out in the westernmost exposures of the lower plate in the Whipple Mountains. Consequently a palinspastic reconstruction would compress the allochthons

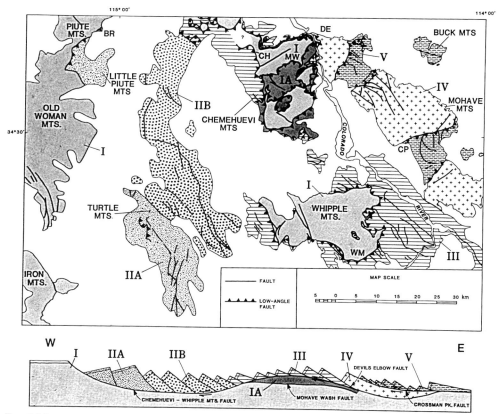

FIG. 5.(b)

together so that they overlay western parts of the lower plate (Davis *et al.* 1982; Howard *et al.* 1982a, b). Only in the Old Woman–Piute break-away area are Tertiary volcanic rocks found in lower-plate position.

Unidirectional slip of imbricate allochthons

Upper-plate transport sense on each fault, where known, was to the NE (Davis *et al.* 1980; John & Howard 1982; Howard *et al.* 1982a; John this volume). Stratal tilts (Fig. 3), slickensides, offset plutonic contacts, and a coarse sedimentary breccia that is offset from unique source rocks all confirm this transport. The transport direction holds even for the structurally deepest faults and allochthons.

Detachment faults define a series of stacked allochthons in the central part of the extensional corridor. Each of the metamorphic core complexes exposes at least two stacked low-angle faults (Shackelford 1976; Frost 1981; Adams

et al. 1982; Frost & Martin 1982a; John 1982; Mathis 1982; Spencer & Turner 1982; Wilkens & Heidrick 1982; Spencer 1985).

In the Chemehuevi Mountains (John 1982, this volume), the deepest exposed detachment fault, the Mohave Wash fault, offset plutonic contacts in its allochthon 1–2 km NE (Fig. 5a & b). The allochthon is 0 to 800 m thick and it is roofed by the younger Chemehuevi detachment fault, with probably tens of kilometres displacement. The structurally higher and older low-angle Devils Elbow fault also has large separation; it is truncated to the E by the lower Chemehuevi fault. These three faults project down-dip to the E under a large allochthon or allochthons in the Mohave Mountains (Fig. 5a & b) at least 1 km thick, and 15 by 25 km wide in map view. This large allochthon in turn is overlain by higher, smaller allochthons above the low-angle Crossman Peak fault (Howard *et al.* 1982a). The allochthons above the Crossman Peak fault each show top-to-the-NE separation.

The allochthons in the extensional corridor are shingled, many are tilted, and some of them are upended so that SW-facing Miocene strata that cap crystalline basement rocks are steeply dipping or even overturned. The tilted blocks, now slices of upended crust, must thin and terminate down-section between faults, in the NE transport direction. The allochthons are viewed as imbricated in a manner analogous to major thrust fault systems. Commonly imbricate thrust allochthons thicken away from the transport direction (Boyer & Elliott 1982), whereas imbricate extensional allochthons are inferred to thin in the transport direction (Fig. 5b, bottom).

The palaeodepth of the easternmost exposures of the sole faults in the Chemehuevi and Whipple Mountains at the time of fault initiation is inferred to have been at least 10–15 km in places. This inference derives from the structural interpretation that an intact allochthon in the Mohave Mountains above these faults (IV in Fig. 5b) exposes 10–15 km of crustal section that was detached, upended and moved off the core complexes during faulting (Howard *et al.* 1982a). This tilted section consists mostly of Proterozoic gneiss, cut by unbroken early Miocene dykes (now gentle dipping), and capped by lower Miocene volcanic strata (now sub-vertical) (see Fig. 4). Its palaeothickness is indicated by the stratal and dyke orientations and by its structural integrity for 15 km across-strike (Howard *et al.* 1982a). Proterozoic gneiss is granulite-textured only in the structurally deeper part, consistent with inferred crustal position. Likewise, medium-grained Tertiary dyke rocks are found only in the deeper part, whereas all Tertiary dykes in the shallower part are fine-grained. The faults and lower plate that underlie this block, in the area from which it slid and rotated, must have initiated at depths as great or greater than the palaeothickness of the block. Based on a 10- to 15-km palaeodepth of the sole faults in the core complexes, the stacked low-angle faults formed at various levels throughout the upper crust.

The shingled allochthons, representing many kilometres of original crustal section, now total a structural thickness less than 2 km thick over the core complexes. In places the allochthons were completely removed before post-extensional fanglomerates and basalts lapped across denuded mid-crustal rocks 10–15 Ma (e.g. Dickey *et al.* 1980; Davis *et al.* 1980). It is thought that erosion contributed little to this denudation, based on field relations and on the short time interval between tectonism and overlap (Davis *et al.* 1980). The denudation is considerably greater than the average thickness of erosional debris represented by syntectonic clastic deposits and can be attributed primarily to tectonic thinning. We conclude therefore that tectonic thinning and extension of the upper crust above the sole faults locally amounted to several hundred percent or more in order to account for the thinning. Extension of this order is also suggested by the steep to overturned stratal tilts within allochthons (Fig. 3) (cf. Wernicke & Burchfiel 1982; Gans & Miller 1983). Across the width of the extensional corridor the extension amounted to at least 50 km, or about 100 percent average extension. This estimate is based on 30–40 km separation between footwalls and hanging walls, suggested to match; (i) belts of metamorphosed Palaeozoic strata from the Riverside to the Buckskin Mountains (W. J. Carr pers. comm. 1977); (ii) Proterozoic granite and diabase from the western to the eastern Whipple Mountains (Davis *et al.* 1982); and (iii) a dyke swarm from the Whipple to the Mohave Mountains (G. A. Davis pers. comm. 1981; Howard *et al.* 1982a). These ranges are in the central part of the corridor; if displacement increases cumulatively northeastward as expected, a separation of at least 50 km is predicted at the NE margin of the corridor. This analysis concurs with a 50-km separation farther to the SE, in the Harcuvar Mountains area (Fig. 2), suggested by Reynolds & Spencer (1985).

Initial dip of faults

The detachment faults are now domed around the metamorphic core complexes, but were originally probably more planar and dipped gently northeastward in the direction of transport. Evidence outlined below suggests that the faults cut consistently down crustal section to the NE.

In western exposures the lower plates expose initially shallower crustal rocks than in eastern exposures. The Crossman Peak fault in the Mohave Mountains cuts across the thick, upended crustal section in the footwall (IV in Fig. 5b), from vertical Tertiary strata in the SW to basement rocks that were initially 10–15 km deeper, measured perpendicular to the Proterozoic–Tertiary unconformity, in the NE (Howard *et al.* 1982a). In lower plates in the Chemehuevi, Sacramento, and Whipple Mountains core complexes, deeper level rocks lie to the E of initially shallower rocks. Before extension, the middle Proterozoic granites and diabases that occur only in westernmost exposures of the footwall of the Whipple Mountains detachment fault, typically lay only within the top 5 km of the crust, as measured orthogonally below lower Miocene strata in upper-plate tilt blocks in several ranges

(Fig. 4). Deeper level rocks including Cretaceous plutonic rocks and mylonitic gneisses lie in central and eastern exposures of core-complex footwalls (Davis *et al.* 1980, 1982; John 1982). Mesozoic mylonitic gneisses in the Chemehuevi, Whipple, Sacramento, and Rawhide Mountains core complexes dip gently westward under higher level footwall rocks (Davis *et al.* 1980; McClelland 1982; John, this volume); a geometry consistent with deeper structural levels to the E. A zoned Cretaceous pluton below the Chemehuevi detachment fault contains quartz veins and sparsely mineralized joints suggestive of moderate to high plutonic levels in the western exposures of the Chemehuevi Mountains. In the eastern exposures the pluton floor grades structurally downward *lit-par-lit* with older gneiss below, suggesting greater palaeodepth to the E.

K–Ar biotite dates of pre-Tertiary rocks are Miocene in the central and eastern parts of the lower plates in the Whipple and Chemehuevi Mountains, but are Mesozoic in western parts of the lower plates in these ranges (Davis *et al.* 1982; John 1982; Martin *et al.* 1981; M. A. Pernokas, pers. comm. 1982; D. L. Martin, pers. comm. 1981). This eastward decrease of K–Ar dates with greater inferred palaeodepth is consistent with greater Miocene extensional unroofing and thermal quenching of deeper, hotter rocks to the E. Other factors that probably affect K–Ar dates in the area include strain or heating near the major faults (Martin *et al.* 1981), and extension-related intrusions. These factors do not explain eastward younging. Dyke swarms that may be extension-related are concentrated in the western parts of the Chemehuevi and Whipple Mountains lower plates (Carr *et al.* 1980; Davis *et al.* 1980, 1982; John 1982), and therefore do not explain the young K–Ar dates from the E.

Fault rocks also suggest eastward-increased palaeodepth. Eastern exposures of the Chemehuevi detachment fault include deep-formed cataclasites (John, this volume), whereas western exposures show breccias and minor cataclasites inferred to have formed at lesser depth. Gouge overprints both, and can be ascribed to faulting at shallow levels (Sibson 1977) as tectonic unloading progressed and the overburden thinned. Fault zones tend to widen with depth according to Sibson (1977), a relation that may be reflected in eastward-increased thickness of chlorite breccia as mapped below detachment faults in both the Whipple and Sacramento Mountains by Davis *et al.* (1982) and McClelland (1982).

We conclude that the faults initially cut down crustal section in the NE direction of transport. The present domal geometry in the core complexes resulted, in part, from upwarping (Howard *et al.* 1982b; Spencer 1982, 1984). Because the faults nowhere expose granulite facies or other lower-crustal rocks of Tertiary age, despite tens of kilometres of continuous exposure down-dip, the basal faults in the core complexes initially must have dipped no more than a few degrees. Palaeodepth comparisons of footwall plutonic rocks from up-dip and down-dip exposures suggest that the Chemehuevi and Mohave Wash faults dipped initially between about 5° and 15° (John, this volume).

Both steep and gentle initial dips can be inferred for upper-plate faults above the major detachment faults in the core complexes. An originally sub-horizontal orientation can be inferred for a shallow upper-plate detachment fault within the Tertiary stratigraphic section in the Sacramento Mountains, for it follows footwall bedding throughout many kilometres of exposure (McClelland 1982; Spencer & Turner 1982, 1983). Original orientations are likewise inferred for a pair of sub-horizontal faults in the Turtle Mountains, where Proterozoic diabase dykes are little rotated from their regionally consistent pre-Tertiary orientation. Many upper-plate faults initiated at steep dips, based on high angles between faults and bedding. A 90° average angle between upper-plate faults and beds, suggestive of initially vertical faults, was estimated for the Rawhide Mountains (Shackleford 1976) and Turtle Mountains (Howard *et al.* 1982b). Using data shown in Fig. 3, we now estimate that fault-bedding angles average about 60° in the Turtle Mountains and about 90° throughout the core complexes and the Mohave Mountains area. These values suggest that the initial dip of many of the faults, where they came to the surface, was in this range. Such estimates must be used with caution, because dip patterns (Fig. 3) are complicated by the effects of overturned beds, fault drag, antithetic faults, multi-stage faulting and rotation (cf. Gans & Miller 1983), and deposition during growth faulting (Frost 1981). The primary dip of the major Crossman Peak fault in the Mohave Mountains could have been any angle from horizontal to vertical, depending on its age relative to tilting of its footwall block. If bedding in the footwall, which is at 90° to the fault, was only marginally tilted when the fault formed, the fault originally could have been steep and only later rotated to the sub-horizontal, in the same way as faults at Yerington, Nevada and in the Egan Range, Nevada, have (Proffett 1977; Gans & Miller 1983).

Most of the faults in the extensional corridor cut indiscriminately across crystalline and stratified rocks. These faults were not guided by stratigraphic layering or older faults which elsewhere have guided some low-angle normal faults (e.g. Royse *et al.* 1975).

The faults in the core complexes and the Mohave Mountains project eastward under the relatively unbroken Hualapai Mountains along the E side of the corridor (Fig. 2). Lucchitta & Suneson (1981) reported that the major detachment fault in the Rawhide Mountains dips at a gentle inclination to the NE under rocks that are continuous with undeformed rocks of the Colorado Plateau. The fault there juxtaposes upper-crustal rocks—Tertiary strata and their basement of coarse-grained Proterozoic granite —upon mid-crustal mylonitic gneiss (Shackelford 1976; Suneson 1980). This juxtaposition suggests that substantial crustal section was cut out where the exposed fault system roots.

Conclusions

The fault system in the Colorado River extensional corridor accommodated at least 50 km of shear down to the E, along which the crust extended, to palaeodepths of at least 10 to 15 km. We find little evidence in ranges we have studied of ductile strain or magmatic inflation sufficient in magnitude to accommodate more than a small fraction of the extension, even at the mid-crustal levels now exposed. We are led, therefore, to favour a model in which the crust in California moved southwestward out from under the crust in Arizona on this fault system (Shackelford 1981; Reynolds & Spencer 1985; Wernicke 1985), as indicated in Figs 5(b) (bottom) and 1(d). An alternative model where the crust extends by the formation of giant lenses or boudins (Davis 1980; Hamilton 1982; Adams *et al.* 1982) seems applicable to this extensional corridor only if the lenses are part of a unidirectional simple-shear system. No known complementary slip system at any exposed level is opposite in sense and could allow a symmetrical lense or boudin mechanism such as depicted in Fig. 1(c). Other tilt domains in regions to the S and W of this extensional corridor may reflect intersecting shear zones that alternate in shear sense. Most importantly, however, there is no evidence known in the relatively unbroken terrane to the NE of the extensional corridor of major down-to-the-W extensional faults that could balance the shear and provide symmetry.

The rooted fault model of Wernicke (1981, 1985; see also Coward 1984), appears applicable

in explaining the unidirectional slip in this area. In terms of this model, the crust in California and W-central Arizona moved out southwestward from under the Colorado Plateau (Fig. 1d). This model can be tested by geophysical experiments now in progress or planned by three groups: CALCRUST (a consortium of California university scientists); COCORP (the Consortium for Continental Reflection Profiling), and PACE (Pacific to Arizona Crustal Experiment of the USGS). Together they are studying a crustal transect across the southwestern United States that crosses the Colorado River extensional corridor.

Crustal thinning normally results in rise of the Moho and net subsidence of the ground surface (Le Pichon & Sibuet 1982). In the Colorado River region, middle-crustal rocks in the core complexes rose 10–15 km, and now stand higher than their surroundings. Unloading, leading to the isostatic rise of the denuded core complexes, undoubtedly accounts for part of the uplift along the relatively narrow belt of core complexes. Simple unloading seems unlikely to account for all of the uplift, however, for there is neither evidence nor likelihood that the base of the crust is similarly domed along this narrow belt. Even if the doming were related to flexing above unseen or unsuspected deeper extensional faults (e.g. Bartley & Wernicke 1984; Wernicke *et al.* 1985b), the uplift of middle-crustal rocks to the surface would still have required major updoming deeper in the crust. Thermal history studies of the Old Woman–Piute range, in the headwall area, show that Tertiary uplift and denudation there were relatively minor (Knoll *et al.* 1985), in contrast to the complete removal of the Tertiary upper crust in the central belt of the metamorphic core complexes. If there is no corresponding dome on the Moho under the core complexes, then evidence should be sought to establish whether the lower crust was ductilely redistributed or else inflated by magmatic additions at depth under the core complexes.

ACKNOWLEDGMENTS: Will Carr first introduced us to the extensional fault system in the Colorado River area and for this we thank him along with numerous other colleagues who furthered our understanding of it, especially Greg Davis and Eric Frost. We also thank Ernie Anderson, Gordon Haxel, Warren Hamilton, Will Carr, Greg Davis, John Platt, Jon Spencer, Michel Seguret and an anonymous reviewer for critiques that improved the paper; but we hold none of them responsible for our conclusions. Gregory Davis and Gordon Lister kindly sent us a copy of a 1985 manuscript of theirs that treats many of the same problems with which we have grappled.

References

ADAMS, M.A., HILLEMEYER, F.L. & FROST, E.G. 1982. Anastomosing shear zones – a geometric explanation for mid-Tertiary crustal extension in the detachment terrane of the Colorado River region, CA, AZ, NV. *Abstr. with Programs geol. Soc. Am.* **15**, 375.

ALLMENDINGER, R.W., SHARP, J.W., VON TISH, D., SERPA, L., BROWN, L., KAUFMAN, S., OLIVER, J. & SMITH, R.B. 1983. Cenozoic and Mesozoic structure of the eastern Basin and Range province, Utah, from COCORP seismic-reflection data. *Geology*, **11**, 532-6.

ANDERSON, J.L. & ROWLEY, M.C. 1981. Synkinematic intrusion of peraluminous and associated metaluminous granitoids, Whipple Mountains, California. *Can. Min.* **19**, 83-101.

ARMSTRONG, R.L. 1972. Low-angle (denudation) faults, hinterland on the Sevier orogenic belt, eastern Nevada and western Utah. *Bull. geol. Soc.* **82**, 43-58.

BARTLEY, J.M. & WERNICKE, B.P. 1984. The Snake Range decollement interpreted as a major extensional shear zone. *Tectonics*, **3**, 647-57.

BOYER, S.E. & ELLIOTT, D. 1982. Thrust systems: *Bull. Am. Ass. Pet. Geol.* **66**, 1196-230.

BRUN, J-P. & CHOUKROUNE, P. 1983. Normal faulting, block tilting and décollement in a stretched crust. *Tectonics*, **2**, 345-56.

CAMPBELL, R.H. YERKES, R.F. & WENTWORTH, C.M. 1966. Detachment faults in central Santa Monica Mountains, California. *U.S. geol. Surv. Prof. Pap.* **550-C**, 1-11.

CARR, W.J. & DICKEY, D.D. 1976. Cenozoic tectonics of eastern Mojave Desert. *U.S. geol. Surv. Prof. Pap.* **1000**, 75.

—, — & QUINLIVAN, W.D. 1980. Geologic map of the Vidal NW, Vidal Junction, and parts of the Savahia Peak SW and Savahia Peak quadrangles, San Bernardino County, California (1:24,000). *U.S. geol. Surv. Map I-1126*.

COLLETA, B. & ANGELIER, J. 1982. Sur les systèmes de blocs faillés basculés associés aux fortes extensions: étude préliminaire d'exemples ouest-américains (Nevada, U.S.A. et Basse-Californie, Mexique). *C.R. Acad. Sc. Paris*, **294 (II)**, 467-9.

COLLIER, J.T. 1960a. *Geology and mineral resources of Township 7 North, Ranges 21 and 22 East, San Bernardino Base and Meridian, San Bernardino County, California.* South Pac. Co., Land Dep. San Francisco.

—— 1960b, *Geology and mineral resources of Township 8 North, Ranges 21 and 22 East, San Bernardino Base and Meridian, San Bernardino County, California.* South. Pac. Co., Land Dep. San Francisco.

CONEY, P.J. 1974. Structural analysis of the Snake Range 'décollement', east-central Nevada: *Bull. geol. Soc. Am.* **85**, 973-8.

—— 1979. Tertiary evolution of Cordilleran metamorphic core complexes. *In*: ARMENTROUT, J.W. *et al.* (eds) *Cenozoic paleogeography of western United States. Soc. econ. Paleontol. and Mineral., Pac. Sect. III*, 15-28.

COOKSLEY, J.W. JR 1960a. *Geology and mineral resources of Township 7 North, Ranges 17-18 East, San Bernardino Base and Meridian, San Bernardino County, California.* South. Pac. Co., Land Dep. San Francisco.

—— 1960b. *Geology and mineral resources of part of Township 6 North, Ranges 17-18 East, San Bernardino Base and Meridian, San Bernardino County, California.* South. Pac. Co., Land Dep. San Francisco.

COWARD, M.P. 1984. Major shear zones in the Precambrian crust; examples from NW Scotland and southern Africa and their significance. *In*: KRONER, A. & GREILING, R. (eds) *Precambrian tectonics illustrated*, pp. 207-35. Stuttgart, E. Schweizerbart'sche Verlagsbucjhhandlung (Nagele u. Obermiller).

CRITTENDEN, M.D., JR, CONEY, P.J. & DAVIS, G.H. (eds) 1980. Cordilleran metamorphic core complexes. *Mem. geol. Soc. Am.* **153**, 490 pp.

DAVIS, G.A., ANDERSON, J.L., FROST, E.G. & SHACKELFORD, T.J. 1980. Mylonitization and detachment faulting in the Whipple-Buckskin-Rawhide Mountains terrane, southeastern California and western Arizona. *In*: CRITTENDEN, M.D., JR, CONEY, P.J. & DAVIS, G.H. (eds) *Cordilleran metamorphic core complexes. Mem. geol. Soc. Am.* **153**, 79-129.

——, ——, MARTIN, D.L., KRUMMENACHER, D., FROST, E.G. & ARMSTRONG, R.L. 1982. Geologic and geochronologic relations in the lower plate of the Whipple detachment fault, Whipple Mountains, southeastern California: a progress report. *In*: FROST, E.G. & MARTIN, D.L. (eds) *Mesozoic-Cenozoic tectonic evolution of the Colorado River region, California, Arizona and Nevada, (Anderson-Hamilton volume)*, pp. 408-32. Cordilleran Publishers, San Diego.

DAVIS, G.H. 1980. Structural characteristics of metamorphic core complexes, southern Arizona, *In*: CRITTENDEN, M.D., JR, CONEY, P.J. & DAVIS, G.H. (eds) *Cordilleran metamorphic core complexes. Mem. geol. Soc. Am.* **153**, 35-77.

—— 1984. *Structural geology of rocks and regions*, 491 pp. John Wiley & Sons, New York.

DENNIS, A.J., TAVARES, L., ROSS, M. & BOSWORTH, W. 1983. Extensional and transcurrent tectonics superimposed on a convergent history. An example from the Sierra Las Pintas, Northern Baja, Mexico. *Abstr. with Programs Geol. Soc. Am.* **15**, 556.

DICKEY, D.D., CARR, W.J. & BULL, W.B. 1980. Geologic map of the Parker NW, Parker, and parts of the Whipple Mountains SW and Whipple Wash Quadrangles, California and Arizona (1:24,000). *U.S. Geol. Surv. Map I-1124.*

EATON, G.P. 1982. The Basin and Range Province:

Origin and tectonic significance. *Ann. Rev. Earth planet. Sci.* **10**, 409–40.

FROST, E.G. 1981. Structural style of detachment faulting in the Whipple Mountains, California, and Buckskin Mountains, Arizona. *Ariz. geol. Soc. Dig.*, **XIII**, 25–9.

—— & MARTIN, D.L. 1982a. Comparison of Mesozoic compressional tectonics with mid-Tertiary detachment faulting in the Colorado River area, California, Arizona and Nevada. *In*: COOPER, J.D. (compiler), *Geologic excursions in the California desert.* Geol. soc. Am. Cordilleran Section, 78th Annu. Meet. Anaheim. California, April 19–21, 1982. pp. 113–59.

—— & —— (eds) 1982b. *Mesozoic–Cenozoic tectonic evolution of the Colorado River region, California, Arizona and Nevada, (Anderson-Hamilton volume),* 608 pp. Cordilleran Publishers, San Diego.

—— & OKAYA, D.A. 1985. Geometry of detachment faulting in the Old Woman-Turtle-Sacramento-Chemehuevi Mountains region of SE California. *Eos.* **66**, 978.

GANS, P.B. & MILLER, E.L. 1983. Style of mid-Tertiary Extension in East-Central Nevada, *In*: *Geologic Excursions in the Overthrust Belt and Metamorphic Core Complexes of the Intermountain Region. Utah Geol. Mineral Surv., Spec. Stud. 59, Guidebk.-Part I*, pp. 108–39.

HAMBLIN, W.K. 1965. Origin of 'reverse drag' on the down-thrown side of normal faults. *Bull. Geol. Soc. Am.* **76**, 1145–64.

HAMILTON, W. 1982. Structural evolution of the Big Maria Mountains, northeastern Riverside County, southeastern California. *In*: FROST, E.G. & MARTIN, D.L. (eds) *Mesozoic-Cenozoic tectonic evolution of the Colorado River region, California, Arizona and Nevada, (Anderson-Hamilton volume)*, pp. 1–27. Cordilleran Publishers, San Diego.

HOWARD, K.A., GOODGE, J.W. & JOHN, B.E. 1982a. Detached crystalline rocks of the Mohave, Buck, *In*: FROST, E.G. & MARTIN, D.L. (eds) *Mesozoic-Cenozoic tectonic evolution of the Colorado River region, California, Arizona, and Nevada, (Anderson-Hamilton volume)*, pp. 377–90. Cordilleran Publishers, San Diego.

——, STONE, P., PERNOKAS, M.A. & MARVIN, R.F. 1982b. Geologic and geochronologic reconnaissance of the Turtle Mountains area, California: West border of the Whipple detachment terrane. *In*: FROST, F.G. & MARTIN, D.L. (eds) *Mesozoic-Cenozoic tectonic evolution of the Colorado River region, California, Arizona, and Nevada, (Anderson-Hamilton volume)*, pp. 341–54. Cordilleran Publishers, San Diego.

JOHN, B.E. 1982. Geologic framework of the Chemehuevi Mountains, southeastern California. *In*: FROST, E.G. & MARTIN, D.L. (eds) *Mesozoic-Cenozoic tectonic evolution of the Colorado River region, California, Arizona, and Nevada, (Anderson-Hamilton volume)*, pp. 317–25. Cordilleran Publishers, San Diego.

—— This volume. Geometry and evolution of a mid-crustal extensional fault system: Chemehuevi Mountains, southeastern California, pp. 313–35.

—— & HOWARD, K.A. 1982. Multiple low-angle Tertiary faults in the Chemehuevi and Mohave Mountains, California and Arizona. *Abstr. with Programs geol. Soc. Am.* **14**, 175.

KNOLL, M.A., HARRISON, T.M., MILLER, C.F., HOWARD, K.A., DUDDY, I.R. & MILLER, D.S. 1985. Pre-Peach Springs Tuff (18 m.y.) unroofing of the Old Woman Mtns crystalline complex, southeastern California: Implications for Tertiary extensional tectonics. *Abstr. with Programs geol. Soc. Am.* **17**, 365.

LE PICHON, X. & SIBUET, J.-C. 1982. Passive margins: A model of formation. *J. geophys. Res.* **86**, 3708–20.

LIGHT, T.D., PIKE, J.E., HOWARD, K.A., McDONNELL, J.R., SIMPSON, R.W., RAINES, G.L., KNOX, R.D., WILSHIRE, H.G. & PERNOKAS, M.A. 1983. Mineral resource potential map of the Crossman Peak Wilderness Study Area (5–7B), Mohave County, Arizona (1:48,000). *U.S. geol. Surv. Map MF-1602-A.*

LUCCHITTA, I. & SUNESON, N. 1981. Comment on 'Tertiary tectonic denudation of a Mesozoic-early Tertiary(?) gneiss complex, Rawhide Mountains, western Arizona'. *Geology*, **9**, 50–2.

McCLELLAND, W.C. 1982. Structural geology of the central Sacramento Mountains, San Bernardino County, California. *In*: FROST, E.G. & MARTIN, D.L. (eds) *Mesozoic-Cenozoic tectonic evolution of the Colorado River region, California, Arizona, and Nevada, (Anderson-Hamilton volume)*, pp. 401–6. Cordilleran Publishers, San Diego.

MARTIN, D.L., KRUMMENACHER, D. & FROST, E.G. 1981. Regional resetting of the K-Ar isotopic system by mid-Tertiary detachment faulting in the Colorado River region, California, Arizona, and Nevada. *Abstr. with Programs Geol. Soc. Am.* **13**, 504.

——, —— & —— 1982. K-Ar geochronologic record of Mesozoic and Tertiary tectonics in the Big Maria-Little Maria-Riverside Mountains terrane. *In*: FROST, E.G. & MARTIN, D.L. (eds) *Mesozoic-Cenozoic tectonic evolution of the Colorado River region, California, Arizona, and Nevada, (Anderson-Hamilton volume)*, pp. 518–49. Cordilleran Publishers, San Diego.

MATHIS, R.S. 1982. Mid-Tertiary detachment faulting in the southeastern Newberry Mountains, Clark County, Nevada. *In*: FROST, E.G. & MARTIN, D.L. (eds) *Mesozoic-Cenozoic tectonic evolution of the Colorado River region, California, Arizona, and Nevada, (Anderson-Hamilton volume)*, pp. 326–40. Cordilleran Publishers, San Diego.

MILLER, C.F., HOWARD, K.A. & HOISCH, T.D. 1982. Mesozoic thrusting, metamorphism, and plutonism, Old Woman-Piute Range, southeastern California. *In*: FROST, E.G. & MARTIN, D.L. (eds) *Mesozoic-Cenozoic tectonic evolution of the Colorado River region, California, Arizona, and Nevada, (Anderson-Hamilton volume)*, pp. 562–81. Cordilleran Publishers, San Diego.

MILLER, D.M. & HOWARD, K.A. 1985. Bedrock geologic map of the Iron Mountains quadrangle, San Bernardino and Riverside Counties, California (1:62500). *U.S. geol. Surv. Map MF-1736.*

PIERCE, W.G. 1963. Reef Creek detachment fault, northwestern Wyoming. *Bull. geol. Soc. Am.* **74**, 1225-36.

PROFFETT, J.M., JR 1977. Cenozoic geology of the Yerington District, Nevada, and implications for the nature and origin of Basin and Range faulting. *Bull. Geol. Soc. Am.* **88**, 247-66.

REYNOLDS, S.J. & SPENCER, J.E. 1985. Evidence for large-scale transport on the Bullard detachment fault, west-central Arizona. *Geology*, **13**, 353-6.

ROYSE, F., JR, WARNER, M.A. & REESE, D.L. 1975. Thrust belt structural geometry and related stratigraphic problems, Wyoming–Idaho–northern Utah. *In*: BOLYARD, D.W. (ed.) *Deep drilling frontiers of the central Rocky Mountains. Rocky Mtn Assoc. Geol. 1975 Symp.* pp. 41–54.

SHACKELFORD, T.J. 1976. *Structural geology of the Rawhide Mountains, Mohave County, Arizona.* Ph.D. Thesis, Univ. Southern California, Los Angeles, 175 pp.

—— 1981. Reply to comment on 'Tertiary tectonic denudation of a Mesozoic–early Tertiary(?) gneiss complex, Rawhide Mountains, western Arizona. *Geology*, **9**, 51.

SIBSON, R.H. 1977. Fault rocks and fault mechanisms. *J. geol. Soc. London*, **133**, 191–213.

SMITH, R.B. & BRUHN, R.L. 1984. Intraplate extensional tectonics of the eastern Basin-Range: Inferences on structural style from seismic reflection data, regional tectonics, and thermal-mechanical models of brittle–ductile deformation. *J. geophys. Res.* **89**, 5733–62.

SPENCER, J.E. 1982. Origin of folds of Tertiary low-angle fault surfaces, southeastern California and western Arizona. *In*: FROST, E.G. & MARTIN, D.L. (eds) *Mesozoic–Cenozoic tectonic evolution of the Colorado River region, California, Arizona, and Nevada, (Anderson-Hamilton volume)*, pp. 123–34. Cordilleran Publishers, San Diego.

—— 1984. Role of tectonic denudation in warping and uplift of low-angle normal faults. *Geology*, **12**, 95–8.

—— 1985. Miocene low-angle faulting and dike emplacement, Homer Mountain and surrounding areas, southeastern California and southernmost Nevada. *Bull. Geol. Soc. Am.* **96**, 1140–55.

—— & TURNER, R.D. 1982. Dike swarms and low-angle faults, Homer Mountain and the northwestern Sacramento Mountains. *In*: FROST, E.G. & MARTIN, D.L. (eds) *Mesozoic–Cenozoic tectonic evolution of the Colorado River region, California, Arizona, and Nevada, (Anderson-Hamilton volume)*, pp. 97–108. Cordilleran Publishers, San Diego.

—— & —— 1983. Geologic map of part of the northwestern Sacramento Mountains, southeastern California. *U.S. geol. Surv. Open-file Rep. 83–614.*

STEWART, J.H. 1980. Regional tilt patterns of late Cenozoic basin–range fault blocks, western United States. *Bull. geol. Soc. Am.* **91**, 460–4.

STONE, P. & HOWARD, K.A. 1979. Compilation of geologic mapping, Needles 1° × 2° sheet, California and Arizona (1 : 250,000). *U.S. geol. Surv. Open-file Rep. 79–388.*

——, —— & HAMILTON, W. 1983, Correlation of metamorphosed Paleozoic strata of the southeastern Mojave Desert region, California and Arizona. *Bull. geol. Soc. Am.* **94**, 1135–47.

SUNESON, N.H. 1980. *The origin of bimodal volcanism, west-central Arizona*, Ph.D. Thesis, Univ. California, Santa Barbara, 293 pp.

THOMPSON, G.A. & BURKE, D.B. 1974. Regional geophysics of the Basin and Range Province. *Ann. Rev. Earth planet. Sci.* **2**, 213–38.

WERNICKE, B. 1981. Low-angle normal faults in the Basin and Range province: nappe tectonics in an extending orogen. *Nature, Lond.* **291**, 645–6.

—— 1985. Uniform-sense simple shear of the continental lithosphere. *Can. J. Earth Sci.* **22**, 108–25.

—— & BURCHFIEL, B.C. 1982. Modes of extensional tectonics. *J. struct. Geol.* **4**, 105–15.

——, GUTH, P.L. & AXEN, G.J. 1985a. Tertiary extensional tectonics in the Sevier thrust belt of southern Nevada. *In*: LINTZ, J., JR (ed.) *Western geological excursions, 4*, pp. 473–510. Dept. geol. Sciences, Mackay School of Mines, Reno, Nev.

——, WALKER, J.D. & BEAUFAIT, M.S. 1985b. Structural discordance between Neogene detachments and frontal Sevier thrusts, central Mormon Mountains, southern Nevada. *Tectonics*, **4**, 213–46.

WILKENS, J. JR & HEIDRICK, T.L. 1982. Base and precious metal mineralization related to low-angle tectonic features in the Whipple Mountains, California and Buckskin Mountains, Arizona. *In*: FROST, E.G. & MARTIN, D.L. (eds) *Mesozoic–Cenozoic tectonic evolution of the Colorado River region, California, Arizona, and Nevada, (Anderson-Hamilton volume)*, pp. 182–203. Cordilleran Publishers, San Diego.

WRIGHT, L.A., OTTON, J.K. & TROXEL, B.W. 1974. Turtleback surfaces of Death Valley viewed as phenomena of extensional tectonics. *Geology*, **2**, 53–5.

YOUNG, R.A. 1966. Cenocoic geology along the edge of the Colorado Plateau in northwestern Arizona. *Diss. Abstr. Section B*, **27**, 1994.

KEITH A. HOWARD, US Geological Survey, Menlo Park, CA 94025, USA.

BARBARA E. JOHN, US Geological Survey, Menlo Park, CA 94025, and Department of Geological Sciences, University of California, Santa Barbara, CA 93106, USA.

Geometry and evolution of a mid-crustal extensional fault system: Chemehuevi Mountains, southeastern California

B.E. John

SUMMARY: The extensional fault system exposed in the Chemehuevi Mountains area of the southern Cordillera provides data on the mode of mid-crustal accommodation to continental extension. A stacked sequence of three mid-Tertiary low-angle normal faults cut gently down-section through deformed Proterozoic and Mesozoic crystalline basement below Cenozoic strata. Hanging wall blocks are consistently displaced relatively NE across these three detachment faults, recording unidirectional extension of quartzofeldspathic crust at palaeodepths of 6–10 km. The two structurally deepest faults in the sequence are exposed over 22 km in a down-dip direction, across a total area in excess of 350 km^2, and were initiated with a regional dip of less than 15° NE. Both of the structurally deepest faults are corrugated parallel to the direction of transport; wavelengths of the corrugations range between 200 m and 10 km, and amplitudes range from 30 to 400 m. These undulations are broad mullion structures that developed coeval with fault slip. Amplitude and wavelength vary with footwall rock type and pre-existing structural grain. Slip on the faults at the present level of exposure was accomplished by brittle deformation, with the generation of gouge, breccias, rocks of the cataclasite series, and rare pseudotachylites. Major mylonite zones in the Chemehuevi Mountains are older and unrelated to the extensional faulting. These data support the conclusion that mid-crustal extension in the Chemehuevi Mountains area was accommodated by an asymmetrical normal-slip shear system. Extension occurred along seismically active, gently NE-dipping, undulating surfaces. During their evolution they rose from middle- to upper-crustal depths.

Shallow-crustal structure associated with Cenozoic continental extension is relatively well documented from geological studies in the northern Basin and Range (Stewart 1980; Proffett 1977; Proffett & Dillas 1984). Knowledge of deeper-crustal structure, however, is based largely on geophysical studies and limited well data (Anderson et al. 1983; Smith & Bruhn 1984; Allmendinger et al. 1983). As most of these data represent an indirect observation of continental extension, the mode of mid-crustal accommodation to stretching remains poorly understood. Published studies on the geometry and kinematics of extensional regimes often present models that are confined to the geometry of deformation within the upper few kilometres of the Earth's surface and lose validity with greater structural depth, or are based on inadequate knowledge of the timing of structural events. This paper reports on a mid-crustal extensional fault system exposed in the Chemehuevi Mountains area of the southern Cordillera. Extension was accomplished here along a stacked sequence of very low-angle normal or detachment faults with unidirectional slip. Above the regionally developed Chemehuevi detachment fault, the hanging wall block is distended by innumerable high-angle faults. Structurally below the Chemehuevi detachment fault lies the smaller-displacment Mohave Wash fault. Little deformation occurred in the footwall to this fault

system. Both the Mohave Wash and Chemehuevi faults are broadly corrugated parallel to the direction of transport, and were originally formed with regional dips of less than 15° NE. Slip on the faults at palaeodepths of 6–10 km, the present level of exposure, was accomplished by brittle deformation. This paper seeks to document the geometry and evolution of a mid-crustal continental extensional fault system in an exceptionally well-exposed area, in order to constrain better models of crustal extension.

Regional setting

Major zones of thrust faulting, folding, and metamorphism have been documented through the eastern Mojave and Sonoran Deserts of California and Arizona (Fig. 1). Thrust faults and folds of late-Mesozoic age, marked by deformed Palaeozoic and Mesozoic strata and crystalline basement (Howard et al. 1980; Miller et al. 1982; Hamilton 1982; Frost & Martin 1982a), can be traced into the region from the Sevier orogenic belt of Utah and Nevada (Armstrong 1968; Burchfiel & Davis 1981). Thick zones of mylonitic gneiss that outcrop in eastern California and western Arizona are believed to be of similar age to the Mesozoic thrusting (John 1982, 1986; Howard et al. 1982c; Shackelford 1980; Davis et al. 1982). In

From COWARD, M.P., DEWEY, J.F. & HANCOCK, P.L. (eds), 1987, *Continental Extensional Tectonics*, Geological Society Special Publication No. 28, pp. 313–335.

B.E. John

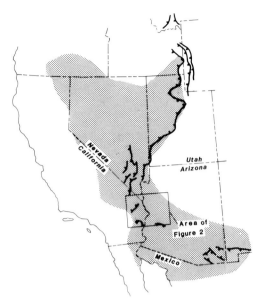

FIG. 1. Tertiary extension (shaded) overprints an area previously affected by Mesozoic compression in the North American Cordillera. The Colorado River extensional corridor lies between the central Mojave Desert in California, and the unbroken Colorado Plateau in Arizona.

the southern Cordillera, evidence of the thrust belt includes unroofed basement-involved ductile nappes, thrust faults and folds that are commonly associated with Cretaceous plutonic rocks (Davis *et al*. 1980; Howard *et al*. 1980; Coney & Harms 1984). Mid-Tertiary extension lay astride this belt and distended an already deformed or heterogeneous crust.

The Chemehuevi Mountains area lies in the central part of a 100-km wide zone of extension, termed the Colorado River extensional corridor, which is centred along the Colorado River trough (Fig. 2). Major mid-Tertiary extension involving the upper and middle crust was accomplished along brittle, E-dipping, low-angle normal or detachment faults (Howard & John, this volume). As a consequence of this deformation, crystalline rocks, including mylonites that resided at palaeodepths of at least 6–10 km in the crust, are juxtaposed against volcanic rocks erupted at the surface 18 Ma.

The western margin or breakaway zone of the Colorado River extensional corridor lies between the Turtle and Old Woman Mountains in

California (John & Howard 1982) (Fig. 2). The breakaway exposes Tertiary faults that dip E into the corridor, and cut gently W-dipping Tertiary strata unconformably overlying Proterozoic granites and gneisses (Howard *et al*. 1982a). Offset structural and stratigraphic markers in the pre-Tertiary crystalline basement of the hanging wall and footwall indicate that down-to-the-E separation on the fault(s) was no more than 2–3 km either vertically or horizontally (Howard & John, this volume).

Low-angle normal or detachment faults are exposed around the domal metamorphic core complexes (Coney 1980) in the central part of the extensional corridor, including the Whipple and Rawhide Mountains (Davis *et al*. 1980; Frost & Martin 1982b), Chemehuevi Mountains (John 1982), Sacramento Mountains (McClelland 1982; Spencer 1985), and the Dead Mountains (Spencer 1985). These exposures apparently represent the sole fault(s) to the extensional fault system. Cumulative slip on this fault (or faults) increases northeastward across the extensional corridor, and totals an estimated 50 km, or 100% average extension regionally (Howard & John, this volume). The northeastward increase in cumulative slip results from displacement on numerous hanging wall faults that fed displacement into the detachment(s). Transport of the upper plate of each fault, where known, was to the NE (Davis *et al*. 1980; John & Howard 1982; Howard *et al*. 1982a; Spencer 1985). This transport direction holds even for the structurally deepest exposed faults in the system. Regional field relations indicate that the faults cut consistently down-section northeastwards, in the direction of tectonic transport (Howard & John, this volume). This relation implies that the fault system had a shallow NE dip away from the breakaway region.

The eastern limit of marked extension lies to the W of the Hualapai Mountains in Arizona, approximately 100 km NE of the breakaway. The Chemehuevi Mountains are in the central part of the corridor along the belt of metamorphic core complexes. The range is flanked by the regionally developed Chemehuevi detachment fault which projects at depth beneath the Hualapai Mountains and toward the Colorado Plateaus.

The Chemehuevi Mountains and nearby ranges are framed by the early-Miocene and Oligocene(?) low-angle extensional faults. In contrast, in the northern Basin and Range Province most ranges are fronted by younger high-angle faults (Stewart 1971; Eaton 1982).

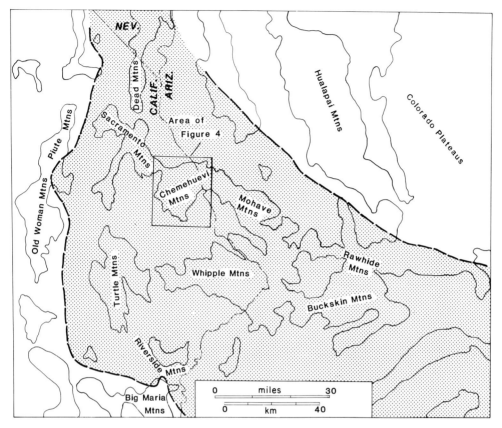

FIG. 2. Map of the Colorado River extensional corridor (shaded between the heavy dashed lines) in California and Arizona, as defined in Howard & John (this volume). The Chemehuevi Mountains (outlined in box) lie in the central belt of metamorphic core complexes that include from N to S, the Dead, Sacramento, Chemehuevi and Whipple Mountains. The eastern limit of extension marked by highly faulted and tilted blocks lies W of the Hualapai Mountains. Detachment faults exposed around the core complexes dip under the Hualapai Mountains and Colorado Plateau.

Geology of the Chemehuevi Mountains

Three structural plates or allochthons, separated by three Tertiary low-angle normal or detachment faults, have been recognized in the Chemehuevi Mountains. The footwall or 'autochthon, A', of the Chemehuevi Mountains includes the structurally deepest exposed rocks in the range, below the deepest exposed detachment, the Mohave Wash fault (Fig. 3). Successively higher plates or allochthons are termed B, C and D (Figs 3 & 4a, b). Because the low-angle normal or detachment faults juxtapose mainly crystalline rocks of different structural levels from the upper and middle crust, usually with a gross lithological 'mis-match', it is necessary to separate rocks by their relative structural

position. Rocks in the Chemehuevi Mountains are divided into two assemblages defined by their relative structural positions and lithology (Fig. 3). The structurally deeper rock assemblage (I) consists of a large, crudely zoned plutonic suite of probable Cretaceous age, that intrudes foliated mylonitic gneiss at least 1.5 km thick, and makes up most of the footwall, A, and lowest allochthon, B. These two plates are separated by the Mohave Wash fault (Figs 3 & 4). The higher rock assemblage (II) lies above the Chemehuevi detachment fault in allochthon C, and above the Devils Elbow fault in allochthon D. Assemblage (II) consists of Proterozoic igneous and metamorphic rocks, and an overlying Oligocene(?) and Miocene volcanic and sedimentary sequence. Locally, intrusive rocks of assemblage (I) are found above the Chemehuevi detachment fault, and some

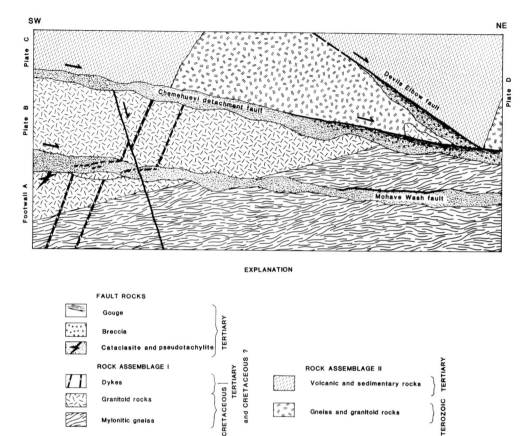

FIG. 3. Schematic composite section through the extensional fault system in the Chemehuevi Mountains. The range is cut by three low-angle normal or detachment faults—from structurally deepest to highest; the Mohave Wash, Chemehuevi and Devils Elbow faults. Each fault shows NE separation of its hanging wall. Variation in fault rock type and progressive reworking, from SW to NE, is shown diagramatically.

assemblage (II) rocks occur below the Chemehuevi fault (Fig. 4a). Each fault has normal-slip displacement shallow rocks against deeper-crustal rocks. This juxtaposition forms a distinctive tectonic layering (Fig. 3). Howard *et al.* (1982b) constructed a generalized crustal column for the extensional corridor. The reconstructed column indicates a gross 5–10 km scale layering of the crystalline upper and middle crust throughout the Colorado River area.

In this paper I use the terms low-angle normal and detachment fault interchangeably. The term low-angle normal fault implies knowledge of fault orientation and shear sense during slip, and conveys significant information about the geometry of the faults. Recognizing that the term detachment fault has been used without consistent meaning (cf. Pierce 1973; Carr &

Dickey 1976; Reynolds & Spencer 1985), I will use it here for major unrotated, low-angle normal faults, to conform with previous usage in the region (Davis *et al.* 1980; Frost & Martin 1982a).

The time of initiation of extensional faulting is not well constrained, but is probably late Oligocene or early Miocene. In the nearby Whipple and Buckskin Mountains (Fig. 2), syntectonic sediments and interstratified volcanic rocks deposited in basins that developed during extension have been dated as early Miocene and late Oligocene (Davis *et al.* 1980, 1982). Cenozoic deformation in the Chemehuevi Mountains ended by the late Miocene; basalt plugs and local flows, dated at 11.6 ± 1.2 Ma (K-Ar, whole rock—J. Nakata pers. comm., 1984), intrude or overlie and fuse cataclasites in the Chemehuevi detachment fault zone in the central part of the range. This relation indicates that movement had ceased on the Chemehuevi detachment fault by the late Miocene. Undeformed Pliocene sedimentary rocks and Quaternary deposits overlap the exposed fault system.

Rock assemblage (I)

Crystalline rocks of the footwall, A, and the lowest allochthon, B, outcrop in the central part of the range (Fig. 4a), and consist mostly of Proterozoic layered gneisses and migmatites, Cretaceous granitic rocks, and a dense swarm of younger Cretaceous(?) and Tertiary dykes.

The gneissic rocks of assemblage (I) consist of strongly foliated, variably mylonitized, layered orthogneisses and paragneisses of Proterozoic age. These upper greenschist- to lower amphibolite-facies rocks form a coherent gently (15°) SW-dipping sequence in the eastern part of the range, a steeply dipping (60–90°), NE-striking zone in the northern part of the range, and a long screen within the Cretaceous plutonic suite. The mylonitic gneisses outcrop beneath the detachment faults only in the northern and eastern parts of the range (Fig. 4a). Both the gently and steeply dipping mylonitic gneisses are *L–S* tectonites with a sub-horizontal NE–SW-trending mineral-elongation lineation which parallels the linear fabric component of other mylonites in the region (Coney 1980; Davis *et al.* 1980; Rehrig & Reynolds 1980).

Intruding the layered gneiss and migmatite complex and underlying most of the southern and central Chemehuevi Mountains is the plutonic suite of the Chemehuevi Mountains, of probable Late Cretaceous age (John 1982). The suite forms a concordant, irregularly zoned plutonic body, and comprises five phases, spanning a wide compositional range from hornblende- and sphene-rich quartz diorite and granodiorite, through biotite granodiorite, to leucocratic garnet-bearing, muscovite–biotite monzogranite. These intrusive phases are crudely concentric, the younger and more highly differentiated rocks occur towards the centre.

Foliated quartz diorite and granodiorite are the oldest phases of the suite. Locally these units are foliated and lineated with the same mylonitic fabric as the layered gneisses. A porphyritic granodiorite to monzogranite mass intrudes the older granodiorite. It is the most extensive phase of the suite. The eastern contact of this phase, against the base of mylonitic gneisses, is defined by fine- to medium-grained granitic sills in a *lit-par-lit* arrangement. The base dips gently

southwestward under the pluton. The porphyritic granodiorite unit contains, and intrudes small enclaves, as well as a very large screen, of mylonitized layered gneiss, and is, therefore, post-mylonitic. Two-mica granodiorite to monzogranite form the youngest member of the suite. The distribution of distinctive compositional types and the attitudes of plutonic contacts are the main means for measuring the separation on the low-angle normal faults.

The porphyritic granodiorite yielded a 64 Ma K–Ar cooling age on biotite (John 1982). This date indicates that the mylonitic gneisses had acquired their fabric by the end of the Cretaceous. The mylonitic fabric is apparently unrelated to mid-Tertiary extensional faulting that coincidentally parallels the lineation direction. U–Pb dating of the plutonic suite is in progress to further constrain the timing. The consistent NE–SW lineation trend observed in the Chemehuevi Mountains and throughout the region implies, by analogy with other orogenic belts, that movement along mylonitic shear zones was either NE or southwestward (Escher & Watterson 1974).

The youngest intrusions recognized in the footwall, A, and the lowest allochthon, B, form dense swarms of mafic and silicic dykes in the western and central part of the range. The dykes are centred in the Cretaceous plutonic suite, and locally account for as much as 10% of the rock volume. They form two roughly orthogonal sets orientated ENE, and N to WNW. Intrusive relations between some of the NE-trending dykes and phases of the plutonic suite suggest that the dykes may be synplutonic, i.e. Late Cretaceous or older. The NW-trending dykes cut them and possibly are Miocene based on a K–Ar date (Frost *et al.* 1982). In the southern Chemehuevi Mountains is a second set of NE-trending mafic dykes, presumably Miocene, which intrude the Chemehuevi detachment fault, and exhibit substantial fracturing that resulted from subsequent fault movement. These dykes indicate that some intrusion was synchronous with detachment faulting.

Rock assemblage (II)

Crystalline rocks of assemblage (II) outcrop in allochthons C and D, above the Chemehuevi detachment fault in the western Chemehuevi Mountains and above the Chemehuevi and Devils Elbow faults in the eastern part of the area (Fig. 4a). Proterozoic granites and gneisses without a mylonitic fabric, and therefore texturally unlike those in rock assemblage (I), are the major crystalline rock types in assemblage (II).

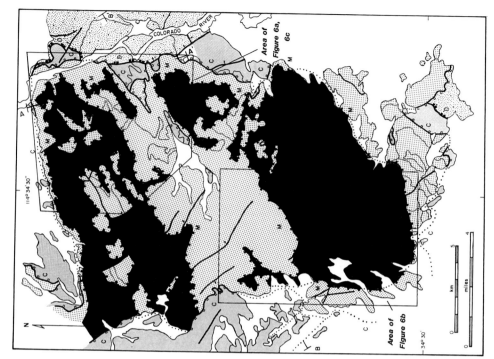

FIG. 4(b)

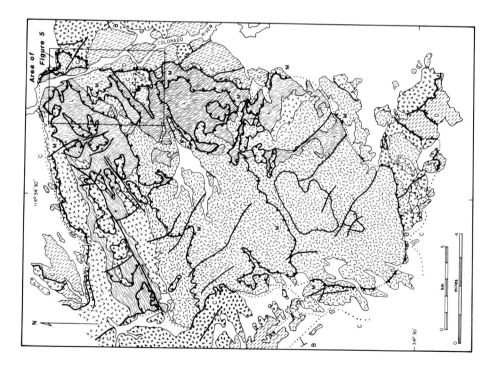

FIG. 4(a)

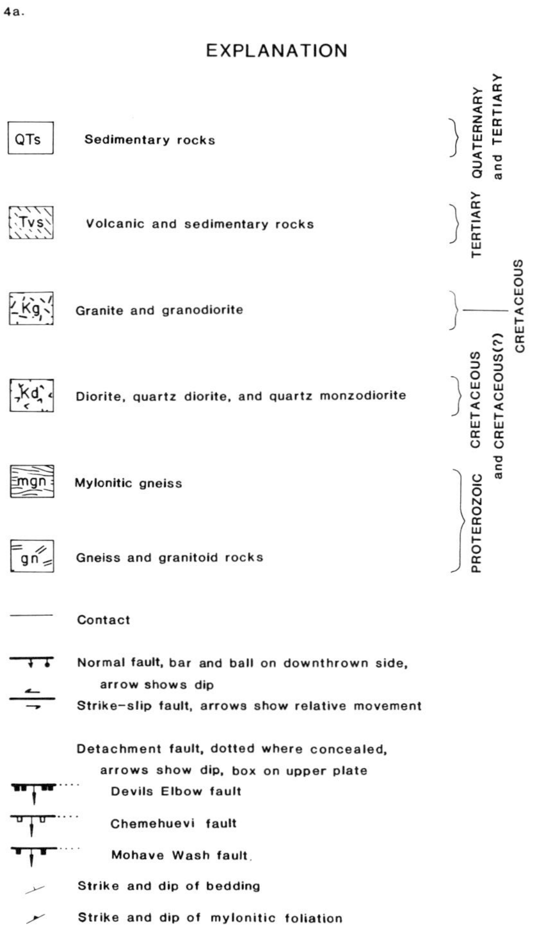

4b.

EXPLANATION

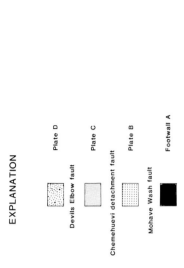

Plate D

Devils Elbow fault

Plate C

Chemehuevi detachment fault

Plate B

Mohave Wash fault

Footwall A

FIG. 4. (a) Generalized geological map of the Chemehuevi Mountains area in California and Arizona. The three detachment faults are indicated by M = Mohave Wash fault; C = Chemehuevi fault; and D = Devils Elbow fault. (b) Tectonic map of the Chemehuevi Mountains portraying the Tertiary detachment faults and intervening plates. Unpatterned areas outline post-detachment deposits that are Pliocene and younger. The patterned areas outline plates discussed in the text. The footwall, A, is the structurally deepest plate exposed. Plate B lies above the Mohave Wash fault. Plate C lies above the regionally developed Chemehuevi detachment fault. The structurally highest plate, D, is above the Devils Elbow fault, in the southern and eastern part of the range. Plates C and D, both of which are broken and shingled by numerous E-dipping(?) normal faults, moved together during slip on the Chemehuevi detachment fault, after the Devils Elbow fault became inactive.

4a.

EXPLANATION

QTs   Sedimentary rocks

Tvs   Volcanic and sedimentary rocks

Kg   Granite and granodiorite

Kd   Diorite, quartz diorite, and quartz monzodiorite

mgn   Mylonitic gneiss

gn   Gneiss and granitoid rocks

} QUATERNARY and TERTIARY

} TERTIARY

} CRETACEOUS

} CRETACEOUS and CRETACEOUS(?)

} PROTEROZOIC and CRETACEOUS

——— Contact

Normal fault, bar and ball on downthrown side, arrow shows dip

Strike-slip fault, arrows show relative movement

Detachment fault, dotted where concealed, arrows show dip, box on upper plate

Devils Elbow fault

Chemehuevi fault

Mohave Wash fault

Strike and dip of bedding

Strike and dip of mylonitic foliation

Distinctive Proterozoic ophitic diabase sheets, striking NW and dipping steeply, intrude the non-mylonitic gneisses and granites. Unlike rock assemblage (I), none of the crystalline rocks exposed in rock assemblage (II) exhibit a mylonitic fabric. Non-mylonitic gneisses assigned to assemblage (II) outcrop in plate B in the southern part of the range, and are inferred as lying above an unexposed upper-shear-zone margin or mylonite front.

Volcanic and sedimentary rocks of Tertiary age encircle the range above the Chemehuevi detachment fault and Devils Elbow fault, and lie both unconformably and in fault contact above the crystalline rocks just described. The deformed Tertiary rocks are divided into three major lithological sequences, from oldest to youngest, mafic and intermediate lavas, an ash-flow tuff considered to be the Peach Springs Tuff of Young & Brennan (1974), and a thick sequence of alluvial fan deposits and breccias with thin interbedded mafic and silicic flows and tuffs. An estimated thickness of the Tertiary section is of the order of 2–3 km. The age of the older sequence of volcanic rocks is not accurately known. Most of the faulted Tertiary rocks in the region around the Chemehuevi Mountains are between 17 and 22 Ma (Howard & John, this volume). In the Whipple Mountains, however, volcanic rocks have ages as old as 26 Ma. This age range suggests that the older sequence is of latest-Oligocene or early-Miocene age. The Peach Springs Tuff outcrops in both the eastern and western parts of the range, and has a K–Ar age of 18.1±0.6 Ma (Howard et al. 1982a).

Within the faulted Tertiary sedimentary sequence are large (up to 1 km in greatest dimension) lenses of monolithologic breccia. These megabreccia lenses are composed of shattered Proterozoic granites and gneisses of assemblage (II) and the Cretaceous granitic rocks and younger dykes of assemblage (I). Deposits of this type are characteristic of landslides in arid environments (Krieger 1978), and may represent seismically triggered debris derived from over-steepened or unstable fault scarps. The granitic megabreccia deposits and alluvial sediments lie within the tilted Tertiary sequence above the Chemehuevi fault in the eastern part of the range. Clast types match source regions of restricted outcrop in plates A and B less than 8 km away in the central Chemehuevi Mountains. Similarity in fracture intensity and alteration between exposed cataclasites and the granite megabreccias suggests that these syntectonic deposits may have resulted from the exhumation of the detachment faults during progressive extension. This is supported by the presence of clasts of chlorite-and epidote-altered cataclasite, elsewhere associated with the faults, in allochthonous alluvial fan deposits younger than the megabreccias.

Style and sequence of Tertiary deformation

All the rock types in assemblages (I) and (II) were mildly to intensely deformed during the mid- to late-Tertiary. The deformation produced a fault system comprised of at least three allochthons, separated by three brittle, low-angle normal faults (from structurally deepest to most shallow), the Mohave Wash, Chemehuevi Mountains and Devils Elbow detachment faults (Figs 3, 4 & 5). Criteria for the recognition of each fault, separating the allochthons, include types of rocks juxtaposed, style and intensity of the brittle deformation and related fault rocks, amount of reworking of fault rocks, and relative structural position and continuity of outcrop. Of the three faults, the Chemehuevi fault is of the greatest significance regionally and is the youngest. It is here equated with the Whipple Mountains detachment fault of Carr & Dickey (1976) and the Whipple detachment fault of Davis et al. (1980) exposed in the Whipple Mountains 20 km to the S, and with the Sacramento detachment fault of McClelland (1982) exposed just NW of the Chemehuevi Mountains in the Sacramento Mountains (Fig. 2).

From the evidence of offset markers, preserved striae, drag folds, minor faults within related cataclasites, and the SW dip of Tertiary strata in the Chemehuevi Mountains, it is estimated that slip on each of the low-angle normal faults resulted in northeastward (040–060°) transport of successively higher plates or allochthons. The detachment faults cut down-section in the direction of tectonic transport, and record unidirectional extension of the upper and middle crust. The upper and middle crust as a whole extended non-uniformally–rocks above the Chemehuevi detachment fault were extended along a series of steep normal faults, while the footwall apparently remained largely undeformed. Plutonic contacts in allochthon B are separated from the footwall, A, along the Mohave Wash fault by ~2 km. Separation of plate B from plate C along the Chemehuevi detachment fault is at least 8 km. Movement of the structurally highest plate, D, above plate C on the Devils Elbow fault is likewise believed to be many kilometres. Plates C and D behaved as a single plate during the most recent motion on the Chemehuevi detachment fault.

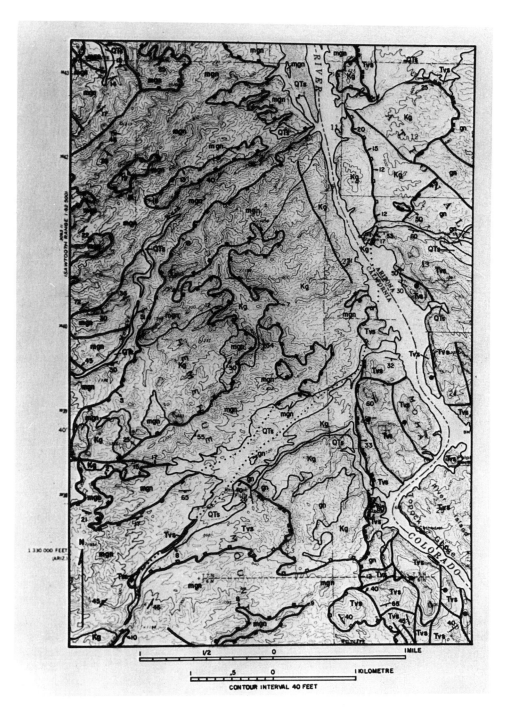

FIG. 5. Geological map of part of the eastern Chemehuevi Mountains (outlined in Fig. 4a), showing the stacked sequence of detachment faults. Symbols used are the same as those in Fig. 4.

At outcrop scale, each fault is approximately planar, but when viewed at map scale, the two structurally deepest faults are corrugated parallel to the NE transport direction. Orthogonal to these are broad NNW-trending antiformal and synformal undulations of the fault surfaces (Cameron & Frost 1981; John 1982, 1984; Spencer 1984).

Dips on each detachment fault vary from horizontal or very gently inclined along the troughs or crests of the mullion structures, to as much as 40° on the steeper flanks or strike-slip portions of the faults.

Mohave Wash fault

The lowest detachment fault, the Mohave Wash fault, occurs wholly within the crystalline rocks of assemblage (I), except in the very southernmost part of the range (Fig. 4a). The fault is exposed as a sinuous trace over more than 350 km² in the Chemehuevi Mountains (Fig. 4). An initial NE dip of the fault, in the transport direction, is suggested by several lines of evidence (Howard & John, this volume). An initial average dip of the Mohave Wash fault of 15°NE, which implies cutting through nearly 6 km of crustal section over 22 km, is considered to be the maximum possible, based on the lack of significant chemical, textural and mineralogical variations within the porphyritic granodiorite phase of the plutonic suite across 15 km of strike (John 1982, and unpublished work). Therefore the original dip of the faults was probably less than 15°NE, and could have been as low as 5° regionally. This corroborates data from the fault zone, which indicate relatively little changes in fault rock type, deformation mechanism and metamorphic grade in the footwall.

Correlation of a moderately dipping, roughly N-trending internal contact within the plutonic suite in the footwall, A, and in the lowest allochthon, B, and numerous truncated screens of older wall-rocks within the plutonic suite, indicate ~2 km ENE–WSW separation on the Mohave Wash fault. Sub-horizontal striae preserved along the fault trend 040–060°, and indicate the direction of most recent movement.

Deformation within autochthon A and plate B

Autochthon A and lowest allochton B, as exposed in the Chemehuevi Mountains, are largely undeformed internally. Sparse, discontinuous ductile shear zones or mylonites (up to 1 m thick) cut all rock types in assemblage (I). These are concentrated zones of high strain, locally with variably orientated foliation and mineral-elongation lineations. Stereo-plots of the foliation and lineations show no consistent orientation. Where dykes or compositional layering in the crystalline rocks are cut by these shear zones, separations up to tens of centimetres have been measured. Numerous small microfaults and vein-like intrusions are common throughout the autochthon and lowest allochthon, and are concentrated near both the Mohave Wash and Chemehuevi detachment faults.

Moderate to steeply dipping (50–80°) normal faults with strikes ranging from 110 to 170° cut autochthon A and allochthon B, some truncating and others truncated by the Mohave Wash fault (Figs 3, 4 & 5). These faults have tens to hundreds of metres of separation, and are nowhere known to cut the structurally higher Chemehuevi detachment fault. Locally preserved striae indicate nearly pure dip-slip movement. Because slip occurred on the steep normal faults both before and after movement on the Mohave Wash fault, it is reasonable to conclude that these steeper faults were active concurrent with faulting along the Chemehuevi detachment.

Several NE-trending (050–060°) strike-slip faults truncate the Mohave Wash fault, and are older than the latest movement on the Chemehuevi detachment. Dip of the faults is between 40 and 80°, but tends to mimic the foliation in the steeply dipping mylonitic gneisses in the northern Chemehuevi Mountains. Left-lateral separation on the northern strike-slip fault (Fig. 4) may be as much as several hundred metres.

One klippe of a small displacement low-angle fault, mapped as part of the footwall, A, outcrops in the southwestern part of the range (Figs 3 & 4a, b). Irregular plutonic contacts cut by the fault are not significantly offset, indicating probably less than one hundred metres separation.

Both the normal and strike-slip faults, are planar discontinuities marked by coherent breccias and cataclasites. Locally, a microbreccia layer one millimetre to several centimetres thick marks the most recent fault trace. The cataclasites are composed primarily of quartz, plagioclase and potassium-feldspar, the milled-down equivalent of the wall-rock, in a matrix of hematite (or specular hematite) ±calcite ±quartz±azurite±malachite±barite. In contrast, the low-angle fault is marked by coherent cataclasites composed of quartz, plagioclase and potassium-feldspar, with the retrograde mineral assemblage of chlorite±albite±epidote±clinozoisite±sericite and rare calcite.

Taken as a group the normal and strike-slip faults, and microfaults cutting the footwall, A, and allochthon B, can account for a few percent extension, below the regionally developed Chemehuevi detachment fault. Displacement within the thin ductile shear zones can account for even less extension. Dyke rocks, only some of which are coeval with the extension, intrude the footwall, A, and allochthon B and constitute up to 10% of the rock volume in the western half of the Chemehuevi Mountains. Dyke intrusion therefore accounts for no more than 5% extension overall in the footwall of the regionally developed Chemehuevi detachment fault. Footwall accommodation to movement on the regionally developed Chemehuevi detachment fault was therefore small.

Chemehuevi detachment fault

The Chemehuevi detachment fault lies 0–750 m above the older Mohave Wash fault, and generally separates rock assemblage (I) of the footwall, A, and plate B, from rock assemblage (II) and plate C. The fault juxtaposes Miocene ashflow tuffs and lavas directly on the plutonic suite and underlying mylonitized gneisses. The depth at which the fault was initiated is estimated as at least 6 km, because structurally intact blocks above the Chemehuevi detachment fault in the western Chemehuevi Mountains and along the Colorado River have minimum palaeothicknesses (measured perpendicular to the Tertiary unconformity) up to 6 km (Fig. 4). The 'toes' of these blocks have either been eroded, or are covered by structurally higher blocks; the palaeothickness of the blocks provides a minimum estimate of crustal thickness above the fault prior to their detachment, rotation and northeastward translation. From regional arguments put forward by Howard & John (this volume), it can be inferred that the easternmost exposures of the Chemehuevi and Whipple detachment fault(s) were initiated at depths of 10 and 15 km. Juxtaposition of Tertiary strata down against plate B implies that the Chemehuevi detachment fault has at least 6 km and perhaps 10–15 km of crustal excision and vertical displacement. A more detailed discussion of initial dip will further constrain this estimate.

Horizontal separation of crystalline rocks on the Chemehuevi detachment fault is a minimum of 8 km NE, and displacement is probably of the order of 20–40 km. Broad areas of slickensides occur along the fault. The striae are sub-horizontal, and regionally trend 220–240° parallel to the dip direction of the overlying

rotated Tertiary strata. Assuming that the Tertiary succession was horizontal prior to detachment faulting, NE upper-plate slip can be inferred from the direction of tilted strata, the orientation of striae, observed offset on minor normal faults within related cataclasites, and the geometry of drag folds in plates C and D. Intrusive rocks of the plutonic suite crop out just E of the Colorado River above the Chemehuevi fault (Figs 3 & 4). The restored position of these rocks in the footwall, A, suggests a minimum of 8 km northeastward horizontal separation of plate C along the Chemehuevi detachment fault, from what is now the N-central part of the range. This estimate is based on the location of the northeastern limit of the Cretaceous granite and granodiorite phases of the plutonic suite in the footwall, A, and plate B (Fig. 4). A reasonable estimate of slip on the Chemehuevi fault in the Chemehuevi Mountains would be on the order of 20–40 km, based on the overall increase in displacement noted regionally by Howard & John (this volume) across the extensional corridor. Estimates of 30–40 km separation have been suggested for the Whipple detachment fault by G. A. Davis (pers. comm. 1981) and Howard *et al.* (1982a). To the W, in the headwall region of the extensional corridor, displacement is significantly less (Howard & John, this volume). The youngest deformed Miocene rocks show separation on the fault of 8 km or less, based on the presence of garnet-bearing, muscovite–biotite monzogranite clasts in the syntectonic deposits, that are areally restricted within the footwall (A).

Both the Chemehuevi and Mohave Wash faults are corrugated parallel to the NE transport direction, but are not everywhere parallel to each other. Locally plate B is cut out, and plate C lies in direct tectonic contact with plate A along the Chemehuevi fault. This relationship suggests that movement had ceased on the Mohave Wash fault, while the Chemehuevi detachment fault was still active. The Mohave fault may have been an early splay that became inactive, and was cut by the new Chemehuevi detachment fault which was more favourable for slip during the evolution of the fault system.

Unlike the deeper Mohave Wash fault, the Chemehuevi fault is not cut by younger high-angle normal faults. Numerous high-angle faults cut rocks above the Chemehuevi detachment fault (Figs 4a, b & 5), and account for extreme extension of the hanging wall. For simplicity only a few of the largest faults are shown in Fig. 4; I have mapped many others (John, unpublished work; Miller *et al.* 1983). None of these faults, however, can be traced across the detachment into plate B. The Chemehuevi detachment fault is preserved within a few degrees of the initial orientation, and is not a steep normal fault that has been rotated during progressive extension. As with the Mohave Wash fault, exposure of the Chemehuevi detachment fault over an area in excess of 350 km^2 and 22 km across strike, with only small changes in crustal level and nature of related fault rocks, limits the initial dip of the fault to a very low angle in this region. Deepening of the Chemehuevi fault by 2–4 km across the range (SW–NE) is inferred, compatible with an initial regional dip of 5–15° NE as described for the structurally deeper Mohave Wash fault.

Devils Elbow fault

The Devils Elbow fault, the structurally highest exposed detachment fault, can be traced along-strike for roughly 6 km along both sides of the Colorado River. This limited exposure precludes detailed analysis of the geometry. In excellent exposures along the W side of the river (Fig. 5), the fault juxtaposes Tertiary fanglomerates and crystalline-clast megabreccias in plate D, against granites of the plutonic suite in plate C. The fault is marked by a moderately E-dipping (34°) planar surface, on which striae plunge 30–060°. Based on the orientation of preserved striae, SW dip of the overlying Tertiary strata, and observed offsets on minor normal faults within the related breccias and cataclasites, the hanging wall of the Devils Elbow fault is inferred to have moved NE. It is truncated in at least two places by the structurally deeper Chemehuevi fault. Separation of plate D from plate C on the Devils Elbow fault is estimated as 3–8 km, using the base of the Tertiary section as a datum (John, unpublished work). No source of the rocks above the fault has been recognized in the footwall, A.

Cumulative separation of plate D from the footwall, A, is the combined displacement of the Mohave Wash fault (~2 km), the Chemehuevi detachment fault (>8 km), and earlier slip on the Devils Elbow fault (~4–8 km). Estimated minimum horizontal slip on the composite fault system exceeds 22 km, the present width of the Chemehuevi detachment fault exposure around the range.

Deformation within plates C and D

Deformation above the regionally developed Chemehuevi detachment fault accounts for the extreme extension of the upper crust above the largely undeformed footwall. Plates C and D were extended along innumerable steeply

dipping (60–80°) normal faults with strikes ranging from 135 to 160°, and oblique-slip faults trending 045–090° (Figs 4 & 5). These faults have tens of metres to over one kilometre of separation, and are never seen to cut the Chemehuevi detachment fault.

Both the normal and oblique-slip faults, where well exposed, are irregular planar discontinuities characterized by thin zones of hematite-rich gouge and breccia, commonly with calcite vein-fill.

Structures in the hanging wall of the Chemehuevi detachment fault are best preserved in the E-central part of the range (Fig. 4). There cross-cutting relationships between faults suggest a complex history of repeated high-angle faulting (normal and oblique-slip), to produce both the steeply and gently dipping faults exposed.

Fault corrugation: mullion structures

The synchronous development of Tertiary low-angle normal faults and broad undulations in these faults is well documented along the Colorado River trough (Wilkens & Heidrick 1982; Cameron & Frost 1981; Frost et al. 1982; John 1984). The undulations form generally orthogonal sets that trend NE and NNW. The origin of these undulations is currently a topic of interest among numerous geologists in the region (Rehrig & Reynolds 1980; Frost 1981; Spencer 1982; John 1984; Spencer 1984).

The two structurally deepest detachments in the Chemehuevi Mountains, the Chemehuevi and Mohave Wash faults, are corrugated parallel to the NE direction of transport during fault slip. Other, broader undulations trending N-NW perpendicular to the slip direction, with wavelengths of 10–50 km, are discussed later. It is thought that the corrugations along the slip direction developed during fault movement as primary mullion structures based on the detailed analysis that follows. The amplitude and wavelength of the corrugations vary with footwall rock type and pre-existing structural grain, and also differ between the two faults.

Minimum-relief contour maps have been constructed from 1:24,000 scale mapping for both the Mohave Wash and Chemehuevi detachment faults (Fig. 6a–c) in areas where the faults are best preserved (Fig. 4). The maps (Fig. 6) were constructed in a manner similar to that used by Spencer (1985). From these maps comparisons are made regarding the influence of footwall rock type and fabric on the fault shape, relative amplitude and wavelength of corrugations associated with the two faults, and down-dip

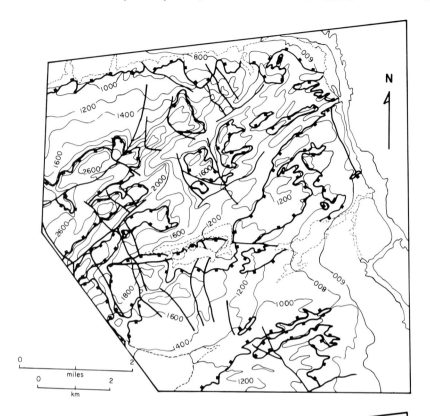

FIG. 6(a)

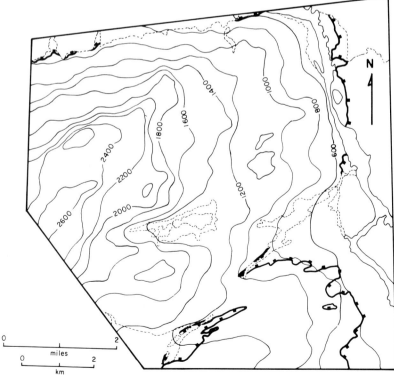

FIG. 6(b)

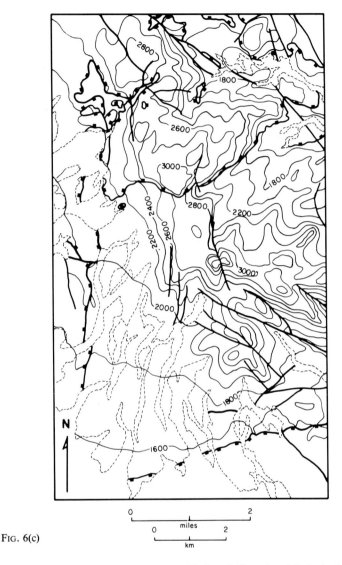

FIG. 6(c)

FIG. 6. Minimum-relief contour maps of the Mohave Wash and Chemehuevi faults in the areas outlined in Fig. 4(b). Contour interval for each map 200ft. (a) Structure contour map of the Mohave Wash fault in the northeastern part of the Chemehuevi Mountains. Footwall rocks are both sub-horizontally and sub-vertically foliated mylonitic gneiss. (b) Structure contour map of the Chemehuevi detachment fault in the same area as Fig. 6(a). The footwall of the fault consists of sub-horizontally and sub-vertically foliated mylonitic gneiss. (c) Structure contour map of the Mohave Wash fault in the southwestern part of the Chemehuevi Mountains. Footwall rocks are isotropic Cretaceous granitic rocks.

irregularities of the fault surfaces. Differences in form between the Mohave Wash and Chemehuevi detachment faults may be attributed in part to the high-angle faults that cut the Mohave Wash, but not the Chemehuevi fault. Of the three detachment faults exposed in the Chemehuevi Mountains, the geometry of the Mohave Wash fault is best characterized.

Mohave Wash fault

The geometry of the Mohave Wash fault is dominated by a series of NE-trending mullion structures. They are corrugations having wavelengths of 200 m to 1 km and amplitudes of up to 150 m where the fault cuts sub-horizontally foliated mylonitic gneisses (Fig. 6a). Locally the fault has small parasitic undulations with amplitudes as low as 30 m. Where the Mohave Wash fault cuts homogeneous granite, the wavelengths are up to 3 km and the amplitudes as much as 390 m (Fig. 6c). Antiformal corrugations commonly project along their lengths into synformal corrugations in a down-dip direction along the fault. In addition, the noncylindrical appearance of the corrugations seen in the structure contour maps probably reflects, in part, unrecognized younger normal and strike-slip faults that cut the Mohave Wash fault.

The long dimensions of the mullion structures are oriented $055 \pm 5°$. Inasmuch as slickensides on the fault surfaces are orientated $040 - 060°$, the latest fault movement roughly paralleled the axes of the mullion structures.

Along the strike-slip segments or lateral walls of the corrugations, crystalline rocks of the two adjacent plates have been dragged past each other. Originally steep NE- and NW-striking dykes of the Cretaceous(?) and/or Tertiary dyke swarms are fractured and rotated into subparallelism with the gentle dipping fault zone. Throughout the zone of cataclasis the dykes are clearly recognizable, as shown in Fig. 3, but fracture intensity and rotation increase near the upper margin where offset is greatest. This relationship of increased fracture intensity and dyke rotation within the fault zone is consistent enough to be used to estimate the original position of eroded parts of either the Mohave Wash or Chemehuevi detachment faults, and help constrain the contour maps.

Chemehuevi detachment fault

The Chemehuevi detachment fault surface has broader NE-trending corrugations than the Mohave Wash fault. Where the Chemehuevi fault truncates sub-horizontally foliated gneisses in the footwall (Fig. 6b), the fault is corrugated with wavelengths of 1.5–3 km and amplitudes of only 50–100 m. Above undeformed granites in the western part of the range, the wavelengths vary up to 8–10 km and the amplitudes vary between 150 and 300 m. In the northernmost part of the range, where vertically foliated mylonitic gneisses make up the footwalls of both the Mohave Wash and Chemehuevi faults (Fig. 4), the amplitude of corrugations on each of the two faults increases to nearly 400 m, and the wavelength is approximately the same as elsewhere. As with the Mohave Wash fault, corrugations of the Chemehuevi detachment fault apparently porpoise from antiformal to synformal, in the transport direction.

A section (Fig. 7) drawn perpendicular to the corrugations (Fig. 4b) illustrates differences in relative amplitude and wavelength between the two faults where they cut the same footwall rock type. The section emphasizes the cross-cutting nature of the faulting with respect to the pre-existing mylonitic fabric. The two faults anastomose both along strike (NW-trend) and down-dip (NE-trend) (Fig. 8). In places the faults are separated by nearly 1 km of coherent rock. Elsewhere the two faults are separated by hundreds of metres of altered cataclasites; locally, the Chemehuevi detachment fault truncates the Mohave Wash fault (Figs 4 & 9).

Devils Elbow fault

Throughout its relatively limited exposure, the Devils Elbow fault is apparently either very broadly warped or uncorrugated in the slip direction. The structurally deeper Chemehuevi detachment fault is corrugated in a broad antiform–synform mullion pair where it truncates a NW-trending warp in the Devils Elbow fault in the eastern part of the range (Fig. 4).

Northwest-trending fault undulations

Broad undulations of the two structurally deepest fault zones, with wavelengths of 10–50 km, trend NNW, orthogonal to the mullion structures. These larger undulations combine with the NE-trending mullion structures to produce the domal topography characteristic of the metamorphic core complexes W of the Colorado River in California (Cameron & Frost 1981; Spencer 1984). Possible origins of these features are discussed in a later section.

Evidence for a syntectonic origin of the corrugations

Warps of the detachment faults along the Colorado River trough have been attributed to folding of the faults by Cameron & Frost (1981), Davis *et al.* (1982), and Spencer (1982, 1984), whereas Woodward & Osborn (1980) and Wilkens & Heidrick (1982) described some as primary megagrooves. The wave-like pattern of parallel NE-trending undulations formed along the Mohave Wash and Chemehuevi fault zones are not folds, but primary grooves or syntectonic corrugations. Amplitude and wavelength of the corrugations differ along the three main faults. The corrugated Chemehuevi fault cuts the more planar Devils Elbow fault (Fig. 5). Both the Mohave Wash and Chemehuevi detachment faults truncate pre-existing gently W-dipping mylonitic foliation in the eastern part of the range (Figs 7 & 9). This fabric is cut by the undulating faults, and not folded into

B.E. John

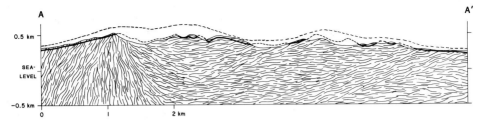

FIG. 7. Geological section along the line A–A' (Fig. 4b), drawn NW–SE normal to the corrugation axes. Corrugations of the Mohave Wash fault cut the mylonitic foliation.

FIG. 8. Geological section along B–B' (Fig. 4a), drawn SW–NE parallel to the corrugation axes. The Tertiary section is repeated by numerous faults above the regionally developed Chemehuevi detachment fault. The Mohave Wash fault is truncated by the structurally higher Chemehuevi fault in the W, and inferred to be cut in the E. Patterns shown are the same as in Fig. 4.

FIG. 9. Left: view NE from the central part of the Chemehuevi Mountains showing the stacked sequence of Tertiary detachment faults. The Mohave Wash fault (M) separates gently dipping mylonitic gneisses in the footwall from equivalent rocks in plate B. Rocks above the Chemehuevi detachment fault (C) across the Colorado River in Arizona, are Cretaceous granitic rocks. Rocks above the Devils Elbow fault (D) are Proterozoic gneisses and granites, and unconformable Tertiary strata.
Right: view SE from the northeastern part of the Chemehuevi Mountains showing the discordance between gently SW-dipping mylonitic foliation, and the E-dipping Mohave Wash fault.

concordance with them. The thickness of cataclasites and breccias associated with the two faults varies with relative position on the corrugations. The corrugation axes and lateral walls parallel the 040–060° slip on the faults. In the northern part of the range where steeply dipping mylonites make up the footwall (Fig. 4), extension was apparently more easily accommodated by broad, high-amplitude undulations and tear faults. This contrasts with the high-frequency, low-amplitude corrugations that formed where the faults cut sub-horizontally foliated mylonites in the eastern part of the range.

Fault rocks

Rocks produced by slip on the detachment faults in the Chemehuevi Mountains include incoherent gouge, breccia, rocks of the cataclasite series, and rare protomylonite and pseudotachylite.

Following the conceptual model of Sibson (1977, 1983), these fault rocks can be interpreted as a depth series formed roughly at crustal depths from 0 to 5 km (gouge and breccia), 5 to 10 km (breccia and cataclasite) and >10 km (protomylonite). Thin mylonites 0.01–1 m thick are present, but no major zones of mylonite can be related to the detachment faulting in the Chemehuevi Mountains. Fluids associated with the faulting hydrothermally altered intrafault cataclasites and breccias. From SW to NE in the transport direction across the range, fault rocks associated with detachment faulting change progressively in alteration mineral assemblages, in nature of active deformation mechanism, and in amount of reworking of the fault rocks.

Rocks produced by slip on the Mohave Wash fault include crush breccias, cataclasites and locally pseudotachylite. Thickness of these fault rocks varies from less than 2 m to more than 100 m. The retrograde mineral assemblage associated with the fault zone is consistently lower greenschist facies (e.g. chlorite±epidote±albite±clinozoisite±sericite±actinolite±calcite). The northeasternmost exposures show evidence of reworking of these rocks at shallower structural levels to form gouge and breccia, rich in hematite and calcite, that overprint earlier cataclasites. A general lack of reworking of fault rocks elsewhere along the fault, and its small displacement, suggests that the Mohave Wash fault was active for a relatively short time; the cataclasites suggest generation at intermediate crustal depths (Sibson 1977).

Fault rocks associated with the Chemehuevi fault include gouge, crush breccias and cataclasites. Thick zones of altered cataclasite are reworked into thinner zones of breccia. This sequence of cross-cutting or reworked fault rocks suggests that the depth of faulting became progressively shallower during fault evolution owing to progressive normal faulting and tectonic unroofing. The most recently active fault surface outcrops as planar zones, typical of shallow-level faults, marked in eastern exposures by the juxtaposition of hematite-rich breccias against chlorite- and epidote-rich cataclasites (Fig. 3). These relations suggest that the Chemehuevi detachment fault evolved from a wide zone of cataclasite at mid-crustal depths, to a narrower zone of breccia within the upper crust, to a sharp planar discontinuity marked by breccia and gouge locally at shallow-crustal depths of 0–5 km. Cataclasites beneath the fault are typically tens of metres thick. Locally, flow-laminated breccias as thick as 1 m are preserved in the synformal hinges. In western exposures,

the Chemehuevi fault juxtaposes Proterozoic granites and gneisses of assemblage (II) down on Cretaceous granites from assemblage (I). Rocks of both the hanging wall and footwall are intensely fractured, and show limonitic alteration apparently superimposed on pervasive chlorite and epidote mineralization. In these western exposures, the fault is marked by breccia and cataclasite, lacking any throughgoing planar surface. The absence of gouge and of a planar fault surface in western exposures of the Chemehuevi detachment fault suggests that slip there may have ceased at some intermediate depth in the upper crust (>5 km). If so, movement on the eastern portion of the fault may have continued after the western portion locked.

The Devils Elbow fault is marked by a gouge and breccia zone less than 2 m thick beneath an extremely planar fault surface. Footwall granitic rocks are highly fractured crush breccias and cataclasites, which contain chlorite- and epidote-alteration mineral assemblages. The cataclasites are reworked as clasts in younger scaly gouge, reflecting continued faulting. The gouge, planar fault surface, and thinness of the fault zone suggest that the most recent movement on the Devils Elbow fault was at a shallow crustal level, probably less than 5 km.

Cataclastic rocks along the detachment fault zones in the Chemehuevi Mountains provide evidence of either high strain rates or temperatures low enough for frictional processes (cataclastic flow and frictional sliding) to have dominated deformation at the present level of exposure. Elongate quartz and alkali feldspar suggests that in the structurally deepest exposures of the Mohave Wash fault incipient crystal plastic behaviour in quartz and pressure solution apparently became important deformation mechanisms.

Rare cross-cutting veins of pseudotachylite a few millimetres to centimetres thick and as much as 0.5 m long occur in and adjacent to the Mohave Wash fault zone in the southwestern part of the area. The pseudotachylite, identified microscopically by R. H. Sibson (1984, pers. comm.), resulted from frictional melting during faulting. Its presence in the Mohave Wash fault zone suggests that the fault was seismically active during at least part of its movement history as a low-angle normal fault. Similar veins are found along the Chemehuevi detachment fault, although none are unambiguously pseudotachylite. The Mohave Wash and Chemehuevi detachment faults are also characterized by a high concentration of cross-cutting mineralized veins and fractures. The veins are host to chlorite and epidote and/or calcite and hematite vein-fill.

Cross-cutting relationships between the veins and fractures, and their proximity to the faults, imply episodic fracturing and fluid flow associated with detachment faulting.

Along both the Mohave Wash and Chemehuevi detachment faults cataclasites are thickest on the lateral walls of the mullion structures, and thinnest on the crests and troughs. Along the Mohave Wash fault cataclasites vary in thickness from less than 2 m over an antiformal crest, to greater than 100 m locally across the lateral wall of one of the mullion structures. Thickness variations along the Chemehuevi detachment fault are less well documented but apparently similar. Other properties being equal (slip, strain rate, thermal gradient, etc.) cataclasis was apparently more widespread along the sides, or strike-slip portions, of the mullion structures.

Fault-zone evolution

The fault system in the Chemehuevi Mountains evolved over roughly 5–10 My. Initial extension was accommodated at palaeodepths of greater than 6–10 km by the gently NE-dipping Mohave Wash fault. The upper crust was apparently being pulled apart simultaneously along steeply dipping normal faults. The small-displacement Mohave Wash fault is interpreted as representing an early stage of the regionally extensive Chemehuevi detachment fault which became active with continued extension at upper mid-crustal levels. Footwall accommodation (within the autochthon, A, and plate B) to movement on the Chemehuevi fault was minor, but included the development of normal and strike-slip faults, microfaults, local ductile shear zones and dyke emplacement. With continued extension upper-crustal volcanic and sedimentary rocks were rotated along high-angle normal faults above the Chemehuevi detachment fault, to a position against the mid-crustal footwall rocks. Examination of fault rocks associated with the Chemehuevi fault, and syntectonic alluvial fan deposits suggests that movement on the detachment continued up to very shallow crustal levels (0–5 km), and locally breached the surface leading to wholesale denudation of the fault zone.

Discussion

The tendency for the crust to extend in one particular mode is influenced by thermal gradient, and to a lesser extent, strain rate, depth, rock type, asssociated fluids and pre-existing struc-tures or crustal heterogeneity. The Chemehuevi Mountains provide an example of mid-crustal accommodation to continental stretching, in which some of the effects of these variables can be evaluated. Deformation in the Chemehuevi Mountains took place along gently NE-dipping detachment fault zones that cut discordantly across heterogeneous crystalline rocks. The faults had low initial dips, and accommodated up to 100% extension. Above the regionally developed detachment faults, extension took place along a system of steeper normal faults which probably fed displacement into the detachment(s) (Davis *et al.* 1980; Howard *et al.* 1982a). The mapped fault geometry and inferred evolution of the fault system, place certain constraints on models of continental extension.

Detachment faults within the Chemehuevi Mountains area were initiated with a regional dip of 5–15° NE. Minor pseudotachylite associated with the low-angle normal faults suggests that they were seismically active during at least part of their movement history. The presence of cataclasites but absence of thick zones of associated mylonite indicate that the faults were active at a low angle within the brittle regime, at crustal depths of 6–10 km. Seismologists have yet to find earthquake evidence for seismic slip on low-angle normal faults. Fault-plane solutions of large normal-faulting earthquakes throughout the world appear at the time of movement to have dips of 30–60° throughout the 'brittle' upper crust (Eyidogan & Jackson 1985; Jackson & McKenzie 1983). The Chemehuevi Mountains are therefore particularly significant, emphasizing the paradox that needs to be resolved between field evidence and seismic data concerning the nature of crustal accommodation to continental extension.

The field evidence from the Chemehuevi Mountains also challenges the common assumption that low-angle normal faults theoretically cannot move in that orientation. Jackson & McKenzie (1983) suggest that new generations of high-angle faults are required during progressive extensional deformation, because of the decrease in effectiveness of gravity to overcome friction on a fault plane, as the dip of a fault decreases. I suggest that movement may have been aided in the Chemehuevi Mountains area by intermittent high(?) fluid pressure. Altered intrafault cataclasites and breccias, and associated veins showing repeated fracturing, fluid flow and mineralization, suggest that detachment faulting may have been accompanied by episodic high fluid pressure. A similar relationship has been documented by Power (unpubl. work) along detachment faults in the

Riverside Mountains approximately 50 km to the S. He suggests that intermittent high fluid pressure may have diminished the frictional resistance, and effective normal stress along the fault(s), and allowed movement at a low dip. As in the Chemehuevi Mountains, extensional deformation in the Riverside Mountains was confined to the brittle regime. Bartley & Glazner (1985) have gone a step further in proposing a model for the initiation of low-angle normal faults, through the reorientation of stress trajectories by periodic sealing of a geothermal system.

The NE-trending corrugations on the Chemehuevi and Mohave Wash fault developed coeval with slip. Shovel or scoop-shaped faults present in the Chemehuevi Mountains resulted where antiformal crests were eroded or else truncated by a later detachment fault, and are not the original fault geometry. I suspect that most scalloped or cuspate-shaped faults commonly described in other areas of continental extension may be characteristic of high structural levels in the crust. Quaternary normal-fault scarps along the Wasatch front, Utah, (Smith & Bruhn 1984), the Pearce and Tobin scarps associated with the 1915 Pleasant Valley earthquake in Nevada (Wallace 1984) and scarps from the 1969–70 Gediz earthquakes in Turkey (Ambraseys & Tchalenko 1972) all have cuspate forms at the surface. Each of these faults dips steeply (50–70°), with scallops measuring from hundreds of metres to several kilometres. The more continuous sub-horizontal mullion structures described in this paper may represent the downward continuations of cuspate fault scarps.

The detachment faults in the Chemehuevi Mountains are shown to be initially continuous sub-horizontal surfaces that are corrugated parallel to the NE transport direction. Orthogonal to these are broad NNW-trending undulations of the fault surfaces. These undulations may be the result of crustal flexing due to isostatic rebound following denudation (Howard *et al.* 1982a; Spencer 1984), reverse drag above a young high-angle normal fault (Gibbs 1984; Gans *et al.* 1985; Wernicke *et al.* 1985), ramping of the faults 'down' in the direction of transport (John 1984; Coward 1984), or some combination of the above. Spencer (1984) argues that the broad NNW-trending undulations of the detachment surfaces along the Colorado River trough and in southern Arizona are a product of isostatic uplift following tectonic denudation. Wernicke *et al.* (1985) suggest that the folding of detachments along axes perpendicular to the transport direction occurs as a result of reverse drag along younger, deeper faults. However, inasmuch as no younger faults have been recognized cutting the Chemehuevi fault, arching of the range orthogonal to the transport direction is unlikely to be the result of reverse drag.

An alternative, perhaps complementary explanation of the undulations with axes perpendicular to the transport direction is a ramp–flat pair in the detachment fault system (Fig. 10). This geometry has been inferred by Gibbs (1984) in interpretations of seismic sections from the North Sea, and may account for some of the irregularities in reflectors on the COCORP Sevier Desert line (Allmendinger *et al.* 1983).

With specific reference to the Chemehuevi Mountains area, this fault geometry could provide a mechanism for continued movement on different parts of the once continuous Chemehuevi detachment fault, at different times. Figure 10 outlines the schematic evolution of the fault system across the extensional corridor and the Chemehuevi Mountains. In this model, the extensional fault system initially cut steeply down-section from the headwall region in the Old Woman–Piute Mountains area, and flattened at a depth of ~6 km. The small-separation Mohave Wash fault is portrayed as an early ramp splay that is cut off by younger movement along the Chemehuevi detachment fault, as the fault cut into the hanging wall with progressive extension. With continued extensional deformation, the ramp is domed causing cessation of slip on the structural flat to the W. Continued down-slope movement on the eastern portion of the fault would thin and eventually denude the ramp, reworking structurally deeper cataclasites into gouge and breccia. Isostatic rise, as outlined by Spencer (1984) would enhance the already domal form of the detachment fault system, and produce the subdued arch of the fault surface we see today.

This model allows for local exhumation of the detachment fault(s), to provide detritus including altered lower-plate cataclasites that were shed into basin(s) in the eastern part of the range. A cross-section drawn parallel to the slip direction on the detachment faults (Fig. 8) requires a major displacement fault repeating the Tertiary section near what is now the inflection point of the dome. This fault may be a 'young' fault feeding slip into the eastern part of the Chemehuevi detachment fault. As the western segment of the Chemehuevi detachment fault became inactive due to doming the eastern portion moved down-slope under the influence of gravity to produce the very shallow fault rocks associated with the latest movement on the faults in the eastern part of the range (Fig. 10).

There appears to be some influence of pre-existing structures on the overall geometry of the

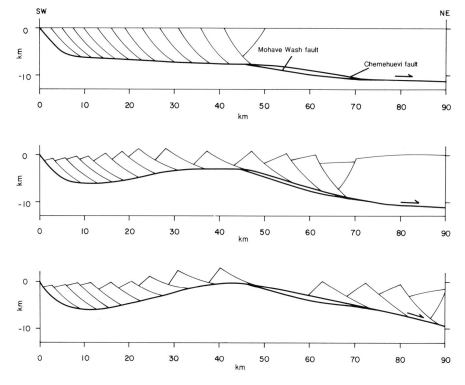

Fig. 10. Schematic evolution of the extensional fault system in the Chemehuevi Mountains area, outlined in the text and modified after Spencer 1984. The top diagram shows the initial trajectory of the fault system, from the breakaway in the Old Woman–Piute Mountains area, NE across the extensional corridor. With continued extensional deformation, the ramp is domed and progressively denuded. Final slip on the Chemehuevi fault along the eastern slope of the dome is gravity driven, at very shallow crustal levels. Implied in this model is a transition from brittle to ductile deformation associated with extension at greater structural depths, under what is now Arizona.

fault system. Undeformed granitoids, sub-horizontally foliated gneiss, and sub-vertically foliated gneiss in the footwalls of the two lower detachment faults are each associated with different scales in amplitude and wavelength of the syntectonic corrugations and apparently influenced their shapes. Steep strike-slip faults are most common within the sub-vertically foliated gneisses, paralleling the foliation. Corrugation amplitudes and wavelengths are greater in sub-vertical than in sub-horizontal gneisses.

On a crustal scale, the fault system may have ramped down through the undeformed granitoids and flattened within the sub-horizontal gneisses. In the Chemehuevi Mountains (Fig. 9), the angular discordance between the sub-horizontal foliation and detachment faults is ~20°, and very little slip was accommodated by movement parallel to foliation. These earlier structures apparently influ-

enced but did not overwhelmingly control the position and geometry of the extensional faults.

Concluding remarks

This paper documents the geometric evolution of an extensional fault system in an area of heterogeneous continental crust. The geometry and evolution of the extensional fault system exposed in the Chemehuevi Mountains area has basic similarities with those documented for classic fold and thrust belts (Boyer & Elliot 1982; Bally et al. 1966), but opposite in sense of movement. Thrust systems have two possible propagation sequences. Piggy-back thrust propagation arises if a younger thrust develops in the footwall of an older thrust. The sequence of fault generation in the Chemehuevi Mountains is analogous but opposite to that outlined above, as the Chemehuevi fault developed in the hanging wall of the earlier Mohave Wash fault. This relationship implies that extensional fault systems may propagate towards the hanging wall, in the direction of transport.

ACKNOWLEDGMENTS: Thanks are due to K. A. Howard, W. L. Power, G. A. Davis, E. G. Frost, J. L. Anderson and D. M. Miller for countless discussions and field trips pertaining to detachment faulting. R. H. Sibson and R. E. Anderson provided much needed tutoring on the nature of continental fault zones. Special thanks are due to my field assistants, in particular V. L. Hansen and L. L. Glick for their time, energy and sweat. Without them this study would not have been possible. Financial support from the U.S. Geological Survey Graduate Intern Program is gratefully acknowledged. Finally, I thank R. H. Sibson, M. W. Reynolds, K. A. Howard and an anonymous reviewer for helpful, critical reviews of the manuscript.

References

ALLMENDINGER, R.W., SHARP, J.W., VON TISCH, P., SERPA, L., BROWN, L., KAUFMAN, S., OLIVER, J. & SMITH, R.B. 1983. Cenozoic and Mesozoic structure of the eastern Basin and Range province, Utah, from COCORP seismic reflection data. *Geology,* 11, 532–36.

AMBRASEYS, N.N. & TCHALENKO, J.S. 1972. Seismotectonic aspects of the Gediz Turkey, earthquake of March 1970. *Geophys. J. R. astron. Soc.,* 30, 229–52.

ANDERSON, R.E., ZOBACK, M.L. & THOMPSON, G. 1983. Implications of selected subsurface data on the structural form and evolution of some basins in the northern Basin and Range Province, Nevada and Utah. *Bull. geol. Soc. Am.* 94, 1055–72

ARMSTRONG, R.L. 1968. Sevier orogenic belt in Nevada and Utah. *Bull. geol. Soc. Am.* 79, 429–58.

BALLY, A.W., GORDY, P.L. & STEWART, G.A. 1966. Structure, seismic data and orogenic evolution of the southern Canadian Rocky Mountains. *Bull. Can. Pet. Geol.* 14, 337–81.

BARTLEY, J.M. & GLAZNER, A.F. 1985. Hydrothermal systems and Tertiary low-angle normal faulting in the southwestern United States. *Geology,* 13, 562–4.

BOYER, S.E. & ELLIOT, D. 1982. Thrust systems. *Bull. Am. Ass. Pet. Geol.* 66, 1196–230.

BURCHFIEL, B.C. & DAVIS, G.A. 1981. Mojave Desert and Environs. In: ERNST, W.G. (ed.) *The Geotectonic Development of California,* pp. 217–52. Prentice-Hall Inc., New Jersey.

CAMERON, T.E. & FROST, E.G. 1981. Regional development of major antiforms and synforms with detachment faulting in California, Arizona, Nevada and Sonora. *Abstr. with Programs geol. Soc. Am.* 13, 421–2.

CARR, W.J. & DICKEY, D.D. 1976. Cenozoic tectonics of the eastern Mojave Desert. *U.S. geol. Surv. Prof. Pap. 1000,* 75 pp.

CONEY, P.J. 1980. Cordilleran metamorphic core complexes: an overview. In: CRITTENDEN, M.D., CONEY, P.J. & DAVIS, G.H. (eds) *Cordilleran Metamorphic Core Complexes Mem. geol. Soc. Am.* 153, 7–31.

—— & HARMS, T.A. 1984. Cordilleran metamorphic core complexes: Cenozoic extensional relicts of Mesozoic compression. *Geology,* 12, 550–4.

COWARD, M.D. 1984. Major shear zones in the Precambrian crust; examples from NW Scotland and southern Africa and their significance. In: KRONER, A. & GREILING, R. (eds) *Precambrian Tectonics Illustrated,* pp. 207–35. E. Schweizerbart'sche Verlagsbuchhandlung, Stuttgart.

DAVIS, G.A., ANDERSON, J.L., FROST, E.G. & SHACKELFORD, T.J. 1980. Mylonitization and detachment faulting in the Whipple–Buckskin–Rawhide Mountains terrane, southeastern California and western Arizona. In: CRITTENDEN, M.D., CONEY, P.J. & DAVIS, G.H. (eds) *Cordilleran Metamorphic Core Complexes, Mem. geol. Soc. Am.* 153, 79–129.

——, ANDERSON, J.L., MARTIN, D.L., KRUMMENACHER, D., FROST, E.G. & ARMSTRONG, R.L. 1982. Geologic and geochronologic relations in the lower plate of the Whipple detachment fault, Whipple Mountains, southeastern California: a progress report. In: FROST, E.G. & MARTIN, D.L. (eds) *Mesozoic–Cenozoic Tectonic Evolution of the Colorado River Region California, Arizona and Nevada (Anderson-Hamilton volume),* pp. 409–32. Cordilleran Publishers, San Diego.

EATON, G.P. 1982. The Basin and Range province: origin and tectonic significance. *Ann. Rev. Earth planet. Sci.* 10, 409–40.

ESCHER, A. & WATTERSON, J. 1974. Stretching fabrics, folds and crustal shortening. *Tectonophysics,* 22, 223–31.

EYIDOGAN, H. & JACKSON, J. 1985. A seismological study of normal faulting in the Demirci, Alasehir and Gediz Earthquakes of 1969–70 in western Turkey: implications for the nature and geometry of deformation in the continental crust. *Geophys. J. R. astron. Soc.* 81, 569–607.

FROST, E.G. 1981. Structural style of detachment faulting in the Whipple Mountains, California, and Buckskin Mountains, Arizona. In: STONE, C. & JENNY, J.P. (eds) *Az. geol. Soc. Dig.* XIII, 25–9.

—— & MARTIN, D.L. (eds) 1982a. *Mesozoic–Cenozoic Tectonic Evolution of the Colorado River Region, California, Arizona and Nevada (Anderson-Hamilton volume),* 608 pp. Cordilleran Publishers, San Diego.

—— & MARTIN, D.L. 1982b. Comparison of Mesozoic compressional tectonics with mid-Tertiary detachment faulting in the Colorado River area, California, Arizona and Nevada. In:

COOPER, J.D. (ed.) *Geologic Excursions in the California Desert, geol. Soc. Am. Field Trip Volume and Guide*, pp. 111–59.

——, CAMERON, T.G. & KRUMMENACHER, D. 1982. Mid-Tertiary detachment related deformation in the Chemehuevi Mountains, and its implications for regional crustal extension. *Abstr. with Programs geol. Soc. Am.* **14**, pp. 164.

GANS, P.B., MILLER, E.L., McCARTHY, J. & OULDCOTT, M.L. 1985. Tertiary extensional faulting and evolving ductile–brittle transition zone in the northern Snake Range and vicinity: New insight from seismic data. *Geology*, **13**, 189–93.

GIBBS, A.D. 1984. Structural evolution of extensional basin margins. *J. geol. Soc. London*, **141**, 609–20.

HAMILTON, W. 1982. Structural evolution of the Big Maria Mountains, southeastern Riverside County, southeastern California. *In*: FROST, E.G. & MARTIN, D.L. (eds) *Mesozoic–Cenozoic Tectonic Evolution of the Colorado River Region, California, Arizona and Nevada (Anderson-Hamilton volume)*, pp. 1–27. Cordilleran Publishers, San Diego.

HOWARD, K.A. & JOHN, B.E. This volume. Crustal extension along a rooted system of low-angle normal faults: Colorado River extensional corridor, California and Arizona.

——, MILLER, C.F. & STONE, P. 1980. Mesozoic thrusting in the eastern Mojave Desert, California. *Abstr. with Programs geol. Soc. Am.* **12**, pp. 112.

——, STONE, P., PERNOKAS, M.A. & MARVIN, R.F. 1982a. Geologic and geochronologic reconnaissance of the Turtle Mountains area, California: west border of the Whipple detachment terrane. *In*: FROST, E.G. & MARTIN, D.L. (eds) *Mesozoic–Cenozoic Tectonic Evolution of the Colorado River Region, California, Arizona and Nevada (Anderson-Hamilton volume)*, pp. 341–54. Cordilleran Publishers, San Diego.

——, GOODGE, J.W. & JOHN, B.E. 1982b. Detached crystalline rocks of the Mohave, Buck and Bill Williams Mountains, western Arizona. *In*: FROST, E.G. & MARTIN, D.L. (eds) *Mesozoic–Cenozoic Tectonic Evolution of the Colorado River Region, California, Arizona and Nevada (Anderson-Hamilton volume)*, pp. 377–90. Cordilleran Publishers, San Diego.

——, MILLER, D.M. & JOHN, B.E. 1982c. Regional character of mylonitic gneiss in the Cadiz Valley area, southeastern California. *In*: FROST, E.G. & MARTIN, D.L. (eds) *Mesozoic–Cenozoic Tectonic Evolution of the Colorado River Region, California, Arizona and Nevada (Anderson-Hamilton volume)*, pp. 441–7. Cordilleran Publishers, San Diego.

JACKSON, J. & McKENZIE, D. 1983. Geometrical evolution of normal fault systems. *J. struct. geol.* **5**, 471–82.

JOHN, B.E. 1982. Geologic framework of the Chemehuevi Mountains, southeastern California. *In*: FROST, E.G. & MARTIN, D.L. (eds) *Mesozoic–Cenozoic Tectonic Evolution of the Colorado River Region, California, Arizona and Nevada*

(Anderson-Hamilton volume), pp. 317–25. Cordilleran Publishers, San Diego.

—— 1984. Primary corrugations in Tertiary low-angle normal faults, SE California: Porpoising mullion structures? *Abstr. with Programs geol. Soc. Am.* **16**, pp. 291.

—— 1986. Evidence for late Mesozoic thrusting in the Chemehuevi Mountains area, southeastern California. *Abstr. with Programs geol. Soc. Am.* **18**, pp. 122.

—— & HOWARD, K.A. 1982. Multiple low-angle Tertiary faults in the Chemehuevi and Mohave Mountains, California and Arizona. *Abstr. with Programs geol. Soc. Am.* **14**, pp. 175.

KRIEGER, M.L. 1978. Large landslides composed of megabreccia interbedded in Miocene basin deposits, southeastern Arizona. *U.S. geol. Surv. Prof. Pap. 1008*, 25 pp.

McCLELLAND, W.C. 1982. Structural geology of the central Sacramento Mountains, San Bernardino Country, California. *In*: FROST, E.G. & MARTIN, D.L. (eds) *Mesozoic–Cenozoic Tectonic Evolution of the Colorado River Region, California, Arizona and Nevada (Anderson-Hamilton volume)*, pp. 401–6. Cordilleran Publishers, San Diego.

MILLER, C.F., HOWARD, K.A. & HOISCH, T.D. 1982. Mesozoic thrusting, metamorphism, and plutonism, Old Woman–Piute Range, southeastern California. *In*: FROST, E.G. & MARTIN, D.L. (eds) *Mesozoic–Cenozoic Tectonic Evolution of the Colorado River Region, California, Arizona and Nevada (Anderson-Hamilton volume)*, pp. 561–81. Cordilleran Publishers, San Diego.

MILLER, D.M., JOHN, B.E., ANTWEILER, J.C., SIMPSON, R.W., HOOVER, D.B., RAINES, G.L. & KREIDLER, T.J. 1983. Mineral Resource Potential Map of the Chemehuevi Mountains Wilderness Study Area (CDCA-310), San Bernardino County, California. *U.S. geol. Surv. Misc. Field Studies Map MF-1584-A*, 1:48,000.

PIERCE, W.G. 1973. Principle features of the Heart Mountain fault and the mechanism problem. *In*: DEJONG, K.A. & SCHOLTEN, R. (eds) *Gravity and Tectonics*, pp. 457–71. John Wiley & Sons Inc., New York.

POWER, W.L. 1986. Mechanics of low-angle extensional faulting in the Riverside Mountains, southeastern California. Unpubl. M.A. Thesis, U.C. Santa Barbara.

PROFFETT, J.M., JR 1977. Cenozoic geology of the Yerington District Nevada, and implications for the nature and origin of Basin and Range faulting. *Bull. geol. Soc. Am.* **88**, 247–66.

PROFFETT, J.M. JR & DILLAS, J.H. 1984. Geologic map of the Yerington District, Nevada. *Nev. Bur. Mines and Geol. Map* 77, 1:24,000.

REHRIG, W.A. & REYNOLDS, S.J. 1980. Geologic and geochronologic reconnaissance of a northwest-trending zone of metamorphic complexes in southern Arizona. *In*: CRITTENDEN, M.D., CONEY, P.J. & DAVIS, G.H. (eds) *Cordilleran Metamorphic Core Complexes. Mem. geol. Soc. Am.* **153**, 131–58.

REYNOLDS, S.J. & SPENCER, J.E. 1985. Evidence for large-scale transport on the Bullard detachment fault, west-central Arizona. *Geology*, 13, 353–6.

SHACKELFORD, T.J. 1980. Tertiary tectonic denudation of a Mesozoic–early Tertiary(?) gneiss complex, Rawhide Mountains, western Arizona. *Geology*, 8, 190–4.

SIBSON, R.H. 1977. Fault rocks and fault mechanisms. *J. geol. Soc. London*, 133, 191–213.

—— 1983. Continental fault structure and the shallow earthquake source. *J. geol. Soc. London*, 140, 741–67.

SMITH, R.B. & BRUHN, R.L. 1984. Intraplate extensional tectonics from the eastern Basin-Range: inference from seismic reflection data, regional tectonics, and thermal–mechanical models of brittle–ductile deformation. *J. geophys. Res.* 89, 5733–62.

SPENCER, J.E. 1982. Origin of folds of Tertiary low-angle fault surfaces, southeastern California and western Arizona. *In*: FROST, E.G. & MARTIN, D.L. (eds) *Mesozoic–Cenozoic Tectonic Evolution of the Colorado River Region, California, Arizona and Nevada (Anderson-Hamilton volume)*, pp. 123–34. Cordilleran Publishers, San Diego.

—— 1984. Role of tectonic denudation in warping and uplift of low-angle normal faults. *Geology*, 12, 95–8.

—— 1985. Miocene low-angle normal faulting and dike emplacement, Homer Mountain and surrounding areas, southeastern California and southernmost Nevada. *Bull. geol. Soc. Am.* 96, 1140–55.

STEWART, J.H. 1971. Basin and Range structure: A system of horsts and grabens produced by deep-seated extension. *Bull. geol. Soc. Am.* 82, 1019–44.

—— 1980. Regional tilt patterns of late Cenozoic basin-range fault blocks, western United States. *Bull. geol. Soc. Am.* 91, 460–4.

WALLACE, R.E. 1984. Faulting related to 1915 Earthquake in Pleasant Valley, Nevada. *U.S. geol. Surv. Prof. Pap. 1274A*, pp. A1–A33.

WERNICKE, B. 1985. Uniform-sense normal simple shear of the continental lithosphere. *Can. J. Earth Sci.* 22, 108–25.

——, WALKER, J.D. & BEUFAIT, M.S. 1985. Structural discordance between Neogene detachments and frontal Sevier thrusts, central Morman Mountains, southern Nevada. *Tectonics*, 4, 213–46.

WILKENS, J. JR & HEIDRICK, T.L. 1982. Base and precious metal mineralization related to low-angle tectonic features in the Whipple Mountains, California and Buckskin Mountains, Arizona. *In*: FROST, E.G. & MARTIN, D.L. (eds) *Mesozoic–Cenozoic Tectonic Evolution of the Colorado River Region, California, Arizona and Nevada (Anderson-Hamilton volume)*, pp. 182–209. Cordilleran Publishers, San Diego.

WOODWARD, R.J. & OSBORN, G.M. 1980. Low-angle detachment faulting and multiple deformation of the central Buckskin Mountains, Yuma County, Arizona. *Abstr. with Programs geol. Soc. Am.* 12, pp. 245.

YOUNG, R.A. & BRENNAN, W.J. 1974. Peach Springs Tuff: It's bearing on the structural evolution of the Colorado Plateau and development of Cenozoic drainage in Mohave County, Arizona. *Bull. geol. Soc. Am.* 85, 83–90.

BARBARA E. JOHN, Department of Geological Sciences, University of California, Santa, Barbara, CA 93106, USA and US Geological Survey, 345 Middlefield Road, Menlo Park, CA 94025, USA.

Rupture characteristics of normal faults: an example from the Wasatch fault zone, Utah

R.L. Bruhn, P.R. Gibler, & W.T. Parry

SUMMARY: The Salt Lake fault segment is one of several independent rupture segments in the Wasatch normal fault zone, Utah. The segment is about 35 km long and consists of several, approximately linear fault sections that intersect in geometrical barriers defined by bends and branching of the fault trace. The dips of these fault sections vary based on a preliminary model of the fault zone, with estimated dips ranging from 45 to 90°. The palaeo-stress tensor was characterized by sub-vertical maximum principal compressive stress, a minimum principal stress axis trending about 050° and $\phi \approx 0.2 - 0.5$. The average slip direction across the fault segment was $\approx 240°$. Three large, non-conservative barriers occur within the fault segment—at the northern and southern ends of the segment, and a branch point in the centre of the segment. Bifurcation of the rupture zone into two primary fault systems has presumably increased the fracture toughness of the northern part of the segment due to the overlap of secondary faulting adjacent to the primary fault planes. Two large historic earthquakes in the eastern Basin and Range and Rocky Mountain transition region have ruptured bifurcated fault zones similar in structure to the Salt Lake segment; the Hebgen Lake, Montana earthquake ($M = 7.5$) in 1959 and the Borah Peak, Idaho earthquake ($M = 7.3$) in 1983. The earthquake foci were located at depths of 12–18 km and the ruptures propagated towards the regions of fault-zone bifurcation in both cases. A characteristic earthquake ($M \approx 7$–7.5) may initiate at either the centre or the southern end of the Salt Lake segment. In the first case, the rupture would propagate bilaterally, but in the latter case the rupture would propagate unilaterally to the N. A unilateral propagation direction is preferred based on inferences drawn from the structural geology of the segment and direct comparison with the rupture traces of the Borah Peak and Hebgen Lake earthquakes.

Processes of crustal extension break the upper crust into a mosaic of blocks separated by normal and transcurrent fault zones. Large normal fault zones, which extend for hundred's of kilometres along strike are divided into structural segments that differ in their geometrical, seismogenic, and long-term displacement characteristics. Fault-zone segments in the Basin and Range and Rocky Mountain Provinces of the western United States, for example, are ten's of kilometres long and defined by major variations in the geometry of the fault zone, along-strike variations in displacement and differing earthquake rupture histories (Zoback 1983; Schwartz & Coppersmith 1984; Wallace 1984; Smith & Bruhn 1984; Crone & Machette 1984; Doser 1985a,b). Individual rupture segments are capable of generating $M = 7$–7.5 earthquakes.

Rupture characteristics of fault-zone segments control the generation of earthquakes. This paper presents a study of the structural geology of the Salt Lake segment (Fig. 1), one of several independent rupture segments in the Wasatch fault zone proposed by Schwartz & Coppersmith (1984). Our purpose is to infer certain rupture characteristics of the segment from its structure. The rupture segment is marked by prominent fault-line scarps in Quaternary surface deposits and has undergone at least two, and probably four, earthquakes of $M = 7$–7.5 during the last 8000 years (Schwartz & Coppersmith 1984). These characteristic earthquakes presumably ruptured most if not all of the 35-km long segment.

Rupture barriers

The asperity and barrier models of fault zones provide two extreme views of rupture initiation and propagation during earthquakes (Aki 1979). In the asperity model, a large earthquake initiates when the the strongest part (an asperity) of the rupture segment fails, while in the barrier model, ruptures initiate in the weaker parts of the fault zone and either arrest or bypass the stronger parts (barriers). The two models are in reality, not mutually exclusive. For example, the strength of barriers may increase after rupturing in a seismic event, evolving into asperities, or strong patches, within the fault zone (King 1983). Here, we briefly discuss the structural characteristics of the geometrical barrier, in order to provide a framework for interpreting

From COWARD, M.P., DEWEY, J.F. & HANCOCK, P.L. (eds), 1987, *Continental Extensional Tectonics*, Geological Society Special Publication No. 28, pp. 337–353.

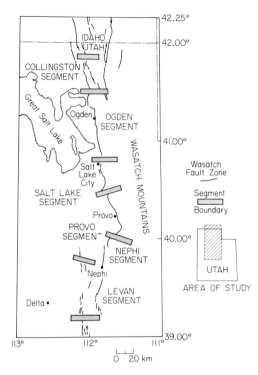

FIG. 1. Regional map of the Wasatch fault zone showing rupture segments proposed by Schwartz & Coppersmith (1984).

the structural geology of a fault zone in terms of potential rupture characteristics.

Geometrical barriers represent jogs or bends in the fault zone marked by lateral offset of fault sections or changes in strike and dip. The conservative and non-conservative barrier are two, fundamentally different structures, that have important implications for rupture characteristics (King & Yielding 1984). The fault slip vector in a conservative barrier is constant on both sides of the barrier, paralleling the intersection line between the two adjacent fault sections that intersect in the barrier. That is, the two fault sections form a cylindrical surface. Conversely, a non-conservative barrier develops in regions where the slip vector changes between two adjacent fault sections. Faulting in the conservative barrier may be accommodated in a relatively narrow zone because intensive fracturing of the country rock is not necessary in order to transfer motion between the two intersecting sections of the fault zone. Rupturing through a non-conservative barrier, on the other hand, requires extensive fracturing of the country rock and development of a new, third direction of faulting in order to transfer motion between

adjacent sections of the fault zone. Consequently, an extensive network of subsidiary faults must form in the barrier.

These subsidiary faults have a fundamental role in controlling both the arrest and initiation of earthquake ruptures according to the hypotheses of King & Yielding (1984) and King & Nabelek (1985). The broadly distributed subsidiary faults will be activated as a rupture propagates through the barrier, effectively blunting the tip of the rupture and diffusing energy into a large volume of fractured rock adjacent to the primary fault zone. This process will inhibit rupture propagation, either slowing the rupture or even causing its arrest. In addition, activation of the subsidiary fault sets will cause mutual interference and interlocking of faults, creating new asperities that must be broken before another rupture can propagate in the barrier. In effect, the previously activated, non-conservative barrier becomes a zone of increased resistance to rupture and must be broken prior to the next characteristic earthquake. If several barriers exist within the rupture segment, then the one with the least fracture toughness may fail first, initiating the large earthquake.

An alternative, but complimentary, view of the non-conservative barrier's influence on rupture initiation arises from considering the flow of fluids into the fault zone. The large fracture density of non-conservative barriers means that they are likely sites for enhanced fracture permeability and hence, increased fluid access into the fault zone. Fluids may affect faulting in two primary ways; time-dependent chemical weakening (Das & Scholz 1981), and the reduction of effective normal stress due to fluid pressure. Indeed, the quasi-static phase of rupture growth is thought to be strongly dependent on the access of chemically reactive fluids to the expanding rupture front in the time period prior to the unstable, coseismic phase of propagation (Das & Scholz 1981). Obviously, fluids entering the non-conservative barrier may weaken previously developed asperities. However, the barrier will also act as a conduit for fluid flow into adjacent sections of the primary fault zone. There, the fluid will be confined to a narrower, more concentrated zone of faulting than in the barrier, where the fluids must spread through a large volume of rock containing faults of several different orientations. Therefore, fluid infiltration into the narrow, primary fault zone adjacent to the barrier may better enhance growth of a discrete rupture to critical dimensions than in the wider and structurally complex barrier itself. In this view, a new rupture is expected to initiate either within or near the zone of intersection between the barrier and the more structurally discrete fault section.

Several criteria exist for identifying geometrical barriers in fault zones (King 1983; King & Yielding 1984; King & Nabelek 1985). An abrupt offset, bend or branching in the trace of a fault zone is sufficient to identify a barrier. The presence of a non-conservative barrier in a normal fault zone is indicated by changes in either the amount or directions of slip on two adjacent fault sections leading to (i) development of a third direction of faulting in the barrier, (ii) breakup of the hanging wall into ridges and troughs above the barrier, (iii) development of enhanced fracture permeability and hydrothermal fluid flow, and (iv) the possibility of diffuse seismicity associated with the failure of asperities within the barrier over time.

The concept of purely conservative and non-conservative barriers is of course a geometrical abstraction. We do not imply that nil subsidiary faulting occurs in conservative barriers. Indeed, subsidiary faults do form, but the volume of rock affected is presumably much smaller than in the non-conservative barrier.

Tectonics of Wasatch fault zone

The Wasatch normal fault zone extends for 370 km along the eastern edge of the Basin and Range Province in southern Idaho and Utah (Fig. 1). The fault zone has a pronounced footwall escarpment, with up to 3 km of relief, separating alluvium-filled valleys to the W from the Wasatch Mountains to the E (Gilbert 1928). Total throw across the fault zone varies along strike, with estimates ranging from 2.6 to 4 km based on gravity models (Zoback 1983) to a maximum of ≥ 11 km just S of Salt Lake City, Utah, in the central part of the fault zone (Parry & Bruhn 1986).

The Wasatch fault zone is divided into structural segments defined by differences in the geometry of the fault trace, variations in footwall topography, gravity anomalies and earthquake rupture history (Schwartz & Coppersmith 1984). The segments have strike lengths of 35–70 km and their ends are marked by E-striking faults and basement ridges that subdivide Neogene basins in the hanging wall of the fault zone (Zoback 1983; Schwartz & Coppersmith 1984). Each segment has undergone multiple episodes of surface faulting during the Pleistocene and Holocene and is thought capable of generating characteristic earthquakes of $M = 7$–7.5 based on fault displacements

measured in trenches placed across fault-line scarps. The recurrence intervals on individual segments are estimated to be as short as 4580 yr with an average recurrence interval for characteristic earthquakes of 400–600 yr for the entire Wasatch fault zone (Swan et al. 1980; Schwartz et al. 1983). The Wasatch fault zone has not had a characteristic earthquake during historic times, but it is associated with a diffuse, N–S zone of seismicity (Arabasz et al. 1980).

Structure of Salt Lake rupture segment

The Salt Lake segment is one of several independent rupture segments proposed by Schwartz & Coppersmith (1984). The fault segment extends for ≈ 35 km and is marked by a series of discontinuous fault-line scarps that bifurcate in the northern half of the segment, forming two primary fault zones (Fig. 2; Marsell 1969). These fault-line scarps form several, approximately linear sections between 3 and 12 km in length that are separated by abrupt bends in the trace of the fault zone. These bends have been classified as either conservative or non-conservative barriers based on the criteria listed in Table 1.

The footwall of the Salt Lake segment is composed of Precambrian through to Cenozoic strata, Precambrian metamorphics and a quartz monzonite intrusion of Oligocene age (Fig. 2). The rupture segment is superimposed on the Uinta Arch, an E-trending anticlinorium that developed during the late Mesozoic and early Tertiary as a result of thrust faulting and folding during the Sevier–Laramide Orogeny. The Uinta Arch was subsequently intruded by quartz monzonite during the Oligocene (Crittenden 1976). The trend of the arch is anomalous with respect to the regional, N–S grain of Sevier and Laramide structures in adjacent parts of Utah and Wyoming. This anomalous trend is partly due to the ancient structure of the late Proterozoic Uinta sedimentary basin, which originally crossed the Wasatch Mountains in the area of the Uinta Arch. The possible influence of pre-Neogene crustal structure on the Salt Lake rupture segment has been briefly discussed by Zoback (1983) and Smith & Bruhn (1984).

The time of origin of the Salt Lake rupture segment is poorly constrained. Normal faulting post-dated intrusion of the Little Cottonwood stock at 31.1 ± 0.9 Ma (Crittenden et al. 1973). Hydrothermal muscovite in cataclasite at the southern end of the rupture segment formed at 17.6 ± 0.7 Ma, indicating that faulting began by latest early Miocene (Parry & Bruhn 1986).

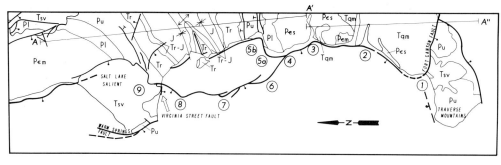

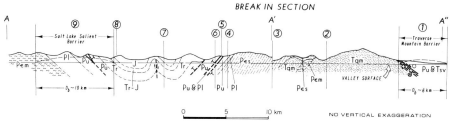

BREAK IN SECTION

0   5   10 km   NO VERTICAL EXAGGERATION

EXPLANATION

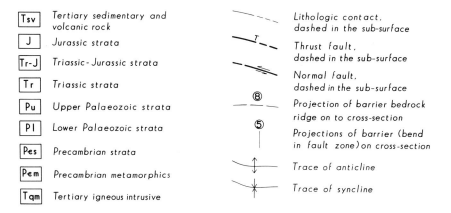

Tsv	Tertiary sedimentary and volcanic rock
J	Jurassic strata
Tr-J	Triassic-Jurassic strata
Tr	Triassic strata
Pu	Upper Palaeozoic strata
Pl	Lower Palaeozoic strata
Pes	Precambrian strata
Pem	Precambrian metamorphics
Tqm	Tertiary igneous intrusive

Lithologic contact, dashed in the sub-surface

Thrust fault, dashed in the sub-surface

Normal fault, dashed in the sub-surface

⑧ Projection of barrier bedrock ridge on to cross-section

⑤ Projections of barrier (bend in fault zone) on cross-section

Trace of anticline

Trace of syncline

FIG. 2. Geological map and cross-section of the Wasatch Mountain front and Salt Lake rupture segment. Barriers in the fault zone are numbered and projected onto the footwall cross-section. Geology from Davis (1983a, b) and Wasatch fault trace from Marsell (1969).

This cataclasite, which consists of deformed quartz monzonite, has been uplifted ≥11 km within the fault zone.

Palaeo-slip direction and stress tensor

The palaeo-slip directions and characteristics of the palaeo-stress tensor in the Salt Lake fault segment were estimated from the analysis of mesoscopic fault populations in the fault zone

and adjacent footwall. Four structural domains were chosen for study; three domains in the Salt Lake segment and one in the E-trending section of the Wasatch fault zone at the southern end of the segment (Fig. 3). The domains were distributed along the length of the fault segment to test for possible spatial variations in displacement directions or stress tensor characteristics. The Red Butte and Olympus Cove domains were located in Mesozoic and Palaeozoic strata in the northern and central parts of the segment, respectively. The Draper and Fort Canyon

TABLE 1. *Barrier Classification.*

Barrier	Structural characteristics	Barrier type
1	TF, HB, TH, SE, OF	Non-conservative
2	B	Conservative
3	B	Conservative
4*	BR, TF, HB	Non-conservative
5a*	B, ID	Non-conservative
5b*	B, TF(?), ID	Non-conservative
6	B	Conservative(?)
7	B	Conservative(?)
8	B	Conservative(?)
9	TF, BR, HB, SE, OF	Non-conservative

* This branch point and two bends considered as one composite, non-conservative barrier.

Structural characteristics

   B – Bend in trace
  BR – Branching of fault trace
  OF – Lateral offset of two primary rupture traces
  TF – Three directions of large-scale faulting
  HB – Hanging wall breakup or basement ridge
  TH – Abrupt difference in primary fault throw
  ID – Dip incompatible with conservation of slip
       on adjacent fault section
  SE – Diffuse seismicity

domains were located at the southern end of the segment in quartz monzonite of the Little Cottonwood stock.

Faults within each domain form several sets that cut the rock on the metre to centimetre scale (Fig. 4). The age of faulting is not well constrained. The Draper and Fort Canyon domains are located within the primary fault zone, in the carapace of cataclasite on the margins of the Little Cottonwood stock, and must have formed since 17.6 ± 0.7 Ma (Parry & Bruhn 1986). Faults in the Red Butte and Olympus Cove domains form part of an extensive population of normal and normal-oblique-slip faults that occur in the footwall along the entire length of the fault segment. These faults are subsidiary faults that developed in footwall strata immediately adjacent to the primary fault zone, but there is no independent evidence for their time of origin.

The mesoscopic fault populations in each domain are composed of a mixture of mutually offsetting, normal, oblique-slip and pure strike-slip faults. Slickensides in each domain generally form two or more spatial maxima (Fig. 4),

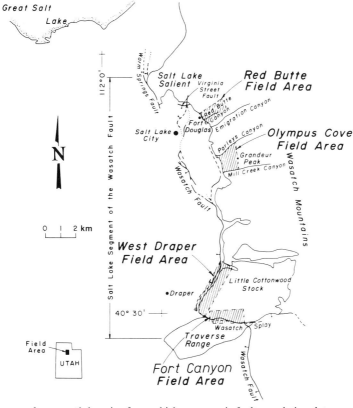

FIG. 3. Locality map of structural domains from which mesoscopic fault population data were collected for palaeo-stress study (after Gibler 1985).

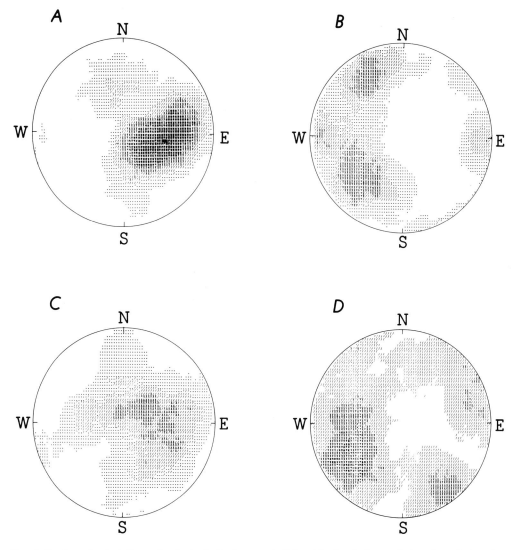

FIG. 4. Contoured orientations of poles to fault planes and slickensides for fault populations in each domain of Fig. 3. Red Butte Canyon—129 faults (a) and slickensides (b); Olympus Cove—105 faults (c) and slickensides (d); West Draper—110 faults (e) and slickensides (f); Fort Canyon—106 faults (g) and slickensides (h). Contour intervals are 0,2,4,6, & 8 standard deviations above a random distribution as plotted on lower hemisphere, equal-area projections.

except in the Fort Canyon domain, where they form a broad partial girdle in the stereo-plot. The other three domains contain a prominent maximum trending 230 to 250°, with subsidiary maxima plunging at moderate angles into either the northern or southern quadrants.

The principal directions and stress ratio parameter $\phi = \sigma_2 - \sigma_3 / \sigma_1 - \sigma_3$ of the palaeo-stress tensor in each domain were estimated from the geometry and slip directions of the palaeo-fault populations using an inversion method described

by Michael (1984). The information required for the inversion method was the orientation and slip direction of each fault in the population. The following assumptions were required to generate a system of linear equations for solution using a singular-value, decomposition computer routine described by Lawson & Hanson (subroutine SVA, 1974). (i) All faults within the population slipped during a single episode of homogeneous deformation. (ii) The palaeo-stress tensor was constant in orientation and

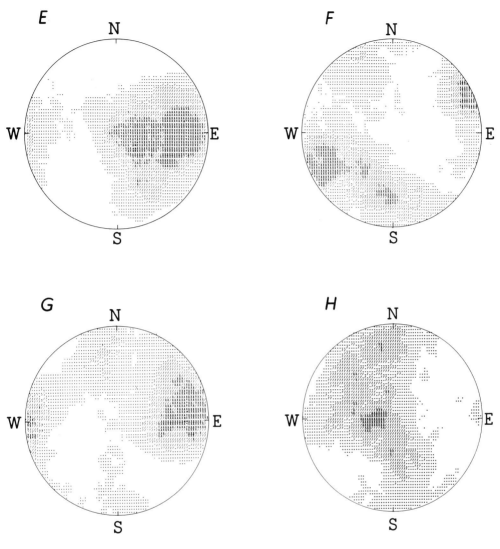

F_{IG}. 4. (*cont.*)

magnitude during the deformation event. (iii) Slip on individual fault planes was parallel to the maximum resolved shear-stress vector on the fault plane. (iv) Faults slipped at a constant, but unknown, value of shear stress. Further discussion of the method is given by Michael (1984). Here, we wish to emphasize the highly restrictive nature of the assumptions required to set up a mathematical inversion problem and suggest that the results must be treated as only an approximation of the true characteristics of the stress tensor during faulting.

The principal palaeo-stress directions were consistent in each domain, σ_1 plunged steeply

and σ_3 plunged gently to either the WSW or ENE (Fig. 5; Table 2). The average direction of σ_3 was $050° \pm 5°$ with a maximum variation in trend of only $11°$. The stress parameter, ϕ, varied from a high of 0.54 in Red Butte to a low of 0.21 in Fort Canyon (Table 2).

The results of the palaeo-stress inversion method are reasonable, based on several independent lines of evidence. The steeply dipping palaeo-σ_1 directions calculated by the inversion program are expected in an extensional terrane. The trend of σ_3 should lie close to, but not necessarily parallel to, the trend of maximum extension in domains where $\phi > 0$. Indeed, the

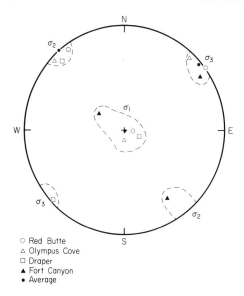

○ Red Butte
△ Olympus Cove
□ Draper
▲ Fort Canyon
● Average

FIG. 5. Palaeo-principal deviatoric stress orientations from each of four domains in Fig. 3 based on inversion of fault plane and slickenside data summarized in Fig. 4. σ_1—maximum principal compressive stress, σ_2—intermediate principal stress, σ_3—least principal stress. Trend and plunges of each stress axis are recorded in Table 2.

TABLE 2.

Domain	σ_1	σ_3	ϕ
Red Butte	095°/83°	054°/00°	.54
Olympus C.	180°/82°	044°/07°	.50
Draper	113°/77°	227°/04°	.42
Fort CYN.	301°/66°	056°/10°	.21

σ_1 – Trend/plunge of maximum principal stress
σ_3 – Trend/plunge of minimum principal stress
ϕ = Stress ratio parameter

direction of slip, and therefore extension, on a fault is a function of the fault's orientation, the principal stress directions and the parameter, ϕ (Angelier 1979). Most importantly, the σ_3 directions are sub-parallel to the trend of the prominent set of slickensides in all domains except Fort Canyon, where the slickensides are broadly distributed about a partial girdle (Fig. 4). The average trend of σ_3 (050 or 230°) is also similar to the slip directions on Quaternary fault surfaces measured by Pavlis & Smith (1980) on the Warm Spring and Virginia Street faults at the northern end of the Salt Lake segment (Fig. 2). Slickensides on the NW-striking Warm Spring fault form two sets, the oldest trending 288° and

the youngest 239°. The Virginia Street fault surface strikes N80°E and also contains two sets of slickensides, one trending 255° and the other 233°. Finally, notice that $\phi>0$ in all of the domains, consistent with the observed coexistence of normal, oblique and strike-slip faults. If $\phi=0$, then slip on all faults, regardless of their orientation should be down-dip, or nearly so, depending on the amount of physical interaction between blocks of material within the deforming domain (Angelier 1979).

Fault zone structure

The surface trace of the Wasatch fault zone consists of a series of Quaternary fault-line scarps that extend throughout the Salt Lake segment. In the southern and northern parts of the segment these fault-line scarps cut into bedrock. Unconsolidated surface deposits are faulted directly against large, striated bedrock surfaces on the Warm Spring and Virginia Street faults at the northern end of the segment (Fig. 2; Gilbert 1928; Pavlis & Smith 1980). The surface trace of the fault zone is comprised of several linear to curvilinear fault sections that vary in length from ≈3 to ≈12 km (Fig. 2). These sections are separated by bends in the trace of the fault zone which form geometrical barriers. The bends are tentatively classified as either conservative or non-conservative barriers based on the criteria listed in Table 1. One fundamental criterion for identifying a large, non-conservative barrier is that a third direction of faulting is developed in the zone of intersection between two adjacent sections of the primary fault zone. Such structures are evident at the southern and northern ends of the Salt Lake segment, where large bedrock ridges (Salt Lake salient and Traverse Mountains, Fig. 2) extend westward into the hanging wall and are bounded by sets of W- to SW-striking secondary faults. A similar structure consisting of a buried bedrock ridge and W-striking faults occurs in the central part of the fault segment based on gravity modelling (Cook and Berg 1961; Zoback 1983). These sub-surface structures intersect the bifurcation point of Quaternary fault line-scarps in the centre of the fault segment (barrier 4, Fig. 2; Table 1). Notably, each of the large, non-conservative barriers is associated with extensive palaeo and contemporary hydrothermal spring activity, indicating that these structures represent zones of enhanced permeability and fluid flow in the fault zone. The greatest displacement across the fault segment is at the southern end, near the Traverse Mountains.

Structure of non-conservative barriers

Traverse Mountains

The Traverse Mountains occur at the structural boundary between the Salt Lake and Provo rupture segments as proposed by Schwartz & Coppersmith (1984). Here, we focus on the northern part of the barrier, which consists of a triple junction of three large faults; (i) the southern section (Draper section) of the Salt Lake segment, which strikes ≈035° (fault section A, Fig. 6); (ii) a SSW-striking normal fault zone along the northwestern edge of the Traverse Mountains (fault B, Fig. 6), and (iii) the E-striking Fort Canyon fault (fault C, Fig. 6) that extends eastward to intersect the Deer Creek normal fault and northern end of the Provo rupture segment of the Wasatch fault zone.

The Wasatch fault zone extends into bedrock forming a carapace of cataclasitic and phyllonitic quartz monzonite along the western and southern margins of the Little Cottonwood stock in the Traverse Mountain barrier (Fig. 2). This faulted carapace has been uplifted ≈11 km in the last 17.6±0.7 My (Parry & Bruhn 1986). The fault zone dips between 30 and 40°S on the

southern margin of the stock (fault C, Fig. 10) where Palaeozoic strata and Tertiary volcanics are faulted directly against the igneous rock (Fig. 2; Gilbert 1928; Bullock 1954; Houghton 1985). Shear band fabrics in relic patches of phyllonite preserved in the fault zone indicate dextral-normal slip when the rock was at depths near the brittle–ductile transition. This sense of slip is consistent with displacement on younger, brittle faults formed in the footwall at the centre of the triple junction, where striations on the most prominent set of normal faults plunge to the SW (Parry & Bruhn 1986).

Salt Lake Salient

A large ridge of Tertiary and Palaeozoic bedrock extends westward from the Wasatch Mountains at the northern end of the Salt Lake segment (Fig. 2). Gravity and drill data from the valley immediately to the W of the salient indicate that it continues in the sub-surface as a large, W-trending bedrock ridge and fault system that extends across the width of the valley (Cook & Berg 1961; Zoback 1983).

The western margin of Salt Lake salient is marked by the Warm Springs fault, a N-striking fault that dips ≈70°W and separates Quaternary sediments in the hanging wall from footwall rocks comprised of Palaeozoic and Tertiary strata. The salient is separated from Precambrian metamorphic rock on its eastern margin by a large, W-dipping normal fault that has a throw of ≈1.5 km (Fig. 2). The interior of the salient contains several NNW- and NE-striking normal faults that post-date the deposition of Oligocene rocks (van Horn 1981).

Structurally, the salient forms a non-conservative barrier separating the Salt Lake and Ogden rupture segments (Schwartz & Coppersmith 1984). This barrier is defined by several different fault zones with variable trends, including the W-striking Virginia Street fault along the southern edge of the salient, the N-striking Warm Springs fault along its western margin, and N- to NE-striking normal faults at the southern end of the Ogden rupture segment. The curvilinear normal fault zone marking the eastern boundary of the salient was certainly active during the late Tertiary, and may have been partly reactivated during the Quaternary as fault-line scarps in the Salt Lake segment project directly into this fault zone (Fig. 2; Marsell ·1969).

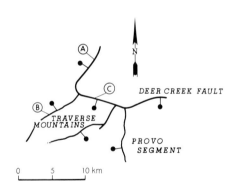

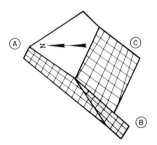

FIG. 6. Fault traces at Traverse Mountain barrier (top) and block-model of the fault geometry (bottom) in the northern part of the barrier.

Bifurcation Zone

Quaternary fault-line scarps bifurcate into two sets in the central part of the rupture

346 *R.L. Bruhn* et al.

segment (Fig. 2, barrier 4), forming a younger western and perhaps somewhat older, eastern branch of surface faulting (Fig. 2; Marsell 1969; van Horn 1972). However, according to van Horn (1972) remnants of the older set of fault-line scarps occur in the western fault branch, indicating that the two branches may have been activated simultaneously during at least some earthquakes.

The position of fault-zone bifurcation occurs at a major boundary in the structure of the hanging wall basin. Here, the basin is separated into two parts, a southern, deeper part containing up to ≈ 1 km of sedimentary fill and a more shallow, northern part in which the fill is only several hundred metres thick (Cook & Berg 1961; Zoback 1983). This boundary is marked by a W-trending gravity gradient that extends across the basin and is interpreted by Cook & Berg (1961) and Zoback (1983) as a system of bedrock ridges and faults.

The two 90° bends in the eastern fault branch (barriers 5a & b; Fig. 2) are also tentatively classified as non-conservative barriers based on, (i) the observation that the E-striking fault section between the two bends dips northward, and (ii) the inferred slip direction on the fault zone as a whole is to the SW. Slip in this direction cannot be transferred on to an E-striking fault with northward dip, and therefore the bends must be non-conservative barriers. Notably, this abrupt, eastward deflection in the fault-line scarps occurs where a zone of E-striking Mesozoic thrust faults (Mount Raymond thrust system), exposed in the mountain front, intersects the Wasatch fault zone (Fig. 2). The northward dip of the normal-fault section between bends No. 5a and 5b clearly reflects partial reactivation of this ancient, N-dipping zone of thrust faulting.

Fault-zone geometry

The fault-line scarps in the Salt Lake rupture segment define several, approximately linear fault sections that vary in length from 3 to 12 km (Fig. 2). The dip of the fault zone presumably changes between these sections, particularly when they intersect in a conservative barrier, across which the slip vector is preserved and the fault geometry remains cylindrical. Here, we construct a preliminary model of the fault zone utilizing information about the strike of fault sections, the inferred slip direction in the fault zone, and the characteristics of the palaeo-stress tensor. In constructing this model we assume that (i) the surface traces of fault-line scarps in the rupture segment represent the strike of bedrock faults at depth; (ii) the palaeo-stress

tensor characteristics determined by structural analysis of mesoscopic fault populations are representative of the stress system in which the fault zone evolved; and (iii) the slip direction on a fault plane is defined by the trace of the maximum resolved shear-stress vector on to that plane, which is a function of the fault orientation, palaeo-principal stress direction and stress parameter ϕ (Angelier 1979).

The southern part of the Salt Lake segment extends from Traverse Mountain barrier to the fault-trace bifurcation point. This part of the fault zone contains three sections of variable strike connected by two conservative barriers (barriers 2 & 3; Fig. 2). The fault section south of barrier 2 strikes 035°, forming the northern part of the triple-array of faults intersecting in Traverse Mountain barrier (Figs 2 & 6). The maximum dip of this fault section is estimated at 65° by the geometrical construction shown in Fig. 7, which was accomplished as follows. The slip direction on the Fort Canyon fault is estimated as 22°/242° using the palaeo-stress orientations and ϕ-value from the Fort Canyon domain and the mapped attitude of the fault (fault 2, Fig. 7). The fault plane is shown in the figure with all possible ranges of slip direction for $0 < \phi < 1$, with the preferred-slip estimate based on $\phi = 0.2$ shown as the small, black arrow. There is no information about the slip direction on fault B (Fig. 6) other than that it has a normal com-

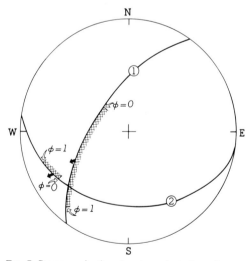

FIG. 7. Stereo-projection showing orientation of Fort Canyon fault, (z) best-estimate of orientation of Draper fault section (*l*) at the southern end of Salt Lake segment, and slip direction for various ϕ-values of palaeo-stress field. Preferred slip direction on Draper section is 240° on a fault plane dipping 65° to the NW. Lower hemisphere, equal-area projection. See text for discussion.

ponent of displacement with the NW side downthrown. We seek solutions for dips of the Draper fault section in the Salt Lake segment (fault 1, Fig. 7) that are compatible with (i) the strike of the fault section, (ii) coincide with the trace of maximum palaeo-shear stress on the modelled fault plane, and (iii) result in extension across fault B (Fig. 6) given the previously estimated slip direction on the Fort Canyon fault. This is just a procedure in which the displacements around the triple junction of the three faults is assumed to sum to zero. A satisfactory solution of 65° places no compression across fault B in the triple junction; the estimated dip on the Draper fault section (fault 1, Fig. 7) would decrease with increasing amounts of extension across fault B.

The maximum dip angles of the two fault sections N of the Draper fault section can then be estimated because each section is connected to the adjacent one by a conservative barrier. This requires that the slip direction is the same on each fault section and that they intersect in a line parallel to the slip direction—i.e. the fault zone is geometrically cylindrical. The results are shown in the fault-zone map of Fig. 8. The dip angles of 45–55° estimated in these sections are consistent with estimates by Bashore *et al.* (1981) based on seismic refraction-reflection data in the same area.

The bifurcation point (barrier 4, Fig. 2) represents a break in the cylindrical geometry of the southern part of the fault zone. The dip angles for fault sections in the western branch N of the bifurcation point have been estimated by assuming that all bends between point barrier 4 and the southern edge of Salt Lake salient are conservative barriers. This assumption is tentative; we do the modelling simply to provide a preliminary model of fault-zone geometry that can be tested and refined in the future.

The dip of the N-striking fault section between bends barriers 7 and 8 is estimated assuming an average slip direction of 240° for the entire fault zone and using the palaeo-stress data from the Red Butte domain, where $\phi = 0.5$. In doing this we make the additional assumption that changes in slip vector along the length of the fault zone are related to differences in vector plunge rather than direction. The solution for a series of fault planes dipping between 20 and 80°W is shown in Fig. 9 where the orientation of the maximum shear-stress vector for this palaeo-stress system is plotted as a series of three curves for $\phi = 0, 0.5$ and 1.0. Notice that the slip direction of 240° does not intersect the $\phi = 0.5$ shear-stress curve, but lies a few degrees to the N of this curve at its closest point of approach. A fault dipping 50°W lies nearest to this latter curve and is therefore the preferred dip estimate. The dip angles of the remaining fault sections were then found assuming a cylindrical fault-zone surface (Fig. 8).

Rupture characteristics

The structure and geometry of a fault zone must strongly influence the propagation of earthquake ruptures. Here, we consider the large, $M \approx 7$–7.5 earthquake, which would originate within the segment and rupture most, if not all, of its length. We do not consider the problem of ruptures that may initiate outside the segment and propagate into it, this problem requires more knowledge of the structure of adjacent segments than is presently available. We are interested in identifying likely sites for the initiation of a characteristic earthquake rupture and probable sites of rupture arrest.

Presumably, a characteristic earthquake initiates as a quasi-statically growing rupture reaches critical dimensions, causing unstable propagation of the rupture front at near sonic velocity (Das & Scholz 1981). This region of quasi-static growth should occur near the frictional/quasi-plastic transition depth, the depth of maximum crustal shear strength. Fault

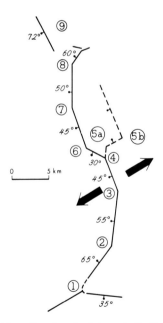

FIG. 8. Map of surface fault trace in the Salt Lake segment with preferred dip angles based on geometrical modelling. Numbers of barriers same as those in Fig. 2 and Table 1. See text for discussion.

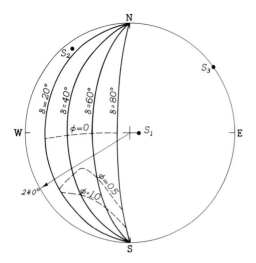

FIG. 9. Stereo-plot of N-striking faults with dips (δ) between 20 and 80°W and slip lines for palaeo-stress field in the Red Butte Canyon domain (Table 2). Slip directions for $\phi = 0$, 0.5 and 1.0 are defined by intersections of great circles defining fault planes with lines of constant ϕ. Best estimate for slip in a 240° direction is a fault plane dipping 50°. See text for discussion.

rock exhumed in the footwall of the Wasatch fault zone at Traverse Mountain barrier was originally deformed at the frictional/quasi-plastic transition at depths greater than 11 km at about 17 Ma (Parry & Bruhn 1986). The palaeo-thermal gradient estimated during development of this fault rock is $\approx 30°C\ km^{-1}$, similar to the contemporary thermal gradient in this part of the Basin and Range. This minimum depth estimate for maximum crustal shear strength is also consistent with the observed depth distribution of small earthquakes in the Wasatch Front region and rheological models of the brittle–ductile transition (Meissner & Strehlau 1982; Sibson 1982; Smith & Bruhn 1984). Consequently, we infer that the rupture nucleation region will be at depths >11 km, a value that is consistent with the locations of large earthquake foci in the western US.

The lateral position of rupture initiation within a fault zone is particularly important for earthquake prediction, in that instrumentation to detect the quasi-static phase of rupture growth should be located as close as possible to the potential focus. Estimating the relative fracture toughness of barriers within the fault zone may provide a simple, geometrical approach to this problem according to King & Yielding (1984). They hypothesize that ruptures will nucleate at the non-conservative barrier with the

least fracture toughness. A non-conservative barrier forms a volume of high-asperity density within the fault zone and the weakest barrier will rupture first given uniform loading along the length of the zone. Presumably, a rupture originating from the failed barrier will have sufficient fracture energy to propagate through adjacent fault sections with lower asperity densities than in the barrier. In this view, asperities in the fault zone arise from variations in structural geometry and the barrier is both a potential source and arrest zone for ruptures.

The population of secondary faults in a non-conservative barrier forms a mutually interlocking system of slip planes which effectively blunt the tip of a propagating rupture, forming a plastic tip-zone in fracture-mechanics terminology (King & Yielding 1984). Here, plastic deformation is used in an approximate sense, implying distortion of the material by contemporaneous slip on a population of discrete faults that mutually interfere and interlock with one another. The radius (r) of the plastic tip zone is given, for an ideal elastic–plastic material, by the relationship

$$r = \frac{\pi}{8}\left[\frac{K_f^2}{S_y^2}\right], \qquad (1)$$

where K_f = fracture toughness and S_y = yield stress at the edge of the plastic tip zone (Rudnicki 1980). King & Yielding (1984) used the dimensions of after-schock zones to estimate r in the El Asnam fault zone, Algeria. Here, we use the dimensions of barriers mapped on the surface as estimates of r.

The magnitude of S_y, the yield stress, is not known. The true value could lie anywhere between the shear strength of intact rock as measured experimentally to the value of typical stress drops during large earthquakes, that is from 100's to less than 10 MPa (King & Yielding 1984). We evade this problem by comparing only the relative dimensions of individual barriers using the following relationship derived from (1):

$$\frac{K_{f1}}{K_{f2}} = \left[\frac{r_1}{r_2}\right]^{1/2}, \qquad (2)$$

where the indices refer to two individual barriers. S_y is assumed constant within the two barriers.

The radii of the Salt Lake and Traverse Mountain barriers are estimated as ≈ 5 and ≈ 3 km, respectively, based on the projection of their mapped widths on to the cross-section of the footwall in Fig. 2. The barriers are approximated by a circular cylinder of radius *r* dipping W to SW into the sub-surface. Indeed, one could argue that the vertical dimension of the barriers might be expected to expand with depth, as secondary faulting extends through an increasing thickness of the overlying hanging wall. However, this effect should be similar for each barrier, and consequently their relative dimensions should remain similar to those measured at the surface. The two estimates of barrier radii indicate that Traverse Mountain barrier has a lower fracture toughness than Salt Lake salient.

The rupture characteristic of the fault zone between Salt Lake salient and the point of bifurcation (barrier 4) can be interpreted in two fundamentally different ways. First, one can consider simply the dimensions of the bifurcation zone, which extends from the bifurcation point (barrier 4) to barrier 5b to the E and barrier 6 to the W (Fig. 2), a region $\approx 3 \times 6$ km in surface area (Fig. 2). The radius of the cross-section of an equivalent, right cylinder dipping westward at 45 to 50° is ≈ 2 km. The fracture toughness of this barrier is then estimated as about 80% that of Traverse Mountain barrier, indicating that the branch point zone may represent the most likely site of rupture nucleation for a characteristic earthquake because it has the lowest estimated fracture toughness of the three prominent, non-conservative barriers.

There is, however, an alternative interpretation for the mechanical characteristics of the northern half of the rupture segment. Detailed mapping of the footwall has revealed that numerous, conjugate normal faults are developed in a zone ≈ 1–2 km wide adjacent to the primary rupture traces (R.L. Bruhn unpublished data). These faults form two, conjugate normal fault sets in cross-section, which are geometrically similar to Riedel and anti-Riedel shears described by Tchalenko (1970) for strike-slip faults. The zone of secondary, conjugate faulting associated with each primary fault trace must overlap in the northern half of the fault segment, forming a broad zone of intense secondary deformation (Fig. 10). Two possible interpretations are shown in the cross-sections (Fig. 10), one in which the two primary faults have the same dips and another, in which the faults intersect at depth. Presently, there is insufficient information to prefer one interpretation to the other. The important point is that the northern half of the rupture segment is characterized by a much broader zone of secondary faulting than the southern half, where only one primary fault zone is present.

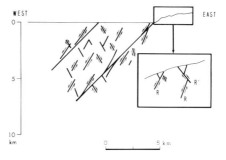

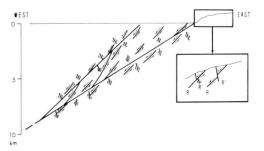

FIG. 10. Schematic cross-sections illustrating possible structure of the branched fault zone in the northern half of the Salt Lake segment. Conjugate faults in the footwall are interpreted as Riedel and anti-Riedel shears to two primary fault zones. (a) The two primary fault branches are assumed to dip at the same angle. (b) The two primary fault branches may converge at depth.

The broad zone of crustal damage in the bifurcated part of the rupture segment must influence rupture propagation in the same manner as a non-conservative barrier; effectively blunting the tip of a propagating rupture and locking the fault zone because of mutual interference between conjugate sets of secondary faults. Consequently, we speculate that the fracture toughness of the northern part of the rupture segment must be significantly greater than in the region S of the bifurcation point. If this speculation is correct, then Traverse Mountain barrier represents the most likely site for rupture initiation based on a fracture-toughness criterion. The highly fractured barrier must also provide a conduit for the introduction of hydrothermal fluids into the narrow, primary fault zone immediately to the N (fault section A, Fig. 6). Conceivably, quasi-static growth of large, coherent ruptures may be facilitated in this narrow, discrete fault section, where fluid flow is channelled rather than spread over the large volume of geometrically complex fault systems in the barrier. In either case, Traverse Mountain barrier is considered fundamental to the process of rupture initiation.

Discussion

The Salt Lake segment has not experienced a characteristic earthquake in historic time and this means that the inferred rupture characteristics are speculative and untested. Consequently, we wish to compare the structure of the segment with that of similar ruptures formed during large, historical earthquakes in the eastern Basin and Range and Rocky Mountains. The bifurcated, surficial rupture traces of the Hebgen, Montana ($M=7.5$, 1959) and Borah Peak, Idaho ($M=7.3$, 1983) earthquakes are geometrically similar to the Salt Lake rupture segment (Fig. 11). The focus of each earthquake was located near the end of the single set of scarps and the rupture propagated towards the bifurcated part of the fault zone, in the manner inferred for the Salt Lake segment. The Hebgen Lake event is particularly interesting, in that a $M=6$ earthquake occurred near the point of rupture branching immediately prior to the main shock, which then ruptured at the SE end of the zone of surface faulting (Dozer 1985a, b). The foci at Hebgen Lake and Borah Peak were both located at depths between 12 and 18 km, similar to that estimated for a characteristic earthquake focus on the Salt Lake segment.

Unfortunately, no structural studies equivalent to that reported here for the Salt Lake segment have been done on the Hebgen or Borah Peak faults. A cross-section of the bifurcated fault zone at Hebgen Lake constructed from the distribution of aftershocks is similar in overall geometry to that of cross-section b in Fig. 10 from the Salt Lake segment (Dozer 1985a, b). In addition, Crone & Machette (1984) speculate that the Borah Peak rupture may have encountered a barrier at the N end of the fault zone, near the bifurcation point in the rupture trace (Fig. 11). Certainly, detailed structural studies of the Hebgen Lake and Borah Peak rupture zones are warranted in the future, and will provide an important analogy for the Salt Lake segment.

The mechanical characteristics of a rupture segment must evolve over time, and barriers are particularly sensitive to changes in the stress field. Consider the Salt Lake segment, where the fault zone consists of several fault sections of different strike and dip (Fig. 8). The slip vector on individual sections between either conservative or non-conservative barriers will be deter-

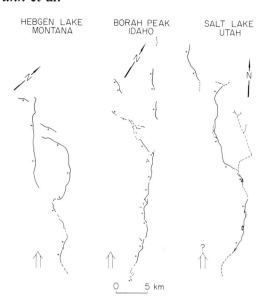

FIG. 11. Rupture traces of the Borah Peak, Idaho and Hebgen Lake, Montana earthquakes compared with the trace of surface rupturing in the Salt Lake segment. The large arrows indicate the directions of unilateral propagation during the Borah Peak and Hebgen Lake events. Borah Peak rupture trace after Crone & Machette (1984), Hebgen Lake trace after Myers & Hamilton (1964).

mined by the orientation and stress parameter of the tectonic stress field (Angelier 1979). If the stress field changes in either orientation or principal-stress ratio over time, then the slip vectors on the various fault sections must also change, possibly causing previously conservative barriers to evolve into non-conservative ones. Likewise, the resistance to rupture propagation in a non-conservative barrier could decrease in some cases. These processes may significantly alter the rupture characteristics of the fault zone. Consequently, one of the most important challenges in studying fault zones is understanding the spatial and temporal evolution of geometrical barriers and the effect of this evolution on palaeo and future earthquake ruptures.

The Salt Lake rupture segment may be undergoing such an evolutionary change in barrier structure at present. According to this study the least principal palaeo-stress was oriented sub-horizontal at $\approx 050° \pm 5°$ with $0.2 < \phi < 0.5$ (Table 2), but estimates of the contemporary stress tensor indicate that the least principal stress is now oriented $073° \pm 15°$ with $\phi \approx 0$ (Zoback 1983, 1985). Alternatively, Arabasz (1985) and Arabasz & Julander (in press) estimate that $\phi \approx 1$ based on their seismicity studies of the southernmost part of the Wasatch fault zone and Basin and Range–Colorado Plateau transition zone. Further understanding of this important problem, which will be common to most fault zones, requires detailed knowledge of the history of growth of the fault zone, better understanding of possible influences of the fault zone itself on the local stress tensor, and the temporal history of stress changes.

Subdivision into planar and curvi-planar sections is a fundamental characteristic of large fault zones. The preliminary model of the Salt Lake segment (Fig. 8) illustrates that in general, adjacent sections will have different dips, and that a dip-angle quoted for one part of the fault zone may not be applicable a few kilometres distant. The concept of conservative and non-conservative barriers in a normal fault zone then becomes important in predicting sub-surface geometry. In particular, the ability to predict dips in adjacent sections separated by conservative barriers, when the true dip of one section is known, is useful. Also, one must recognize that this procedure cannot be used on sections separated by a non-conservative barrier. Another important point is that the curvi-planar trace of a fault zone does not necessarily imply listric geometry at depth. Curvi-planar traces may arise from the linking of either planar or listric fault sections. For example, we cannot predict from our modelling in this study whether or not the fault zone decreases in dip with depth or remains planar. In general, two adjacent fault sections intersecting in a conservative barrier must be both planar or alternatively, they both must be listric. Intersections of two planes with mixed geometry must create a non-conservative barrier in a normal fault zone.

Conclusions

The Salt Lake rupture segment is composed of several, approximately linear fault sections that intersect in geometrical barriers defined by bends and branching of the fault trace. The dips of these fault sections vary based on a preliminary model of the fault zone, with estimated dips ranging from 30 to 90°.

The palaeo-stress tensor was characterized by sub-vertical maximum principal compressive stress, a minimum principal-stress axis trending about 050° and $\phi \approx 0.2$ to 0.5. The average slip direction across the fault section was $\approx 240°$.

A characteristic earthquake rupture originating within the Salt Lake segment is most likely to initiate at the southern end of the segment, either at or adjacent to Traverse Mountain barrier and to propagate northward based on qualitative estimates on the distribution of fracture toughness and fluid access to the fault zone. An alternative rupture initiation point would be located in the centre of the segment, at the point of fault-zone bifurcation. Three large, non-conservative barriers occur within the fault segment—at the northern and southern ends of the segment, and a branch point in the centre of the segment. Bifurcation of the rupture zone into two primary fault systems has presumably increased the fracture toughness of the northern part of the segment due to the overlap of secondary faulting adjacent to the primary fault planes.

Two large historic earthquakes in the eastern Basin and Range and Rocky Mountain transition region have ruptured in bifurcated fault zones; the Hebgen Lake, Montana earthquake ($M = 7.5$) in 1959 and the Borah peak, Idaho earth quake ($M = 7.3$) in 1983. The rupture foci were located at depths of 12–18 km and the ruptures propagated towards the regions of fault-zone bifurcation in both cases. The foci depths and directions of rupture propagation were both analogous to the inferred rupture characteristics of the Salt Lake segment.

ACKNOWLEDGMENTS: This work was supported by U.S. Geological Survey Earthquake Hazards Program grant No. 14-08-00011-G-886 to R.L.B. and W.T.P. and by American Chemical Society grants 14179AC2 and 17405AC2-C to R.L.B. The palaeo-stress analysis formed part of an MS thesis project for P.R. Gibler at the University of Utah. We thank W.J. Arabasz, J. Pechman, R.B. Smith and D.P. Schwartz for discussions concerning the structural and seismogenic characteristics of normal faulting.

References

AKI, K. 1979. Characteristics of barriers on earthquake faults. *J. geophys. Res.* **84**, 6140–8.

ANGELIER, J. 1979. Determination of the mean principal directions of stresses for a given fault population. *Tectonophysics*, **56**, T17–T26.

ARABASZ, W. 1985. Earthquake behavior in the Wasatch front area: Association with geologic structure, space-time occurrence and stress state, Proceedings of conference XXVI, A workshop on 'evaluation of regional and urban earthquake hazards and risk in Utah'. *U.S. Geol. Surv. Open-file Rep.* **84–763**, 310–39.

—— & JULANDER, D.R. In press. Geometry of seismically active faults and crustal deformation

352 R.L. *Bruhn* et al.

within the Basin and Range–Colorado Plateau transition in Utah. *Geol. Soc. Am. Spec. Pap. Extensional Tectonics.*

—— , SMITH, R.B. & RICHENS, W.D. 1980. Earthquake studies along the Wasatch front, Utah: Network Monitoring, seismicity and seismic hazards. *Bull. seis. Soc. Am.* **70**, 1479–500.

BASHORE, W.M., SMITH, R.B., ZANDT, G. & ANSORGE, J. 1981. Upper crustal structure of the Salt Lake Valley and the Wasatch front from seismic modelling. *Eos.* **62**, 961.

BULLOCK, R.L. 1954. The geology of Lehi quadrangle, Utah. Unpubl. M.Sc. Thesis, Brigham Young Univ.

COOK, K.L. & BERG, J.W. JR 1961. Regional gravity survey along the central and southern Wasatch front, Utah. *U.S. Geol. Surv. Prof. Pap.* **316-E**, 75–89.

CRITTENDEN, M.D. JR 1976. Stratigraphic and structural setting of the Cottonwood area, Utah: *In*: HILL, J.G. (ed.) *Geology of the Cordilleral Hingeline* pp. 281–317. Rocky Mtn Assoc. of Geologists, Denver.

—— , STUCKLESS, J.S., KISTLER, R.W. & STERN, T.W. 1973. Radiometric dating of intrusive rocks in the Cottonwood area Utah. *U.S. Geol. Surv. J. Res.* **1**, 173–8.

CRONE, A.J. & MACHETTE, M.N. 1984. Surface faulting accompanying the Borah Peak earthquake, central Idaho. *Geology*, **11**, 664–7.

DAS, S. & SCHOLZ, C.H. 1981. Theory of time-dependent rupture in the earth. *J. geophys, Res.* **86**, 6039–51.

DAVIS, F.D. 1983a. Geologic map of the central Wasatch front, Utah. *Utah geol. Min. Surv. Map,* **55-A**, scale 1:1000,000.

—— 1983b. Geologic map of the southern Wasatch front, Utah. *Utah geol. Min. Surv. Map,* **55-B**, scale 1:100,000.

DOSER, D.I. 1985a. Source parameters and faulting processes of the 1959 Hebgen Lake, Montana earthquake sequence. *J. geophys. Res.* **90**, 4537–56.

—— 1985b. The 1983 Borah Peak, Idaho and 1959 Hebgen Lake, Montana earthquakes: Models for normal fault earthquakes in the Intermountain Seismic Belt. *Proc. Workshop XXVIII on the Borah Peak, Idaho, earthquake, U.S. Geol. Surv. Open-file Rep.* **85–29**, 368–84.

GIBLER, P.R. 1985. Bedrock deformation along the Salt Lake segment of the Wasatch fault: implications for stress magnitudes, stress directions and seismicity, unpubl. MSc. Thesis, Univ. of Utah.

GILBERT, G.K. 1928. Studies of Basin-Range structure. *U.S. Geol. Surv. Prof. Pap.* **153**, 92 pp.

HOUGHTON, W. 1985. *Structural geology of the Deer Creek and Wasatch fault.* Unpubl. MSc. Thesis, Univ. of Utah.

KING, G. 1983. The accommodation of large strains in the upper lithosphere of the earth and other solids by self-similar fault systems: the geometrical origin of b-value. *Pageoph.* **121**, 761–814.

—— & NABELEK, J.L. 1985. Role of fault bends in the initiation and termination of earthquake rupture. *Science*, **228**, 987.

—— & YIELDING, G. 1984. The evolution of a thrust fault system: processes of rupture initiation, propagation and termination in the 1980 El Asnam (Algeria) earthquake. *Geophys. J.R. astron. Soc.* **7**, 915–33.

LAWSON, C.L. & HANSON, R.J. 1974. *Solving Least Squares Problems*, 340 pp. Prentice-Hall Inc., New Jersey.

MARSELL, R.E. 1969. The Wasatch fault zone in north central Utah. *In*: JENSEN, M.L. (ed.) *Guidebook of northern Utah, Utah geol. Min. Surv. Bull.* **82**, 125–39.

MEISSNER, R. & STREHLAU, J. 1982. Limits of stresses in continental crusts and their relationship to the depth-frequency distribution of shallow earthquakes. *Tectonics*, **1**, 73–89.

MICHAEL, A.J. 1984. Determination of stress from slip-data: faults and folds. *J. geophys. Res.* **89**, 11, 517–26.

MYERS, W.B. & HAMILTON, W. 1964. Deformation accompanying the Hebgen Lake earthquake of August 17, 1959. *U.S. Geol. Surv. Prof. Pap.* **435**, 37–98.

PARRY, W.T. & BRUHN, R.L. 1986. Pore fluid and seismogenic characteristics of fault rock at depth of the Wasatch Fault, *Utah. J. geophys. Res.* **91**, 730–44.

PAVLIS, T.L. & SMITH, R.B. 1980. Slip vectors from faults near Salt Lake City from Quaternary displacement and seismicity. *In*: ARABASZ, W.J., SMITH, R.B. & RICHINS, W.D. (eds) *Earthquake Studies in Utah 1850–1978*, pp. 378–82. Univ. of Utah.

RUDNICKI, J.W. 1980. Fracture mechanics applied to the Earth's crust. *Ann. Rev. Earth planet. Sci.* **8**, 489–525.

SCHWARTZ, D.P. & COPPERSMITH, K.J. 1984. Fault behavior and characteristic earthquake; Examples from the Wasatch and San Andreas fault zone. *J. geophys. Res.* **89**, 5681–98.

—— , HANSON, K.L. & SWAN, F.H. III 1983. Paleoseismic investigations along the Wasatch fault zone: An update. *In*: Geologic Excursions in Neotectonics and Engineering Geology in Utah, Guidebook, geol. Soc. Am. part IV, pp. 45–8.

SIBSON, R.H. 1982. Fault zone, models heat flow and depth distribution of earthquakes in the continental crust of the United States. *Bull. seis. Soc. Am.* **72**, 151–63.

SMITH, R.B. & BRUHN, R.L. 1984. Intra-plate extensional tectonics of the eastern Basin-Range: inferences of structural style from seismic reflection data, regional tectonics and thermal-mechanical models of brittle–ductile deformation. *J. geophys. Res.* **89**, 5733–62.

SWAN, F.H. III, SCHWARTZ, D.P. & CLUFF, L.S. 1980. Recurrence of moderate-to-large magnitude earthquakes produced by surface faulting on the Wasatch fault zone. *Bull. seis. Soc. Am.* **70**, 1431–62.

TCHALENKO, J.S. 1970. Similarities between shear

zones of different magnitudes. *Bull. geol. Soc. Am.* **81**, 1625–40.

VAN HORN, R. 1972. Map showing relative ages of faults in the Sugarhouse Quadrangle, Salt Lake County, Utah. *U.S. geol. Surv. Map*, **GQ-1-7667-B**, scale 1:24,000.

—— 1981. Geologic map of pre-Quaternary rocks of the Salt Lake City North Quadrangle. *U.S. geol. Surv. Map*, **1-1330**, scale 1:24,000.

WALLACE R.E. 1984. Pattern and timing of Late Quaternary faulting in the Great Basin Province and relation to some regional tectonic features. *J. geophys. Res.* **89**, 5763–9.

ZOBACK, M.L. 1983. Structure and Cenozoic tectonism along the Wasatch fault zone, Utah. *Mem. geol. Soc. Am.* **157**, 3–27.

—— 1985. Constraints on in-situ stress field along the Wasatch front. *Proc. Conf. XXVI, A workshop on 'evaluation of regional and urban earthquake hazards and risk in Utah'*, *U.S. geol. Surv. Open-file Rep.* **84–763**, 286–309.

RONALD, L. BRUHN, PAMELA, R. GIBLER & WILLIAM, T. PARRY, Department of Geology and Geophysics, University of Utah, Salt Lake City, Utah 84112, USA.

Topography and origin of the southern Rocky Mountains and Alvarado Ridge

G.P. Eaton

SUMMARY: The southern Rocky Mountains of the western United States and their structural continuation southward to the Mexican border represent the crest of a bilaterally symmetrical, continental feature of large dimensions, the Alvarado Ridge. It is characterized by long, gentle topographic rises with systematic, concave-upward slopes on which elevation declines in a quasi-exponential manner. The rises were originally blanketed with clastic sediments, a few tens to hundreds of metres thick; their erosional source being at the ridge crest. The blanket on the E rise is well preserved and has been undisturbed for nearly 5 Ma, save for regional Neogene warping and local, near-crest faulting associated with uplift of the ridge.

A comparative study of variations in regional elevation, gravity and crustal thickness suggest that the Alvarado Ridge and its rises are isostatically compensated and that almost none of the compensation involves an Airy crustal root. The flexural rigidity of the lithosphere is likewise believed to play but a minor role in the origin of the regional topography. Instead, the data are interpreted as confirming the hypothesis of distributed lithospheric thinning continuous and non-continuous in nature, and related thermotectonic uplift. Elevation of the ridge crest took place above the axis of an elongate, rapidly developing, asthenospheric bulge along which extensional strain in the shallow crust was limited to a central corridor only 150–200 km wide. The relatively low density and geometrical configuration of that bulge supports the topography. Heat-flow data in the region are in accord with this model.

The purpose of this paper is to describe a mammoth topographic ridge in the eastern Cordillera of the western United States and to demonstrate the relationship of this ridge to the young, high mountains that constitute its crest, to the axial rift that is enclosed by these mountains and to the sloping plains on either side. All these features, save the ridge itself, are well known (the southern Rocky Mountains, the Rio Grande rift, the Colorado Plateau and the Great Plains) and, individually, all have been the subject of much published literature, most if not all of which has been aimed at piecemeal rationales of origin and history that have failed to explain (or even to identify) the nature of the region as a whole. After describing the topography of this whole region, the present paper attempts a qualitative explanation of its origin. It is believed to be largely a function of distributed subcrustal lithospheric thinning and related extensional strain of a geographically limited nature in the crust. Deformation began in the Oligocene and culminated with great uplift in latest Miocene and early Pliocene time, creating a magnificent mountain range that rivals the Alps in elevation and grandeur.

Characteristics of a continental ridge

General aspects

Continental lithospheric rifting leads to local crustal thinning, extensional faulting, and graben subsidence, but equally characteristic is the uplift of a pair of bordering mountain ranges, a sediment source for both graben and ridge flank deposition, as well as the development of a topographic arch that is characterized by gentle, outward-sloping, concave rises adjoining the mountains. Such arches have been described as 'broad domal uplifts', 'plateau uplifts', or 'topographic swells', but, on close inspection, they are found to be remarkably similar in profile to ocean-loaded, slowly spreading ridges (Eaton, in press), hence, the descriptive term 'continental ridge' seems preferable, despite an acknowledged difference in genesis between this feature and a spreading ocean ridge. The characteristics of symmetry and concave flanks are generally always present, whether the continental crust has parted in the

From COWARD, M.P., DEWEY, J.F. & HANCOCK, P.L. (eds), 1987, *Continental Extensional Tectonics*, Geological Society Special Publication No. 28, pp. 355–369.

early stages of drifting to admit and accrete mafic magmas of mantle origin (as in axial portions of the Red Sea) or not (as in the Gulf of Suez, the East African rift system or the Rio Grande rift). In the case of pre-drift continental rifting, the continuity of Precambrian basement rocks across the region is preserved, including the area beneath the graben floor.

Characteristics of the Alvarado Ridge

The southern Rocky Mountains, *sensu lato*, (Eaton, in press) constitute the crest of a continental ridge that trends S from Casper, Wyoming to El Paso, Texas (Fig. 1). It has been dubbed the Alvarado Ridge after the first European explorer (the Spaniard, Hernando de Alvarado) to cross it at its mid-latitudes in 1540. Throughout southern Colorado and all of New Mexico, a narrow, irregular ribbon-like structural depression, the Rio Grande rift, lies between the ridges that constitute the southern Rocky Mountains. Earlier Laramide mountain ranges of different orientation were created on this site during a long period of NE-directed compression, but the topographic relief associated with them was substantially reduced by erosion before the late Oligocene. Lateral stream planation produced a major, SE-sloping, erosion surface across the region that had what was probably an isostatically adjusted, average maximum elevation of less than 900 m, according to interpretations of comprehensive palaeofloral data (Epis & Chapin 1975). Owing to widespread magmatism that accompanied this earlier deformation in the area that was to become the ridge crest, it is postulated that the lithosphere was already locally thin prior to the onset of the extensional episode that created the Alvarado Ridge. Ridge formation, then, resulted from further subcrustal thinning of the lithosphere distributed over a wide region.

The E rise of the Alvarado Ridge (see Fig. 2), which achieved its final profile during the last phases of extensional tectonism less than 7 Ma, is similar in configuration and scale to the W rise

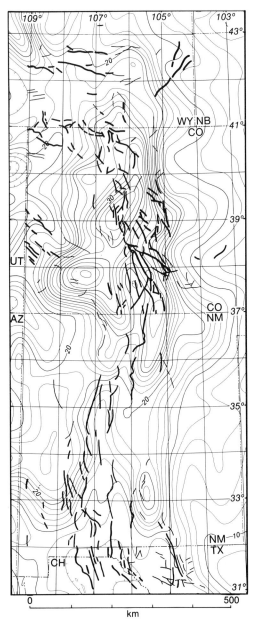

FIG. 1. Major young extensional faults and smoothed topography of the crest and upper flanks of the Alvarado Ridge. Smoothing by 45' squared average moving on a 15' grid. Contour interval is 100 m. Index contours are labelled in hundreds of metres, thus, 20 signifies 2000 m. Double letters identify individual states, as follows: AZ = Arizona; CH = Chihuahua (Mexico); CO = Colorado; NB = Nebraska; NM = New Mexico; TX = Texas; UT = Utah; and WY = Wyoming. (From Eaton, in press.)

—— Normal faults with known or inferred Neogene displacement

—— Other normal faults, age of displacement unknown or believed pre-Neogene

of the Mid-Atlantic Ridge, despite the isostatically-depressing effect of the ocean load on the Mid-Atlantic Ridge (Eaton, in press). In both cases the cross-sectional configuration appears to be related to outward lateral thickening of the lithosphere, but the fundamental cause of the thickness variations is quite different. The

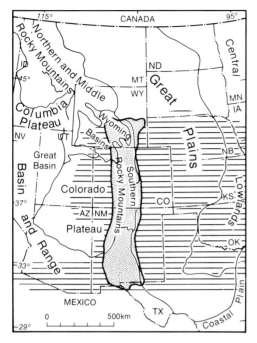

FIG. 2. Index map showing key elements of the Alvarado Ridge in relation to political boundaries (dash-dot lines) and physiographic province boundaries (thin solid lines); some of the latter provinces are grouped together and labelled. The words 'Southern Rocky Mountains' mark two areas of definition of that province: (i) Fenneman's (1931) *physiographic* range is outlined by a thin, irregular line running from the southern half of eastern Wyoming S through central Colorado and the northern quarter of central New Mexico; (ii) Eaton's (in press) *tectonic* range (the crestal region of the Alvarado Ridge) is outlined by a heavy solid line and stippled; it embraces all of Fenneman's southern Rocky Mountains and small parts of several adjoining physiographic provinces, as well as the Rio Grande rift. Horizontal ruling identifies still recognizable parts of the W and E rises. The westward slope of the W rise is interrupted by a sharp uplift near the western and southwestern edges of the Colorado Plateau. That uplift was associated with concomitant extension in the Basin and Range Province. Double letters identify individual states, as follows: AZ = Arizona; CO = Colorado; ID = Idaho; IA = Iowa; KS = Kansas; MN = Minnesota; MT = Montana; NB = Nebraska; ND = North Dakota; NV = Nevada; OK = Oklahoma; SD = South Dakota; TX = Texas; UT = Utah; and WY = Wyoming.

cause in the oceanic case is the lateral translation and time-dependent thickening of a thermal boundary layer that is created continuously at the ridge crest. The cause in the continental case being the rise of asthenosphere

beneath a thinning, pre-existing lithospheric plate that was originally of more or less uniform thickness.

The W rise of the Alvarado Ridge is considerably more complex and the cover sediments there are less extensively preserved. Scattered outcrops suggest an original extent and character like those of the E rise, here utilized in defining the precise configuration of the ridge. Coeval sedimentary rocks are found within the Rio Grande rift, between the bracketing ranges of the southern Rocky Mountains.

Topographic aspects of the southeastern US Cordillera

Transverse topographic profiles

In an effort to define the precise cross-sectional configuration of the Alvarado Ridge, especially its flanking rises, 24 topographic profiles were prepared from a digital data base. E-trending, major river valleys, such as those of the Platte, Arkansas and Canadian, were avoided in fixing the location for the profiles. Three profiles (one near the S end, one near the middle and one near the N end of the ridge) are shown in Fig. 3. Others are shown in a related paper (Eaton, in press, fig. 6). Bilateral symmetry is strongly apparent in the upper part of Fig. 3; is present, but less obvious, in the middle diagram, and is seemingly absent in the lower part of Fig. 3. Note that the E rise of the ridge is still sloping eastward at the E edge of the figure on all three profiles.

In the middle diagram of Fig. 3, the southern Rocky Mountains province is identified following the definition of both Fenneman (1931) and Eaton (in press). Elsewhere, Fenneman's purely physiographic definition is tectonically and geophysically inadequate. The W rise of the ridge, as seen in the middle diagram, includes Fenneman's Colorado Plateau physiographic province and the Great Basin section of his Basin and Range Province. The E rise includes the Great Plains and Central Lowland physiographic provinces (see Fig. 2). It is a central argument of this paper that the Neogene uplift of most of these provinces was synchronous and was genetically linked, hence, their Neogene geological histories should no longer be considered on a province-by-province basis. Note that the eastern part of the Colorado Plateau slopes westward as a mirror image of the upper Great Plains. Farther W it is interrupted on the W by the sharply uplifted E rim of the Great

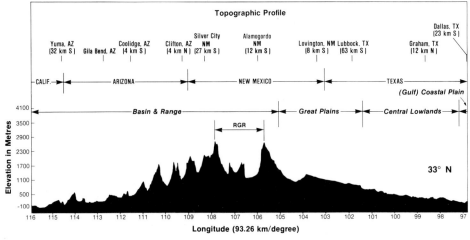

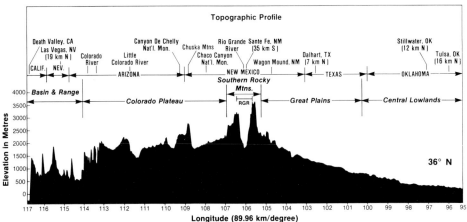

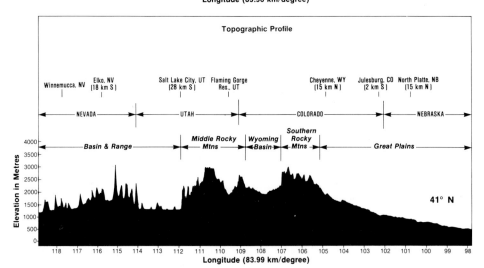

FIG. 3. Topographic profiles across the Alvarado Ridge along parallels 33, 36 and 41°N. Vertical exaggeration is approximately 100:1, but varies slightly among the profiles owing to latitudinal variation of the horizontal scale. First-order bilateral symmetry can be seen in the upper and middle diagrams. Note especially in the middle diagram how the topography of the eastern part of the Colorado Plateau is a mirror image of the western part of the Great Plains. The labelled physiographic provinces of Fenneman (1931) are of limited utility in tectonic analysis here. Letters RGR identify Rio Grande rift.

Basin, a separate, but coeval extensional province (Fig. 2).

The E rise of the Alvarado Ridge is similar on all three profiles in Fig. 3. It is a long, gentle, concave-upward slope that stretches eastward for many hundreds of kilometres. If an analysis of the topography of the ridge is to be undertaken, the eastern part of the crest and the E rise would seem to be the optimum place to make it. This rise is today drained by major rivers, however, and we must first ask to what extent the shape of the rise may have been modified by erosion.

Significance of the sedimentary cover on the rises

Figure 4 shows the present distribution of continental sedimentary rocks of Miocene and Pliocene age that were deposited during the tectonic episode that created the Alvarado Ridge. Many additional outcrops of these sediments are too small to illustrate at the scale of this figure (see for example, Eaton, in press, fig. 4b). The largest continuous remnants are those on the E rise. The youngest sediments there (labelled in Fig. 5 as 'Ogallala cover') are approximately 4.5 Ma old. The cover has been little disturbed since that time, except for local erosion. Major river valleys, their courses obvious in Fig. 4, have cut down into or locally through it. Elsewhere, however, the very gently sloping surface is as featureless as a billiard table.

Those parts of the rise undisturbed by erosion (more than 400,000 km² of the Ogallala cover are essentially unmodified) provide a singular opportunity to define the precise cross-sectional shape of the E rise after the last uplift of the ridge. They thus make possible a direct comparison of the configuration of a continental rise with its oceanic counterpart (one that occupies an environment generally protected from erosion but modified somewhat by sedimentation).

Configuration of the E rise

The three topographic profiles discussed earlier have been extended eastward (Fig. 5) into Louisiana (upper diagram), Arkansas (middle diagram), and Illinois (lower diagram), respectively. The cross-sectional extent of the Ogallala cover is labelled in each of these diagrams. It is widest in the lower diagram and narrowest in the upper. A smooth profile has been passed along the upper surface of the cover in each diagram and extrapolated beyond its eroded edges by extending it across (or above) the highest parts of the adjoining, eroded topography. The lower

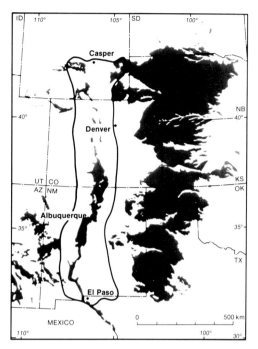

FIG. 4. Distribution of Miocene and Pliocene sedimentary rocks (shaded) on the Alvarado Ridge (after Eaton, in press). These sediments lie in a chain of deep medial grabens and in thin blankets on the flanking rises of the ridge. They were deposited at the latter locales as extensive sheets of fluviatile sediments locally interbedded with rhyolitic tuffs and, close to the ridge crest, with basalt flows. Much of the original cover on the W rise has been lost to erosion.

diagram best illustrates the method of drawing these curves.

Elevations across the E crest and rise were sampled at 50 km intervals out to a distance of 600 km, and at 100 km intervals beyond that. The results, corrected for differences in vertical exaggeration which arose from machine preparation of the original plots, and arbitrarily fixed as to initial distance ($D=0$ km) at the E edge of the crest of the mountains, were reduced arithmetically to a fictitious elevation of sea-level ($H=0$) at an arbitrary distance of 1300 km along each profile. Enclosed families of these profiles are shown in Fig. 6 in the form of two sets of envelopes, each bounding the smoothed profiles in the latitudinal span with which they are identified.

Additional profiles were prepared in the same manner for the northern Rocky Mountains and the northern Great Plains, as well as for the region S of El Paso, Texas, beyond the S end of the Alvarado Ridge. Although they are grossly

360   *G.P. Eaton*

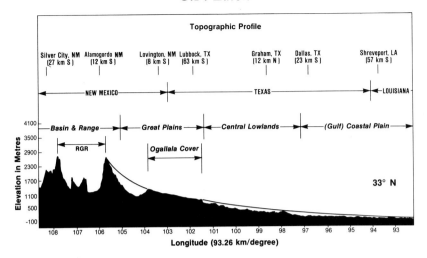

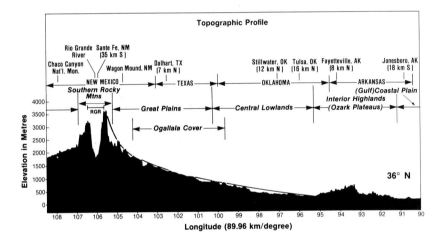

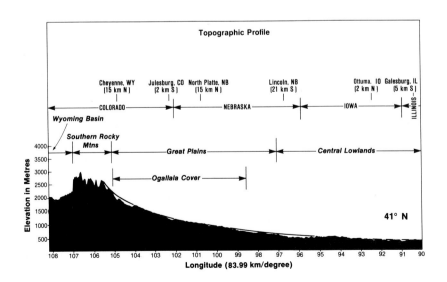

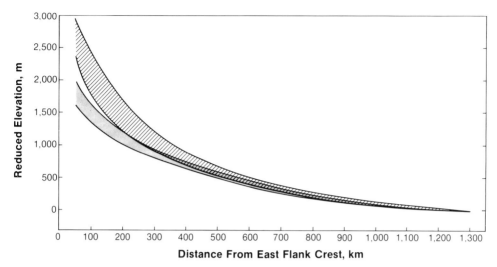

FIG. 6. Pairs of envelopes enclosing the smooth curves relating elevation and distance on the E rise. Nine topographic profiles between 36 and 40°N latitude fall within the diagonally hachured, upper pair. Six profiles near the N and S ends of the range fall within the lower, shaded pair. An anomalous zone of irregular topographic profiles less than 2° wide crossing the Wichita, Arbuckle and Ouachita Mountains in southern Oklahoma was omitted from consideration. Quaternary faulting seemingly unrelated to the origin of the rise has been observed there. All profiles were reduced to an elevation datum of 0 m at 1300 km.

similar in general form to those shown in Figs 3 & 5, that is, a mountain crest is adjoined to the E by a generally E-sloping plain, the slope of that plain is much gentler in these other areas and far less systematic in its variation of elevation with distance. In some places, the regular upward concavity that characterizes the E rise of the Alvarado Ridge out to 1300 km is absent.

Average topographic profile

Determination of an average profile
A single, arithmetic average profile representing the E flank of the main part of the ridge was derived for the purpose of analysis. It is shown by the heavy dots in both parts of Fig. 7, being more readily visible in the lower part, where a precise curve has been fitted to the data. It was traced out to 1300 km, the maximum distance on most of the individual profiles from this portion of the ridge for which an eastward regional slope was still apparent, and extrapolated mathematically from there.

The upper part of Fig. 7 shows three analytical curves produced in a brief series of attempts to fit simple mathematical functions to the observational data, as has been done for oceanic ridges. None is wholly acceptable. The observational data do not yield to such an approach, but an exponential decay comes closest to mimicking the observed topography, as curve (b) demonstrates. There is actually no geological reason to anticipate that elevations on a continental ridge-rise complex would behave as they do in the oceanic case, where a semi-constant spreading rate allows us to relate distance to lithospheric age and where conductive cooling of a lithospheric plate produces ocean-floor depths that increase as the square-root-of-age (Parsons & Sclater 1977).

Curve fitting with a quintic spline
Failure to find a precise analytical function relating rise elevation and distance led to the application of a curve-fitting technique that would provide a basis for extrapolation. Three functions were considered: the polynomial function

FIG. 5. Eastern parts of the topographic profiles of Fig. 3 extended to the E. The span of the Neogene sedimentary rocks on the E rise is identified here with the words 'Ogallala Cover'. Fitted to the profiles and extending W to the eroded top of the eastern ridge crest is a smooth line pinned to the cover and used to define the shape of the rise. E of the eroded edge of the Ogallala Cover this line is drawn so as to graze the top of the highest topography everywhere except near the Ozark Plateaus, mountains that are believed to have been high-standing before the last pulse of uplift of the Alvarado Ridge began some 4–7 Ma. Letters RGR identify Rio Grande rift.

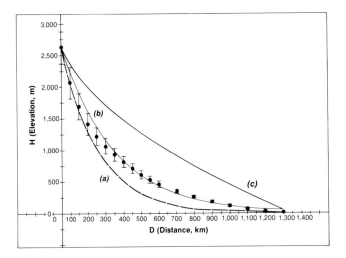

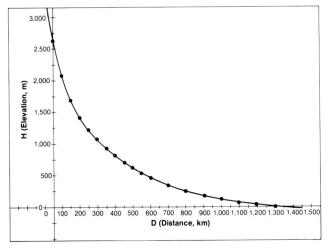

FIG. 7. Average topographic profile for the E rise (shown in the upper diagram as heavy dots with error bars) based on an arithmetic average of all the profiles bounded by the upper envelope in Fig. 6. The vertical exaggeration of this figure has been increased relative to that of Figs 3, 5 & 6. At the top, analytical curves derived in an attempt to match the relationship between elevation and distance are plotted with the observed data. Curves (a) and (b), shown as a heavy dashed and thin solid line, respectively, have the form $H = H_0 \cdot \exp(-cD)$. Curve (c), shown as a continuous heavy solid line, has the form $H = H_0 - kD^{1/2}$. In the lower diagram the observational data have been fitted with a natural quintic spline curve (solid line) that makes extrapolation to points a short distance beyond the sampled data range possible. Such extrapolation allows calculation of an average maximum height for the range, as well as a determination of the distance at which tilting of the lithospheric surface terminates.

and rational function were rejected and the natural spline function (Schultz 1973; de Boor 1978) was chosen. Two quantities were sought from the data: (i) a determination of the distance at which the systematic decay of elevation ends, thus marking the distal edge of the region of lithospheric warping associated with ridge uplift; and (ii) an original, average maximum elevation for the upper E flank of the ridge crest.

In the first case, it was assumed that the initial, undeformed state of the topography was one of essential horizontality and low regional relief. That the expectation of such a condition is not unreasonable on geological grounds follows from the fact that for the whole of the Cretaceous the area of the Great Plains was a sub-horizontal continental platform, occupied by an extensive, shallow sea. The western part of the region was doubtless flexed and tilted during

crustal loading that accompanied the Sevier, and perhaps the Laramide, compressional events, but the E edge of the depressing load lay at the western margin of the Colorado Plateau, 500 km W of the axis of what was to become the Neogene Alvarado Ridge and nearly 2000 km from what was to become the toe of its E rise. Visco-elastic flexural tilting created by such a load at the latter distance, especially after a lapse time (since loading) of 4×10^7 yr, can generally be ignored (see Walcott 1970, 1976). On this basis, the distance to the distal edge of the E rise was calculated using a quintic spline.

The quintic spline is a function that is four times continuously differentiable, is a piece-wise quintic polynomial and provides a quadratic extrapolation scheme, clearly superior to the linear extrapolation scheme provided by the natural *cubic* spline. The quintic spline provides an approximation of order 6 for the function itself, of order 5 for the first derivative, and of order 4 for the second derivative. In employing it for extrapolation, it yields meaningful results out to distances of four data intervals beyond the sampling range. The extrapolation polynomial used in this case yielded a distance to the edge of tilting (the toe of the rise) of 1450 km, the point where $dH/dD = 0$ and a distance beyond the sampling range of only one and one-half intervals, well within the allowable distance for reasonable accuracy.

In the second case, the prediction of an original average maximum elevation for the eastern ridge crest, a quantity that is far from constant in the empirical data, was attempted. Viewed from the E, the ridge crest has been serrated by erosion, hence, values of elevation at $D = 0$ vary widely. In fitting smooth curves to the many individual topographic profiles, the point from which horizontal distance was measured was arbitrarily chosen to be the E edge of the easternmost high topography in the crestal region of the ridge. Because of the serrate topography, however, the first elevation sampled for the fitted curves was at $D = 50$ km (on some profiles it was at $D = 100$ km), the value at $D = 0$ being regarded as unreliable owing to its great variability. For this reason, the ordinate axis in Fig. 7 has been placed at $D = 50$.

As before, the quintic spline provides an extrapolation polynomial that allows the calculation of an elevation at $D = 0$, as well as at distances W of $D = 0$, such as at the top of the W-facing scarp that bounds the E side of the axial graben. Extrapolation yielded a value of 3392 m at $D = 0$, but because the elevation at $D = 1300$ km was set arbitrarily to 0 in the arithmetic reduction of each of the profiles contributing to the average, one must add back the actual average elevation, 350 m, at that distance. The average elevation at $D = 0$ is thus 3742 m (12,274 ft). Farther W, at the top of the E scarp of the principal axial valley (where application of that term is appropriate), the calculated value of average elevation is 3938 m (almost 13,000 ft). Elevations at that location have been greatly and irregularly reduced by erosion since the last pulse of uplift, between 4 and 7 Ma. Original elevations may have been higher, as are the very highest of the individual peaks in the region today.

Extrapolation to such a location assumes that the original, pre-erosion topographic profile did not pass through an inflectional point W of $D = 0$ and thus did not experience a westward decrease in slope. This assumption has neither a foundation nor a possible refutation in observational fact. Prior to graben subsidence, the

highest elevations along the ridge may have been greater than those at the top of the eastern graben wall, but it seemed unreasonable to attempt to calculate elevations there using the spline function, given our ignorance of the actual configuration of the initial topography.

Origin of the ridge topography

The relationship of topography, gravity and crustal thickness

We turn now to a consideration of the process of formation of the Alvarado Ridge and its rifted, spiny backbone, the southern Rocky Mountains and Rio Grande rift. Three hypotheses are considered: (i) development of an Airy crustal root and resultant epeirogenic uplift, with shallow, local spreading at the crest; (ii) elastic flexure of the lithosphere on either side of a long, narrow zone of uplift created by lithospheric heating and intrusion; and (iii) passive extensional necking of the lithosphere and regional thermal uplift. In order to begin, it is necessary to ask if a topographic feature of such dimensions and such recent origin (average maximum height, nearly 4000 m; approximate half-width, 1450 km; and age, less than 20 Ma, with the latest, most pronounced phase of uplift at 7–4 Ma) is isostatically compensated and, if so, by what mechanism and at what depth.

Figure 8 is a map of crustal thickness of the whole of the ridge and of the surrounding terrain (the ridge crest is shaded). Figure 8(b)–(d) presents profiles of gravity, topography and crustal thickness along the three lines identified.

Profile 1 (Fig. 8b) provides a partial answer to the question of the efficacy and nature of buoyant support for the young regional topography. The Bouguer gravity profile (curve CBA) is a mirror image of the smoothed topography (curve S-TOPO) with respect to long and intermediate wavelengths (note, particularly, the systematic relationship within the shaded zone of this figure on the middle and upper E rise), suggesting that the ridge is, indeed, buoyantly supported. This conclusion appears to be substantiated by the free–air (S-FAA) and isostatic (A-HIA) anomalies which are generally everywhere less than 40 mGal and, along the E rise, generally less than 20 mGal. Even at this level, the principal departures of isostatic anomalies from values near zero have shorter wavelengths than the gross topographic feature illustrated. They reflect relatively shallow crustal sources.

The ridge crest has an associated positive free–air anomaly of more than 60 mGal, suggesting that it may be only partially compensated. It is probable that this anomaly is simply a function of the tendency of such anomalies to reflect a direct relation to pronounced local topography. Whereas free–air anomalies involve the fewest assumptions in their calculation, they also tend to reflect all departures from mass homogeneity, including that of the topography (and the density contrast between rock and air). This effect is very large in mountainous terrain, as near the ridge crest (Karner & Watts 1983). For this reason, little significance is attached to it. As to the nature of the isostatic support for the ridge, there is little variation in absolute depth to the M discontinuity in the reach from beneath the summit of the ridge crest all of the way to eastern Kansas, far down the E rise.

Profile 2 (Fig. 8c) reveals a thinned crust under the ridge crest and a corresponding axial graben, as might be expected, but no significant variation across the entire Texas portion of the E-rise. In Fig. 8(a) crustal thinning is shown as persisting over the entire southern half of the ridge crest, as well as over the northern seventh. Only under its Colorado portion is this feature apparently not characterized by crustal thinning. Examination of Fig. 8(d) reveals that the highest topography along the ridge crest (that part in Colorado) is underlain by the thickest crust and that as the crust thins, both to the N and S, elevation declines. In this part of its character, at least, there appears to be a component of Airy support for the very highest parts of the ridge.

Isostatic relations for the areally extensive E rise (it is approximately $11° × 15°$ in dimensions) were subjected to a further brief examination, the results of which are shown in Fig. 9. The relationship between complete Bouguer gravity and average topography for 127 data locations is plotted in Fig. 9. Variation in elevation for the population as a whole ranges from 130 to 2140 m and Bouguer gravity, from -2 to -221 mGal. Two local areas were excluded in the sampling, one of them, the buried, ribbon-like Keweenawan rift in the northern Great Plains (crossing parts of Nebraska, Iowa and Kansas) and the other,

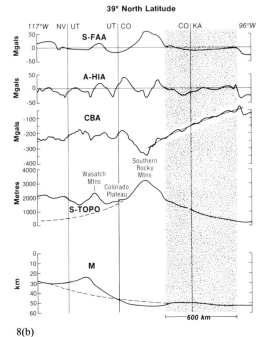

8(b)

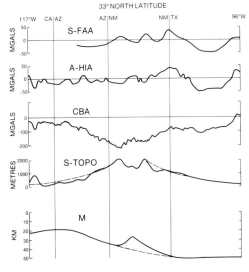

PROFILE 2: Gravity, Topography and M Discontinuity

8(c)

8(a)

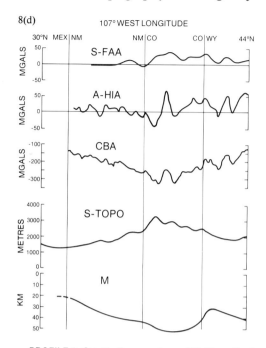

8(d)

107° WEST LONGITUDE

PROFILE 3: Gravity, Topography and M Discontinuity

FIG. 8. Crustal thickness, gravity and average elevation across the western United States between longitudes 96° and 117°W (data from Allenby & Schnetzler 1983, Diment & Urban 1981, McGinnis *et al.* 1979, Society for Exploration Geophysicists 1982, and Woollard 1966). (a) Map of crustal thickness based on published reversed and unreversed seismic refraction profiles. (b) Profiles of the smoothed free–air gravity field (S-FAA), Airy-Heiskanen isostatic gravity field (A-HIA; $T = 30$ km), complete Bouguer gravity field (CBA); $45' \times 45'$ average topography (S-TOPO) and the Mohorovicic discontinuity (M) along Profile 1, at 39°N latitude. Relations within the shaded area are discussed in the text. The pecked line on the W side of the S-TOPO curve is a mirror image of the E flank and rise. Departure of actual topography from it is the result of uplift of the Wasatch Mountains and back-tilting of the Colorado Plateau in central Utah (see Fig. 2 for map relationships). The subjective dashed line drawn through part of the M curve is intended to show how the crust might have varied in thickness across the area prior to pronounced crustal thinning beneath the eastern Great Basin of western Utah (UT) and development of a broad shallow hull beneath the southern Rocky Mountains in central Colorado (CO). (c) Gravity, topography and depth to the base of the crust at 33°N latitude. Labels as in diagram (b). Pecked lines drawn through the profile of topography are mirror images of one another, reflecting first-order bilateral symmetry. Dashed line drawn at base of M curve shows presumed configuration of the base of the crust prior to crustal thinning beneath the ridge crest's axial graben. (d) Longitudinal profiles down the

the narrow Wichita Mountains uplift in the southern Great Plains (in parts of Oklahoma and Texas). Both are characterized by narrow, highly elongate gravity highs with steep flanking gradients (Society for Exploration Geophysicists 1982). Neither appears to be isostatically compensated.

A linear least-squares fit is shown in Fig. 9. Parameters of fit are: (i) coefficient of correlation, 0.94; (ii) coefficient of determination, 0.88 and (iii) standard deviation of elevation, 51. The regional topography of the E rise is apparently compensated and this compensation has little if anything to do with systematic variations in the thickness of the crust. Because thinning of continental crust results in subsidence, but thinning of mantle lithosphere leads to regional uplift, this latter phenomenon would seem to be the principal cause of regional uplift here, perhaps complicated by additional contributions from systematic lateral variations in temperature and, hence, density, within the lithosphere.

Detailed modelling of the gravity field of the ridge and E rise is beyond the scope of this paper, owing to the need for complex stripping of the gravitational effect of a Phanerozoic section that undergoes significant changes in thickness and lithology across the region. A simple, first-order calculation is sufficient, however, to test the general efficacy of lithospheric thinning as a source for the observed major variation in gravity across the E rise. Assuming, for the sake of simple argument, that there is little contribution to long-wavelength variations in regional gravity from the near-surface geology, the rather large observed change that is accompanied by a variation in elevation of 1600 m, but by little change in crustal thickness, could be generated by a variation in thickness of the mantle lithosphere (mean density 3.26 mg m^{-3}, overlying asthenosphere of density 3.20 mg m^{-3}) of 70 km, distributed over a horizontal distance under the central and upper parts of the E rise of 600 km.

Thermal state of the lithosphere

Thermal data from Colorado, New Mexico and southeastern Wyoming define a conspicuous belt of anomalously high heat flow along the crest of the Alvarado Ridge. Values greater than 84 mW m^{-2} (2 HFU) are found from the southern boundary of New Mexico northward to the Colorado/Wyoming border (Decker &

W side of the ridge crest and southern part of the medial graben. Labels as in diagrams (b) and (c). The highest elevations here appear to be supported by the thickest crust.

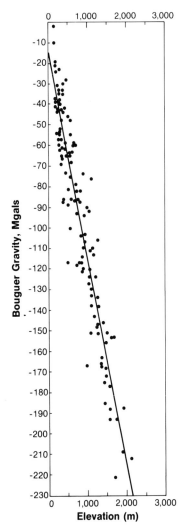

FIG. 9. Bouguer gravity versus 45 × 45′ average elevation on the E rise of the Alvarado Ridge. Measurements were made at 127 data locations ranging in elevation from 130 to 2140 m. Line of least-squares fit is represented by the equation: $-G$ (in mGal) = 15.92 + 0.099 H (in m).

Smithson 1975; Decker *et al.* 1980; Edwards *et al.* 1978; Lachenbruch & Sass 1977; Reiter *et al.* 1975; Reiter *et al.* 1978).

The heat-flow data are sufficiently abundant over much of the length of the ridge crest and adjoining provinces to permit contouring at an interval of 20 mW m^{-2} (~0.5 HFU) (Edwards *et al.* 1978; Morgan 1982; Reiter *et al.* 1975; Seager & Morgan 1979). A broad band of heat-flow sites where values equal to, or greater than 105 mW m^{-2} have been determined characterizes an irregular corridor of the ridge crest. Values on either side of this band fall

everywhere to less than 85 mW m^{-2} and generally to less than 65 mW m^{-2}, remaining a little higher on the Colorado Plateau than on the Great Plains. Decker *et al.* (1984) observed a systematic contrast in heat flux between the medial rift and its bordering ramparts in Colorado. The mean value for the rift is about 113 mW m^{-2} and that for the adjoining mountains, 92 mW m^{-2}.

While heat-flow along the full length of the ridge crest is anomalously high, some of it is clearly related to relatively recent, shallow-crustal intrusion of basaltic magmas, a form of convective mass transport of heat through the lithosphere. A comparison of heat-flow values from several continental rifts by Morgan (1982, 1983) indicates that there is a strong association of high mean heat-flow (and high local variability) with rifts characterized by young volcanism, as well as an association of lower mean heat-flow with non-volcanic rifts. The large, local variability of observed values in the southern Rocky Mountains and Rio Grande rift has rightly led several investigators to attribute a significant part of the anomalously high heat-flow there to shallow-crustal sources such as magmatic intrusions and forced hydrothermal convection (Clarkson & Reiter 1984; Decker *et al.* 1984; Morgan 1982, 1983). Nevertheless, a high degree of coherence in the large-scale, regional anomaly pattern suggests a component from a deep thermal source, as well, and has led to several attempts to model such a component with significant warping of isotherms at deeper levels (Clarkson & Reiter 1984; Mayhew 1982; Seager & Morgan 1979).

Significant sections of the medial rift are entirely free of Neogene volcanic rocks, for example, in a 300 km long stretch that includes the Blue, San Luis and upper Arkansas river valleys between Kremmling and Alamosa, Colorado, hence, the implication of shallow-crustal magma as the *sole* cause for high heat-flow seems debatable, although it is possible that the lower part of the lithosphere has parted to admit magma that has not made its way to the surface everywhere. Unless there is a pronounced decrease in thermal gradient below the level of measurement, however, purely conductive heat-flow values exceeding 100 mW m^{-2} imply the existence of equilibrium geotherms that exceed the solidus above the M discontinuity for all but the thinnest crust. On the basis of these facts, therefore, I favour components from both sources in the area of the medial rift.

Elevated equilibrium geotherms have been the subject of two studies. Mayhew (1982) modelled a step 35 km high on the 550°C Curie isotherm from an analysis of regional magnetic data. The isotherm shoals from a depth of 50 km under the

E rise (the base of the crust) to 15 km beneath the ridge crest. Clarkson & Reiter (1984) modelled a step 54 km high on the 1221°C isotherm across the W flank of the province. It shoals from 86 to 32 km depth. They suggested that values of this sort are achieved 20 Ma after initiation of such a step. As noted above, extension here has been underway since the late Oligocene. The sedimentary record shows that broad, shallow extensional basins began to develop locally during the late Oligocene and continued to develop into the Miocene. In contrast, the *middle* Miocene marked the time of initial deposition of crest-derived sediments on the E rise of the ridge (Eaton, in press), signifying that the first strong uplift took place at that time.

If the upwarped-geotherm model is valid and taking as given that the lithosphere is a thermal boundary layer, elevation of the isostatically compensated ridge crest is attributable to the buoyancy of a hot asthenospheric ridge beneath it, perhaps aided by lateral temperature variations in the lithosphere. What is far from clear, however, is just what the goeometric configuration of the lithosphere/asthenosphere boundary was immediately prior to the onset of extension. Magmatism characterized the central corridor of what is now the ridge crest during the Oligocene. The implication of such magmatism is one of crustal melting and, hence, of the existence of a locally thinned lithosphere that would not have had time to cool, thicken, and subside substantially before notable local extension began along the central corridor. Perhaps the area was moderately high during this period, but, as noted above, the crestal area was apparently less than 1000 m high during part of the Oligocene and the 35 Ma-old Wall Mountain ash-flow tuff swept southeastward across the crestal area without topographic impediment (Epis & Chapin 1975).

The regional existence of an asthenospheric ridge beneath the Rio Grande rift has long been suspected (Decker & Smithson 1975; Cordell 1978; Ramberg *et al.* 1978; Seager & Morgan 1979). A recent study of teleseismic *P*-wave delays ·(Davis *et al.* 1984) revealed the presence of delay residuals of up to 1.5 sec beneath the regioh. The pattern of delays across the long line of profile correlates well with the Bouguer gravity field of Fig. 8(b) & (c). The delays were ascribed to a rise of the lithosphere/asthenosphere boundary. The top of the upwarp was postulated to lie at a depth of 65–70 km and to fall to 130–135 km beneath the Colorado Plateau 425 km to the W. It also falls to depths of 185–190 km at an equal distance beneath the Great Plains to the E. Out to this distance, then, the maximum struc-

tural relief at the base of the lithosphere is 115–125 km. At the surface, the maximum topographic relief over the same span is roughly 3.0 km. The observed contrast in depth to the asthenosphere on either side of the ridge is roughly paralleled by a contrast in P_n values in the lower lithosphere: W rise, 7.8 km sec^{-1}; ridge crest, 7.6 km sec^{-1}, and E rise, 8.2 km sec^{-1} (Seager & Morgan 1979).

What is the basis for the great width of the ridge, a feature nearly 3000 km wide? If the asthenospheric bulge beneath it has but a fraction of its total width and if the continental lithosphere has a characteristic thickness of the order of 90–130 km, it seems unlikely to be supported to any significant degree by the flexural rigidity of the lithosphere, especially given the elevated heat-flow in the region. The magnitude of the force on the surface of a lithospheric plate (in this case, an upward-acting, or negative, load arising from the buoyancy of both the asthenospheric ridge at its lower surface and of any relatively light magmatic masses that may have been emplaced within it) is but one of several factors that dictates the amplitude and wavelength of the resultant flexure (Walcott 1970). We are interested primarily in bending of the plate that may take place beyond the edge of the load. Calculation of the flexural rigidity for the lithosphere beneath the Interior Plains of Canada (the geological setting most closely analogous to the Great Plains) yielded a figure of 4×10^{30} dyn cm (Walcott 1970) and similar calculations for the Alps, Appalachians and Himalayas yielded a range of values from 10^{30} to 5×10^{32} dyn cm (Karner & Watts 1983). The Alvarado ridge would require a value much greater than these to account for its full dimensions if its configuration stems solely from a flexure associated with simple uplift at the crest of the ridge.

The preferred model, then, is that of distributed lithospheric thinning. The moderately elevated, observed heat-flow values beneath the E rise suggest that if the asthenosphere beneath it is elevated as a result of such thinning, then the recency of last uplift (4–7 Ma) relative to the thermal time constant for the crust and lithosphere is such that the maximum pulse of elevated heat flux through the rises has yet to be sensed at the surface (Lachenbruch & Sass 1977). Morgan (1983) has examined this phenomenon in detail with regard both to slow and rapid dynamic thinning of the lithosphere, concluding that there is considerable delay in the development of a surface heat-flow anomaly after thermally induced uplift has occurred. The only signal of thinning one might expect to see at the surface on the flanks of the Alvarado Ridge would thus be an increase in regional topographic elevation.

The ridge seems to match well the genetic model of Rowley & Sahagian (1986) who proposed that the characteristics of such structures are most readily explained by continuous non-uniform stretching of the mantle in a polygonal region beneath a locally thinned and rifted, and regionally uplifted, crust.

Based on the distribution of Neogene normal faults, the crust at the summit of the Alvarado Ridge is significantly stretched only within an axial corridor 150–200 km wide. The width of a nearly coincidental belt of highly discontinuous Neogene volcanic fields of fundamentally basaltic character is similar. Beyond the edges of this corridor there is a virtual absence of evidence that the crust beneath the adjoining rises is extended. On the other hand, modelling of P_n delays on the E side suggests that the lithosphere thickens outward to at least 425 km in that direction and possibly continues to thicken out to 600 km, where the reliable seismic delay data end and where one is nearly eight times as far from the axis of the ridge as is the E edge of the belt of normal faulting and obvious crustal stretching. At this point, however, one is still only halfway out to the foot of the broad regional topographic arch and related regional Bouguer gravity anomaly. At 1,450 km, the value of the parameter, 0, of Rowley & Sahagian (1986) exceeds 80°, thus yielding the cross-sectional appearance of a highly and broadly thinned mantle lithosphere. Clearly, this ridge is ripe for quantitative modelling.

Although many of the observational data required have been presented or referred to in this paper, a critical and singular problem will severely limit the choice of models: the rapidity of nearly 3 km of uplift. Although the first record of regional unroofing of the Precambrian basement and its Palaeozoic cover resulting from Neogene uplift seems to have occurred at approximately 17 Ma in Colorado and was perhaps as much as 5 Ma later in West Texas (Eaton, *in press*), it followed very closely in time (less than 18 Ma) the existence of a limited maximum regional elevation of less than one km in Oligocene time. The simple conductive rise of geotherms through the lithosphere is incapable of explaining the origin of the Alvarado Ridge.

ACKNOWLEDGMENTS: Two friends and exacting critics, Warren Hamilton and Paul Morgan, tackled an early version of the manuscript and suggested much that led to its improvement. They are absolved of further responsibility: any remaining shortcomings are due to me. I am indebted to my Texas A&M colleague, Charles K. Chui, for pointing me towards the application of the natural spline for extrapolation and for the development of a computer program that would fit the elevation data for the E rise of the Alvarado Ridge. Finally, I wish to acknowledge the effective and willing assistance of Laurie Price and Melvin Lasell, who aided me in the compilation, processing and modelling of some of the data.

References

ALLENBY, R.J. & SCHNETZLER, C.C. 1983. United States crustal thickness. *Tectonophysics*, **93**, 13–31.

DE BOOR, C. 1978. *A practical guide to splines, Appl. Math. Sc. 27.* Springer-Verlag, New York, 392 pp.

CHAPIN, C.E. 1971. The Rio Grande rift, Part 1: Modification and additions. *In: The San Luis Basin. New Mexico geol. Soc. Guidebook 22,* pp. 191–201.

CLARKSON, G. & REITER, M. 1984. Analysis of terrestrial heat-flow profiles across the Rio Grande rift and Southern Rocky Mountains in Northern New Mexico. *In:* BALDRIDGE, W.S., DICKERSON, P.W., RIECKER, R.E. & ZIDEK, J. (eds) *Rio Grande rift: Northern New Mexico, New Mexico geol. Soc. 35th Ann. Field Conf.* pp. 39–44.

CORDELL, L. 1978. Regional geophysical setting of the Rio Grande rift. *Bull. geol. Soc. Am.* **89**, 1073–1090.

DAVIS, P.M., PARKER, E.C., EVANS, J.R., IYER, H.M & OLSEN, K.H. 1984. Teleseismic deep sounding of the velocity structure beneath the Rio Grande rift. *In:* BALDRIDGE, W.S., DICKERSON, P.W., RIECKER, R.E. & ZIDEK, J. (eds) *Rio*

Grande rift: Northern New Mexico, New Mexico geol. Soc. 35th Ann. Field Conf. pp. 29–38.

DECKER, E.R. & SMITHSON, S.B. 1975. Heat flow and gravity interpretation across the Rio Grande rift in southern New Mexico and west Texas. *J. geophys. Res.* **80**, 2542–52.

——, BAKER, K.H., BUCHER, G.J. & HEASLER, H.P. 1980. Preliminary heat flow and radioactivity studies in Wyoming. *J. geophys. Res.* **85**, 311–21.

——, BUCHER, G.J., BUELOW, K.L. & HEASLER, H.P. 1984. Preliminary interpretation of heat flow and radioactivity in the Rio Grande rift zone in central and northern Colorado. *In:* BALDRIDGE, W.S., DICKERSON, P.W., RIECKER, R.E. & ZIDEK, J. (eds) *Rio Grande rift: Northern New Mexico. New Mexico geol. Soc. 35th Ann. Field Conf.* pp. 45–50.

DIMENT, W.H. & URBAN, T.C. 1981. Average elevation map of the conterminous United States (Gilluly averaging method). *U.S. geol. Surv. geophys. Inv. Map GP-933.* 1:2,500,000.

EATON, G.P. in press. A tectonic redefinition of the Southern Rocky Mountains. *Tectonophysics,* **132**.

EDWARDS, C.L., REITER, M., SHEARER, C. & YOUNG, W. 1978. Terrestrial heat flow and crustal radioactivity in northeastern New Mexico and southeastern Colorado. *Bull. geol. Soc. Am.* **89**, 1341–50.

EPIS, R.C. & CHAPIN, C.E. 1975. Geomorphic and tectonic implications of the post-Laramide, late Eocene erosion surface in the Southern Rocky Mountains. *In*: CURTIS, B.F. (ed.) *Cenozoic history of the Southern Rocky Mountains, Mem. geol. Soc. Am.* **144**, 45–74.

FENNEMAN, N.M. 1931. *Physiography of Western United States*. McGraw-Hill Book Co., New York, 534 pp.

KARNER, G.D. & WATTS, A.B. 1983. Gravity anomalies and flexure of the lithosphere at mountain ranges. *J. geophys. Res.* **88**, 10449–77.

LACHENBRUCH, A.H. & SASS, J.H. 1977. Heat flow in the United States and the thermal regime of the crust. *In*: HEACOCK, J.G. (ed.) *The nature and physical properties of the earth's crust, Am. geophys. Union geophys. Mono.* **20**, 626–75.

MCGINNIS, L.D., WOLF, M.G., KOHSMANN, J.J. & EVANS, C.P. 1979. Regional free air gravity anomalies and tectonic observations in the United States. *J. geophys. Res.* **84**, 591–601.

MAYHEW, M.A. 1982. Application of satellite magnetic anomaly data to Curie isotherm mapping. *J. geophys. Res.* **87**, 4846–54.

MORGAN, P. 1982. Heat flow in rift zones. *In*: PALMASON, G. (ed.) *Continental and oceanic rifts, Am. geophys. Union and geol. Soc. Am. Geodyn. Ser.* **8**, 107–22.

—— 1983. Constraints on rift thermal processes from heat flow and uplift. *Tectonophysics*, **94**, 277–98.

PARSONS, B. & SCLATER, J.G. 1977. An analysis of the variation of ocean floor bathymetry and heat flow with age. *J. geophys. Res.* **82**, 803–28.

RAMBERG, I.B., COOK, F.A. & SMITHSON, S.B. 1978. Structure of the Rio Grande rift in southern New Mexico and west Texas based on gravity interpolation. *Bull. geol. Soc. Am.* **89**, 107–23.

REITER, M., SHEARER, C. & EDWARDS, C.L. 1978. Geothermal anomalies along the Rio Grande rift in New Mexico. *Geology*, **6**, 85–8.

——, EDWARDS, C.L., HARTMAN, H. & WEIDMAN, C. 1975. Terrestrial heat flow along the Rio Grande rift, New Mexico and southern Colorado. *Bull. geol. Soc. Am.* **87**, 811–18.

ROWLEY, D.B. & SAHAGIAN, D. 1986. Depth-dependent stretching. *Geology*, **14**, 32–5.

SCHULTZ, M.H. 1973. *Spline analysis*. Prentice-Hall, Englewood Cliffs, New Jersey, 156 pp.

SEAGER, W.R. & MORGAN, P. 1979. Rio Grande rift in southern New Mexico, west Texas, and northern Chihuahua. *In*: RIECKER, R.E. (ed.) *Rio Grande rift: tectonics and magmatism*, pp. 87–106. Am. geophys. Union, Washington, D.C.

Society for Exploration Geophysicists 1982. *Gravity anomaly map of the United States, exclusive of Alaska and Hawaii*. Tulsa, Oklahoma, 1:2,500,000.

WALCOTT, R.I. 1970. Flexural rigidity, thickness, and viscosity of the lithosphere. *J. geophys. Res.* **75**, 3941–54.

—— 1976. Lithospheric flexure, analysis of gravity anomalies, and the progression of seamount chains. *In*: SUTTON, G.H., MANGHNANI, M.H. & MOBERLY, R. (eds) *The geophysics of the Pacific Ocean basin and its margin, Am. geophys. Union geophys. Mono.* **19**, 431–8.

WOOLLARD, G.P. 1966. Regional isostatic relations in the United States. *In*: STEINHART, J.S. & SMITH, T.J. (eds) *The earth beneath the continents, Am. geophys. Union geophys. Mono.* **10**, 557–94.

GORDON, P. EATON, Office of the President, Iowa State University, Ames, Iowa 50011, USA.

Kinematics of Basin and Range intraplate extension

P.K. Eddington, R.B. Smith & C. Renggli

SUMMARY: Strain rates assessed from brittle fracture (associated with historic earth-quakes) and total brittle-ductile deformation measured from geodetic data have been com-pared to estimates of palaeostrain, from Quaternary geology for the intraplate Great Basin part of the Basin and Range Province, western United States. These data provide an assess-ment of the kinematics and mode of lithospheric extension that the western U S Cordillera has experienced from the past few million years to the present. Strain and deformation rates were determined by the seismic-moment-tensor method using historic seismicity and fault-plane solutions for sub-regions of homogeneous strain. Contemporary deformation (with maximum-deformation rates) in the Great Basin occurs principally along the active seismic zones: (i) the southern Intermountain Seismic Belt (ISB), 4.7 mm a^{-1}; (ii) along the western boundary, the Sierra Nevada front, 1.6 mm a^1 (28.0 mm a^{-1} if the M 8.3 1872 Owen Valley, California earthquake is included); and (iii) along the W-central Nevada seismic belt, 7.5 mm a^{-1}. The integrated opening rate across the entire Great Basin is accommodated by E–W extension at 8–10 mm a^{-1} to the N which diminishes to 3.5 mm a^{-1} to the S. These results show 8–10 mm a^{-1} contemporary extension across the entire Great Basin associated with earthquakes that compares to the ≤ 9 mm a^{-1} value determined from intraplate tectonic models (constrained by satellite geodesy) implying that contemporary strain is generally released by earthquakes. Zones of maximum lithospheric extension correspond to belts of thin crust, high heat flow, and Quaternary basaltic volcanism, suggesting that these parameters are related through the mechanism of extension such as a stress relaxation, allowing buoyant uplift and ascension of magmas.

Contemporary strain and deformation rates have been determined from geodetic measurements yielding maximum deformation of 11.2 mm a^{-1} in the Hebgen Lake, Montana portion of the Intermountain Seismic Belt; 3.6 mm a^{-1} in the Walker Lane, Nevada area; and 2.5 mm a^{-1} in the Owens Valley, California area adjacent to the Sierra Nevada front. Palaeostrain and deformation rates principally from Quaternary fault-displacement rates gave deformation rates of 7.4 mm a^{-1} along the southern ISB. Geodetically determined deformation rates compare well with rates determined from seismic moments, whereas poorly constrained palaeo-strain rates from Quaternary geology are ~10 times smaller than contemporary rates except in parts of central and southern California, Wyoming, parts of Utah, and along the Idaho–Wyoming border.

The Great Basin sub-province of the Basin and Range Province, western US, is an area of active E–W lithospheric extension (Fig. 1). The presence of this strain regime has been inferred from many types of geological and geophysical data summarized by Smith & Sbar (1974); Eaton et al. (1978); Zoback et al. (1981). Quantitative estimates of contemporary deformation and magnitudes of extension rates have been dif-ficult to obtain; however, various authors have made estimates of reginal extension using studies of seismicity, fault-plane geometries, intraplate tectonic models, and geodetic measurements (Proffett 1977; Greensfelder et al. 1980; Minster & Jordan 1984; Savage 1983). In this study, the seismic moment-tensor method was employed to determine strain and deformation rates of discrete areas of homogeneous strain and overall Great Basin opening rates. These data were then compared to strain rates estimated from geodetic measurements and to palaeostrain rates calculated from geological data.

Strain rates from earthquake data

Brittle strain release in the lithosphere is primar-ily expressed by earthquakes that can be used to assess regional strain (see e.g. Greensfelder et al. 1980; Doser & Smith 1982, 1983; Hyndman & Wiechert 1983; Wesnousky et al. 1982a). Earth-quake magnitudes with fault-plane orientations derived from fault-plane solutions were used to determine the seismic-moment tensors that in turn were used to calculate the strain-rate tensor (Kostrov 1974). The results of these calculations provided data on strain and deformation rates that characterize the kinematics of Great Basin intraplate extension.

Cenozoic history of the Great Basin

Great Basin extension began with the cessation of subduction along the W coast of North America about 30 Ma. Prior to this extensional regime, Mesozoic volcanism was associated with

From COWARD, M.P., DEWEY, J.F. & HANCOCK, P.L. (eds), 1987, *Continental Extensional Tectonics*, Geological Society Special Publication No. 28, pp. 371–392.

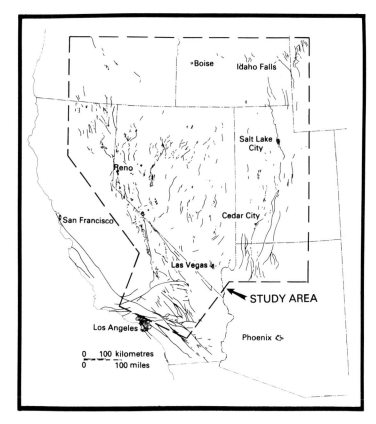

Fig. 1. Active fault map of Great Basin study area (inner area). Faults of late-Cenozoic age (principally Quaternary). Data taken from published and unpublished sources (references on file at the University of Utah).

subduction that produced a calc-alkaline volcanic arc. East of this arc, a foreland belt of folding and thrusting, associated with the Sevier and Laramide Orogenies produced crustal compression and lithospheric shortening in areas that were later affected by late Cenozoic extension.

During the Miocene, about 30–40 Ma, subduction was nearing its conclusion and WSW–ENE extension began in the Great Basin region, possibly as a result of back-arc spreading and stress relaxation of the lithosphere (Scholz *et al.* 1971; Zoback *et al.* 1981). A second period of Great Basin regional extension followed about 10–13 Ma (Zoback *et al.* 1981), initially in the southern Basin and Range of Arizona and northern Mexico (Thompson & Burke 1974). Marking the beginning of this extensional episode, the direction of extension rotated counterclockwise ~45° to a WNW–ESE direction (Zoback *et al.* 1981). Further evidence of these

two periods of Great Basin extension comes from palinspastic reconstructions of reflection profiles in western Utah (von Tish *et al.* 1985).

Normal faulting that developed during the latter period of crustal extension has largely overprinted evidence of the earlier periods of extension and compression (Eaton *et al.* 1978). However, in some areas, contemporary strain may be accommodated by movement on pre-existing faults developed during the early periods of deformation (Zoback & Zoback 1980; Smith & Bruhn 1984).

The Great Basin is still undergoing active E–W extension as evidenced by the province-wide seismicity and numerous normal-faulting fault-plane solutions (Smith 1978; Smith & Lindh 1978; Zoback & Zoback 1980). Some possible causes of this lithospheric extension have been suggested as pure crustal stretching, passive or active magmatic intrusion, crustal underplating, or a combination of these mechanisms (Lachenbruch & Sass 1978). It appears that some mantle upwelling probably accompanied Great Basin extension to produce the widespread, late Tertiary basaltic volcanism (Best & Hamblin 1978) and the E–W symmetry of gravity and regional topography of the province (Eaton *et al.* 1978).

Great Basin topography is dominated by N-trending, normal-fault-bounded ranges separated at 25 km average intervals by alluvium-filled basins. The region has generally high elevations from 1 to 1.5 km and is charac-

terized by high heat flow exceeding 90 mWm^{-2} (Lachenbruch & Sass 1978), low Bouguer gravity (Eaton *et al.* 1978), a thin crust, 24–34 km, and low *Pn* velocities (Smith 1978). The seismicity (Fig. 2) occurs along diffuse bands up to 200 km wide.

Earthquake history of the Great Basin

Seismicity within the Great Basin (Fig. 2) has been concentrated along the eastern province margin associated with the southern Inter-

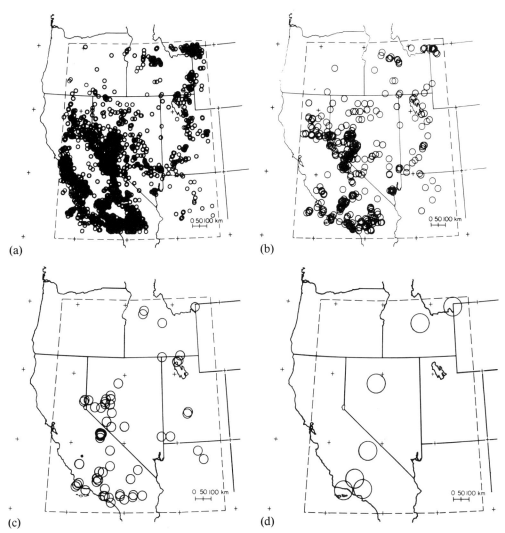

(a)

(b)

(c)

(d)

FIG. 2. Earthquake epicentre maps from regional network and historic data compiled for this study. Data cover period, 1900–1981 plus the 1983, Borah Peak, Idaho earthquake sequence: (a) $M_L > 4$; (b) $M_L > 5$; (c) $M_L > 6$, and (d) $M_L > 7$.

mountain Seismic Belt (ISB); along the western-province margin associated with the Sierra Nevada front, and in central Nevada (Smith 1978). Large magnitude, $M > 6.5$, Great Basin earthquakes have occurred principally in central Nevada, in Owens Valley, California and at locations of pronounced changes in the trend of the southern ISB.

Great Basin seismicity has been characterized primarily by dip-slip and oblique-slip events throughout most of the region, including nine $6.5 < M < 7.5$ normal-faulting events that produced scarps (Smith 1978; Smith & Lindh 1978). Strike-slip and oblique-slip events have occurred along the region's southern and southwestern borders. Most earthquakes in the Great Basin occur at depths less than 15 km and approximately 80% are less than 10 km (Smith & Sbar 1974; Sibson 1982; Smith & Bruhn 1984).

Hypocentres of the largest, $M > 7$, earthquakes, however, were located at greater depths, e.g. ~ 15 km (Smith & Richins 1984), near the hypothetical brittle–ductile transition. The large magnitude, $M > 7$, earthquakes can be clearly correlated with surface-breaking faults. However, for smaller earthquakes, generally less than $M6.5$, there is a lack of surface faulting.

It has been theorized that large earthquakes nucleate near the brittle–ductile transition where lithospheric loading is the principal contributor to deviatoric stress, but where strain rates, at ~ 10^{-4} sec^{-1} relieve the stored energy (Smith & Bruhn 1984; Sibson 1982). Smith & Bruhn's (1984) Great Basin rheological model suggests multiple brittle–ductile transition zones, where the multiplicity corresponds to changes in rock type with depth. The shallowest ductile zone is about 7 km deep, near the 80th percentile in focal-depth distribution for the Wasatch and Sierra Nevada fronts.

The study area for this paper includes the intraplate extensional domains of the Great Basin and surrounding areas, principally southwestern Montana, western Wyoming, southeastern Idaho, eastern California, and southeastern Oregon (Fig. 1). The transition from the Basin and Range to the San Andreas Fault, including the White Wolf, Lone Pine and Garlock faults, was also included.

In summary, the objectives of the study were: (i) to determine the contemporary strain and deformation rates of this region of intraplate extension using the seismic-moment-tensor method; (ii) to compare the contemporary strain rates with geodetically and geologically determined Quaternary strain rates; and (iii) to assess the kinematics of Great Basin extension.

Strain determination from earthquake data

Strain-rate calculation from the seismic-moment tensor

The seismic-moment method described here was used to calculate stresses, strains and seismic moments from earthquake magnitudes and fault-plane solutions following the methods outlined by Kostrov (1974), Anderson (1979), Molnar (1979) and Doser & Smith (1982, 1983). The process involves the following steps:

Conversion of magnitudes to scalar moments

The seismic moment and seismic-moment rates of a single fault are given by:

$$M_0 = \mu A u \tag{1a}$$
$$\dot{M}_0 = \mu A \dot{u} \tag{1b}$$

where M_0 is the seismic moment, u is the displacement, A is the fault-plane area, μ is the shear modulus, and $\dot{u}$ and $\dot{M}_0$ are the slip rate and moment rate respectively (after Aki 1966). Seismic moments can also be estimated from empirical magnitude–moment relationships and from inferred palaeoslip rates based upon the dating of Quaternary faults. For this study, seismic moments for large earthquakes were taken from published sources, when possible; otherwise, the following magnitude–moment relations were used:

$$\log(M_0) = 1.1 M_L + 18.4 \tag{2a}$$
Utah (extension, after Doser & Smith 1982),

$$\log(M_0) = 1.5 M_L + 16.0 \tag{2b}$$
California (compressive strike-slip (Thatcher & Hanks 1973)).

Equation (2a) was applied to the Great Basin extensional and oblique-slip events and equation (2b) was used for the Great Basin-southern California transition, oblique- and strike-slip events. The magnitudes were converted to the local (Richter) magnitude, M_L, scale.

The next step was to associate a regional stress-field orientation with regions of homogeneous strain (Fig. 3); to be defined later. The stress orientations from observed fault-plane solutions for a given area were weighted and averaged, providing the average stress orientation. This direction was assumed for all earthquakes in a given area.

Calculate, sum and diagonalize moment tensors

The strike, dip and rake of the assumed fault plane for individual earthquakes were used to determine the moment tensor. The data for the fault plane, along with the scalar moment, M_0, were used to find the moment tensor according to equations given by Aki & Richards (1980, p. 106).

The moment-tensor eigenvalues and the eigenvectors were then calculated. The eigenvalues compare to the principal stress values (Kostrov 1974; Aki & Richards 1980). The moment tensors of individual events were then summed by component and the resulting regional moment tensors were diagonalized.

Strain and deformation rates

Assuming linear elasticity, the moment tensor can be converted to the strain-rate tensor using Kostrov's (1974) equation:

$$\dot{\epsilon}_{ij} = \frac{\Sigma \, m_{ij}}{(2\mu\triangle V\triangle t)} \quad (3)$$

$\dot{\epsilon}_{ij}$ are the strain-rate tensor components, m_{ij} are the moment-tensor components. The summation respresents the component summation of moments described above. $\triangle V$ is the volume of the lithospheric block defined by the surface dimensions of the homogeneous areas (Fig. 3) and the estimated maximum depth of earthquake hypocentres at 15 km, $\triangle t$ is the time difference between first and last events, and μ is the shear modulus assumed to be 3.3×10^{11} dyn cm^{-2} (Molnar 1979).

To find the maximum strain rates in the horizontal plane, the two-by-two strain-rate matrix (4) was then diagonalized.

$$\begin{matrix} \dot{\epsilon}_{11} & \dot{\epsilon}_{12} \\ \dot{\epsilon}_{21} & \dot{\epsilon}_{22}. \end{matrix} \quad (4)$$

Examples of the calculations and a detailed description of this method is given in Eddington (1986).

Homogeneous seismic source areas

One goal of this study was to determine detailed local and regional strain rates. To determine local strain rates, Kostrov's method was applied to the smaller areas of assumed homogeneous strain release shown in Fig. 3. The boundaries of these smaller areas were previously established by Renggli & Smith (1984) based on: (i) unifor-

mity of fault types and orientations such as are discussed in the paper by Greensfelder *et al.* (1980); (ii) similarities of fault-plane solution P and T axes (minimum and maximum principal-stress axes); and (iii) similarities in Quaternary geology. The three criteria were usually compatible, although an occasional fault-plane solution displayed P and T axes inconsistent with area surface geology and other fault-plane solutions.

Limits and accuracy

The accuracy of the method described above is limited primarily by discretization approximations, incompleteness and/or vagueness in the earthquake catalogues and fault-plane solution data, and incorrect magnitude–moment determinations.

The discrete area subdivisions described above, assume a volume of homogeneous strain. Although the area boundaries were chosen to enclose geologically and geophysically homogeneous regions, it is obvious that real strain fields are not completely homogeneous in discrete blocks, nor will they change magnitude and orientation discontinuously at block boundaries. Consequently, the area boundaries shown in Fig. 3 could be misplaced up to 10–20 km introducing up to ±5% error in strain magnitude and ± 15% error in strain direction.

Incompleteness of the earthquake data, particularly the percentage of events for which fault-plane solutions have been determined, is a second limitation. The method requires that both a magnitude and a fault-plane solution be given for each earthquake. The fault-plane solution gives the principal stress orientation. Unfortunately, less than 1% of the earthquakes used had fault-plane solutions; however, most events of $M>6$ in each area had solutions. The need for fault-plane solutions for each earthquake was alleviated by averaging the stress orientations of the available fault-plane solutions and applying the resulting 'average fault-plane solution' to each earthquake. This required an assumption of uniform strain release for all earthquakes regardless of magnitude. We know that in many areas of the Great Basin $M<4$ events produce a variety of fault-plane orientations, sometimes not the same as for the larger, $M>6$, events in the same area. Since fault-plane solutions for larger magnitude events were usually available and since larger events account for most of the seismic moment in any area (an increase of 1 in magnitude equals multiplying the moment by 10) the effect of this assumption

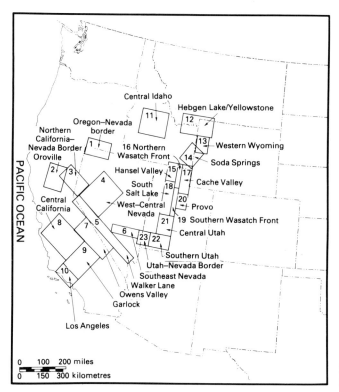

FIG. 3. Index map of sub-regions of assumed homogeneous strain.

on the accuracy of the strain rates is less than 5%.

A further limitation arises from variations in the type of magnitudes used, M_L, m_b, or M_s. The earthquake data in many of the older catalogues did not specify which magnitude scale was selected. The main earthquake file used here was a combination of several independently compiled catalogues. Simply treating all magnitudes the same would introduce significant error when they were converted to moments. Fortunately, several independent sources were available which gave magnitude scales for many of these events. The USGS, Great Basin Study provided a carefully prepared earthquake catalogue that covered the period from 1900 to 1977 (Askew & Algermissen 1983). Magnitude data from the University of Utah Seismograph Stations were correlated with USGS files and with published data on specific events (for example the work by Hanks *et al.* (1975) for California earthquakes) helped to minimize the error caused by incorrect magnitude-scale assumptions to less than 10%.

Errors can also be introduced in the magnitude–moment conversion even if proper magnitude scales are assumed. Hanks & Boore (1984) suggested that different magnitude scales established for different parts of California are not really characteristic of different areas, but are dependent on the range of the earthquake magnitudes used to produce them. Their assertion is that log (moment) versus magnitude is not a linear relationship, but that the magnitude of the slope of the curve increases with increasing earthquake magnitude. Thus, if only large-magnitude earthquakes were used to establish a linear magnitude–moment relationship, the slope of that line would be too steep and moments for small earthquakes would be underestimated. Conversely, if only smaller magnitude events were used, the slope would be small and the moments for larger earthquakes would be underestimated.

The primary magnitude-moment relation used in this study, equation (2a) (Doser & Smith 1982), was based on spectral analyses of extensional earthquakes in Utah with magnitudes in the range $3.7 < M_L < 6.6$. An earthquake magnitude outside this range might be converted inaccurately to a seismic moment. However, since smaller earthquakes have orders of magnitude less impact on the total moment than larger events and since moments for most $M_L > 7$ earthquakes were taken from independently determined results in the literature, possible non-linearity of the magnitude–moment relation contributed less than 5% underestimation of moment in any given area.

Since smaller earthquakes, with magnitudes $M < 4$, are not included from earlier periods of recording this also adds to the seismic-moment underestimation. However, since large-magnitude earthquakes contribute most of the moment, the underestimation from both incorrect magnitude–moment conversions and incomplete small-earthquake listings was estimated to be less than 5%.

Another possible limitation of determining strain rates from earthquake data is the assumption of an idealized, brittle medium. There is evidence that at about 10–20 Ma, the Great Basin stress field rotated about 45° (Zoback *et al.* 1981) from WSW–ENE to WNW–ESE. Reactivation of pre-existing faults by the present stress field could have introduced error into the results of this study. However, Kostrov's (1974) method (equation (3)), assumes statistical distributions and orientations of dislocations in the deforming material. Hence, fault-plane orientations for all events were not necessary for the calculation.

The most important limitation in magnitude–moment conversions is the variation in seismic-moment determinations for large earthquakes.

For example, Hanks *et al.* (1975) determined a moment for the 1952 Fort Tejon, California earthquake of 9.0×10^{17} dyn-cm, while Sieh (1977) gave a moment range of 5.0×10^{17} to 8.7×10^{17} dyn-cm for the same event. Recorded seismic moments can vary by a factor of 3. This corresponds to a possible error of $\pm 300\%$ in strain-rate calculations.

Seismic moments were taken from the results of other workers for 12 earthquakes (Table 1) ranging in magnitude from $6.1 < M < 7.9$. However, independent moments were not found for the large central Nevada earthquakes. The error in seismic-moment determinations for large earthquakes using magnitude–moment relations may be as much as a factor of 3 because of scatter in magnitude–moment curves. Hence, a $\pm 300\%$ error is possible depending on whether the moment came from an independent calculation or from a magnitude–moment relationship.

The total possible error in strain- and deformation-rate calculations due to these limitations is $\pm 325\%$ in magnitude and $\pm 15\%$ in direction. The error in strain magnitude is almost entirely a result of the uncertainty in seismic-moment determinations for large earthquakes, which exceeds all other sources of error.

Earthquake data

The earthquake catalogue (Table 2) produced for this study contains a listing of the felt and instrumentally recorded earthquakes in the western US Cordillera during the nineteenth and

TABLE 1. *Seismic moments for large earthquakes of the Great Basin and surrounding region.*

Earthquake		Magnitude	Moment dyne-cm	Reference
California	Jan. 9, 1857	$M_s 8.3$	5.3–8.7×10^{27}	Sieh (1977)
			9.0×10^{27}	Hanks *et al.* (1975)
	March 26, 1872	$M_s 8.3$	5.0×10^{26}	Hanks *et al.* (1975)
	March 15, 1946	$M_L 6.0$	1.0×10^{25}	Hanks *et al.* (1975)
	July 21, 1952	$M_L 7.7$	2.0×10^{27}	Hanks *et al.* (1975)
	July 21, 1952	$M_L 6.0$	3.0×10^{25}	Hanks *et al.* (1975)
	July 29, 1952	$M_L 6.0$	3.0×10^{25}	Hanks *et al.* (1975)
	Feb. 9, 1971	$M_L 6.4$	1.0×10^{26}	Hanks *et al.* (1975)
Utah	1934	$M_L 6.6$	7.7×10^{25}	Doser & Smith (1982)
Hebgen Lake	1959	$M_L 7.5$	1.0×10^{27}	Doser (1985)
Idaho	1975	$M_L 6.2$	1.5×10^{25}	Doser (1985)
Yellowstone	1975	$M_L 6.1$	7.5×10^{24}	Doser (1985)
Borah Peak	1983	$M_L 7.3$	3.3×10^{26}	Doser (1985)

twentieth centuries up to and including much of 1981. Before 1962, earthquake recording was hampered by a lack of regional seismograph-network coverage and the USGS file was the prime source of information. Only earthquakes recorded after 1900 were considered accurate enough and the files sufficiently complete for use in this study. Because of their large size and impact on the calculations, the 1857, M_s 8.3 Fort Tejon, California, and the 1872, M_s 8.3 Owens Valley, California, earthquakes were included in this study. All events (including earthquakes) within the Nevada nuclear test site studied were removed from the catalogues to eliminate bias from the introduction of nuclear blasts that would not be distinguished from natural events.

The record of post 1900, $M>4$ earthquakes, was considered to be reasonably complete, since the number of $M>4$ events recorded this century varies little from year to year. Figure 2(a) is a

map of all $M>4$ earthquakes within the study area. A file, complete down to $M>4$, was considered sufficient since most seismic moment in any area comes from the larger earthquakes. For example, in the study region, 3637 $M>4$ earthquakes produced a total seismic moment of 2.2×10^{28} dyn-cm; 572 $M>5$ events yielded 2.1×10^{28} dyn-cm; 80 $M>6$ events yielded 2.0×10^{28} dyn-cm; and 7 $M>7$ earthquakes produced 1.8×10^{28} dyn-cm. These data demonstrate that the 3630 earthquakes with magnitudes $4<M<7$ accounted for only 18% of the seismic moment released in all $M>4$ earthquakes; whereas the seven $M>7$ earthquakes produced the remaining 82% of the moment.

The primary earthquake catalogue was produced by choosing one file as the base, then comparing all other files to it. Events from other files that were not found in the key file were added to a master catalogue. The final master

TABLE 2. *Earthquake data, periods of data coverage and sources.*

Period of Time Covered	Source
1 1900–1981 including 1983 Borah Peak, Idaho data	University of Utah Seismograph Stations, Salt Lake City
2 1900–1980 possible gaps from 1900–1970	University of Nevada Network, Reno
3 1928–1980 1900–1973 1900–1974 1910–1974	National Geophysical Solar Terrestrial Data Center—Four files used; PDE (USCGS–USGS): Oregon State University: Division of Mines and Geology (California): University of California at Berkeley
4 1932–1981 Preliminary determinations of epicentres for 1975–1977 and for 1980–1981	California Institute of Technology Southern California Network
5 Aug. 1978–Jan. 16, 1982	USGS, Southern Basin and Range Network
6 July 26, 1974–Nov. 10, 1978	Montana earthquake data from 'Historical seismicity and earthquake hazards in Montana'
7 1969–Nov. 30, 1981	USGS, southern California Network, Menlo Park, California—summary data
8 Jan. 1, 1973–June 30, 1980	University of California Network, Berkeley, California
9 1900–1977	USGS Great Basin file, USGS Open-file report 83–86, (1983)

file used the Askew & Algermissen (1983) Basin and Range file as a standard for correlation. Events were chronologically listed and duplicates were removed. The 1983 Borah Peak, Idaho, M_L7.3 earthquake and aftershocks were added from the University of Utah files. For comparisons, when any two earthquakes had origin times closer than 10 sec and epicentres closer than 15 km, they were considered duplicates and the master-file location was used. Table 2 includes a list of the earthquake catalogues used in this compilation.

Cordilleran seismicity

The data used in this study included ~ 50,000 earthquakes out of the ~ 120,000 events summarized in the various catalogues. The area covered by the main earthquake data file extended from longitude 100–130° W and from latitude 30–50° N. Figure 2(a) shows the seismicity confined primarily to the study area: ~ longitude 109°30′ W to 125° W and latitude 33°30′ N to 46° N.

The areas of principal active seismicity occurred at or near locations of changes in direction of the ISB, along the Great Basin's western

border, in central Nevada, and along the San Andreas Fault and its associated faults. Almost half of the earthquakes studied were located in the San Andreas, Garlock, and White Wolf fault zones (in the central California, Garlock, and Los Angeles areas). Figure 2(d) shows that, of the seven $M>7$ earthquakes that occurred in the study area, three were located in the Los Angeles and Garlock areas; one $M>7$ event occurred in each of the Owens Valley, California; W-central Nevada; Hebgen Lake/Yellowstone Park; and central Idaho areas.

Fault-plane solutions

The fault-plane solution data used in this study were compiled by Renggli & Smith (1984; and unpublished data) primarily from the data of Smith & Lindh, (1978, Table 5-1). These data were augmented by fault-plane solutions for the M_L7.5, 1959, Hebgen Lake, Montana earthquakes (Doser 1984); for the 1983, M_L7.3, Borah Peak earthquake sequence (Doser 1985); and focal mechanisms of large Great Basin, pre-1964, earthquakes based on surface-wave analyses by Patton (in press). T-axes of these fault-plane solutions are presented in Fig. 4 and

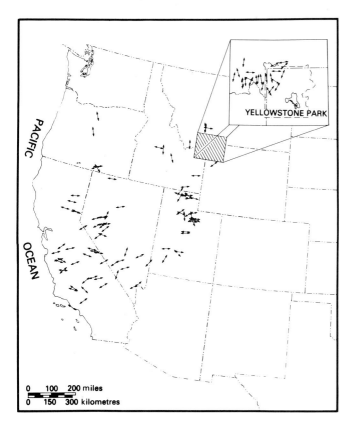

FIG. 4. Map of T (tension) axes from fault-plane solutions of the Great Basin. Data taken from Smith & Lindh (1978); Doser (1984); Kienle & Couch (unpubl. data, 1977); and Patton (in press).

380 *P.K. Eddington* et al.

show the direction of regional strain accompanying the earthquakes.

Contemporary strain rates

Strain rates from historic earthquakes

A summary of the moment tensor strain and deformation rates is presented in Tables 3 and 4 and shown in Fig. 5. Time periods for given areas vary according to the data available but were generally from 1900 to 1981. Figure 5 also includes some of Anderson's (1979) results for southern California.

The general results show a principal E–W direction of extension for the seismically active parts of the Great Basin. E–W extension was dominant on the W edge of the Great Basin. In Idaho, Montana, and Wyoming, extension was accommodated by a large N–S component. In Utah, extension trended NW–SE. Some exceptions were in South Salt Lake Provo, central Utah, and Utah–Nevada border areas (areas 18, 20, 21 and 23) where the principal horizontal strain corresponded to compression rather than extension. This pattern is consistent with a rotation of the stress field from σ_1 approximately vertical and σ_2 and σ_3 in the horizontal plane, to σ_3 vertical and σ_1 and σ_2 in the horizontal plane. The South Salt Lake region (area 18) has had little earthquake activity in historic time and accordingly has a low deformation rate of only 0.001 mm a^{-1}; too small to be considered reliable. (Also see Smith *et al.* (1984) for detailed discussion of strain rates in Utah.)

The Colorado Plateau–Great Basin transition (area 20), may be influenced by the neighbouring N–S compression of the northern Colorado Plateau. The central Utah area would seem geographically to be more closely associated with the Great Basin; however, here, the stress orientation of the area was determined primarily from a single event with a near-vertical nodal plane on the extreme eastern edge of the area. The stress orientation for the Utah–Nevada border area was dominated by a single large strike-slip event, $M6.1$, 1966. This solution is anomalous, hence the stress orientation may not be adequately accounted for. However, the strike-slip nature of this earthquake is the first of many that extend westward across southern Nevada.

The largest Great Basin deformation rates were associated with the western margin along the northern California–Nevada border (1.6 mm a^{-1}), in W-Central Nevada (7.5 mm a^{-1}), along the Walker Lane (2.9 mm a^{-1}), and in

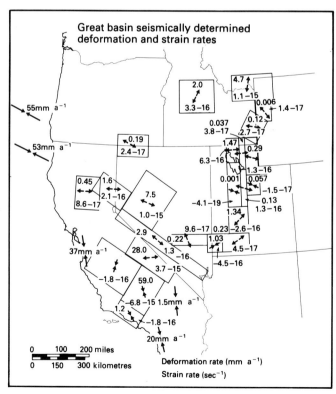

FIG. 5. Great Basin seismically determined strain/deformation rates. In each area, top value is deformation rate in mm a^{-1}, bottom value is strain rate in sec^{-1}; second number is power of 10; from Hyndman & Wiechert (1983); from Anderson (1979).

TABLE 3. *Number of earthquakes, maximum magnitude (M_{max}), principal moment tensor component (M_1) per anum, horizontal deformation rates, and maximum horizontal strain rates for homogeneous areas of the Great Basin..*

Area No.	Area Name	Number of earthquakes	M_{max}	M_1 (dyn-cm a^{-1})	Horizontal deformation (mm a^{-1})	Strain rate (sec^{-1})
1	Oregon–Nevada Border	71	5.0 M_s	2.3×10^{23}	0.2	2.4×10^{-17}
2	Oroville	590	6.0 M_s	7.6×10^{23}	0.5	8.6×10^{-17}
3	Northern California –Nevada Border	1429	6.4 M_L	1.7×10^{24}	1.6	2.1×10^{-16} N90°W
4	W-central Nevada	2533	7.8 M_L	1.9×10^{25}	7.5	1.0×10^{-15} N69°W
5	Walker Lane	2237	6.0 M_L	1.8×10^{24}	2.9	9.6×10^{-17} N46°W
6	SE Nevada	118	6.0 m_b	5.5×10^{23}	0.22	9.6×10^{-17} N22°W
7	Owens Valley	3809	8.3 M_s	4.9×10^{25}	28.0	3.7×10^{-15} N83°E
8	Central California	20827	6.9 M_L	3.3×10^{24}	1.1	1.8×10^{-16} N19°E
9	Garlock	5647	8.3 M_s	8.9×10^{25}	59.0	6.8×10^{-15} N13°W
10	Los Angeles	4175	6.3 M_L	2.4×10^{24}	1.2	1.8×10^{-16} N27°W
11	Central Idaho	918	7.3 M_L	4.5×10^{24}	2.0	3.3×10^{-16} N29°E
12	Hebgen Lake	1332	7.6 M_L	4.5×10^{24}	4.7	1.1×10^{-15} N11°E
13	Western Wyoming	1159	4.5 M_L	6.7×10^{22}	0.07	1.4×10^{-17} N41°W
14	Soda Springs	242	5.0 M_L	1.9×10^{23}	0.12	2.7×10^{-17}
15	Hansel Valley	1944	6.8 M_L	1.8×10^{24}	1.5	6.3×10^{-16} N67°E
16	Northern Wasatch Front	166	5.7 M_L	7.9×10^{22}	0.04	3.8×10^{-17} N78°E
17	Cache Valley	789	5.9 M_L	4.1×10^{23}	0.29	1.3×10^{-16} N79°W
18	South Salt Lake	141	5.4 M_L	3.7×10^{21}	0.001	-4.1×10^{-19} N66°W
19	Southern Wasatch Front	520	5.7 M_L	1.7×10^{23}	0.13	1.3×10^{-16} N76°E
20	Provo	249	5.7 M_L	3.2×10^{22}	0.06	1.5×10^{-17} N37°E
21	Central Utah	962	6.9 M_L	2.2×10^{24}	1.3	2.6×10^{-16} N35°W
22	Southern Utah	234	5.5 M_L	1.5×10^{23}	0.23	4.5×10^{-17} N59°E
23	Utah–Nevada Border	94	6.3 M_L	5.8×10^{23}	1.0	4.5×10^{-16} N64°E

TABLE 4. *Comparison of strain and deformation rates using geological (palaeoearthquake), contemporary seismicity and geodetic data.*

Area	Geological		Earthquake		Geodetic	
	Deformation rate (mm a^{-1})	Strain rate (sec^{-1})	Deformation rate (mm a^{-1})	Strain Rate (sec^{-1})	Deformation rate (mm a^{-1})	Strain Rate (sec^{-1})
Oregon–Nevada border			0.19	2.4×10^{-17}		
Oroville, California			0.5	8.6×10^{-17}		
Northern California–Nevada border	0.02	2.6×10^{-18}	1.6	2.1×10^{-16}		
W-central Nevada	0.08	1.3×10^{-17}	7.5	1.0×10^{-15}	2.0	1.6×10^{-15}
Walker Lane, SE Nevada	0.001	3.8×10^{-19}	2.9	1.3×10^{-16}	3.6	1.9×10^{-15}
Owens Valley			0.22	9.6×10^{-17}		
Central California	4.0	-1.9×10^{-16}	1.1	-1.8×10^{-16}	2.5	2.5×10^{-15}
Garlock	2.5	4.4×10^{-16}	59.0	-6.8×10^{-15}	1.8	-2.9×10^{-15}
Los Angeles	49.3	-1.1×10^{-14}	1.2	-1.8×10^{-16}	11.2	-5.1×10^{-15}
Central Idaho*	0.08	1.3×10^{-17}	2.0	3.3×10^{-16}	13.5	-4.8×10^{-15}
Hebgen Lake/Yellowstone Park	0.24	3.5×10^{-17}	4.7	1.1×10^{-15}	11.2	8.9×10^{-15}
Western Wyoming	0.74	2.9×10^{-16}	0.07	1.4×10^{-17}		
Soda Springs	0.14	3.8×10^{-17}	0.12	2.7×10^{-17}		
Hansel Valley	0.11	4.8×10^{-17}	1.5	6.3×10^{-16}		
Northern Wasatch Front	0.25	1.9×10^{-16}	0.04	3.8×10^{-17}	0.6	3.2×10^{-16}
Cache Valley	0.01	4.4×10^{-17}	0.29	1.3×10^{-16}		
South Salt Lake	0.03	1.3×10^{-17}	0.001	-4.1×10^{-19}		
Southern Wasatch Front	0.31	2.4×10^{-16}	0.13	1.3×10^{-16}		
Provo	0.03	1.2×10^{-17}	0.06	-1.5×10^{-17}		
Central Utah	0.38	1.2×10^{-16}	1.3	-2.6×10^{-16}		
Southern Utah	7.4	9.8×10^{-16}	0.23	4.5×10^{-17}		
Utah–Nevada Border			1.0	-4.5×10^{-16}		

* from Scott *et al.* (In press)

the Owens Valley (28.0 mm a^{-1}) (areas 3, 4, 5 and 7). Deformation in the Owens Valley area was exceptionally high because of the 1872, M_s 8.3, Owens Valley earthquake.

Another region of high strain rate occurred along the Great Basin's eastern border. Deformation rates of 1.0–4.7 mm a^{-1} were determined in areas where the trend of the ISB changes: for example in the Hebgen Lake/Yellowstone Park; Hansel Valley, northern Utah; Central Utah; and Utah–Nevada border areas (areas 12, 15, 21 and 23).

Deformation of 2.0 mm a^{-1} in the Central Idaho area was due principally to the 1983, M_L7.3 Borah Peak, Idaho, earthquake and aftershock and does not fit either of the two trends mentioned above. The central Idaho area may be associated with NW extension of the Great Basin eastern margin.

With the exception of the Owens Valley area, deformation rates in these areas thus range from 1 to 9 mm a^{-1}; about 10 times greater than in other areas of the Great Basin. However, they were much less than the 59 mm a^{-1} deformation rate calculated for the Garlock fault zone of southeastern California. Note that most of the Garlock area moment came from the 1857, M_s 8.3 Fort Tejon earthquake produced by fracture on the San Andreas Fault along the S edge of the Garlock area.

Geodetically determined strain rates

Geodetic (trilateration and triangulation) networks have been used by several workers to determine strain rates. For purposes of comparison, Savage's (1983) summary of strain rates of different USGS trilateration networks was used along with modifications and additions taken from Savage *et al.* (1985) and Snay *et al.* (1984).

Some problems associated with geodetic determinations are inaccurate measurements because of inconsistent station locations and measuring techniques. Also a factor in the usefulness of geodetic measurements is the sparseness of measurements throughout the western US, with the exception of California. A summary of deformation and strain rates derived from geodetic data is presented in Fig. 6.

Geodetic strain rates were only available in about half of the areas considered in the seismic strain-rate determinations. In many areas where geodetic strain measurements were available, strain and deformation rates were close to the values measured seismically. However, in some cases the geodetic rates were 10–20 times larger (Table 4).

In most cases, geodetically determined strain rates were higher probably because seismically determined strains were from broader regions and thus represent spatial sampling differences. Geodetic networks were usually three to five times smaller than the areas used in this study and focused on the most actively deforming regions. Consequently, higher strain rates would be expected for geodetic network results.

The Walker Lane area (area 5) was an example of different areal coverage with different contemporary strain rates. The seismically and geodetically determined strain rates for this area, 1.3×10^{-16} sec^{-1} and 1.9×10^{-15} sec^{-1} respectively, differ by more than order of magnitude. However, the seismic and geodetic deformation rates for the area were 2.9 mm a^{-1} from earthquake data, and 3.6 mm a^{-1} measured geodetically (Savage 1983). The earthquakes on the Excelsior fault were probably the source of most deformation in this area and were sampled by both methods. Thus, when area size discrepancies are eliminated, the resulting deformations agree within the accuracies of the methods.

Palaeostrain rates from geological data

Palaeostrain determinations

Strain rates from geological data (slip rates on faults) were determined using a conversion of fault slip-rates to seismic moment rates. Mapped slip rates and fault-plane geometries were used to determine the scalar moment rates following the equation (1b). From the seismic moment rate, $\dot{M}_0$ strain rate can be found using:

$$\dot{\epsilon} = \frac{\dot{M}_0 \, k}{\mu \, l_1 l_2 l_3} \,, \qquad \text{(Anderson 1979)} \qquad (5)$$

where l_i = volume dimensions of the homogeneous seismic area, $k = 0.75$ an empirically determined constraint, (Doser & Smith 1983) $\dot{\epsilon}$ = scalar strain rate, and $\dot{M}_0$ = scalar moment rate. Moments for faults in the western US (Fig. 7) used here were calculated previously by Smith (1982) and unpublished data, assuming an average fault dip of 60°.

Fault-slip data covered a range in ages of faulting from ~ 10,000 yr to 10 Ma. Geological displacement rates for the Wasatch Front were determined from fault segmentation and slip rates by Schwartz & Coppersmith (1984). Palaeodeformation rates calculated for areas in

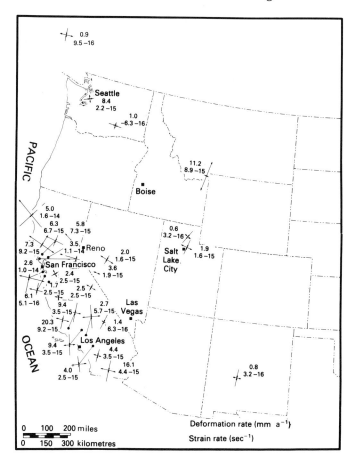

FIG. 6. Western US geodetically determined extensional deformation and strain rates. The top number is deformation rate (mm a^{-1}) and the bottom is strain rate (sec^{-1}). The second number is power of 10. Data are from Savage (1983), Savage *et al.* (1985), and Snay *et al.* (1984).

southern California by Anderson (1979) were also included in Fig. 8. Results for the Borah Peak, Idaho, earthquake area are from Scott *et al.* (in press).

Faults were grouped into the same areas as used in the seismic strain-rate determinations where possible. The seismic-moment rates were summed following equation (5). Because of a lack of detailed information on the direction of fault slip, the direction of extension was assumed to be E–W for the Great Basin. N–S compression was assumed for areas associated with the San Andreas fault system (the central California and Los Angeles areas) and in Idaho and Montana.

Accuracy of palaeostrain results

The primary limitation of the geological data lies in its interpretation and completeness. For the results to be complete, all faults with significant displacement must be included and assigned accurate slips, areas, and displacement ages. While there were numerous references to Holocene and Quaternary faults throughout the region, less than 30% had published slip rates. Fault dips at depth must also be accurately estimated since low-angle normal-fault dips yield higher horizontal extension-rate estimates. This study assumes a 60° average fault dip (Smith 1982) but horizontal extension would increase by 1.5 for 40° fault dips.

Second, even if surface exposures of faults are adequate and all major faults have been studied in an area, only large earthquakes, $M > 6.5$, will have produced surface displacements in the first place. Consequently, palaeostrain determinations in a given area would be underestimated.

Slip-rate data in western Nevada and eastern California were so sparse that regional strain-rate estimates are totally unreliable. The problem was less pronounced along the Intermountain Seismic Belt because of the extensive study by Doser & Smith (1982, 1983).

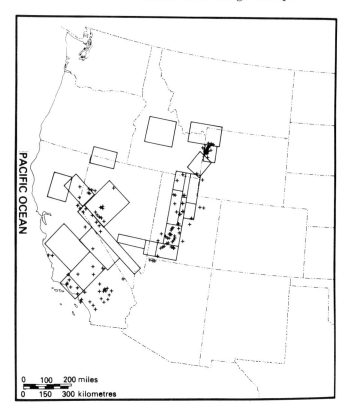

FIG 7. Location of faults with late-Cenozoic displacement rates used in this study. Data from Smith (unpubl. data, 1982), and Thenhaus & Wentworth (1982). Crosses, +, indicate centres of mapped faults for which slip rates were available.

Palaeostrain results

Palaeodeformation rates (Fig. 8 and Table 5) yield the highest values in two regions; Hebgen Lake, Montana–Yellowstone Park, 0.24 mm a^{-1}; and in western Wyoming, 0.74 mm a^{-1}. Here, the ISB changes from a N–S trend in Utah to a NNE–SSW trend in southeastern Idaho and western Wyoming. High deformation rates were also calculated for the central and southern Utah areas, 0.38 and 7.4 mm a^{-1}, where the ISB again changes trend from N–S in most of Utah to E–W in SE Nevada. Seismic results offer a more reliable measure of strain concentration in these regions than do palaeostrain results.

Pre-historic slip-rate data for the W side of the Great Basin were considered incomplete resulting in unreliably low deformation rates. Figure 1 shows that both the E and W margins of the Great Basin are candidates for $M > 7$ earthquakes and inherent high deformation, yet insufficient data on mapped faults and slip rates on the W margin exist to accurately assess pre-historic slip.

Comparisons of contemporary and palaeostrain rates

Table 4 demonstrates that palaeostrain rates are often one to two orders of magnitude lower than contemporary strain rates. The exceptions to this pattern were: (i) the Los Angeles, western Wyoming, south Salt Lake, southern Utah, and northern Wasatch Front areas where the palaeo-deformation rates of 49.3, 0.74, 0.03, 7.4, and 0.25 mm a^{-1} were significantly larger than seismically determined rates of 1.2, 0.07, 0.001, 0.23, and 0.04 mm a^{-1}; and (ii) in the Idaho–Wyoming area—0.14 versus 0.12 mm a^{-1}; central California—4.0 versus 1.1 mm a^{-1}; Cache Valley, Utah—0.1 versus 0.3 mm a^{-1}; and the southern Wasatch Front—0.31 versus 0.13 mm a^{-1} areas where palaeostrain versus seismically determined deformation rates were within a factor of 4. These results suggest that historic seismicity and deformation in the above areas have been at lower than average levels, since the seismic

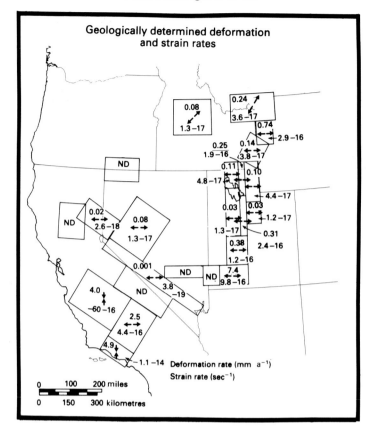

FIG. 8. Great Basin palaeostrain and deformation rates from geological data. Top value is deformation rate in mm a^{-1}; bottom value is strain rate in sec^{-1}; second number is power of 10. See Fig. 5 for comparison.

values are no larger than the underestimated palaeodeformation values. It is also possible that these areas have more complete geological data than other areas.

Palaeostrain rates in Fig. 8 also show that deformation along the ISB, up to 7.4 mm a^{-1} in the southern Utah area, was greater than along the western margins of the Great Basin with up to 0.08 mm a^{-1} in the W-central Nevada area. This result is the opposite of that determined using earthquake data where deformation rates along the ISB were as high as 2.8 mm a^{-1}, in the Hebgen Lake–Yellowstone area, and deformation rates in the western half of the Great Basin were as high as 7.5 mm a^{-1} in the W-central Nevada area. Again this difference is probably due to insufficient geological data.

For comparison, Anderson (1979) calculated a deformation rate of 20 mm a^{-1} from geological data in the Los Angeles area compared to 1.2 mm a^{-1} from the earthquake contribution. Likewise, he estimated deformation rates of 8.0

and 1.5 mm a^{-1} in the Garlock and Owens Valley (California) areas where seismicity rates were 59.0 mm a^{-1} in the Garlock area and 28.0 mm a^{-1} in Owens Valley.

Comparisons of contemporary and palaeo-deformation support the concept of anomalous Wasatch Front low seismicity. The northern Wasatch Front area (area 16) contains the Wasatch fault, the primary surface-breaking fault of the eastern Great Basin. The northern Wasatch Front area is also bordered on the E and W by the seismically active Cache Valley and Hansel Valley areas. In contrast, the northern Wasatch Front area has been seismically quiet throughout historic time. Less than 200 earthquakes have been recorded in that block in the last 78 years. The maximum magnitude earthquake to be recorded in the area during this time period was $M_L = 5.7$.

Smith (1978) suggested that this 'seismic gap' along the northern Wasatch fault is temporary and might be 'filled' at a later time. The deformation rate from seismicity for the northern Wasatch Front was 0.04 mm a^{-1} and for the southern Wasatch Front, 0.13 mm a^{-1}. In contrast, the geologically determined rates were 0.25 N and 0.31 mm a^{-1} S. The higher palaeo-deformation values suggest that contemporary seismic quiescence is indeed anomalous.

Comparisons of Great Basin extension rates

Overall Great Basin deformation patterns were used to assess the general kinematics of intraplate deformation in this region (Fig. 9). Deformation and strain rates were calculated across the entire Great Basin along three profiles (B–B′, B–B″ and C–C′, Fig. 9). The components of the deformation along the profiles were summed to give the integrated opening rate of the Great Basin.

Profile B–B′, a line across northern California, Nevada, and northern Utah had a 10.0 mm a^{-1} deformation rate. Profile, B–B″, is an E–W line with an 8.4 mm a^{-1} rate. The southern line, C–C′, is an E–W line across SE California, southern Nevada, and southern Utah; here, the deformation rate diminishes to 3.5 mm a^{-1}. However, if the 1872 M_s8.3 Owens Valley earthquake is included and projected on to C–C′, the deformation rate increases to 29.2 mm a^{-1}. The extension rates found along these profiles are summarized in Table 5. When strain rates were considered, it was found that B–B′ experienced 2.7×10^{-16}sec^{-1}, B–B″ yielded 2.2×10^{-16}sec^{-1} and C–C′ yielded 1.4×10^{-16}sec^{-1}.

The deformation rate in the northern Great Basin is more than twice as high as the southern Great Basin (without including the Owens Valley earthquake). This pattern implies fan-shaped opening of the Great Basin similar to a pattern that was deduced from Cenozoic fault patterns by Wernicke *et al.* (1982).

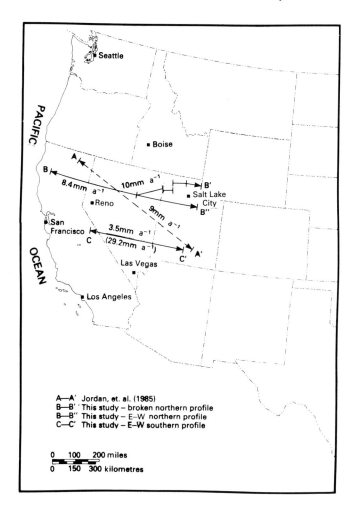

FIG. 9. Great Basin regional extension. A–A′ is from Jordan *et al.*'s (in press) intraplate kinematic model of motion between North American and Pacific Plates constrained by satellite ranging data; B–B′, B–B″, and C–C′ from this study. Value in parentheses below C–C′ includes deformation from the Owens Valley, California, 1872 earthquake.

TABLE 5. *Great Basin strain rates, deformation rates, and total extension from this and other studies.*

Reference	Strain rate (sec^{-1})	Deformation rate (mm a^{-1})	Total extension (%)
This Study			
Profile B–B′	2.6×10^{-16}	10.0	~10
B–B″	2.2×10^{-16}	8.4	~10
C–C′	1.3×10^{-16}	3.5	<10
Other Studies			
Jordan *et al.* (In press)			
A–A′		<9	
Wright (1976)			
north		5.8–7.5	~10
south		3.7–10.1	10–50
Proffett (1977)		200	30–35
Thompson & Burke (1974)	3.2×10^{-16}	8	~10
Eaton *et al.* (1978)	3.2×10^{-16}	8	~10
Zoback *et al.* (1981)			15–39
Minster & Jordan (1984)			
geology[1]		3–20	
heat flow[2]		3–12	
palaeoseismicity[3]		1–12	
seismicity[4]		5–22	

[1] Hamilton & Myers (1966); Stewart (1978); Davis (1980); Proffett (1977).
[2] Lachenbruch (1979); Lachenbruch & Sass (1978).
[3] Wallace (1978); Thompson & Burke (1974); Greensfelder *et al.* (1980).
[4] Greensfelder *et al.* (1980); Anderson (1979).

Earthquake induced deformation rates of 10.0 mm a^{-1} on B–B′ and 8.4 mm a^{-1} on B–B″ determined along the two northern profiles shown in Fig. 9 compare well with deformation rates determined from other studies. For example, Lachenbruch & Sass (1978) determined 5–10 mm a^{-1} extension for the Great Basin using heat-flow constraints and thermal models of extension.

Jordan *et al.* (in press) estimated a deformation rate across the Great Basin of equal to or less than 9 mm a^{-1} (along profile A–A′ in Fig. 9) from North American–Pacific Plate intraplate tectonic models, while the seismically determined deformation rate along line B–B″ was 8.4 mm a^{-1} (Table 5)—a remarkable similarity for two different methods. This result implies that the North American–Pacific Plate interaction, modelled by Jordan *et al.* (in press), may contribute a significant component to Great Basin extension. This comparison also leads to the conclusion that much of the Great Basin

extension is expressed as earthquake-generated brittle fracture.

Geologically determined palaeodeformation rates established by other workers (Table 5) ranged from 1–20 mm a^{-1}, except for Proffett's (1977) deformation rate of about 200 mm a^{-1}. A range of 1–20 mm a^{-1} is consistent with the deformation produced by contemporary seismicity. These comparisons suggest that since geologically inferred and contemporary strain rates are similar, the mechanism that facilitates Great Basin extension today operated throughout Quaternary time. Had the mechanism changed, we would expect to see greater differences in deformation rates between the contemporary and palaeoestimations.

Similar contemporary- and palaeo-strain rates in the Great Basin suggest that the seismic record, though experiencing short-term local variability, is a reasonable indicator of future seismicity on a regional scale. This conclusion is analogous to the findings of Wesnousky *et al.*

(1982a, 1982b) who found for Japanese seismicity that contemporary variations in seismic activity were determined to be short-term effects that disappeared over periods of many hundreds of years.

Conclusions

This study has shown that, on a regional scale, contemporary strain rates from seismicity are comparable to strain rates determined from modern, geodetic measurements. Comparisons with palaeostrain rates determined from geological data are, however, generally unreliable because of insufficient geological data on slip rates.

Regionally, an E–W Great Basin maximum extension rate of 8–10 mm a^{-1} was determined from earthquake data. Locally, contemporary strain was concentrated at changes in direction of trend of the Intermountain Seismic Belt along the Great Basin eastern boundary; along the western margin of the Great Basin; in central Nevada; and in some other scattered areas primarily on region boundaries. Great Basin contemporary deformation rates in the range 1–28 mm a^{-1} were found in this study. By comparison, rates of 20–50 mm a^{-1} were

determined for active interplate subduction in the Pacific Northwest calculated from seismicity by Hyndman & Wiechert (1983). Likewise slip rates along the San Andreas Fault ranged from 45 to 55 mm a^{-1} based upon seismicity data (Anderson 1979). Thus, Great Basin deformation rates from seismicity were, on average, from 2 to 10 times lower than plate-convergence rates.

Patterns of seismicity and high deformation rates of the Great Basin show that most brittle fracture occurs along its margins and along the central Nevada seismic belt. The stress release and accompanying crustal fracture represented by this seismicity may have accommodated magma ascension through the lithosphere, in some cases to the surface. Figure 10, is a map of Quaternary volcanism for the last 5 Ma (Smith & Luedke 1984; and the seismically determined deformation rates of this study. These data suggest that brittle fracture and subsequent magma intrusion has persisted concomitantly along the edges of the Great Basin for at least the last few million years.

The local and regional deformation-rate results, summarized above, imply that brittle fracture has been produced as the principal strain-release mechanism, although it may ultimately be driven by creep and flow at greater

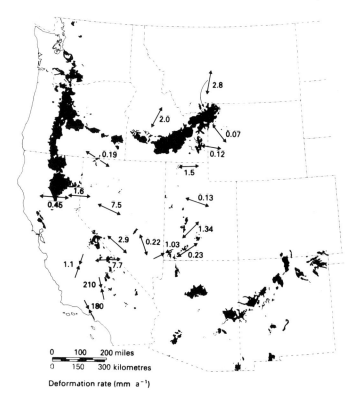

FIG. 10. Western US volcanism and seismically determined deformation rates. Volcanism is from Smith & Luedke (1984) and deformation rates are in mm a^{-1}.

lithospheric depths. It follows that most Great Basin extension has thus been expressed as brittle fracture in the upper crust and that the amount of creep in the whole of the lithosphere probably does not exceed that of brittle strain.

ACKNOWLEDGMENTS: The research presented here was supported by NASA research grant No. NAG 5-164 on the relationship between the contemporary deformation of the Great Basin and the San Andreas Fault. Support for computer time and plotting was from the USGS grant No. 14-08-0001-21983. Part of this research was done while one of us (P.K.E.) was a Visiting Graduate Fellow at the Lunar and Planetary Institute, Houston, Texas, which is operated under contract NASW3389.

We particularly acknowledge the earthquake data generously given to us by: R. Cockerham, USGS, Menlo Park, California; H. Kanamori, California Institute of Technology; A. Ryall, University of Nevada; B. A. Bolt, University of California at Berkeley; S. T. Algermissen, B. Askew, and A. Rogers of the USGS Golden, Colorado; and the University of Utah Seismograph Stations for regional-network earthquake data. W. Nagy assisted in manuscript and figure preparation.

We thank M. Bauer, D. Galagher and S. Willett who helped compile much of the geological and geophysical information in the early stages of this project, D. Doser who offered advice on the seismic moment methodology, and G. Randall who assisted with the initial compilation of earthquake data. Discussions with P. Lowman, NASA Goddard Space Flight Center regarding the objectives and geological data were appreciated. J. Pechmann and W. P. Nash offered criticism and review of the manuscript.

References

AKI, K. 1966. Generation and propagation of G waves from the Nigata earthquake of June 16, 1964, 2. Estimation of earthquake moment, release energy, and stress drop from the G-wave spectrum. *Bull. Earthqk Res. Inst. Tokyo Univ.* **44**, 73–88.

—— & RICHARDS, P. 1980. *Quantitative Seismology*, pp. 105–19. W. H. Freeman, San Francisco, California.

ANDERSON, J.G. 1979. Estimating the seismicity from geological structure for seismic-risk studies. *Bull. seism. Soc. Am.* **69**, 135–58.

ASKEW, B. & ALGERMISSEN, S.T. 1983. An earthquake catalog for the Basin and Range province 1803–1977. *U.S. geol. Surv. Open-file Rep.* 83–86.

BEST, M.G. & HAMBLIN, W.K. 1978. Origin of the northern Basin and Range province: Implications from the geology of its eastern boundary. *In:* SMITH, R.B. & EATON, G.P. (eds) Cenozoic Tectonics and Regional Geophysics of the Western Cordillera, Mem. geol. Soc. Am. **152**, 313–40.

DAVIS, G.A. 1980. Problems of intraplate extensional tectonics western United States: *In: Continental Tectonics*, pp. 84–95. Nat. Acad. Sci. Wash. D. C.

DOSER, D.I. 1984. *Source parameters and faulting processes of the August 1959 Hebgen Lake, Montana earthquake sequence*, Ph.D. Thesis, Univ. of Utah, 152 pp.

—— 1985. Source parameters and faulting processes of the 1959 Hebgen Lake, Montana earthquake sequence. *J. geophys. Res.* **90**, 4537–56.

—— & SMITH, R.B. 1982. Seismic moment rates in the Utah region. *Bull. seis. Soc. Am.* **72**, 525–51.

—— & —— 1983. Seismicity of the Teton–Southern Yellowstone Region, Wyoming, *Bull. seis. Soc. Am.* **73**, 1369–94.

EATON, G.P., WAHL, R.R., PROSTKA, H.J., MABEY, D.R. & KLEINKOPF, M.D. 1978. Regional gravity and tectonic patterns: Their relation to the late Cenozoic epeirogeny and lateral spreading in the western Cordillera; In: SMITH, R.B. & EATON, G.P. (eds) *Cenozoic Tectonics and Regional Geophysics of the Western Cordillera, Mem. geol. Soc. Am.* **152**, 51–91.

EDDINGTON, P.K. 1985. *Kinematics of Great Basin intraplate extension from earthquake, geodetic and geologic information*. Unpubl. MSc. Thesis, Univ. of Utah.

GREENSFELDER, R.W., KINTZER, F.C. & SOMERVILLE, M.R. 1980. Seismotectonic regionalization of the Great Basin, and comparison of moment rates computed from Holocene strain and historic seismicity: (summary) *Bull. geol. Soc. Am.* **97**, 518–23.

HAMILTON, W. & MYERS, W.B. 1966. Cenozoic tectonics of the western United States. *Rev. Geophys.* **4**, 509–49.

HANKS, T.C. & BOORE, D.M. 1984. Moment–magnitude relations in theory and practice. *J. geophys. Res.* **89**, 6229–35.

——, HILEMAN, J.A. & THATCHER, W. 1975. Seismic moments of the larger earthquakes of the southern California region. *Bull. geol. Soc. Am.* **86**, 1131–9.

HYNDMAN, R.D. & WIECHERT, D.H. 1983. Seismicity and rates of relative motion on the plate boundaries of western North America. *Geophys. J. R. astron. Soc.* **72**, 59–82.

JORDAN, T.H., MINSTER, J.B., CHRISTODOULIDIS, D.C. & SMITH, D.E. In press. Constraints on western U.S. deformation from satellite laser ranging.

KOSTROV, V.V. 1974. Seismic moment and energy of earthquakes, and seismic flow of rock. *Izvestiya Earth Phys.* **1**, 23–40.

LACHENBRUCH, A.H. 1979. Heat flow in the Basin and Range province and thermal effects of tectonic extension. *Pageoph.* **117**, 34–50.

—— & SASS, J.H. 1978. Models of an extending lithosphere and heat flow in the Basin and Range province. *In:* SMITH, R.B. & EATON, G.P. (eds) *Cenozoic Tectonics and Regional Geophysics of the Western Cordillera, Mem. geol. Soc. Am.* **152**, 209–50.

MINSTER, J.B. & JORDAN, T.H. 1984. Vector constraints on Quaternary deformation of the western United States east and west of the San Andreas fault. *In*: CROUCH, J.K. & BARBMAN, S.B. (eds) *Tectonics and Sedimentation along the California margin, Soc. econ. Paleontol. and Mineral., Pac. sect.* **38**, 1–16.

MOLNAR, P. 1979. Earthquake recurrence intervals and plate tectonics, *Bull. seis. Soc. Am.* **69**, 115–33.

PATTON, H.J. In press. P-wave fault-plane solutions and the generation of surface waves by earthquakes in the Western United States.

PROFFETT, J.M. JR 1977. Cenozoic geology of the Yerington district, Nevada and implications for the nature of and origin of Basin and Range faulting, *Bull. geol. Soc. Am.* **88**, 247–66.

RENGGLI, C. & SMITH, R.B. 1984. Estimates of crustal extension for the Basin–Range/southern San Andreas associated with active seismicity (abstract). *Earthqk Notes*, **55**, 29.

SAVAGE, J.C. 1983. Strain accumulation in western United States, *Ann. Rev. Earth planet. Sci.* **11**, 11–43.

—, LISOWSKI, M. & PRESCOTT, W.H. 1985. Strain accumulation in the Rocky Mountain states. *J. geophys. Res.* **90**, 10, 310–20.

SCHOLZ, C.H., BARAZANGI, M. & SBAR, M.L. 1971. Late Cenozoic evolution of the Great Basin, Western United States, as an ensialic interarc basin. *Bull. geol. Soc. Am.* **82**, 2979–90.

SCHWARTZ, D.P. & COPPERSMITH, K.J. 1984. Fault behavior and characteristic earthquakes: Examples from the Wasatch and San Andreas fault zones. *J. geophys. Res.* **89**, 5681–98.

SCOTT, W.E., PIERCE, K.L. & HAIT, M.H. JR In press. Quaternary tectonic setting of the 1983 Borah Peak earthquakes, Central Idaho.

SIBSON, R.H. 1982. Fault zone models, heat flow, and the depth distribution of earthquakes in the continental crust of the United States. *Bull. seis. Soc. Am.* **72**, 151–63.

SIEH, K.E. 1977. *A study of Holocene displacement history along the south-central reach of the San Andreas fault.* Ph.D. Thesis, Stanford Univ. California.

SMITH, R.B. 1978. Seismicity, crustal structure, and intraplate tectonics of the interior of the western Cordillera. *In*: SMITH, R.B. & EATON, G.P. (eds) *Cenozoic Tectonics and Regional Geophysics of the Western Cordillera, Mem. geol. Soc. Am.* **152**, 111–44.

—— 1982. Intraplate seismo-tectonics and mechanisms of extension in the western United States, (abstract). *AGU Chapman Conference on Fault Behavior and Earthquake Generation Process*, Snowbird, Utah.

—— & BRUHN, R.L. 1984. Intraplate extensional tectonics of the eastern Basin–Range: Inferences on structural style from seismic reflection data, regional tectonics and thermal-mechanical models of brittle/ductile deformation. *J. geophys. Res,* **89**, 5733–62.

—— & LINDH, A.G. 1978. Fault-plane solutions of the western United States: a compilation. *In*: SMITH,

R.B. & EATON, G.P. (eds) *Cenozoic Tectonics and Regional Geophysics of the Western Cordillera, Mem. geol. Soc. Am.* **152**, 107–9.

—— & RICHINS, W. 1984. Seismicity and earthquake hazards of Utah and the Wasatch Front: Paradigm and paradox. *U.S. geol. Surv. Open-file Rep. 84–763, 73–112.*

—— & SBAR, M. 1974. Contemporary tectonics and seismicity of the western United States with emphasis on the Intermountain Seismic Belt, *Bull. geol. Soc. of Am.* **85**, 1205–18.

——, EDDINGTON, P. & LEU, L.L. 1984. Strain Rates in Utah from Seismic Moments, Paleoslip, and Geodetic Surveys, *U.S. geol. Surv. Open-file Rep. 84–763*, pp. 422–437.

SMITH, R.L. & LUEDKE, R.G. 1984. Potentially active volcanic lineaments and loci in western conterminous United States. *In*: *Explosive Volcanism: Inception, Evolution, and Hazards*, pp. 47–66. Nat. Res. Counc., National Academy Press, Wash. D.C.

SNAY, R.A., SMITH, R.R. & SOLER, T. 1984. Horizontal strain across the Wasatch Front near Salt Lake City, Utah. *J. geophys. Res.* **89**, 1113–22.

STEWART, J.H. 1978. Basin and Range structure in western North America: A review, *In*: SMITH, R.B. & EATON, G.P. (eds) *Cenozoic Tectonics and Regional Geophysics of the Western Cordillera, Mem. geol. Soc. Am.* **152**, 1–13.

THATCHER, W. & HANKS, T.C. 1973. Source parameters of southern California earthquakes. *J. geophys. Res.* **78**, 8547–76.

THENHAUS, P.C. & WENTWORTH, C.M. 1982. Map showing zones of similar ages of surface faulting and estimated maximum earthquake size in the Basin and Range province and selected adjacent areas. *U.S. geol. Surv. Open-file Rep. 82–742.*

THOMPSON, G.A. & BURKE, D.B. 1974. Regional geophysics of the Basin and Range province. *Ann. Rev. Earth planet. Sci.* **2**, 213–38.

VON TISH, D.B., ALLMENDINGER, R.W. & SHARP, J.W. 1985. History of Cenozoic extension in central Sevier Desert, west-central Utah, from COCORP seismic reflection data. *Bull. Am. Assoc. Pet. Geol.* **69**, 1077–87.

WALLACE, R.E. 1978. Patterns of faulting and seismic gaps in the Great Basin province: in Proc. Conf. VI, Methodology for Identifying Seismic Gaps and Soon-to-Break Gaps. *U.S. geol. Surv. Open-file Rep. 78–943.*

WERNICKE, B.P., SPENCER, J.E., BURCHFIEL, B.C. & GUTH, P.L. 1982. Magnitude of extension in the southern Great Basin. *Geology*, **10**, 499–502.

WESNOUSKY, S.G., SCHOLZ, C.H. & SHIMAZAKI, K. 1982a. Deformation of an island arc: Rates of moment release and crustal shortening in intraplate Japan determined from seismicity and Quaternary fault data. *J. geophys. Res.* **87**, 6829–52.

——, ——, —— & MATSUDA, T. 1982b. Earthquake frequency distribution and the mechanics of faulting. *J. geophys. Res.* **88**, 9331–40.

WRIGHT, L. 1976. Late Cenozoic fault patterns and stress fields in the Great Basin and westward displacement of the Sierra Nevada block. *Geology*, **4**, 489–94.

ZOBACK, M.L. & ZOBACK, M.D. 1980. State of stress in the conterminous United States. *J. geophys. Res.* **85**, 6113–56.

——, ANDERSON, R.E. & THOMPSON, G.A. 1981. Cainozoic evolution of the state of stress and style of tectonism of the Basin and Range province of the Western United States. *Phil. Trans. R. Soc. London,* **300**, 407–34.

PAUL K. EDDINGTON & ROBERT B. SMITH, Department of Geology and Geophysics, University of Utah, Salt Lake City, Utah 84112 USA, and Casper Renggli Institute for Geophysics, Swiss Federal Institute of Technology, ETH-Honggerberg, CH-8093, Zurich, Switzerland.

Footwall structural evolution of the Tucki Mountain detachment system, Death Valley region, southeastern California

K.V. Hodges, J.D. Walker & B.P. Wernicke

SUMMARY: Tucki Mountain lies within the central portion of the Death Valley extended terrain. Its structure is dominated by the Cenozoic Tucki Mountain detachment system, a complex and long-lived extensional feature which places weakly metamorphosed–unmetamorphosed strata on middle to upper greenschist facies metamorphic rocks. Detailed analysis of tectonites in the footwall of the detachment system has led to the identification of seven phases of ductile structures. The earliest are latest Mesozoic–earliest Tertiary(?) isoclinal folds and associated schistosity which may have been related to compressional deformation. All subsequent generations of structures developed during Cenozoic extension at intermediate–upper crustal levels. Structures of D_3 and D_5 age are markedly asymmetric and record simple-shear deformation along the detachment system. Kinematic analysis of these structures indicates consistent NNW movement of the hanging wall relative to the footwall throughout the history of the fault zone. This extension direction is inconsistent with the overall N45W–S45E direction indicated for the Death Valley region by the orientation of major transfer faults like the Death Valley and Furnace Creek fault zones. The discrepancy may reflect late-stage changes in the regional extension direction from N–S to NW–SE, or a partitioning of overall NW–SE extension into domains of variably orientated local extension.

One of the most striking consequences of Cenozoic extensional tectonics in the Basin and Range Province of western North America was the transport of large tracts of intermediate P/T metamorphic rocks to shallow crustal levels. These crystalline terrains, which form the footwalls of the Cordilleran 'metamorphic core complexes' of Davis & Coney (1979), are usually separated from unmetamorphosed hanging wall rocks by low-angle, structurally complex fault zones or 'detachments'. Structures observed within the metamorphic footwalls are commonly diachronous N of Arizona: ductile, Mesozoic compressional structures have been overprinted by ductile to brittle, Cenozoic extensional structures (e.g. Armstrong 1982). Although diachroneity complicates structural analysis in many 'core complexes', integrated structural and geochronological studies in several of them have illuminated a common developmental sequence of footwall extensional structures in the detachment zone: (i) early development of mylonitic planar and linear fabrics under amphibolite–middle greenschist facies metamorphic conditions, followed by (ii) brittle–ductile deformation under lower greenschist facies conditions, succeeded by (iii) brittle extensional faulting (e.g. the southern Arizona Complexes—Davis 1980, the Whipple Mountains of southeastern California—Davis et al. 1983 and the Ruby Mountains of eastern Nevada—Snoke & Lush 1984). This temporal progression of deformational style mimics the *spatial* variations that might be expected along a major crustal shear zone as it passes from deeper to shallower crustal levels (e.g. Sibson 1977), a similarity that has prompted several workers (e.g. Wernicke 1981; Armstrong 1982; Davis et al. 1983; Snoke & Lush 1984) to postulate that the observed developmental sequence of detachment-zone structures in 'metamorphic core complexes' is the natural consequence of transporting footwall crystalline rocks from the middle crust to the upper crust along deeply rooted, low-angle normal shear zones (Fig. 1).

If the model illustrated in Fig. 1 is correct, it should be possible to track changes (if any) in extension direction between footwall and hanging wall during the development of 'core complexes' through kinematic analysis of progressively younger extensional structures in the detachment zone. We have attempted to test this hypothesis in a portion of the Basin and Range Province where the interplay of associated strike-slip- and normal-fault systems are thought to provide independent constraints on the regional direction of Tertiary extension—the Tucki Mountain area of the Death Valley extended terrain, southeastern California.

Regional Setting

The Death Valley region (Fig. 2) has been the site of large-scale extension since at least early

From COWARD, M.P., DEWEY, J.F. & HANCOCK, P.L. (eds), 1987, *Continental Extensional Tectonics*, Geological Society Special Publication No. 28. pp. 393–408.

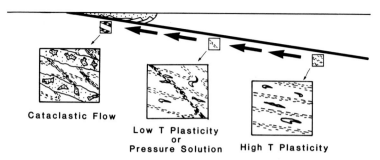

Cataclastic Flow

Low T Plasticity
or
Pressure Solution   High T Plasticity

FIG. 1. Hypothetical model of the development of rock fabrics during movement on a detachment system. As footwall rocks are extracted from beneath the hanging wall, they pass through progressively lower temperature deformational regimes. At middle crustal levels, deformation occurs principally through dislocation creep and dynamic recrystallization. At shallower levels, these fabrics are overprinted by structures characteristic of dislocation glide (e.g. mechanical twins) or pressure solution. Finally, near the surface, deformation is accommodated by cataclastic flow.

Miocene time (Cemen *et al.* 1982). This extension was accommodated in the upper crust by listric and low-angle planar normal faults and by NW-trending, right-lateral strike-slip faults which served as 'transfers' between normal-fault systems. At the surface, most of the normal-fault systems shown in Fig. 2 dip W–NW at intermediate–low angles ($<50°$), although subsequent folding produced locally complex fault geometries. Movement along these fault systems consequently led to an eastward tilting of the ranges in the area, exposing a bedrock stratigraphy from Precambrian (>1400 Ma) crystalline basement to Upper Palaeozoic carbonate rocks. In several ranges, the Precambrian section was subjected to regional metamorphism, but the prevailing P/T conditions varied significantly from range to range. For example, clastic and carbonate rocks of the late Precambrian Pahrump Group in the Funeral Mountains experienced metamorphic conditions as high as ~975 K and ~900 MPa, whereas stratigraphically equivalent rocks in the Panamint Mountains reached a maximum of ~975 K at ~300 MPa (Labotka 1980, 1981). Available geochronological data suggest that much of the metamorphism throughout the Death Valley region occurred in middle Jurassic time (e.g. DeWitt *et al.* 1984; Labotka *et al.* 1985), contemporaneous with deformation in the Sevier foreland fold and thrust belt at this latitude (Burchfiel & Davis 1975); thus, both high- and low-pressure regional metamorphism of equivalent stratigraphy indicates large-scale structural imbrication at intermediate crustal levels during Sevier compressional orogenesis.

Several lines of evidence have been used to argue that subsequent Cenozoic extension in the region was directed uniformly NW–SE. First, the northerly trend of W-dipping normal-fault systems and the eastward tilting of the ranges is consistent with general top-to-the-W displacement. Secondly, the transfer faults in the region (with the exception of the Garlock Fault) consistently trend NW. Contemporaneous movement along *en échelon* transfers like the Death Valley and Furnace Creek fault zones (Fig. 2) imply approximately N45W–S45E extension (Burchfiel & Stewart 1966). Thirdly, pre-Cenozoic reconstructions of the central Death Valley area based on late Precambrian–Palaeozoic stratigraphic facies and thickness trends suggest that at least some portions of the Panamint Mountains were transported up to 80 km northwestward during late Cenozoic extension (Stewart 1983). Finally, three NW-plunging domal fault surfaces along the western foot of the Black Mountains (the Death Valley 'turtlebacks') have been interpreted as kilometre-scale mullion structures indicating NW–SE extension (Wright *et al.* 1974).

The Tucki Mountain area

Tucki Mountain occupies a central position within the Death Valley extended terrain and constitutes the northern termination of the Panamint Range (Fig. 2). The northern Panamint Range features a composite tectonic window which may be described conveniently in terms of two structural elements (Fig. 3): a lower plate, consisting of a middle–upper greenschist facies section ranging from middle Proterozoic crystalline basement to late Precambrian miogeoclinal strata, as well as the latest Cretaceous–earliest Palaeocene Skidoo granitic

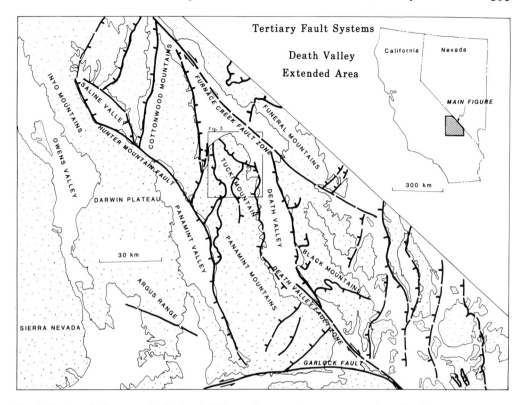

FIG. 2. Tertiary fault systems in the Death Valley region. Boxed area corresponds to Fig. 3.

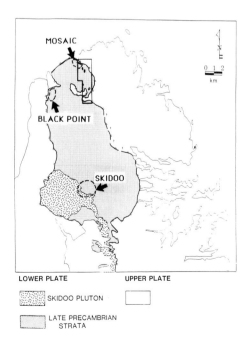

pluton; and an upper plate, composed of lower greenschist facies to unmetamorphosed units ranging from late Precambrian miogeoclinal rocks to Tertiary syn-extensional, alluvial fan deposits ('fanglomerates').

The contact between the upper and lower plates is marked by several temporally distinct faults. Although the geometrical relationships between these structures are complex and constitute a major focus of our ongoing research in the area, a few general relations are certain. First, all of these faults place younger rocks on older rocks. In many instances the faults mark a metamorphic discontinuity with lower grade or unmetamorphosed units in the hanging wall and higher grade rocks in the footwall. These

FIG. 3. Generalized tectonic map of the Tucki Mountain area. Individual faults making up the detachment system are not distinguished; only the composite upper plate – lower plate boundary is shown. Structural sub-areas are enclosed by dashed lines. Boxed area corresponds to Fig. 8.

characteristics imply a normal-fault geometry. Secondly, faults which form the margin of the window dip eastward at moderate angles (10–70°) on the eastern edge of the window, northward ~20° at the northern terminus of the window and westward at shallow angles (<20°) on the western edge of the window. Thus, the upper plate/lower plate contact forms a N-plunging antiformal surface. At the northern end of the range, the surface has been exhumed and forms a 'turtleback' reminiscent of those on the western flank of the Black Mountains. The consequent continuous exposure of the upper plate/lower plate contact reveals a smoothness which belies the diachroneity of the different faults that form the surface, suggesting that it roughly corresponds to the 'sole' detachment for the Tucki Mountain normal-fault system. Thus, although different upper plate faults were operative at different times, lower plate structures within the Tucki Mountain detachment zone (as we will subsequently call the upper plate/lower plate contact) should record the cumulative effects of the extensional history.

One of the oldest window-bounding faults is truncated by structures related to the Little Chief granite stock in the central Panamint Range (McDowell 1974). Rb–Sr isotopic data for plagioclase, biotite and hornblende separates, from this stock, yield an internal isochron corresponding to 10.8±0.3 Ma (McKenna 1985). Consequently, elements of the Tucki Mountain extensional system appear to be older than 11 Ma, but regional considerations suggest that they are unlikely to be older than early Miocene. The youngest faults in the system (along the western margin of the window) cut Tertiary fanglomerates with interstratified basalts and tuffs which yield Pliocene K–Ar ages (Hall 1971; W. Hildreth, unpubl. data). Thus, at least some of the movement on the Tucki Mountain system must be late Pliocene–Recent in age.

Structure

General comments

Three sub-areas in the lower plate of the Tucki Mountain window were selected for detailed structural analysis: Mosaic Canyon, Black Point, and Skidoo (Fig. 3). Thanks to extreme topographic and structural relief, as well as an arid environment, these sub-areas provide essentially complete exposure of tectonites in the uppermost 200 m of the lower plate. Within each sub-area, overprinting

relationships were used to define the relative age of various structural elements. Generally, two to five generations of structures were discerned in each sub-area. Structural correlations between sub-areas were made principally on the basis of structural style in rocks of similar mechanical properties, and to a lesser extent on orientation. Integration of fabric data from the three sub-areas led to the identification of seven deformational 'phases' in the lower plate tectonites. Many of these 'phases' are best interpreted as snapshots of a continuous deformational process rather than episodic phenomena, although we infer a significant gap in time between D_{1-2} and D_3. D_3 through D_5 were most strongly pronounced in the uppermost few hundred metres of the lower plate and are interpreted as being related directly to movement on the detachment system.

D_{1-2}

The oldest structural elements in the lower plate include typically recumbent, isoclinal to tight folds and associated axial planar schistosity. Folds of this age vary from angular to curved non-parallel in profile and have highly attenuated limbs and thickened hinges. Most are cylindrical on outcrop scale, but wide variations in measured axes and axial planes in a single sub-area (Fig. 4a,b) suggest non-cylindricity at larger scales. Height–width ratios (following the terminology of Hansen 1971) vary from 100 to 5. In general, these folds are not markedly asymmetric and they have no consistent sense of vergence.

In Mosaic Canyon, early isoclinal folds with amplitudes of up to 30 m are refolded by isoclinal folds with amplitudes up to 15 m (Fig. 5a). Both fold sets have an associated axial planar foliation and approximately the same morphology; in the absence of refolding relationships, it was extremely difficult to assign an individual isoclinal or tight fold to 'D_1' rather than 'D_2'. Consequently, we assign all early isoclinal to tight folds and their accompanying foliations to a collective deformational phase D_{1-2}.

F_{1-2} folds strongly transposed an earlier compositional layering (S_0, presumed to be bedding), such that S_0 is sub-parallel to S_{1-2} except in the hinges of F_{1-2} folds. In impure carbonate lithologies, S_{1-2} is defined by the alignment of phlogopite porphyroblasts and the elongation of calcite, quartz and plagioclase grains. Undulose extinction and optically discernable sub-grains are common in quartz. Large (>2 mm) calcite grains are surrounded by small (<0.5 mm), dynamically recrystallized calcite grains. The

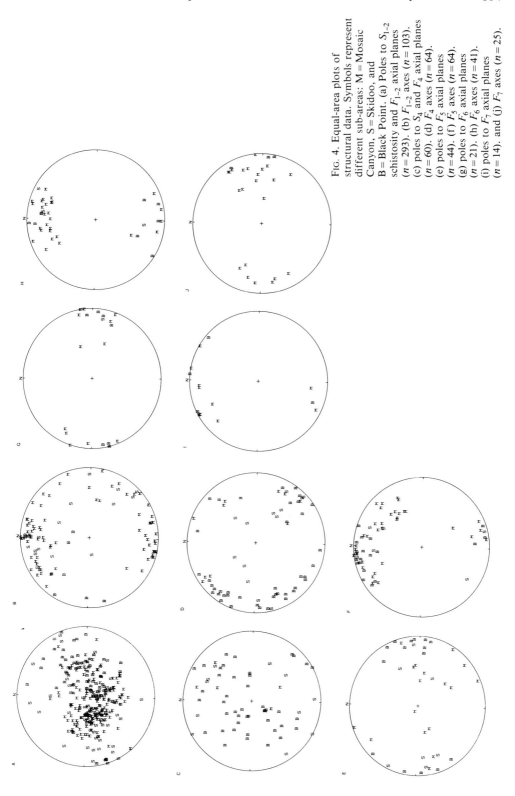

FIG. 4. Equal-area plots of structural data. Symbols represent different sub-areas: M = Mosaic Canyon, S = Skidoo, and B = Black Point. (a) Poles to S_{1-2} schistosity and F_{1-2} axial planes ($n=293$). (b) F_{1-2} axes ($n=103$). (c) poles to S_4 and F_4 axial planes ($n=60$). (d) F_4 axes ($n=64$). (e) poles to F_5 axial planes ($n=44$). (f) F_5 axes ($n=64$). (g) poles to F_6 axial planes ($n=21$). (h) F_6 axes ($n=41$). (i) poles to F_7 axial planes ($n=14$). and (j) F_7 axes ($n=25$).

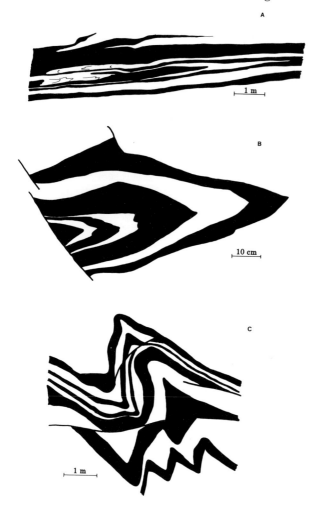

FIG. 5. Fold morphology.
Drawings represent principal
sections of representative
structures. (a) F_{1-2}. (b) F_4. (c) F_5.

larger grains show pervasive mechanical twinning. Generally, the twin planes have a preferred orientation sub-parallel to S_{1-2}, but it is possible that the twins were formed during lower temperature D_3 deformation rather than D_{1-2} (see below).

In pelitic to psammitic lithologies, S_{1-2} is defined by the preferred orientation of mica and chloritoid porphyroblasts and by the elongation of quartz grains. The elongate quartz grains characteristically have well-developed subgrains. Most chloritoids contain an internal foliation defined by quartz, mica and ilmenite inclusions. This foliation is always optically continuous with S_{1-2}. Many of the chloritoids exhibit rotational structure (Fig. 6), indicating growth during D_{1-2} simple-shear deformation. Asymmetrical pressure shadows, predominantly composed of quartz and muscovite with grano-

blastic polygonal texture, indicative of dynamic recrystallization, are associated with the chloritoids. The sense of rotation recorded by these microstructures is generally consistent within a single thin section but varies from sample to sample; consequently, the chloritoids do not provide clear constraints on the kinematics of D_{1-2} deformation.

D_3

A variety of mesoscopic and microscopic structures indicative of extensional strain are superimposed on D_{1-2} structures and are collectively termed D_3. One of the most striking of these is a stretching lineation (L_3) which is common in all three sub-areas. It is best developed along S_{1-2} surfaces in impure carbonate lithologies (Fig. 7a). In conglomeratic lithologies, L_3 corresponds to

FIG. 6. Photomicrograph (plane light) of chloritoid schist from the Black Point sub-area. Note rotation of chloritoid in S_{1-2} and overprinting by S_3 extensional crenulation cleavage. Section orientated N15W, with W to the left.

the long axis of stretched cobbles. Orientations of L_3 are remarkably consistent throughout the northern Panamint Range. Least-squares analysis of L_3 data collected over the 20 km^2 Mosaic Canyon sub-area (Fig. 8) yields a mean orientation of 13° to N16W with a 2σ uncertainty of only 16°.

Boudinage on a scale ranging from centimetres to metres is pervasive in the sub-areas studied. A small percentage of the observed boudins were symmetrical. The neck areas of symmetrical boudins contain secondary quartz + calcite + plagioclase pods which exhibit a granoblastic polygonal fabric in thin section. In a few instances, three-dimensional exposures of symmetrical boudins suggest that the structures are generally cylindrical, such that the neck lines maintain constant orientations up and down plunge. Where observed, the necklines always lie within the S_{1-2} plane and have a mean orientation of 12° to N83E.

Asymmetrical boudinage (Platt & Vissers 1980) is common in the impure marbles found in lower Mosaic Canyon (Fig. 7b). Here, polished exposures in the canyon walls look like stretched-pebble conglomerates, although the stratigraphic interval to which these marbles belong is generally devoid of carbonate conglomerates. Close inspection of the 'pebbles' reveals that some contain intrafolial isoclinal folds of apparent D_{1-2} age, indicating that the conglomeratic nature of the rocks is the result of pervasive D_3 boudinage. A complete progression from asymmetrical 'pinch and swell' to boudinage can be observed in the canyon, and leads to the model of 'pseudo-conglomerate' formation shown in

Fig. 9. In Frame B, planar and listric ductile shear zones develop at intermediate angles (20–60°) with respect to S_0 (as transposed into S_{1-2}). Ductility contrasts between centimetre-scale interbeds lead to décollement horizons at the upper and lower contacts of competent beds, which act as roof and floor faults for the ductile normal shears. In Frame C, continuing movement leads to major local thinning of the competent layers along ductile normal-shear zones, and a net rotation of these zones toward parallelism with S_0 and S_{1-2}. Compositional layering *within* lithons often exhibits a reverse drag or 'rollover' geometry. Penetrative ductile stretching of the lithons between normal shears leads to an overall thinning of competent layers and enhances the asymmetry of the lithons. In Frame D, the lithons become individual asymmetrical boudins—'clasts' in the pseudo-conglomerate. In some cases, the lithons appear to have behaved more rigidly during D_3 extension and rotated as blocks in a direction antithetic to the sense of movement along the normal-shear zones. This behaviour is also exhibited by boudinaged granitic dykes which cut quartz-rich metasediments in the Black Point area. Throughout the Tucki Mountain area, the ductile normal-shear zones associated with D_3 asymmetrical boudinage consistently strike ENE and dip to the NNW.

The uppermost lower plate exposures in the Black Point sub-area are of quartz-rich diamictites. Cobbles of quartzite, amphibolite, pelitic gneiss and marble are conspicuously flattened in the S_{1-2} plane. In this sub-area, asymmetrical boudinage is of less importance than an unusual composite fabric (Fig. 7c) which we also attribute to D_3. Quartz, pelitic gneiss and carbonate cobbles are commonly deformed into sigmoidal forms, such that the central portion of a clast makes an angle of less than 45° with S_{1-2} and the 'tails' of the clast are asymptotic to S_{1-2}. More micaceous interbeds within the diamictite exhibit mesoscopic Type I S–C fabric (Lister & Snoke 1984) of D_3 age. In general, the shear planes (C) coincide with S_{1-2} and the 'schistosity' (S) lies sub-parallel to the central portion of the sigmiodally deformed cobbles.

The ductile normal-shear zones common in impure carbonates (Fig. 7b) appear as bands of fine-grained, (<0.3 mm) dynamically recrystallized calcite in thin section. Microscopic structures of D_3 age are more varied in pelitic and psammitic lithologies. Extensional crenu-

lation cleavage (Platt & Vissers 1980) with a pronounced listric form is common in the Black Point area (Fig. 6). These microscopic 'normal faults' appear to offset millimetre-scale compositional layering, but 'sole' into the S_{1-2} schistosity. There is no apparent compositional variation between the cleavage zones and the surrounding material. In orientated samples, these cleavages uniformly exhibit a top-to-the-NW sense of offset.

The structurally highest psammitic rocks at Black Point and Skidoo exhibit both Type I and more commonly Type II S–C fabric (Lister & Snoke 1984) in thin section. Figure 10 represents a line drawing from a Skidoo thin section which is orientated approximately N15W. In this S–C tectonite, porphyroblasts of chloritoid are variably retrograded to chlorite and biotite. Extension fractures perpendicular to S_{1-2} are

(a)

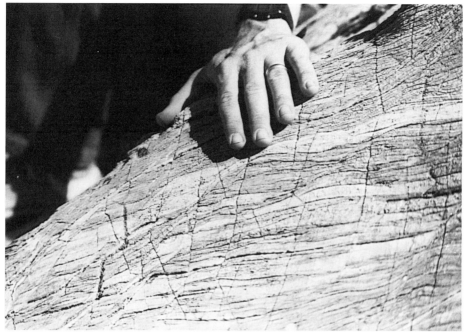

(b)

(c)

FIG. 7. Mesoscopic D_3 extensional structures. (a) Stretching lineation in impure carbonate lithology, lower Mosaic Canyon. Mechanical pencil points 15° to N15W. (b) Asymmetrical boudinage in lower Mosaic Canyon. Outcrop oriented NNW–SSE with NNW to the left. (c) Asymmetrically deformed diamictite, Black Point sub-area. Outcrop oriented NW–SE with NW to the right.

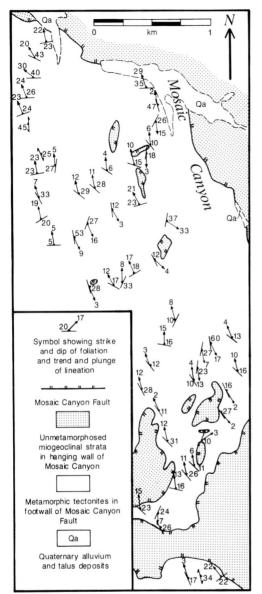

FIG. 8. Orientations of L_3 stretching lineations in the Mosaic Canyon area. The lineations are developed in 'S_3' planes (strongly modified S_{1-2}), whose orientations are also shown. Here the Mosaic Canyon Fault represents the Tucki Mountain detachment system.

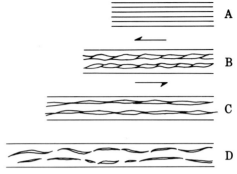

FIG. 9. Developmental model for 'pseudo-conglomerate'. See text for explanation.

axes are commonly aligned sub-parallel to L_3 in strongly lineated rocks. We interpret this as reflecting rotation of the earlier folds during D_3 simple-shear deformation. S_{1-2} surfaces appear to have acted as shear planes during the formation of many D_3 S–C fabrics. Except where features such as extensional crenulation cleavage are well developed, it is difficult to identify an angular discordance between S_{1-2} and planar fabrics of D_3 age. We believe that the dominant foliation in areas strongly affected by D_3 is a highly modified S_{1-2} fabric and might best be considered an S_3 fabric.

D_4

The D_4 event is represented by tight folds which are angular non-parallel in profile (Fig. 5b). They are moderately non-cylindrical, and axial orientations of F_4 folds are highly variable (Fig. 4c, d). Height–width ratios vary from 2 to 5. F_4 folds are generally symmetrical and thus have no clear sense of vergence.

F_4 folds in pelitic and carbonate lithologies often have an associated S_4 axial planar fabric. In some pelitic thin sections, this fabric is defined by secondary chlorite and white mica. Most often, it takes the form of pressure solution cleavage.

D_5

Markedly asymmetrical folds with height–width ratios of 0.5–2 are characteristic of D_5. They are angular to curved non-parallel in profile (Fig. 5c), and generally non-cylindrical at outcrop scale. The orientations of F_5 folds are variable (Fig. 4e, f). The vergence of F_5 fold trains varies systematically with axial orientation; N- to NE-trending fold sets verge

filled with secondary biotite which appears to be compositionally equivalent to the biotite 'fish' which are common in the thin section.

In many instances, the D_3 features described above have strongly modified D_{1-2} structures and fabrics. In the Mosaic Canyon sub-area, F_{1-2}

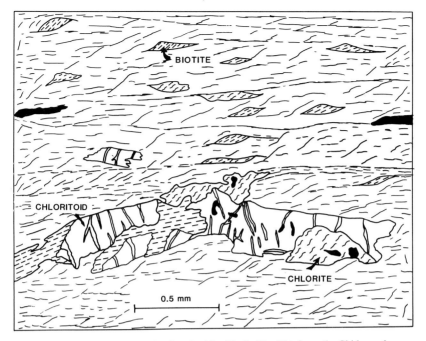

FIG. 10. Line drawing of photomicrograph of mylonitic chloritoid schist from the Skidoo sub-area.

eastward, whereas NW-trending sets verge westward. There is no apparent axial planar fabric associated with F_5 folding.

Folds with orientations and morphology similar to the lower plate F_5 were also observed in the upper plate at Mosaic Canyon. In both the Mosaic Canyon and Black Point areas, the actual upper plate/lower plate contact is marked by a cataclastic fault zone from <1 m to >100 m thick. This zone is characterized by highly fractured metre-scale blocks of lower plate and upper plate lithologies in a matrix of centimetre- to millimetre-scale fault breccia or gouge. Variations in cement composition have led to the development of patchy compositional layering within the fault gouge. This layering is spectacularly deformed by asymmetrical folds which also appear similar to the lower plate F_5. In a few instances, the axial plane of a lower plate F_5 structure may be traced upward into the cataclastic zone. Most commonly, however, F_5 folds in the lower plate and similar folds in the fault zone increase in asymmetry and degree of overturning near the bounding faults of the cataclastic zone and do not affect these surfaces. Collectively, these observations lead us to conclude that the asymmetric folds in the upper plate and the fault zone are indeed D_5 structures, and that they developed synchronously with relative movement between the upper and lower plates along the cataclastic zone.

D_6

Structures of D_6 age include mesoscopic and macroscopic, broad to open folds. These folds are curved parallel in profile, with height–width ratios of ≤ 0.3. They are extremely cylindrical and F_6 axes and axial planes from throughout the study area cluster rather tightly (Fig. 4g, h). The mean F_6 axial orientation is 19° to the N.

D_7

The latest lower plate structures observed at Tucki Mountain are broad, curved-parallel warps with a mean trend of 19° to N78E (Fig. 4i, j). These structures generally have height–width ratios less than 0.2 and are apparently quite cylindrical. Together, F_6 and F_7 folds form broad, 'dome and basin' interference patterns. Metre-scale examples are especially common in the Mosaic Canyon sub-area (Fig. 11).

Timing of lower plate structural events

The age of D_{1-2}–D_7 in the lower plate is bracketed between the intrusion of the Skidoo pluton and deposition of modern alluvial fan deposits.

The Skidoo granitoid commonly exhibits complicated intrusive relationships with its

FIG. 11. Dome and basin structures formed by the interference of F_6 and F_7 fold sets, Mosaic Canyon sub-area. View is approximately down-plunge on a set of F_7 open fields orientated ~N80E. F_6 axes are roughly orthogonal to F_7 at this outcrop (i.e. within the plane of the photograph). Compass shown for scale is 7 cm across.

country rocks. Centimetre- to metre-scale apophyses of granite permeate the country rocks near the margins of the main intrusive body in the Skidoo sub-area. These apophyses are deformed by F_{1-2} folds and were boudinaged during D_3. Available K–Ar mica and Rb–Sr whole-rock geochronological data suggest that the Skidoo pluton is latest Cretaceous–earliest Palaeocené in age (W. Hildreth, unpublished data; M. Hubbard, unpublished data), implying a maximum age of latest Mesozoic for D_{1-2}. Relationships between S_{1-2} fabrics and metamorphic porphyroblasts (see above) further suggest that D_{1-2} was roughly synchronous with regional prograde metamorphism in the northern Panamint Range. Attempts to constrain the age of metamorphism in the *central* Panamint Range directly, using Ar–Ar systematics in micas and amphiboles (Labotka *et al.* 1985) have yielded data suggestive of two metamorphic events (middle Jurassic and latest Cretaceous). It appears that the second of these was the dominant phase of metamorphism in the northern Panamint Range.

The association between D_3 deformation and retrograde metamorphic minerals in pelitic and psammitic lithologies suggests an interval of uplift, cooling, and consequent retrograde metamorphism between D_{1-2} and D_3. Structures of D_3 age are most strongly developed in the structurally highest portions of the lower plate and dominate the mesoscopic fabric of tectonites within a few hundred metres of the detachment system. D_3 kinematic indicators (see below) suggest extension sub-parallel to S_{1-2} accompanying top-to-the-NW simple shear, a geometry more consistent with Tertiary extension than Mesozoic compression at this latitude. For these reasons, we interpret structures of D_3 age and younger as Tertiary extensional phenomena.

D_5 was the first deformational phase which affected both lower plate and upper plate lithologies at Tucki Mountain and apparently records the final juxtaposition of footwall and hanging wall along the detachment system. The associated cataclastic fault zone carries poorly consolidated fanglomerates in its hanging wall near the Black Point sub-area. Interbedded basalts within these fanglomerates yield Pliocene K–Ar ages (Hall 1971; W. Hildreth, unpubl. data). Thus, D_5–D_7 must be Pliocene-Recent in age.

Kinematic analysis of extensional structures

Of the many structures of apparent Tertiary age at Tucki Mountain, only those belonging to D_3 and D_5 readily lend themselves to kinematic analysis. Asymmetrical boudinage, extensional crenulation cleavage and S–C fabrics record effectively ductile normal faulting at all scales during D_3 deformation. One of the most important characteristics of these structures at Tucki Mountain is that they consistently exhibit a top-to-the-NW sense of shear. As pointed out by Lister & Snoke (1984), minor asymmetrical structures associated with a large-scale shear zone need not always reflect the bulk shear sense due to local strain inhomogeneities. In the northern Panamint Range, however, the ubiquity of top-to-the-NW minor structures suggests that this was the bulk shear sense during D_3.

Two approaches may be used to deduce the direction of D_3 extension. First, normals to the necklines of concentric, symmetrical boudins within S_{1-2} should be parallel to the extension direction. In Mosaic Canyon, where three-dimensional exposures of symmetrical boudins are most common and geometrical corrections for post-D_3 deformation are minimal, this approach yields a direction of 10° to N10W. Secondly, L_3 stretching lineations in Mosaic Canyon have a mean orientation of 13° to N16W. The agreement between these approaches and the great consistency of L_3 orientations over large tracts of the lower plate strongly suggest a NNW extension direction during D_3.

As mentioned previously, the vergence of F_5 fold sets varies systematically with axial orientation. Coupled with our interpretation that F_5 folding was related to movement along the Tucki Mountain detachment system, this characteristic suggests that a slip-line analysis (Hansen 1971) of F_5 folds may constrain the late-stage transport direction along the detachment. Figure 12 shows the axial orientation of mesoscopic F_5 fold sets for which the vergence direction could be determined. Throughout the area, E-vergent fold sets outnumber W-vergent fold sets; however, both senses of vergence are represented in each sub-area. Together, the data define a relatively narrow zone of overlap which corresponds to a separation angle of approximately 10°. The bulk D_5 transport direction should be within this angle provided that the following conditions are met (Hansen 1971): (i) the analysed structures belong to a single order; (ii) they are located between adjacent axial surfaces of the next lower order F_5 folds; and (iii) the folded surfaces were

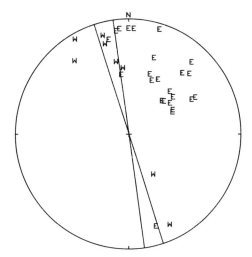

FIG. 12. Separation angle analysis of F_5 fold sets for which vergence is known. E = folds belonging to east-vergent sets; W = folds belonging to west-vergent fold sets. Superimposed vertical planes enclose the region of mixed vergence. $n = 32$.

planar before folding, or F_5 was the latest fold phase affecting the rocks in question. Most F_5 folds in the Tucki Mountain area appear to belong to a single mesoscopic order, extenuating the first and second conditions. Because F_4 folds are locally developed and generally mesoscopic, the surfaces folded by F_5 were essentially S_{1-2} strongly modified by D_3 extension. It is reasonable (but impossible to prove) that this fabric was quasi-planar prior to F_5 folding. In any event, F_6 and F_7 structures are broad and clearly did not affect F_5 geometries significantly. For example, the separation arc shown in Fig. 12 lies between N8W and N18W. If we assume that F_6 fold axes were sub-horizontal prior to F_7 folding, we may eliminate D_7 effects on F_5 orientations by restoring the mean F_6 orientation to horizontal in each sub-area and rotating F_5 orientations in the same fashion. Similar assumptions and data manipulations permit corrections for D_6. The 'restored' F_5 data yield a narrower separation arc, lying between N3W and N1E, which is not so very different from the 'unrestored' arc. Thus, we interpret the F_5 data as indicative of a NNW–SSE extension transport direction during D_5.

Discussion

Kinematic analysis of D_3 and D_5 structures indicates that top-to-the-NNW simple shear was the dominant mode of extension throughout much of the history of the Tucki Mountain detachment system. Despite the present anti-formal shape of the detachment, D_3 and D_5 extension directions were approximately the same in all sub-ares, regardless of position on the anticline. This characteristic, which the Tucki Mountain area shares with many core complexes (e.g. Snoke & Lush 1984), suggests that the detachment was initially more planar, and that its modern morphology resulted from subsequent macroscopic folding. We attribute the broad arching of this surface to reverse-drag flexure caused by top-to-the-W displacement on a younger, structurally lower detachment system exposed along the eastern foot of the Panamint Range. Reconstructions of the detachment system pre-folding configuration using this model for the folding mechanism imply a shallow west-ward dip for the detachment system during D_3–D_5. Provided that the simplistic developmental model shown in Fig. 1 is generally correct, our data suggest that the displacement direction along the detachment system did not change significantly as the lower plate rocks were deformed, first in the ductile regime (D_3) and subsequently in the brittle–ductile regime (D_5) during extension.

The apparent movement direction for the Tucki Mountain detachment system is nearly orthogonal to that which might be inferred from the westward stratal tilt associated with upper plate splay faults. Consequently, we suggest discretion in the use of hanging wall tilt directions to deduce the bulk extension direction for a detachment system. It seems likely that such analyses will often indicate the direction of extension *within* the hanging wall rather than the relative displacement across the 'sole' detachment.

It is also noteworthy that the NNW bulk elongation indicated by lower plate tectonites is inconsistent with the commonly assumed N45W extension direction for the Death Valley region as a whole. This discrepancy may be resolved if: (i) the transfer faults in the region (which constitute the principal evidence for N45W extension) dip shallowly and have a significant dip-slip component; or (ii) the development of the transfers post-dates movement along the Tucki Mountain detachment system, such that the orientation of the transfers indicates a recent change in the extension direction in the Death Valley region; or (iii) displacement along the Tucki Mountain detachment system reflects only the local extension direction rather than that of the Death Valley region as a whole.

The first of these propositions is difficult to verify because major transfers, such as the Death Valley and Furnace Creek fault zones, are generally not exposed. However, COCORP seismic reflection profiling in the southern Death Valley shows a W-dipping, low-angle reflector, the surface projection of which coincides with the approximate trace of the Death Valley fault zone (Serpa et al. 1985). If both the Furnace Creek and Death Valley fault zones have this geometry, then overall NNW extension might be possible, but it would require a significant reverse component of movement along these transfers. Such displacement seems unlikely in light of the distribution of extensional basins in the region.

The likelihood of the second possibility depends upon the age of inception of the transfer faults in the area. Although Cemen et al. (1984) argue for early Miocene–Recent movement along the Furnace Creek fault zone, most of the evidence for early movement is based on the age of basin-fill deposits thought to be associated with this structure. Given the structural complexity of the Furnace Creek area, it seems equally plausible, to us, that the Miocene deposits were associated with fault systems which pre-dated the Furnace Creek fault zone. To our knowledge, none of the available data *require* movement on the NW-trending transfers in the Death Valley area prior to the late Pliocene time.

It is equally possible that the displacement direction for the Tucki Mountain detachment system does not coincide with the regional extension direction. Overall extension in a given direction could be accommodated by variably oriented (but compatible) strains in different domains within the region. For example, the orientation of the Garlock fault zone (Fig. 2), and its significance as a boundary between a relatively unextended terrain to the S and a highly extended terrain to the N, virtually requires roughly E–W extension in the southern Death Valley region (Davis & Burchfiel 1973). Provided that at least part of the movement along the NW-trending strike-slip faults in the central and northern Death Valley region was concurrent with activity along the Garlock Fault, then a zone of displacement transfer between domains of E–W and NW–SE extension must occur in the southern Panamint Range. Much of this area is incompletely mapped, but normal-fault zones in the southern Panamints with regionally anomalous NE–SW trends may indicate the nature of the transfer zone. The 'anomalous' extension direction recorded by mesoscopic structures associated with the Tucki Mountain detachment system could be explained similarly.

Conclusions

Seven phases of ductile to brittle–ductile deformation have been identified in the mesoscopic
and microscopic structures of the Tucki Mountain metamorphic terrain. F_{1-2} isoclinal folds
and the dominant schistosity over much of the
terrain (S_{1-2}) developed synchronously with
latest Mesozoic–earliest Tertiary (?) regional
metamorphism. D_3 structures indicate top-to-
the-NNW simple-shear deformation and are
thought to record the early stages of movement
on the Tucki Mountain detachment system.
Subsequent D_4 and D_5 structures are also consistent with non-coaxial strain, and kinematic
analysis of F_5 folds indicates continued NNW
extension. F_6 and F_7 folds result in gentle dome
and basin structure on a mesoscopic scale.

The inferred kinematics of D_3 and D_5 deformation suggest that the displacement direction,
along the Tucki Mountain detachment, remained constant (NNW) throughout much of the
movement history of the feature. Tilt directions
of strata within hanging wall splays do not
accurately describe overall movement on the
detachment system, which suggests that caution
is required when applying this technique in other
extensional terrains. At first glance, NNW-
extension accommodated by the Tucki Mountain detachment seems inconsistent with the
more westerly bulk extension direction commonly inferred for the region from the orientation of major transfer faults. This apparent
paradox can be reconciled if the transfers
developed more recently than D_3–D_5 displacement on the detachment, or if the kinematics of
Tertiary deformation in the Death Valley region
were characterized by complex interactions between domains of variably orientated extension.
The available data permit either solution.

ACKNOWLEDGMENTS: We would like to thank B.C.
Burchfiel for useful discussions concerning Death
Valley geology. M. Harding, L. Hodges, M. Hubbard,
L. McKenna, and J. Stock provided able field assist-
ance. This research was funded by National Science
Foundation grants EAR-8319767 to B.P.W and
EAR-8319768 to K.V.H.

References

ARMSTRONG, R.L. 1982. Cordilleran metamorphic
core complexes – from Arizona to southern
Canada. *Ann. Rev. Earth planet. Sci.* **10**, 129–54.

BURCHFIEL, B.C. & STEWART, J.H. 1966. 'Pull-apart'
origin of the central segment of Death Valley,
California. *Bull. geol. Soc. Am.* **77**, 439–40.

—— & DAVIS, G.A. 1975. Nature and controls of
Cordilleran orogenesis, western United States:
extensions of an earlier synthesis. *Am. J. Sci.*
275-A, 363–96.

CEMEN, I., DRAKE, R. & WRIGHT, L.A. 1982. Strati-
graphy and chronology of the Tertiary sedimentary
and volcanic units at the southern end of the
Funeral Mountains, Death Valley Region, Cali-
fornia. *In:* COOPER, J.D. *et al.* (eds) *Geology
of Selected areas in the San Bernardino
Mountains, Western Mojahve Desert, and
Southern Great Basin, California*, pp. 77–88.
Shohone, CA, Death Valley Publishing
Company.

——, WRIGHT, L.A., DRAKE, R.E. & JOHNSON, F.C.
1984. Cenozoic deformation and sedimentation,
southeasternmost part of the Furnace Creek Fault
Zone, Death Valley, California. *Abstr. with
Programs geol. Soc. Am.* **16**, 466.

DAVIS, G.A. & BURCHFIEL, B.C. 1973. Garlock Fault:
an intra-continental transform structure, southern
California. *Bull. geol. Soc. Am.* **84**, 1407–22.

——, LISTER, G.S. & REYNOLDS, S.J. 1983. Interpretation of Cordilleran core complexes as evolving shear zones in an extensional orogen. *Abstr.
with Programs geol. Soc. Am.* **15**, 311.

DAVIS, G.H. 1980. Structural characteristics of metamorphic core complexes, southern Arizona. *Mem.
geol. Soc. Am.* **153**, 35–77.

—— & CONEY, P.J. 1979. Geological development of
the Cordilleran metamorphic core complexes.
Geology, **7**, 120–4.

DEWITT, E., MILLER, D.M. & SNOKE, A.W. 1984.
Mesozoic regional metamorphic terranes, Western
U.S. *Abstr. with Programs geol. Soc. Am.* **16**,
487.

HALL, W.E. 1971. Geology of the Panamint Butte
Quadrangle, Inyo County, California. *U.S. geol.
Surv. Bull.* **1299**, pp. 67.

HANSEN, E. 1971. *Strain Facies*, p. 207. Springer-
Verlag, New York.

LABOTKA, T.C. 1980. Petrology of a medium-pressure
metamorphic terrane, Funeral Mountains, California. *Am. Mineral.* **65**, 670–89.

——, 1981. Petrology of an andalusite-type regional
metamorphic terrane, Panamint Mountains, California. *J. Petrol.* **22**, 261–96.

——, WARASILA, R.L. & SPANGLER, R.R. 1985.
Polymetamorphism in the Panamint Mountains,
California: a ^{39}Ar–^{40}Ar study. *J. geophys. Res.*
90, 10359–71.

LISTER, G.S. & SNOKE, A.W. 1984. S–C Mylonites.
J. struct. Geol. **6**, 617–38.

MCDOWELL, S.D. 1974. Emplacement of the Little
Chief Stock, Panamint Range, California. *Bull.
geol. Soc. Am.* **85**, 1535–46.

MCKENNA, L.W. 1986. New Rb–Sr constraints on the
age of detachment faulting in the Panamint
Range, Death Valley, CA. *Abstr. with Programs
geol. Soc. Am.* **18**, 156.

PLATT, J.P. & VISSERS, R.L.M. 1980. Extensional structures in anisotropic rocks. *J. struct. Geol.* **2**, 397–410.

SERPA, L., DeVOOGD, B., OLIVER, J. & WRIGHT, L. 1985. Late Cenozoic structural evolution of the Death Valley region from COCORP seismic profiles. *Abstr. with Programs geol. Soc. Am.* **17**, 407.

SIBSON, R.H. 1977. Fault rocks and fault mechanisms. *J. geol. Soc. London*, **133**, 191–213.

SNOKE, A.W. & LUSH, A.P. 1984. Polyphase Mesozoic–Cenozoic deformational history of the northern Ruby Mountains – East Humbolt Range,

Nevada. *Geol. Soc. Am. Field Trip Guidebook, Annual Meeting, Reno, Nevada*, pp. 232–60.

STEWART, J.H. 1983. Extensional tectonics in the Death Valley area, California: Transport of the Panamint Range structural block 80 km. northwestward. *Geology*, **11**, 153–7.

WERNICKE, B. 1981. Low-angle normal faults in the Basin and Range Province – nappe tectonics in an extending orogen. *Nature*, **291**, 645–8.

WRIGHT, L.A., OTTON, J.K. & TROXELL, B.W. 1974. Turtleback surfaces of Death Valley viewed as phenomena of extensional tectonics. *Geology*, **2**, 53–4.

K.V. HODGES, Department of Earth, Atmospheric and Planetary Sciences, Massachusetts Institute of Technology, Cambridge, Massachusetts.

J.D. WALKER, Department of Geology, Kansas University, Lawrence, Kansas.

B.P. WERNICKE, Department of Geological Sciences, Harvard University, Cambridge, Massachusetts.

Extension and its influence on Canadian Cordilleran passive-margin evolution

B. Thompson, E. Mercier & C. Roots

SUMMARY: The proto-Pacific margin of North America remained passive for the main part of 1.4 Ga. The stratigraphy that accumulated can be split into four major time-rock sequences; each may be considered a separate passive-margin sequence. The margin, initiated at about 1500 Ma, was remodelled by extensional (rift) episodes. Geological evidence for a 780 Ma extension event is documented here; subsidence analysis supports a 550 to 600 Ma separation event (Bond & Kominz), and stratigraphic and structural evidence from the northern Canadian Cordillera suggests 370 Ma extension. Each event is interpreted as the precursor to, and initiator of, passive-margin sedimentation.

    Fold- and thrust-belt trends reflect passive-margin geometry. In the Ogilvie Mountains an abrupt right-angle bend in structural trend was inherited from 775 Ma extension faults.

For 1.4 Ga the proto-Pacific margin of North America remained mainly passive—a remarkably long period compared with the passive margin sequences in the Appalachians and Alps, which lasted 250 Ma or less before collapse and the onset of mountain building. More ancient examples like the early Proterozoic Coronation miogeocline evolved in only 10 Ma (Hoffman 1983). The Cordilleran margin was protected from plate convergence for a long time, but this doesn't explain the distribution of stratigraphic thicknesses and facies through time. The process that 'drives' subsidence, conductive cooling of a thermal anomaly, reaches equilibrium in about 200 Ma or less (McKenzie 1978). Subsidence potential decreases to zero in that time; yet the Cordilleran passive-margin succession contains thick shallow-water siliclastic and carbonate sequences of Middle Proterozoic, Upper Proterozoic and Phanerozoic ages. A single continental rift and separation event can account for only a part of this stratigraphy.

An alternative is to view the stratigraphy as an overlapping succession of discrete passive-margin sequences. In this way the longevity problem is eased because repeated 'thermal events' (stretchings?) are implied—each event creating potential for isostatic subsidence in response to conductive cooling.

Multiple rift events are not a new idea. Burchfiel & Davis (1975) suggested continental breakup around 1500 Ma followed by renewed extension around 800 Ma; a 550 Ma separation event is predicted by tectonic subsidence curves for Lower Palaeozoic shelf carbonates (Bond & Kominz 1984) and structural and sedimentological evidence suggests a period of continental extension in the northern Canadian Cordillera during the late Devonian and early Carboniferous (Abbott 1982; S.P. Gordey, in prep. K.R.

McClay & J.G. Abbott, pers. comm. 1984). The strata that accummulated following each event exhibit the characteristics of passive-margin sequences.

This paper focuses on one stretching episode; that at 780 Ma which initiated deposition of the Windermere Supergroup (the second passive-margin sequence). Discussion then turns to the 600–480 Ma time interval in the northern Cordillera, where extension-related volcanism occurred while shelf carbonates accumulated inboard from them. Finally the controls of early extension patterns on the trend of Mesozoic folds and thrusts are examined. Data come from the northwesternmost part of the Canadian foreland fold and thrust belt; the Ogilvie Mountains (Fig. 1).

Setting

The four passive-margin sequences that make up the Cordilleran miogeocline fall in the intervals: 1500–800 Ma (Fig. 1, Belt–Purcell sequence or Wernecke, Pinguicula and Mackenzie Mountain sequence—first passive-margin sequence); 800–600 Ma (Fig. 1, Windermere sequence—second passive-margin sequence); 600–370 Ma (Lower Palaeozoic sequence—third passive-margin sequence); and 370–180 Ma (Upper Palaeozoic and Lower Mesozoic sequence—fourth passive-margin sequence). The margin was presumably initiated during continental fragmentation about 1500 to 1700 Ma (Burke & Dewey 1973; Sears & Price 1978; McMechan & Price 1982), and modified by extensional events that preceded each passive-margin sequence.

Evidence of rifting takes different forms. For the 1500–800 Ma (first) sequence (Obradovich & Peterman 1968; Obradovich et al.), basin shape, facies and thickness are the prime indicators (the

From COWARD, M.P., DEWEY, J.F. & HANCOCK, P.L. (eds), 1987, *Continental Extensional Tectonics*, Geological Society Special Publication No. 28, pp. 409–17.

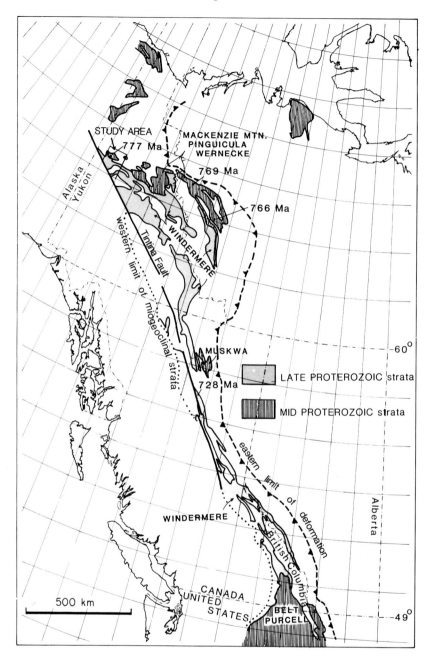

FIG. 1. Distribution of middle and late Proterozoic strata in the Canadian Cordillera. Dates refer to age of base of late Proterozoic Windermere Supergroup (second passive-margin sequence): 777 Ma (zircon Pb/Pb; from mafic volcanics in graben-fill succession; Roots, *et al.*, in prep.); 769 and 766 Ma (Rb/Sr isochrons; from dykes that intrude middle Proterozoic Mackenzie Mountains Supergroup and are interpreted as coeval with volcanic flows at the base of the Windermere Supergroup; Armstrong *et al.* 1982); 728 Ma (zircon Pb/Pb; from granitoid gneiss that conformably underlies Windermere Supergroup; Evenchick *et al.* 1984). Names applied to middle Proterozoic strata are: Belt and Purcell; Muskwa; Wernecke, Pinguicula, and Mackenzie Mountains. Name applied to late Proterozoic strata is: Windermere. Heavy solid lines are right-lateral transcurrent faults of Mesozoic age; dotted line is locus of significant overlap between exotic terranes to the W and autochthonous miogeoclinal strata to the E.

base of the sequence is not exposed). Preserved today are the contents of large and apparently separate basins that extend eastward onto the craton as much as 400 km (Price 1964; Harrison 1972; Aitken 1982; Young *et al.* 1979; Delaney 1981; Mitchell 1984; Hoyl 1984). The basins may represent E-trending failed arms or aulacogens formed during continental separation (e.g. Burke & Dewey 1973) or their shape might result from subsidence along pre-existing weaknesses in the E–W structural grain of the underlying crystalline basement (Harrison & Reynolds 1976). Regardless of basin origin, a continental margin seems necessary to support westward-thickening prisms of up to 15 km of shallow-water strata (Gabrielse 1976).

Extension faults, uplifted blocks stripped of stratigraphy now preserved in clasts filling adjacent half-grabens, and thick mafic volcanics, are evidence of rifting at the start of the 800–600 Ma Windermere (second) sequence (Stewart 1972, 1976; Lis & Price & 1976; Eisbacher 1981; McMechan & Price 1982; Thompson & Eisbacher 1984; Thompson 1984).

Stratigraphic and structural evidence of extension prior to the 550–370 Ma Cambrian–Devonian sequence is wanting, but the tectonic subsidence derived from back-stripping Cambrian and Lower Ordovician strata agrees with that modelled for the drift phase of instantaneously rifted continental lithosphere (Bond & Kominz 1984).

Evidence of extension at the start of the 370–180 Ma Devonian–Jurassic (fourth) sequence comes from the northern Canadian Cordillera where chert-pebble conglomerate and gritty sandstone occupy fault-bounded basins separated by uplifted and partially eroded blocks (Gordey, in prep.).

The three youngest passive-margin sequences span about 200 Ma each—the time required to re-establish conductive equilibrium after instantaneous rifting (McKenzie 1978; Jarvis & McKenzie 1980). Had rifting not recurred, the margin would presumably have lost its potential for subsidence. This leaves unexplained, as much as 600 Ma of subsidence for the Wernecke, Pinguicula and Mackenzie Mountains sequence in the northern Canadian Cordillera and the Belt–Purcell sequence in the southern Canadian Cordillera (Fig. 1). Chronostratigraphical constraints are few, but this interval may itself contain one or more 'rift' pulses. Sedimentation may have ended prior to a 1250–1300 Ma metamorphic/intrusive event (McMechan & Price 1982) in the S, an interpretation favoured by magnetostratigraphical analysis (Elston 1984). In the northern

Cordillera, Middle Proterozoic sedimentation can be broken into at least two discrete episodes (Eisbacher 1981; Young *et al.* 1979) that are inferred to span 1500–1200 Ma and 1200–900 Ma. In the Ogilvie Mountains, extension faults and associated half-grabens formed about 1200 Ma; if this 'event' corresponds in time with the metamorphic/intrusive event in the S, it could represent a time of transtension and transpression along the Cordilleran margin.

Mesozoic deformation of the Cordilleran margin produced structural salients and re-entrants along the eastern (foreland) side of the deformed belt. They mimic the geometry of the depositional margin (Price 1981; McMechan 1981; Thompson, in press). The abrupt northward swing of structural trends in the Ogilvie Mountains coincides with a northward swing of late Proterozoic extensional features (Fig. 2). This is evidence that the Mesozoic structural grain may have been dictated by older structures.

Evidence of extension at 777 Ma in the Ogilvie Mountains

In the Ogilvie Mountains the clearest evidence of late Proterozoic extension is the existence of faults that separate uplifted and eroded blocks on one side, from half-grabens filled with the eroded detritus on the other. The faults dip N and NE and cut bedding at steep angles (45–90°). Conglomerates in the half-grabens contain only clasts eroded from the adjacent uplifted block.

An example is illustrated schematically in Fig. 3. N of the Harper Fault (Fig. 2), the graben fill is a kilometre or more thick and contains numerous outsized clasts and olistoliths suggesting its deposition in the form of debris flows. The conglomerate rests on 2 km of late Proterozoic shallow-water carbonate. S of the fault, a thin sequence (±20 m) of conglomerates rests directly on mid-Proterozoic argillite and quartzite—the carbonates that should intervene are missing (Fig. 3). Clast type, size, and distribution demonstrate that the stratigraphy missing from the uplifted block now occupies the half-graben. Intercalated with the conglomerate and bounded by the Harper Fault, are 1200 m of mafic marine and non-marine volcanic flows and breccias (Roots 1982, 1983; Roots & Moore 1983); zircons from a felsic unit high in the succession give a 777 (+47, −31) Ma date (Roots, in prep.). The conglomeratic facies grades laterally into fluvial pebble conglomerate and sandstone, and red weathering siltstone and mudstone containing suncracks; a marine com-

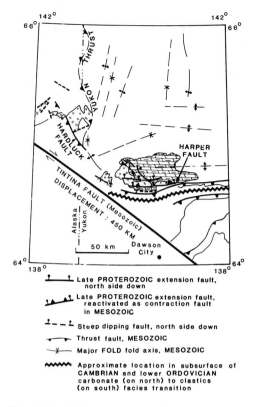

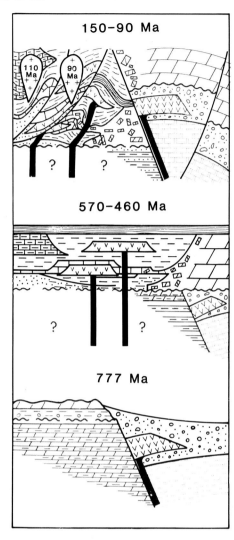

FIG. 2. Simplified tectonic map of the western Ogilvie Mountains showing the main structures. Diagonal cross pattern is middle Proterozoic strata (first passive-margin sequence; Wernecke Supergroup and Pinguicula? Group); light dotted pattern represents late Proterozoic rift assemblage, the earliest deposits of Windermere Supergroup (second passive-margin sequence). Some of the steep dipping faults may be reactivated late Proterozoic extension faults.

FIG. 3. Schematic cross-section showing three stages in the geological evolution of the western Ogilvie Mountains. In stage 1 (777 Ma) motion on the Harper Fault produced a half-graben and adjacent uplifted block; the graben was filled with coarse conglomerates and volcanics. In stage 2 (600–480 Ma) extension produced a trough filled by sandstone turbidites, shales, discontinuous carbonates and mafic volcanics; the trough was bordered to the N by a stable carbonate shelf and to the S by an inferred clastic source terrain. In stage 3 (150–90 Ma) the Harper Fault was reactivated as a contraction fault, as thrusts and folds migrated across the region from S–N. Numbers in legend boxes refer to the following stratigraphic groups: 1 = Quartet Group; 2 = Gillespie Lake Group; 3 = Pinguicula Group; 4 = Kechika Group; 5 = Road River Group.

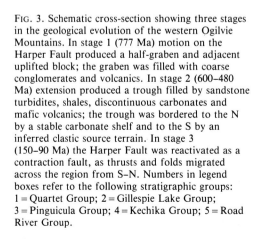

Cambrian to Devonian

[5]	chert shale ;	[4]	argillaceous limestone
	shale ;	v v v / v v v v	volcanics
	limestone ;		dolomite
	shale sandstone ;		gritty sandstone

Upper Proterozoic (rift assemblage)

	conglomerate ;	V V V V / V V V V	volcanics

Middle Proterozoic

	shale pebbly mudstone;	[3]	dolomite
[2]	argillaceous dolomite ;	[1]	sandstone shale

ponent is represented by shallow-water dolomite and turbiditic siltstone and shale.

In Alaska (Fig. 2), conglomerate next to the Hardluck Fault fines southeastward. This and stratigraphical omission NE of the fault (Brabb & Churkin 1965; Young 1982), suggest that the Hardluck Fault was also a late Proterozoic extension feature.

Alluvial fans are the initial stratigraphical deposits of many rifted continental margins; in the Ogilvie Mountains, they are coastal fans (Rust 1979). A modern example of coastal fans developing in a rift environment is the Gulf of Aqaba where detritus eroded from the uplifted Sinai Peninsula is funnelled into a few fans that prograde into the gulf (e.g. at Neviot).

In the Ogilvie Mountains the three extension-related elements: graben and fill, extension fault, and eroded block, are rarely preserved together. All but the roots of some extension faults are eroded and former grabens are represented by stratigraphical remnants of conglomerate. The compilation of extension-related features assumes that each is related to the same 780 Ma event (Fig. 2). Together they define a diffuse zone that bends towards the northwest.

Evidence for 750–800 Ma extension elsewhere in the Cordillera

Fault-bounded basins filled with locally derived conglomerate, typify initial late Proterozoic deposits in the Mackenzie Mountains (Eisbacher 1981; Ruell 1982; Young *et al.* 1979), in the northern (Gabrielse & Taylor 1982; Gabrielse 1972), central (McMechan & Thompson 1985) and southern Canadian Rocky Mountains (Lis & Price 1976; McMechan & Price 1982), and along the US Cordillera to southern California (Stewart 1972, 1976; Miller *et al.* 1973; Wright *et al.* 1976).

Timing is constrained by dates from the northern Canadian Cordillera (Fig. 1). Dykes interpreted as feeders of volcanic flows at the base of the rift succession in the Mackenzie Mountains, give Rb–Sr isochron dates of 766 (± 24) and 769 (± 27) Ma (Armstrong *et al.* 1982), consistent with the Ogilvie zircon dates. In the northern Rocky Mountains, gneissic granite beneath Upper Proterozoic pebble conglomerate gives a 728 (+8, −7) Ma zircon age, representing a probable lower limit for Upper Proterozoic deposition there (Evanchick *et al.* 1984).

In the southern Rocky Mountains, volcanics at the base of the Upper Proterozoic succession give K–Ar dates ranging from 233 to 918 Ma (Miller *et al.* 1973) with 827 to 918 Ma the

likeliest period of rifting. Unlike the northern data, these ages are poorly constrained.

Consistency of dates from the northern Canadian Cordillera suggests rifting between 720 and 780 Ma. If mafic-dyke intrusion is evidence of extension, a set of 740 Ma dykes cutting 2750 Ma basement in the Beartooth Mountains of Wyoming and Montana (Baadsgaard & Mueller 1973) suggests extension in the craton of the northwestern US and conterminous Canada during the 720 and 780 Ma interval.

Evidence for early Palaeozoic extension in the Ogilvie Mountains

A prominent facies boundary (Fig. 2) separates the Ogilvie Mountains into northern and southern halves. On the N the 777 Ma rift assemblage is unconformably overlain by shelf carbonate of lowest Cambrian through Lower Ordovician age; on the S is a thick succession of gritty quartzose sandstone, limestone, maroon- and green-weathering argillite, and mafic volcanics of latest Proterozoic through Lower Ordovician age. The volcanics consist of mafic flows and breccias that form narrow (1–3 km) linear belts; they probably occurred as fissure eruptions (Thompson & Roots 1982; Roots 1982).

This clastic-volcanic succession was deposited in an E–W-trending trough-like feature. A proximal southern margin and source terrain is suggested by sandstone gravity flows which become increasingly coarse southward and contain sole markings (flutes) indicating S–N transport.

Therefore Cambrian and Lower Ordovician palaeogeography suggests a narrow extended basin bordered to the N by a broad shallow-water carbonate shelf, and to the S by a landmass that provided terrigenous sediment.

Evidence for 550 to 600 Ma extension elsewhere in the Cordillera

Bond & Kominz (1984) have summarized the stratigraphical evidence for continental extension and separation at about 550 to 600 Ma in the southern Canadian Cordillera. Coarse arkosic and feldspathic sandstone, pebble conglomerate, and scattered occurrences of mafic volcanics are present in western facies of the basal unit of the Lower Palaeozoic sequence.

In parts of the southern Canadian Rocky Mountains, the Windermere Supergroup is truncated by Lower Palaeozoic quartzite (Aitken 1969). In the same region, graded-stratified conglomerate and massive pebbly sandstone turbidite, high in the Windermere Supergroup, are analogous to feeder canyon deposits cut into a continental slope (Hein & Arnott 1983; Arnott 1984), hinting at a nearby source. The contact between Windermere and Lower Palaeozoic assemblages is paraconformable or gradational in most parts of the Canadian Cordillera. In all, stratigraphical and structural evidence for extension and separation at this time is far from complete.

The best evidence for a 550 Ma separation comes from the subsidence analysis of Middle Cambrian through Lower Ordovician strata by Bond & Kominz (1984). The form of the tectonic subsidence curves fits that calculated for thermal subsidence of an instantaneously rifted continental margin (McKenzie 1978). Projecting the tectonic subsidence curves backward to time zero indicates a time of separation between 550 and 600 Ma.

Bond & Kominz's (1984) estimate for time of separation along the southern Canadian Cordilleran margin is supported by their global analysis (Bond *et al.* 1984) of subsidence characteristics for late Proterozoic and early Cambrian passive margins. Separation and thermal subsidence apparently occurred between 625 and 555 Ma along nearly 18,000 km of passive margins.

Discussion

If the North American proto-Pacific margin was initiated by 1500 Ma continental breakup, why did rifting recur, and why was the entire margin involved? Vink *et al.* (1984) point out that continental margins are presently rifted and segmented in preference to adjacent oceanic lithosphere. Thus spreading ridges penetrate continental crust as they propagate and where spreading is slow, ridges jump into nearby continental lithosphere. The continental margin is thus segmented and presumably attenuated. Once a strip of continental crust has been separated, thinned lithosphere beneath the newly modified continental margin can rethicken and subside isostatically and the stage is set for deposition of a new passive-margin sequence.

Would either process, rift propagation and/or ridge-jumping, have affected the entire 5000 + km of the North American proto-Pacific margin? Vink *et al.*'s (1984) examples support this possibility. Lomonosov Ridge and Baja

California are strips of continental crust less than 150 km wide and more than 1000 km long separated from the North American and Eurasian Plates respectively. In each case the responsible rift did not propagate along the oceanic–continental boundary but opted for a continental pathway just within continental lithosphere. Similarly, ridge-jumps separated the Seychelles continental fragment from the Indian Plate, and the Rockall continental fragment from Greenland. In each example, 1000 or more km of the continental margin are affected. Presumably a rift will propagate so long as continental margin is available, in the case of the North American-proto Pacific, 5000 km.

Breakup ages determined from tectonic subsidence curves (Bond *et al.* 1984), palaeomagnetic data (Piper 1983) and early Cambrian faunal endemism (Kirschvink 1984) suggest segmentation of a super-continent between 555 and 625 Ma. Interestingly, the proto-Pacific margin of North America is unattached in the speculative reconstruction of continents prior to 560 Ma (fig. 4 cf. Bond *et al.* 1984, based on data from Smith *et al.* 1981). In other words, it already displayed rift and drift symptoms as though it had been created by an earlier continental separation.

Poor age control on late Proterozoic deposits in the Cordillera led Bond *et al.* (1984) to downplay the 750–800 Ma extension event in favour of a 70 Ma rift interval preceding 555–625 Ma continental breakup. The best stratigraphical and structural evidence for extension exposed in the northern Canadian part of the Cordillera is about 780 Ma, however. Rather than opt for one age determination or the other, I suggest that the North American margin was affected by both stretching events, separated by about 100 to 150 Ma of passive-margin sedimentation (Windermere Supergroup, second passive-margin sequence).

Influence of rift geometry on Mesozoic fold and thrust trends

The Harper and Hardluck Faults were reactivated as contraction faults in the Mesozoic (fig. 3; Young 1982). Mesozoic folds and thrusts run parallel to them, suggesting that the right-angle bend in the fold and thrust belt is inherited.

The abrupt northward bend of the continental margin is also reflected in the distribution of Lower Palaeozoic carbonate and shale facies (Clough & Blodgett 1984). The change from shallow-water carbonates in the NE to deeper water shale in the SW follows the late Proterozoic extension features.

The influence of palaeogeography and early structure on fold- and thrust-belt trend was demonstrated for the arc of the Mackenzie Mountains (Aitken & Long 1978), structural divergence along the northern Rocky Mountains (Thompson, in press), the curvilinear trend of the Kootenay Arc in the southern Rocky Mountains (Price 1981), and the abrupt bend in the foothills and Lewis thrust at Crowsnest Pass in the southern Rocky Mountains (McMechan 1981; Norris 1968).

Conclusion

The Cordilleran miogeocline includes at least four overlapping passive-margin sequences.

Each was initiated by a thermal event associated with crustal extension. One of these, at about 780 Ma, is well exposed in the Ogilvie Mountains where it can be accurately dated. A 550 to 600 Ma extension event is less well documented.

The 780 Ma event may have produced the right-angle bend in the continental margin that is now emphasized by folds and thrusts in the western Ogilvie Mountains.

ACKNOWLEDGMENTS: This paper summarizes some results from an ongoing field mapping programme in west central Yukon Territory by the Geological Survey of Canada. We would like to thank Jim Aitken, Margot McMechan and Dirk Templeman-Kluit who suggested improvements to an earlier version of the manuscript.

References

ABBOTT, J.G. 1982. Structure and stratigraphy of the MacMillan fold belt: Evidence for Devonian faulting, *Department of Indian and Northern Affairs, Open File, May 1982.*

AITKEN, J.D. 1969. Documentation of the Sub-Cambrian unconformity, Rocky Mountains Main Ranges, Alberta. *Can. J. Earth Sci.* **6**, 193–200.

—— 1982. Precambrian of the Mackenzie Fold Belt— a stratigraphic and tectonic overview. *In*: HUTCHINSON, R.W., SPENCE, C.D. & FRANKLIN, J.M. (eds) *Precambrian Sulphide Deposits*, **25**, 150–61.

—— & LONG, D.G.F. 1978. MacKenzie tectonic arc – Reflection of early basin configuration? *Geology*, **6**, 626–9.

ARMSTRONG, R.L., EISBACHER, G.H. & EVANS, D. 1982. Age and stratigraphic-tectonic significance of Proterozoic diabase sheets, MacKenzie Mountains, northwestern Canada. *Can J. Earth Sci.* **19**, 316–23.

ARNOTT, R.W.C. 1984. Proximal channel deposits of the Hadrynian Hector Formation, Lake Louise, Alberta. Unpubl. MSc Thesis, Univ. Alberta, 149 pp.

BAADSGAARD, H. & MUELLER, A. 1973. K–Ar and Rb–Sr Ages of Intrusive Precambrian Mafic Rocks, Southern Beartooth Mountains, Montana and Wyoming. *Bull. geol. Soc. Am.* **84**, 365–3644.

BOND, C. & KOMINZ, A. 1984. Construction of tectonic subsidence curves for the early Palaeozoic miogeocline, southern Canadian Rocky Mountains: Implications for subsidence mechanisms, age of breakup and crustal thinning. *Bull. geol. Soc. Am.* **95**, 155–73.

—— , NICKESON, A. & KOMINZ, A. 1984. Breakup of a supercontinent between 625 Ma and 555 Ma: new evidence and implications for continental histories. *Earth planet. Sci. Lett.* **70**, 325–45.

BRABB, E.E. & CHURKIN, M. JR. 1965. Preliminary geologic map of the Eagle D-1 quadrangle, east-central Alaska. *U.S. Geol. Surv., Open-File Rep.* 249.

BURCHFIEL, B.C. & DAVIS, A. 1975. Nature and controls of Cordilleran orogenesis western United States: Extensions of an earlier synthesis. *Am. J. Sci.* **275-A**, 363–96.

BURKE, K. & DEWEY, J.F. 1973. Plume-generated triple junctions: Key indicators in applying plate tectonics to old rocks. *J. Geol.* **81**, 406–33.

CLOUGH, G. & BLODGETT, R.B. 1984. Lower Devonian basin to shelf carbonates in outcrop from the western Ogilvie Mountains, Alaska and Yukon Territory. *In*: *Carbonate In Subsurface and Outcrop*, pp. 57–81. 1984 C.S.P.G. Core Conference, Canadian Society of Petroleum Geologists.

DELANEY, G.D. 1981. The mid-Proterozoic Wernecke Supergroup, Wernecke Mountains, Yukon Territory. *In*: CAMPBELL, F.H.A. (ed.) *Proterozoic Basins of Canada, Geol. Surv. Can. Pap.* **81–10**, 1–24.

EISBACHER, G.H. 1981. Sedimentary tectonics and glacial record in the Windermere supergroup, Mackenzie Mountains, Northwestern Canada. *Geol. Surv. Can Pap.* **80–27**, pp. 40.

ELSTON, P. 1984. Magnetostratigraphy of the Belt Supergroup. A synopsis. *In*: WARREN HOBBS, S. (ed.) *The Belt, Montana Bureau of Mines Special Publication 90, Abstr. with Summaries*, pp. 88–90.

EVENCHICK, A., PARRISH, R. & GABRIELSE, H. 1984. Precambrian gneiss and late Proterozoic sedimentation in north-central British Columbia. *Geology*, **12**, 233–7.

GABRIELSE, H. 1972. Younger Precambrian of the Canadian Cordillera. *Am. J. Sci.* **272**, 521–36.

—— 1976. Environments of Canadian Cordillera depositional basins. *Am. Assoc. Pet. Geol. Mem.* **25**, 492–502.

—— & TAYLOR, G.C. 1983. Geological maps and cross-sections of the Cordillera from near Fort Nelson, British Columbia to Gravina Island, southeastern Alaska. *Geol. Surv. Can. Open File No. 864.*

GREEN, L.H. 1972. Geology of Nash Creek, Larsen Creek and Dawson map-areas, Yukon Territory. *Geol. Surv. Can.* **364**, 157.

HARRISON, J.E. 1972. Precambrian Belt basin of northwestern United States: Its geometry, sedimentation and copper occurrences. *Bull. geol. Soc. Am.* **83**, 1215–40.

HARRISON, J.E. & REYNOLDS, M.W. 1976. Western U.S. continental margin: A stable platform dominated by vertical tectonics in the late Precambrian. *Abstr. with Programs geol. Soc. Am.* **8**, 905.

HEIN, J. & ARNOTT, R. 1983. Precambrian Miette conglomerates, Lower Cambrian Gog Quartzites and modern braided outwash deposits, Kicking Horse Pass area. *Can. Soc. Pet. Geol. Field Trip Guidebook.*

HOFFMAN, P.F. 1983. Three stage subsidence of the 1.9 GA Coronation Margin. *Abstr. with Programs geol. Assoc. Can.* **8**, A33.

HOY, T. 1984. The Purcell Supergroup near the Rocky Mountain Trench, southeastern British Columbia. *In*: WARREN HOBBS, S. (ed.) *The Belt, Mont. Bur. Min. Geol. Spec. Publ.* **90**, 36–8.

JARVIS, G.T. & MCKENZIE, P. 1980. Sedimentary basin formation with finite extension rates. *Earth planet. Sci. Lett.* **48**, 42–52.

KIRSCHVINK, A., ROZANOV, Y., BARR, T.D. & ZHURAVLEV, A. 1984. The destruction of paleo Pangea (?) in the Early Cambrian. *Abstr. Int. geol. Cong. Moscow.*

LIS, M.G. & PRICE, R.A. 1976. Large-scale block faulting during deposition of the Windermere Supergroup (Hadrynian) in southeastern British Columbia. *Geol. Surv. Can. Pap.* **76-1A**, 135–6.

MCKENZIE, D. 1978. Some remarks on the development of sedimentary basins. *Earth planet. Sci. Lett.* **40**, 25–32.

MCMECHAN, M.E. 1981. The Middle Proterozoic Purcell Supergroup in the southwestern Rocky and southeastern Purcell Mountains, British Columbia and the initiation of the Cordilleran miogeocline, southern Canada and adjacent United States, *Bull. Can. Pet. Geol.* **29**, 583–621.

—— & PRICE, R.A. 1982. Superimposed low-grade metamorphism in the Mount Fisher area, southeastern British Columbia—implications for the East Kootenay Orogeny, *Can. J. Earth Sci.* **19**, 476–89.

—— & THOMPSON, R.I. 1985. Geology of the Southeastern Quadrant of Monkman Pass Map Area (93I). *Geol. Surv. Can. Open-file Rep. No. 1150.*

MILLER, F.K., MCKEE, E.H. & YATES, R.G. 1973. Age and correlation of the Windermere Group in northeastern Washington. *Bull. geol. Soc. Am.* **84**, 3723–30.

MITCHELL, W.R. 1984. Tectonic setting and development of the Belt Basin, northwestern United States. *In*: WARREN HOBBS, S. (ed.) *The Belt, Mont. Bur. Min. Geol. Spec. Publ.* **90**, 44–6.

PRICE, R.A. 1964. The Precambrian Purcell System in the Rocky Mountains of southern Alberta and British Columbia. *Bull. Can. Pet. Geol.* **12**, 399–426.

—— , 1981. The Cordilleran foreland thrust and fold belt in the southern Canadian Rocky Mountains. *In*: PRICE, N.J. & MCCLAY, K.R. (eds) *Thrust and Nappe Tectonics*, Spec. Publ. geol. Soc. London, **9**, 427–48.

OBRADOVICH, J.D. & PETERMAN, Z.E. 1968. Geochronology of the Belt Supergroup, Montana. *Can. J. Earth. Sci.* **5**, 737–47.

——, ZARTMAN, R.E. & PETERMAN, Z.E. 1984. Update of the geochronology of the Belt Supergroup. *In*: WARREN HOBBS, S. (ed.) *The Belt, Mont. Bur. Min. Geol. Spec. Publ.* **90**, 82–4.

PIPER, J.D.A. 1983. Proterozoic palaeomagnetism and single continent plate tectonics. *Geophys. J. R. astron. Soc.* **74**, 163–97.

ROOTS, C.F. 1982. Ogilvie Mountains project, Yukon; part B: Volcanic rocks in north-central Dawson map-area. *Geol. Surv. Can. Pap.* **82-1A**, 411–4.

—— 1983. Mount Harper complex, Yukon: Early Palaeozoic volcanism at the margin of the Mackenzie platform. *Geol. Surv. Can. Pap.* **83-1A**, 423–7.

—— & MOORE, M. JR. 1983. Proterozoic and early Palaeozoic volcanism in the Ogilvie Mountains: An example from Mount Harper, west-central Yukon. *In*: *Yukon Exploration and Geology, 1982*, pp. 55–62. Exploration and Geological Services Northern Affairs Program, Indian and Northern Affairs Canada.

RUELL, J.C.L. 1982. Depositional environments and genesis of stratiform copper deposits of the Redstone Copper Belt, Mackenzie Mountains, N.W.T. *In*: HUTCHINSON, R.W., SPENCE, C.D. & FRANKLIN, J.M. (eds) *Precambrian Sulphide Deposits, H.S. Robinson Memorial Volume*, Geol. Assoc. Can. Spec. Pap. **25**, 701–37.

RUST, B.R. 1979. Facies Models 2. Coarse Alluvial Deposits. *In*: WAKER, R.G. (ed.) *Facies Models, Geoscience, Canada Reprint Series 1*, pp. 9–21.

SEARS, J.W. & PRICE, R.A. 1978. The Siberian connection: A case for Precambrian separation of the North American and Siberian cratons. *Geology*, **6**, 267–70.

SMITH, A.G., HURLEY, A.M. & BRIDEN, J.C. 1981. Phanerozoic Paleocontinental World Maps, pp. 102. Cambridge University Press.

STEWART, J.H. 1972. Initial deposits in the Cordilleran geosyncline: Evidence of a late Precambrian (less than 850 m.y.) continental separation. *Bull. geol. Soc. Am.* **83**, 1345–60.

—— 1976. Late Precambrian evolution of North America: Plate tectonics implication. *Geology*, **4**, 11–15.

THOMPSON, R.I. 1984. Late Proterozoic extension and its influence on Mesozoic deformation, western

Ogilvie Mountains, Yukon. *Abstr. with Programs Can. Soc. Pet. Geol.*

—— In press. Stratigraphy, Structural analysis, and tectonic evolution of the Halfway River map area (94B), northern Rocky Mountains, British Columbia. *Geol. Surv. Can. Mem.*

—— & EISBACHER, G.H. 1984. Late Proterozoic rift assemblages, northern Canadian Cordillera. *Abstr. with Programs geol. Soc. Am.* **116**, 336.

—— & ROOTS, C.F. 1982. Ogilvie Mountains project, Yukon; part A: A new regional mapping program. *Geol. Surv. Can. Pap.* **82-1A**, 403–11.

VINK, G.E., MORGAN, W.J. & ZHAO, W.-L. 1984. Preferential Rifting of Continents: A Source of Displaced Terranes. *J. geophys. Res.* **89**, 10,072–6.

WRIGHT, L.A., TROXEL, B.W., WILLIAMS, E.G., ROBERTS, M.T. & DIEHL, P.E. 1976. Precambrian sedimentary environments of the Death Valley region eastern California. *In*: TROXEL, B.W. & WRIGHT, L.A. (eds) *Geological features Death Valley, California, Calif. Div. Mines Geol. Spec. Rep.* **106**, 7–15.

YOUNG, G.M. 1982. The late Proterozoic Tindir Group, east-central Alaska: Evolution of a continental margin. *Bull. geol. Soc. Am.* **93**, 759–83.

—— , JEFFERSON, C.W., DELANEY, G.D. & YEO, G.M. 1979. Middle and late Proterozoic evolution of the northern Canadian Cordillera and Shield. *Geology*, **7**, 125–8.

BOB THOMPSON, Geological Survey of Canada, Vancouver, British Columbia, Canada V6B 1R8.
ERIC MERCIER, L'Université des Sciences et Technique de Lille, France.
CHARLIE ROOTS, Carleton University, Ottawa, Canada K1S 5B6.

Lithospheric extension on the Antarctic Peninsula during Cenozoic subduction

S.W. Garrett & B.C. Storey

SUMMARY: The magmatic arc of the Antarctic Peninsula displays a wide range of features related to extensional tectonics at a convergent margin. Cenozoic extensional features are concentrated in a linear belt on the western side of the peninsula. The West Coast Magnetic Anomaly (WCMA) indicates the presence of a composite batholith 90 km wide and 1 500 km long, part of which may have been emplaced during an initial splitting of the continental arc. Horst and graben structures subsequently developed in segments bounded by continental fracture zones reflecting those of the oceanic lithosphere. This suggests the influence of processes associated with the late stages of subduction. The arrival of segments of the ocean ridge at the trench may have resulted in the extension and uplift of the adjacent portion of the continental plate. The final set of these interactions began at about 7 Ma opposite the northern Antarctic Peninsula and coincided with the dramatic slowing of spreading at the surviving ocean ridge and the development of continental alkaline volcanism. Continued extension in response to the tendency of the subducted plate to continue sinking led to total failure of the continental lithosphere and the opening of Bransfield Strait, a marginal basin floored by oceanic crust.

The Antarctic Peninsula (Fig. 1) is a narrow strip of continental crust flanked by the oceanic crust of the Drake Passage (Barker & Burrell 1977), South Pacific Ocean (Herron & Tucholke 1976; Cande et al. 1982), the Scotia Sea (Barker & Hill 1981) and the Weddell Sea (Barker & Jahn 1980; LaBreque & Barker 1981). The formation of much of the exposed continental crust of the peninsula was associated with the subduction of proto-Pacific Ocean lithosphere from at least the Triassic onwards. Accretionary and magmatic processes during the Mesozoic and Cenozoic both thickened and widened the crust against a fragment of ancient crystalline basement now located beneath the E coast (Storey & Garrett 1985). The limited lateral extent of the continental plate may have allowed a sensitive response to variations in both the spreading and subduction rates of the surrounding oceanic plates.

For much of the Mesozoic the Antarctic Peninsula lay within a broad region of extensional tectonism associated with the breakup of Gondwanaland (Dalziel et al., this volume). In the Southern Andes and South Georgia a marginal basin opened which was floored by oceanic crust. In the peninsula, which was probably geographically continuous with the Southern Andes and South Georgia during this time, evidence of extension is limited to a series of fault-controlled sedimentary basins along the eastern (back-arc) margin (Farquharson et al. 1984). This extension on the peninsula may be related to marginal basin development or may be due to the formation of half-grabens along the western margin of the Weddell Sea. Swarms of andesitic, basaltic and amphibolitic dykes are also common within the arc but radiometric dates are too few to constrain the periods of intra-arc extension they represent.

The W coast of the Antarctic Peninsula displays a set of extensional features of probable Cenozoic age (Storey & Garrett 1985). Magnetic anomalies indicate the presence of a linear batholith which follows the arcuate trend of the peninsula in western Palmer Land and offshore of Graham Land (Renner et al. 1982, 1985). This batholith may contain gabbroic plutons intruded during crustal extension. A series of horsts and grabens delineated by block faults are present both above and to the W of the magnetic batholith. The most spectacular representative of these structures is the linear graben of George VI Sound (King 1964; Bell 1975; Edwards 1979; Crabtree et al. 1985). Similar features may be present elsewhere between the mainland and the western archipelagoes and have been detected on the margins of Bransfield Strait, an extensional marginal basin floored by oceanic crust (Ashcroft 1972). Alkaline volcanic rocks are present on Alexander Island and in the northern Antarctic Peninsula (Saunders & Tarney 1982). A combination of all these features is found within and adjacent to Bransfield Strait flanking the narrow strip of young oceanic crust.

The suite of extensional structures present along the W coast of the peninsula is regarded as illustrating various stages of development of a marginal basin during the Cenozoic. The Cenozoic subduction history of the Antarctic Peninsula is well documented (Barker 1982)

From COWARD, M.P., DEWEY, J.F. & HANCOCK, P.L. (eds), 1987, *Continental Extensional Tectonics*, Geological Society Special Publication No. 28, pp. 419–431.

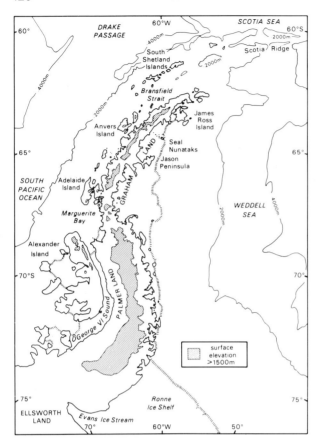

FIG. 1. The Antarctic Peninsula; location map and surface elevation.

and continental extension during this era is more clearly understood than that during the Mesozoic. We therefore confine ourselves to a description of Cenozoic continental extension and a discussion of its relationship with the subduction of oceanic lithosphere.

Regional gravity, aeromagnetic, geological and topographic data are used to constrain a new series of crustal cross-sections illustrating extensional features. Aeromagnetic and gravity anomaly maps are presented by Renner *et al.* (1985). We have selected linear anomalies from these data for interpretation using two-dimensional methods. Firstly, magnetic profiles were filtered by Werner-based deconvolution to provide estimates of depth to magnetic sources (Hartman *et al.* 1971), whilst gravity anomalies were inverted using the method of Bott (1960). These initial models were refined using polygonal techniques for both gravity and magnetic data (Talwani *et al.* 1959; Talwani 1965), combined in a computer program described by Lee (1979).

Initial stages of intra-arc extension: the West Coast Magnetic Anomaly and mafic magmatism

The regional magnetic field over the Antarctic Peninsula (Fig. 2) is dominated by the West Coast Magnetic Anomaly (WCMA) recognized by Renner *et al.* (1982). The most significant attributes of this feature, visible on the aeromagnetic anomaly map (Renner *et al.* 1985), are its linear and positive nature and the high magnetic gradients along its margins. Profile data often reveal a considerable degree of internal complexity (Fig. 3) but despite this the WCMA may be divided into two main components. A narrow western component (area 1 in Fig. 2) becomes progressively separated northwards along the length of the peninsula from a broader eastern component (area 2 in Fig. 2). The two components are adjacent over western Palmer Land, become divided over the

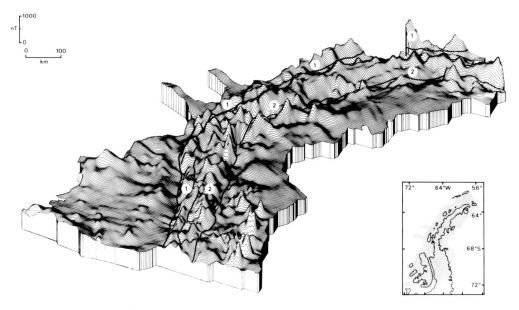

FIG. 2. Isometric view of the residual magnetic field over the Antarctic Peninsula. Area 1: western component of the West Coast Magnetic Anomaly (WCMA). Area 2: eastern component of the WCMA.

archipelago to the W of Graham Land and ultimately flank Bransfield Strait (Fig. 3). Renner *et al.* (1985) only considered the eastern component of the WCMA offshore of northern Graham Land and concluded that the WCMA narrowed northwards. A careful comparison of profiles has subsequently confirmed the identity and continuity of the western component (Fig. 3) and we conclude that the WCMA becomes wider to the N with the separation of the two components.

The bodies causing the WCMA have been successfully modelled with a near-vertical magnetization (Fig. 3) approximating that of the Earth's present field direction. Values of intensity of magnetization of up to 3 A m^{-1} have been used, although it was necessary to introduce higher values for the northern parts of the western body. Longshaw & Griffiths (1983) reported high inclinations for the remanent field of some Jurassic rocks from the Antarctic Peninsula, and so the high field inclination used in modelling of the WCMA does not assist in determining the age of the causative body. If the remanent component of the WCMA body is large, however, the positive polarity of the anomaly does imply that the source bodies were intruded during discrete time intervals when the field occupied a normal orientation. Thus the body causing the WCMA probably did not continuously develop throughout the long history of the arc. The depths to the top of

the modelled bodies were constrained by depth-to-magnetic-source solutions of between 4 and 6 km below sea-level for the western component and around 2 km for the eastern component. The shallowest modelled bodies are in western Palmer Land, but the causative body may also lie close to outcrop offshore of Graham Land.

The WCMA is restricted to the western half of Palmer Land and offshore of Graham Land. The remainder of the Mesozoic–Cenozoic magmatic arc in eastern Palmer Land, Alexander Island and Graham Land shows magnetic anomalies of limited lateral extent indicating individual, unconnected mafic plutons (Ashley 1962; Allen 1966; Crawford *et al.* 1986). These represent the development of mafic plutons throughout the history of the arc. By contrast the linear and continuous nature of the WCMA suggests a composite linear batholith (Renner *et al.* 1982) representing an unusual development within the arc. A positive gravity anomaly associated with the WCMA (Renner *et al.* 1985) indicates that the magnetic batholith is mafic in composition. The WCMA flanks major rifts such as Bransfield Strait and George VI Sound. Storey & Garrett (1985) suggested that the upwelling of mafic magma during crustal extension through the early stages of rift formation might have given rise to parts of the batholith.

The WCMA may be reflected in the outcrop geology in areas where the modelled bodies and

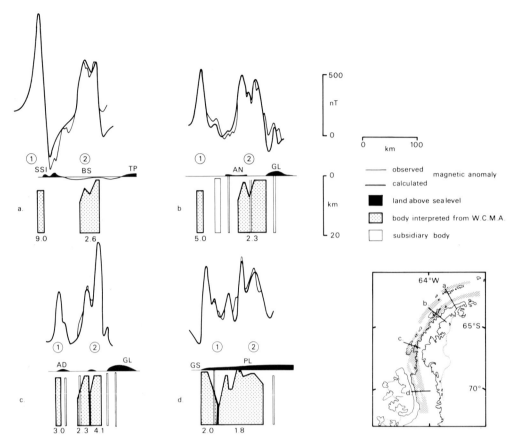

FIG. 3. Interpreted profiles across the West Coast Magnetic Anomaly (WCMA). Inset shows position of profiles in relation to the WCMA (stippled). Eastern and western components are labelled as in Fig. 2. Intensity
of magnetization of modelled bodies given in A m^{-1}. SSI = South Shetland Islands; BS = Bransfield Strait;
TP = Trinity Peninsula; AN = Anvers Island; GL = Graham Land; AD = Adelaide Island; GS = George VI
Sound; PL = Palmer Land. Profile 3d at same latitude as section in Fig. 4.

depth-to-source solutions are shallow. In
western Palmer Land the western component of
the WCMA correlates with gabbroic plutons
which apparently post-date the main calc-
alkaline batholith (S.M. Harrison, pers.
comm.). Elsewhere there is no clear indication
that the WCMA is associated with distinctive
lithologies. Investigation of mafic rocks in
southern Graham land by A.B. Moyes has
shown that rocks on the W coast are richer in
magnetite than those on the E coast but otherwise are petrographically similar. Some of the
mafic rocks on the W coast, however, have rare-
earth element patterns similar to gabbroic rocks
associated with the Mesozoic marginal basin in
South Georgia. This suggests that there may be a
petrogenetic distinction between arc-related
mafic magmatism and that associated with intra-

arc extension. At present we visualize the source
of the WCMA as being a composite mafic batholith rich in magnetite and a diagnostic rare-earth
element pattern but otherwise petrologically indistinguishable from other calc-alkaline mafic
magmas.

Radiometric dating of plutonic rocks (Rex
1976; Pankhurst 1982a) shows that before 160 Ma
the magmatic arc was restricted to the E coast of
the peninsula, whereas in the last 60 Ma the arc
has been restricted to the W coast. In the intervening 100 My plutonism was common across the
width of the peninsula. Given the coincidence of
the WCMA with the area of Tertiary plutonism,
its close association with late-stage rifting structures and a preliminary assessment of field
relations in north-west Palmer Land, we tentatively assign a Tertiary age to the body causing the

WCMA. If the continental lithosphere was placed under tension at this time it would probably have failed preferentially at a line of weakness such as the western edge of the Mesozoic arc. This corresponds to the arc splitting phase of Karig (1971). Early-Tertiary major crustal extension would have resulted in the intrusion of a linear batholith containing the available mafic magma from the arc. Such intra-arc extension may be reflected in outcrop by the block faults controlling the intrusion of mafic material in the vicinity of Anvers Island (Hooper 1962) where many plutons have been dated as Tertiary in age (Rex 1976). Continued extension may be represented by the 'post-Andean' mafic dykes found throughout the peninsula (e.g. Dewar 1970).

Block faulting and graben formation

Many authors (e.g. Adie 1964) have noted evidence for a pervasive late-Tertiary block faulting and uplift event that might be largely responsible for the present physiography of the Antarctic Peninsula (Curtis 1966). Several of the faults are illustrated on the regional geological maps (British Antarctic Survey 1979, 1981a, 1981b, 1982). Satellite imagery displays several additional lineaments thought to represent crustal fractures (Fig. 6) and radio-echo sounding of the ice sheet confirms that many of these features are underlain by major sub-glacial troughs (Crabtree 1981). Where geological control exists these lineaments correspond to normal faults or shear zones cutting rocks of the Mesozoic–Cenozoic arc (e.g. Matthews 1983a).

The dominant feature of physiography on the Antarctic Peninsula is the mainland plateau (Fig. 1). It averages 30–100 km wide, reaches a maximum elevation of 2652 m and is continuous for 1800 km, although it is dissected at several latitudes by major transverse fractures. Detailed mapping of the geology of southern Graham Land confirms that the plateau is a horst (Moyes & Hamer 1984) rather than a simple erosional feature (Linton 1964). The horst occupies the majority of central Graham Land, but radio-echo sounding reveals that it only forms the eastern half of Palmer Land (Crabtree *et al.* 1985). A negative Bouguer anomaly of −1000 gu over the Palmer Land plateau reflects significant crustal thickening to compensate for the elevated terrain (Renner *et al.* 1985).

A belt of grabens and associated faults is found along the length of the peninsula to the W of the plateau horst. Bransfield Strait is a marginal basin formed within a graben bounded by the S Shetland Islands where large normal faults show a substantial late-Pliocene displacement (Barton 1965). Deep channels and faults in the vicinity of Anvers Island suggest that grabens may be present between the island and the mainland. Marguerite Bay is probably a graben with adjacent islands showing normal faulting along its margins (British Antarctic Survey 1981b; Matthews 1983a,b). The clearest graben is that of George VI Sound between Alexander Island and Palmer Land. Evidence for normal faulting within and adjacent to the sound has been summarized by Crabtree *et al.* (1985). Bouguer anomalies adjacent to northern George VI Sound indicate that the crust beneath the graben may be 5 km thinner than that beneath Palmer Land and Alexander Island (Renner *et al.* 1985) (Fig. 4). This may have resulted from local crustal stretching and attenuation. The pattern of block faulting and crustal thinning seems less apparent in southern George VI Sound.

Two linear, positive gravity anomalies run parallel to George VI Sound on Alexander Island (Butler 1975) and Palmer Land (Butler & McArthur 1983). They have a similar wavelength and lateral extent suggesting a common tectonic origin probably related to Cenozoic block faulting. The Bouguer anomaly over western Palmer Land corresponds to the western component of the WCMA (Renner *et al.* 1985) and has been modelled successfully using the body shape derived during magnetic modelling at this latitude (Figs 3 & 4). A density contrast of 0.2 Mg m^{-3} was used, based on measurements of rock densities by Butler & McArthur (1983). The eastern component of the WCMA was also incorporated into the gravity model and arbitrarily assigned a density contrast of 0.1 Mg m^{-3}. The Bouguer anomaly over central Alexander Island corresponds to the outcrop of the Lully Foothills Formation (Burn 1984) and was successfully modelled using a contrast of 0.3 Mg m^{-3} based on rock densities measured by L.J.S. Sturgeon (Fig. 4).

The models derived from the gravity anomalies give an indication of the amplitude of Cenozoic block faults. A minimum throw of 4 km is suggested for the faults on Alexander Island, and a value up to 10 km is proposed for the eastern edge of the western component of the WCMA in Palmer Land. These faults are all marked by deep sub-glacial troughs which elsewhere obscure the characteristics of other Cenozoic fractures. We suggest that the predominant extension direction was perpendicular to the oceanic trench but few indications of the

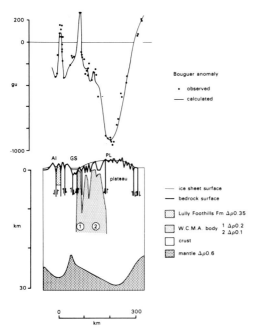

FIG. 4. Interpreted gravity profile between Palmer
Land and Alexander Island at latitude 71°S.
WCMA body shape as derived in Fig. 3d. Density
contrasts in Mg m^{-3}. AI = Alexander Island;
GS = George VI Sound; PL = Palmer Land.

fault kinematics can be found. A southward
regional tilting is observable in Alexander Island
(Bell 1975) but no systematic regional tilting
strikes parallel to the faults.

Many of the crustal fractures follow the trend
of earlier structural features. The western edge
of the plateau horst corresponds to the eastern
edge of the WCMA in Palmer Land and Graham
Land (Fig. 3). The presence of a dense mafic
batholith beneath the WCMA appears to have led
to subsidence relative to the plateau horst when
the crust was placed under tension. This caused
the formation of channels between the western
archipelago and Graham Land. Crustal fractures
appear to have formed along the edges of the
batholith, for example the eastern coastline of
George VI Sound, the western coast of Adelaide
Island and the southeastern limit of ocean crust in
Bransfield Strait.

The separation of the two components of the
WCMA may be a primary feature or reflect
crustal extension within the batholith after intrusion. The two components show the greatest
divergence across Bransfield Strait where they are
about 50 km further apart than in western Palmer
Land (Fig. 3). Thirty-two km of this separation
may be attributed to the semi-oceanic crust

(Ashcroft 1972) whilst the remaining 20 km may
be attributed to ensialic block faulting. The two
components also became separated by as much as
30 km to the W of Anvers Island. There is no
evidence at present for offshore basins at this
latitude but fracturing and alkaline volcanics are
well represented onshore. Further S, the two
components of the WCMA are separated by the
mountains of Adelaide Island where there is
evidence of block faulting (Dewar 1970). In
Palmer Land the two components are separated
by a major fracture system but extension was
accommodated by structures to the W, beneath
George VI Sound and in Alexander Island.

Alkaline basaltic volcanism

During the later part of the Cenozoic there was a
marked change in the type of volcanic activity
throughout the Antarctic Peninsula. The calc-
alkaline activity of the Mesozoic and early Tertiary was replaced by more alkaline volcanism (7
Ma–Recent) which has previously been related to
an extensional regime (Baker *et al.* 1977;
Saunders & Tarney 1982). Exposures of alkali
volcanic rocks occur mainly N of a line between
Anvers Island and Jason Peninsula (Fig. 1). To
the E of the plateau, eroded basalt and palagonite
breccia cones (Saunders 1982; Gonzalez-Ferran
1983) may still be active. Massive olivine tholeiites
and hawaiites of Cenozoic age (Baker 1972) occur
as the James Ross Island Volcanic Group (Nelson
1966). To the W of the plateau, alkaline and
olivine basalts occur on the S Shetland Islands
(less than 2 Ma, Pankhurst & Smellie 1983), on
other islands of the Bransfield Strait (Bell 1984)
and adjacent to the Gerlache Strait (Hooper 1962;
Gonzalez-Ferran & Katsui 1970).

Pankhurst (1982b) has shown that the volcanic
rocks of the E coast indicate small degrees of
melting of a deep garnet-peridotite mantle source
more typical of extensional tectonics away from
convergent plate boundaries. Alkali volcanism
on the W coast was located closer to the trench
and to the complex volcanism (Weaver *et al.*
1979) associated with the Bransfield Strait
marginal basin. The close relationship in space
and time of the eastern and western alkaline
volcanism and the Bransfield Strait volcanism
suggests that they may reflect coincident activity
in the asthenospheric mantle. The volcanic rocks
adjacent to the Bransfield Strait are influenced by
a complex source region and passage to the
surface via a fracture system associated with a
total extensional failure of the continental
lithosphere. There is no distinctive magnetic
anomaly associated with the western volcanic

rocks as anomalies may be masked by the WCMA. The E coast alkali volcanic rocks give large magnetic anomalies of high frequency indicating shallow sources of limited extent (Fig. 5), and have possibly risen to the surface by means of fracture systems that resulted from a limited brittle failure of the lithosphere, best illustrated by the linear alignment of Seal Nunataks (Gonzalez-Ferran 1983).

In the Alexander Island area, late Cenozoic (3.9±0.4 to 7.5±0.4 Ma, R.J. Pankhurst, pers. comm.) alkali volcanic rocks and hyaloclastites are closely related to major fracture systems (Bell 1973; Care 1980; Burn & Thomson 1981). They lie on approximately NE–SW lines parallel to the trend of dykes cutting the exposures of volcanic rocks. Alkali basalts within the Merrick Mountains were tentatively dated at 6 Ma (Halpern 1971).

Alkaline volcanism is typically found in an intraplate setting and may represent a fundamental change of tectonic environment on the Antarctic Peninsula in the late Cenozoic. Although the alkaline volcanism within the peninsula has been broadly related to extensional tectonics, the amount of associated extension is believed to be limited as the volcanic rocks give shallow magnetic source solutions and are associated with localized fracture systems. The volcanism may be more strongly related to a high heat-flow regime following lithospheric stretching and attenuation.

Marginal basin formation: Bransfield Strait

The marginal basin of Bransfield Strait (Ashcroft 1972) is floored by semi-oceanic crust (Davey 1972) formed within the last 1.3 Ma (P.J. Roach pers. comm.). The axial and off-axis volcanic rocks, associated with this spreading, display a complex chemistry with features indicative both of island-arc and ocean-floor volcanism (Weaver *et al.* 1979). The major and trace element relationships imply much complexity in the source region and processes of magma generation. This may be expected in the initial stages of back-arc diapirism in an environment where island-arc magmatism had been taking place during the previous 100 My (Pankhurst & Smellie 1983). Fuller reviews of the geochemical and geodynamic processes involved in the formation of the marginal basin are given by Weaver *et al.* (1979), Saunders & Tarney (1982) and Barker & Dalziel (1983).

Bransfield Strait does not represent a unique, localized feature but rather the most fully

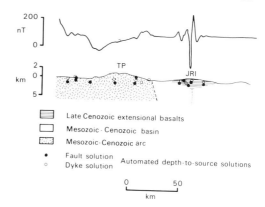

FIG. 5. Aeromagnetic profile across James Ross Island. Solutions for the depth to the top of dyke-like and fault-like bodies derived using the method of Hartman *et al.* (1971). TP = Trinity Peninsula; JRI = James Ross Island.

developed rift within the W coast extensional zone. The total failure of the continental lithosphere was preceded by intrusion in the WCMA body, major crustal extension and the development of continental alkaline volcanism. Adjacent parts of the continental alkali basalt field were still active during the opening of the Bransfield Strait.

Continental extension and Cenozoic subduction history

The Antarctic Peninsula as a broad tectonic entity is delimited to the N by the fragmentation of the southern Scotia Ridge (Fig. 1) and to the S by the abrupt topographic and geophysical discontinuity adjacent to the Evans Ice Stream (Behrendt 1964; Doake *et al.* 1983). The peninsula may be divided into four broad physiographic segments based upon the trend and nature of features developed during Cenozoic extension and uplift (Fig. 6). The northernmost segment contains the marginal basin of Bransfield Strait flanked by the two components of the WCMA, the S Shetland Islands and plateau horst of Trinity Peninsula. Structures within this segment strike at 060°. The next segment contains the Graham Land plateau horst and western archipelago including Anvers Island and Adelaide Island. There is evidence of fracturing and possible grabens coincident with the WCMA between the islands and mainland. Structures strike between 040° and 015°. The third segment contains the wider plateau horst of northern Palmer Land, bounded to the W by

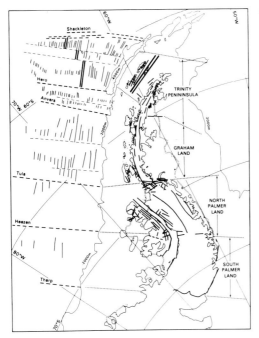

FIG. 6. Major crustal lineaments on the Antarctic Peninsula, as interpreted from satellite imagery and available geological and geophysical data. The continental segmentation is defined by development of Cenozoic extensional features. The simplified structure of the adjacent ocean floor is shown after Barker (1982) with identified magnetic anomalies and major fracture zones.

the WCMA. The graben of George VI Sound is flanked by major linear mountain ranges and other structures which are associated with block faulting on Alexander Island and strike at 170°. In the southernmost segment, topography on Alexander Island is more subdued and George VI Sound is wider. Structures strike at about 070°.

The simple segmentation defined by structure and physiography does not account for all along-strike variations in Cenozoic geology. In the- Graham Land segment alkaline volcanic rocks are present in the vicinity of Anvers Island and on Jason Peninsula but are not known near Adelaide Island, the WCMA bifurcates between the two islands, and the strike of the major fractures varies by 25°. This may be due to additional segmentation within Graham Land as suggested by Hawkes (1981). Otherwise the segmented development of Cenozoic extension and uplift adequately explains the crustal pattern. The segments are bounded by fracture zones which presumably accommodated the differ-

ences in stress between adjacent areas during extension. These continental fractures correspond to major fracture zones on the oceanic crust (Fig. 6). As the oceanic fractures may have existed for only about 30 My prior to the cessation of subduction, it seems likely that continental extension was related to processes operative during the closing stages of subduction.

The simple pattern of magnetic anomalies in the southeast Pacific Ocean (Herron & Tucholke 1976) indicates that the Cenozoic subduction history was dominated by the arrival of successive segments of the ocean ridge at the trench. The resulting ridge crest–trench collisions may have provided a suitable mechanism for the development of the extensional features. A thermal input to the overriding plate may have accompanied the arrival of the hot, young oceanic lithosphere at the trench leading to uplift (Barker 1982). Subduction probably terminated after this and a release of horizontal compressive stress in the overriding plate may have resulted in extension.

A second mechanism for continental extension may be associated with trench suction (Forsyth & Uyeda 1975). The last set of ridge crest–trench collisions had significant consequences for both the subducting and the overriding plates. Spreading at the adjacent ocean ridge opposite Anvers Island slowed dramatically (Fig. 7) in response to collision at 6.5 Ma, whilst opening of the Drake Passage effectively ceased (Barker & Burrell 1977). The inception of olivine-basaltic magmatism in the corresponding segment of the overriding plate dates from this time (Baker *et al.* 1977). Continued subduction of the oceanic plate resulted in collision at 4 Ma and in the virtual cessation of spreading at the ocean ridge before the remaining spreading centre reached the trench. This produced further extension of the continental plate in response to the tendency of the subducted plate to continue sinking (Barker 1982), and culminated in the total failure of the continental lithosphere and the formation of Bransfield Strait. We suggest a similar extensional response of the crust may have occurred during a rapid slowing of spreading at the ocean ridge during the early Tertiary (Fig. 7), with partial failure of the continental lithosphere and the intrusion of at least part of the magnetic batholith along the length of the peninsula. A major change in the regime of the overriding plate during the early Cenozoic is also suggested by a trenchward 'jump' of the magmatic arc at this time on to Alexander Island (Thomson *et al.* 1983). The change in plate motions may be associated with

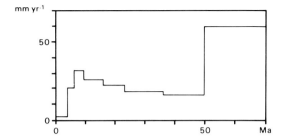

FIG. 7. Cenozoic half-spreading rates at the ocean ridge adjacent to the Antarctic Peninsula, after Barker (1982), Cande *et al.* (1982), and Herron & Tucholke (1976).

a major reorganization in the triple junction between Africa, Antarctica and South America around 60–65 Ma and consequently a major change in the movement path of Antarctica relative to Africa and South America (Lawver *et al.* 1985).

We have developed a simple model for a possible sequence of Cenozoic plate interactions using the time-scale of Barker (1982) for the cessation of subduction (Fig. 8). Corroborating evidence is provided by a date of 15 Ma from a camptonite dyke on Alexander Island (Rex 1970) consistent with the predicted age of crustal extension in this region. Although there was a marked cor-

respondence between the onset of the voluminous alkaline volcanism in the northern part of the peninsula and the rapid slowing of spreading on the neighbouring ocean ridge, alkali volcanism on Alexander Island and the southern part of the peninsula also date from this time. The cessation of activity at the adjacent ocean ridge may therefore have invoked a widespread thermal response in the asthenosphere beneath the peninsula and resulted in extrusion of alkali basalt outside the northern segment. As Cenozoic alkali basalts are widespread throughout the remainder of W Antarctica (e.g. LeMasurier & Rex 1982), however, the alkaline volcanism may be related to

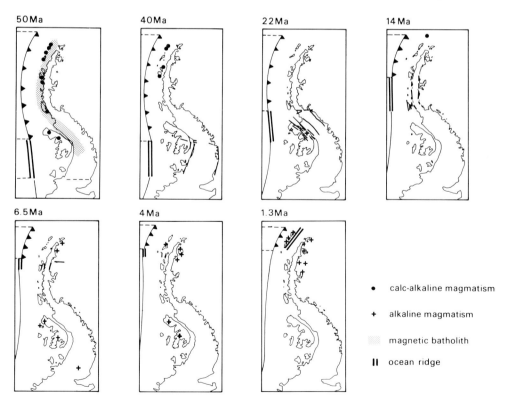

FIG. 8. A simplified model for the development of Cenozoic extensional features on the continental lithosphere during the cessation of subduction.

an even broader thermal regime independent of convergent margin tectonism.

Comparison with the Pacific margin of the American continents

The Cenozoic histories of arc development in the Antarctic Peninsula and Basin and Range Province of North America exhibit many similarities. The extension on the Antarctic Peninsula began as a result of a slowing of plate convergence rates with a westward relocation or narrowing of the locus of magmatic arc activity. Intra-arc or back-arc extension accompanied the intrusion of part of the magnetic batholith. The first well-documented intra-arc extension in the Basin and Range Province occurred at 37 Ma in response to a similar slowing of plate motions (Engebretson *et al.* 1984). Tilted strata and passively emplaced batholiths suggest extension by as much as 100% (Zoback *et al.* 1981) which accompanied a further reduction of convergence velocities. Between 22 and 18 Ma the North American arc narrowed sharply from a width of 600 to 200 km with the accompanying development of a back-arc spreading regime on the continental lithosphere. This westward relocation of arc activity took place after plate motion fell below 50 mm yr^{-1} (Engebretson *et al.* 1984). The major magnetic anomaly along the Great Valley (Zietz *et al.* 1969) and offshore British Columbia (Coles & Currie 1977) may also owe its origin to plate interactions similar to those proposed for the WCMA on the Antarctic Peninsula.

The symmetrical pattern of back-arc extension in the Basin and Range (Eaton 1984) developed during the closing stages of subduction (Scholtz *et al.* 1971) and was then replaced by an oblique extension (Zoback *et al.* 1981) related to the lateral passage of the North American and Pacific Plates after ridge crest–trench collision (Atwater 1970). Volcanism had changed from a calc-alkaline to bimodal type. There is evidence

that this continued extension in the Basin and Range Province resulted from the relocation of asthenospheric activity from beneath the East Pacific Rise to beneath the western Cordillera (Gough 1984). This may be similar to the relocation of mantle thermal activity from beneath the Aluk Ridge to beneath the Bransfield Strait and Antarctic Peninsula, resulting in the alkaline volcanism that continues to the present day.

In the Southern Andes the Cenozoic collision of the ridge crest with the trench (Herron *et al.* 1981) also led to the cessation of calc-alkaline magmatism and to the development of alkali volcanism in response to continental extension (Baker *et al.* 1981). Some small degree of oblique subduction may still occur (Barker & Dalziel 1983), however, and extensional features on the continental crust are obscured by a major transcurrent fault system (Winslow 1982).

The arrival of the oceanic ridge crest along the E Pacific margin during the Cenozoic was in general preceded or followed by the development of an extensional stress field within the continental plate. Possible mechanisms of continental extension include trench suction, mantle convection, thermal expansion and the release of compressive stress following ridge crest–trench collision. Continental extension during periods of a decreasing continent–ocean convergence rate forms a contrast to back-arc extension on oceanic lithosphere during periods of an increasing ocean–ocean convergence rate (Furlong *et al.* 1982) and compression in the overriding plate during periods of increasing continent–ocean convergence rates (Engebretson *et al.* 1984).

ACKNOWLEDGMENTS: We thank our many colleagues in the British Antarctic Survey who either participated in the geophysical field work or who took part in discussions of the data. J.A. Jones provided valuable assistance in implementing the depth to magnetic source computer program provided by A.P.R. Cooper (Scott Polar Research Institute).

References

ADIE, R.J. 1964. Geological history. *In*: PRIESTLEY, R.E., ADIE, R.J. & ROBIN, G. DE Q. (eds) *Antarctic Research*, pp. 118–62. Butterworth, London.

ALLEN, A. 1966. A magnetic survey of north-east Trinity Peninsula, Graham Land. *Sci. Rep. Br. Antarct. Surv.* **49**, 32 pp.

ASHCROFT, W.A. 1972. Crustal structure of the South Shetland Islands and Bransfield Strait. *Sci. Rep. Br. Antarct. Surv.* **66**, 43 pp.

ASHLEY, J. 1962. A magnetic survey of north-east Trinity Peninsula, Graham Land: I. Tabarin

Peninsula and Duse Bay. *Sci. Rep. Falkld. Isl. Depend. Surv.* **35**, 35 pp.

ATWATER, T. 1970. Implications of plate tectonics for the Cenozoic evolution of western North America. *Bull. geol. Soc. Am.* **81**, 3513–36.

BAKER, P.E. 1972. Recent volcanism and magmatic variation in the Scotia Arc. *In*: ADIE, R.J. (ed.) *Antarctic Geology and Geophysics*, pp. 857–60. Universitetsforlaget, Oslo.

—— , BUCKLEY, F. & REX, D.C. 1977. Cenozoic volcanism in the Antarctic. *Phil. Trans. R. Soc.*

London, **B279**, 131–42.

——, REA, W.J., SKARMETA, J., CAMINOS, R. & REX, D.C. 1981. Igneous history of the Andean Cordillera and Patagonian Plateau around latitude 46° S. *Phil. Trans. R. Soc. London*, **A303**, 105–49.

BARKER, P.F. 1982. The Cenozoic subduction history of the Pacific margin of the Antarctic Peninsula: ridge crest–trench interactions. *J. geol. Soc. London*, **139**, 787–801.

—— & BURRELL, J. 1977. The Opening of Drake Passage. *Mar. Geol.* **25**, 15–34.

—— & DALZIEL, I.W.D. 1983. Progress in geodynamics in the Scotia arc region. *In*: CABRE, R. (ed.) Geodynamics of the eastern Pacific region, Caribbean and Scotia arcs. *Am. geophys. Union Geodyn. Ser.* **9**, 137–70.

—— & HILL, I.A. 1981. Back-arc extension in the Scotia Sea. *Phil. Trans. R. Soc. London*, **A300**, 249–62.

—— & JAHN, R.A. 1980. A marine geophysical reconnaissance of the Weddell Sea. *Geophys. J. R. astron. Soc.* **63**, 271–83.

BARTON, C.M. 1965. The geology of the South Shetland Islands. III. The stratigraphy of King George Island. *Sci. Rep. Br. Antarct. Surv.* **44**, 33 pp.

BEHRENDT, J.C. 1964. The crustal geology of Ellsworth Land and southern Antarctic Peninsula from gravity and magnetic anomalies. *J. geophys. Res.* **69**, 2047–63.

BELL, C.M. 1973. The geology of Beethoven Peninsula, south-western Alexander Island. *Bull. Br. Antarct. Surv.* **32**, 75–83.

—— 1975. Structural geology of parts of Alexander Island. *Bull. Br. Antarct. Surv.* **41 & 42**, 43–58.

—— 1984. The geology of islands in Bransfield Strait. *Bull. Br. Antarct. Surv.* **63**, 41–55.

BOTT, M.H.P. 1960. The use of rapid digital computing methods for direct gravity interpretation of sedimentary basins. *Geophys. J.R. astron. Soc.* **3**, 63–7.

BRITISH ANTARCTIC SURVEY. 1979. *British Antarctic Territory geological map, Sheet 2*, 1:500 000, BAS 500G series. Geology compiled by E.A. FLEMING & J.W. THOMSON. British Antarctic Survey, Cambridge.

—— 1981a. *British Antarctic Territory geological map, Sheet 3*, 1:500 000, BAS 500G series. Geology compiled by J.W. THOMSON & J.S. HARRIS. British Antarctic Survey, Cambridge.

—— 1981b. *British Antarctic Territory geological map, Sheet 4*, 1:500 000, BAS 500G series. Geology compiled by J.W. THOMSON. British Antarctic Survey, Cambridge.

—— 1982. *British Antarctic Territory geological Map, Sheet 5*, 1:500 000, BAS 500G series. Geology compiled by J.W. THOMSON, J.S. HARRIS, P.D. ROWLEY *et al.* Cambridge, British Antarctic Survey.

BURN, R.W. 1984. The geology of the LeMay Group, Alexander Island. *Sci. Rep. Br. Antarct. Surv.* **109**, 65 pp.

—— & THOMSON, M.R.A. 1981. Late Cenozoic tillites associated with intraglacial volcanic rocks, Lesser Antarctica. *In*: HAMBREY, M.J. & HARLAND, W.B. (eds) *Earth's pre-Pleistocene glacial record*, pp. 109–203. Cambridge University Press.

BUTLER, P.F. 1975. A linear Bouguer anomaly in central Alexander Island. *Bull. Br. Antarct. Surv.* **41, 42**, 147–50.

—— & MCARTHUR, M. 1983. A regional Bouguer anomaly map of north-western Palmer Land. *Bull. Br. Antarct. Surv.* **52**, 245–9.

CANDE, S.C., HERRON, E.M. & HALL, B.R. 1982. The early Cenozoic tectonic history of the south-east Pacific. *Earth planet. Sci. Lett.* **57**, 63–74.

CARE, B.W. 1980. The geology of Rothschild Island, north-west Alexander Island. *Bull. Br. Antarct. Surv.* **50**, 87–112.

COLES, R.L. & CURRIE, R.G. 1977. Magnetic anomalies and rock magnetisations in the southern Coast Mountains, British Columbia: possible relation to subduction. *Can. J. Earth. Sci.* **14**, 1753–70.

CRABTREE, R.D. 1981. Subglacial morphology in northern Palmer Land, Antarctic Peninsula. *Ann. Glac.* **2**, 17–22.

——, STOREY, B.C. & DOAKE, C.S.M. 1985. The structural evolution of George VI Sound, Antarctic Peninsula. *In*: HUSEBYE, E.S., JOHNSON, G.L. & KRISTOFFERSEN, Y. (eds) Geophysics of the Polar Regions, *Tectonophysics*, **114**, 431–42.

CRAWFORD, I.A., GIRDLER, R.W. & RENNER, R.G.B. 1986. Interpretation of aeromagnetic anomalies over the Staccato Peaks area of Alexander Island. *Bull. Br. Antarct. Surv.* **70**, 41–53.

CURTIS, R. 1966. The petrology of the Graham Coast, Graham Land. *Sci. Rep. Br. Antarct. Surv.* **50**, 51 pp.

DALZIEL, I.W.D., STOREY, B.C., GARRETT, S.W., GRUNOW, A.M., HERROD, L.D.B. & PANKHURST, R.J. This volume. Extensional tectonics and the fragmentation of Gondwanaland.

DAVEY, F.J. 1972. Marine gravity measurements in Bransfield Strait and adjacent areas. *In*: ADIE, R.J. (ed.) *Antarctic Geology and Geophysics*, pp. 39–45. Universitetsforlaget, Oslo.

DEWAR, G.J. 1970. The geology of Adelaide Island. *Sci. Rep. Br. Antarct. Surv.* **57**, 84 pp.

DOAKE, C.S.M., CRABTREE, R.D. & DALZIEL, I.W.D. 1983. Subglacial morphology between Ellsworth Mountains and Antarctic Peninsula: new data and tectonic significance. *In*: OLIVER, R.L., JAMES, P.R. & JAGO, J.B. (eds) *Antarctic Earth Science*, pp. 270–3. Cambridge University Press.

EATON, G.P. 1984. The Miocene Great Basin of western North America as an extending back-arc region. *In*: CARLSON, R.L. & KOBAYASHI, K. (eds) Geodynamics of back-arc regions. *Tectonophysics*, **102**, 275–95.

EDWARDS, C.W. 1979. New evidence of major faulting on Alexander Island. *Bull. Br. Antarct. Surv.* **49**, 15–20.

ENGEBRETSON, D.C., COX, A. & THOMPSON, G.A. 1984. Correlation of plate motions with continental tectonics: Larimide to Basin-Range. *Tectonics*, **3**, 115–9.

FARQUHARSON, G.W., HAMER, R.D. & INESON, J.R. 1984. Proximal volcaniclastic sedimentation in a Cretaceous back-arc basin, northern Antarctic Peninsula. *In*: KOKELAAR, B.P. & HOWELLS, M.F. (eds) *Marginal Basin Geology, Spec. Publ. geol. Soc. London*, pp. 219–29.

FORSYTH, D.W. & UYEDA, S. 1975. On the relative importance of the driving forces of plate motion. *Geophys. J.R. astron. Soc.* **43**, 163–200.

FURLONG, K.P., CHAPMAN, D.S. & ALFELD, P.W. 1982. Thermal modelling of the geometry of subduction with implications for the tectonics of the overriding plate. *J. geophys. Res.* **87**, 1786–802.

GONZALEZ-FERRAN, O. 1983. The Seal Nunataks: an active volcanic group on the Larsen Ice Shelf, West Antarctica. *In*: OLIVER, R.L., JAMES, P.R. & JAGO, J.B. (eds) *Antarctic Earth Science*, pp. 334–7. Cambridge University Press.

—— & KATSUI, Y. 1970. Estudio integral del volcanismo reciente cenozoico superior de las islas Shetland de Sur, Antarctica. *Ser. cient. Inst. Antarct. Chil.* **1**, 123–74.

GOUGH, D.I. 1984. Mantle upflow under North America and plate dynamics. *Nature, London*, **311**, 428–33.

HALPERN, M. 1971. Evidence for Gondwanaland from a review of West Antarctic radiometric ages. *In*: QUAM, L.O. (ed.) *Research in the Antarctic*, pp. 717–30. Am. Assoc. Adv. Sci.

HARTMAN, R.R., TESKEY, J. & FRIEDBERG, J.L. 1971. A system for rapid digital aeromagnetic interpretation. *Geophysics*, **36**, 891–918.

HAWKES, D.D. 1981. Tectonic segmentation of the northern Antarctic Peninsula. *Geology*, **9**, 220–4.

HERRON, E.M. & TUCHOLKE, B.E. 1976. Sea-floor magnetic patterns and basement structure in the southeastern Pacific. *In*: HOLLISTER, C.D., CRADDOCK, C. *et al. Init. Rep. D.S.D.P.* **35**, pp. 263–78. U.S. Govt. Printing Office, Washington.

——, CANDE, S.C. & HALL, B.R. 1981. An active spreading centre collides with a subduction zone: a geophysical survey of the Chile margin triple junction. *Mem. geol. Soc. Am.* **154**, 683–701.

HOOPER, P.R. 1962. The petrology of Anvers Island and adjacent islands. *Sci. Rep. Br. Antarct. Surv.* **34**, 69 pp.

KARIG, D.E. 1971. Origin and development of marginal basins in the western Pacific. *J. geophys. Res.* **76**, 2542–61.

KING, L. 1964. Pre-glacial geomorphology of Alexander Island. *In*: ADIE, R.J. (ed.) *Antarctic Geology*, pp. 53–64. Amsterdam, North-Holland Publishing Company.

LABRECQUE, J.L. & BARKER, P.F. 1981. The age of the Weddell Basin. *Nature, London,* **290**, 489–92.

LAWVER, L.A., SCLATER, J.G. & MEINKE, L. 1985. Mesozoic and Cenozoic reconstructions of the South Atlantic. *Tectonophysics*, **114**, 233–54.

LEE, M.K. 1979. Two dimensional gravity and magnetic interpretation (Version 2). Program GAM2D. *BGS Computer Program Report Series*, **32**, 30 pp.

LEMASURIER, W.E. & REX, D.C. 1982. Volcanic record of Cenozoic Glacial History in Marie Byrd Land and Western Ellsworth Land: revised Chronology and Evaluation of tectonic factors. *In*: CRADDOCK, C. (ed.) *Antarctic Geoscience*, pp. 725–34. University of Wisconsin Press, Madison.

LINTON, D.L. 1964. Landscape evolution. *In*: PRIESTLEY, R.E., ADIE, R.J. & ROBIN, G. DE Q. (eds) *Antarctic Research*, pp. 85–99. Butterworth, London.

LONGSHAW, S.K. & GRIFFITHS, D.H. 1983. A palaeomagnetic study of Jurassic rocks from the Antarctic Peninsula and its implications. *J. geol. Soc. London*, **140**, 945–54.

MATTHEWS, D.W. 1983a. The geology of Pourquoi Pas Island, northern Marguerite Bay, Graham Land. *Bull. Br. Antarct. Surv.* **52**, 1–20.

—— 1983b. The geology of Horseshoe and Lagotellarie islands, Marguerite Bay, Graham Land. *Bull. Br. Antarct. Surv.* **52**, 125–54.

MOYES, A.B. & HAMER, R.D. 1984. The geology of the Arrowsmith Peninsula and Blaiklock Island, Graham Land, Antarctica. *Bull. Br. Antarct. Surv.* **65**, 41–55.

NELSON, P.H.H. 1975. The James Ross Island Volcanic Group of north-east Graham Land. *Sci. Rep. Br. Antarct. Surv.* **54**, 62 pp.

PANKHURST, R.J. 1982a. Rb–Sr geochronology of Graham Land, Antarctica. *J. geol. Soc. London*, **139**, 701–11.

—— 1982b. Sr-isotope and trace element geochemistry of Cenozoic volcanic rocks from the Scotia Arc and the northern Antarctic Peninsula. *In*: CRADDOCK, C. (ed.) *Antarctic Geoscience*, pp. 229–34. University of Wisconsin Press, Madison.

—— & SMELLIE, J.L. 1983. K–Ar geochronology of the South Shetland Islands, Lesser Antarctica: apparent lateral migration of Jurassic to Quaternary island arc volcanism. *Earth planet. Sci. Lett.* **66**, 214–22.

RENNER, R.G.B., DIKSTRA, B.J. & MARTIN, J.L. 1982. Aeromagnetic surveys over the Antarctic Peninsula. *In*: CRADDOCK, C. (ed.) *Antarctic Geoscience*, pp. 363–7. University of Wisconsin Press, Madison.

——, STURGEON, L.J.S. & GARRETT, S.W. 1985. Reconnaissance gravity and aeromagnetic surveys of the Antarctic Peninsula. *Sci. Rep. Br. Antarct. Surv.* **110**, 50pp.

REX, D.C. 1970. Age of a camptonite dyke from south-east Alexander Island. *Bull. Br. Antarct. Surv.* **23**, pp. 103.

—— 1976. Geochronology in relation to the stratigraphy of the Antarctic Peninsula. *Bull. Br. Antarct. Surv.* **43**, 49–58.

SAUNDERS, A.D. 1982. Petrology and geochemistry of alkali basalts from Jason Peninsula, Oscar II Coast. *Bull. Br. Antarct. Surv.* **55**, 1–9.

—— & TARNEY, J. 1982. Igneous activity in the southern Andes and northern Antarctic Peninsula: a review. *J. geol. Soc. London*, **139**, 691–700.

SCHOLTZ, C.H., BARAZANGI, M. & SBAR, M.L. 1971. Late Cenozoic evolution of the Great Basin, western United States as an ensialic interarc basin. *Bull. geol. Soc. Am.* **82**, 2979–90.

STOREY, B.C. & GARRETT, S.W. 1985. Crustal growth of the Antarctic Peninsula by accretion, magmatism and extension. *Geol. Mag.* **122**, 5–14.

TALWANI, M. 1965. Comparison with the help of a digital computer of magnetic anomalies caused by bodies of arbitrary shape. *Geophysics,* **30**, 797–817.

——, WORZEL, J.L. & LANDISMAN, M. 1959. Rapid gravity computations for two dimensional bodies with application to the Mendocino submarine fracture zone. *J. geophys. Res.* **64**, 49–59.

THOMSON, M.R.A., PANKHURST, R.J. & CLARKSON, P.D. 1983. The Antarctic Peninsula—a late Mesozoic–Cenozoic arc (review). *In*: OLIVER, R.L., JAMES, P.R. & JAGO, J.B. (eds) *Antarctic Earth Science*, pp. 289–94. Cambridge University Press.

WEAVER, S.D., SAUNDERS, A.D., PANKHURST, R.J. & TARNEY, J. 1979. A geochemical study of magmatism associated with the initial stages of back-arc spreading. *Contrib. Mineral. Petrol.* **68**, 151–69.

WINSLOW, M.A. 1982. The structural evolution of the Magellenes Basin and neotectonics in the southernmost Andes. *In*: CRADDOCK, C. (ed.) *Antarctic Geoscience*, pp. 143–54. University of Wisconsin Press, Madison.

ZIETZ, I., BATEMAN, P.C., CASE, J.R., CRITTENDEN, M.D., GRISCOM, A., KING, E.R., ROBERTS, E.R. & LORENTZEN, G.R. 1969. Aeromagnetic investigation of Crustal Structure for a strip across the western United States. *Bull. geol. Soc. Am.* **80**, 1703–14.

ZOBACK, M.L., ANDERSON, R.E. & THOMPSON, G.A. 1981. Cainozoic evolution of the state of stress and style of tectonism of the Basin and Range province of the western United States. *Phil. Trans. R. Soc. London,* **A300**, 407–34.

S.W. GARRETT & B.C. STOREY, British Antarctic Survey, High Cross, Madingley Road, Cambridge CB3 0ET, UK.

Extensional tectonics and the fragmentation of Gondwanaland

I.W.D. Dalziel, B.C. Storey, S.W. Garrett, A.M. Grunow, L.D.B. Herrod & R.J. Pankhurst

SUMMARY: Evidence of widespread lithospheric extension, bimodal volcanism, and uplift and erosion, accompanying the fragmentation of Gondwanaland, is reviewed. One regime of extensional phenomena appears to be intimately associated with a Pacific-margin convergent-plate regime. A second appears to bear no direct geometrical relationship to the margin, but may reflect a thermal anomaly that resulted in the breakup of Gondwanaland. Possible causes of this anomaly are discussed. The two regimes overlap in space and time in the South Atlantic–Weddell Sea area. A causal relationship between the two is possible but remains non-proven.

Tectonic environment

The fragmentation of Gondwanaland was preceded and accompanied by a variety of manifestations of an extensional tectonic environment affecting a very large area of the Earth's lithosphere. The significance of these phenomena lies in their potential for contributing to an understanding of the long-term and large-scale dynamic behaviour of the crust and mantle. Apart from their diverse characteristics and their broad spatial and temporal scope, the phenomena are significant in that they followed a long period of comparative tectonic stability in the interior of the supercontinent. Moreover, they overlap, in space and time, other phenomena related to ocean–continent lithospheric convergence along its proto-Pacific margin and so have a direct bearing on the possibility of a genetic relationship between convergent-margin tectonics and continental breakup.

In this paper we outline the important features of this large-scale extensional tectonic environment. We refer to preliminary results of a joint UK–US project in Antarctica which has been initiated in an attempt to shed more light on the tectonic evolution of West Antarctica and its relation to East Antarctica (Dalziel & Pankhurst 1985, in press; Natural Environment Research Council 1984, 1985).

The basic history and geometry of rifting and the subsequent ocean-floor spreading that resulted in fragmentation of the Gondwanaland super-continent is reasonably well established (Norton & Sclater 1979; Lawver et al. 1985) and is not described in detail here. Poorly understood, however, because of ice cover and inaccessibility, is the evolution of the floor of the Weddell Sea between the Antarctic Peninsula magmatic arc and the East Antarctic craton (Fig. 1). Although Mesozoic magnetic anomalies

have been tentatively identified in the north-eastern Weddell Sea (La Brecque & Barker 1981), their distribution does not yet lead to a clear picture of the geometry and age of spreading. Some reconstructions of the Gondwanaland supercontinent in this area (e.g. Norton & Sclater 1979) result in the well-known 'overlap' of the continental crust of the Falkland Plateau with that of the Antarctic Peninsula. This contrasts strongly with the rather close 'fit' of the Brazilian and West African margins of the South Atlantic Ocean. It may be partially explained by extreme extension of the continental lithosphere in the South Atlantic–Weddell Sea area accompanied by motion of continental fragments in West Antarctica relative to the Gondwanaland craton (Dalziel & Elliot 1982; Dalziel & Grunow 1985; Dalziel et al., in press; Garrett et al., in press; Grunow et al., in press).

There was, in this area, associated with the unusually broad zone of continental extension developed during Gondwanaland breakup, widespread igneous activity including emplacement of the Karoo–Ferrar–Tasman dolerite suite, formation of new ocean floor and crustal anatexis (Fig. 2). Along the active portion of the Pacific margin of the disintegrating supercontinent there was contemporaneous development of extensional marginal basins within and behind the magmatic arc (Fig. 3). Uplift and erosion were also widespread (Fig. 2).

The timing of the extensional tectonic phenomena associated with breakup and Pacific-margin processes is imprecise. They appear to span a considerable range with no known date for the initiation of continental breakup. The main igneous activity associated with continental extension appears to date from the early Jurassic or even the late Triassic in South America, southern Africa, and Antarctica. The widespread Karoo–Ferrar–Tasman

From COWARD, M.P., DEWEY, J.F. & HANCOCK, P.L. (eds), 1987, *Continental Extensional Tectonics*, Geological Society Special Publication No. 28, pp. 433–441.

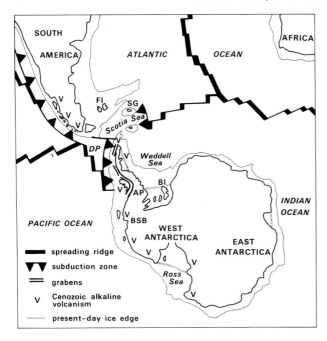

FIG. 1. The South Atlantic–Weddell Sea region. A sketch map of plate boundaries during the Cenozoic, plotted on a reconstruction at anomaly 6 time (20 Ma). AP = Antarctic Peninsula; FI = Falkland Islands; SG = South Georgia; BI = Berkner Island; DP = Drake Passage; BSB = Byrd Subglacial Basin.

dolerites, for example, are mainly Lower–Middle Jurassic (Cox 1978). Graben infilled with Middle- to Upper-Jurassic lavas and pyroclastic deposits in South America may have originated in the late Jurassic (Gust *et al.* 1985). The age of the oldest oceanic lithosphere in the South Atlantic is approximately 130 Ma Early Cretaceous: Rabinowitz & La Brecque 1979). Extensional phenomena more directly related to Pacific-margin tectonics in this region occurred within the same time-span. Gabbros associated with back-arc basin formation on South Georgia were emplaced in the early Jurassic (Storey & Macdonald 1984). The main development of the 'Rocas Verdes' back-arc basin along the western margin of southernmost South America and South Georgia took place during the latest Jurassic and Early Cretaceous (for review see Dalziel 1981).

In the following sections we describe the tectonic phenomena associated with these extensional regimes leading to the fragmentation of Gondwanaland and back-arc basin formation in the South Atlantic–Weddell Sea region and discuss their significance.

Intra-continental extension

There is direct evidence of significant extension of continental lithosphere in southern South America and West Antarctica during the mid Mesozoic. No reliable quantitative estimates of

the amount of extension are yet available, but the nature of the geophysical, structural and stratigraphical evidence and the fact that the extension was accompanied by widespread crustal anatexis suggests that it was substantial.

In southern South America widespread formation of grabens and half-grabens accompanied by widespread silicic to bimodal volcanism occurred in the late Triassic to middle and late Jurassic (Natland *et al.* 1974; Bruhn *et al.* 1978; Gust *et al.* 1985). Most of these structures trend approximately NNW (Fig. 2) parallel to the structural grain of the underlying rocks which are widely interpreted as representing a Gondwanaland-margin fore-arc accretionary prism, magmatic arc, and back-arc basin or fore-deep (Barker in Dalziel *et al.* 1976; Forsythe 1982; Dalziel & Forsythe 1985; Gust *et al.* 1985). The bounding faults are reported to be steeply dipping for the most part, but listric profiles have been observed at depth in some seismic sections (Gust *et al.* 1985). Basin formation culminated with the development of the Early Cretaceous 'Rocas Verdes' basin along the Pacific margin (Dalziel 1981) (Fig. 3). Basins associated with bimodal volcanism also developed in southern Africa over the same time-span. These are located in the Cape fold belt, on the Agulhas Bank, and in the Orange Basin (Lock *et al.* 1975; Du Toit 1979).

Studies of the sub-ice topography of West Antarctica reveal deep basins separating upstanding continental blocks (Jankowski &

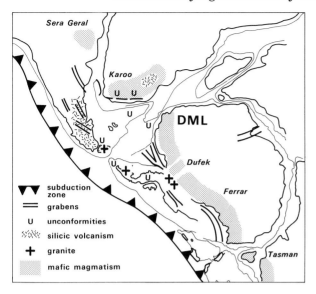

FIG. 2. Gondwanaland reconstruction of Lawver *et al.* (1985) at M12 time (137 Ma). West Antarctica has been displaced relative to East Antarctica by an arbitrary amount to remove overlap of the Antarctic Peninsula and Falkland Plateau. Mesozoic extensional features illustrated. DML = Dronning Maud Land.

Drewry 1981; Doake *et al.* 1983). Aeromagnetic data suggest that the topographic depressions between the Antarctic Peninsula and Ellsworth Mountains represent extensional grabens bounded by normal faults with displacements of several kilometres (Garrett *et al.*, in press). The presence of material of high magnetic susceptibility beneath the central zone of one of the most clearly developed West Antarctic basins, the Byrd Subglacial Basin (Fig. 1) suggests the presence of volcanic rocks along its axis, further supporting the possibility of an extensional origin (Jankowski & Drewry 1981).

Geophysical data obtained by Soviet Antarctic expeditions are consistently interpreted by Russian scientists in terms of rift valleys penetrating the interior of West Antarctica from the Weddell Sea basin (Masolov *et al.* 1981), while West German marine geophysical data are interpreted by Hinz (1981) as indicating that the bedrock trough separating Berkner Island (Fig. 1) from the East Antarctic craton is an extensional feature of late Mesozoic age. This trough penetrates southward to the Pensacola Mountains where the large, layered mafic body of early Jurassic age known as the Dufek intrusion is located (Fig. 2) (Behrendt *et al.* 1981). The Dufek intrusion is a pyroxene gabbro–dolerite body of continental tholeiitic affinity, related to the Ferrar Dolerites group, with strongly developed mineralogical and cryptic layering apparently of Skaergaard–Bushveldt type. Hence there is evidence that much of the crustal extension in West Antarctica could be coeval with the fragmentation of Gondwanaland. Preliminary

palaeomagnetic results, from our joint UK–US project rule out large-scale movement of continental blocks forming West Antarctica during or since the break up of Gondwanaland, but do suggest limited movement of the blocks (rotations of about 20° and latitude changes ≤20°) during breakup (Dalziel & Grunow 1985; Grunow *et al.*, in press).

Igneous activity

Even apart from the generation of the lithosphere forming the floors of the southern oceans, several different categories of igneous activity can be distinguished and identified as being associated with the break up of Gondwanaland (Fig. 2).

Firstly, there was the well-known voluminous eruption of tholeiitic flood basalts and emplacement of dolerite sills, dykes and larger, layered intrusions in East Antarctica, South Africa, Tasmania, South America and the Falkland Islands. These mafic rocks are predominantly basaltic in composition with a tholeiitic character, although more acidic compositions occur locally. They show a wide range in initial Sr^{87}/Sr^{86} ratios (0.703–0.7153) which relate to some distinctive geographical variations. Two major provinces have been recognized in East Antarctica (Faure *et al.* 1979; Kyle *et al.* 1981); rocks of the Ferrar supergroup along the Transantarctic Mountains, which includes the Kirkpatrick Basalt group, the Ferrar Dolerite group and the Forrestal Gabbro group which in-

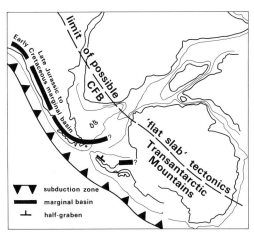

FIG. 3. Reconstruction (as in Fig. 2) showing early Cretaceous marginal-basin development and limit of influence of possible 'flat-slab' subduction. CFB = Cape fold belt.

cludes the Dufek intrusion referred to above, are enriched in lithophile elements and have high Sr^{87}/Sr^{86} ratios, whereas the Dronning Maud Land basalt flows and intrusions (Fig. 2) have lower ratios more typical of other continental tholeiitic provinces. A similar variation is seen in the Karoo supergroup of South Africa (see Dingle *et al.* 1983 for review) and the Tasman dolerites typically have high ratios (Kyle *et al.* 1981). The chemical variation may be due to progressive contamination of basaltic magma by crustal material (Faure *et al.* 1982), although Kyle *et al.* (1983) concluded that the primary magmas must have had an elevated initial ratio due to a heterogeneous upper mantle. Although much of this igneous activity was coeval and erupted over a short time-span (179 ± 7 Ma), the Sera Geral rocks of South America were emplaced in the Cretaceous, reflecting the diachronous nature of the extensional phenomena.

In southern South America a further extremely prominent category of igneous activity that was broadly contemporaneous with the breakup of Gondwanaland can be identified. This activity was dominated by a widespread silicic, locally bimodal volcanic suite culminating in a Middle- to Upper-Jurassic volcanic field which is widely known as the Tobifera (literally tuffaceous) or Porphyritica Formation (Natland *et al.* 1974). It contains a large volume of rhyolitic pyroclastics associated with a small volume of basaltic and intermediate rock types, and extends from the Pacific margin (where it appears to grade into a narrow zone of intermediate composition) to the Malvinas Basin between mainland South America and the Falkland Islands (Bruhn *et al.* 1978; Dalziel 1981; Gust *et al.* 1985). It has a more geographically restricted South African counterpart in the Suurberg basalts and rhyolites and the Hoachanas basalts found in drill holes along the southwestern African continental margin (Gerrard & Smith 1982; Bristow & Saggeson 1983). The basalts were generated by partial melting of the mantle and are chemically similar to flood basalts although the degree of crustal contamination is unclear. The South American rhyolites appear to be products of the crustal anatexis of sedimentary source material as a result of the input of hot basaltic magma into the base of the crust (Gust *et al.* 1985). Granitic orthogneiss of late Jurassic age in the Cordillera Darwin of the southern Andes (Darwin granite suite) may represent the deeper seated equivalent of the silicic volcanics (Nelson *et al.* 1980; Herve *et al.* 1981). This middle- to late-Jurassic igneous activity was closely related to the graben formation outlined earlier. Rapid changes in the thicknesses of volcanic deposits across normal faults have been proved by drilling. Indeed, the volcanics are locally confined to the grabens (Natland *et al.* 1974). This association, together with the composition of the rocks, invites comparison with the Basin and Range Province of the western United States (Bruhn *et al.* 1978; Gust *et al.* 1985).

Although the rocks of the Antarctic Peninsula Volcanic group (Thomson *et al.* 1983) are in part contemporaneous with the Tobifera group and its equivalents in southern Africa, they are essentially calc-alkaline and variations in composition occur transverse to the arc suggesting a direct relationship to subduction at the continental margin. No bimodal volcanic field comparable to the Tobifera is known at present on the Antarctic continent. Preliminary results of our ongoing project in West Antarctica indicate, however, that the middle Jurassic granitic plutons of the Ellsworth Mountains–Whitmore Mountains crustal block (Webers *et al.* 1983) are S-type peraluminous leucogranites (Vennum & Storey, in press) with comparatively high initial Sr^{87}/Sr^{86} ratios (0.7077–0.722; Millar & Pankhurst, in press) and may, like the Darwin granite suite of southern Chile, represent the products of crustal anatexis. Because they are the same age as the Ferrar supergroup, both elements of a bimodal suite of plutonic rocks related to the breakup of Gondwanaland are thus present in Antarctica (Dalziel *et al.*, in press). In this case the two members of the suite are geographically distinct (Fig. 2) but it should be pointed out that it is not unusual for the mafic member of such a suite to be concentrated along the periphery of the zone of acid magmatism (Hildreth 1981). While all the mafic rocks are generally regarded as belonging to the continental flood-type tholeiitic association, they are unusual in that even the least-evolved mafic members have trace element distributions and Sr-isotope compositions more characteristic of old sialic continental crust. The Ferrar suite, like the Tasman suite, possesses these characteristics virtually to the exclusion of mantle-derived features. They imply such a high degree of crustal contamination that massive melting and incorporation of lower crust or 'fossilized' underlying lithosphere, with an anomalous long-term enrichment in lithophile elements, is indicated (Kyle *et al.* 1983). This can be seen as a consequence of a newly developed thermal regime related to the disruption of the pre-existing stable crust–mantle system of Gondwanaland.

Back-arc extension

It is now well established that a back-arc basin ('Rocas Verdes' basin) floored at least partly by quasi-oceanic crust developed along the Pacific margin of southernmost South America and South Georgia in the late Jurassic or earliest Cretaceous (Dalziel 1981; Storey & Macdonald 1984). Mafic complexes, pillow lavas, sheeted dykes and layered gabbros cut and overlie the Upper Jurassic silicic volcanic rocks that were extruded during the phase of more widespread extension from the late Triassic to the middle to late Jurassic described above. The basin closely follows the present continental margin around the Patagonian orocline (Fig. 3) and is the most southerly part of a composite back-arc basin that extended north almost as far as the equator and was uplifted and destroyed in the mid-Cretaceous (Chotin 1976; Dalziel 1986). The opening of this composite basin appears to have been closely controlled by the Pacific–continental-margin plate convergence. Northwards it diverges from the Atlantic Ocean basin and is separated from it by the Trans-Amazonian Shield. The southeastern limit is unknown. It clearly extended onto the northern Scotia Ridge, and it may have been related in some way to the opening of the Weddell Sea basin (Barker *et al.*, in press), but it is now trun-cated by the younger oceanic lithosphere of the Scotia Sea. The back-arc basins (Farquharson *et al.* 1984) manifested as half-grabens on the side of the developing Weddell Sea may represent its southerly continuation (Fig. 3).

Erosional unconformities

The existence of major erosional unconformities beneath Upper Triassic, Jurassic and Lower Cretaceous strata in southern South America, southern Africa and the Antarctic Peninsula has been known for many years (Du Toit 1937; King 1962; Bibby 1966; Dalziel & Elliott 1973). The uplift and erosion preceding the deposition of the overlying strata occurred in a number of pre-existing types of tectonic environments, and immediately pre-dated the graben formation and Triassic, Jurassic and Cretaceous igneous activity associated with rifting of the Gondwanaland continent.

The pre-existing tectonic environments include the following elements of the late Palaeozoic–Mesozoic Gondwanaland proto-Pacific margin: (i) accretionary prisms in Tierra del Fuego and Patagonia (Dalziel & Elliot 1973; Dalziel & Forsythe 1985) and the Antarctic Peninsula (Storey & Garrett 1985); (ii) a magmatic arc in eastern South America at approximately 48°S (Gust *et al.* 1985); (iii) a back-arc (fore-deep) basin in the Cape fold belt (Lock *et al.* 1975); and (iv) the Gondwanaland Craton in the eastern Falkland Plateau (Barker, Dalziel *et al.* 1976). The ages of the oldest strata overlying the unconformities vary from Triassic to Early Cretaceous. In southern South America the rocks above the unconformity are Jurassic volcanics or sedimentary strata associated with the extensive graben formation described above. Further N in South America the overlying strata are Triassic. Within the Antarctic Peninsula fluviatile conglomerates and interbedded volcanic rocks, of probable early Cretaceous age, accumulated in local fault-bounded basins on an uplifted accretionary prism terrain (Farquharson 1983). Marine seismic surveys in the eastern Weddell Sea have revealed a surface interpreted as a 'Weddell Sea unconformity' of mid- to late-Jurassic age (Hinz 1984; Haughland *et al.* 1985). The surface separates presumed continental basement from overlying sedimentary strata of late Mesozoic and Cenozoic age. Thus, wherever timing can be determined with confidence, the regional uplift and erosion appear to have immediately preceded some of the extensional phenomena described above.

Discussion

We have outlined evidence of widespread extension of continental lithosphere in the South Atlantic–Weddell Sea region during and after the breakup of Gondwanaland. Initial extension in the mid Mesozoic is indicated by the extensive development of the Jurassic mafic-igneous rocks of the Ferrar–Karoo–Tasman suite, the Mesozoic age of the Weddell Sea floor and its rift extensions into the continent, and the presence in West Antarctica and southern South America of middle Jurassic granitic and rhyolitic rocks that appear to represent the products of crustal anatexis. All the tectonic and igneous phenomena listed coincided with the subduction of proto-Pacific oceanic lithosphere beneath the super-continent. Indeed, it has been suggested that the opening of the southern oceans was initiated as a back-arc phenomenon (Cox 1978). An alternative hypothesis is that presented by Anderson (1982, 1984) who suggested that super-continent breakup may reflect heat build-up due to thermal insulation of the mantle throughout a long period of continental stability. In either case it must be concluded that the acid-igneous rocks signify the production of S-type magmas in a non-collisional environment.

In supporting the hypothesis that the breakup of Gondwanaland was initiated as a Pacific margin back-arc phenomenon, Gust *et al.* (1985) viewed the late Jurassic-Early Cretaceous Rocas Verdes back-arc basin, in the southernmost Andes, as the culmination of the extension that accompanied the silicic Jurassic magmatism. They related the silicic volcanism and opening of the Rocas Verdes and South Atlantic basins to a tectonic and magmatic event associated with the steepening of the down-going slab following a period of 'flat-slab' subduction that resulted in the Gondwanide deformation of the Cape fold belt (Lock 1980) (Fig. 3). Within this model the bimodal mafic and felsic magmatic rocks of the Ferrar–Karoo–Tasman suite and the West Antarctic granitic rocks would also be related to Pacific-margin processes, specifically the steepening of the down-going slab. It is difficult, however, to envisage a causal relationship between circum-Pacific events and the Karoo dolerites and Drakensburg volcanics along the southeastern margin of Africa. Moreover, the Gondwana cover-sequence (Beacon supergroup) rocks of the Transantarctic Mountains, stratigraphically equivalent to the folded sedimentary strata of the Cape fold belt (Cape and Karoo supergroups), are mostly undeformed

despite the presence of the Jurassic Ferrar dolerites. Thus there is no evidence throughout the length of most of the Transantarctic Mountains for the presence in the early Mesozoic of a flat lithospheric slab that could have steepened to allow an extensional regime to develop in West Antarctica during the Jurassic–Cretaceous. The Rocas Verdes basin does, however, appear to have resulted from an extensional stress regime directly related to plate convergence along the Pacific margin. The basin is the southernmost part of a 7,500-km-long composite early-Cretaceous marginal basin closely following the Pacific margin of South America as far N as the Gulf of Guayaquil (5°S), the northern part of which has no associated silicic-volcanic field comparable to that of southern South America. The composite basin closed in the mid-Cretaceous during the period of high spreading rates and rapid elongation of the spreading ridge in the South Atlantic (Dalziel 1986). This also suggests tectonic control effected by the stress regime along the convergent Pacific margin.

In contrast to the above hypothesis, there may also have been an extensional stress regime in the South Atlantic–Weddell Sea region that was independent of this Pacific-margin stress system. The pattern of extensional features in this area is very inhomogeneous and may have been controlled by earlier basement trends. These extensional phenomena may be related to a thermal event, independent of convergent-margin geometry, which subsequently led to the breakup of Gondwanaland. This may initially have resulted in the emplacement of large volumes of mantle-derived mafic magma (the Ferrar–Karoo–South America (?Tobifera) mafic suite) which caused large-scale melting of the crust and formation of the felsic members of the bimodal suite, the granitic plutons of West Antarctica and the felsic-volcanic rocks of South America (Tobifera) and South Africa. Kyle *et al.* (1981) concluded that the Ferrar supergroup formed in response to a rise in mantle geotherms independent of any plate boundary. We accept this possibility and conclude that both the mafic and felsic rocks may be related to an intracontinental thermal event heralding the breakup of Gondwanaland. The mantle heterogeneity, inferred from the high initial Sr ratios for some of the mafic rocks, may have occurred as a result of large-scale recycling of crustal material into the mantle during subduction. The restriction of this to distinct provinces and the presence of contemporaneous subduction-related processes along the Pacific margin suggest that this may have been inherited from a previous orogenic episode, and was not coeval with this thermal event. The magmatic activity could clearly be categorized as an 'ignimbrite flare-up' comparable to the well-known event in the western United States (Lipman 1980). The thermal event was initiated 80 Ma prior to the first sea-floor magnetic anomalies. Continental tholeiitic magmatism continued during break-up in South Africa and South America as the South Atlantic opened northward resulting in intrusion of the Sera Geral.

We do not, as yet, have sufficient data to distinguish between these two hypotheses, but are presently inclined toward the view that two discrete but overlapping extensional tectonic regimes may have been operating, both during and after the breakup of Gondwanaland. One set of extensional phenomena appears to be intimately associated with a Pacific-margin regime, another set appears to bear no direct relationship to that margin. The two overlap in space and time in the South Atlantic–Weddell Sea region.

Finally, it should be pointed out that events similar to those accompanying the breakup of Gondwanaland have continued in the area of southernmost South America and the Antarctic Peninsula during the Cenozoic (Fig. 1). Extension closely controlled by the geometry of the Pacific margin (Garrett & Storey this volume) has culminated in the opening of the Bransfield Strait over the past 2 My (Barker & Dalziel 1983). More widespread back-arc extension accompanied by alkaline volcanism occurs well to the E of the Pacific margin in Patagonia,

Tierra del Fuego, and the Antarctic Peninsula (Tectonic Map of the Scotia Arc, 1:3,000,000, BAS [Misc. 3] British Antarctic Survey, Cambridge, 1985). The eruption of large volumes of alkali flood basalts also accompanied crustal extension in central West Antarctica during the Cenozoic (LeMasurier & Rex 1982). In all cases, extension followed uplift.

Conclusions

There is evidence of widespread lithospheric extension and bimodal volcanism accompanying the fragmentation of Gondwanaland in the South Atlantic–Weddell Sea region. These phenomena may provide useful data for a better understanding of large-scale tectonic processes, and suggest that the limited microcontinental movements in this area may be partially due to widespread lithospheric extension. Present data indicate that back-arc effects of Pacific-margin subduction, and the effects of a larger extensional and thermal regime that resulted in the breakup of Gondwanaland, may be superimposed in the region. A causal relationship between the two is possible but remains non-proven.

ACKNOWLEDGMENTS: Our work is supported by the Division of Polar Programs of the National Science Foundation, Washington, DC, USA (Grant No. DPP 82-13798 to I.W.D.D.) and by the British Antarctic Survey, Natural Environment Research Council, UK. We appreciate the constructive reviews of P.F. Barker and R.L. Bruhn.

References

ANDERSON, D.L. 1982. Hotspots, polar wander, Mesozoic convection, and the geoid. *Nature*, **297**, 391–3.
ANDERSON, D.L. 1984. The earth as a planet: paradigms and paradoxes. *Science*, **223**, 347–55.
BARKER, P.F. & DALZIEL, I.W.D. 1983. Progress in Geodynamics in the Scotia arc region. *In*: CABRE, R. (ed.) Geodynamics of the eastern Pacific region, Caribbean and Scotia arcs. *Am. geophys. Union Geodyn. Ser.* **9**, 137–70.
—, —, & STOREY, B.C. In press. Tectonic development of the Scotia arc region. *In*: TINGEY, R. (ed.) *Antarctic Geology*, Oxford University Press.
—, —, et al. 1976. *Init. Reps D.S.D.P.* **36**, pp. 1080. Washington, D.C., U.S. Government Printing Office.
BIBBY, J.S. 1966. The stratigraphy of part of northern Graham Land and the James Ross Island Group. *Sci. Rep. Br. Antarct. Surv.*, **63**, pp. 37.
BRISTOW, J.W. & SAGGESON, E.P. 1983. A general account of Karoo volcanicity in southern Africa. *Geol. Res.* **72**, 1015–60.

BRUHN, R.L., STERN, C.R. & DE WIT, M.J. 1978. Field and geochemical data bearing on the development of a Mesozoic volcano-tectonic rift zone and back-arc basin in southern South America. *Earth planet. Sci. Lett.* **41**, 32–46.
CHOTIN, P. 1976. Essai d'interprétation de Bassin Andin Chileono–Argentine en tant que bassin marginal. *Ann. Soc. geol. Nord.* **96**, 177–84.
COX, K. 1978. Flood basalts, subduction, and the break-up of Gondwanaland. *Nature*, **274**, 47–9.
DALZIEL, I.W.D. 1981. Back-arc basin in the southern Andes: a review and critical reappraisal. *Phil. Trans. R. Soc. London*, **A300**, 319–35.
—— 1986. Collision and cordilleran orogenesis: an Andean perspective. *Collision Tectonics, Spec. Publ. geol. Soc. London*, **19**, 389–404.
—— & ELLIOT, D.H. 1973. The Scotia arc and Antarctic margin. *In*: NAIRN, A.E.M. & STEHLI, F.H. (eds) *The Ocean Basins and Margins, I. The South Atlantic*, pp. 171–246. Plenum Press, New York.
—— & —— 1982. West Antarctica: problem child of Gondwanaland. *Tectonics*, **1**, 3–19.

—— & FORSYTHE, R.D. 1985. Andean evolution and the terrane concept. *In*: HOWELL, D.G. *et al.* (eds) Circum-Pacific Terranes. *Am. Assoc. Pet. Geol. Spec. Publ. Circum-Pacific Coun. Energy and Mineral Reasons, Earth Sci. Ser.* **1**, 565–81.

—— & GRUNOW, A.M. 1985. The Pacific margin of Antarctica: terranes within terranes within terranes. *In*: HOWELL, D.G. *et al.* (eds) Circum-Pacific Terranes. *Am. Assoc. Pet. Geol. Spec. Publ. Circum-Pacific Coun. Energy and Mineral Resources, Earth Sci. Ser.* **1**, 555–64.

—— & PANKHURST, R.J. 1985. Joint UK–US West Antarctic Tectonics Project 1983–84. *Ant. J. U. S.* **19**, 35–6.

—— & —— In press. Joint UK–US West Antarctic Tectonics Project 1984–85. An Introduction. *Proc. Sixth Gondwana Conference, Columbus, Ohio, August 1985, Am. geophys. Union.*

——, GARRETT, S.W., GRUNOW, A.M., PANKHURST, R.J., STOREY, B.C. & VENNUM, W. R. In press. The Ellsworth–Whitmore mountains crustal block: its role in the tectonic evolution of West Antarctica. *Proc. Sixth Gondwana Conference, Columbus, Ohio, August 1985, Am. geophys. Union.*

DINGLE, R.V., SIESSER, W.G. & NEWTON, A.R. 1983. *Mesozoic and Tertiary Geology of southern Africa.* 375 pp. A.A. Balkema, Rotterdam.

DOAKE, C.S.M., CRABTREE, R.D. & DALZIEL, I.W.D. 1983. Subglacial morphology between Ellsworth Mountains and Antarctic Peninsula: new data and tectonic significance. *In*: OLIVER, R.L., JAMES, P.R. & JAGO, J.B. (eds) *Antarctic Earth Science*, pp. 270–3. Australian Academy of Sciences, Canberra.

DU TOIT, A.L. 1937. *Our Wandering Continents*, 366 pp. Oliver and Boyd, Edinburgh.

DU TOIT, S.R. 1979. The Mesozoic history of the Agulhas Bank in terms of plate tectonic history. *Geol. Soc. Sth Afr. Spec. Publ.* **6**, 197–203.

FARQUHARSON, G.W. 1983. Evolution of late Mesozoic sedimentary basins in the northern Antarctic Peninsula. *In*: OLIVER, R.L., JAMES, P.R. & JAGO, J.B. (eds) *Antarctic Earth Science*, pp. 270–3. Australian Academy of Sciences, Canberra.

——, G.W., HAMER, R.D. & INESON, J.R. Proximal volcaniclastic sedimentation in a Cretaceous back-arc basin, northern Antarctic Peninsula. *In*: KOKELAAR, B.P. & HOWELLS, M.F. (eds) *Marginal Basin Geology*, pp. 219–29. Blackwell Scientific Publications, Oxford.

FAURE, G., BOWMAN, J.R. & ELLIOT, D.H. 1979. The initial $^{87}Sr/^{86}Sr$ ratios of the Kirwan Volcanics of Dronning Maud Land: comparison with the Kirkpatrick Basalt, Transantarctic Mountains. *Chem. Geol.* **26**, 77–90.

——, PALE, K.K. & ELLIOT, D.H. 1982. Systematic variations of $^{87}Sr/^{86}Sr$ ratios and major element concentrations in the Kirkpatrick Basalt of Mt Falla, Queen Alexandra Range, Transantarctic Mountains. *In*: CRADDOCK, C. (ed.) *Antarctic Geoscience*, pp. 715–23. University of Wisconsin Press, Madison.

FORSYTHE, R.D. 1982. The late Palaeozoic to early Mesozoic evolution of southern South America: a plate tectonic interpretation. *J. geol. Soc. London*, **139**, 671–82.

GARRETT, S.W. & STOREY, B.C. This volume. Lithospheric extension on the Antarctic Peninsula during Cenozoic subduction.

——, HERROD, L.D.B. & MANTRIPP, D.E. In press. Crustal structure of the area around Haag Nunataks, West Antarctica: implications of rifting for Gondwanaland reconstruction. *Proc. Sixth Gondwana Conference, Columbus, Ohio, August 1985, Am. geophys. Union.*

GERRARD, I. & SMITH, G. C. 1982. Post-Paleozoic succession and structure of the southeastern African continental margin. Studies in Continental Margin Geology. *Mem. Am. Assoc. Pet. Geol.* **34**, 49–74.

GRUNOW, A.M., DALZIEL, I.W.D. & KENT, D. V. In press. Ellsworth–Whitmore mountains crustal block, Western Antarctica: new palaeomagnetic data and their tectonic significance. *Proc. Sixth Gondwana Conference, Columbus, Ohio, August 1985, Am. geophys. Union.*

GUST, D.A., BIDDLE, K.T., PHELPS, D.W. & ULIANA, M.A. 1985. Associated Middle to Late Jurassic volcanism and extension in southern South America. *Tectonophysics*, **116**, 223–53.

HAUGLAND, K., KRISTOFFERSEN, Y. & VELDE, A. 1985. Seismic investigations in the Weddell Sea embayment. *Tectonophysics*, **114**, 293–313.

HERVE, F., NELSON, E., KAWASHITA, K. & SUAREZ, M. 1981. New isotopic ages and the timing of orogenic events in the Cordillera Darwin, Southernmost Chilean Andes. *Earth planet. Sci. Lett.* **55**, 257–65.

HILDRETH, W. 1981. Gradients in silicic magma chambers: implications for lithospheric magmatism. *J. geophys. Res.* **86**, 10153–92.

HINZ, K. 1981. A hypothesis on terrestrial catastrophes. Wedges of very thick oceanward dipping layers beneath passive continental margins – their origin and palaeoenvironmental significance. *Geol. Jahrb. Hannover*, **22**, 3–28.

—— 1984. Results of Geophysical Investigations in the Weddell Sea and the Ross Sea, Antarctica. *Proc. 11th World Petroleum Congress, London, 1983*, pp. 279–91. Wiley, New York.

JANKOWSKI, E.J. & DREWRY, D.J. 1981. The structure of West Antarctica from geophysical studies. *Nature*, **291**, 17–21.

KING, L.C. 1962. *Morphology of the Earth*, 609 pp. Hafner Publishing Company, New York.

KYLE, P.R., ELLIOT, D.H. & SUTTER, J.F. 1981. Jurassic Ferrar Supergroup tholeiites from the Transantarctic Mountains, Antarctica, and their relationship to the initial fragmentation of Gondwana. *In*: CRESSWELL, M.M. & VELLA, P. (eds) *Gondwana Five*, pp. 283–7. A.A. Balkema, Rotterdam.

—— , PANKHURST, R.J. & BOWMAN, J.R. 1983. Isotopic and chemical variations in Kirkpatrick Basalt Group rocks from southern Victoria Land. *In*: OLIVER, R.L., JAMES, P.R. & JAGO, J.B. (eds) *Antarctic Earth Science*. pp. 234–7. Australian Academy of Science, Canberra.

LA BREQUE, J. & BARKER, P.F. 1981. The age of the Weddell Basin. *Nature*, **290**, 489–92.

LAWVER, L.A., SCLATER, J.G. & MEINKE, L. 1985. Mesozoic and Cenozoic reconstructions of the South Atlantic. *Tectonophysics*, **114**, 233–54.

LE MASURIER, W.E. & REX, D.C. 1982. Volcanic record of Cenozoic glacial history in Marie Byrd Land and Western Ellsworth Land: revised chronology and evaluation of tectonic factors. *In*: CRADDOCK, C. (ed.) *Antarctic Geoscience*. pp. 725–34. University of Wisconsin Press, Madison.

LIPMAN, P.W. 1980. Cenozoic volcanism in the western United States: implications for continental tectonics. *Studies in Geophysics: Continental Tectonics*, pp. 161–74. National Academy of Sciences, Washington, D.C.

LOCK, B.E. 1980. Flat-plate subduction and the Cape fold belt of South Africa. *Geology*, **8**, 35–9.

—— , STONE, R., COATES, A.T. & HUTTON, C.J. 1975. Mesozoic nonarc-type sedimentary basins within the Cape fold belt of southern Africa. *Proc. 9th International Congress of Sedimentology*, **6**, 217–25.

MASOLOV, V.N., KURININ, R.G. & GRIKUROV, G.E. 1981. Crustal structure and tectonic significance of Antarctic rift zones (from geophysical evidence). *In*: CRESSWELL, M.M. & VELLA, P. (eds) *Gondwana Five*, pp. 303–9. A.A. Balkema, Rotterdam.

MILLAR, I.A. & PANKHURST, R.J. In press. Geochronology of the region between the Antarctic Peninsula and the Transantarctic Mountains, Haag Nunataks and Mesozoic granitoids. *Proc. Sixth Gondwana Conference, Columbus, Ohio, August 1985*.

NATLAND, M.L., GONZALES, E., CANON, A. & ERNST, M. 1974. A system of stages for correlation of Magallanes Basin sediments. *Geol. Soc. Am. Mem.* **139**, pp. 126.

NATURAL ENVIRONMENT RESEARCH COUNCIL 1984. *Annual Report of British Antarctic Survey*. Cambridge.

—— 1985. *Annual Report of British Antarctic Survey*. Cambridge.

NELSON, E.P., DALZIEL, I.W.D. & MILNES, A.G. 1980. Structural geology of the Cordillera Darwin: collision-style orogenesis in the southernmost Chilean Andes. *Eclog. geol. Helv.* **73**, 729–51.

NORTON, I.W. & SCALTER, J.G. 1979. A model for the evolution of the Indian Ocean and the break-up of Gondwanaland. *J. geophys. Res.* **84**, 6803–30.

RABINOWITZ, P.D. & LA BRECQUE, J.L. 1979. The Mesozoic South Atlantic Ocean and evolution of its continental margins. *J. geophys. Res.* **84**, 5973–6002.

STOREY, B.C. & GARRETT, S.W. 1985. Crustal growth of the Antarctic Peninsula by accretion, magmatism and extension. *Geol. Mag.* **122**, 5–14.

—— & MACDONALD, D.M. 1984. Processes of formation and filling of a Mesozoic back-arc basin on the island of South Georgia. *In*: KOKELAAR, B.P. & HOWELLS, M.F. (eds) *Marginal Basin Geology*, pp. 207–18. Blackwell Scientific Publications, Oxford.

THOMSON, M.R.A., PANKHURST, R.J. & CLARKSON, P.D. 1983. The Antarctic Peninsula: a Late Mesozoic-Cenozoic arc. *In*: OLIVER, R.L., JAMES, P.R. & JAGO, J.B. (eds) *Antarctic Earth Science*, pp. 289–94. Australian Academy of Science, Canberra.

VENNUM, W.R. & STOREY, B.C. In press. Petrology, geochemistry, and tectonic setting of granitic rocks from the Ellsworth–Whitmore mountains crustal block and Thiel Mountains, West Antarctica. *Proc. Sixth Gondwana Conference, Columbus, Ohio, August 1985, Am. geophys. Union*.

WEBERS, G.F., CRADDOCK, C., ROGERS, M.A. & ANDERSON, J.J. 1983. Geology of Pagano Nunatak and the Hart Hills. *In*: OLIVER, R.L., JAMES, P.R. & JAGO, J.B. (eds) *Antarctic Earth Sciences*, pp. 251–5. Australian Academy of Sciences, Canberra.

I.W.D. DALZIEL* & A.M. GRUNOW, Lamont-Doherty Geological Observatory of Columbia University, Palisades, New York 10964, USA.

B.C. STOREY, S.W. GARRETT, L.D.B. HERROD & R.J. PANKHURST, British Antarctic Survey, Natural Environment Research Council, High Cross, Madingley Road, Cambridge CB3 0ET, UK.

*Present address: Institute for Geophysics, University of Texas at Austin, 4920 North IH 35, Austin, TX 78751, USA.

Extension in the
NW European Continental Shelf

Extensional structures on the western UK continental shelf: a review of evidence from deep seismic profiling

M.J. Cheadle, S. McGeary, M.R. Warner & D.H. Matthews

SUMMARY: BIRPS deep seismic reflection data collected on the western United Kingdom continental shelf show the existence of a wide variety of sedimentary basins, most of which originated during Palaeozoic–Mesozoic crustal extension. Symmetrical interior-fracture basins are numerous, but more complex basins are also common and show the importance of fault reactivation and the influence of pre-existing structures on basin development. All of the major basement-penetrating faults are interpreted as having been reactivated. They do not visibly cut through the entire crust and into the upper mantle. The crystalline crust thins dramatically beneath the basins indicating local crustal extensions of up to 60%, although regional extension is less than 30%.

The typical BIRPS profile shows a highly reflective lower crust sandwiched between an unreflective upper crust and upper mantle. This pattern of reflectivity appears to be characteristic of deep seismic data collected from within extended regions. The relatively small amount of extension which has affected this region suggests that the highly reflective lower crust is more likely to be due to lithological variation formed by mafic igneous intrusion and underplating during crustal extension than to extensional ductile fabrics within the lower crust.

BIRPS (British Institutions Reflection Profiling Syndicate) has collected over 3000 km of high-quality, deep (15-sec two-way travel time), marine seismic reflection data on the continental shelf N, W and S of Britain (Fig. 1). Much of the continental crust in this region has experienced major post-orogenic extension during periods of late Palaeozoic and Mesozoic rifting (Naylor & Shannon 1982; Ziegler 1982). This extension overprinted earlier Caledonian (600–400 Ma) and Variscan (370–270 Ma) structures, produced the large sedimentary basins and thin crust of the continental shelf and possibly contributed to the origin of the thin crust of mainland Britain itself (25–33 km: Bamford et al. 1978; Matthews 1986).

In this paper we present our general conclusions about crustal extension based on the BIRPS data set and provide examples of the data (Figs 2–9) which demonstrate the range of structural styles visible on the continental shelf to the W of Britain. It is not our intention here to discuss specific local features in detail, except in so far as they serve as examples of the overall pattern. The interested reader is referred to several detailed and other more preliminary accounts of the data which have been published elsewhere (MOIST: Brewer & Smythe 1984; WINCH: Brewer et al. 1983; Hall et al. 1984; SWAT: BIRPS & ECORS 1986; Matthews & Cheadle 1986), and to the original data which are available at the cost of reproduction from the Edinburgh office of the British Geological Survey. For a description of the field techniques used and

the data-processing sequence involved in producing the BIRPS seismic profiles see Warner (1986a).

There are three features which are consistently well imaged on BIRPS data: large sedimentary basins, major basin-bounding faults which cut deep into the continental basement, and strong sub-horizontal reflections from the lower crust and Moho. Each of these features is discussed below.

Sedimentary basins

Figure 1 shows the location of the major sedimentary basins crossed by the BIRPS seismic profiles. Three main types of basin occur: simple fault-bounded tilted half-grabens (northern Scotland: MOIST (Brewer & Smythe 1984), DRUM (McGeary & Warner 1985)), more complex basins locally controlled by major dipping structures (eastern North Celtic Sea basin: SWAT 4 and the Western Approaches basin: SWAT 6 & 7 (BIRPS & ECORS 1986), and symmetrical basins with no major controlling structure seen on the seismic data (western North Celtic Sea basin: SWAT 5 (BIRPS & ECORS 1986). Most can be classified as interior fracture basins according to the classification scheme of Kingston et al. (1983). The basins often have a complicated history, however, with a sequence of several rifting events punctuated by phases of uplift and minor compression; for example the South Celtic Sea basin (Kammerling 1979).

From COWARD, M.P., DEWEY, J.F. & HANCOCK, P.L. (eds), 1987, *Continental Extensional Tectonics*, Geological Society Special Publication No. 28, pp. 445–465.

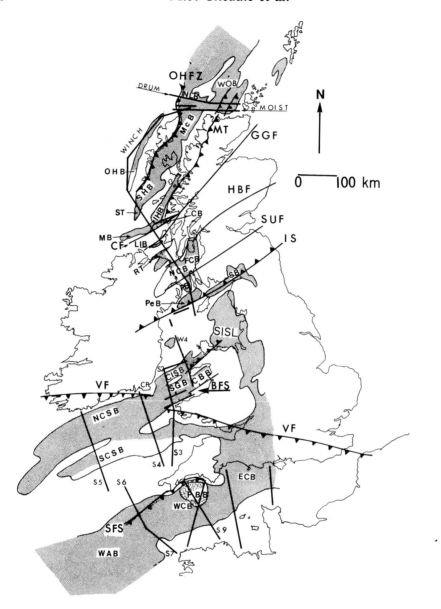

FIG. 1. Location of BIRPS deep profiles to the N, W and S of Britain. Labelled profiles discussed in text: W4=Winch 4; S2, S3, S4, S5, S6, S7 and S9=SWAT profiles 2 to 7 and 9. Stipple pattern marks the extent of the post-orogenic basins crossed by the profiles: CB=Colonsay basin; CBB=Cardigan Bay basin; CISB=Central Irish Sea basin; ECB=Eastern Channel basin; FCB=Firth of Clyde basin; IHB=Inner Hebrides basin; LIB=Loch Indaal basin; MB=Malin basin; McB=Minch basin; NCB=North Channel basin; NCSB=North Celtic Sea basin; NLB=North Lewis basin; OHB=Outer Hebrides basin; PeB=Peel basin; PB=Portpatrick basin; PBB=Plymouth Bay basin; RT=Rathlin Trough; SB=Solway basin; SCSB=South Celtic Sea basin; SGB=St George's Channel basin; SHB=Sea of Hebrides basin; ST=Stanton Trough; WAB=Western Approaches basin; WCB=Western Channel basin; WOB=Western Orkneys basin. CP=Carnsore Point. Major faults shown: BFS=Bala fault system; CF=Colonsay fault; GGF=Great Glen Fault; HBF=Highland Boundary Fault; IS=Iapetus Suture; MT=Moine Thrust; OHFZ=Outer Hebrides fault zone; SFS=Scilly fault system; SISL=South Irish Sea lineament; SUF=Southern Uplands Fault; VF=Variscan front.

The stratigraphy of the commercially prospective basins in the W and S of the region is usually well known from commercial drilling. Far less is known about the basins in the N. Generally the sediments visible on the seismic reflection data are Permian and younger in the S and Devonian and younger in the N (Naylor & Shannon 1982; Ziegler 1982). This age division relates directly to the age of the last major orogeny to have affected the region, i.e. the Caledonian to the N and the Variscan to the S. Only sediments younger than these major compressional events are clearly imaged on BIRPS profiles. For example, the low-grade metamorphic Devono–Carboniferous sediments of southern England which were involved in the Variscan orogeny are not seismically reflective (Fig. 8). The lack of reflections from pre- and syn-orogenic sediments may be explained by the effects of folding and faulting, which will reduce the continuity and planar areal extent of sedimentary reflectors and by those of compaction, induration and metamorphism which will tend to reduce impedance contrasts.

Sedimentary basins need not necessarily be the results of crustal extension and indeed many authors have suggested alternative mechanisms of basin formation (for a short, recent review see Weijemars (Appendix) 1985). The evidence provided by BIRPS deep reflection data suggests, however, that most of the basins profiled are related to crustal extension. Moho-depth reflections show that the crystalline crust thins dramatically beneath the basins. In addition, the geometry of the basins themselves and in particular the detailed relationship between sediments and faults provide support for an extensional origin.

Most of the BIRPS data reveal a highly reflective lower crust (Figs 2, 3, 7, 8, 9 & 10), the base of which appears to coincide with the Moho as defined by seismic refraction experiments (Barton *et al.* 1984; Matthews 1986). If it is assumed that the refraction Moho corresponds at least approximately to the compositional base of the crust, then most of the basins visible on the BIRPS data lie above thinned continental crust (Figs 2, 3, 7 & 9; Brewer *et al.* 1983; BIRPS & ECORS 1986). It is likely that the crust of this region was of at least average thickness (35 km: Cogley 1984) immediately after the Variscan and Caledonian Orogenies. Therefore the

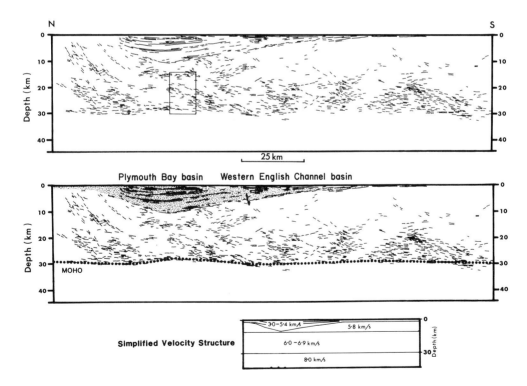

FIG. 2. Interpreted line drawing of SWAT 9, based on a line-drawing depth migrated profile. Plymouth Bay basin shaded. Western English Channel basin unshaded. No vertical exaggeration. The migration velocities (inset) were constrained in the upper crust by stacking velocities and in the lower crust by regional refraction surveys (Edwards & Blundell 1984). Box shows location of Fig. 10(b) which is unmigrated.

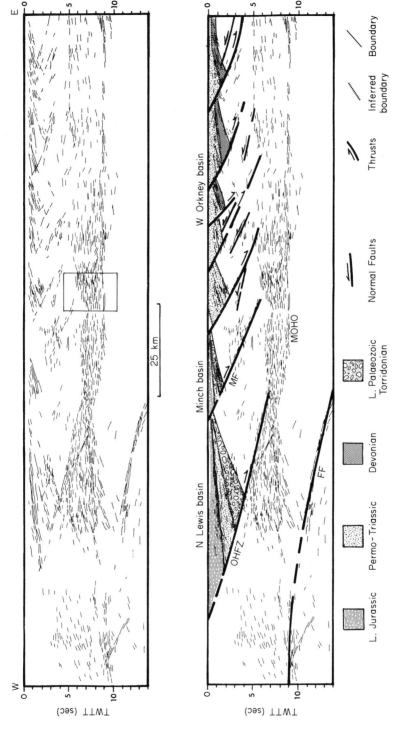

FIG. 3. Line drawing and interpretation of DRUM, unmigrated profile. The position of the stratigraphic boundaries between the sedimentary units is poorly constrained. FF=Flannan fault; MF=Minch fault; OHFZ=Outer Hebrides fault zone. Horizontal to vertical scale is 1:1 for 5 km sec^{-1}. Top 14 seconds of data only. Box shows locations of Fig. 10(c).

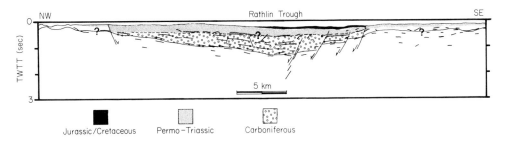

FIG. 4. Interpreted line drawing of part of WINCH 2, unmigrated profile showing Rathlin Trough, after Hall *et al.* 1984. The position of the stratigraphic boundaries between the sedimentary units is poorly constrained. Horizontal to vertical scale is 1:1 for 5 km sec⁻¹. Top 3 seconds only.

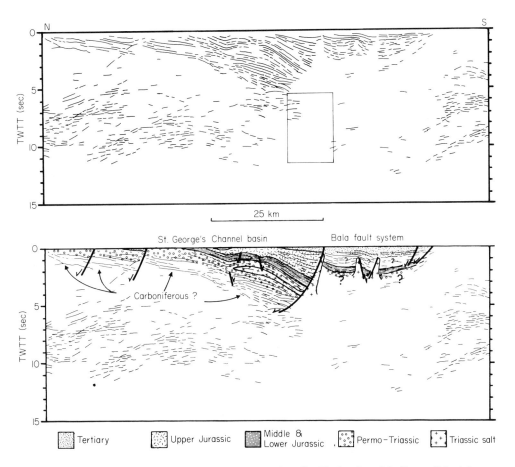

FIG. 5. Line drawing and interpretation of SWAT 2, unmigrated profile. The location of the Permo–Triassic/ Carboniferous boundary is poorly constrained, as is the stratigraphic succession within the Bala fault system. Horizontal to vertical scale is 1:1 for 5 km sec⁻¹. Box shows location of Fig. 10(d).

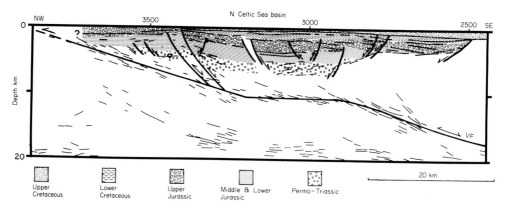

FIG. 6. Interpreted line drawing of the northern part of SWAT 4, based on a depth migrated profile. Velocities constrained by stacking velocities. No vertical exaggeration. Anticlinal structures related to Tertiary compression. Basin poorly constrained at the bottom of the sedimentary sequence and at the northernmost end. Top 20 km of data only.

origin of these basins must be related to crustal thinning. Basin-forming mechanisms that do not involve extension, such as those proposed by O'Connell & Wasserburg (1967), Falvey (1974), Turcotte & Ahern (1977), Middleton (1980) and Neugebauer (1983) may also lead to thinned continental crust. The depth of the larger basins imaged and the extreme reduction in thickness of the basement below them, however, seems too large to be explained solely by these mechanisms that would produce basins of at most 2–3 km depth. For example, the North Celtic Sea basin (Fig. 7) is approximately 8 km deep and its basement thins from approximately 32 km beneath its flanks to 18 km beneath its centre. Furthermore, other complications such as magma intrusion would only serve to thicken the crust. Therefore most of the basins seem to have an origin dominated by crustal extension.

The elongate geometry of most of the imaged basins (Fig. 1) is also characteristic of extensional basins. Perhaps the best seismic reflection evidence for an extensional origin is the detailed internal geometry of the basins themselves, such as the presence of sedimentary thickness variation controlled by non-vertical normal faults. Although such geometries are readily apparent on SWAT 2, for example (Fig. 5), they may be difficult to discern in complex deep basins (SWAT 5: Fig. 7).

Some of the shallower basins have more ambiguous origins, and additional evidence for an extensional origin is provided by regional geological information such as the occurrence of contemporaneous volcanics with extensional tectonic affinities or the offset of major tectonic elements or markers.

Wrench faulting is difficult to identify solely on the basis of two-dimensional reconnaissance BIRPS

surveys. Complicated fault zones on some of the profiles, however, may be strike-slip faults (for example at the southern margin of the South Celtic Sea basin on SWAT 4, Fig. 9). This evidence together with existing tectonic interpretations of the UK continental shelf (Kammerling 1979; Gibbs 1984; Day 1986; Beach *et al.* this volume) suggests that all of the larger basins have been affected to some extent by strike-slip faulting. In many cases, however, major pre-existing structures are not significantly offset (Fig. 1), precluding a true pull-apart origin for the basins.

Most of the basins appear to be roughly in isostatic equilibrium. This is apparent on both gravity and deep seismic data. Elastic flexure is of only minor importance (Warner 1986b). One consequence of this is that the Moho is at approximately the same two-way time beneath both the crystalline basement and the deepest basins (Figs 2,7 & 9). Migration of the data to give a true depth-section shows that the Moho clearly rises beneath the larger basins. Figure 2 shows this for the Plymouth Bay basin.

Basement faults

The BIRPS profiles have been surprisingly successful in obtaining reflections from major faults which cut deep into the basement. In many cases we have been able to identify these reflectors uniquely and we are often able to trace them onto land using shallow commercial data. These faults have a variety of shapes, ages and relationships to the surface geology, however, a consistent pattern seems to be emerging.

The most striking result is the importance of pre-existing basement structure, particularly thrusts, in determining how the crust responds to extensional stress (Cheadle *et al.* 1984; Cheadle & Warner, in prep). The major structures that we image, including the easterly dipping reflectors N of Scotland, the Outer Hebrides fault zone, the Iapetus Suture, the South Irish Sea lineament, the Variscan front, and the Scilly fault system (Fig. 1), appear to have been active as extensional faults and contain large sedimentary basins in their hanging walls. We interpret these faults to be older structures which have been reactivated during crustal extension. Evidence for this reactivation will be discussed below for some of these features. There may be ambiguity in some individual cases, yet the consistency with which the surface traces of these structures invariably correspond to the inferred offshore locations of major thrusts mapped on land is a compelling argument for reactivation. In addition, two major Caledonian strike-slip faults, the Great Glen Fault and Bala fault system, also appear to have been reactivated as normal faults. In fact, in our data, we do not see any major basement-penetrating normal faults which are unambiguously 'new'. The smaller, high-angle faults within the basins are generally not well imaged directly and cannot be traced into the basement.

The faults within the basement, that we are able to image, appear with a variety of shapes ranging from simple planar faults (Fig. 3) to faults with a more complicated ramp and flat geometry (Fig. 6). In general we do not see faults with a classic listric shape within the basement, although the dip of many of the faults changes with depth. Their mean dip ranges from 15–35°. Some of these faults were steeper at inception, however. None of the major normal faults are shallow enough in dip to be classified as sub-horizontal normal detachments in the sense of Wernicke (1985). Nowhere do we see fault-plane reflections which cut entirely through the crust. We do see sub-crustal reflections which may be interpreted as shear zones or tectonic discontinuities within the mantle (McGeary & Warner 1985) but these are never continuous with faults seen within the upper crust.

Lower crust

A conspicuous feature of most of the BIRPS data is the presence of a highly reflective lower crust, the base of which appears to coincide with the Moho as defined by seismic refraction (Matthews 1986; Barton *et al.* 1984). In detail, the character of this reflective zone varies along the length of the lines. Some areas show many strong continuous sub-horizontal reflections, up to 15 km in length, (Fig. 10a) while in others the reflective zone is less regular and contains many dipping and hyperbolic

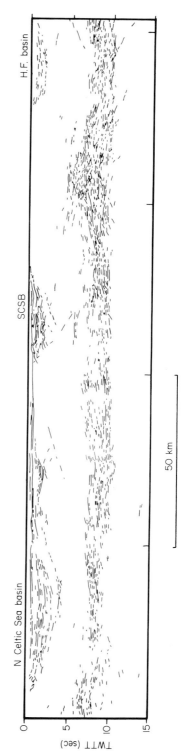

FIG. 7. Line drawing of SWAT 5, unmigrated profile showing symmetrical sag basin geometry of the North Celtic Sea basin and the South Celtic Sea basin (SCSB). H.F. Basin: Haig Fras basin. Horizontal to vertical scale is 1:1 for 5 km sec⁻¹.

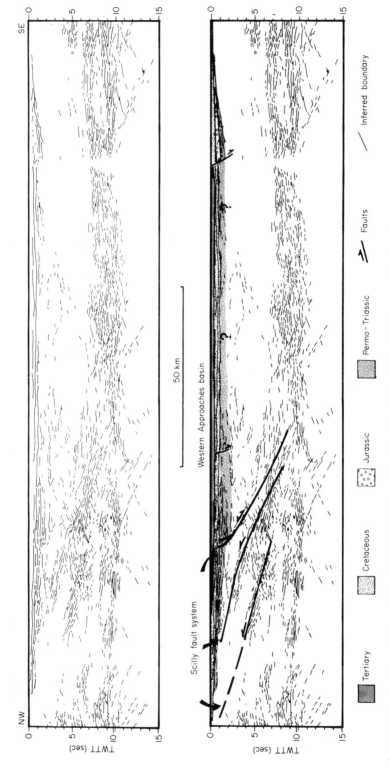

FIG. 8. Line drawing and interpretation of SWAT 6 and 7, unmigrated profiles. The position of the bottom of the basin is poorly constrained. Horizontal to vertical scale is 1:1 for 5 km sec⁻¹.

events (Fig. 10b). The reflections may increase in amplitude and coherence towards the base of the crust and terminate with a bright Moho reflection (Fig. 10c) and in a few areas reflections are poorly developed (Fig. 10d). The thickness of the reflective lower crust also varies, although it often remains of approximately constant thickness over large portions of the data. It consistently occupies only the lower third to half of the crust.

Many origins have been proposed for the reflections in the lower crust (Fuchs 1969; Meissner 1973; Phinney & Jurdy 1979; McKenzie 1984; Matthews & Cheadle 1986) which include: ductile flow in the lower crust produced during crustal extension, igneous intrusion and differentiation associated with increased geothermal gradient, the presence of fluids in the lower crust, and compositional layering and/or horizontal fabrics developed during compressional deformation.

The rapid increase in the quantity and quality of deep continental seismic reflection data has led to several recent reviews of the origin and classification of lower crustal reflective zones (Finlayson & Mathur 1984; Meissner 1986; Allmendinger *et al.* this volume). Each has been based largely on a single data set collected within the confines of one continent. Consensus exists that the reflective zone is intimately related to the last major tectono-thermal event to affect the region and that thermo-mechanical processes have produced the structures from which the reflections originate. The classification schemes of the various authors are incompatible, however, perhaps because of the variability of acquisition techniques and data quality. For example, much of Allmendinger *et al.*'s 'orogenic fabric' from the Basin and Range Province would be classified by Finlayson & Mathur (1984) as 'Archaean less reflective fabric', while the hyperbolic 'cratonal fabric' of Allmendinger *et al.* is not observed in the Australian Craton, and crust with prominent hyperbolic events is observed in Phanerozoic crust on the DEKORP II profile (DEKORP Research Group 1985). The four examples of the reflective lower crust from the BIRPS data set shown in Fig. 10 are all from unequivocal Phanerozoic crust and have been selected from beneath sedimentary basins. They show the possible variability in character of the lower crustal reflective zone within a single province affected by the same last tectono-thermal event: crustal extension. We conclude that there can be considerable variation in lower crustal reflector continuity and geometry within a given region and that the complex patterns may represent the superposition of several geological events. Simple classification schemes based on styles of lower crustal reflectivity may not be applicable worldwide.

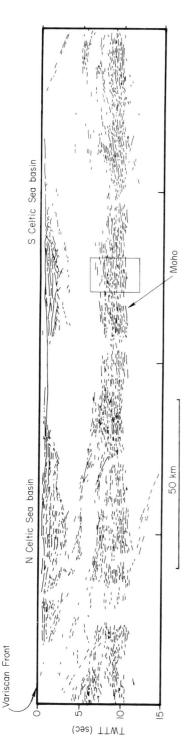

Fig. 9. Line drawing of SWAT 4, unmigrated profile showing variation in thickness of the reflective lower crust beneath the sedimentary basins. Horizontal to vertical scale is 1:1 for 5 km sec⁻¹. Box shows location of Fig. 10(a).

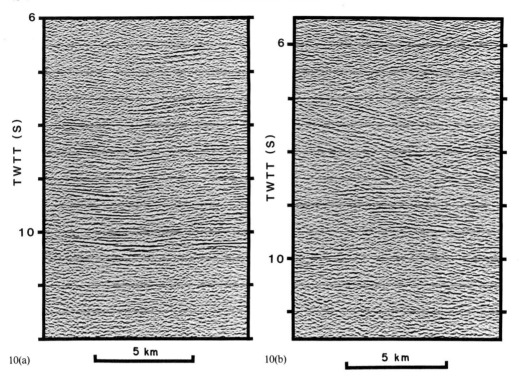

10(a)   5 km   10(b)   5 km

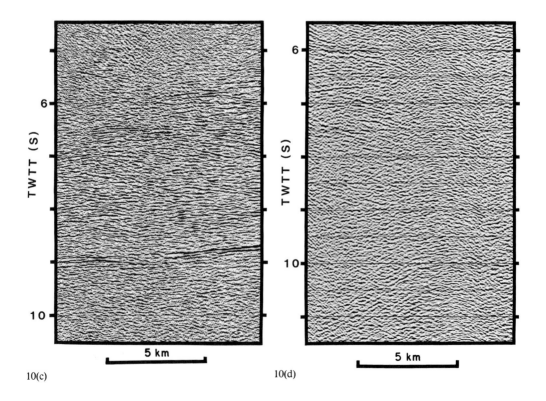

10(c)   5 km   10(d)   5 km

A more general and we suspect fundamental observation is the consistent absence of large areas of prominent reflections in the crystalline upper crust. This is true even when mid-and deep-crustal rocks occur at the surface. Part of the BIRPS data were collected over exposed Lewisian rocks N and W of the Hebrides. The Laxfordian and Scourian sub-divisions of the Lewisian have been suggested as analogues for the middle and lower crust respectively (Weaver & Tarney 1984). On the BIRPS seismic data from this area we see a well-developed reflective zone in the present-day lower crust, but no reflections within the exposed Lewisian basement. Therefore the present-day lower crust of the UK must in some way be different from the Lewisian rocks at the surface. This difference may be due to intense deformation which has drastically reduced the continuity and extent of the reflectors within the Lewisian or more likely may be because the Lewisian is not a good analogue for the lower crust. Other deep reflection profiling of exposed granulite terrains, in the Adirondacks of the eastern US (Klemperer *et al.* 1985) and the Kapuskasing zone in eastern Canada (Cook 1985) has also shown a largely unreflective upper crust. Indeed the occurrence of a highly reflective lower crust sandwiched between an essentially unreflective upper crust and unreflective upper mantle (the 'typical BIRP' of Matthews 1986) is seen on many seismic profiles from all over the world.

The 'typical BIRP' reflection pattern is most prevalent in regions of thin to average crustal thickness (< 40 km), that contain sedimentary basins and that have arguably been affected by processes related to crustal extension. Consider for example the Mesozoic rift domain of the North Atlantic realm (Fig. 11). Most of the profiles recorded within the region show the 'typical BIRP' reflection pattern (Brewer *et al.* 1983; BIRPS & ECORS 1986; Bois *et al.* 1986; Meissner 1986; Schilt *et al.* 1983; Hutchinson *et al.* 1986). Perhaps the most significant profile is the COCORP Southern Appalachian line (Cook *et al.* 1983) (Fig. 12) which shows prominent Moho depth reflections on its eastern end, where the crust is thin (30 km) and has been affected by Permo–Triassic rifting. It

shows no reflections on the western end, where crust is thick (45 km) and unaffected by rifting.

If the reflective lower crust is linked with crustal extension then two origins for the reflections are likely: lithological variation formed by igneous intrusion, underplating, and differentiation (Hildreth 1981), and fabrics produced by ductile flow in the lower crust. The occurrence of a highly reflective lower crust in regions such as western Europe, where recognized extension is generally less than 30% (Kusznir & Park this volume), and the high impedance contrasts of interlayered mafic and felsic rocks suggests that the former origin is more important.

Regional structural style

The region traversed by the BIRPS surveys can be divided into four areas on the basis of age and location. These areas are discussed below to present the variation in basin geometry and structural style of the region.

N Scotland

The northern BIRPS lines, WINCH 1 & 2 and MOIST, traverse the West Orkney, Minch and North Lewis basins and reveal a series of deep (up to 9 km), simple, half-grabens bounded by easterly dipping normal faults (with dips of 20–25° to the E) (Fig. 3) (Smythe *et al.* 1982; Brewer *et al.* 1983; Brewer & Smythe 1984; Brewer & Smythe 1986). The dip of these faults at inception was 30–40°.

The stratigraphy of these basins is not well known (Binns *et al.* 1974; Chesher *et al.* 1983), because of the problems of subdividing monotonous red beds and a lack of commercial drilling. In the E the basins are Devonian and Permo–Triassic in age, but westwards Permo–Triassic sediments become more numerous (Fig. 3). The North Lewis basin is probably Permo–Triassic to Lower Jurassic in age (Binns *et al.* 1974) but Precambrian Torridonian sediments may be present at depth (Brewer & Smythe 1986). The basin-bounding faults themselves have been interpreted by Brewer *et al.*

FIG. 10. Examples of the variation in style and character of reflectivity of the lower crust on BIRPS profiles. All examples are from 'young', Phanerozoic crust, and from beneath large sedimentary basins which have an extensional origin. All are shown at the same size and scale (1:1 for 5 km sec^{-1}).
(a) Highly 'layered' lower crust showing many strong continuous sub-horizontal reflections. From SWAT 4, beneath South Celtic Sea basin (Fig. 9).
(b) Complexly reflective lower crust revealing many dipping and hyperbolic events. From SWAT 9, beneath Plymouth Bay basin (Fig. 2).
(c) Highly reflective lower crust, but with amplitude and coherence increasing towards the bottom and terminating with a bright Moho event. From DRUM, beneath Permo–Triassic basins at centre of line (Fig. 3).
(d) Poorly reflective lower crust. From SWAT 2 beneath St. George's Channel basin (Fig. 5).

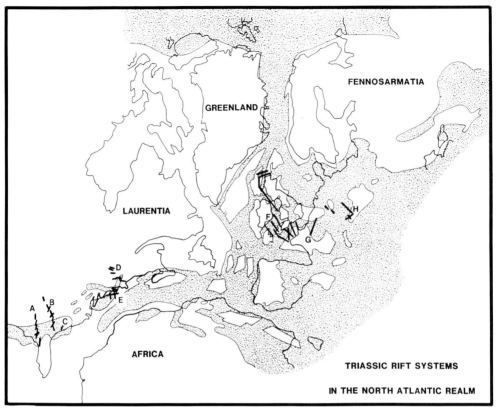

FENNOSARMATIA

GREENLAND

LAURENTIA

AFRICA

TRIASSIC RIFT SYSTEMS

IN THE NORTH ATLANTIC REALM

11(a)

(1983) and Brewer & Smythe (1984) as reactivated Caledonian thrusts. This interpretation was based on the correlation with surface geology and the detailed relationships of the reflectors. Syn-extensional normal faults, including the Minch fault to the S of the DRUM profile (WINCH 2: Brewer & Smythe 1986), appear to sole into the reactivated structures at depth. The Outer Hebrides fault zone (Outer Isles thrust) is approximately planar, and can be followed as a continuous reflector to within 5 km of the Moho, projecting roughly to a normal sense offset in the Moho. Brewer & Smythe (1984), and Peddy (1984) have suggested that it can be extrapolated to cut the Moho. Wernicke (1986), on the basis of gentle warping of the Moho reflections, suggests that both the Outer Hebrides and Minch faults extend through the lithosphere. However, if they do so then they are unreflective and there is no direct evidence to suggest that they continue into the mantle below the Moho.

The Flannan structure (Fig. 3) is our best example of an upper mantle reflector. We interpret this reflector as a tectonic discontinuity or shear zone based on its dip ($\sim 35°$) and its relation to the upper-crustal reflectors (McGeary & Warner 1985). This reflector does not extend through the upper crust but flattens and merges with the lower crust from below (Matthews & Cheadle 1986). It is not known whether this sub-Moho feature is extensional or compressional in origin.

The other basin-bounding faults (the easterly dipping reflectors of Brewer & Smythe 1984) are less planar and may be gently listric, especially at depth. The rollover of the sediments within the easternmost basins further suggests that the faults are listric at depth. The reflectors defining these faults on both MOIST and DRUM (Fig. 3) extend at most to only 19 km depth and terminate about 10 km above the Moho. The absence of deeper reflections led Brewer & Smythe (1984) to suggest that the faults probably sole out at these depths.

The N Scottish basins clearly have an extensional origin which may be analogous to simple domino-faulting models (Emmons & Garrey 1910; Morton & Black 1975). Using the simple relationship (Wernicke & Burchfiel 1982) between the dip of

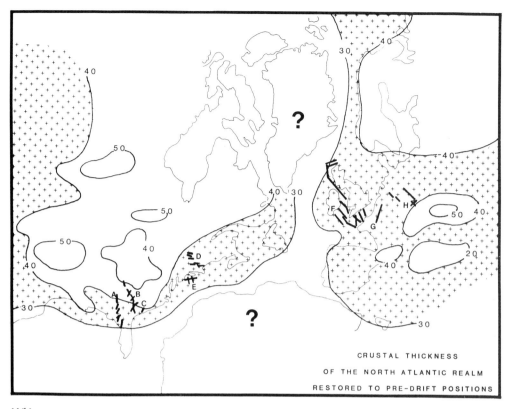

11(b)

FIG. 11. Maps of the North Atlantic Realm restored to pre-drift positions (after Smith *et al.* 1981). (a) Shows Triassic rift systems (after Ziegler 1982) (b) shows approximate present-day crustal thickness (after Beloussov & Pavlenkova 1984 and Condie 1982).

The locations of the seismic surveys are shown in bold lines: A—COCORP Florida and Georgia (Phase II) profiles (McBride *et al.* 1985); B—COCORP Georgia (Phase I) and Tennessee profiles (Cook *et al.* 1983); C—COCORP Charlston profiles (Schilt *et al.* 1983); D—COCORP Northern Appalachian profiles (Ando *et al.* 1984; Klemperer *et al.* 1985); E—USGS Long Island Sound profiles (Hutchison *et al.* 1986); F—BIRPS profiles (Smythe *et al.* 1982; Brewer *et al.* 1983; BIRPS & ECORS 1986; McGeary & Warner 1985); G—ECORS profiles (BIRPS & ECORS 1986; Bois *et al.* 1986); H—DEKORP and other West German profiles (DEKORP Research Group 1985; Meissner 1986).

sediments (20°) and the dip of the bounding faults (20–25°), and assuming rigid-block (domino) rotation allows an approximate crustal extension of about 50–60% to be calculated. Wernicke *et al.* (1985) have performed a similar calculation using different dips and predict an extension of 80–100%. Both of these are only approximate estimates because the geometry of the faults and the behaviour of the individual fault blocks are more complex than in a simple domino model. Individual fault blocks vary in thickness and the basin-bounding faults to the E of the Outer Hebrides fault zone are not planar

and become more shallow to the E. These estimates of the extension suggest that the original crustal thickness was 42–56 km and that the Caledonian crust of mainland Britain was of similar thickness. Erosion and extension has reduced this to around 32 km (Bamford *et al.* 1978).

Much of the rotation of the blocks must have been accommodated by distributed deformation in the lower crust and possibly the upper mantle. The absence of a major half-graben and hence a major normal fault to the W of the planar Outer Hebrides fault zone, the rapid lateral termination of the basins

458   *M.J. Cheadle* et al.

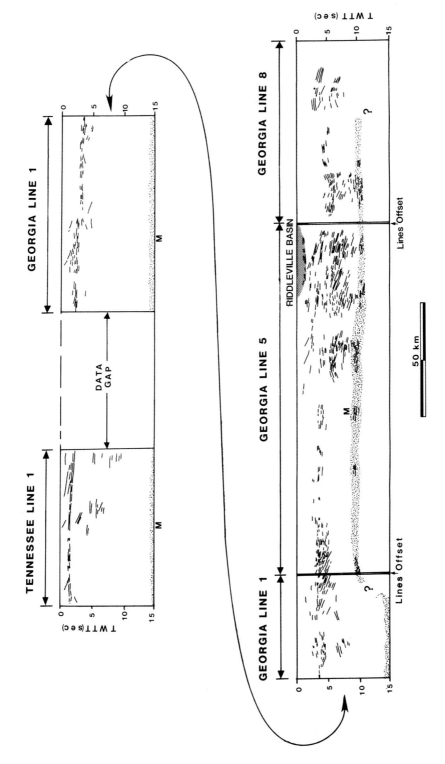

FIG. 12. Line drawing of COCORP Tennessee and Georgia (Phase I) unmigrated profiles (after Cook *et al.* 1983), showing presence of Permo–Triassic Riddleville basin, Moho depth reflections and the inferred position of the Moho (shaded and labelled M). Horizontal to vertical scale is 1:1 for 5 km sec^{-1}.

at the Scottish coastline, and the change in basin geometry to the N (Naylor & Shannon 1982) further suggests extensive distributed crustal deformation.

SW Scotland–Northern Ireland

The complex of small interior fracture and wrench basins which lie between Northern Ireland and SW Scotland were crossed by the central part of the WINCH survey (Brewer & Smythe 1986; Hall *et al.* 1984) and are typical of the smaller basins traversed by the BIRPS profiles. These basins: the Stanton Trough, Colonsay basin, Loch Indaal basin, Rathlin Trough, Portpatrick basin, Peel basin, North Channel and Firth of Clyde basins, are all relatively shallow (less than 5 km depth) and have variable histories. Much of the older sedimentation in the North Channel and Firth of Clyde basins, the offshore continuation of the Midland Valley, was Devonian in age and is not well resolved by the reflection profiling. Most of the basins are symmetrical faulted basins containing Carboniferous to Mesozoic sediments (Hall *et al.* 1984). True half-grabens are rare; the exception being the Loch Indaal basin bounded by the south-easterly dipping Loch Gruinart fault. An extensional history for the basins is difficult to determine from the profiles. The regional geology, however, (Leeder 1982; Anderton *et al.* 1979) suggests that both the Carboniferous and Permo–Triassic were periods of crustal extension. An example of one of the basins is shown in Fig. 4.

Hall *et al.* (1984) conclude that most of the basins are in some way related to pre-existing basement structures and in particular to the major Caledonian sub-vertical strike-slip faults. The Colonsay basin is bounded by the southwesterly extensions of the Great Glen Fault, the Colonsay fault to the S and the Dubh Artach fault to the N. The Peel basin is a broad syncline with little obvious control by old faults, however, it lies in the hanging wall of the Iapetus Suture and may be related to reactivation of this feature. The Mesozoic basins are not super-imposed on the Upper Palaeozoic basins so that the stress regime must have changed between the Devono–Carboniferous rifting and wrenching, and the later Mesozoic events.

Irish and Celtic Sea

The Celtic Sea is underlain by two complex ENE-trending parallel interior fracture basins, the North and South Celtic Sea basins. S of Carnsore Point the North Celtic Sea basin terminates in a series of complex structural units, the St Georges Channel basin, the Cardigan Bay basin and the Central Irish Sea basin (Fig. 1).

The North and South Celtic Sea basins contain Permo(?)–Triassic to Tertiary sediments (Naylor & Shannon 1982), however, the basins differ in their detailed history, the South Celtic Sea basin having suffered more from Cimmerian compressional events (Kammerling 1979). Both have been affected by intermittent compressional events during the Tertiary.

The NCSB and its along-strike continuations, the Central Irish Sea basin and Cardigan Bay basin (Fig. 1), have been traversed four times by the BIRPS survey which has shown the complex lateral variation within these basins. Fig. 13 is a cartoon of these lines. WINCH 4 reveals the Central Irish Sea basin to be a complex faulted basin bounded to the S by a reactivated northward-dipping Caledonian thrust fault (35° mean dip), the South Irish Sea lineament (Brewer *et al.* 1983). SWAT 2 (Fig. 5) crosses the Central Irish Sea basin and the St Georges Channel basin and shows a deep (8–10 km) basin cut by a major northward-dipping listric fault. The apparent shallowing of sediment dips with depth towards the fault (Fig. 5) is due to the presence of a Triassic salt pillow within the sedimentary sequence. This fault correlates with the offshore continuation of the Caledonian Bala fault system (Barr *et al.* 1981) and may be another example of the importance of fault reactivation. Several other apparently planar northward-dipping normal faults also cut the basin.

SWAT 4 (Fig. 6) shows the NCSB lying in the hanging wall of a major SSE-dipping reflector (average dip 17°) which exhibits ramp and flat geometry. This reflector has a Variscan trend (100°, BIRPS & ECORS 1986), is located at the inferred offshore outcrop of the Variscan front (Dunning 1977) and hence has been identified as the Variscan front (BIRPS & ECORS 1986). The coincidence of local changes of trend of the Irish coastline, the basin margin (Fig. 1) and faults and structures within the basin itself (Fig. 14), from the usual Caledonian trend to a Variscan trend in the vicinity of this reflector lead to the conclusion that Variscan structure is locally important in controlling the geometry of the basin. Although the precise relationship between the sediments and the Variscan front is unclear due to lack of resolution in the data, the close proximity of the sedimentary reflectors to the Variscan front, and the continuous unfaulted form of the uppermost ramp of the fault suggests that the Variscan front itself may have acted as a normal fault, possibly during the Permo–Triassic history of the basin. Indeed, the absence of control by other Variscan structures elsewhere within the basin and the shallowing and widening of the basin above the Variscan front relative to the geometry of the basin to the NE and SW of SWAT 4 (SWAT 2 and 5, figs 5 & 7) support this

460 *M.J. Cheadle* et al.

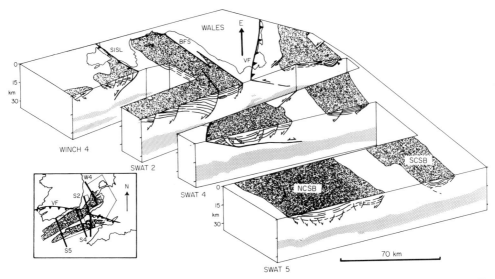

FIG. 13. Schematic block diagram of BIRPS profiles which cross the North and South Celtic Sea basins. All profiles are shown at the same scale (1:1 for 5 km sec⁻¹) and are accurately located relative to each other. Basins and reflective lower crust shaded. Note orientation arrow; E is towards the top of the page. Inset map shows the location of the profiles and the block diagram relative to SW Britain and Eire. BFS=Bala fault system; NCSB=North Celtic Sea basin; SCSB=South Celtic Sea basin; SISL=South Irish Sea lineament; VF=Variscan front. Profiles: W4= WINCH 4; S2=SWAT 2; S4=SWAT 4; S5=SWAT 5.

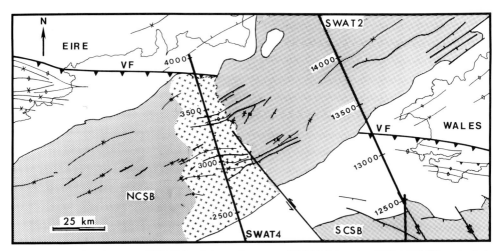

FIG. 14. Detailed location map of SWAT 2 and the northern part of SWAT 4, based on BGS 1:250,000 geological maps: Nymphe Bank, Lundy and Cardigan Bay, (Dunning 1985). NE–SW Caledonian trends and E–W Variscan trends are clearly shown both within and outside basins. The offset of the Variscan front across the North Celtic Sea basin is due to the extensional origin of the basin. Basins are shaded. Cross pattern shows region where trends within the North Celtic Sea basin become more E–W. NCSB=North Celtic Sea basin; SCSB=South Celtic Sea basin; VF=Variscan front.

conclusion. Although the arguments for the reactivation of the Variscan front are persuasive, the fact that the NCSB lies in the hanging wall of the reflector, the apparently continuous character of the reflector, and its ramp and flat geometry are not in themselves diagnostic of reactivation. A similar geometry could be produced by differential stretching of a planar dipping horizon (N.J. White pers. comm.) and simple subsidence of the basin above a horizon similar to the Faille du Midi (Bois *et al.*

1986) could produce the fault geometry. A combination of both of these mechanisms could explain the observed geometry of the fault and the thinning of the basement below it (Fig. 15). A detailed subsidence history of the basin remains to be determined, however. Both the detailed internal geometry and the overall form of the basin visible on SWAT 4 preclude a purely normal-fault origin for the basin. Differential stretching of the entire crust above and below the Variscan front and associated subsidence can to a large extent account

for the basin shape. The Variscan front, therefore, is not a classic detachment fault in the sense of Wernicke (1985a). The situation is further complicated by later Tertiary compressional events which produced the gentle anticlinal structure visible in Fig. 6.

Further to the W, SWAT 5 reveals a deep (8 km) 50-km wide, symmetrical basin with no major fault control (Fig. 7). The upper crustal basement below the basin is presumably cut by many small-displacement normal faults.

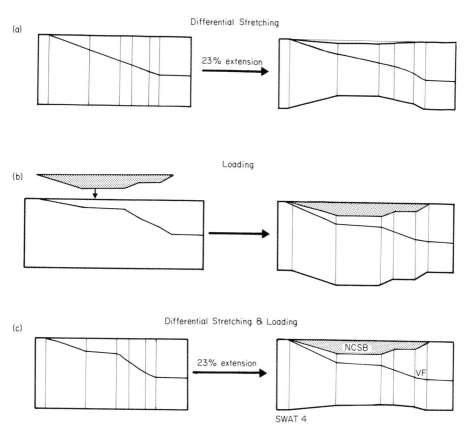

FIG. 15. Cartoon showing how the processes of differential stretching and loading may produce structures with similar shape to the Variscan front. (a) Shows differential stretching of an original planar horizon which soles out at the location of the top of the reflective lower crust. Structure is stretched by the amount calculated from SWAT 4 (23% extension) assuming that the crystalline crust was of constant thickness prior to stretching and that there has been no volume loss or addition during stretching. (b) Shows the effect of pure subsidence due to a load with the shape of the North Celtic Sea basin on a constant thickness crust containing a major structure. This figure shows that the present shape of the Variscan front may be produced by pure subsidence of a structure similar in shape to the Faille du Midi (Bois *et al.* 1986). (c) Shows the initial shape, of the Variscan front, required to produce the present-day shape of the structure as a result of a combination of differential stretching and loading during the formation of the North Celtic Sea basin. Model (c) assumes the crystalline crust was of constant thickness prior to stretching and that there has been no volume loss or addition during stretching. Models (a) and (c) assume isostatic equilibrium.

All models are used merely to demonstrate that the present-day geometry of the North Celtic Sea basin and the Variscan front and present-day crustal thickness cannot be used alone to suggest that the Variscan front has been reactivated as a normal fault. They are not used to predict the original shape of the Variscan front prior to stretching. Other evidence, discussed in the text suggests that the fault has been reactivated to some extent during stretching.

M.J. Cheadle et al.

These rapid lateral changes in basin shape can be accommodated by NE–SW-trending strike-slip faults that effectively subdivide the NCSB into a series of sub-basins. The sub-basins themselves are often controlled by major pre-existing basement weaknesses. The thin crystalline crust beneath these deep, sub-basins (~ 18–22 km) suggests that they have an extensional origin and indicate local crustal extensions of up to 40%.

Channel and Western Approaches

The Western Approaches basin is a wide (150 km), deep (5–6 km) basin which extends between the basement massifs of SW England and Brittany (Fig. 8). It is separated from the similar, shallower (3–4 km) Western Channel basin to the E by the Start–Cherbourg Ridge. Both basins have a complex Mesozoic history and were initiated by Permo–Triassic rifting. Overall basin geometry is similar to the symmetrical basins of the western NCSB and the Northern Ireland/southern Scottish basins but differs in depth and size. Both basins are extensively faulted having suffered a repeated history of rifting and inversion (Ziegler 1982). The Scilly fault system (BIRPS & ECORS 1986), a major Variscan thrust system (35° mean dip), shows evidence of reactivation along the northern margin of the Western Approaches basin (Fig. 8). Other Variscan structures also appear to affect the overall geometry of the English Channel basin.

An anomalous basin lies off axis, beneath the Western Channel basin in Plymouth Bay (Fig. 2). This major, deep (~ 9 km), Permo–Triassic interior sag basin has a roughly circular form (Ziegler 1982; Day 1986) and is unlike most of the other basins profiled by BIRPS. The base of the basin appears unfaulted, at least within the limits of resolution of the seismic survey, though the northern margin is not clearly imaged and could be fault bounded. The thinning of the basement below the basin (Fig. 2) indicates that it originated as a result of crustal extension. It may be a pull-apart bounded by N–S-trending strike-slip faults (Day & Edwards 1983) that were not crossed by the BIRPS profiles.

Discussion

The 3000 km of deep seismic profiles recorded by BIRPS on the western UK continental shelf provides a large body of data from which to study the structural style and processes of crustal extension.

The major conclusion about basin geometry that must be drawn from this data is the importance of pre-existing basement structure as a control for both the locations and shapes of the basins. All of the major basin-bounding faults imaged are interpreted as being reactivated earlier features and indeed their shapes often influence the complex geometry of the basins (see Figs 3,5,6 & 8). None of these faults visibly cut through the entire crust and into the upper mantle as has been suggested in the Basin and Range Province of the western USA and for the MOIST data by Wernicke *et al.* (1985).

The importance of pre-existing structural control on the UK continental shelf may be related to the relatively small amount of extension that affected the region—about 30% (Kusznir & Park this volume). Larger amounts of extension may be more conducive to the generation of new faults due to the rotation and subsequent faulting of pre-existing structures and because igneous and thermal overprinting may effectively anneal older structures.

The symmetrical geometry of the North Celtic Sea basin shown on SWAT 5 is typical of basins formed in the absence of major basement control. The width and depth of these symmetrical basins may vary considerably. The distinct difference in structural style between the basins N of Scotland and those to the S may result from several factors— differences in original basement, the age and amount of extensional deformation, the effect of local strike-slip faulting, and the influence of pre-existing structures within the basement. The same factors are probably also responsible for the complex variation along-strike seen within several of the larger basins in the S, for example the North Celtic Sea basin.

The appearance of a flat Moho on seismic records underscores dramatically the dangers of interpreting seismic reflection time-sections. In fact, the Moho shallows by about 3 km beneath the sedimentary basins which are mostly in isostatic equilibrium.

A comparison of the BIRPS data with worldwide seismic data suggests that the existence of a highly reflective lower crust sandwiched between essentially unreflective upper crust and mantle, in many regions, is significant. We find that this characteristic is more prevalent on data collected from regions of extended continental crust. Of extreme importance is the variation in thickness of the reflective zone beneath the large sedimentary basins, which may place constraints on how the zone relates to crustal extension. The data are to some extent ambiguous; it is sometimes difficult to define the top and bottom of the zone, and data quality varies. Yet many profiles show little change in reflective-zone thickness between the flanks and centre of the basins (for example, SWAT 4, fig. 9). This suggests that either the zone did not pre-date crustal extension, or that extension in the lower crust was distributed over areas much wider than the basins themselves and hence the change in thickness of the zone is beyond the resolution of the data. Another possibility is that extension in the lower crust has been transferred by decollement away from the basins into other regions of the crust. The last explanation is considered unlikely because of the absence of reflections from such decollements.

The lower-crustal reflectivity is most likely due to lithological contrasts formed as a result of mafic-igneous intrusion, underplating and differentiation at lower crustal levels during crustal extension. Herzberg *et al.* (1983) point out that primary magmas from the mantle will be more dense than typical mid–upper crustal rocks at 10 kb. Hence they will tend to underplate felsic–intermediate continental crust. Extensional ductile fabrics are considered to be a less likely explanation for the reflectivity since most of the region was extended by less than 30%.

The variable character of the lower-crustal reflections could be explained by variations in the pre-intrusion crustal composition, the sizes and forms of the intrusive and underplating bodies, and the degree of lower-crustal melting and meta-morphism caused by the bodies. It should be noted, however, that reflections recorded from gneissic layering in metamorphic core complexes in the western US (Reif & Robinson 1981; Hurich *et al.* 1985) provide evidence that ductile fabrics are capable of producing reflections and may therefore account for some of the reflectivity beneath the largest basins.

A mafic lower crust is further supported by the composition of granulite xenolith populations, which are generally basic, in contrast to the exposed granulite terrains which are more acidic (Hunter & Cheadle in prep.). The absence of upper-crustal reflections may be due to the difficulty of uplifting large slices of high-density lower crust during orogenesis. The rheology of such crust would make decollement formation extremely favourable at the top of the mafic lower crust.

Intrusion and underplating of large volumes of igneous rock during extension would also imply that estimates of extension based on constant crustal volume are likely to be minimum estimates. Therefore extension may be greater than can be calculated with simple conservation of crustal volume calculations.

There are four distinct data sets available to the earth scientist interested in extension: (i) earthquake data; (ii) gravity, magnetic and conductivity data; (iii) outcrop geology; and (iv) seismic data. Each of these types of data provides a different and selective sub-set of information. Earthquakes reveal the nature of brittle failure in tectonically active regions. Gravity, magnetic and conductivity data can be used to constrain mass and fluid distributions. Field work and other geological techniques provide a huge quantity of varied information based on exposed rock; although not everything (particularly the lowermost crust) is exposed. Finally, seismic data can only reveal features which are reflective. Thus, different researchers may reach different conclusions based on the bias of their own data-set. We hope in the future to work in tectonically active areas, where the seismic information can be integrated with both earthquake and other geophysical data, and outcrop studies.

ACKNOWLEDGMENTS: We would especially like to thank R. Renner and N.J. White who in a fair world would have been co-authors of this paper. Two almost anonymous referees are also thanked. Of course none of this would have been possible without the expertise, cooperation and never-ending patience of our contractors: GECO UK (WINCH and DRUM), Merlin Profilers and Seismograph Services (England) Ltd., (SWAT) and Western Geophysical (MOIST). Funding is from the Natural Environment Research Council through the Deep Geology Committee, Department of Earth Sciences, Cambridge, Contribution No. 726. Last but not least we must thank Bev Smith for typing and putting up with endless corrections to the manuscript.

References

ALLMENDINGER, R.W., HAUGE, T., HAUSER, E.C., POTTER, C. & OLIVER, J. This volume. Tectonic heredity and the layered lower crust in the Basin and Range Province, western United States.

ANDERTON, R., BRIDGES, P.H., LEEDER, M.R. & SELLWOOD, B.W. 1979. *A dynamic stratigraphy of the British Isles*, 301 pp. George Allen and Unwin, London.

ANDO, C.J., CZUCHRA, B.L., KLEMPERER, S.L., BROWN, L.D., CHEADLE, M.J., COOK, F.A, OLIVER, J.E., KAUFMAN, S., WALSH, T., THOMPSON, J.B., LYONS, J.B. & ROSENFELD, J.L. 1984. Crustal profile of mountain belt: COCORP deep seismic profiling in New England Appalachians and Implications for architecture of convergent mountain chains. *Bull. Am. Assoc. Pet. Geol.* **68**, 819–37.

BAMFORD, D., NUNN, K., PRODEHL, C. & JACOB, B. 1978. LISPB–IV. Crustal structure of northern Britain. *Geophys. J.R. astron. Soc.* **54**, 43–60.

BARR, K.W., COULTER, V.S. & YOUNG, R. 1981. The geology of the Cardigan Bay-St. George's Channel Basin, In: ILLING, L.V. & HOBSON, G.D. (eds) *Petroleum Geology of the Continental Shelf of Northwest Europe*, pp. 432–43. Heyden, London.

464 *M.J. Cheadle* et al.

BARTON, P.J., MATTHEWS, D.H., HALL, J. & WARNER, M. 1984. Moho beneath the North Sea compared on normal incidence and wide-angle seismic records. *Nature*, **308**, 55–6.

BEACH, A., BIRD, T. & GIBBS, A. This volume. Extensional tectonics and crustal structure: Deep seismic reflection data from the northern North Sea Viking graben.

BELOUSSOV, V.V. & PAVLENKOVA, N.I. 1984. The types of the Earth's crust. *J. Geodyn.* **1**, 167–83.

BINNS, P.E., McQUILLIN, R. & KENOLTY, N. 1974. The geology of the Sea of Hebrides. *Rep. Inst. geol. Sci.* London, **73/4**, pp. 43.

BIRPS & ECORS. 1986. Deep seismic reflection profiling between England, France and Ireland. *J. geol. Soc. London.* **143**, 45–52.

BOIS, C., DAMOTTE, B., MASCLE, A., CAZES, M., TORREILLES, G., GALDEANO, A., HIRN, A., MATTE, P. & RAOULT, J.F. 1986. Deep seismic profiling of the crust in Northern France: program ECORS. *In*: BARAZANGI, M. & BROWN, L.D. (eds) *Reflection Seismology: A Global Perspective, Am. geophys. Union geodyn. Ser.* **13**, 21–9.

BREWER, J.A. & SMYTHE, D.K. 1984. MOIST and the continuity of crustal reflector geometry along the Caledonian–Appalachian orogeny. *J. geol. Soc. London*, **141**, 105–20.

—— & —— 1986. Deep Structure of the foreland to the Caledonian Orogen, NW Scotland: Results of the BIRPS WINCH profile. *Tectonics*, **5**, 171–94.

——, MATTHEWS, D.H., WARNER, M.R., HALL, J.R., SMYTHE, D.K. & WHITTINGTON, R.J. 1983. BIRPS deep seismic reflection studies of the British Caledonides. *Nature*, **305**, 206–10.

CHEADLE, M.J., WARNER, M.R. & MATTHEWS, D.H. 1984. Thrust fault reactivation – evidence from BIRPS data. *Abstr. with Programs geol. Soc. Am.* **16**, 463.

CHESHER, J.A., SMYTHE, D.K. & BISHOP, P. 1983. The geology of the Minches, Inner Sound and sound of Raasay. *Rep. Inst. geol. Sci. London*, **83/6**.

COGLEY, J.G. 1984. Continental margins and the extent and number of the continents. *Rev. Geophys. Space Phys.* **22**, 101–22.

CONDIE, K.C. 1982. *Plate Tectonics and Crustal Evolution*, 2nd edn, 310 pp. Pergamon Press, Oxford.

COOK, F.A. 1985. Geometry of the Kapuskasing structure from a lithoprobe pilot reflection survey. *Geology*, **13**, 368–71.

——, BROWN, L.D., KAUFMAN, S. & OLIVER, J.E. 1983. The COCORP seismic reflection traverse across the southern Appalachians. *Am. Assoc. Pet. Geol. Studies in Geology*, **14**, 61 pp.

DAY, G.A. 1986. The Hercynian Evolution of the South West British continental margin. *In*: BARAZANGI, M. & BROWN, L.D. (eds) *Reflection Seismology: The continental crust, Am. geophys. Union Geodyn. Ser.* **14**, 233–41.

—— & EDWARDS, J.W.F. 1983. Variscan thrusting in the basement of the English Channel and S.W. Approaches. *Proc. Ussher Soc.* **5**, 432–6.

DEKORP RESEARCH GROUP 1985. First results and preliminary interpretation of deep reflection seismic recordings along profile DEKORP 2 – South. *J. Geophys.* **57**, 137–63.

DUNNING, F.W. 1977. La Chaine Varisque d' Europe Moyen et Occidentale. *Colloq. international Centr. Recherche Scientifique*, **243**, 165–80.

—— (ed.) 1985. *Geological structure of Great Britain, Ireland and surrounding seas*, Geol. Soc. London Map Chart.

EDWARDS, J.W.F. & BLUNDELL, D.J. 1984. Summary of seismic refraction experiments in the English Channel, Celtic Sea and St. Georges Channel. *IGS Report No. 144*, 14 pp.

EMMONS, W.H. & GARREY, G.H. 1910. General Geology. *In*: RANSOME, F.L. *et al.* (eds) *Geology and ore deposits of the Bullfrog District, Bull. U.S. geol. Surv.* **407**, 19–89.

FALVEY, D.A. 1974. The development of continental margins in plate tectonic theory. *APEA J.* **14**, 95–106.

FINLAYSON, D.M. & MATHUR, S.P. 1984. Seismic refraction and reflection features of the lithosphere in northern and eastern Australia, and continental growth. *Ann. Geophys.* **2**, 711–22.

FUCHS, K., 1969. On the properties of deep crustal reflectors. *Z. Geophys.* **35**, 133–49.

GIBBS, A.D. 1984. Structural evolution of extensional basin margins. *J. geol. Soc. London*, **141**, 609–20.

HALL, J., BREWER, J.A., MATTHEWS, D.H. & WARNER, M.R. 1984. Crustal structure across the Caledonides from the 'WINCH' seismic reflection profile: Influences on Midland Valley evolution. *Trans. R. Soc. Edinburgh Earth Sci.* **75**, 97–109.

HERZBERG, C.T., FYFE, W.S. & CARR, M.J. 1983. Density constraints on the formation of the continental Moho and crust. *Contrib. Mineral. Petrol.* **84**, 1–5.

HILDRETH, W. 1981. Gradients in silicic magma chambers: Implications for lithospheric magmatism. *J. geophys. Res.* **86**, 10153–92.

HURICH, C.A., SMITHSON, S.B., FOUNTAIN, D.M. & HUMPHREYS, M.C. 1985. Seismic evidence of mylonite reflectivity and deep structure in the Kettle dome metamorphic arc complex, Washington. *Geology*, **13**, 577–80.

HUTCHINSON, D.R., GROW, J.A. & KLITGORD, K.D. 1986. Crustal reflections from the Long Island platform of the U.S. Atlantic continental margin. *In*: BARAZANGI, M. & BROWN, L.D. (eds) *Reflection Seismology: the Continental Crust, Am. geophys. Union Geodyn. Ser.* **14**, 173–88.

KAMMERLING, P. 1979. The geology and hydrocarbon habitat of the British Channel Basin. *J. Pet. Geol.* **2**, 75–93.

KINGSTON, D.R., DISHROON, C.P. & WILLIAMS, P.A. 1983. Global basin classification system. *Bull. Am. Assoc. Pet. Geol.* **67**, 2175–93.

KLEMPERER, S.L., BROWN, L.D., OLIVER, J.E., ANDO, C.J., CZUCHRA, B.L. & KAUFMAN, S. 1985. Some results of COCORP seismic reflection profiling in the Grenville-age Adirondack Mountains, New York State. *Can. J. Earth Sci.* **78**, 141–53.

KUSZNIR, N.J. & PARK, R.G. This volume. The extensional strength of the continental lithosphere: its dependence on geothermal gradient, crustal composition and crustal thickness.

LEEDER, M.R. 1982. Upper Palaeozoic basins of the British Isles – Caledonian inheritance versus Hercynian plate margin processes. *J. geol. Soc. London*, **139**, 479–91.

MCBRIDE, J.H., NELSON, K.D., ARNOW, J.A., OLIVER, J.E., BROWN, L.D. & KAUFMAN, S. 1985. New COCORP profiling in the south-eastern U.S. coastal plain: Late Palaeozoic suture and Mesozoic rift basin. *Eos.* **66**, 359.

MCGEARY, S.E. & WARNER, M.R. 1985. Seismic profiling the continental lithosphere. *Nature*, **317**, 795–7.

MCKENZIE, D. 1984. A possible mechanism for epeirogenic uplift. *Nature*, **307**, 616–8.

MATTHEWS, D.H. 1986. Seismic reflections from the lower crust around Britain. *In*: DAWSON, J. B. (ed.) *Nature of the Lower Continental Crust, Spec. Publ. geol. Soc. London*. pp. 11–21.

—— & CHEADLE, M.J. 1986. Deep reflections from the Caledonides and Variscides west of Britain and comparison with the Himalayas. *In*: BARAZANGI, M. & BROWN, L.D. (eds) *Reflection Seismology: A Global Perspective, Am. geophys. Union Geodyn. Ser.* **13**, 5–19.

MEISSNER, R. 1973. The Moho as a transition zone. *Geophys. Surv. Dordrecht*, **1**, 195–216.

—— 1986. Twenty years of deep seismic reflection profiling in Germany – A contribution to our knowledge on the nature of the Lower Variscan crust. *In*: DAWSON, J. B. (ed.) *Nature of the Lower Continental Crust, Spec. Publ. geol. Soc. London*.

MIDDLETON, M.F. 1980. A model of intracratonic basin formation, entailing deep crustal metamorphism. *Geophys. J.R. astron. Soc.* **61**, 1–14.

MORTON, W.H. & BLACK, R. 1975. Crustal attenuation in Afar. *In*: PILGER, A. & ROSSLER, A. (eds) *Afar Depression of Ethiopia, Inter-Union Commission on Geodynamics, Int. Symp. Afar region and related rift problems, Proc. Sci. Rep. No. 14*, pp. 53–65. E. Schweizerbartsche Verlagsbuchhandlung, Stuttgart, Germany.

NAYLOR, D. & SHANNON, P. 1982. *Geology of Offshore Ireland and West Britain*, 161 pp. Graham & Trotman Ltd., London.

NEUGEBAUER, H.J. 1983. Mechanical aspects of continental rifting. *Tectonophysics*, **94**, 91–108.

O'CONNELL, R.J. & WASSERBURG, G.J. 1967. Dynamics of the motion of a phase change boundary to changes in pressure. *Rev. Geophys.* **5**, 329–410.

PEDDY, C.P. 1984. Displacement of the Moho by the Outer Isles thrust shown by seismic modelling. *Nature*, **312**, 628–30.

PHINNEY, R.A. & JURDY, D.M. 1979. Seismic imaging of deep crust. *Geophysics*, **44**, 1637–60.

REIF, D.M. & ROBINSON, J.P. 1981. Geophysical, geochemical and petrographic data and regional correlation from the Arizona State A-1 Well, Pinal County, Arizona. *Arizona geol. Soc. Dig.*, **13**, 99–109.

SCHILT, F.S., BROWN, L.D., OLIVER, J.E. & KAUFMAN, S. 1983. Subsurface structure near Charleston, South Carolina – Results of COCORP reflection profiling in the Atlantic coastal plain. *In*: GOHN, G.S. (ed.) *Studies related to the Charleston, South Carolina earthquake of 1886 – tectonics and seismicity, U.S. geol. Surv. Prof. Pap.* **1313**, H1–H14.

SMITH, A.G., HURLEY, A.M. & BRIDEN, J.C. 1981. *Phanerozoic palaeocontinental world maps*, 102 pp. Cambridge University Press.

SMYTHE, D.K., DOBINSON, A., McQUILLIN, R., BREWER, J.A., MATTHEWS, D.H., BLUNDELL, D.J. & KELK, B. 1982. Deep structure of the Scottish Caledonides revealed by the MOIST reflection profile. *Nature*, **299**, 338–40.

TURCOTTE, D.L. & AHERN, J.L. 1977. On the thermal and subsidence history of sedimentary basins. *J. geophys. Res.* **82**, 3762–66.

WARNER, M.R. 1986a. Deep seismic reflection profiling of the continental crust at sea. *In*: BARAZANGI, M. & BROWN, L.D. (eds) *Reflection Seismology: A Global Perspective, Am. Geophys. Union Geodyn. Ser.* **13**, 281–6.

—— 1986b. In press. The Moho, isostasy and deep seismic reflections. *Geophys. J. R. astron. Soc.*

WEAVER, B.L. & TARNEY, J. 1984. Major and trace element composition of the continental lithosphere. *In*: POLLACK, H. N. & MURTHY, V. R. (eds) *Structure and Evolution of the Continental Lithosphere, Phys. Chem. Earth Oxford*. **15**, 39–68.

WEIJERMARS, R. 1985. In search for a relationship between harmonic resolutions of the geoid, convective stress patterns and tectonics in the lithosphere: a possible explanation for the Betic-Rif orocline. *Phys. Earth planet. Inter.* **37**, 135–48.

WERNICKE, B. 1985. Uniform-sense normal simple shear of the continental lithosphere. *Can. J. Earth Sci.* **22**, 108–25.

—— 1986. Whole-lithosphere normal simple shear: An interpretation of deep-reflection profiles in Great Britain. *In*: BARAZANGI, M. & BROWN, L.D. (eds) *Reflection Seismology: The Continental Crust, Am. Geophys. Union Geodyn. Ser.* **14**, 331–9.

—— & BURCHFIEL, B.C. 1982. Modes of extensional tectonics. *J. struct. Geol.* **4**, 104–15.

——, WALKER, J.D. & BEAUFAIT, M.S. 1985. Structural discordance between Neogene detachments and frontal Sevier thrusts, Central Mormon Mountains, southern Nevada. *Tectonics*, **4**, 213–46.

ZIEGLER, P.A. 1982. *Geological Atlas of Western and Central Europe*, 130 pp. Shell International Petroleum, Maatshappij B.V.

M.J. CHEADLE, S. MCGEARY, M.R. WARNER & D.H. MATTHEWS, BIRPS, Bullard Laboratories, Department of Earth Sciences, University of Cambridge, Madingley Road, Cambridge CB3 0EZ, UK.

Extensional tectonics and crustal structure: deep seismic reflection data from the northern North Sea Viking graben

A. Beach, T. Bird & A. Gibbs

SUMMARY: A preliminary interpretation of a deep seismic reflection profile across the northern North Sea provides an insight into the crustal structure beneath the major extensional rift, the Viking graben. The Viking graben was initiated during the early Mesozoic and evolved during the Jurassic–Cretaceous into an asymmetrical half-graben, fault-bounded on its western side. Deep seismic reflections enable an interpretation of the position of the Moho to be made, and an estimate of the amount of crustal extension, within the plane of the section, of 50% has been calculated. The pre-Mesozoic crust has been thinned to a minimum of 14 km, but generally varies from 15–20 km beneath the rift. Interpretation of extensional faults within the Jurassic generally gives less than 50% extension, and much of the early Mesozoic faulting is probably not imaged. Calculation of Mesozoic subsidence in the graben leads to an estimated stretching factor of 3 or greater. A larger scale of linked tectonics involving major strike-slip movements along the length of the graben is invoked to explain the discrepancy between subsidence and crustal extension. Fault-related subsidence occurred in three distinct phases of finite duration—during the Triassic (40 My), the late Jurassic (30 My), and the early Tertiary (30 My). During the late stages of pervasive crustal thinning (late Jurassic–Early Cretaceous) a series of major fault and shear zones developed, dipping E and passing through the crust, offsetting the Moho. The change in tectonic style corresponds to a change from a dominantly extensional to a dominantly strike-slip mode of rift evolution. The seismic profile also images the Magnus basin related to the Great Glen fault system, and the Horda Platform near the coast of Norway.

The Viking graben is a major Mesozoic rift basin in the northern North Sea (Ziegler 1982). Seismic refraction data (Solli 1976), gravity surveys (Donato & Tully 1981) and theoretical modelling (McKenzie 1978) have led to the general acceptance of an extensional tectonic origin for the Viking graben, involving an early Mesozoic phase of extension and fault-controlled subsidence, followed by a more regional thermal-contraction subsidence. The early success of the BIRPS deep seismic relection profiling (Smythe *et al.* 1982) and the results from COCORP (Smithson *et al.* 1979) led to the planning and acquisition during 1983 of a deep seismic line, recorded to 15 sec TWT, across the N Viking graben. The principal aims of this acquisition were to provide constraints on the geometry of the Viking graben and its extensional faults, to provide data on the geometry of crustal thinning beneath the graben, and to provide an insight into the relationship between the shallow extensional features of the sedimentary basin and the deep crustal thinning.

The seismic profile was shot from N of the Shetland Islands to the coast of Norway near Bergen, a length of approximately 340 km, in a NW–SE direction. The line crossed what was considered structurally the simplest part of the Viking graben, and its location is shown on Fig. 1. At its NW end, the line crosses the N Shetland Spur, a large rotated crustal block, with an eroded crest

and a thin cover of Tertiary sediment that marks the beginning of the development of Atlantic-rift margin structures. It then passes across the Magnus basin, a major Mesozoic extensional basin bounded on its SE side by a fault related to the Great Glen Fault lineament. Between the Magnus basin and the Viking graben lies the complexly faulted area making up the northern part of the Shetland Terrace system of Jurassic fault blocks. The Viking graben is approximately 70 km across on this line, and the Jurassic and Cretaceous sequences gradually thin eastwards onto the Horda Platform, of offshore Norway. The features referred to are located on Fig. 1. The profile is discussed here using a series of simplified line drawings, vertical exaggeration being introduced to fit them to page size. Copies of the original, detailed and normal-scale drawings are available from the authors on request.

Acquisition and processing

Standard oil industry exploration seismic techniques were modified to effectively image the deep crustal boundaries as well as maintain acceptable definition of the shallower supra-crustal structure with which the petroleum industry is more familiar. The data were acquired in May 1983 by Western Geophysical using their super-wide airgun array (6276 in³, 2000 psi) towed at a depth of 7.5 m. A

From COWARD, M.P., DEWEY, J.F. & HANCOCK, P.L. (eds), 1987, *Continental Extensional Tectonics*, Geological Society Special Publication No. 28, pp. 467–476.

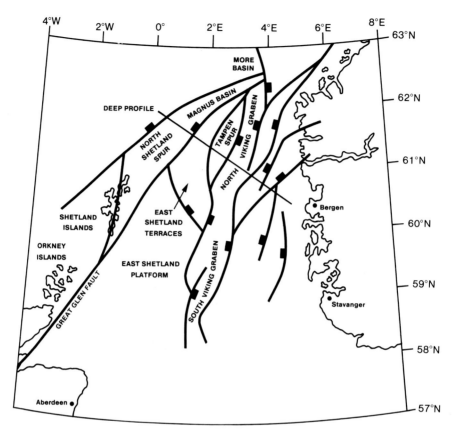

Fig. 1. Location of the deep seismic reflection profile across the northern North Sea, in relation to principal Mesozoic tectonic elements.

shot interval of 50 m permitted the 15 sec record-length required for the deep (50 km) targets to be obtained. The standard 300 m 120-channel hydrophone streamer was towed at 10–12 m average depth with 25 m group length. Western Geophysical tested a variety of processing routines before adopting an optimal sequence with the following features:

1 sample rate 4 ms;
2 predictive deconvolution before stack with 280 ms operator length and 32 ms lag applied to 6 sec only;
3 60—fold stack using stacking velocities derived from velocity spectra;
4 predictive deconvolution after stack,
    (i) 260 ms operator length and 36 ms lag applied from 0–6 sec and,
    (ii) 340 ms operator length and 80 ms lag applied from 6–15 sec;
5 dip filter +/− 7 ms per trace;
6 adjacent trace sum to output a 50 m trace-spacing;

7 migration by the finite-difference method using 90% stacking velocities 0–4 sec; 4000 m sec^{-1} interval velocity 4–7 sec; 5000 m sec^{-1} 7–10 sec; 6000 m sec^{-1} 10–15 sec following structure;
8 time variant band-pass filters ranging from 8 Hz cut at 18 db/octave, 55 Hz high cut at 36 db/octave over 0–2 sec TWT to 4 Hz low cut at 18 db/octave, 20 Hz high cut at 36 db/octave over 10–15 sec TWT interval;
9 equalization using 100 ms window robust automatic gain control;
10 gun-and-cable static correction to sea level datum (12 ms).

Seismic zonation and structure

Figure 2 portrays in a simplified fashion the continuity and strength of reflections on the profile, and shows several features in common with other deep seismic profiles. Cretaceous and Tertiary sedi-

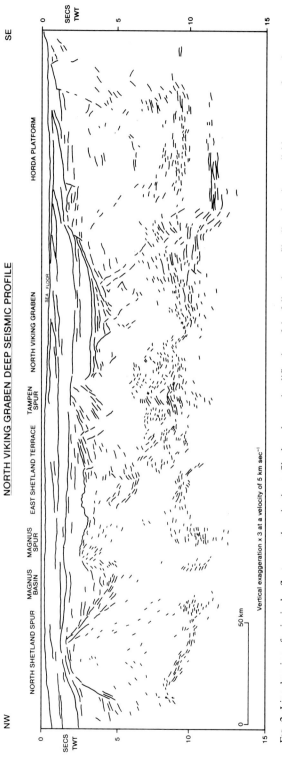

Fig. 2. Line drawing of principal reflectors on the seismic profile, based on a simplification of the full-scale profile (line drawing available on request from the authors), and with a three-fold reduction in horizontal scale.

mentary sequences appear as a well-layered series of continuous seismic reflections. A strong base Cretaceous event is seen over much of the section, with the exception of the middle of the Viking graben and Magnus basin. Reflections from the Jurassic are more discontinuous and become weaker down through the Triassic. Top basement is not imaged over most of the line, with the exception of the eastern end, where metamorphic rocks rise to the sea bed. The inferred pre-Mesozoic basement generally has no strong seismic character. For example, the N Shetland Spur is seismically featureless from top basement at 2 sec TWT down to 9 sec TWT. Under the Shetland Terrace this zone is still present, though not continuous, and under the Viking graben the featureless zone is only 2 sec TWT in thickness. There is a strong contrast between the seismic character of the middle crust and that of the lower crust. A zone of very strong reflections, varying in thickness from 0.5–2 sec TWT, is variably developed along the length of the profile. A combination of seismic reflection and refraction data from the Central graben enabled Barton *et al.* (1984), and Barton & Wood (1984) to interpret the position of the Moho as corresponding closely to the base of the zone of strong reflections. This interpretation has been applied to other deep seismic data (e.g. BIRPS & ECORS 1986; Hall *et al.* 1984) and is adopted here.

Some significant lateral variations in seismic character of the deep crust are noted. The strongest and deepest reflections are seen at the eastern end of the line, immediately overlain by a transparent zone and another zone of reflections. Moving W, the zone of reflections is well developed below the Viking graben, whereas in contrast it is poorly developed beneath the Magnus basin. A similar thickness of Mesozoic–Tertiary sediments in both basins suggests that the difference is a real geological feature, and not an effect of dissipated energy beneath the Magnus basin. In the intervening area, i.e. below the East Shetland Terrace, the zone of reflections gradually rises from E to W, and at the same time decreases in strength. This gross lateral variation in crustal seismic character is referred to again later.

Depth conversion, extension and subsidence

In order to provide an estimate of crustal thinning beneath the Viking graben, it is necessary to convert the principal structures on the profile from a time to a depth position. Crustal velocity data required to accomplish this is sparse. From a seismic refraction profile across the N Viking graben, Solli (1976) determined one velocity of 6.1 km sec^{-1} for the whole of the pre-Mesozoic crust. Further, more detailed seismic experiments are needed to determine vertical and lateral variations in seismic velocity (cf. Barton & Wood 1984). The most important effect on depth conversion is the relative thickness of low-velocity sediment and higher velocity basement. Thus a first-order measurement of crustal thickness can be obtained from applying a uniform velocity of 6.1 km sec^{-1}. Velocities in the overlying sedimentary sequences are known from drill-hole data, and the following were applied to the profile: Tertiary 2.0 km sec^{-1}; upper Cretaceous 2.7 km sec^{-1}; lower Cretaceous, Jurassic, Triassic 3.2 km sec^{-1}. Finally, the narrow zone of very strong reflections at the base of the crust was assigned a velocity of 7 km sec^{-1} (cf. Barton & Wood 1984; Bucovics & Ziegler 1985). The depth-converted profile is shown in Fig. 3.

Figure 3 shows that, assuming an initially uniform crustal thickness of 30–32 km, there has been thinning of the crust to a minimum of 14 km below both the Magnus basin and Viking graben and this is interpreted as a 50% extension of the whole profile, within the plane of the section. In the centre of the Viking graben, the maximum extension of the crust would be 130% ($\beta = 2.3$). The crust reaches a thickness of 30 km below the Horda Platform. In the absence of any contrary information, the pre-Mesozoic crust has been assumed to be of uniform thickness and the statement of 50% extension must be qualified by this (cf. Smythe *et al.* 1980).

The application of the McKenzie (1978) model allows a relationship between crustal thinning and basin subsidence to be established. To this end a basement-subsidence curve has been calculated for the Viking graben, following the methods outlined by Sclater & Christie (1980) and Sawyer *et al.* (1982). Since no wells penetrate the deep Viking graben (e.g. top Jurassic estimated to be at a depth of about 5 km) to top basement, the approach of relying on back-stripping of specific wells to elucidate the basin subsidence history (e.g. Christie & Sclater 1980; Wood 1981; Barton & Wood 1984) has not been adopted. The anomalies associated with specific well locations can be avoided and a more region-wide subsidence curve obtained, by setting up a seismic stratigraphy for the deepest part of the basin. The generalized nature of the Tertiary and Cretaceous sections can be ascertained from well data, but the Jurassic and Triassic are assumed to be dominated by claystone and sandstone respectively for decompaction procedures. Although this results in a less accurate subsidence curve in detail, it provides a curve that truly addresses the problem of overall basin subsidence.

The calculated curve is shown in Fig. 4. This was based on a compilation of average sediment type

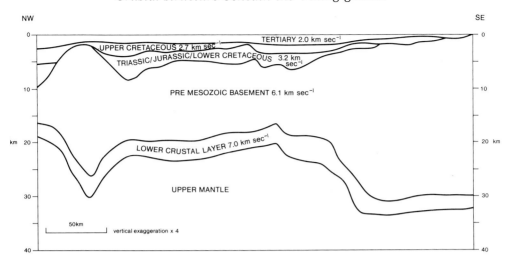

FIG. 3. Depth conversion of the seismic profile based on a simple velocity structure for the crust.

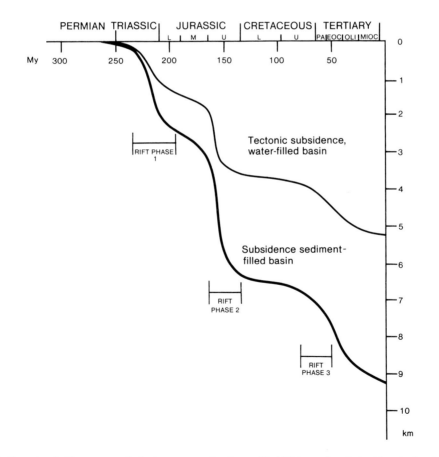

FIG. 4. Tectonic subsidence curves for both a water- and sediment-filled Viking graben derived by a back-stripping procedure, based on a combination of well and seismic stratigraphical data.

taken in 300-m units from the present, back to base Triassic, with a present depth of 9 km in the graben. Back-stripping was carried out by removing 600 m at a time, and decompacting all the underlying sediments along known, generalized compaction curves for Mesozoic sediments in North Sea basins. Figure 4 shows both the tectonic subsidence curve for a waterfilled basin, and basement subsidence for a basin filled with sediment at a constant average density. The effects of sea-level change and palaeobathymmetry have been ignored because accurate data are not available and because their effect on the overall subsidence curve is only second order.

Subsidence related to extensional faulting is known to have occured during the Triassic and the late Jurassic and Early Cretaceous (e.g. Badley *et al.* 1984). However, fault-related subsidence on the principal boundary faults of the Viking graben continued through the Cretaceous and into the early Tertiary. It is not possible simply to identify an early phase of rifting and a subsequent phase of thermal subsidence, as in the McKenzie model, in the Viking graben. Jarvis & McKenzie (1980) discuss the evolution of basins with finite rifting times, and the total thermal and tectonic subsidence in a basin which is independent of the number of stretching events, their duration, etc. Thus, if·it is assumed that final equilibrium of the North Sea stretching events has been reached, then a total stretching factor of 3 is established from Jarvis & McKenzie (1980) for the basin centre.

Rapid subsidence during extension occurred over approximately 40 My during the Triassic and earliest Jurassic. A stretching factor of 1.5 is estimated from this portion of the curve (using standard crustal thicknesses etc, Dewey 1982). There was a time gap of about 30 My before the onset of a second phase of rifting subsidence during the late Jurassic, which lasted for about 30 My. As a first approximation it is estimated, in the calculation of a stretching factor from a standard crust model, that the effect of rifting over a finite period of time counteracts the effect of superimposing this rifting on the thermal subsidence from the earlier rift phase. The stretching factor for the Jurassic phase is thus estimated to lie in the range 1.8–2.2. This provides a cumulative stretching factor for the graben centre of approximately 3.0. Although subsidence continued to be fault-controlled during the Cretaceous, the geometry found is not characteristic of extensional subsidence (Badley *et al.* 1984). The fault relation is most probably an expression of the mechanism by which the crust responds to regional thermal subsidence by movement along deep-seated faults. However, a third phase of extensional subsidence in the Viking graben area is thought to have occurred during the Late Cretaceous to Palaeocene (cf. Dewey 1982),

and the stretching factor is estimated to be 1.1 over a period of about 30 My. The cumulative stretching factor for the centre of the Viking graben, estimated from the basin subsidence, may thus be as high as 3.3.

There is a discrepancy between the stretching factor interpreted from the basin-centre subsidence history (3.3), and the crustal thinning, beneath the graben, measured from the profile (2.3). The estimates quoted above are based on a standard ratio of crustal thickness to lithospheric thickness (31/125, cf. Dewey 1982) and an increase in the thickness of the pre-Mesozoic crust has the effect of (i) increasing the estimate of crustal extension, and (ii) decreasing the value of the cumulative stretching factor for the observed amount of subsidence. The two estimates can be made broadly compatible in this way, though there are no geological data available on the thickness of the pre-Mesozoic crust. For example, for the crust at the eastern end of the profile beneath the Horda Platform, an increase in average crustal velocity from 6.1 (used here) to 6.7 in the lower half of the crust would increase an estimate of crustal thickness from 32 to 40 km, and a seismic refraction experiment should be designed to gather more detailed deep-crustal seismic velocities (cf. Barton & Wood 1984).

Geological models for the profile

Interpretation of the early extensional phase

A simple geological model for the profile is presented in this section, and the discussion here centres on the interpretation of Fig. 2 as shown in Fig. 5.

Thinning of the whole or lower crust is seen over the section from the Magnus basin to the E side of the Viking graben, and this is related in time to the deposition of the overlying Triassic–Jurassic sequence. After the main phase of extensional history, the mechanism of movement changed from one affecting the whole of the lower crust, to one of a much more discrete nature—movement occurred on primary fault/shear zones that cut right through the crust and offset the Moho. The latter mechanism accounts for only a small amount of extension in the plane of the profile ($\beta = 1.05$), compared with the total measured crustal extension ($\beta = 1.5$). However, it is the major through-crust fault zones that impart the most obvious geometric features seen on the profile, i.e. the asymmetry and down-to-the-E rooting of the Viking graben structures. The relatively insignificant contribution of these large structures to the overall extension leaves unanswered the question of how Triassic–Jurassic faults in the shallow crust relate to the extension in the lower crust, and to lithospheric structure.

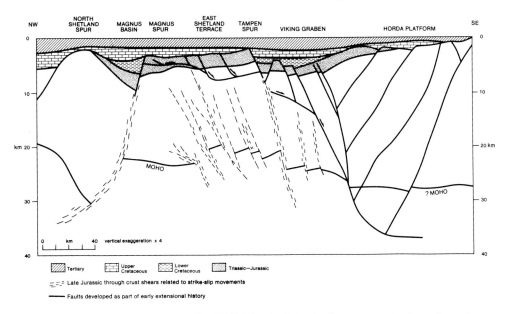

FIG. 5. Simple geological model for the profile, highlighting the distinction between an early phase of extension on an easterly dipping detachment, and a later phase of movement on steeper, through-crust shears. Note four-fold vertical exaggeration.

Faults have been imaged to a depth of 6–8 km beneath the Tampen Spur, and a fault detachment is interpreted from the geometry of extension and rotation of Triassic to early Jurassic reflectors in the eastern part of the East Shetland Platform (cf. Gibbs 1983, 1984). On a restoration of the Viking graben boundary fault at a mid-Jurassic time, this structural style is expected to continue eastwards. The position of this detachment cannot be determined from the profile, and the position marked in Fig. 5 is highly speculative. The important points that are clear, however, are that (i) principal Triassic–Jurassic extensional faults dip consistently to the E across the East Shetland Terrace and into the Viking graben, and (ii) a distinct ramp down-to-the-E of the basal extensional detachment is thus constrained to root into the lower crust beneath the eastern side of the Viking graben. Is this a 'blind' detachment within the lower crust, or does it cut down into the upper mantle?

Both hypotheses are admissible. In the former, the detachment would be 'pinned' once the crust returned to normal thickness, unaffected by early-Mesozoic extension, below the Horda Platform (Fig. 6). In the latter hypothesis, the detachment would ramp into the mantle as a major zone of movement, and ultimately link into the decoupling surfaces of contemporaneous plate motions. The strong, sub-horizontal reflections at 11–12 sec TWT beneath the Horda Platform (Fig. 2) may be interpreted as indicating the position of the Moho here. The presence of a seismically transparent zone immediately above these reflections, with the characteristically 'noisy' lower crust above this, however, leads to the preferred interpretation that these strong reflectors are within the upper mantle, imaging the major extensional detachment as it ramps down beneath the Moho (Fig. 6). The Moho lies above this at 9–10 sec TWT (about 28–30 km in Fig. 3). An experiment designed to determine deep-crustal seismic velocities may help answer this problem. Early-Mesozoic basin development thus occurred in the hanging wall above a gently, easterly dipping deep-crustal detachment shear zone, analogous to that described by Wernicke (1981).

Interpretation of the subsequent strike-slip phase

Several different geometric models of the development of extensional basins have been proposed, largely following the formulation of the McKenzie (1978) model and in an attempt to elucidate mechanisms of crustal extension. Two broad categories can be recognized:

1 The suggestion that major, gently dipping detachment zones pass through the crust, and that basins develop in the overlying hanging wall. Crustal extension occurs by deep-crustal

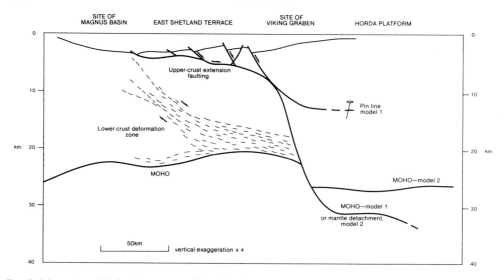

FIG. 6. Schematic models for the geometry of the Triassic–early Jurassic extensional phase.

ductile movements and separation across the low-angle detachment. Brittle extensional faulting in the upper-crustal hanging wall decouples at or above the low-angle detachment, (Wernicke 1981; Allmendinger *et al.* 1983; Anderson *et al.* 1983; Brun & Choukroune 1983).

2 The suggestion that a series of moderate to steeply inclined fault zones cut through the crust from shallow to deep levels, imparting a domino structure to the crust. Crustal extension occurs by dip-slip on the fault set and the rotation of the major crustal blocks bounded by these faults (Wernicke & Burchfiel 1982; Le Pichon *et al.* 1982; Jackson & McKenzie 1983; Brun & Choukroune 1983).

The major fault bounding the Magnus basin is interpreted as a Mesozoic strike-slip reactivation of the Great Glen fault system. The part of this fault that forms the boundary to the Moray Firth basin is known to have Mesozoic strike-slip movements (McQuillin *et al.* 1982; Flinn 1975). Further, this lineament extends to the NE as a Mesozoic strike-slip zone in the offshore Norway area (Hamar & Hjelle 1984; Gabrielson & Robinson 1984; Bucovics & Ziegler 1985). The Magnus basin has the geometry of a pull-apart basin against this strike-slip fault zone, analogous to the Unst and Fair Isle basins (cf. Johnson & Dingwall 1981; Flinn 1969). The subsidence histories of the Magnus basin and the Viking graben are very similar in both the timing and amounts of subsidence. In particular, both record a later Jurassic to Early Cretaceous subsidence at variance with the crustal extension across the major boundary faults. In addition, both

basins are bounded by late Jurassic fault zones that cut steeply through the crust and which are interpreted as offsetting the Moho. It is suggested that this geometry is a result of major crustal strike-slip movements along both the Magnus basin and the Viking graben. On a regional scale, the Viking graben during the late Jurassic and Early Cretaceous has been interpreted by Beach (1985) as a major sinistral transtensional pull-apart basin. This is seen in the fault geometry in plan view— side-stepping major faults linked by extensional cross-faults (e.g. Fig. 2) and in the rectangular, steep-sided nature of the late Jurassic–Early Cretaceous depocentres. Both the level of detachment of these structures and the isostatic compensation depth for the late Jurassic basin developments are inferred as being sub-crustal.

Seismic reflection data only indirectly address the problem of determining strike-slip movements along extensional basins through measurements of extension and subsidence, and do not permit accurate estimates of the magnitudes of movement to be made. The Viking graben movements involved both transpressional and transtensional elements (cf. the East Shetland Terrace structure, Fig. 5, Hamar & Hjelle 1984; Gabrielson & Robinson 1984). The problem of the overall strike-slip movement along the Viking graben could be addressed by measuring amounts of extension and/or contraction along several profiles of variable orientations. From these data, a strain model for the strike-slip basin evolution could be deduced. Preliminary estimates indicate that across a graben width of 100 km affected by strike-slip movements, up to 50 km offset may have occurred across the graben.

A further programme of combined seismic reflection and refraction profiles is required to further elucidate this problem.

Conclusions

1 Two different models for crustal extension could be applied to the development of the N Viking graben:
   (i) A Sevier Desert (Allmendinger *et al.* 1983) model with a gently dipping detachment shear zone passing eastwards down through the crust.
   (ii) A domino model with extensional fault zones passing from the upper to lower crust and offsetting the Moho.

2 Elements of the geometry of both models can be recognized on the deep profile.
3 Model (i) is applied to the early-Mesozoic development (Triassic–early Jurassic) in a dominantly extensional mode.
4 Model (ii) is applied to the late-Jurassic–Early-Cretaceous development in a dominantly strike-slip mode.
5 Early-Mesozoic crustal extension (50%) is compatible with basin subsidence and a McKenzie-type model can be applied.
6 Late Jurassic crustal extension (5%) is not compatible with basin subsidence ($\beta = 2$), and a model of strike-slip development across the plane of the profile, with fault detachment in the upper mantle, is applied.

References

ALLMENDINGER, R.W., SHARP, J.W., VON TISH, D., SERPA, L., BROWN, L., KAUFMAN, S., OLIVER, J. & SMITH, R.B. 1983. Cenozoic and Mesozoic structure of the eastern Basin and Range province, Utah, from COCORP seismic-reflection data. *Geology*, **11**, 532–6.

BADLEY, M.E., EGEBERG, T. & NIPEN, O. 1984. Development of rift basins illustrated by the structural evolution of the Oseberg feature, Block 30/6, offshore Norway. *J. geol. Soc. London*, **141**, 639–51.

BARTON, P. & WOOD, R. 1984. Tectonic evolution of the North Sea Basin: crustal stretching and subsidence. *Geophys. J. R. astron. Soc.* **79**, 987–1022.

——, MATTHEWS, D., HALL, J. & WARNER, M. 1984. Moho beneath the North Sea compared on normal incidence and wide angle seismic records. *Nature*, **308**, 55–6.

BEACH, A. 1985. Some comments on sedimentary basin development in the northern North Sea. *Scott. J. Geol.* **21**, 493–512.

BIRPS & ECORS 1986. Deep seismic reflection profiling between England, France and Ireland. *J. geol. Soc. London*, **143**, 45–52.

BRUN, J.P. & CHOUKROUNE, P. 1983. Normal faulting, block tilting and decollement in a stretched crust. *Tectonics*, **2**, 345–56.

BUCOVICS, C. & ZIEGLER, P.A. 1985. Tectonic development of the mid-Norway continental margin. *Mar. Pet. Geol.* **2**, 2–22.

CHRISTIE, P.A.F. & SCLATER, J.G. 1980. An extensional origin for the Buchan and Witchground Graben in the North Sea. *Nature*, **283**, 729–32.

DEWEY, J.F. 1982. Plate tectonics and the evolution of the British Isles. *J. geol. Soc. London*, **139**, 371–414.

DONATO, J.A. & TULLY, M.C. 1981. A regional interpretation of North Sea gravity data. *In*: ILLING, L.V. & HOBSON, G.D. (eds) *Petroleum Geology of the Continental Shelf of NW Europe*, 65–75. Heydon, London.

FLINN, D. 1969. A geological interpretation of the aeromagnetic maps of the continental shelf around Orkney and Shetland. *Geol. J.* **6**, 279–92.

—— 1975. Evidence for post Hercynian transcurrent movement of the Great Glen Fault in the Moray Firth. *Scott. J. Geol.* **11**, 266–7.

GABRIELSON, R.H. & ROBINSON, C. 1984. Tectonic inhomogenities of the Kristiansand—Bodo Fault complex, offshore Mid-Norway, *In*: *Petroleum Geology of the North European Margin*, pp. 397–406. Graham and Trotman Limited, London.

GIBBS, A.D. 1983. Balanced cross-section constructions from seismic sections in areas of extensional tectonics. *J. struct. Geol.* **5**, 153–60.

—— 1984. Structural evolution of extensional basin margins. *J. geol. Soc. London*, **141**, 609–20.

HALL, J., BREWER, J.A., MATTHEWS, D.H. & WARNER, M.R. 1984. Crustal structure across the Caledonides from the WINCH seismic reflection profile: influences on the evolution of the Midland Valley of Scotland. *Trans. R. Soc. Edinburgh, Earth Sci.* **75**, 97–109.

HAMAR, G.P. & HJELLE, K. 1984. Tectonic framework of the More Basin and the northern North Sea. *In*: *Petroleum Geology of the North European Margin*, pp. 349–58. Graham and Trotman Limited, London.

JACKSON, J. & MCKENZIE, D. 1983. The geometrical evolution of normal fault systems. *J. struct. Geology*, **5**, 471–82.

JARVIS, G.T. & MCKENZIE, D.P. 1980. Sedimentary basin formation with finite extension rates. *Earth Planet. Sci. Lett.* **48**, 42–52.

JOHNSON, R.J. & DINGWALL, R.G. 1981. The Caledonides, their influence on the stratigraphy of the NW European Continental Shelf. *In*: ILLING, L.V. & HOBSON, G.D. (eds) *Petroleum Geology of NW Europe*, pp. 85–97. Heydon, London.

LE PICHON, X., ANGELIER, J. & SIBUET, J.C. 1982. Subsidence and stretching, *In*: WATKINS, J.S. & DRAKE, C.L. (eds) *Studies in Continental Margin Geology, Mem. Am. Assoc. Pet. Geol.* **34**, 731–42.

MCKENZIE, D.P. 1978. Some remarks on the development of sedimentary basins. *Earth planet. Sci. Lett.* **40**, 25–32.

MCQUILLIN, R., DONANTO, J.A. & TULSTRUP, J. 1982.

Development of basins in the Inner Moray Firth and the North Sea by crustal extension and dextral displacement of the Great Glen Fault. *Earth planet. Sci. Lett.* **60**, 127–39.

SAWYER, D.A., SWIFT, B.A., SCLATER, J.G. & TOKSOZ, M.N. 1982. Extensional model for the subsidence of the northern US Atlantic Continental margin. *Geology*, **10**, 134–40.

SCLATER, J.G. & CHRISTIE, P.A.F. 1980. Continental stretching; an explanation of the post mid-Cretaceous subsidence of the Central North Sea Basin. *J. geophys. Res.* **85**, 3711–39.

SMITHSON, S.B., BREWER, J.A., KAUFMAN, S., OLIVER, J.E. & HURICH, C.E. 1979. Structure of the Laramide Wind River uplift, Wyoming from COCORP deep reflection data and from gravity data. *J. geophys. Res.* **84**, 5955–72.

SMYTHE, D.K., SKUCE, A.G. & DONATO, J.A. 1980. Geological objections to an extensional origin for the Buchan and Witchground Graben in the North Sea. *Nature*, **287**, 467–8.

——, DOBINSON, A., McQUILLAN, R., BREWER, J.A., MATTHEWS, D.H., BLUNDELL, D.J. & KELK, B. 1982. Deep structure of the Scottish Caledonides revealed by the MOIST reflection profile. *Nature, Lond.*, **299**, 338–40.

SOLLI, M. 1976. En seismisk skorpeundersokelse Norges-Shetland. Unpubl. Ph.D. Thesis, Univ. Bergen.

WERNICKE, B. 1981. Low-angle faults in the Basin and Range Province: nappe tectonics in an extending orogen. *Nature*, **291**, 645–8.

WERNICKE, B. & BURCHFIEL, B.C. 1982. Modes of extensional tectonics. *J. struct. Geol.* **4**, 105–15.

WOOD, R.J. 1981. The subsidence history of Conoco well 15/30-1, Central North Sea. *Earth planet. Sci. Lett.* **54**, 306–12.

ZIEGLER, P.A. 1982. *Geological Atlas of Western and Central Europe*, 130 pp. Shell Internationale Petroleum Maatschappij BV, Hague.

ALASTAIR BEACH*, TIM BIRD* & ALAN GIBBS*, Exploration Division, Britoil plc, 150 St Vincent Street, Glasgow G2 5LJ, UK.

*Present address: Midland Valley Exploration Limited, 14 Park Circus, Glasgow G3 6AX, UK.

A compilation and regional interpretation of the northern North Sea gravity map

F. Zervos

SUMMARY: A Bouguer anomaly map of the northern North Sea between the Shetland Islands and Norway has been compiled based on four different data sources. The gravity effect of the Devonian to recent sediments was calculated along six published seismic profiles crossing the area and a regional gravity anomaly map produced on the assumption that the sedimentary basin structure is two dimensional. Regional consideration of the gravity field revealed the presence of a mass excess beneath the low-density sediments within the Viking graben. This high-amplitude, long-wavelength anomaly is explained by thinning of the crust from 30 km beneath the flanks to 10 km beneath the centre of the graben, excluding the thickness of the sediments. Crustal thickness along the profiles was derived using the regional gravity field and from this a contour map of the Moho was produced. Predictions obtained from the gravity data confirm the crustal structure derived so far from seismic experiments in the North Sea. For comparison a three-dimensional model of crustal thickness was constructed and a second contour map of the Moho was produced. The Moho contour maps derived from the two-dimensional and three-dimensional models show close agreement, demonstrating that a two-dimensional approach is justified in this case.

The geology of the northern North Sea sedimentary basins is fully described in earlier work (Hardman 1980; Glennie 1984) and only a brief summary is given here.

The pre-Devonian basement, where sampled, usually consists of medium- to high-grade metamorphic rocks, deformed during the Caledonian Orogeny. During the Devonian and Carboniferous continental and shallow marine sedimentation occurred mainly in the Midland Valley graben and Orcadian basin. Two basins, separated by the mid North Sea–Ringkobing Fyn High and containing continental, fluvial, aeolian and sabka deposits, were formed during the Permian. The depocentre of the Northern Permian Basin is located to the E of the Central and Viking grabens although it is evident that the rift formation of these grabens was initiated in the early Permian. The three-armed graben system was established during the Triassic when further subsidence and deposition occurred. A subsequent rifting phase occurred from mid-Jurassic to mid-Cretaceous times, since when there has been continuous subsidence and deposition of up to 4 km of sediments.

Lithospheric-stretching models have been invoked to explain the development of the Central, Witchground and Viking grabens since the early Permian. The early Mesozoic rifting phases are associated with extension of the lithosphere and the formation of a more widespread saucer-shaped basin with subsequent thermal relaxation of the stretched lithosphere.

Bouguer anomaly gravity values over the northern North Sea are generally higher than − 10 mGal despite the fact that there are up to 9 km of low-density sediments within the grabens. Collette *et al.* (1965) first suggested that this isostatic equilibrium was achieved by thinning of the crust since Permian times. Subsequent refraction experiments in the Viking (Solli 1976), Witchground/Buchan (Christie & Sclater 1980) and Central grabens (Wood & Barton 1983) have confirmed this picture of crustal thinning beneath the grabens. Donato & Tully (1981) analysed nine regional gravity profiles and predicted a maximum thinning of about 10 km beneath both the Viking and Central grabens. They calculated only 5 km thinning beneath the Outer Moray Firth Basin (Witchground/Buchan grabens) whilst Dimitropoulos & Donato (1981) predicted no significant thinning beneath the Inner Moray Firth basin where a large negative gravity anomaly is situated.

This paper presents the results of a study of the Moho topography based on an investigation of the gravity field of the northern North Sea (Fig. 1). Gravity data from the Norwegian sector was combined with published BGS data in the UK sector to compile a Bouguer gravity anomaly map of the whole northern North Sea. Recent seismic reflection and refraction data have also provided greater control for the gravity models than was available for previous studies (e.g. Donato & Tully 1981).

Data sources and reliability

The Bouguer anomaly gravity map was compiled from four data sets which are described below. Their distribution is shown in Fig. 2, with the map area enclosed by heavy lines.

From COWARD, M.P., DEWEY, J.F. & HANCOCK, P.L. (eds), 1987, *Continental Extensional Tectonics*, Geological Society Special Publication No. 28, pp. 477–493.

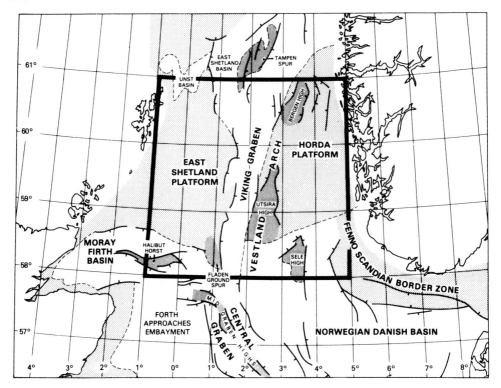

FIG. 1. Major structural units of the northern North Sea with the area of interest enclosed by heavy line.

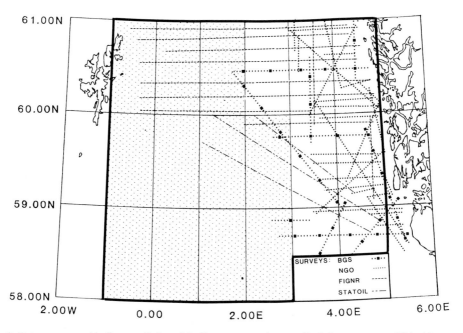

FIG. 2. Data sources used in the compilation of the Bouguer anomaly map. Shaded area covers published Bouguer anomaly maps by BGS.

Gravity surveys:

1 Maps of the British Geological Survey 1:250 000 Bouguer anomaly gravity map series. Each map covers an area of 2° long. by 1° lat. and is contoured at an interval of 2 mGal. Most surveys were run on a N–S, E–W rectangular grid, with average line spacing of 12×7 km respectively. Analysis of the cross-over values at line intersections reveals the internal consistency of the surveys. The absolute accuracy was established by linking readings into harbour bases connected to stations in the National Gravity Reference Net 1973 (NGRN 73). Internal accuracy is estimated to be 1–2 mGal for recent surveys but variations between lines of up to 4 mGal exist in older surveys, due to the lower navigation accuracy and greater instability of meter platforms (Tully & Donato 1985). Apart from the rectangular grid, a number of BGS lines run across the Viking graben into the Norwegian sector were used as a framework to which all other surveys in this sector were referred. The calculated anomalies on these lines were estimated to be accurate to within 2 mGal.

2 A survey carried out by the Federal Institute of Geosciences and Natural Resources (FIGNR), Hannover, in 1974. Data cover an area from the Shetland Islands to the Norwegian coast, between 60°N and 62°N. Plaumann (1979) discusses the results of the marine gravity measurements. Discrepancies with BGS data are probably due to two breakdowns of the gravimeter, platform vibration on the two grid tie-lines and a large (12 mGal) non-linear drift, all of which reduced the accuracy of this survey. As a result approximately 25% of the FIGNR data were discarded because misties with BGS data exceeded 3 mGal and no consistent offset could be applied.

3 A survey, mainly in the Norwegian sector, carried out by Western Geophysical for Statoil who kindly made the results available.

4 A survey conducted jointly by the US Army Topographic Command and the Geographical Survey of Norway (NGO) in 1970. Approximately 40% of the data were discarded because misties with other data sets were greater than 3 mGal.

Gravity anomalies in all the surveys were calculated using the International Gravity Formula of the Geodetic Reference System 1967 (IGF 67) and referred to the International Gravity Standardisation Net of 1971 (IGSN 71). The NGO survey was originally tied to the European Calibration System 1962 and the anomalies were calculated using the 1930 International Gravity Formula. A correction of −7.5 mGal was applied to convert the data to the IGF 67 (average +7.2 mGal over the area) and to refer it to the IGSN 71 (average −14.7 mGal) (Hospers & Finnstrom 1984).

General discussion of the main gravity anomalies

The most striking feature of the Bouguer anomaly map (Fig. 3) is the absence of a large negative anomaly corresponding to the position of the major North Sea graben system. Anomalies mostly range between −5 and +20 mGal, clearly indicating the presence of some form of isostatic compensation beneath the sedimentary basins.

The following simple interpretation of the major anomalies refers to features numbered on Fig. 3. The faults indicated are based on the tectonic maps of the North Sea (Hamar, 1979; Day *et al.* 1981) and outline the main graben features.

UK sector

Steep gradients occur in the western Viking graben area associated with boundary faults along the graben (1), (2), (3). A broad gravity anomaly (2) occurs on the upthrown side of these faults. Donato & Tully (1982) have suggested that this anomaly together with a related magnetic anomaly can be ascribed to the presence of a buried granite batholith on the upthrown side of the fault. The East Shetland Platform area (4) exhibits a complex pattern of highs and lows with no obvious trend. A narrow low occurs to the NE of Unst and Fetlar (5), which corresponds to the location of the Unst basin of Permo–Triassic and younger rocks. Elongate gravity highs (6) extend to the NE away from the southern end of Shetland. These may indicate the presence of a major fault which could be considered either as a splay or as the extension of the Great Glen Fault to the NE (Flinn 1961; Pitcher 1969; Bott & Watts 1970). These highs are more likely to be associated with a belt of basic igneous rocks (possibly bounded by a major fault) such as is observed inland (McQuillin & Brooks 1967). Towards the southern edge of the East Shetland Platform a deep gravity low (7) correlates with an area of thickened sediments assumed to be of Permo–Triassic and/or Devonian age beneath a Tertiary cover. The Inner Moray Firth basin is bounded to the N by the Caithness Ridge which appears on the map as a narrow E–W-trending gravity high (8). The Halibut Horst, a buried Devonian ridge to the E of the Inner Moray Firth, can be seen as a positive anomaly (9).

Norwegian sector

Along the coast a gravity gradient (10) clearly indicates the presence of major faults which mark

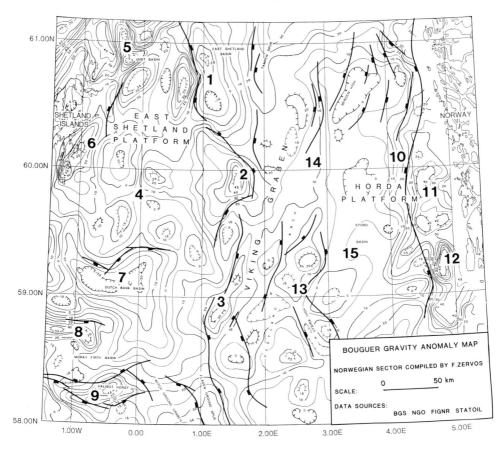

FIG. 3. Bouguer anomaly map of the northern North Sea. Gravity anomalies are calculated using the IGF 1967 and referred to the IGSN 1971 and a density of 2.67 g cm^{-3} was used for the Bouguer corrections.

the western boundary of the Norwegian continental platform. Two distinctive gravity highs (11, 12) occur on the upthrown side of these faults. Hospers & Finnstrom (1984) have calculated maximum source depths of 5–10 km for these anomalies, on the basis of half-width estimates for buried spheres and horizonal cylinders. This would seem to be too deep to be reconciled with the known basement depth of 1–2 km (Hamar *et al.* 1980) which suggests that they are not due to sharp basement topography. Alternatively, it is quite possible that the elongate gravity ridge reflects basement lithology, which in this case would mean the presence of rocks of relatively high density within the basement. Both features (11) and (12) have associated magnetic anomalies, with the contours showing much more irregularity than in the surrounding areas (Hospers & Rathore 1984), and could be due to the presence of basic igneous rocks within the basement as suggested by Hospers &

Finnstrom (1984). Another indication supporting this suggestion is the fact that late Carboniferous–Jurassic igneous rocks are known to occur nearby on land (Faerseth *et al.* 1976). An area of high gravity anomalies (13) on the eastern side of the Viking graben corresponds to the Utsira High. The extension of the Vestland Arch from the Utsira High to the N is clearly displayed as a series of N–S contours (14) along the eastern edge of the Viking graben. An area of broad gravity lows within the Horda Platform (15) indicate the presence of the N–S elongated Stord basin. This is a large sedimentary basin of Triassic–Jurassic age, about 4 km deep (Hamar *et al.* 1980).

Densities used for gravity modelling

Before any gravity anomalies can be calculated for the gravity backstripping exercise, it is necessary to establish reasonable density values for the various sedimentary layers present in the seismic sections. For this purpose Formation Density Compensation logs (FDC) were examined from 58 wells shown in Fig. 4. Density values were averaged every 50 ft down the well and a mean density was chosen for individual stratigraphic units marked on the seismic profiles. Obviously the FDC logs were usually only run over limited sections within each well and not all stratigraphic units were present in all wells. Nevertheless, by using 58 wells an adequate number of observations was obtained.

The following stratigraphic units were considered: Eocene–Recent, Palaeocene, Upper Cretaceous, Lower Cretaceous, Jurassic, Triassic, Permian–Carboniferous–Devonian. The histogram of densities for the above units and the densities chosen for gravity modelling are shown in Fig. 5. Some units exhibited large variations in density, associated with lithological changes and the considerable variation in the depth of burial, e.g. depth of the Devonian varied from 2 to 5 km.

Salt was encountered on profile 5 (Fig. 6) buried beneath Triassic sediment at a depth of approximately 6 km. This was known to be a local structure and as such it was replaced in the model by a Permo–Triassic layer of density 2.6 g cm^{-3} (rather than using salt density of 2.1–2.4 g cm^{-3}), (Parasnis 1979). Densities of 2.72 and 2.62 g cm^{-3} were assumed for the basement and granites, respectively.

Two-dimensional modelling

The gravity field of the northern North Sea has been interpreted with the aid of six long gravity profiles across the Viking graben (Fig. 4). The profiles are based on the results of six published interpreted seismic sections each 285 km long, shown in Fig. 6. Sections 1, 3 and 5 have been taken from Ziegler (1982 p. 54) and sections 2, 4 and 6 from Glennie (1984 p. 36). Along each profile a two-dimensional model of the sedimentary basin has been constructed in order to backstrip its gravity effect.

The accuracy of the published seismic profiles was checked against released wells along them (Fig. 6) and was found to be accurate to within 100 m. Obviously, for the gravity modelling, folds and faults on the seismic sections were simplified, so a maximum discrepancy of 400 m can be found between gravity models and actual seismic sections. Because of this simplification a 2–3 mGal error can be introduced.

Acidic intrusions

Two major granites not included in the seismic sections were taken into account based on positive evidence from published material and well inspection. The granite on profile 3 (Viking graben granite, Fig. 6) located at the eastern edge of the

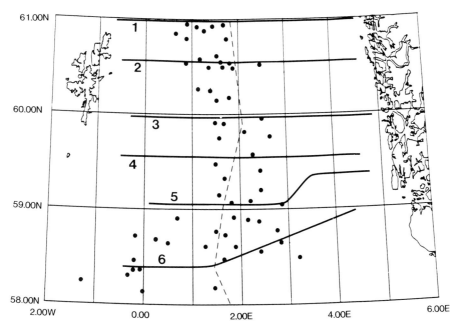

FIG. 4. Gravity–seismic profiles and wells used for deriving densities (58 in all).

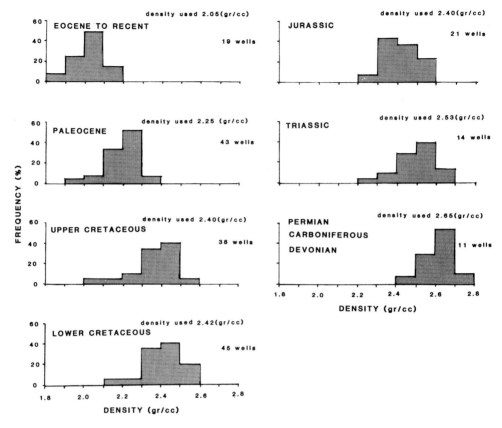

FIG. 5. Density variation for different stratigraphic units in the northern North Sea.

East Shetland Platform at about 60°N 1°E, was proposed by Donato & Tully (1982) and is associated with a pronounced magnetic anomaly of approximately 300 nT amplitude and a negative gravity residual anomaly of approximately 30 mGal. It can be modelled as a cylinder of radius 20 km with its base at 10 km depth.

The second granite (Utsira High granite) appears on profiles 5 and 6 (Fig. 6), having an elongated shape of about 80×40 km, associated with a negative gravity residual anomaly of approximately 37 mGal and a broad magnetic anomaly of 100 nT. Further evidence for this granite comes from the released wells shown in Fig. 7, of which four reached granitic basement and three encountered unspecified igneous/metamorphic basement of possible granitic composition. A two-dimensional gravity model of the Utsira High granite gives the base at 10 km depth. The granite may extend deeper than this but the gravity effect of this was found to be insignificant.

No estimate of the age of the granite can be obtained from the geophysical data. Possible ages to be considered are:

1 Devonian; Late Caledonian plutons of the same general area as the Aberdeenshire gabbros and the coeval granites now known to underlie parts of the North Sea (Frost *et al.* 1981; Donato & Tully 1982).

Key to Fig. 6.

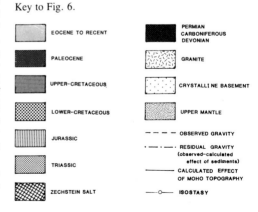

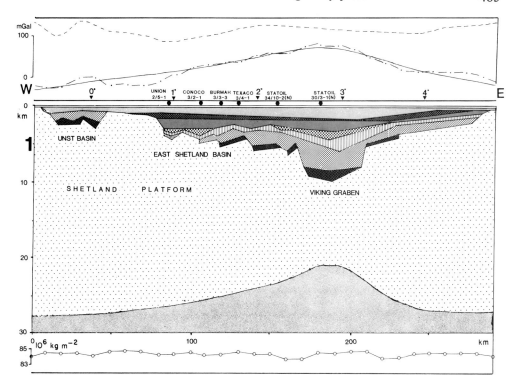

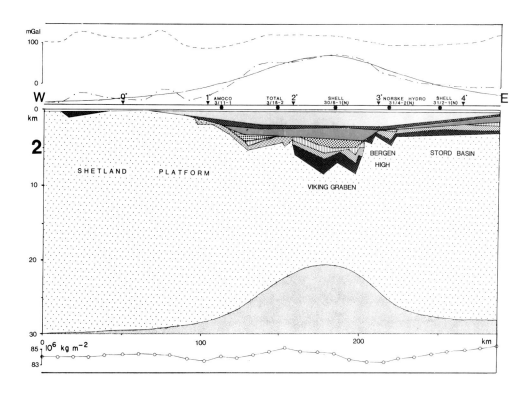

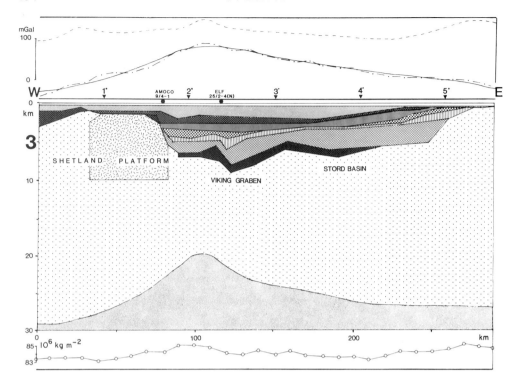

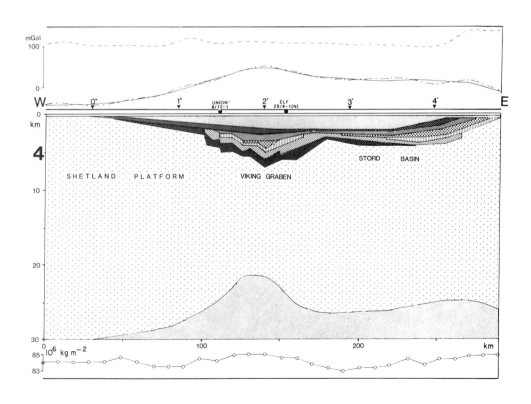

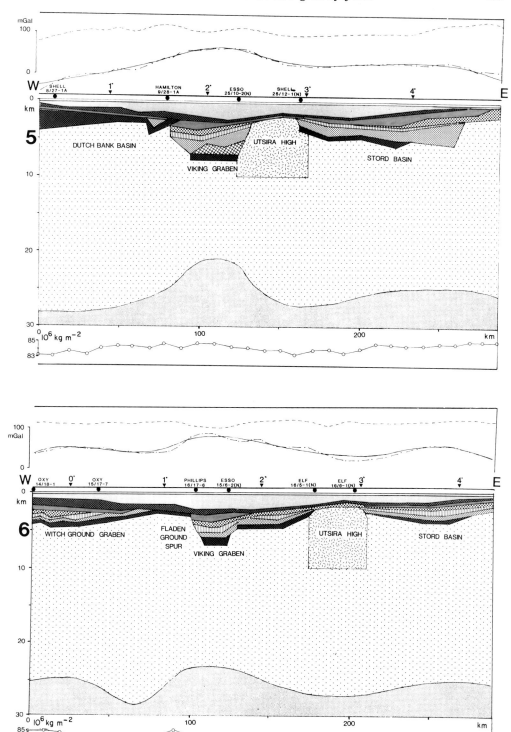

FIG. 6. Gravity–seismic profiles across the northern North Sea, showing the wells used for stratigraphic control.

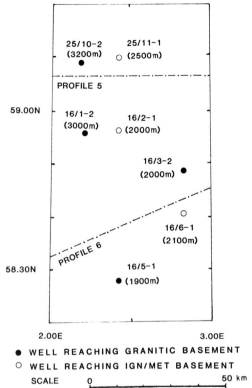

● WELL REACHING GRANITIC BASEMENT
○ WELL REACHING IGN/MET BASEMENT
SCALE   0 _____ 50 km

FIG. 7. Wells supporting the evidence of a granite on profiles 5 and 6 (Fig. 6). The number in brackets is the depth at which the basement was encountered.

2 Late Carboniferous–Permian; early Permian plutonism and volcanism is widespread at the NW European shelf, (Dixon *et al.* 1981; Ziegler 1981).
3 Jurassic; contemporary with the major mid-Jurassic volcanism of the Forties–Witchground area (Howitt *et al.* 1975; Woodhall & Knox 1979; Dixon *et al.* 1981; Ziegler 1981).

It seems most likely, however, particularly on consideration of the stratigraphic history apparently demonstrated by the published profiles (Fig. 6), that the Utsira High granite is similar to the numerous Caledonian granites observed onshore.

Interpretation of the residual anomaly

A large discrepancy was found between observed gravity anomalies and those calculated for the attraction of the sediments in all six profiles in the Viking graben area, although on the flanks a rough agreement was achieved. By subtracting the effect of the sediments from the observed gravity values,

a residual anomaly is produced having an amplitude of approximately 100 mGal and a long wavelength of at least 100 km across the Viking graben (Fig. 6). The residual anomaly can be explained in terms of a thinning of the crust beneath the Stord basin, Witchground and Viking grabens. Attempts were made to match the residual gravity with the calculated gravity effect by varying the Moho topography. A density of 3.35 g cm^{-3} was used for the upper mantle and in this case the density of the crust was assumed to be 2.85 g cm^{-3}, instead of 2.72 g cm^{-3} when the effect of the sediments was calculated to take into account a density increase with depth.

A maximum thinning of the crust of about 20 km beneath the Viking graben was calculated, excluding the sediment thickness and assuming an initial crustal thickness of 30 km. Similar conclusions have been drawn by Donato & Tully (1981) investigating the thickness of the crust using gravity data from the UK sector of the North Sea.

A contour map of Moho depth (Fig. 8) was constructed from the two-dimensional gravity–seismic models (Fig. 6) and this is shown as an isometric projection in (Fig. 9).

Three-dimensional modelling

The two-dimensional gravity modelling assumes infinite extension of the cross-sections along strike. This is approximately the case especially for the Upper Cretaceous and Tertiary sediments, but it is obvious that the shape of the profiles does change in detail along the length of the basin. Three-dimensional modelling represents a more rigorous approach and could be used to check the results of the two-dimensional model. Unfortunately, there is insufficient published data available, particularly in the Norwegian sector, to enable the construction of isopach maps over the whole area.

The regional Bouguer anomaly gravity map (Fig. 10) was therefore compiled from the residual gravity values of the six gravity–seismic profiles (Fig. 6). The map was contoured by hand and wavelengths shorter than 20 km were absent. This map is considered to reflect the gravity effect of the Moho topography through its long-wavelength anomalies. A more accurate model of the Moho could be obtained if any remaining short wavelengths, due to shallow structures, were eliminated mathematically. This was in effect done by digitizing the regional map (Fig. 10) on a 10 km grid and applying a Gaussian filter in the X and Y directions. The filtered map was then used to construct a three-dimensional model of the Moho, assuming a crust/mantle density contrast of 0.5 g cm^{-3} and a crustal thickness of 30 km on either

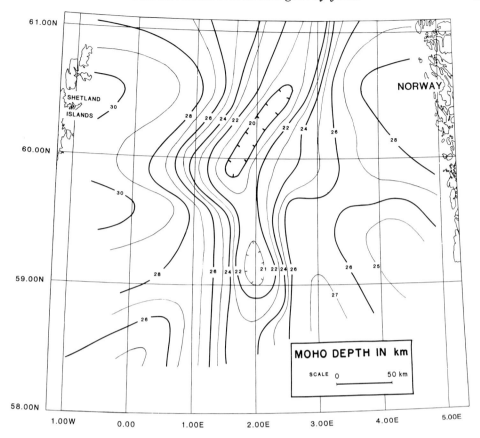

FIG. 8. Moho topography constructed from two-dimensional gravity–seismic models (Fig. 6).

side of the graben. The results from the three-dimensional model (Fig. 11) are very similar to those obtained with the two-dimensional model. The Moho contours follow the same trend and the maximum local discrepancy between models is about 2 km.

Lateral density variations within the crust

Refraction profiles shot across the Viking (Solli 1976) and Witchground/Buchan (Christie 1982) grabens show crustal thinning beneath the grabens but reveal no information about lateral heterogeneity within the crust. Barton & Wood (1984), following the method of Cassell (1982), modelled a laterally varying structure beneath their Central graben refraction profile and their results represent the best-constructed seismic model so far obtained for the crustal structure of the North Sea. They have modelled a high-velocity anomaly within the lower

crust just to the W of the Central graben. Converting seismic velocities to suitable densities, using the range of values possible within the scatter of points shown on a velocity–density plot of Ludwig *et al.* (1970), the gravity anomaly created was found to be less than 16 mGal. The introduction of such an anomaly beneath the Viking graben would introduce an error of only 1 or 2 km in the modelled depth of the Moho topography. For upper-crustal bodies to produce a significant contribution to the positive regional gravity anomaly requires them to have unrealistic dimensions and densities. All the available evidence indicates therefore that crustal thinning is responsible for the observed regional gravity anomaly.

Initial crustal thickness

The estimates of crustal thickness at the margins of the basin have an important effect on the amount of crustal thinning required by the model to fit the

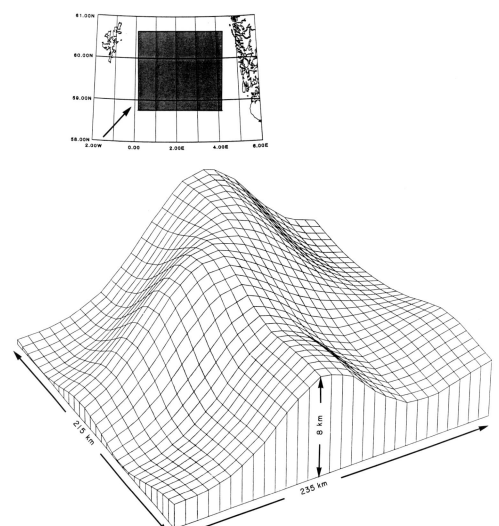

FIG. 9. Isometric projection of Moho topography constructed from Fig. 8. The base of the diagram lies 30 km below sea level. The vertical scale is greatly exaggerated with the maximum relief being approximately 10 km. The location of the study area is shown in the top figure with the arrow pointing in the direction of viewing from an elevation of 35°.

regional gravity high. Refraction experiments indicate that crustal thickness may reach 35 km beneath both Scotland (Bamford *et al.* 1978) and Norway (Cassell *et al.* 1983). In this study it is more appropriate to consider the results of refraction studies at the margin of the northern North Sea sedimentary basin which show Moho depths of 29–32 km W of the Central Graben (Barton & Wood 1984; Sclater & Christie 1980), 30–32 km on the East Shetland Platform (Sclater & Christie 1980) and 27–28 km on the SE margin of the Viking graben falling to 30 km at the Norwegian

coast (Barton & Wood 1984; Cassell *et al.* 1983). The value of 30 km chosen for the gravity modelling is a rough mean of these values and is considered to be a realistic value for the thickness of the crust beneath the Viking graben prior to Permo–Triassic rifting (Zervos & Reay, in prep).

Density contrast

The density contrast at the crust/mantle boundary is fundamental in determining the magnitude of the

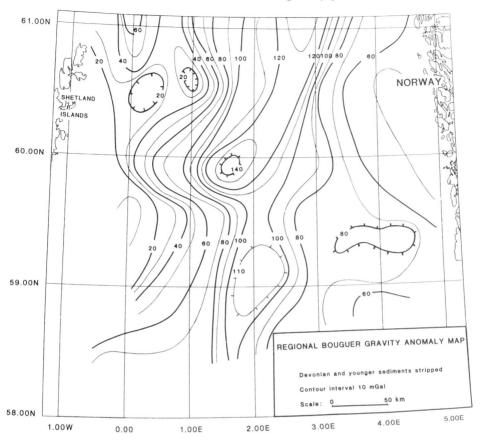

FIG. 10. Regional Bouguer anomaly map contoured from the residual gravity values of the gravity–seismic profiles (Fig. 6).

calculated anomaly. Reference may be made once again to the refraction experiments (Solli 1976; Sclater & Christie 1980; Barton & Wood 1984) which clearly identified a Moho refractor with velocities of 8.3, 8.16 and 8.1 km sec^{-1}, respectively. The lower crustal velocities obtained by Solli (1976) and Sclater & Christie (1980) were poorly constrained and more credence is given to the range of 6.6–7.0 km sec^{-1} given by Barton & Wood (1984) for the lower crust laterally adjacent to the upwelling of the mantle beneath the crust. The above velocities were converted to densities using the velocity density plot by Ludwig *et al.* (1970) giving a density value of 3.35±0.03 g cm^{-3} for the upper mantle and a mean value of 2.85±0.1 g cm^{-3} for the lower crust. The chosen density contrast of 0.5 g cm^{-3} corresponds to the middle of the range, but this uncertainty could lead to slightly different results. It also has to be pointed out that Moho depth determinations greater than 30 km are associated with crustal velocities that

would give rise to a crust/mantle density contrast slightly lower than 0.5 g cm^{-3}. A combination of a crustal thickness of 32 km and density contrast of 0.45 g cm^{-3} yields virtually identical results to the ones described in this paper.

Isostasy

Each gravity profile in Fig. 6 includes a quasi-isostatic vertical mass summation down to 30 km depth. The isostasy curves vary around a mean value of 84 Gg m^{-2}, representing a 30-km thick crust of mean density 2.8 g cm^{-3}. The short-wavelength variation of these curves around a mean value indicates a reasonable isostatic compensation of each profile. There is a slight tendency, however, for the isostasy curve to follow roughly the Moho topography, which can easily be caused by a slight inaccuracy in the estimation of density contrast between lower crust and mantle.

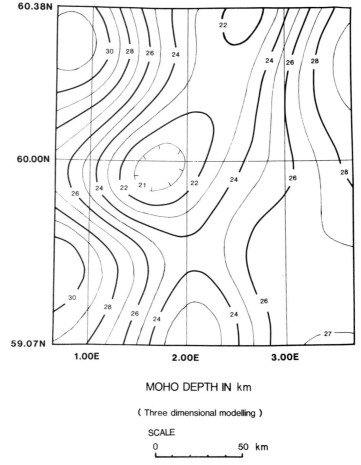

MOHO DEPTH IN km

(Three dimensional modelling)

SCALE

0   50 km

FIG. 11. Moho topography in three-dimensions constructed from the filtered version of the regional Bouguer gravity anomaly map (Fig. 10).

Discussion and conclusions

The sediments were stripped off the sedimentary basin leaving a regional gravity anomaly. The peak of the anomaly is located in the area of the thickest sedimentary section with its wavelength increasing but amplitude decreasing from N to S. The magnitude and wavelengths are similar to those for gravity anomalies observed over the ancient intercontinental rifts (Ramberg 1972; Chase & Gilmer 1973; Ocola & Meyer 1973; Blundell 1978).

The regional anomaly is explained in terms of thinning of the crust beneath the Stord basin, Witchground Viking grabens. These results closely agree with predictions obtained from gravity data for this area (Donato & Tully 1981). The refraction data of Christie & Sclater (1980) and of Wood & Barton (1983) have provided some confirmation of a similar picture below the Witchground and Central

grabens respectively. The profile of Christie & Sclater (1980) crosses the western ends of profiles 3–6 giving a discrepancy of 2 km for the first intersection (profile 3) and less than 1 km for the rest. Their seismic study was combined with independent well subsidence data to show that the crustal structure and basement subsidence patterns are both compatible with a simple uniform extensional mechanism over 60 My for the post-Palaeozoic evolution of the North Sea. A detailed account of this work was given by Barton & Wood (1984) and Barton & Matthews (1984) where no major lateral density variations, seen as variations in velocity, were detected within the crust. The refraction profile was later used to label the Moho depth below the Central graben in a normal-incidence deep-reflection profile coincident to the refraction one (Barton et al. 1984). Profile 1 almost coincides with part of Solli's refraction profile (Ziegler 1982) which yields similar results. On profiles 1 and 2 a short-wavelength discrepancy of 18 mGal maximum can be observed between residual and calculated gravity from Moho topography at the East Shetland Platform area. This is due to either basic igneous rocks such as are seen on the Shetland Islands (McQuillin & Brooks 1967) or small-scale lateral density variations within the pre-Permian basement. Close to the Norwegian coast, however, the Moho depth is found to be approximately 28 km coinciding with the value given by Ramberg *et al.* (1977), deepening rapidly towards the mainland. The possibility of large-scale lateral density variations within the crust, causing the regional anomaly is incompatible with the present geological knowledge of the area. It can be concluded, therefore, that the large-amplitude, long-wavelength positive regional anomaly is due almost entirely to the effects of crustal thinning with possible lateral density variations not affecting the Moho topography by more than 2 km.

The Moho topography in the gravity profiles seems, in the first order, to reflect the shape of the sedimentary basin. The isostasy curves suggest that basement subsidence and sediment loading have been largely accommodated by local Airy-type isostatic equilibration (e.g. Barton & Wood 1984 for the Central graben) rather than by flexure as described by Donato & Tully (1981).

For comparison with the two-dimensional approach of the Moho topography, a three-dimensional model was constructed showing that the contours follow the same trend as in the two-dimensional case with a maximum local discrepancy of about 2 km between the two models. Relief in the Moho is more pronounced in the three-dimensional model but the crustal thinning is still at a maximum under the graben. The two-dimensional approach is adequate in this case because the Tertiary basin which accounts for greater than 60% of the total sediment gravity effect is approximately two-dimensional with length: width ratio >4:1.

The presence of the Utsira High granite resulted in the deviation of the faulted margin around the granite block, giving rise to the fault pattern observed today. There are numerous examples of the control which granites may exhibit during the development of sedimentary basins. These include the Northern Pennines (Bott 1967) and the Market Weighton region (Bott *et al.* 1978). The tectonic influence of this granite was effective during periods of taphrogenic subsidence when faulting permitted the buoyant forces of the low-density intrusion to be accommodated (Zervos & Reay, in prep.). Such a taphrogenic subsidence started in the North Sea during the Permo–Triassic and continued with intervals until the Lower Cretaceous with the development of the Viking, Central and Outer Moray Firth grabens. Further subsidence, due to thermal relaxation of the crust which followed the taphrogenic episode, occurred throughout the Upper Cretaceous and Tertiary periods with minimal associated faulting. This led to the development of the distinctive symmetrical saucer shape of the North Sea basin (Sclater & Christie 1980). This thermal subsidence affected the whole crustal region beneath the North Sea with the granite unable to exhibit any form of control (Zervos & Reay, in prep.). If the granite does date from the Caledonian period then it may have influenced the area before the main North Sea graben system developed. Insufficient knowledge of the distribution of the later Palaeozoic sediments, however, makes any earlier influence impossible to determine.

The gravity interpretation is of course non-unique and a number of different models can be made to fit the regional positive anomaly. They all, however, retain a similar maximum crustal thinning and width of the thinning beneath the Viking graben with the main variation the steepness of the Moho topography towards this maximum. Refraction evidence from Solli (1976), Christie & Sclater (1980), Wood & Barton (1983) and deep-reflection interpretation, Barton *et al.* (1984), Brewer *et al.* (1983), Brewer and Smythe (1984), Hall *et al.* (1984) in the North Sea and surrounding seas suggests that the Moho has a rather smooth swell shape rather than a diapiric structure, even though the latter is numerically agreeable with the data. The model illustrated was chosen because of its compatibility with the refraction data and the present geological knowledge of the northern North Sea area.

ACKNOWLEDGMENTS: The author is grateful to the staff of the Marine Geophysics Research Programme, BGS and especially to Derek Reay for his constant help and inspiration, to Bob McQuillin and Dr Roger Scrutton for their helpful comments and to two anonymous referees. The paper is published with the permission of the Director, British Geological Survey.

References

BAMFORD, D., NUNN, K., PRODEHL, C. & JACOB, B. 1978. LISPB – IV. Crustal structure of Northern Britain. *Geophys. J.R. astron. Soc.*, **54**, 43–60.

BARTON, P.J. & WOOD, R.J. 1984. Tectonic evolution of the North Sea basin. *Geophys. J. R. astron. Soc.*, **79**, 987–1022.

—— & MATTHEWS, D.H. 1984. Deep structure and geology of the North Sea region interpreted from a seismic refraction profile. *Ann. Geophysicae*, **2**, 663–8.

——, MATTHEWS, D., HALL, J. & WARNER, M. 1984. Moho beneath the North Sea compared on normal incidence and wide-angle seismic records. *Nature*, **308**, 55–6.

BLUNDELL, D.J. 1978. A gravity survey across the Garder Igneous Province, SW Greenland. *J. geol. Soc. London*, **135**, 545–54.

BOTT, M.H.P. 1967. Geophysical investigations of the northern Pennine Basement rocks. *Proc. Yorkshire geol. Soc.*, **36**, 139–68.

—— & WATTS, A.B. 1970. Deep sedimentary basins proved in the Shetland–Hebridean continental shelf and margin. *Nature*, **225**, 265–8.

——, ROBINSON, J. & KOHNSTAMM, M.M. 1978. Granite beneath Market Weighton, East Yorkshire. *J. Geol. Soc. London*, **135**, 535–43.

BREWER, J.A. & SMYTHE, D.K. 1984. MOIST and the continuity of crustal reflector geometry along the Caledonian–Appalachian orogen. *J. geol. Soc. London*, **141**, 105–20.

——, MATTHEWS, D., WARNER, M., HALL, J., SMYTHE, D. & WHITTINGTON, R. 1983. BIRPS seismic reflection studies of the British Caledonides. *Nature*, **305**, 206–10.

CASSELL, B.R. 1982. A method for calculating synthetic seismograms in laterally varying media. *Geophys. J.R. astron. Soc.*, **69**, 339–55.

CASSELL, B.R., MYKKELTVEIT, S., KANESTROM, R. & HUSEBYE, E.S. 1983. A North Sea–Southern Norway seismic crustal profile. *Geophys. J.R. astron. Soc.*, **72**, 733–53.

CHASE, G.C. & GILMER, T.H. 1973. Precambrian plate tectonics: the midcontinental gravity high. *Earth planet. Sci. Lett.*, **21**, 70–8.

CHRISTIE, P.A.F. 1982. Interpretation of refraction experiments in the North Sea. *Phil. Trans. R. Soc. London*, **A 305**, 101–12.

—— & SCLATER, J.G. 1980. An extensional origin for the Witchground/Buchan graben in the northern North Sea. *Nature*, **283**, 729–32.

COLLETTE, B.J., LAGAAY, R.A. & RITSEMA, A.R. 1965. Depth of the Mohotovicic-discontinuity under the North Sea Basin. *Nature*, **203**, 688–9.

DAY, G.A., COOPER, B.A., ANDERSEN, C., BURGERS, W., RONNEVIK, H. & SCHONEICH, H. 1981. Regional seismic structure maps of the North Sea. *In*: ILLING, L.V. & HOBSON, G.D. (eds) *The petroleum geology of the Continental Shelf of N.W. Europe*, pp. 76–84. Hayden.

DIMITROPOULOS, K. & DONATO, J.A. 1981. The Inner Moray Firth central ridge, a geophysical interpretation. *Scott. J. Geol.*, **17**, 27–38.

DIXON, J.E., FITTON, J.G. & FROST, R.T.C. 1981. The tectonic significance of the post-Carboniferous igneous activity in the North Sea basin. *In*: ILLING, L.V. & HOBSON, G.D. (eds) *The petroleum geology of the Continental Shelf of N.W. Europe*. pp. 121–37. Hayden.

DONATO, J.A. & TULLY, M.C. 1981. A regional interpretation of North Sea gravity. *In*: ILLING, L.V.

& HOBSON, G.D. (eds) *The petroleum geology of the Continental Shelf of N.W. Europe*, pp. 65–75. Hayden.

—— & —— 1982. A proposed granite batholith along the western flank of the North Sea Viking Graben. *Geophys. J.R. astron. Soc.*, **69**, 187–95.

FAERSETH, R.B., MACINTYRE, R.M. & NATERSTAD, J. 1976. Mesozoic alkaline dykes in the Sunnhordland region, western Norway: ages, geochemistry and regional significance. *Lithos.*, **9**, 331–45.

FLINN, D. 1961. Continuation of the Great Glen Fault beyond the Moray Firth. *Nature*, **191**, 589–91.

FROST, R.T.C., FITCH, F.J. & MILLER, J.A. 1981. The age and nature of the crystalline basement of the North Sea basin. *In*: ILLING, L.V. & HOBSON, G.D. (eds), *The petroleum geology of the Continental Shelf of N.W. Europe*, pp. 43–57. Hayden.

GLENNIE, K.W. 1984. The structural framework and the pre-Permian history of the North Sea Area. *In*: GLENNIE, K.W. (ed.) *Introduction to the Petroleum Geology of the North Sea*, pp. 17–39. Blackwell Scientific Publications.

HALL, J., BREWER, J.A., MATTHEWS, D. & WARNER, M. 1984. Crustal structure across the Caledonides from the 'WINCH' seismic reflection profile: influences on the evolution of the Midland Valley of Scotland. *Trans. R. Soc. Edinburgh Earth Sci.*, **75**, 97–109.

HAMAR, G.P. 1979. *Tectonic map of the North Sea, scale 1:1 000 000*. Statoil, Stavanger.

——, JAKOBSSON, J., KOBSSON, K.H., ORMAASEN, D.E. & SHARPNES, O. 1980. The tectonic development of the North Sea north of Central Highs. *In*: *The sedimentation of the North Sea reservoir rocks*, pp. 1–23. Norwegian Petroleum Society, Oslo. Part III.

HARDMAN, R. 1980. *The sedimentation of North Sea Reservoir Rocks*, 389 pp. Norwegian Petroleum Society, Oslo.

HOSPERS, J. & FINNSTROM, E.G. 1984. The gravity field of the Norwegian sector of the North Sea. *Nor. geol. Unders. Bull.*, **396**, 25–34.

—— & RATHORE, J.R. 1984. Interpretation of aeromagnetic data from the Norwegian sector of the North Sea. *Geophys. Prospect.*, **32**, 929–42.

HOWITT, F., ASTON, E.R. & JACQUE, M. 1975. The occurrence of Jurassic volcanics in the North Sea. *In*: WOODLAND, A.W. (ed.) *Petroleum and the Continental Shelf of North-West Europe Vol. 1. Geology*, pp. 379–87. Applied Science Publ., London.

LUDWIG, J.W., NAFE, J.E., DRAKE, C.L. 1970. Ch. 2, Seismic Refractions. *In*: MAXWELL, A.E. (ed.) *The Sea: Vol 4*, pp. 53–84. John Wiley, New York.

MCQUILLIN, R. & BROOKS, M. 1967. Geophysical surveys in the Shetland Islands. *Geophys. Pap. No. 2, London*, **2**, HMSO.

OCOLA, L.C. & MEYER, R.P. 1973. Central North American Rift System 1: Structure of the axial zone from seismic and gravimetric data. *J. geophys. Res.*, **78**, 5173–94.

PARASNIS, D.S. 1979. *Principles of Applied Geophysics*. 3rd edn. A Halsted Press Book, John Wiley & Sons, New York.

PITCHER, W.A. 1969. Northeast-trending faults of

Scotland and Ireland. *In*: KAY, M. (ed.) *North Atlantic Geology and Continental Drift. Mem. Am. Assoc. Pet. Geol.*, **12**, 724–33.

PLAUMANN, S. 1979. Eine Schwerekarte der Nordsee fur den Bereich ostlich der Shetland Inseln. *Geol. Jahrb., Reihe E: Geophys.*, **14**, 11–23.

RAMBERG, I.B. 1972. Crustal structure across the Permian Oslo Graben from gravity measurements. *Nature*, **240**, 149–53.

—— & GABRIELSEN, R.H., LARSEN, B.T. & SOLLI, A. 1977. Analysis of fracture patterns in southern Norway. *J. R. geol. Min. Soc. Netherlands*, **56**, 295–311.

SCLATER, J. & CHRISTIE, P. 1980. Continental stretching: an explanation of the post-mid-Cretaceous subsidence of the central North Sea Basin. *J. geophys. Res.*, **85**, 3711–39.

SOLLI, M. 1976. En seismisk skorpeundezsokelse Norge-Shetland. Thesis, Univ. Bergen, 155 pp.

TULLY, M.C. & DONATO, J.A. 1985. 1:100 000 northern North Sea Bouguer anomaly gravity map. *Rep. Br. geol. Surv. Vol. 16, No. 6.*

WOOD, R. & BARTON, P. 1983. Crustal thinning and subsidence in the North Sea. *Nature*, **302**, 134–6.

WOODHALL, D. & KNOX, R.W. O'B. 1979. Mesozoic volcanism in the northern North Sea and adjacent areas. *Bull. geol. Surv. G.B.*, **70**, 34–56.

ZIEGLER, P.A. 1981. Evolution of sedimentary basins in north-west Europe. *In*: ILLING, L.V. & HOBSON, G.D. (eds) *The petroleum geology of the Continental Shelf of N.W. Europe*, pp. 3–39. Hayden.

—— 1982. *Geological Atlas of Western and Central Europe.* 130 pp. Elsevier, Amsterdam.

F. ZERVOS, British Geological Survey, Marine Geophysics Research Programme, Murchison House, West Mains Road, Edinburgh EH9 3LA and Grant Institute of Geology, University of Edinburgh, West Mains Road, Edinburgh EH9 3JW.

Fault patterns generated during extensional deformation of crystalline basement, NW Scotland

S.E. Laubach & S. Marshak

SUMMARY: The fracture array in the Lewisian basement of NW Scotland is dominated by two orthogonal sets. Parallel to and perhaps in part reactivating these fractures are two sets of faults, each with apparent normal offset. The NE-trending faults are longer and regionally more significant. The NW-trending faults commonly terminate against NE-trending faults and divide the hanging wall rocks of NE-trending faults into independent blocks. The propagation of principal NE-trending faults into the basement was accommodated discontinuously by relative differential displacement of these crustal blocks. The limited data suggest that incremental slip episodes were down-dip and coaxial on the NE-trending faults, but not on the NW-trending faults. The presence of non-coaxial low-angle slip lineations on NW-trending faults suggests either that master NE-trending faults rotated during progressive deformation, or that the dip of these faults decreases with depth. The dominance of NE-trending faults, and the kinematics of fault movements suggest that movement on the faults accommodated NW–SE extension.

Despite rapid advances in understanding of the geometry of faults associated with extensional deformation (e.g. Wernicke & Burchfiel 1982; Gibbs 1984) questions remain concerning the mechanisms by which extensional fault arrays develop in crystalline basement terranes. The presence of steeply dipping pre-existing fabrics in basement rocks is likely to have an influence on fault-array geometry and on the manner in which faults propagate laterally, and may lead to fault patterns that differ from those found in stratified sedimentary basins, in which the dominant mechanical anisotropy is sub-horizontal.

NW Scotland is a good locality for studying extensional faulting in crystalline basement. Many faults of various sizes are present in the region, and readily recognizable unconformities between basement crystalline rocks and a cover sequence of Torridonian sandstones and Cambro–Ordovician quartzites and carbonates permit determination of fault displacements at some localities. In addition, good exposures of fault-related fracture arrays are present locally within fault blocks, permitting inferences to be drawn regarding the nature of the fault-propagation processes, and kinematic indicators are visible in some fault zones, enabling local determination of shear sense.

This study focuses on the fault array exposed in the autochthonous foreland terrane to the NW of the Moine thrust zone, in the region between the towns of Durness and Scourie where basement is composed of Archaean Lewisian gneiss the fabric of which largely reflects 1.7 Ga Laxfordian metamorphism and deformation (Fig. 1). The study area was first mapped systematically by the BGS (Peach *et al.* 1907) at the turn of the century. Bowes & Leake (1978), Harris *et al.* (1979) and Craig (1983) provide recent reviews of regional geology. There

has recently been intense study of the Moine thrust zone, but little attention has been directed towards the normal faults of the region since the early Geological Survey mapping.

The age of normal faults is poorly constrained. Along strike to the SW of our study area, the faults offset the Scourie dykes and Laxfordian granitic sheets, and thus post-date these features. Recognition of Scourie dykes is difficult in the area N of Rhiconich because they have been transposed into foliation and appear only as amphibolite pods. It is possible that some of the faults were initially active during a proposed late Proterozoic extension event associated with deposition of the Torridonian sandstones (Stewart 1982). Many post-date the Caledonide event, for they offset the Moine Thrust.

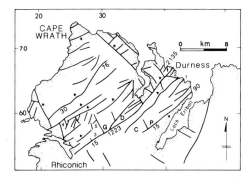

FIG. 1. Generalized fault map of NW Scotland. Diagonal numbers indicate displacement in metres on adjacent fault. Location of stations referred to in Fig. 3, is indicated. Marginal ticks are National Grid coordinates (NC). G = Gaulin; D = Dionard fault; C = Cranstackie; P = Polla fault; S = Sheigra; K = Kinlochbervie.

From COWARD, M.P., DEWEY, J.F. & HANCOCK, P.L. (eds), 1987, *Continental Extensional Tectonics*, Geological Society Special Publication No. 28, pp. 495–499.

The parallelism between faults in NW Scotland and Mesozoic offshore faulting suggests, however, that at least some are coeval with the offshore faults, and therefore are in part Mesozoic (cf. Binns *et al.* 1975; Steel & Wilson 1975).

The purpose of our study is to describe the normal-fault and fracture arrays in a well-exposed basement terrane and to show how normal-fault propagation in a terrane with a pre-existing aniso-tropy parallel to the extension direction has resulted in a pattern of segmented, differentially extended hanging wall blocks bounded by cross-faults. The complex pattern of slip on cross-faults may indicate that master NE-trending normal faults either have a listric shape or have themselves rotated to more gentle dips with increasing throw.

Procedure

This study is based on 1:10,000-scale geological mapping of portions of NW Scotland, detailed examination of individual fault zones, and system-atic fracture measurement and characterization. The 1:10,000 mapping for this study was carried out in two localities: first between Loch Eriboll and the hills W of the A838 road, N of Rhiconich (NC255 521) to Durness (NC402 678), and, second, between Rhiconich and Sheigra (NC188 605). Figure 1 is a generalized compilation that includes our own fault-trace data, data collected by students mapping under the supervision of D.S. Wood, and, in the vicinity of Cape Wrath, data described by Peach *et al.* (1907). Fault zones them-selves are usually poorly exposed, but recent road-cuttings to the NW of Rhiconich provide excellent exposure of the shear surfaces associated with a NW-trending fault zone. Much of our analysis of the NW-trending faults is based on this zone. Faults can be reliably traced for long distances where they cut Torridonian and/or Cambro–Ordovician rocks. In basement gneiss, however, faults are not easily recognized, especially where they are parallel to metamorphic foliation. Exposures for character-ization of fracture arrays in these rocks, however, are good. Fracture arrays were characterized by mapping of all fractures at a scale of 1:250 in representative areas, measuring of all fractures at grid stations, and describing associated alteration, fracture aperture, and mineralogy of associated veins at selected localities.

Observations

Description of faults

The compilation of fault traces (Fig. 1) demon-strates the predominant NE and NW trends of faults in NW Scotland, and indicates that NW-trending minor faults are more widespread than previously recognized. Both NE- and NW-trending faults have steep dips at the surface; NE-trending faults dip primarily to the W, while the dip on NW-trending faults is variable.

The two fault sets differ in several ways. The NE-trending faults tend to have larger throws and longer traces, and to be less numerous than the NW-trending faults. Though three long NW-trending faults are indicated in Fig. 1, their traces are not well constrained. The throw on the NE-trending faults decreases dramatically to the SW. For example, the throw on the Dionard fault is approx-imately 2135 m at Durness, based on the presence of downthrown Moine thrust zone rocks at Sango Bay (NC410 675) in Durness, and is 1223 m at Gaulin (NC302 564), based on offset of the basal Cambrian unconformity. On the B801 road near Rhiconich (NC255 536), this fault terminates and Lewisian marker horizons can be mapped across the fault trace without offset. Displacements are more poorly constrained on the Polla fault, but off-sets across the fault in Cambrian quartzite on Cranstackie (NC355 545) also show a decrease in throw to the S of about 10 m in 1 km. There is no evidence of tilting of hanging wall blocks to the NE.

Figure 1 indicates that regionally the two fault sets are mutually crosscutting. However, it is more common for NW-trending faults to terminate against NE-trending faults. A good example of such a termination is displayed NW of the A838 road (NC310 572). It appears that the NW-trending faults at this locality are not offset by NE-trending faults, since the continuations of these faults cannot be found in the footwall of the NE-trending fault.

The parallelism of post-Caledonide normal-fault arrays with Caledonide structural trends has frequently been noted (e.g. Johnson & Dingwall 1981) and NE-trending normal-fault patterns have been ascribed to a structural inheritance of Caledonide trends. The NE-trending faults in NW Scotland parallel Caledonide trends but are not localized along any Caledonide structures. The NE-trending faults parallel the dominant NE-trending fracture set. The NW-trending faults, on the other hand, frequently parallel the penetrative, steeply dipping Lewisian metamorphic fabric and a fracture set parallel to this fabric; the NW-trending faults therefore appear to have reactivated this fabric as a slip surface.

The morphologies of fault zones for the two fault sets are similar. Where exposed, faults of both sets are characterized by the presence of anastomosing clay-rich gouge zones within broad (1–10 m) zones of cataclastite, breccia and hematite-clay-coated fractured rock. The clay and hematite in the fault gouge are derived from the alteration of both feldspar and mafic minerals. Alteration and bleaching of intact rock in the vicinity of faults also occur, but is confined to narrow centimetre-scale zones adjacent to fractures. Tectonic slivers and inclusions in fault zones may approach a metre in diameter; large inclusions are generally lozenge or phacoid-shaped. Phacoids resulted from progressive linking of through-going fault-parallel shear fractures by short cross-fractures. Brittle grain-size reduction during subsequent fault movements streamlined larger inclusions and produced interstitial gouge. Fractures with quartz-clay alteration similar to that which occurs within faults are also spatially associated with faults (Fig. 2).

Linear grooves and occasionally tectonic 'chatter-marks' and small step-like slickensides are present on fault surfaces. These kinematic indicators were used to deduce slip-direction. Slip-lineation data indicate that the NE-trending faults display dip-slip motion (Fig. 3a). The best exposures of NW-trending faults are on the B801 road near Kinlochbervie (NC225 560) and S of the hill known as Farrmheall (NC298 584). At both these localities, fault surfaces display oblique-slip and low-angle oblique-slip grooves (Fig. 3b). On many surfaces in the Kinlochbervie fault zone, grooves are non-parallel on adjacent gouge surfaces, and indicate that increments of slip were non-coaxial.

Fracture patterns

Basement gneisses contained systematic and non-systematic fractures in a range of orientations prior to the most recent episode of normal faulting. In fact, the presence of open joints partially infilled with Torridonian sediment (Peach *et al.* 1907) indicates that some fractures are pre-Torridonian in age. The most prominent fracture sets strike NE, ENE and NW. Although NE-striking fractures are most common, the ENE-striking set is often as well developed, in terms of frequency and fracture length, as the NE-striking set which is parallel to faults.

Despite the range of fracture orientation, only fractures trending parallel to NE faults display vein fillings and widespread hydrothermal alteration similar to that found along fault zones themselves. These fractures are bordered by distinctive 1–5 cm clay-rich haloes or bleached zones in which the original rock has been altered to quartz-clay-hematite. Vein widths range from millimetres to several centimetres, and are filled with fine-grained quartz and hematite. Figure 2 illustrates the spatial association of halo-bordered fractures with NE-trending faults, and shows their association with regions along strike from fault terminations. Minor, rare alteration haloes are also locally associated with NW-trending faults and fractures, but veined

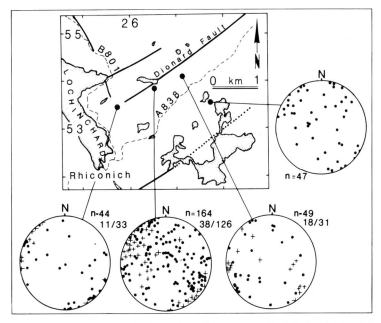

FIG. 2. Fracture patterns and fracture intensity (in numbers of fractures per 5 m²) in the vicinity of the Dionard fault. Lower-hemisphere equal-area plots; dots, poles to tight fractures; crosses, poles to veined fractures. Road number B801 is shown.

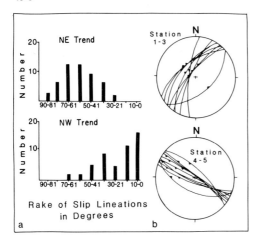

FIG. 3. Slip-lineation data. (a) Histograms indicating number of NW- and NE-trending faults which have slip indicators raking in the indicated range. (b) Equal-area lower-hemisphere plots of slip surfaces and slip lineations from representative stations. See Fig. 1 for station locations.

fractures are rare, and are characterized by small fracture apertures.

Discussion and conclusions

Extension of the crystalline basement in NW Scotland has resulted in an orthogonal fault system. There are at least three mechanisms that could lead to such a pattern. First, the pattern could be the result of a complex tectonic history, involving two (or more) episodes of extension. Second, the pattern could reflect the initial stages of the development of small pull-apart basins associated with regional transcurrent fault movement. Third, the pattern could reflect the result of a single episode of extension in a terrane that possessed pre-existing orthogonal structural weaknesses. The occurrence of mutual cross-cutting relationships between the two fault sets of NW Scotland leads us to favour the third mechanism, but this proposal remains tentative until additional data are obtained concerning the larger NW-trending faults (Fig. 1), against which short NE-trending faults terminate. These fault traces are not well constrained.

The coeval activity of the two mutually orthogonal fault sets does not require that NW Scotland underwent regional biaxial (chocolate–tablet) extension. Observations of associated fracture arrays suggest that the regional extension was dominantly uniaxial, with the principal extension axis orientated NW–SE. Alteration haloes and veins are preferentially associated with NE-

trending fracture sets, indicating that dilation occurred predominantly on NE-trending fractures. Other fracture sets were apparently closed to fluid circulation. Presumably, the planes on which dilation occurred are orientated perpendicular to the extension direction, and therefore, extension was NW–SE.

In the context of a single phase of uniaxial extension, movement on the NW-trending faults is interpreted as reflecting the accommodation of differential extension of the hanging wall along the large NE-trending faults, as has been suggested for faults in Turkey by Şengor (1986). The NW-trending faults are thought to be restricted to the hanging walls of the NE-trending faults, and to divide the hanging walls into discrete blocks which moved independently. Therefore, the decrease in displacement along NE-trending faults occurred in abrupt jumps, though the regional integration of these jumps resulted in a scissors geometry.

If the NW- and NE-trending faults were active simultaneously, the orientation of slip on the NW-trending faults may provide important constraints on the at-depth geometry of the NE-trending faults. Figure 4 illustrates two models of movement of the two fault sets. In both models, the NW-trending faults are considered to be confined to the hanging wall blocks of the NE-trending faults. If the NE-trending faults are strictly planar, slip lineations on the NW-trending faults would be oblique, but would parallel the dip-slip lineations on the NE-trending faults (Fig. 4a). If the NE-trending faults are listric (Fig. 4b), or if the NE-trending faults themselves rotated around a horizontal axis during progressive extension (not shown), hanging wall blocks would rotate, and increments of movement on NW-trending faults would be non-coaxial (cf. Bott 1959; Jackson & McKenzie 1983). Some increments of movement could approach strike-slip orientations (cf. Sengor 1986). Figure 3 illustrates that slip lineations, where visible on the well-exposed NW-trending fault near Kinlochbervie, indicate complex non-coaxial movement with increments of strike-slip movement. Slip lineations on NE-trending faults, by comparison, are down-dip and coaxial. This observation favours either the model shown in Fig. 4(b) or a model in which the NE-trending fault planes rotated during deformation.

The geometry of the fault array in NW Scotland may serve as a model for the geometry of continental rifts propagating into anisotropic basement terranes. The parallelism of the fault sets to basement fabric suggests that their orientation has been controlled by basement-fabric geometry. An anisotropic basement terrane may tend to break up into discrete blocks, during extension, more readily than would a stratified sedimentary terrane. Variations

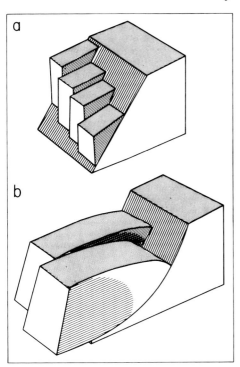

in the development of basement fabric may affect the work required to propagate a rift laterally into unextended basement. This suggestion is based on the observation that the change in character of basement fabric that occurs at the Laxford front near Scourie (S of the map area shown in Fig. 1), correlates with a decrease in throw on NE-trending faults. S of Scourie, NW-trending fabrics are less well developed. Perhaps as a consequence, NW-trending faulting was inhibited; propagation of NE-trending faults may be linked to the ease of formation of the NW-trending cross-faults.

ACKNOWLEDGMENTS: We thank D.E. Anderson, A.M.C. Şengor, and D.S. Wood for helpful discussions. Comments on the manuscript by M.R.W. Johnson were very useful.

FIG. 4. Block diagrams of planar and listric normal faults and the predicted pattern of slip indicators on master and cross-faults. (a) Geometry of hanging wall fault blocks on a planar fault. (b) Geometry of hanging wall fault blocks above a listric fault. Note crossing sets of slip lineations.

References

BINNS, P.E., McQUILLIN, R., FANNIN, N.G.T., KENOLTY, N. & ARDUS, D.A. 1975. Structure and stratigraphy of sedimentary basins in the Sea of the Hebrides and the Minches. *In*: WOODLAND, A.W. (ed.) *Petroleum and the continental shelf of Northwest Europe. 1. Geology*, pp. 93–102. Applied Science Publishers, Barking.

BOTT, M.H.P. 1959. The mechanics of oblique slip faulting. *Geol. Mag.* **96**, 109–17.

BOWES, D.R. & LEAKE, B.E. (eds). 1978. *Crustal evolution in north-western Britain and adjacent regions*, 491 pp. Seel House Press, Liverpool.

CRAIG, G.Y. (ed.). 1983. *Geology of Scotland*, 472 pp. Scottish Academic Press, Edinburgh.

GIBBS, A.D. 1984. Structural evolution of extensional basin margins. *J. geol. Soc. London*, **141**, 609–20.

HARRIS, A.L., HOLLAND, C.H. & LEAKE, B.E. (eds). 1979. *The Caledonides of the British Isles—reviewed*, *Spec. publ. geol. Soc. London*, **8**, 768 pp.

JACKSON, J. & McKENZIE, D. 1983. The geometrical evolution of normal fault systems. *J. struct. Geol.* **5**, 471–82.

JOHNSON, R.J. & DINGWALL, R.G. 1981. The Caledonides: their influence on the stratigraphy of the North West European continental shelf. *In*: ILLING, L.V. & HOBSON, G.D. (eds) *Petroleum Geology of the Continental Shelf of North-West Europe*, pp. 85–97. Heyden, London.

PEACH, B.N., HORNE, J., GUNN, W., CLOUGH, C.T. & HINXMAN, L.W. 1907. The geological structure of the Northwest Highlands of Scotland. *Mem. geol. Surv. U.K.* 668 pp.

ŞENGOR, A.M.C. This volume. Cross-faults and differential stretching of hanging walls in regions of low-angle normal faulting: examples from western Turkey.

STEEL, R.J. & WILSON, A.C. 1975. Sedimentation and tectonism (?Permo–Triassic) on the margin of the North Minch Basin, Lewis. *J. geol. Soc. London*, **131**, 183–202.

STEWART, A.D. 1982. Late Proterozoic rifting in NW Scotland: the genesis of the 'Torridonian'. *J. geol. Soc. London*, **139**, 413–20.

WERNICKE, B. & BURCHFIEL, B.C. 1982. Modes of extensional tectonics. *J. struct. Geol.* **4**, 105–15.

STEPHEN E. LAUBACH & STEPHEN MARSHAK, Department of Geology, University of Illinois, 1301 West Green Street, Urbana, IL 61801, USA.

Timing and style of crustal extension N of the Scottish mainland

S.R. Kirton & K. Hitchen

SUMMARY: The region immediately to the N of the Scottish mainland and W of Orkney and Shetland may be divided into two areas on grounds of structural style. The two areas are separated by a well-defined NE–SW-trending horst, the Solan Bank High. The northwestern area is dominated by listric normal faults downthrowing to the NW. These faults were initiated at two main stages: late, or post Permo–Triassic (but pre-middle Jurassic) and middle Jurassic. A well-defined NW–SE-trending transfer (strike-slip) fault, termed here the Judd fault, is associated with the middle Jurassic faults. The southeastern area is dominated by listric normal faults down-throwing to the SE. These faults were initially Caledonian thrusts which subsequently relaxed during the Permo–Triassic.

The geology of the area to the W of Orkney and Shetland, referred to as the NW margin of Britain, has been the subject of little literature. Cashion (1975) and Ridd (1981) summarized the structure and geology of the West Shetland basin, as revealed by hydrocarbon exploration. Much further S, Brewer & Smythe (1984) used the MOIST seismic line to describe the area immediately to the N of the Scottish mainland. The intervening area has only been described on the basis of gravity and magnetic-field data, shallow reflection seismic and deep refraction seismic data (e.g. Flinn (1969), Bott & Watts (1970), Watts (1971), Bott *et al.* (1974), Smith & Bott (1975)). These limited accounts do not include the area W of Orkney and southern Shetland, for which the deep structure is almost totally unknown. Recent commercial multi-channel seismic data, commercial wells, and BGS shallow boreholes, however, now enable the structure at depth to be determined.

Structure and development of the West Shetland basin and Rona Ridge

Immediately to the W of Shetland is the West Shetland Platform, a large area of crystalline basement partly overlain by Old Red Sandstone (Ridd 1981; Ziegler 1982) (Figs 1 & 2). This is bounded to the NW by a series of *en échelon* faults which downthrow to the NW by up to 6000 m—a figure derived • from unpublished seismic data. These faults are collectively known as the Shetland Spine fault system and form the southeastern boundary of a major half-graben known as the West Shetland basin (Ridd 1981; Ziegler 1982) (Figs 1 & 2). Oceanward from the basin is the steep-sided Rona Ridge, a major basement feature, proven by many of the hydrocarbon exploration wells drilled in the NW margin. Rb–Sr dates from the ridge indicate an age of 2527±73Ma, suggesting that the Rona Ridge is at least partly of late Scourian age (Ritchie & Darbyshire 1984). The Rona Ridge is the most northwesterly feature before the continental basement descends towards the centre of the Faeroe–Shetland Channel (Ridd 1981; Ziegler 1982).

These features are all NE–SW-trending and are the result of listric faults downthrowing to the NW. Interpretation of unpublished seismic data, by the authors, suggests that the listric faulting was the result of crustal extension, mostly in the Jurassic, but that the Shetland Spine fault system may have been initiated in the Permo–Triassic.

Structure to the N of the Scottish mainland

The MOIST seismic line (location given in Fig. 3) shows a number of half-grabens, filled with presumed Upper Palaeozoic and Mesozoic sediments and bounded by listric faults apparently downthrowing to the E (Brewer & Smythe 1984). Interpretation of commercial seismic data shows that these faults actually trend NE–SW and down-throw to the SE. At depth the major faults are gently dipping and are sub-parallel to the Moine Thrust onshore. Brewer & Smythe (1984) have postulated that these faults were initially thrusts in the foreland basement and the Caledonian Orogen and that they have subsequently been reactivated as normal faults in late Palaeozoic and Mesozoic times.

Structural geology W of Orkney

As outlined above, there is a considerable differ-ence between the structural development of the

From COWARD, M.P., DEWEY, J.F. & HANCOCK, P.L. (eds), 1987, *Continental Extensional Tectonics*, Geological Society Special Publication No. 28, pp. 501–510.

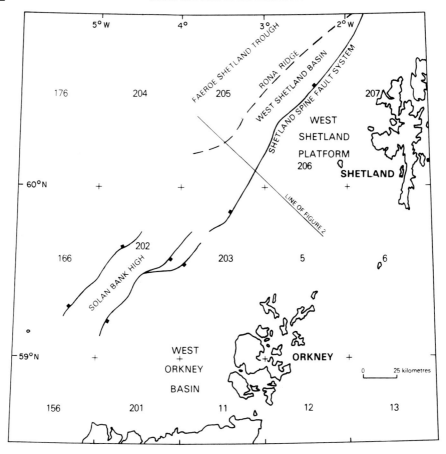

FIG. 1. Major structural features N of the Scottish mainland. The area considered in the paper is W of 3°W and S of 60°30′N. Numbers refer to Department of Energy quadrant numbers.

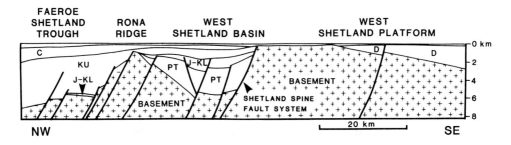

FIG. 2. Schematic section across the West Shetland Platform and Rona Ridge, after Ziegler (1982). Location given in Fig. 1. C=Cainozoic; KU=Upper Cretaceous; KL=Lower Cretaceous; J=Jurassic; PT=Permo–Triassic; D=Devonian.

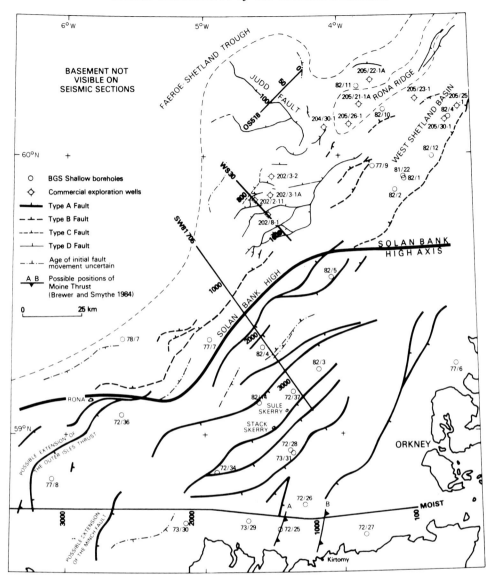

FIG. 3. Map to show types of fault (as defined in text and Fig. 6). Fault positions shown at top Basement level. SW81 705, WS30 and OS 518 are seismic lines shown in Figs 5, 7 & 8 respectively. MOIST is the seismic line described by Brewer & Smythe (1984).

Rona Ridge and the area immediately to the N of the Scottish mainland. To reconcile these differences, commercial multi-channel seismic surveys with a maximum line spacing of 10 km (generally 5 km), commercial deep wells and BGS shallow boreholes have been used to elucidate the structural development of the intervening region.

The structure is best described at top acoustic basement level (Figs 3 & 4) which has been proved

to be Lewisian where drilled. The NE corner of these maps shows the southwesterly termination of the Rona Ridge. Here it is structurally lower and broader than its continuation to the NE. To the SW is the Solan Bank High. This prominent NE–SW trending horst (Figs 3, 4 & 5) is structurally separate from the Rona Ridge although exhibiting a similar orientation. The island of Rona is situated on a minor fault block associated with a fault splay

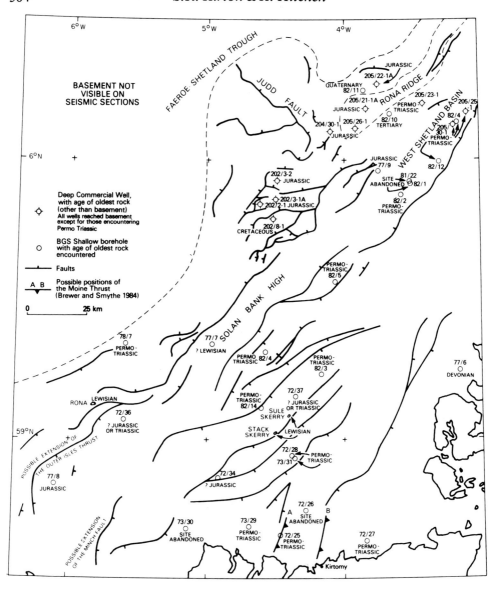

FIG. 4. Map to show age of the oldest sedimentary rocks found in BGS shallow boreholes and commercial wells.

at the southern end of the Solan Bank High. Rona is thus not situated on the Rona Ridge, but to change the nomenclature after such extensive usage would be unsatisfactory and confusing. A NE–SW line divides the area into two parts (Fig. 3). To the SE of this axis is the first of four types of normal faults (type-A faults), and half-graben infills, that occur in the area (Figs 3 & 6A). The type-A faults throw to the SE (but with associated antithetic faults) and may be traced to depth where they flatten out between 17 and 20 km (Brewer & Smythe 1984).

These normal faults are interpreted as being reactivated Caledonian thrusts as suggested by Brewer & Smythe (1984). The initial, normal movement, which has extended the crust by up to 30%, probably occurred during, or before, the Permo–Triassic. This is deduced from the half-graben infill which is known to consist of Permo–Triassic (or older at depth) sedimentary *wedges* (Figs 4, 6A and SE end of Fig. 5). Some of these faults may be continuations of the Outer Isles thrust and the Minch fault whereas others may be con-

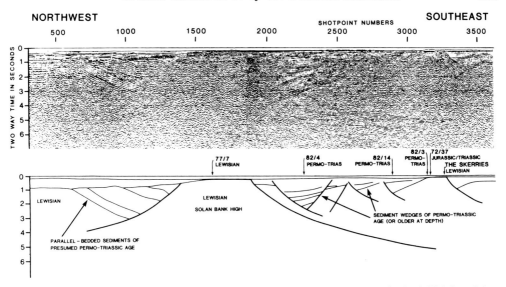

FIG. 5. Seismic line SW81-705 (unmigrated). Location given in Fig. 3. This shows the Solan Bank High bounded to the NW and SE by listric faults and half-grabens. The sediments in the half-graben to the NW are parallel bedded and those to the SE are wedges.

Numbers above the line drawing refer to BGS shallow boreholes shown on Figs 3 & 4. BGS shallow boreholes 77/7, 82/14 and 82/3 are along-strike from the line.

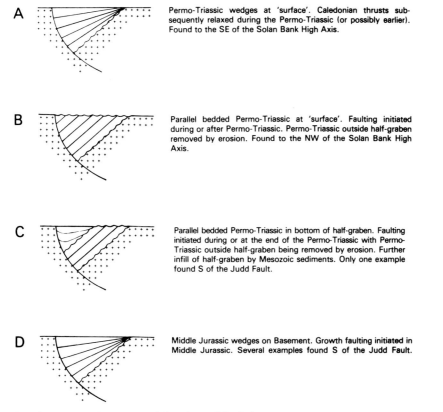

A. Permo-Triassic wedges at 'surface'. Caledonian thrusts subsequently relaxed during the Permo-Triassic (or possibly earlier). Found to the SE of the Solan Bank High Axis.

B. Parallel bedded Permo-Triassic at 'surface'. Faulting initiated during or after Permo-Triassic. Permo-Triassic outside half-graben removed by erosion. Found to the NW of the Solan Bank High Axis.

C. Parallel bedded Permo-Triassic in bottom of half-graben. Faulting initiated during or at the end of the Permo-Triassic with Permo-Triassic outside half-graben being removed by erosion. Further infill of half-graben by Mesozoic sediments. Only one example found S of the Judd Fault.

D. Middle Jurassic wedges on Basement. Growth faulting initiated in Middle Jurassic. Several examples found S of the Judd Fault.

FIG. 6. Summary of the type and inferred age of the faults.

tinuous with smaller N–S-trending faults found onshore, such as those near Kirtomy on the N coast of Scotland (Figs 3 & 4). These faults are associated with ancient valleys filled with Devonian sediments (Peach & Horne 1914; Blackbourn 1981) which may indicate that sediments of similar age occur below the Permo–Triassic sediments offshore.

The remaining three types of normal faults downthrow predominantly to the NW and are found N of the Solan Bank High axis. The type-B faults are the oldest of these three types and are shown in Figs 3, 4, 6B and the NW end of Fig. 5. These faults are associated with half-grabens which contain thick *parallel-bedded* sedimentary sequences not found outside the half-grabens and which are presumed to be Permo–Triassic in age from our knowledge of the regional geology. Such geometry must have arisen by parallel-bedded sediments being deposited over the entire area prior to fault initiation. Subsequent faulting protected the sediments from erosion in the half-graben but erosion removed the sediments from the upstanding blocks. Thus

faulting must have been initiated after sedimentation i.e. post Permo–Triassic times. In one of the half-grabens with this type of geometry the parallel-bedded Permo–Triassic is overlain by a middle Jurassic (and younger) sedimentary wedge. This is called the type-C fault and only one convincing example has been found. This is shown on the northwestern end of Fig. 7 and diagrammatically in Fig. 6C.

The youngest faults (Fig. 6D) are associated with half-grabens which contain wedges of middle Jurassic and younger sediments directly overlying basement (southeastern end of Fig. 7). It is proposed that these faults first moved during the middle Jurassic. Hence there are two ages of fault initiation shown in Fig. 7. The most northwesterly fault was initiated after the Permo–Triassic but before the middle Jurassic, whereas the faults to the SE were initiated in the middle Jurassic. There are also other differences between these two types of faults. The most northwesterly fault is demonstrably listric but the other faults shown in Fig. 7 may be rotational planar faults (Wernicke &

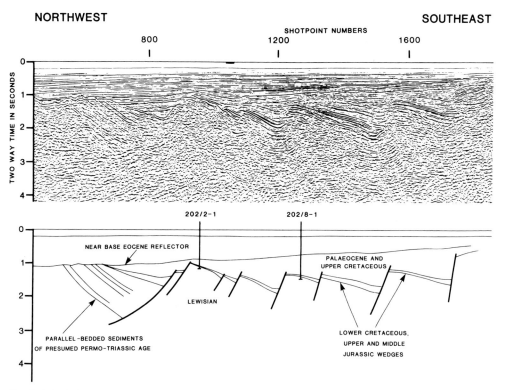

FIG. 7. Seismic line WS 30 (migrated). Location given in Fig. 3. The most northwesterly fault is demonstrably listric and the associated half-graben is filled with parallel-bedded sediments overlain by sedimentary wedges (deepest part of basin is at about 3.5 km depth). The remaining faults cannot be shown to be listric and may be 'domino' faults. The associated half-grabens are filled only with wedging sediments. Numbers above the line drawing refer to released commercial wells shown on Figs 3 & 4.

Burchfiel 1982) or 'domino' faults. This possibility arises as the nature of the fault plane (curved or planar) cannot be seen. Also the dip of the fault blocks, as represented by the top basement reflector, does not increase significantly northwestwards although theory predicts that this ought to be the case if the fault planes are listric.

Depending on the type of faults inferred and the angle of the faults, which cannot be clearly seen on seismic sections, this part of the crust has been extended by between 11 and 23% by the type-D faults.

Transfer faulting: the Judd fault

At the southwestern end of the Rona Ridge is a major NW–SE-trending fault which extends for at least 40 km. It is associated with minor faults of similar trend, which is perpendicular to the main structural trend found along the NW margin of Britain (Figs 3 & 4). This major fault is termed here the Judd fault after the BGS 1:250,000 sheet name for the area.

The Judd fault has a vertical displacement at basement level of approximately 2 sec TWT apparently downthrowing to the NE. On seismic sections it has the appearance of a buried topographic slope rather than a fault (Fig. 8).

The oldest sediments to the NE have not been drilled but on the basis of their seismic character and other regional considerations, it is tentatively suggested that they are of Jurassic age. This is a similar age to that of the main episode of movement on the type-D faults which form a number of fault blocks to the S of the Judd fault. It is unlikely that a normal fault with NW–SE trend would develop by the prevailing stress regime which is parallel to this fault.

It is suggested that this fault, and associated minor faults, are transfer faults as defined by Gibbs (1984), but similar in concept to Bally's transform faults (Bally 1982). If so, the Judd fault developed entirely by lateral movement. Such transfer faults are essential to the development of extensional rift margins but are rarely recognized (Gibbs 1984). The Judd fault is very prominent because of the topographic difference of the basement across the fault. The sense of movement is probably sinistral and it developed thus. The Rona Ridge and the area of shallow basement currently to the SW of the Judd fault acted as an immobile block. A crustal block originally attached to the Rona Ridge separated by extreme crustal extension along the Judd fault and the oceanward fault plane of the Rona Ridge. The detachment of this block and the development of the Judd fault may not have been the result of the 'clean break' but may have resulted in crustal extension S

of the Judd fault prior to complete detachment. The evidence for this is the number of listric fault blocks, instead of the usual single fault plane, that defines the NW edge of the Solan Bank High and the Rona Ridge. Alternatively, the break might have been 'clean', but the Solan Bank High subsequently underwent extension and faulting. This would be in accordance with Gibb's (1984) model where fault activity migrates towards the foreland by footwall collapse.

Age of cessation of fault movement

Most of the faults to the NW of the Solan Bank High axis ceased movement in the Upper Cretaceous or Palaeocene although the Shetland Spine fault system in the S of quadrant 205 forms a marked seabed topographic feature and may still be active (Fig. 1).

The age of cessation of the type-A faults, SE of the Solan Bank High axis, cannot be determined as sediments younger than Permo–Triassic are absent and the faults do not form sea-bed features.

Structural history

Once the ages of fault initiation have been determined (Fig. 6) it is possible to develop a structural history for the area. The oldest proven fault movements in the area are the Caledonian thrust movements of the major type-A faults SE of the Solan Bank High axis. The occurrence of such movements offshore was first suggested by Brewer & Smythe (1984) as a result of their interpretation of a single seismic line (MOIST). Regional seismic interpretation has shown that these thrust movements were probably present over most of the area W of Orkney but that they did not develop further NW than the area that subsequently became the Solan Bank High.

Relaxation of these thrusts in the late Palaeozoic was also postulated by Brewer & Smythe (1984) and again these movements have affected the area W of Orkney as far as the Solan Bank High. Minor faults may have been created at this time paralleling the relaxed thrust faults. These movements which are inferred to be Permo–Triassic at the latest, led to the formation of the southeastern fault of the Solan Bank High. Concomitant with, or slightly later than the relaxation of these thrusts, further crustal extension led to the initiation of the type-B faults, the earliest series of faults which downthrow to the NW. The half-grabens associated with these faults may be grouped together to form part of McLean's (1978) Marginal Belt of basins (see Discussion).

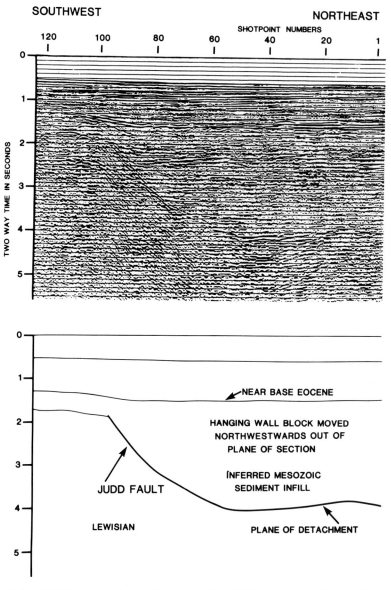

FIG. 8. Seismic line OS 518 (unmigrated). Location given in Fig. 3. This shows the Judd fault and plane of detachment (at about 6 km depth). The sediments in the basin to the NE of the Judd fault do not show the features that would normally be associated with a listric fault (e.g. dipping towards the fault or roll-over) and this is taken as additional evidence to suggest that the Judd fault is a transfer fault. (It should be noted that some of the horizontal 'reflectors' may be multiples).

A period of quiescence must have followed the Permo–Triassic-initiated faulting (although existing faults may have continued to develop) until the middle Jurassic when the major faults of the Rona Ridge developed. At the same time the Judd fault and its associated listric fault blocks, immediately to the S, must also have been initiated. Most faulting ceased during the Upper Cretaceous and Palaeocene although some faults (e.g. the Shetland Spine fault system) may still have been active.

Regional subsidence was initiated during the Palaeocene and continued until the present allowing deposition over the entire area, except for topographic highs near land.

Discussion

Owing to the proximity of this area to the shelf edge, the ages of faulting may be related to the rifting and opening of the North Atlantic. McLean (1978) suggested that a chain of basins existed (those associated with our type-B faults) from the Porcupine Seabight (SW of Ireland) to the area W of Shetland. These basins he termed the Marginal Belt (marginal to the shelf edge) and postulated that they were formed by upper-crustal fracturing in response to oceanward flow of ductile lower lithosphere towards the continental slope (Bott 1971). It is inherent in this model that the continental margin and the Atlantic were in existence by Permo–Triassic times. Such an age is not universally favoured although Russell (1976) and Russell & Smythe (1978) have suggested a Permian age and Haszeldine (1984) a Carboniferous age for earliest North Atlantic rifting.

Le Pichon & Sibuet (1981) disagree with the mechanism proposed by Bott (1971) and their theoretical study shows that oceanic material cannot have been accreted until after the latest period of fault initiation (i.e. after the middle Jurassic). This age is favoured by authors such as Roberts *et al.* (1981).

These conflicting hypotheses show that a definite age for the onset of Atlantic opening cannot yet be proved but suggest that crustal extension along the Atlantic margin was episodic.

Conclusions

Extensional tectonism in this area occurred in two distinct locations and at different times. Listric, transfer and possibly 'domino' faulting was initiated to the NW of the Solan Bank High axis during the middle Jurassic. Relaxation of former Caledonian thrusts to the SE of the Solan Bank High axis was initiated in the Permo–Triassic.

ACKNOWLEDGMENTS: Shell UK Exploration and Production kindly gave permission to reproduce the seismic line in Fig. 5. We would also like to thank Western Geophysical for permission to publish the seismic lines shown in Figs 7 and 8, both of which are taken from speculative data sets, and also D. Barr for constructive criticism of earlier drafts of the manuscript. This paper is published with the permission of the Department of Energy and the Director, British Geological Survey (NERC).

References

BALLY, A.W. 1982. Musing over sedimentary basin evolution. *Phil. Trans. R. Soc. London*, **A305**, 325–38.

BLACKBOURN, G. 1981. Probable Old Red Standstone conglomerates around Tongue and adjacent areas, north Sutherland. *Scott. J. Geol.* **17**, 103–18.

BOTT, M.H.P. 1971. Evolution of young continental margins and formation of shelf basins. *Tectonophysics*, **11**, 319–27.

—— & WATTS, A.B. 1970. Deep sedimentary basins proved in the Shetland–Hebridean continental shelf and margin. *Nature*, **225**, 265–8.

——, SUNDERLAND, J., SMITH, P.J., CASTEN, U. & SAXOV, S. 1974. Evidence for continental crust beneath the Faeroe Islands. *Nature*, **248**, 202–4.

BREWER, J.A & SMYTHE, D.K. 1984. MOIST and the continuity of crustal reflector geometry along the Caledonian–Appalachian orogen. *J. geol. Soc. London*, **141**, 105–20.

CASHION, W.W. 1975. The geology of the West Shetland Basin. In: *Offshore Europe '75 Conference Papers, Paper OE-75, Offshore Services Magazine*, p. 216. Spearhead Publications Ltd.,, Kingston-upon-Thames.

FLINN, D. 1969. A geological interpretation of the aeromagnetic maps of the continental shelf around Orkney and Shetland. *Geol. J.* **6**, 279–92.

GIBBS, A.D. 1984. Structural evolution of extensional basin margins. *J. geol. Soc. London*, **141**, 609–20.

HASZELDINE, R.S. 1984. Carboniferous North Atlantic palaeogeography: stratigraphic evidence for rifting, not megashear or subduction. *Geol. Mag.* **121**, 443–63.

LE PICHON, X. & SIBUET, J-C. 1981. Passive Margins: A model of formation. *J. geophys. Res.* **86**, B5, 3708–20.

McLEAN, A.C. 1978. Evolution of fault-controlled ensialic basins in northwestern Britain. In: BOWES, D.R. & LEAKE, B.E. (eds) *Crustal evolution in northwestern Britain and adjacent regions, Geol. J. Spec. Issue No. 10*, pp. 325–46.

PEACH, B.N. & HORNE, J. 1914. Outliers of Old Red Sandstone between Bighouse Bay and Kyle of Tongue. In: CRAMPTON, C.B. & CARRUTHERS, R.G. *The Geology of Caithness. Mem. geol. Surv. Scotland.*

RIDD, M.F. 1981. Petroleum geology West of Shetlands. In: ILLING, L.V. & HOBSON, G.D. (eds) *Petroleum geology of the continental shelf of north-west Europe*, pp. 414–25. (Inst. Pet. London), Heyden and Son Ltd.

RITCHIE, J.D. & DARBYSHIRE, D.P.F. 1984. Rb-Sr dates on Precambrian rocks from marine exploration wells in and around the West Shetland Basin. *Scott. J. Geol.* **20**, 31–6.

ROBERTS, D.G., MASSON, D.G. & MILES, P.R. 1981. Age and structure of the southern Rockall Trough: new evidence. *Earth planet. Sci. Let.*, **52**, 115–28.

RUSSELL, M.J. 1976. A possible Lower Permian age for the onset of ocean floor spreading in the northern North Atlantic. *Scott. J. Geol.* **12**, 315–23.

—— & SMYTHE, D.K. 1978. Evidence for an early Permian oceanic rift in the northern North Atlantic.

In: NEUMANN, E.R. & RAMBERG, I.B. (eds) *Petrology and geochemistry of continental rifts*, pp. 173–9. Reidel, Dordrecht, Holland.

SMITH, P.J. & BOTT, M.H.P. 1975. Structure of the crust beneath the Caledonian foreland and Caledonian belt of the north Scottish shelf region. *Geophys. J.R. astron. Soc.* **40**, 187–205.

WATTS, A.B. 1971. Geophysical investigations on the continental shelf and slope north of Scotland. *Scott. J. Geol.* **7**, 189–218.

WERNICKE, B. & BURCHFIEL, B.C. 1982. Modes of extensional tectonics. *J. struct. Geol.* **4**, 105–15.

ZIEGLER, P.A. 1982. *Geological atlas of western and central Europe*, pp. 1–130. Shell Internationale Petroleum Maatschappij, BV.

S.R. KIRTON & K. HITCHEN, British Geological Survey, 19 Grange Terrace, Edinburgh EH9 2LF.

Sedimentary structures associated with extensional fault movement from the Westphalian of NE England

C.R. Fielding & G.A.L. Johnson

SUMMARY: Although differential subsidence and extension has been well established as a control on sedimentation for the Dinantian of N England, the continuation of this tectonic regime into Silesian times is less well demonstrated.

The Westphalian (Upper Carboniferous) Coal Measures of the Durham coalfield in NE England, which were deposited on an essentially flat, deltaic plain, display abundant evidence of a subtle structural control on sedimentation. Medium-scale (hundreds of square kilometres) patterns of sedimentation, notably the disposition of major fluvial channel belts, were at times strongly controlled by active, ENE–WSW- and E–W-trending fault lines. The faults represent a response to a broadly N–S directed tension and many resulted from the reactivation of earlier, Caledonide crustal weaknesses.

The effects of such tectonic activity may be seen spectacularly at field-outcrop scale. At an opencast coal mine in southern Co. Durham close to the major Butterknowle fault, an exposed Upper Westphalian A sequence displays a plethora of tectonically associated structures. These include gravity slides, various dewatering structures, claystone dykes, convoluted and internally chaotic sandstone beds, desiccation cracks and signs of vertical drainage in an originally water-logged palaeosol profile, and abrupt bed thickness changes. The existence and orientation of two minor channels on the ESE side of the fault line, and other palaeoflow data, support the hypothesis that the Butterknowle fault displaced downward the area to its ESE at this time.

Fractures across the area of the opencast site were found to contain high concentrations of galena, sphalerite, pyrite/marcasite and other minerals which were apparently introduced at the time of formation of the N Pennine orefield (Carboniferous–Permian).

Across the area that is now northern Britain, the Carboniferous period was characterized by the extension of continental crust and basin subsidence. Recent tectonic models have emphasized the role of crustal attenuation and consequent 'rift and sag' (the model of McKenzie 1978; see Leeder 1982a) and subsidence produced by lithospheric stretching caused by the slab pull force resulting from subduction to the S (Johnson 1982; Bott et al. 1984).

The main phase of rifting and subsidence in northern Britain took place during Dinantian times, and its control on contemporary sedimentation is abundantly demonstrated by sequence thickness changes across the various structural hinge lines (Johnson 1967, 1982), (Figs 1 & 2). Rapid subsidence of the northern Pennine basins in Dinantian times appears to have slowed down through the succeeding Namurian period, coincident with a change from shallow marine to more deltaic environments of sediment deposition. By the beginning of the Westphalian, the original block and trough topography had been essentially eliminated and a wide deltaic plain established across the northern Pennines (Fig. 2). Distributary channels crossed this coastal plain, and were separated by shallow lakes and bays (Fielding 1982, 1984a). Further S in the central Pennines area, the Namurian basin depocentre was maintained through the West-

phalian, though again subsidence rates were reduced, and the coastal-plain environment became established across the entire Pennine province by mid-Westphalian A times (Calver 1969).

In the Durham area, despite the almost uniform sequence of Westphalian strata, evidence of continued extensional faulting has recently been recorded (Fielding 1982, 1984b). The most striking manifestations of such activity are elongate, fault-bounded tracts characterized by expanded vertical sedimentary sequences, impoverishment or wedging out of coal seams, and vertical stacking of fluvial channel-belt deposits (fig. 4, Fielding 1984b). The faults that define such belts, notably the major Ninety Fathom and Butterknowle–Wigglesworth lines, are dominantly orientated ENE–WSW or E–W and, therefore, probably represent the reactivation of older, Caledonide structural weaknesses.

More direct evidence of Westphalian faulting may be seen on the field-outcrop scale. At Buckhead opencast (strip) coal mine in southern Co. Durham (Figs 1 & 2), which straddles part of the Butterknowle–Wigglesworth fault system, recent excavations have exposed a sequence within the Tilley Group of coals (Upper Westphalian A). The exposure displays many syndepositional deformation structures and other features strongly suggestive of a structural control on their formation. It is

From COWARD, M.P., DEWEY, J.F. & HANCOCK, P.L. (eds), 1987, *Continental Extensional Tectonics*, Geological Society Special Publication No. 28, pp. 511–516.

511

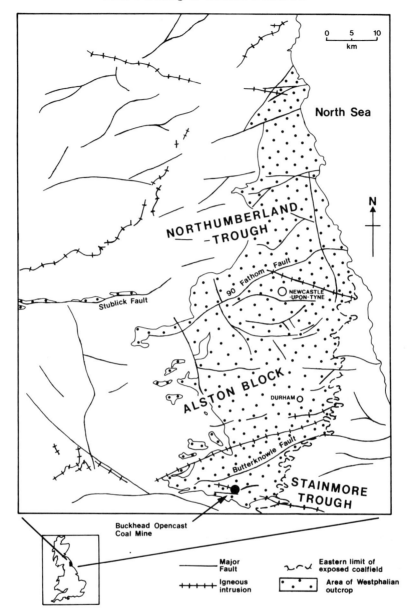

FIG. 1. Map showing the location of the Durham coalfield and Buckhead opencast site, and the regional distribution of major faults.

the purpose of this paper to describe and interpret these structures.

Succession

During the excavation of Buckhead opencast coal mine, (G.R. NZ 133243), the Bottom Tilley coal was uncovered along with an 8.5-m sedimentary sequence overlying the seam (Figs 3 & 4). The sequence, exposed in two adjoining faces, is largely composed of interbedded fine sandstone-to-granulestones and silty claystones (Fig. 4).

Between the two thin leaves of the Bottom Tilley seam, a 2.6-m thick sequence, comprising two coarsening-upward cycles of sub-equal thickness, is developed (Fig. 4). The lower of these reaches fine-sand grade, whereas the higher cycle has coarsened

NORTHERN ENGLAND

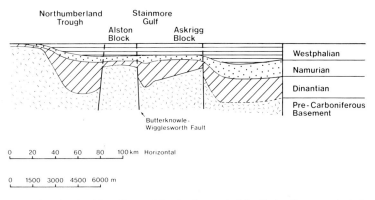

FIG. 2. N–S cross-section showing hinge lines and the development of the Carboniferous geological succession across northern England (after Johnson 1982).

only to siltstone with sandy laminae. Stigmarian rootlets penetrate almost the entire sequence and many are traceable from the lower sequence into the upper one.

The higher coarsening-upward sequence is notable for its containing an assemblage of sandstone-filled cracks, vertical dewatering pipes, and siderite nodules, with vertically orientated long axes, immediately below the upper coal (Fig. 4). The fine-grained sandstone-filled cracks are about 5–20 mm wide, slightly folded, up to 0.3 m long in vertical section, and polygonal in plan view.

Immediately above the upper seam is a series of medium-grained sandstone-to-granulestones interbedded with laminated claystones (Fig. 4). The sandstones contain abundant 'coaly scares', have loaded bases and occasionally show convolute lamination and even complete internal disorganization. Claystone dykes up to 0.15 m in width pass through the basal sandstone into the underlying coal. Interbedded claystones exhibit rare sandy laminae and abundant siderite nodules and lenses.

Higher in the sequence, sandstones are finer grained, and interbedded sediments consist mainly of silty claystones. Burrows referable to *Pelecypodichnus*, *Arenicolites* and *Monocraterion* are common in the sandstones, particularly where thin intercalations of silty claystones are present.

Towards the top of the exposed section, a sequence of interbedded fine-grained sandstones and claystones with a channelized base, display prominent low-angle accretion surfaces (Fig. 4). The Top Tilley coal seam is thought to lie a few metres stratigraphically above the top of the exposed sequence.

Indications of synsedimentary instability are widespread throughout the interval in the form of large-scale loading, various dewatering structures,

abrupt lateral changes in sandstone thickness, character and overall abundance, and listric synsedimentary faults, in addition to previously mentioned dewatering pipes, disrupted bedding and claystone dykes (Fig. 4).

Palaeocurrent measurements from trough cross-bedding and ripple cross-lamination indicate palaeoflow towards the S and SSE. Low-angle accretion surfaces, exposed in two areas, dip towards the SSE and NW (Fig. 4).

Many of the sandstones, particularly the coarser beds, contain an association of euhedral dolomite and pyrite/marcasite cements, which post-date the ubiquitous quartz and kaolinite/illite diagenetic phases. Indeed, many of the sandstones contain veins of pyrite, marcasite, sphalerite, galena, and fluorite, a mineral suite reminiscent of the N Pennine orefield.

Interpretation

The alteration of sharply based sandstones and fine-grained claystones, and palaeocurrent data, imply fluctuating conditions of deposition, varying form high-energy unidirectional flows to quiet-water suspension fall-out. The apparent sheet geometry and flat-lying aspect of most of the sandstones implies deposition by unconfined flows. However, the two units with low-angle accretionary dips are considered as representing channels.

The exposed sequence is interpreted as the deposits of a shallow, subsiding lacustrine basin fed by coarse-grained sediment from a northerly source (Fig. 4). Water depths in the lower part of the sequence (between the two coal seams) were 0–2 m, and in the upper part are uncertain, though the lack of rootlet penetration and a comparison

514   *C.R. Fielding & G.A.L. Johnson*

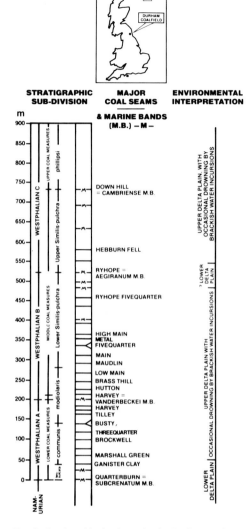

FIG. 3. Stratigraphical column for the Durham coalfield, showing the major coal seams and broad
environmental interpretation.

with similar sequences exposed elsewhere suggest a
likely depth of 3–5 m.

The two areas displaying low-angle accretion
surfaces and channel morphology are interpreted as
the remnants of laterally accreted, minor distributary channels which, from their geometry,
flowed across the shallow basin towards the NE,
though not simultaneously. Geometrical relationships indicate that the channels were about 10 m
wide and 2 m deep.

From their three-dimensional geometry, the
polygonal sandstone-filled cracks are interpreted as

the products of desiccation, and are therefore
indications of a fluctuating water table at the time of
deposition of the sequence.

The various deformational structures, being confined to individual beds or a small number of beds,
are interpreted as having a syndepositional origin.
Such structures, formed by the failure of water-
logged sediment columns, could have been initiated
by the repeated, rapid dumping of sand on to water-
logged (particularly, fine-grained) sediment
surfaces or by tectonic stresses (Leeder 1982b).
Elsewhere in the Durham Coal Measures, syndepositional deformation structures are largely
restricted to load-casting, almost certainly reflecting the former of the two possible mechanisms.
Synsedimentary gravity slides are rare within the
British Coal Measures and particularly so in the
Durham area. Of the two published reports of such
occurrences, one is from the tectonically unstable
South Wales coal field (Elliott & Ladipo 1981).

The abundance and variety of synsedimentary
deformational structures in the Buckhead exposure
are difficult to account for in terms of sedimentary
processes, and a tectonic control on their formation
is thought likely. The most plausible source of
seismic disturbances in the area is the nearby
Butterknowle–Wigglesworth fault system. The
minor channels at Buckhead trend ENE–WSW,
close to the orientation of the Wigglesworth faults,
suggesting that the latter controlled the disposition
of the former (Fig. 4; cf. Fig. 2). Further, palaeocurrent measurements and the orientation of gravity
slides indicate southward-inclined palaeoslopes.

Movement on the Wigglesworth fault is proposed
to explain the observed phenomena. A downthrow
on the SSE side of an arm of the fault located to the
immediate N of the exposure would best explain the
observed palaeocurrent–palaeoslope data. Such a
disturbance, occurring during the deposition of the
sequence above the two thin coals, would have
created an elongate lacustrine hollow which filled
dominantly with silt and mud deposited out of
suspension. Periodic turbidity currents (probably
triggered by seismic disturbances and or
distributary channel flooding) delivered coarser
grained sediment southeastward over the fault scarp
into the basin, which was repeatedly shaken by
further shocks. Twice during this period, minor
distributary channels were attracted into the
elongate lacustrine basin, passing northeastward
along the foot of the fault scarp (Fig. 4). From the
observed bedding relationships, the vertical height
of the fault scarp was probably never greater than a
few metres.

The well-drained palaeosol situated between the
two coals could possibly reflect flexural stress,
resulting in a slight uplift (1–2 m), which preceded
activation of the fault itself.

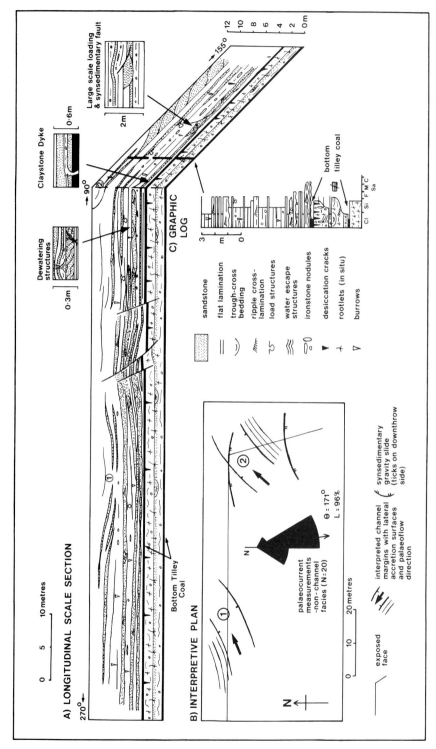

FIG. 4. Scale drawing, sedimentological log and interpretation of the Buckhead exposure.

The exotic cement phases recorded in sandstones are best explained by the passage of solute-charged brines along tension gashes associated with faults which had recently been active, during the late Carboniferous and post-Carboniferous period. It is noteworthy that mineralization was active in the N Pennine orefield for 100 My after the end of the Carboniferous (Dunham 1970) so there was time for the mineral cements to accumulate slowly in the sandstones.

Conclusions

1　Reactivation of Caledonide structural weaknesses in NE England has recently been suggested as a control on sedimentation of the Westphalian (Upper Carboniferous) Coal Measures of the Durham coal field (Fielding 1984a). Evidence for such a control lies in the correspondence between distributary channel belt and major fault trends.

2　More detailed evidence for such a control has been recorded from an opencast coal mine close to the surface trace of the Butterknowle-Wigglesworth fault system. There, within an Upper Westphalian A sequence, numerous syndepositional deformation structures in combination with palaeocurrent data suggest repeated tremors associated with minor fault movements. Such movements evidently created elongate palaeotopographic hollows into which at least two minor distributary channels were attracted. The structural disturbances were preceded by local uplift of 1–2 m, demonstrated by the temporary drainage of a previously and subsequently waterlogged palaeosol.

3　The detailed case study described in this paper demonstrates the application and interpretation of tectonic activity within coastal-plain sequences. Within this context the role played by palaeopedological analysis is of particular importance, having hitherto been somewhat underestimated.

References

Bott, M.H.P., Swinburn, P.M. & Long, R.E. 1984. Deep structure and the origin of the Northumberland and Stainmore troughs. *Proc. Yorkshire geol. Soc.* **44**, 479–95.

Calver, M.A. 1969. Westphalian of Britain. *C.R. 6th Int. Cong. Carb.*, Sheffield 1967, **1**, 233–54.

Dunham, K.C. 1970. Mineralization. *In*: Hickling, G. (ed) *The Geology of Durham County*, pp. 124–133. Nat. Hist. Soc. Northumberland, Newcastle upon Tyne.

Elliott, T. & Ladipo, K.O. 1981. Synsedimentary gravity slides (growth faults) in the Coal Measures of South Wales. *Nature*, **291**, 220–22.

Fielding, C.R. 1982. *Sedimentology and stratigraphy of the Durham Coal Measures, and comparisons with other British coalfields.* Unpubl. PhD Thesis, Univ. Durham.

—— 1984a. Upper delta plain lacustrine and fluviolacustrine facies from the Westphalian of the Durham coalfield, NE England. *Sedimentology*, **31**, 547–67.

—— 1984b. A coal depositional model for the Durham Coal Measures of NE England. *J. geol. Soc. London*, **141**, 919–31.

Johnson, G.A.L. 1967. Basement control of Carboniferous sedimentation in northern England. *Proc. Yorks geol. Soc.* **36**, 175–94.

—— 1982. Geographical change in Britain during the Carboniferous period. *Proc. Yorks geol. Soc.* **44**, 181–203.

Leeder, M.R. 1982a. Upper Palaeozoic basins of the British Isles—Caledonide inheritance versus Hercynian plate margin processes. *J. geol. Soc. London*, **139**, 481–91.

—— 1982b. *Sedimentology.* pp. 344. Allen & Unwin, London.

McKenzie, D. 1978. Some remarks on the development of sedimentary basins. *Earth planet. Sci. Lett.* **40**, 25–32.

C.R. Fielding, Department of Geology and Mineralogy, University of Queensland, St. Lucia, Australia 4067.

G.A.L. Johnson, Department of Geological Sciences, University of Durham, Science Laboratories, South Road, Durham DH1 3LE, UK.

The thermal and mechanical development of the Wessex Basin, southern England

G.D. Karner, S.D. Lake & J.F. Dewey

SUMMARY: The Wessex Basin of southern England is an E–W-trending Late Palaeozoic to Tertiary extensional basin formed on Early Palaeozoic Variscan crust. Extension occured over a protracted period from Late Carboniferous to Cretaceous times resulting in the evolution of four main depocentres or sub-basins; the Channel basin, Winterborne-Kingston Trough, Vale of Pewsey, and Weald basins. Each sub-basin was controlled fundamentally by the normal reactivation of basement thrust faults and wrench or transfer faults. The basement faults represent primary structures associated with the fold-and-thrust terrain of the Devonian–Carboniferous Variscan Orogeny. Subsequent, but synchronous, reactivation of both thrust and transfer faults tended to compartmentalize the basement, leading to discrete depocentres and the production of general, rhomboidal-shaped, sub-basins (characteristic of pull-apart basins in strike-slip terrains).

To investigate the thermo–mechanical properties of the lithosphere during basin formation, 50 boreholes within the Wessex Basin were back-stripped to isolate the driving tectonic subsidence responsible for basin formation. The resultant driving subsidence is characterized by a gentle, sometimes negative, exponential form, with superimposed rapid, discrete, subsidence events. As the geological development of the Wessex Basin was characterized by polyphase extension and the utilization of crustal detachments, the lithospheric model used to determine δ (crustal extension above the detachment) and β (stretching below the detachment) included the effects of depth-dependent stretching and finite re-rifting. From the back-stripping analysis, the basin-wide-averaged upper-crustal extension and lower-crustal/sub-crustal lithospheric stretching were 11 and 5% respectively. The distribution of δ is strongly influenced by the location of growth faults, and hence basement thrust-fault reactivation, suggesting that δ is reflecting the brittle failure and collapse of hanging wall blocks. Repeated slip and block collapse resulted in the polyphase extension responsible for renewed basin subsidence. In contrast, β is uniformly distributed across the basin, suggestive of a ductile failure of the lower crust and responsible for the low-magnitude thermal subsidence. Strain compatibility between the upper-crust and lower-crust/sub-crustal lithosphere is maintained partly within the basin (5%), and partly external to the basin. As the Variscan basal thrust was the fundamental relay (in the sense of Wernicke) responsible for the Wessex Basin formation, we postulate that strain balancing induced a cumulative (essentially thermal) isostatic uplift (of ≈ 60 m) under the northern margin of the Armorican Massif.

To date, the quantitative modelling of intracratonic sedimentary basins has been concerned primarily with the isostatic response of the lithosphere to a single extension event. Such extension predicts two discrete phases of basin development; a rapid subsidence phase related to rifting of the crust and thinning of the sub-crustal lithosphere (i.e. the active phase), followed by a generally negative exponential subsidence phase associated with the conductive cooling of the lithosphere (i.e. the passive phase). In marked contrast to this simple model prediction, many basins exhibit a polyphase rifting history as characterized by episodes of renewed basin subsidence. Often, this renewed subsidence is very rapid and is followed by little, if any, thermal subsidence. Further complexities are introduced in that not all punctuated subsidence phases need be caused by crustal re-rifting. For example, a major complexity in basin development, especially in many European basins, is basin inversion, a process by which a depocentre is transformed into a structural high (while structural highs become depocentres). The very nature of inverting

structural highs into basin subsidence introduces an additional subsidence driving mechanism. Structural high inversion is the consequence of regionally generated compression (or transpression) acting across the same crustal faults which facilitated basin initiation.

Independent of the above complexities, forward modelling has generally failed to reproduce the detailed form of even simple (e.g. young, uniextensional phase) basins, even when factors such as lithospheric flexure, lateral heat-flow, sediment compaction, and eustatic sea-level variations are taken into account (e.g. Watts et al. 1982; Dewey et al. 1984; Beaumont et al. 1982). The purpose of this paper is to investigate the response of the lithosphere to polyphase extension and its implications with respect to sedimentary basin development by combining the results of both forward and inverse modelling. We chose as a suitable example, the Wessex Basin of southern England and the English Channel.

The Wessex Basin (Kent 1949) occupies an area of approximately 80,000 km². The basin is

From COWARD, M.P., DEWEY, J.F. & HANCOCK, P.L. (eds), 1987, *Continental Extensional Tectonics*, Geological Society Special Publication No. 28, pp. 517–536.

bounded to the W by the Cornubian Massif, to the N and E by the London–Brabant platform, and to the S by the Armorican Massif (Fig. 1). The basement consists largely of Devonian and Carboniferous molasse-type sediments deformed by the emplacement of thrust sheets during the Variscan Orogeny. Within the Wessex Basin, Palaeozoic, Mesozoic and Cenozoic sediments have been deposited with an average thickness of ≈ 1500 m, locally exceeding 3500 m. The area is currently attracting considerable exploration interest in the light of recently discovered economic oil and gas reserves.

The stratigraphy, structure and sedimentology of the Wessex Basin has been reported by several authors (e.g. Strahan 1898; Arkell 1947; Falcon & Kent 1950; Phillips 1964; Drummond 1970; Whittaker 1975; Dewey 1982; Drummond 1982; Melville & Freshney 1982; Stoneley 1982; Chadwick 1985). There is still no clear agreement, however, on the structural development of the basin and even less discussion on the mechanisms responsible for its development. Some authors have interpreted the Wessex Basin in the context of lithospheric stretching and crustal rifting (Whittaker 1975; Dewey 1982; Chadwick 1985), while others, notably Drummond (1970), have suggested that wrenching must play a fundamental role. No serious attempt has been made to integrate the entire development history of the basis (tectonic and stratigraphic) with a basin-formation mechanism. Given this, and taking advantage of the access to new data (particularly, recently released borehole data and the deep seismic reflection profiles of the British Institutions Reflection Profiling Syndicate (BIRPS) group, this paper attempts to integrate the geological and structural history of the Wessex Basin and the structure of the Variscan basement with the thermal and mechanical properties of the lithosphere of southern England.

Regional geology and structure

The Wessex Basin was initiated in the Late Carboniferous–early Permian (Knill 1982) with the deposition of continental desert sediments, locally interbedded with Permian volcanics (Knill 1969). Volcanic intrusives and extrusives are rare in the Wessex Basin, the Permian volcanics representing the only significant occurrence. Continental sedimentation continued throughout most of the Permian and Triassic with sediment distribution being strongly controlled by late Variscan topography. The Rhaetian (upper Triassic) marine transgression marked the first onset of marine conditions within the Wessex Basin and the initiation of a marked clay–sandstone–limestone cyclicity that continued throughout the Jurassic

(Hallam 1975). Middle Jurassic bentonites are developed locally, perhaps associated with North Sea volcanism. During the late Jurassic, the seas began to shallow (Sellwood 1978) with the area finally becoming emergent by the middle Tithonian (late Portlandian).

The Early Cretaceous was dominated, initially, by non-marine fluviatile sands and clays, unconformably overlain by Aptian/Albian shallow-marine sediments. Oil generation and migration was probably initiated during this period (Colter & Havard 1981) as oil-saturated conglomerates exist locally within the Wealden (Arkell 1947). The extensive regional distribution of the upper Cretaceous marine chalks is coincident with the global peak in eustatic sea-level (Hays & Pitman 1973; Vail *et al.* 1977; Pitman 1978). Shallow-marine to freshwater sands and clays dominate most of the Tertiary. The Alpine collision (Helvetic phase) in the late Oligocene effectively terminated the development of the Wessex Basin.

The basin consists of four main sub-basins (Fig. 1) of varying geometry, each showing similar structural controls and stratigraphical relationships. The Channel basin developed as a half-graben, the Winterborne–Kingston Trough as a symmetrical graben, the Vale of Pewsey basin as a half-graben, while the Weald basin is more typical of a sag-type basin, although westwards along strike it develops into a half-graben.

Two fundamentally different interpretations have been suggested to explain the structural development of the Wessex Basin, and these differ in the importance attached to the E–W and NW–SE trends which occur within the basin. Dewey (1982) and Stoneley (1982) considered the E–W structures to be fundamental to basin development and suggested that they represented major listric growth faults. Dewey (1982) identified three main phases of crustal rifting; a Triassic event, a more localized Toarcian event, and finally, a late Neocomian event. Chadwick *et al.* (1983) strengthened this interpretation by demonstrating that the E–W growth faults were generated by the normal reactivation of possibly Variscan aged basement thrusts. Further support for a basement (i.e. Variscan thrust) control on basin development was given by Day & Edwards (1983), who traced southward-dipping intrabasement reflectors to surface thrusts, while Lake *et al.* (1984) identified major lineament orientations within the central portion of the Wessex Basin (based on LANDSAT, MSS, and TM data sets) paralleling E–W Variscan basement trends.

Alternatively, some authors have interpreted Wessex Basin development solely in terms of the reactivation of the second dominant trend within the basin, the NW–SE faults. These faults formed

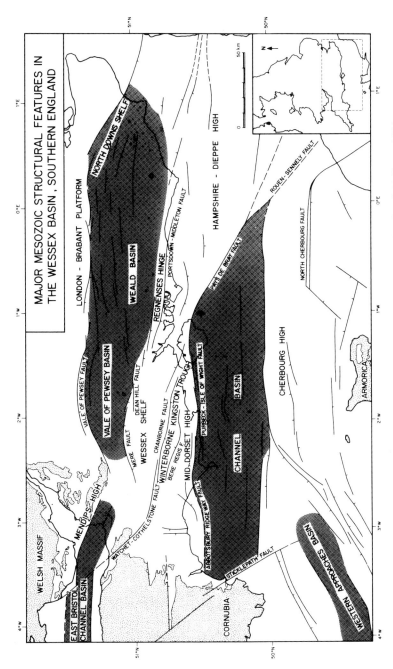

FIG. 1. Major Mesozoic structural features of the Wessex Basin (modified after Stoneley 1982; Allen & Holloway 1984; Sellwood *et al.* 1985). The main depocentres are shown shaded. The stippled area around the basin represents outcropping basement older than Permian.

contemporaneously with the emplacement of Variscan thrust sheets (Coward & Smallwood 1984; Hobson & Sanderson 1983) and acted as transfer faults by facilitating thrust-sheet offsets. For example, the southeastward continuation of the Sticklepath fault has acted as a transfer fault thereby allowing the independent development of the Western Approaches basin relative to the Wessex Basin (Fig. 1). Within the Wessex Basin, the *en échelon* arrangement of NW–SE trends suggests an E–W sinistral shear, and a complementary NW–SE dextral shear (Drummond 1982) during basin formation.

It would seem reasonable to expect that reactivation of both the E–W and the NW–SE faults could occur, thereby compartmentalizing the basement and hence isolating individual depocentres (cf. Isaac *et al.* 1982). The resulting geometry resembles a pull-apart basin (Fig. 1), in broad agreement with the wrench boundaries of the Wessex Basin (i.e. Sticklepath and Pays de Bray faults and the Purbeck–Isle of Wight and mid-Channel faults). The apparent separation between these basin-boundary faults is of the order of 40 km, but, as demonstrated by Stoneley (1982), the maximum horizontal extension across the Purbeck–Isle of Wight fault was only ≈ 2.5 km during the Jurassic–mid-Cretaceous. While crustal extension, and therefore basin initiation, is a consequence of sinistral motion across the NW–SE wrench faults, it is the collapse of the hanging wall block (or thrust sheet) that ultimately determines the basin width even when the absolute amount of extension is relatively small. Localized half-grabens, therefore, form as a consequence of hanging wall collapse. On increasing extension, antithetic faulting becomes important and transforms the half-graben geometry into full, but apparent, symmetrical grabens (e.g. Winterborne–Kingston Trough).

While the NW–SE fault direction is obviously important in the development of the Wessex Basin, it also represents a major fabric which cross-cuts the Variscides of Europe and as such, has controlled the development of many western European basins (e.g. Ziegler 1982; Lake & Karner 1986). In summary, the structural evolution of the Wessex Basin is believed to be fundamentally the result of basement reactivation. The E–W faults, as a consequence of normal reactivation, compensated extension by the upward propagation of growth faulting into the overlying sedimentary cover. The NW–SE faults compartmentalized the basement, thereby producing rhomboidal-shaped depocentres. Intermittent movement along either fault direction resulted in polyphase crustal extension and hence punctuated basin subsidence.

Other lineament and fault trends, while existing, are generally considered insignificant, for example,

the N–S trends S of the Purbeck–Isle of Wight fault (e.g. Arkell 1947; Donovan & Stride 1961). To the N of the Wessex Basin, the only major feature with this trend is the Malvern axis, a probable Precambrian basement feature. As the strong magnetic signature of the axis does not continue southwards into the Wessex Basin (cf. Hawkins 1942; Shackleton 1984), the basement of the Wessex Basin is likely to be solely of Variscan age.

Basin initiation independent of a basement control has been suggested by Falcon & Kent (1950) who postulate the migration of large amounts of Triassic salt as a cause for basin subsidence. Structures formerly attributed to salt movement, such as the Compton Valence anticline and the Fordingbridge High, proved, on drilling, to be low-density intrabasement rocks at shallow depths rather than salt diapirs (Melville & Freshney 1982). Rhys *et al.* (1982) have also shown that in the areas of thickest salt accumulation (i.e. 50 m, Winterborne–Kingston Trough), there is virtually no disruption of bedding as interpreted from seismic reflection imaging.

Mechanisms of basin formation

Sedimentary basins are the consequence of a driving subsidence, the form and distribution of which is dependent on the thermal and mechanical properties of the lithosphere. The history of basin subsidence, therefore, is a sensitive indicator of both the basin initiation mechanism, and the thermal and mechanical properties of the lithosphere, both in rifting, and during the subsequent conductive dissipation of rift-induced heat. The observed negative exponential form of rift basin subsidence (Sleep 1971) is analogous to the exponential decay of oceanic crust subsidence (Parsons & Sclater 1977).

Rift basins can be divided into two main types (Fig. 2), those resulting from lithospheric stretching (McKenzie 1978), and those resulting from crustal/upper-crustal extension (Royden *et al.* 1983; Karner & Dewey 1986). Although their surface expressions may be geometrically similar, the subsidence history is sensitive to the degree of lithospheric heating during rifting. Lithospheric rifting introduces a significant amount of heat into the base of the lithosphere (associated with the passive upwelling of hot asthenospheric material) relative to crustal rifting (cf. Fig. 2b & c). For ease of discussion, the dissipation of this asthenospheric heat will be termed the thermal recovery, or cooling, of the rifted lithosphere, even though nothing is actually heated during the extension process.

The lithospheric stretching model of McKenzie (1978) adequately reproduces the regional observations of intracratonic and rift/passive

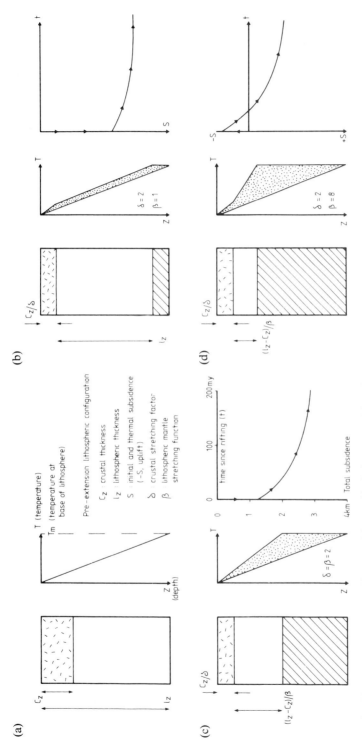

Fig. 2. Lithospheric stretching modifies the thickness of both the crust and the sub-crustal lithosphere. Details of the stretching configuration are strongly controlled by the presence of intracrustal detachments. Delta (δ) represents stretching above the detachment and beta (β) represents either the amount of stretching below the detachment or the degree of sub-crustal heating. The simplest lithospheric stretching model is for depth-independent extension ($\delta = \beta$) in which the pre-event lithospheric configuration (a) is modified to give (b). Two phases are apparent; a rapid subsidence phase and a slower thermal phase. δ controls the total subsidence of which the basin is capable, while β controls the magnitude of the thermal subsidence. In contrast, crustal stretching involves stretching above a detachment (c) and results in a significant reduction in lithospheric heating and therefore the amount of thermal subsidence. General depth-dependent stretching is shown in (d).

margin basins (e.g. Watts *et al.* 1982; Watts & Steckler 1981). The degree of lithospheric stretching can be characterized by the factor β, and predicts an initial rift phase associated with fault-controlled subsidence, followed by a thermal subsidence phase related to the thermal contraction and cooling of the lithosphere (Fig. 2b). As the lithosphere/asthenosphere boundary represents a temperature isotherm, any upward migration of this boundary introduces a temperature perturbation into the lithosphere. Most applications of this model (e.g. Steckler & Watts 1978; Sclater & Christie 1980) assume Airy (local) compensation for both the rift and thermal subsidence phases, that is, a zero flexural strength for the lithosphere. Inclusion of a finite-strength lithosphere helps to explain the overall increase of basin width with time and the progressive onlap of basin-margin sediments during the thermal subsidence phase (Watts *et al.* 1982; Watts & Thorne 1984).

Crustal extension (Royden *et al.* 1983; Karner & Dewey 1986) refers to the tectonic situation whereby extension is confined solely to the crust, the sub-crustal lithosphere playing an entirely (or largely) passive role (Fig. 2c). During extension, strain compatibility must be maintained within the crust and is most simply accommodated by contemporaneous foreland basin formation or regional thrusting in adjacent regions (cf. Karner & Dewey 1986; Christie-Blick & Biddle, in press). Although basins produced by crustal/upper-crustal extension are probably common, little attention has been given to this model. Possible candidates include many of the British offshore basins (on the continental margin) that have been seismically imaged by BIRPS and show Palaeozoic and Mesozoic basins formed along earlier Caledonide and Variscan structural trends (e.g. Brewer & Smythe 1984). Other examples include the Triassic grabens and half-grabens formed within the collapsed hanging wall of reactivated Appalachian thrust sheets along the eastern seaboard of the United States (e.g. the Connecticut, Newark, Culpepper, Riddeville, Bay of Fundy basins and the Brunswick graben).

Strain compatibility can be maintained in other ways, most notably by relaying of extension across crustal/lithospheric detachments (e.g. Wernicke 1985; Ussami *et al.* 1986). Quantitative models for studying the development of · basins above a detachment (e.g. Fig. 2d) have been investigated by Royden & Keen (1980) and Hellinger & Sclater (1983). Though originally designed to investigate basins in which an excess amount of heat was required to explain the high ratio of post-rift to syn-rift sedimentation (i.e. $\delta < \beta$), by symmetry, it is equally applicable to basins in which only minor heating occurs, such as in continental pull-apart

basins or hanging wall basins (e.g. Vienna basin and Limagne graben respectively). The McKenzie model for which $\delta > 1$ and $\beta = 1$ characterizes extension (Fig. 2c) which is confined to the crust (δ defining the crustal extension), with the sub-crustal lithosphere maintaining its thickness during stretching (β defining the stretching or degree of heating within the sub-crustal lithosphere). The resultant lithospheric temperature structure and subsidence for general detachment stretching is shown in Fig. 2d (with $\delta \neq \beta$ and, in this example, a flat detachment at the Moho). Readjustment of the sub-crustal lithosphere introduces a minor thermal anomaly which, on dissipation, produces the usual negative exponential rate of subsidence characteristic of the conductive dissipation of heat.

A variety of methods exist by which the amount of crustal (and we hope lithospheric) extension can be estimated; (i) consideration of pre- and post-stretched crustal thicknesses, while diagnostic of cumulative stretching, fails to address the history of stretching; (ii) examination of fault geometries (e.g. Wernicke & Burchfiel 1982) which tends to produce a minimum estimate of extension; and (iii) comparison of the observed driving subsidence of a basin, obtained from isostatically removing or back-stripping its sediments, with a theoretically determined driving subsidence. We use these techniques in an effort to define the magnitude, distribution, and history of lithospheric extension responsible for Wessex Basin formation.

The subsidence history of a sedimentary basin potentially contains information on the driving subsidence and hence initiating mechanism but sedimentation tends to distort the basin subsidence such that a correction for sediment loading must be applied. The process of back-stripping, as outlined by Steckler & Watts (1978), allows the isolation of the tectonic driving subsidence (Fig. 3). Back-stripping is a two-part process; first, the sediments are decompacted so that an estimate of sediment density through time can be made (assuming that the present-day porosity/depth curve applies at all times during basin development); secondly, the sediments are progressively removed and the isostatic rebound (usually Airy) of the basement monitored (Fig. 3). Airy isostasy refers to a lithosphere with a low flexural strength (Karner & Watts 1982), and while it is an unrealistic description of lithospheric behaviour (except possibly early in basin development), it does not change the form of the subsidence curves (Bond & Kominz 1984; Watts *et al.* 1982). The resultant back-stripped subsidence history can be directly compared to theoretically determined subsidence curves, as for example, in Fig. 3, in which the simple one-layer stretching model of McKenzie (1978) has been used.

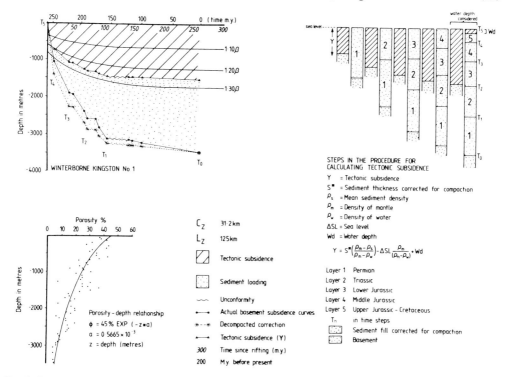

FIG. 3. Procedure (termed back-stripping) for calculating the tectonic subsidence of Wessex Basin boreholes using Winterborne–Kingston No. 1 as an example. Back-stripping requires firstly the decompaction of the sediment back through time, followed by the progressive isostatic removal of sediment from the basement (i.e. basement unloading). Shown for Winterborne–Kingston No. 1 is the actual basement subsidence, the decompacted subsidence, and the basement subsidence corrected for sediment loading (or the tectonic driving subsidence). Sediment-loading induced subsidence (or non-tectonic subsidence) is stippled. The observed and best-fitting porosity curve (in a least-squares sense), obtained from the sonic log of the Winterborne–Kingston No. 1 well is also shown. As no other porosity information was available, this same curve was used for decompacting all Wessex Basin wells.

In order to predict the response of the lithosphere to extension, the pre-stretching lithospheric and crustal thicknesses must be known. Lithospheric thickness is proportional to the thermal age of the basement (Karner *et al.* 1983), that is, the time since the last major thermal event. In southern England, the radiometric age of the low-grade metamorphic basement is 337±5 Ma (K–Ar, Colter & Havard 1981). Similarly, the $^{40}Ar/^{39}Ar$ dating of the middle Devonian basement in Arreton No. 2 borehole is 340±8 Ma. Thus, the pre-extensional lithospheric thickness was approximately 90–125 km. Interpretation of seismic refraction and wide-angle reflection data (e.g. Holder & Bott 1971; Brooks *et al.* 1984) over the Cornubian Massif suggests a pre-basin crustal thickness of 27–32 km, which is consistent with the value of 31.2 km assumed for the subsidence calculations.

Fifty boreholes were back-stripped to determine tectonic driving subsidence within the Wessex

Basin (Fig. 4, Table 1). Airy isostasy was assumed and the effects of eustatic sea-level variations, palaeobathymetry, and erosion were ignored. Figure 4 shows that subsidence within the Wessex Basin is complex, with subsidence magnitude being at a minimum in the northerly region of the basin and increasing towards the Channel. In some regions, the subsidence consists basically of a simple exponential shape punctuated by a number of rapid but small subsidence events (e.g. Nos 30, 35 & 47), whereas other regions show a gentle and continuous (almost linear) subsidence for the entire development history of the basin (e.g. Nos 13, 30, 35 & 37). The truncation of subsidence within the Wessex Basin depocentres (e.g. Nos 18, 23, 31, 46, 49 & 50) undoubtedly represents the effects of syn- to post-upper-Cretaceous inversion and subsequent erosion. Similarly, synchronous structural high inversion resulted in a renewed subsidence phase (e.g. Nos 35, 36, 42 & 47). The initiation of Weald basin subsidence shows and approximately 50 My

TABLE 1. *Summary of Wessex Basin borehole data.*

	Borehole name	N.G.R	Depth to basement (metres)	β	δ	Main finite rifting interval (My)
1	FARINGDON 1	SU324 947	655	1.06	1.06	38
2	COOLES FARM 1	SU018 929	1205	1.05	1.12	79
3	HIGHWORTH 1	SU183 915	1065	1.00	1.09	74
4	WILLESDEN 1	TQ21 83	817	1.04	1.03	24.5
5	SONNINGEYE 1	SU742 759	413	1.05	1.03	91
6	CLIFFE 1	TQ74 76	324	1.05	1.03	30.5
7	HERNE 1	TR18 67	362	1.00	1.03	48
8	BOBBING 1	TQ89 65	384	1.00	1.03	50
9	KINGSCLERE 1	SU499 589	1873	1.05	1.14	130
10	ULSTER DEVIZES 1	ST960 570	946	1.05	1.07	55
11	WARLINGHAM 1	TQ348 572	1373	1.10	1.12	128
12	TATSFIELD 1	TQ41 57	1405	1.05	1.08	69
13	STRAT A1	SU948 528	963	1.05	1.07	148
14	HARMANSOLE 1	TR14 52	527	1.02	1.02	19
15	LYDDEN VALLEY 1	TR37 53	618	1.00?	1.01	6
16	BURTON ROW 1	ST336 521	1105+ (P)	1.00	1.04	58
17	SELWORTHY 1	SS924 462	60	1.01	1.01	25
18	SHALFORD 1	SU989 471	1641	1.02	1.15	50
19	BLETCHINGLY 1	TQ362 477	1910	1.05	1.15	75
20	COLLENDEAN FM 1	TQ248 443	1755	1.05	1.17	75
21	COWDEN 1	TQ467 428	1646 ?	1.05	1.14	81
22	ELHAM 1	TR18 44	487	1.05	1.04	25
23	WESTBURY 1	SU872 429	616+ (T)	1.05	1.11	19
24	SHREWTON 1	SU031 420	1601	1.10	1.15	108
25	PURITON 1	ST319 489	600+ (P)	1.04	1.05	55
26	BRABOURNE 1	TR100 308	627	1.00	1.05	62
27	FOLKESTONE 1	TR23 37	453	1.05	1.04	6
28	BRUTON 1	ST690 328	293	1.00	1.03	25
29	FARLEY SOUTH 1	SU236 285	1679	1.075	1.14	88
30	LOCKERLEY 1	SU307 259	2050 ?	1.10	1.17	93
★ 31	ASHDOWN 2	TQ512 295	1230+ (T)	1.03	1.17	75
32	BOLNEY 1	TQ280 243	2439	1.05	1.16	75
33	BRIGHTLING 1	TQ685 210	1322	1.05	1.11	63
34	HENFIELD 1	TQ182 151	1556	1.06	1.13	75
★ 35	FORDINGBRIDGE 1	SU188 118	1368+ (T)	1.02	1.12	167
★ 36	SOUTHAMPTON 1	SU416 120	1827	1.08	1.15	98
★ 37	MARCHWOOD 1	SU399 112	1725	1.08	1.15	92
38	CRANBOURNE 1	SU034 071	1663	1.075	1.12	87
39	PORTSDOWN 1	SU638 078	1998	1.17	1.18	98
40	WESTHAM 1	TQ610 054	887+ (P)	1.025	1.07	81
41	SEABOROUGH 1	ST435 062	1555	1.10	1.14	39
★ 42	MIDDLETON 1	SU973 015	1607 ?	1.06	1.14	108
43	MARSHWOOD 1	SY389 988	1339 ?	1.04	1.13	67
★ 44	WINTERBORNE KINGSTON 1	SY847 980	3043+ (P)	1.01	1.25	39
★ 45	BERE REGIS 1	SY864 956	1686+ (T)	1.12	1.25	20
★ 46	NETTLECOMBE 1	SY505 954	1910	1.00	1.17	39
★ 47	STOBOROUGH 1	SY913 870	1230+ (T)	1.04	1.24	39
★ 48	WYTCHFARM D5	SY996 855	2703	1.07	1.23	39
★ 49	ARRETON 1	SZ532 858	2423	1.07	1.24	139
50	BH 98/22–1	50° 14′ 39″ N 01° 39′ 22″ W	726+ (T)	1.04	1.07	79

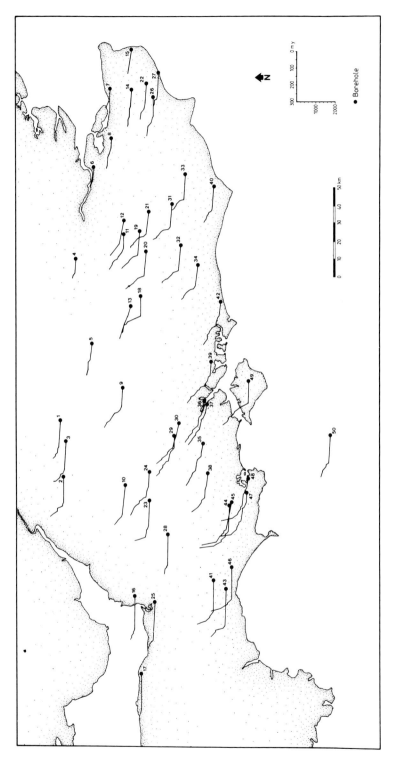

FIG. 4. Distribution of well data within the Wessex Basin showing the form and variation of the tectonic driving subsidence. Borehole numbers refer to information summarized in Table 1.

offset relative to the basin subsidence in the W (Fig. 4), suggesting a migration of rifting from W to E during the Late Palaeozoic–Mesozoic.

As the lithospheric stretching model of McKenzie (1978) has been useful in understanding the development of other intracratonic basins, we have used this model for comparison with the observed subsidence of the Wessex Basin. Rather than showing all the back-stripped subsidence curves of the Wessex Basin, four representative examples have been chosen; Winterborne–Kingston (No. 44, Fig. 4), Southampton (No. 36), Arreton (No. 49) and Ashdown (No. 31). Figure 5 shows that, in general, the observed back-stripped subsidence transects the negative exponential subsidence predicted from the simple lithospheric-stretching model (except Winterborne–Kingston) implying that during rifting, whole-lithospheric failure has not occurred. The degree of involvement of the sub-crustal lithosphere (and asthenosphere) during rifting is dependent on the width (or wavelength) of

the rift sub-basin and the flexural rigidity of the lithosphere (Karner & Dewey 1986). That is, the compensating asthenospheric 'infill' associated with narrow crustal rifts (10–40 km) will tend to be regionally distributed compared to wide rifts (50–100 km), because rift-induced lithospheric heating for low amounts of extension is relatively minor, and hence unable to reset flexural rigidities, and the 'load' wavelength is insufficient to 'activate' the flexural behaviour of the lithosphere. The large variability in the observed subsidence form over relatively short distances would seem to disqualify the uniform lithospheric stretching model as an adequate explanation for Wessex Basin subsidence. Spatially local crustal rifting, however, need not be related to the sub-crustal lithosphere in a one-to-one fashion as required by the McKenzie stretching model. Further, the lack of a significant Moho topography between the basin and the surrounding massifs (e.g. Brooks *et al.* 1984; Holder & Bott 1971; BIRPS–ECORS 1986) strongly

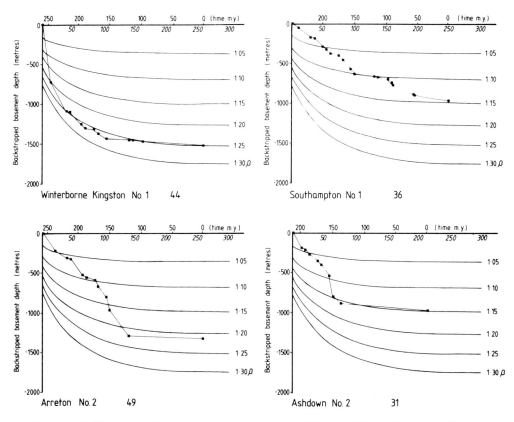

FIG. 5. Four wells (Winterborne–Kingston, Southampton, Arreton and Ashdown) taken to be representative examples of subsidence types within the Wessex Basin are compared to the predicted subsidence from the simple depth-independent lithospheric stretching model of McKenzie (1978) for a range of β values. The general transection of the theoretical curves by the observed driving subsidence implies that the origin of Wessex Basin subsidence is not of this type.

suggests that the upper and lower crusts are accommodating extension in a different way. In particular, we might expect that brittle extension in the upper crust (and hence local failure) is balanced by dominantly ductile extension in the lower-crust/sub-crustal lithosphere (resulting in a broad, regional failure; e.g. Hellinger & Sclater 1983; Karner 1985). Given that the flexural rigidity of the lithosphere has failed to be reset (as a consequence of $\beta < 1.25$), then upper-crustal unloading (i.e. to form spatially local basins) caused by extension will be isostatically compensated by a regional rebound of the lower-crust/sub-crustal lithosphere (cf. Karner & Dewey 1986).

The estimation of β, as in Fig. 5, is somewhat problematical because it represents an estimate of the amount of heat introduced into the sub-crustal lithosphere during rifting. In the original McKenzie model, rifting was considered instantaneous and, as such, tended to maximize the heating of the sub-crustal lithosphere and therefore the magnitude of the post-rift subsidence. More importantly with this model, the magnitude of the thermal subsidence is a direct measure of β. During finite rifting, however, heat is conductively removed from the lithosphere, thereby accentuating the rift subsidence while diminishing the magnitude of the subsequent thermal subsidence. In this case, the thermal subsidence reflects the amount of heat residing in the lithosphere at the end of rifting. To accurately estimate β, therefore, this heat loss during rifting needs to be accounted for. As basement fault reactivation along a listric detachment is known to have played a fundamental role in basin development, we have used a lithospheric-stretching model that includes the effects of décollement extension relaying and finite rifting (Fig. 6).

The estimation of δ, the crustal extension, was relatively straightforward; it represents the maximum observed subsidence of the basin. For each well, δ was assigned according to the maximum back-stripped subsidence, while the

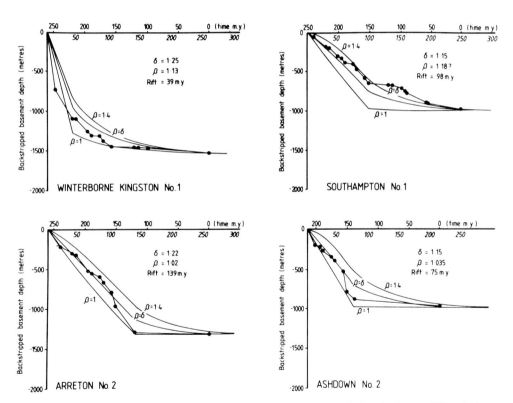

FIG. 6. The stretching model of Fig. 5 assumed instantaneous rifting (which maximises the degree of lithospheric heating) which is obviously violated given the protracted rifting history of the Wessex Basin. The inclusion of finite-rifting in the lithospheric stretching model allows for the cooling of the lithosphere during rifting. To test for depth-dependent stretching, the observed driving subsidence was compared to a range of β's for a δ consistent with the maximum subsidence of the basin. Winterborne–Kingston, the well which most clearly exhibits a simple negative exponential form, suggests that $\delta > \beta$. The other examples still tend to transect the theoretical curves and in the case of Southampton, seem to suggest that $\beta > \delta$.

rifting interval was estimated from the major break in subsidence (thought to represent the rift/cooling transition; cf. Mutter *et al.* 1985). The depth of the intracrustal detachment was assumed to be 15 km, based on Brewer (1984), Williams & Brooks (1985) and Lake & Karner (1986). This information was used to estimate β across the Wessex Basin (Table 1). The resulting distribution of δ within the Wessex Basin shows an apparent increase towards the Channel with major but local variations in the vicinity of growth faults (and hence reactivated basement thrusts), with β being essentially constant, but significantly lower, across the entire basin. In particular, δ and β average 1.11 and 1.05 respectively. The strong correlation between δ and growth faults suggests that block rotation accompanying basement fault reactivation is primarily responsible for local basin subsidence and sediment accumulation. Fault offsets in the Wessex Basin are consistent with the low estimates of δ. Rift-induced lithospheric failure is disqualified since $\delta \neq \beta$, which is also evident in the large variation in rifting times across the basin, even for closely spaced wells (e.g. Fig. 4, Nos 44 & 35, separated by only 40 km). The Winterborne–Kingston well, while showing a negative exponential subsidence form (Fig. 5), also suggests that $\delta > \beta$. Problems remain, however, in that some wells continue to transect even the finite-rifting/cooling subsidence curves, with some estimates of β exceeding δ (e.g. Table 1; Southampton, Middleton, Bere Regis and Wytchfarm D5).

The extension models employed so far consider basin development as a two-phase process; rifting (be it finite), followed by the passive recovery of the lithosphere. However, subsidence within Wessex Basin is characterized by a general subsidence form punctuated by a number of rapid, but finite, renewed subsidence events (Figs 4 & 5). These rapid subsidence phases (which for convenience we will term mechanical) can be correlated in time and space within any one sub-basin (Fig. 7), suggesting that their synchroneity and regional extent may have a tectonic control. Geologically, the rapid phases correspond to the development of a clay facies (associated with a rapid ˙transgression or base-level rise), whereas during the return to the slow, smooth subsidence (termed thermal) phase, a regressive facies is developed. The discontinuous nature of Wessex Basin subsidence suggests that rather than extension occurring as a single event, it may represent the cumulative effect of repeated events. We interpret Wessex Basin subsidence therefore, as the result of polyphase extension, the subsidence of which consists of a general 'background' thermal subsidence reflecting the regional extension of the sub-crustal lithosphere, punctuated by rapid, rift-

induced subsidence events reflecting the local extension of the crust.

The calculation of the rift (or mechanical) and thermal subsidence of the lithosphere due to its finite re-rifting is complicated not only by a constantly varying crust/lithosphere thickness ratio, but also by the persistence of a residual temperature perturbation (associated with preceding rifting events) which modifies the initial thermal conditions for the next rifting event. By extending the formulation by Cochran (1983), we have calculated the finite, re-rifting subsidence history for a number of Wessex Basin wells (in particular, those for which $\delta < \beta$ (marked by stars in Table 1) and which, incidentally, represent the main depo-centres) using the clay facies within the basin as an indicator of rift-onset and length (Table 2; Fig. 8). In all cases, the resultant β value was significantly less than δ (e.g. Fig. 8; average δ and β values for the wells marked with an asterisk in Table 1 are 1.19 and 1.05 respectively) suggesting that much of the lithospheric cooling and subsidence within the Wessex Basin was occurring during prolonged periods of crustal rifting and primarily within the depocentres. We have included the renewed subsidence event at 100 Ma (mid-Cretaceous) even though the driving subsidence is probably independent of extension. More likely, this subsidence phase is an artefact of the failure to consider either sea-level variations and/or palaeobathymetry within the back-stripping analysis.

The Late Cretaceous was characterized by inversion tectonics in which depocentres were inverted into structural highs while structural highs became depocentres. The Southampton region (well No. 36, Fig. 8), in particular, has been involved in Laramide transpression along the Purbeck–Isle of Wight fault. The general variability between rift-length times and rift-subsidence magnitude across the basin tends to confirm the cause of basin subsidence as brittle extension of the upper crust. δ factors therefore, are a function of sediment accumulation following hanging wall collapse of reactivated Variscan thrust sheets, and characterize the total amount of stretching within the crust, whereas β factors are indicative of the total amount of heat added to the sub-crustal lithosphere during polyphase rifting.

It would appear that the relaying of extension above and below the intracrustal detachment within the Wessex Basin produced an apparent strain incompatibility since brittle failure (the average δ over the basin) is greater than the ductile extension (the average β over the basin). However, as suggested by Wernicke (1985), upper-crustal extension is balanced by lower-crust/sub-crustal lithospheric extension, partly within, and partly external to, the region. To balance the measured

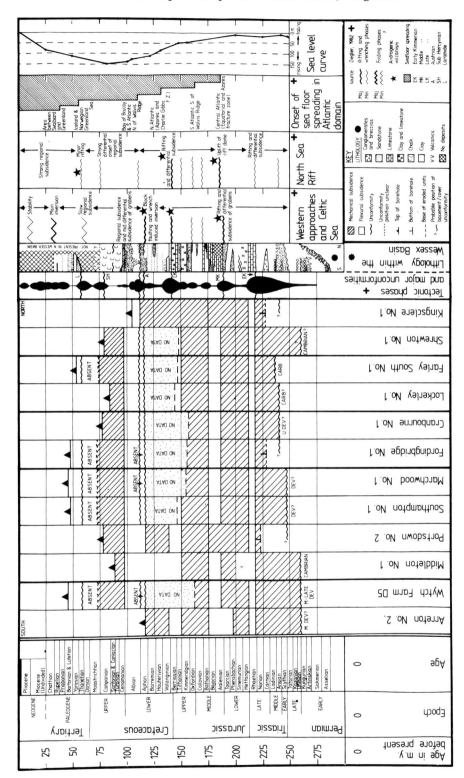

FIG. 7. Correlation of mechanical subsidence (fault induced) and flexural subsidence (thermally induced) with the sandstone/clay/limestone cyclicity within the Winterbourne–Kingston Trough region.

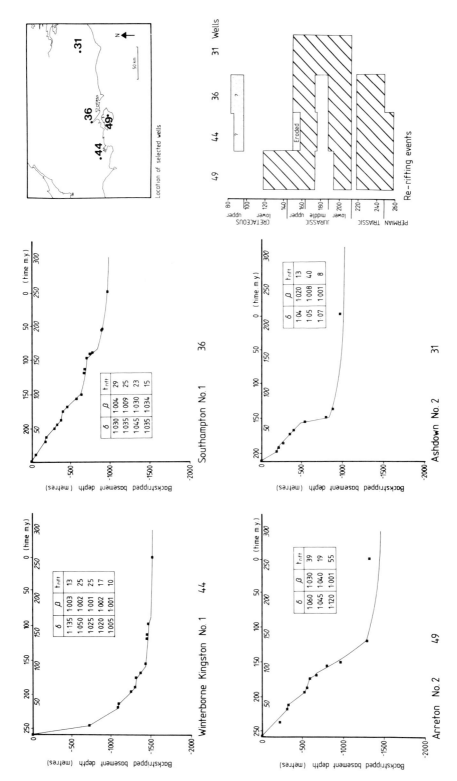

FIG. 8. Comparison of Wessex Basin driving subsidence with a model which includes the complexities introduced by the polyphase, finite re-rifting of the lithosphere (and depth-dependent stretching). The age of rift initiation, and the length of rifting, is defined by the development, and return of, the cyclic clay facies within each sub-basin. In this case, excellent fits are obtained between the observed and theoretical subsidences. In all cases, the cumulative δ (representing crustal extension) is significantly greater than the cumulative β (representing sub-crustal lithospheric stretching).

lithospheric extension within the Wessex Basin requires a 5% extension of the sub-crustal lithosphere beneath the Armorican Massif, in turn inducing a cumulative 60 m (and probably unrecognizable) isostatic uplift over the past 100 My.

Watts *et al.* (1982) have demonstrated that the thermal, and hence the mechanical, recovery of rifted lithosphere causes a stratigraphic basement onlap. Given that lithospheric stretching is minimal within the Wessex Basin (i.e. $\beta < 1.05$), the fact that major transgression has apparently occurred onto the London–Brabant platform from Permian to Cretaceous times (Worsam & Ivimey-Cook 1971; Anderton *et al.* 1979; Allsop *et al.* 1982; Dewey 1982) is problematic. Further, a marine transgression also occurred during the Palaeogene (Arkell 1947, p. 216). To investigate the possible flexural control on Wessex Basin stratigraphy, and in particular, whether the observed stretching history of the basin could account for the observed onlap patterns, we have forward-modelled the Late Palaeozoic–early Mesozoic development of the Wessex Basin (i.e. excluding the inversion-induced subsidence) using the magnitude and distribution of stretching parameters applicable to the Winterborne–Kingston Trough (Table 1). For comparison, we assembled a N–S cross-section across the trough (Fig. 9) and removed the complications introduced by growth faulting and inversion. By equating the depth to the 450°C isotherm (in space and time) with the effective elastic thickness of the lithosphere, it is possible to monitor the thermo–mechanical history of the lithosphere. When this history is linked to the theoretical equations for basin subsidence (e.g. McKenzie 1978; Royden & Keen 1980), the two-dimensional development history of the basin can be modelled as outlined by Watts *et al.* (1982) and Karner (1985). We have also included the eustatic sea-level curve of Pitman (1978), calibrated to a maximum variation of 150 m (Table 2) based on oxygen isotope determinations of the magnitude of the Eocene/Oligocene sea-level fall (Matthews 1984).

As can be seen from Fig. 9, basement onlap occurs only for the Permian section, generally consistent with the observed section in Fig. 9. The lack of a general basement onlap during the thermal subsidence phase is a re-statement of Steckler (1981) and Kusznir & Karner (1985) that sub-crustal lithospheric heating, and hence rigidity resetting, is minimal until $\beta > 2$. The modelling suggests that the basin width should be 350–450 km as a direct consequence of the large (essentially pre-rifting) flexural rigidity of the lithosphere ($T_e = 40$ km). The reduced present-day distribution of upper-Cretaceous sediments within the Wessex Basin (the time of maximum lateral extent), implies a large amount of post-Cretaceous (probably inversion-related) erosion. Further, much of the subsidence in the basin periphery appears to be flexurally induced by the driving subsidence and sediment loading in the main depocentres, thereby explaining the very low apparent extension values ($\delta < 1.05$) observed on the London–Brabant platform. Including a eustatic sea-level curve in the basin modelling produces a basin-wide transgression/regression between 92–256 My after rifting (i.e. syn-post-Jurassic). Though not explicitly modelled, we suggest that the Jurassic clay–sandstone–limestone cyclicity of the Wessex Basin may represent the interplay between the rates of change in sea-level (including sediment loading and supply) and the rift-induced mechanical subsidence (cf. Pitman 1978).

Basin inversion began in the Late Cretaceous and essentially terminated any further development of the sub-basin depocentres (Lake & Karner 1986). Inversion, at least in the Wessex Basin, simply represents the reverse/thrust reactivation of the same basement faults that initiated basin formation. Consequently, only the main basin-bounding faults (both thrust and transfer) were involved in the inversion phase (e.g. Purbeck–Isle of Wight fault). The effects of inversion were twofold; areas that were structural highs during the Permo–Jurassic became sites of subsidence in the Late Cretaceous (the driving subsidence being the loading effect associated with thrust-sheet reactivation leading to the creation of small foreland-type basins), and the uplift and truncation of sediments across the major compressionally reactivated basement faults.

On the cessation of polyphase rifting in the Early Cretaceous, the ensuing thermal subsidence allows a check on the amount of residual heat dissipated from the sub-crustal lithosphere. If basin width continued to increase in the Tertiary, even during a demonstrable sea-level regression, it was most likely the result of continuing thermal subsidence and its associated flexural effects. The Tertiary outcrop of the Wessex Basin (Fig. 10) shows, however, a general regressive sequence in the sense of a progressive decrease in the depositional area with time (and is not simply the result of erosion because each of the Tertiary units were deposited in a proximal environment). Detailed analysis of the facies within these units has shown a sequence of finer onlap and offlap patterns (Fig. 10) that correlate remarkably well with the timing of transgressive/regressive cycles of the Vail *et al.* (1977) curve (Fig. 10). It appears therefore, that as the Tertiary stratigraphy is dominated by second-order eustatic effects, thermal subsidence has been rendered negligible in approximately 35 My, consistent with the low β values estimated from the back-stripped wells (cf. Table 1).

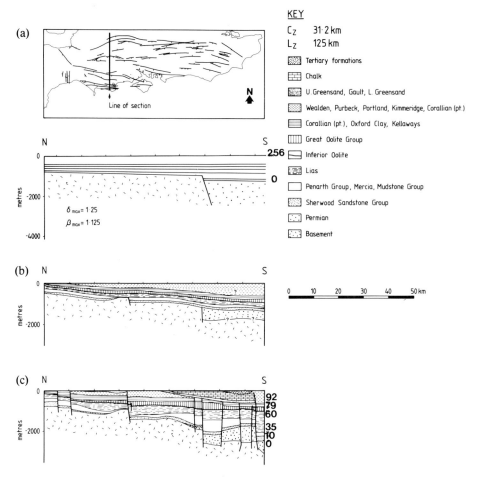

FIG. 9. N–S geological cross-section across the Winterborne–Kingston Trough and adjacent Wessex Shelf based on the data of Whittaker (1985). (a) Present-day structural configuration of the basin. (b) Removal of growth fault and inversion effects and thrust reactivation. (c) Forward modelling of the late Palaeozoic/Mesozoic development of the Wessex Basin using the magnitude and distribution of stretching parameters summarized in Table 1 for Winterborne–Kingston No. 1. The effects of lithospheric flexure, both in space and time, have been included by tracking the depth of the 450°C isotherm following a single, major, rifting event (an adequate approximation for the Winterborne–Kingston well only). The rapid onlap predicted in the N reflects the failure of β to appreciably modify the lithospheric temperature structure. The predicted time-line stratigraphy is a reasonable approximation to the observed stratigraphy.

Conclusions

The Wessex Basin consists of a number of growth-fault-bounded grabens and half-grabens, or sub-basins that owe their existence to the synchronous reactivation of both an E–W and NW–SE basement thrust and transfer faults respectively. Basin initiation began in the Permian with the formation of the Winterborne–Kingston Trough, and migrated discontinuously westwards during the Triassic–Jurassic to form the Channel and Weald basins. The general form of Wessex Basin subsidence, while complex in detail, consists of a 'background', smoothly varying subsidence (sometimes of negative exponential form, but often linear), punctuated by a number of rapid, but smaller, subsidence events. Fifty boreholes were used to determine the form of the tectonic driving subsidence responsible for the development of the Wessex Basin, and in particular, to determine the average crustal extension (δ) and sub-crustal lithospheric stretching/heating (β). As the geological development of the Wessex Basin involved the utilization of crustal detachments and both the finite and repeated rifting of the crust, our subsidence models have also had to include these effects.

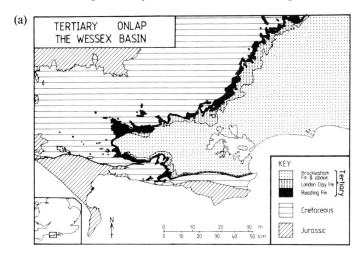

(a) TERTIARY ONLAP THE WESSEX BASIN

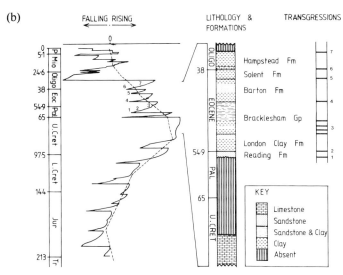

(b)

FIG. 10. (a) Plan view of the stratigraphy in the central portion of the Wessex Basin suggesting a general sea-level fall during the Tertiary in the sense of an increasingly smaller depositional area with time. (b) First- and second-order relative sea-level variations estimated by Pitman (1978) [dashed line] and Vail et al. (1977) [solid line], compared with the Tertiary onlap and offlap patterns of the Wessex Basin. Numbered transgressions in the Vail et al. curve directly relate to observed transgressional phases within the basin. Transgressions from Anderton et al. (1979) and Plint (1983). The Late Cretaceous–Tertiary regional development of the basin appears to be dominated by the effects of eustasy.

Areas of high sedimentation (hence relatively high extension) directly correlate with the existence of growth faults and by inference, regions of basement thrust reactivation. Major sediment thickness variations across the growth faults indicate that the basal sole thrust has accommodated the majority of the extension. Block rotation, accompanying basement fault reactivation and hanging wall collapse, is primarily responsible for local basin development and directly correlates with

δ. By default, δ will tend to be discontinuous and represents the brittle failure of the upper crust. Repeated fault reactivation produces the punctuating subsidence events which are superimposed on to a general, smoothly varying, basin subsidence. In contrast, β values estimated from the backstripped wells are constant across the basin (1.05), but significantly lower than δ values (average of 1.11 using the entire basin, or 1.19 using only the main depocentres). It appears therefore, that the lower-crust/sub-crustal lithosphere has accommodated itself in a different way to the upper crust, consistent with the lack of an observable Moho topography between the basin and the surrounding massifs. While the upper crust appears to have failed in a brittle fashion, the lower crust has failed in a predominantly ductile, and hence continuous, manner. A primarily upper-crustal control on Wessex Basin development is consistent with the general variability in rift-length times and rift-subsidence magnitudes, especially when compared with adjacent wells and the rather small magnitudes of extension involved (maximum 25%). Since $\delta \neq \beta$, whole-scale lithospheric rifting as a cause for Wessex Basin initiation and development is disqualified.

Each lithospheric stretching event predicts two phases of basin formation; an active, rift or mechanical phase (the duration of which is controlled by the length of rifting; 10–50 My), followed by a passive, thermal phase (the duration of which is controlled by the thermal properties of the lithosphere; 80–200 My). Polyphase extension will result in the superposition of a relatively rapid mechanical subsidence on to a more gentle thermal subsidence. Our preferred model for the development of the Wessex Basin therefore, is for the polyphase reactivation of Variscan thrust sheets above a crustal detachment, hanging wall collapse of which results in sub-basin initiation. Depocentre distribution will be controlled by the configuration of reactivated basement faults. While some lower-crust/sub-crustal lithospheric extension occurs within the Wessex Basin region (5%), strain compatibility is primarily maintained by the relaying of extension into the lower-crust/sub-crustal lithosphere across the basal Variscan thrust (itself a depth-dependent intracrustal detachment), much in the same way as envisaged by Wernicke (1985). Given average δ and β values of 1.11 and 1.05, respectively, ductile stretching of the lower-crust/sub-crustal lithosphere occurred over an area approximately twice the size of the brittle extension within the Wessex Basin. We suggest that strain balancing of Wessex Basin extension has induced a cumulative 60 m isostatic but thermal uplift of the northern Armorican Massif over the past 200 My. Regional thermal subsidence of the Wessex Basin was a consequence of the conductive dissipation of rift-induced heat from the lithosphere.

As the Jurassic–Cretaceous basement onlap reported by Dewey (1982) and Anderton *et al.* (1979) from the western Wessex Basin correlates with the major Mesozoic transgression seen in the Vail *et al.* (1977) coastal-onlap curve, and further, that the maximum lateral extent of the Wessex Basin occurred in the Late Cretaceous eustatic high-stand, we suggest that this onlap is related primarily to eustasy and independent of the usual means of producing regional basement onlap, namely via the thermal recovery of the rifted lithosphere (cf. Watts *et al.* 1982). In contrast, the ubiquitous sedimentary cyclicity observed within the Wessex Basin is likely to be the product of the interaction between rates of sea-level change versus the rates and timing of the mechanical subsidence phases. Renewed rifting results in an immediate base-level rise (i.e. a rapid transgressive event) with subsequent sedimentation and regional thermal subsidence producing a regressive sequence as the basin slowly refills.

ACKNOWLEDGMENTS: We would like to thank the many oil companies who allowed us access to their data and Shell Exploration and Production (UK) for permission to publish data from the Lockerly and Farley South boreholes. Our thanks also to J. Pindell, K. Brown and I. Vann for discussions, an anonymous reviewer for helpful comments, and Andy Reid for his drafting assistance. We also wish to acknowledge financial support from NERC (S.D.L.) and the Durham University Research Foundation and the Society of Fellows (G.D.K).

References

ALLEN, D.J. & HOLLOWAY, S. 1984. The Wessex Basin. *Invest. geotherm. potent. U.K. Inst. geol. Sci.* 80 pp.

ALLSOP, J.M., HOLLOWAY, D.W., JONES, C.M., KENOLTY, N., KIRKBY, G.A., KUBALA, M. & SOBEY, R.A. 1982. Palaeogeological maps of the floors beneath two major unconformities in the Oxford–Newbury–Reading area. *Rep. Inst. geol. Sci.* **82/1**, 48–51.

ANDERTON, R., BRIDGES, P.H., LEEDER, M.R. & SELLWOOD, B.W. 1979. A dynamic stratigraphy of the British Isles, 301 pp. George Allen and Unwin Ltd., London.

ARKELL, W.J. 1947. The geology of the country around Weymouth, Swanage, Corfe and Lulworth. *Mem. geol. Surv. U.K.* 386 pp.

BEAUMONT, C., KEEN, C.E. & BOUTILIER, R. 1982. A comparison of foreland and rift margin sedimentary basins. *Phil. Trans. R. Soc. London,* **A305**, 295–317.

BIRPS & ECORS 1986. Deep seismic profiling between England, France and Ireland. *J. geol. Soc. London,* **143**, 45–52.

BOND, G.C. & KOMINZ, M.A. 1984. Construction of tectonic subsidence curves for the early Palaeozoic Miogeocline, southern Canadian Rocky mountains: Implications for subsidence mechanisms, age of breakup, and crustal thinning. *Bull. geol. Soc. Am.* **95**, 155–73.

BREWER, J.A. 1984. Clues to the deep structure of the European Variscides from crustal seismic profiling in North America. *In:* HUTTON, D.H.W. & SANDERSON,

D.J. (eds) *Variscan Tectonics of the North Atlantic Region. Spec. Publ. geol. Soc. London*, **14**, 253–64.

—— & SMYTHE, D.K. 1984. MOIST and the continuity of crustal reflection geometry along the Caledonian–Appalachian orogen. *J. geol. Soc. London*, **141**, 105–20.

BROOKS, M., DOODY, J.J. & AL-RAWI, F.R.J. 1984. Major crustal reflectors beneath SW England. *J. geol. Soc. London*, **141**, 97–104.

BURCHFIEL, B.C. & ROYDEN, L. 1982. Carpathian foreland fold and thrust belt and its relation to the Pannonian and other basins. *Am. Assoc. Pet. Geol*, **66**, 1179–95.

CHADWICK, R.A. 1985. End Jurassic—early Cretaceous sedimentation and subsidence (late Portlandian to Barremian) and the late-Cimmerian unconformity. *In*: WHITTAKER, A. (ed.) *Atlas of Onshore Sedimentary Basins in England and Wales: Post-Carboniferous Tectonics and Stratigraphy*. Blackie, Glasgow.

——, KENOLTY, N. & WHITTAKER, A. 1983. Crustal structure beneath southern England from deep seismic reflection profiles. *J. geol. Soc. London*. **140**, 893–912.

CHRISTIE-BLICK, N. & BIDDLE, K.T. In press. Deformation and basin formation along strike-slip faults. *In*: BIDDLE, K.T.B. & CHRISTIE-BLICK, N. (eds) *Strike-Slip Deformation, Basin formation, and sedimentation, Soc. econ. Palaentol. and Mineral. Spec. Publ.*

COCHRAN, J.R. 1983. Effects of finite rifting times on the development of sedimentary basins. *Earth planet. Sci. Lett.* **66**, 289–302.

COLTER, V.S. & HAVARD, D.J. 1981. The Wytch Farm oil field, Dorset. *In*: ILLING, L.V. & HOBSON, G.D. (eds) *Petroleum Geology of the Continental Shelf of north-west Europe*, pp. 494–503. Heyden and Son Ltd.

COWARD, M.P. & SMALLWOOD, S. 1984. An interpretation of the Variscan tectonics of SW Britain. *In*: HUTTON, D.H.W. & SANDERSON, D.J. (eds) *Variscan Tectonics of the North Atlantic Region. Spec. Publ. geol. Soc. London*, **14**, 89–102.

DAY, G.A. & EDWARDS, J.W.F. 1983. Variscan thrusting in the Basement of the English Channel and SW Approaches. *Proc. Ussher. Soc.* **5**, 432–36.

DEWEY, J.F. 1982. Plate tectonics and the evolution of the British Isles. *J. geol. Soc. London*, **139**, 371–414.

——, KARNER, G.D. & PITMAN, W.C. 1984. Thermo-mechanical properties and evolution of Pull-apart basins (abstract). *Am. Assoc. Pet. Geol.*, **68**, 794.

DONOVAN, D.T. & STRIDE, A.H. 1961. An acoustic survey of the sea floor south of Dorset and its geological interpretation. *Phil. Trans. R. Soc. London*, **A244**, 299–325.

DRUMMOND, P.V.O. 1970. The Mid-Dorset Swell. Evidence of Albian-Cenomanian movements in Wessex. *Proc. Geol. Assoc. London*, **81**, 679-714.

—— 1982. Discussion *In*: STONELEY, R. The structural development of the Wessex Basin. *J. geol. Soc. London*, **139**, 553–4.

FALCON, N.L. & KENT, P.E. 1950. Chalk Rock of Dorset—more evidence of salt? *Geol. Mag.* **87**, 302–3.

HALLAM, A. 1975. *Jurassic Environments*, 269 pp. Cambridge University Press.

HAWKINS, H.L. 1942. Some episodes in the geological history of the South of England. *Q. J. geol. Soc. London*, **98**, 1–19.

HAYS, J.D. & PITMAN, W.C. 1973. Lithospheric plate motion, sea level changes and climatic and ecological consequences. *Nature*, **246**, 18–22.

HELLINGER, S.J. & SCLATER, J.G. 1983. Some comments on two-layer extensional models for the evolution of sedimentary basins. *J. geophys. Res.* **88**, 8251–69.

HOBSON, D.M. & SANDERSON, D.J. 1983. Variscan deformation in southwest England. *In*: HANCOCK, P.L. (ed.) *The Variscan Fold Belt in the British Isles*, pp. 108–129. Hilger. Bristol.

HOLDER, A.P. & BOTT, M.H.P. 1971. Crustal structures in the vicinity of southwest England. *Geophys. J. R. astron. Soc.* **23**, 465–89.

ISAAC, K.P., TURNER, P.J. & STEWART, I.J. 1982. The evolution of the Hercynides of central SW England. *J. geol. Soc. London*, **139**, 523–34.

KARNER, G.D. 1985. *Continental tectonics—a quantitative view of the thermal and mechanical properties of the continental lithosphere in compressional and extensional stress regimes*, 53 pp. Centre National d'Etudes Spatiales, Summer School of Space Physics, Toulouse, France.

——, DEWEY, J.F. 1986. Rifting: Lithospheric versus crustal extension as applied to the Ridge Basin of southern California. *In*: HALBOUTY, M.T. (ed.) *Future petroleum provinces of the world, Am. Assoc. Pet. Geol. Mem.* **40**, 317–37.

—— & WATTS, A.B. 1982. On isostasy at Atlantic-type continental margins. *J. geophys. Res.* **87**, 2923–48.

——, STECKLER, M.S. & THORNE, J.A. 1983. Long-term thermo-mechanical properties of the continental lithosphere. *Nature*, **304**, 250–53.

KENT, P.E. 1949. A structure-contour map of the surface of the buried pre-Permian rocks in England and Wales. *Proc. geol. Assoc. London*, **60**, 87–104.

KNILL, D.C. 1969. The Permian igneous rocks of Devon. *Bull. geol. Surv. G.B.* **29**, 115–38.

—— 1982. Permian volcanism in south-western England. *In*: SUTHERLAND, D.S. (ed.) *Igneous rocks of the British Isles*, pp. 329–32. John Wiley and Sons.

KUSZNIR, N. & KARNER, G.D. 1985. Dependence of the flexural rigidity of the continental lithosphere on rheology and temperature. *Nature*, **316**, 138–42.

LAKE, S.D., MUNDAY, T.J. & DEWEY, J.F. 1984. Lineament Mapping and analysis in the Wessex Basin of southern England: A Comparison between MSS and TM data. *Proc. Anniv. Int. Conf. Satellite Remote Sensing*, Reading, UK. pp. 361–75.

LAKE, S.D. & KARNER, G.D. In press. The structure and evolution of the Wessex Basin, southern England: An example of inversion tectonics. *Tectonophysics*.

MCKENZIE, D. 1978. Some remarks on the development of sedimentary basins. *Earth & planet. Sci. Lett.* **40**, 25–32.

MATTHEWS, R.K. 1984. Oxygen-Isotope Record of Ice-Volume History: 100 Million Year of Glacio-Eustatic Sea-level Fluctuation. *In*: SCHLEE, J.S. (ed.) *Inter-regional unconformities and hydrocarbon accumulation. Am. Assoc. Pet. Geol. Mem.* **36**, 97–107.

MELVILLE, R.V. & FRESHNEY, E.C. 1982. The Hampshire Basin and adjoining areas. British

Regional Geology. *The Hampshire Basin and adjoining areas*, 146 pp. HMSO.

MUTTER, J.C., HEGARTY, K.A., CANDE, S.C. & WEISSEL, J.K. 1985. Breakup between Australia and Antartica: A brief review in the light of new data. *Tectonophysics*, **114**, 255–79.

PARSONS, B. & SCLATER, J.G. 1977. An analysis of the variation of ocean floor bathymetry and heat flow with age. *J. geophys. Res.* **82**, 803–27.

PHILLIPS, W.J. 1964. The structures in the Jurassic and Cretaceous rocks on the Dorset coast between White Nothe and Mupe Bay. *Proc. geol. Assoc. London*, **75**, 373–406.

PITMAN, III, W.C. 1978. The relationship between eustasy and stratigraphic sequences of passive margins. *Bull. geol. Soc. am.* **89**, 1389–403.

PLINT, A.G. 1983. Facies, environments and sedimentary cycles in the Middle Eocene, Bracklesham Formation of the Hampshire Basin: evidence for global sea-level changes? *Sedimentology*, **30**, 625–53.

RHYS, G.H., LOTT, G.K. & CALVER, M.A. 1982. The Winterborne Kingston borehole, Dorset, England. *Rep. Inst. geol. Sci.* **81/3**, 196 pp.

ROYDEN, L. & KEEN, C.E. 1980. Rifting processes and thermal evolution of the continental margin of eastern Canada determined from subsidence curves. *Earth planet. Sci. lett.* **51**, 343–61.

——, HORVATH, F., NAGGMAROSY, A. & STEGENA, L. 1983. Evolution of the Pannonian Basin system 2. Subsidence and thermal history. *Tectonics*, **2**, 91–137.

SCLATER, J.G. & CHRISTIE, P.A.F. 1980. Continental stretching: An explanation of the post-mid-Cretaceous subsidence of the central North Sea Basin. *J. geophys. Res.* **85**, 3711–39.

SELLWOOD, B.W. 1978. Shallow-water Carbonate Environments. *In*: READING, H.G. (ed.) *Sedimentary Environments and Facies*, pp. 259–313. Blackwell Scientific Publications, Oxford.

——, SCOTT, J., MIKKELSEN, P. & ARKROYD, P. 1985. Stratigraphy and sedimentology of the Great Oolite Group in the Humbly Grove Oilfield, Hampshire. *Mar. and Pet. Geol.* **2**, 44–55.

SHACKLETON, R.M. 1984. Thin-skinned tectonics, basement control and the Variscan Front. *In*: HUTTON, D.H.W. & SANDERSON, D.J. (eds) *Variscan Tectonics of the North Atlantic Region*. *Spec. Publ. geol. Soc. London*, **14**, 125–30.

SLEEP, N.H. 1971. Thermal effects of the formation of Atlantic continental margins by continental breakup. *Geophys. J. R. astron. Soc.* **24**, 325–50.

STECKLER, M.S. 1981. The thermal and mechanical evolution of Atlantic type continental margins.

Unpubl. Ph.D. Thesis, Columbia Univ. New York.

—— & WATTS, A.B. 1978. Subsidence of the Atlantic-type continental margin of New York. *Earth planet. Sci. lett.* **41**, 1–13.

STONELEY, R. 1982. The structural development of the Wessex Basin. *J. geol. Soc. London*, **139**, 543–54.

STRAHAN, A. 1898. *The Geology of the Isle of Purbeck and Weymouth. Mem. geol. Surv. UK.*

USSAMI, N., KARNER, G.D. & BOTT, M.H.P. 1986. Crustal detachment during south Atlantic rifting and formation of the Tucano–Gabon basin system. *Nature*, **322**, 629–32.

VAIL, P.R., MITCHUM, JR, R.M. & THOMPSON, III, S. 1977. Seismic stratigraphy and global changes of sea level, Part 3: Relative changes of sea level from coastal onlap. *In*: PAYTON, C.E. (ed.) *Seismic stratigraphy—applications to hydrocarbon exploration. Am. Assoc. Pet. Geol. Mem.* **26**, 63–81.

WATTS, A.B. & STECKLER, M.S. 1981. Subsidence and tectonics of Atlantic type continental margins. *Oceanologica Acta, No. SP., Colloq. C3, Geologie des Marges Continentales, 26 eme, C.G.I*, pp. 143–54.

——, KARNER, G.D. & STECKLER, M.S. 1982. Lithospheric flexure and the evolution of sedimentary basin formation. *In*: The evolution of sedimentary basins. *Phil. Trans. R. Soc. London*, **A305**, 249–81.

—— & THORNE, J. 1984. Tectonics, Global changes in sea-level and their relationship to stratigraphic sequences at the U.S. Atlantic continental margin. *Mar. and Pet. Geol.* **1**, 319–39.

WERNICKE, B. 1985. Uniform-sense normal simple shear of the continental lithosphere. *Can. J. Earth Sci.* **22**, 108–25.

—— & BURCHFIEL, B.C. 1982. Modes of extensional tectonics. *J. struct. Geol.* **4**, 105–15.

WHITTAKER, A. 1975. A postulated post-Hercynian rift valley system in Southern Britain. *Geol. Mag.* **112**, 137–49.

—— (ed.) 1985. *Atlas of Onshore sedimentary basins in England and Wales: Post-Carboniferous Tectonics and Stratigraphy*, 71 pp. Blackie, Glasgow.

WILLIAMS, G.D. & BROOKS, M. 1985. A reinterpretation of the concealed Variscan structure beneath southern England by section balancing. *J. geol. Soc. London*, **142**, 689–96.

WORSSAM, B.C. & IVIMEY-COOK, H.C. 1971. The stratigraphy of the Geological Survey Borehole at Warlingham, Surrey. *Bull. geol. Surv. GB.* **36**, 1–46.

ZIEGLER, P.A. 1982. *Geological Atlas of Western and Central Europe*. Shell International Petroleum Mag. BV, The Hague.

GARRY D. KARNER[1], STUART D. LAKE[2] & JOHN F. DEWEY[3], Department of Geological Sciences, University of Durham, Durham DH1 3LE, UK.

[1] Present address: Lamont-Doherty Geological Observatory, Palisades, New York 10964, USA.
[2] Present address: Shell International Petroleum, Maatschappij BV, The Hague, Nederlands.
[3] Present address: Department of Earth Sciences, University of Oxford, Oxford OX1 2PR, UK.

The Devonian basins of western Norway: tectonics and kinematics of an extending crust

M. Seranne & M. Seguret

SUMMARY: The Devonian basins of western Norway represent shallow to deep exposures of a synthetic extensional sedimentary basin and provide field evidence for ductile extensional deformation within the basin fill and for the evolution of a brittle low-angle fault and ductile shear zone along the basal contact. The motion along this low-angle (5–25°) detachment is synchronous with both deposition and tilting (25°) of the huge (up to 25-km thick) overlapping coarse detrital Middle Devonian series. Such a geometry requires a minimum dip-slip offset of 50 km.

The structural data are consistent with fault-rock associations along the basal contact and with the prograde greenschist metamorphism observed in the southern basin: deeper and deeper levels are observed from N to S. Except along the highly sheared and retrogressed basal shear zone, the footwall remained unaffected by deformation during basin development.

We discuss three crustal models for basin development and propose that the displacement along the basal contact of the basins is transformed into pervasive ductile flow within the lower crust both at some distance to the side of the basin and beneath the basin.

A key problem for large-scale extensional tectonics is to determine the relationships between brittle faulting near to the surface and ductile stretching at depth, which controls the structure and evolution of extensional sedimentary basins.

Using a theoretical approach, McKenzie (1978) proposed a model for lithospheric stretching. Recently, Kuznir and Park (1984) investigated mathematically the deformation of the intraplate lithosphere. They showed that it is closely dependent on the temperature distribution. Faugere & Brun (1984), analysed the stretching-induced structures in small-scale models. Deep seismic reflection profiles (COCORP; MOIST; SWAT; see Allmendinger *et al.* this volume; Cheadle *et al.* this volume) supplied control on the deep crustal structures. They display low-angle normal faults that vanish within the lower third of the crust.

In field examples, such as those in the Basin and Range Province, the accuracy of the observations of the deformation mechanisms should provide better constraints on the models. According to Miller *et al.* (1983) and Gans & Miller (1983), extensional basins are settled over a ductilely stretched crust and they are limited by a horizontal detachment. Wernicke (1981; 1984) and Bartley & Wernicke (1984) proposed a model of large lithospheric low-angle normal faults which allow shear between two large coherent sheets.

The Devonian basins of western Norway (DBWN) provide a new field example of continental extensional tectonics. They display a continuous section from undeformed sediments at the top of the basin fill, to ductile shearing at the basal contact, involving both Devonian metasediments and basement rocks (Seranne & Seguret 1985a). Observations made at different erosional levels aid determination of the geometry, tectonics and kinematics of these extensional basins.

Geological setting

The DBWN include from N to S, the basins of Hornelen, Hasteinen, Kvamshesten and Solund (Fig. 1). They are located on the western side of the Caledonian thrust belt. During the Caledonian Orogeny, Cambro–Silurian rocks related to a passive margin and oceanic origin were thrust eastwards (Hossack & Cooper, in press) above the Scandinavian craton consisting of Precambrian gneisses now outcropping within the More window (Santarelli 1977). The basal contact of the DBWN represents a re-working of the thrust plane as a westwards-sliding normal fault (Hossack, 1984; Norton, 1984; Seranne & Seguret 1985a) (Fig. 1).

Sedimentology

In the Hornelen and Kvamshesten basins, the coarse alluvial fan conglomerates outcropping along the present borders distally grade into alluvial/lacustrine sandstones in the axis of the basins (Steel & Gloppen 1980). In these basins both types of deposits are well organized into 50–200-m thick coarsening- and thickening-upward cycles. It has been demonstrated that sedimentation was largely controlled by tectonics related to the basin formation (Brynhi & Skjerlie 1975; Steel 1976).

The Solund and Hasteinen basins are mostly filled with unsorted and ungraded conglomerates, the grain size of which ranges from very coarse sandstone to cobble. Nilsen (1968) and Indreaver (1980) interpreted these deposits as being formed in humid

From COWARD, M.P., DEWEY, J.F. & HANCOCK, P.L. (eds), 1987, *Continental Extensional Tectonics*, Geological Society Special Publication No. 28, pp. 537–548.

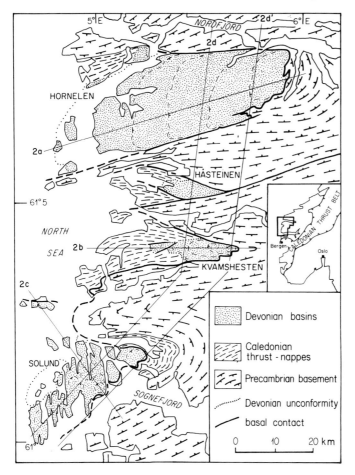

FIG. 1. Generalized geological map of the area.

Geometry

The borders

The basins represent a homogeneous structural setting (Figs 1 & 2). Along the western borders, the Devonian series lies unconformably on the

alluvial fans. The occurrence of sieve and stream flood deposits confirms this interpretation. The pebbles are derived from metamorphic rocks of Cambro–Silurian origin (greywacke, quartzite, siltstone and gabbro) or Precambrian origin (quartzites and gneisses). In addition, very rare pebbles of reddish siltstones are thought to be re-worked material from intrabasinal, fine distal facies of Devonian age.

The bodies of gabbro found in N Solund were interpreted as thrust sheets (Kildal 1970) or as intrusive (Nilsen 1968) but the relationship with the conglomerate argues for an olistolithic origin (Brynhi 1976).

Cambro–Silurian metamorphic rocks. The present eastern margins are low-angle (5–25°) westward-dipping tectonic contacts traditionally interpreted as eastward-moving thrusts (Nilsen 1968; Kildal 1970; Hoisaeter 1971; Steel & Gloppen 1980; Roberts 1983; Sturt 1983). The low-angle eastern contact. evolves along the N and S borders into steeper faults (45–60°) that define a spoon-shape geometry to the basal contact of each basin. This geometry is well preserved in the Hornelen basin in which the present steep N and S borders probably closely fit the original margins (Steel & Gloppen 1980). In contrast, the low-angle faults presently limiting the Solund basin indicate a structure truncated by erosion. Therefore, the Hornelen basin represents a shallow exposure of the DBWN, whereas the Kvamshesten and Solund basins represent deeper exposures of the DBWN. Hossack (1984) suggested that the basal contact of the four basins could constitute a unique westward-sliding normal fault with lateral ramps related to E–W-trending culminations. Our field data support these

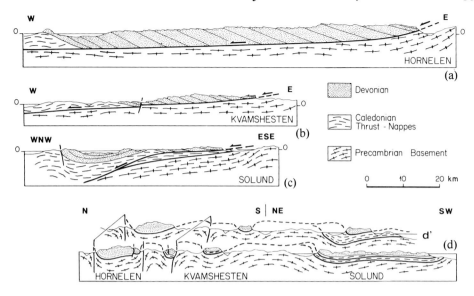

FIG. 2. Longitudinal cross-section of (a) the Hornelen basin; (b) the Kvamshesten basin; (c) the Solund basin; and (d) transverse cross-sections.

assumptions. The Hasteinen basin exhibits a slightly different structure; except for the western unconformable boundary, all the margins are sinistral strike-slip faults, as indicated by micro-structures.

Internal organization of the basins

The Devonian strata generally dip towards the eastern normal fault and at a constant 25° along the axial sections of the basins. The dip decreases, however, close to the eastern normal fault, but increases close to the lateral margins where the strikes tend to be parallel to the faults (Fig. 1).

In the Hornelen and Kvamshesten basins, unconformities with local erosion have been identified in the steeply dipping marginal conglomerates, associated with a significant thickening of the cyclothems towards the basin axis (Bryhni & Skjerlie 1975). This demonstrates an inhomogeneous and syndepositional subsidence. The syncline geometry does not require a later N–S compressional event. The present great stratigraphic thickness of the basin successions (25 km in Hornelen (Bryhni 1964), 7 km in Kvamshesten, 6 km in Solund) strongly contrasts with their small area (2500 km² for the larger one: Hornelen); the stratigraphic thickness does not represent the depth of the basin. The vertical section of sediments above the low-angle fault is observable at Kvamshesten Basin; it does not exceed 1500 m. It is likely that the depth of the basal contact beneath the depositional surface did not exceed 5–10 km (Fig. 2).

Motion along the basal contact

The geometrical features of the basins allow an estimate of the amount of motion along the basal contact. A dip of 25° E of the basal Devonian unconformity, a 65 km length for Hornelen basin and a fault plane dipping westward at an angle of 10°, integrating the deep structural data from the other basins, require a minimum dip-slip offset of 50 km for this basin (Figs 2 & 3). From the analysis of branch-lines and fault cut-off lines, Hossack (1984, Figs 4 & 5) found a similar displacement value.

During basin development, the syntectonic sedimentation occurred in a depocentre located along the eastern fault margin, overlapping the earlier sediments (Fig. 3). The rollover in the hanging wall caused tilting of the Devonian sediments and the motion along the very low-angle fault resulted in a westwards translation of the series and preserved their constant dip of 25° (Fig. 3).

Structural analysis

Hornelen and Kvamshesten basins

Hornelen and Kvamshesten sandstones and conglomerates display an intense fracturing and jointing. Three main orientations can be defined (N 40° E, N 110° E, N 170° E); generally no relative motion, dip-slip or strike-slip, can be determined at outcrop scale along these joints.

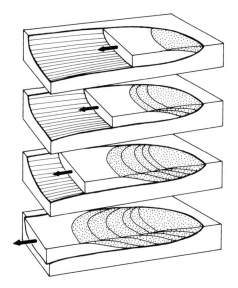

FIG. 3. Cartoon of the basin development (without scale).

Some steeply dipping bedding planes reveal pebbles with long axes re-oriented parallel to the dip-slip direction (Brynhi 1978) and interbedded siltstones show striations on bedding planes in the maximum-dip direction. A fine cleavage often indicates interbed dip-slip movement. Such brittle deformation on a discrete plane results in a finite extension broadly parallel to the axis of the basin and an associated vertical shortening. In these basins, no penetrative deformation is observed; the pebbles are broken only very close to the basal contact.

Solund basin

The conglomerates of the Solund basin contain an outstanding basin-wide anisotropic fabric, interpreted by Nilsen (1968) as a sedimentary fabric. More detailed studies, however, show a relationship between the fabric evolution and that of the regional deformation. This allowed us to define four structural zones from the centre of the basin to the SE basal contact (Fig. 4).

Zone 1

In the centre of the basin, the bedding dips at 25° SE and the landscape is dominated by the repetition of ledges which interrupt the conglomerate scarps. A typical morphological sequence, 10–50 m thick, is composed of a basal division (D1) of poorly consolidated conglomerates, a few metres

thick, grading up into a well-consolidated upper division (D2) (Fig. 5).

The uppermost part (D2b) of D2 is half a metre thick and is characterized by pebbles lying flat on the bedding plane which show no preferred orientation. Within the rest of the morphological sequence, that is in D1 and D2a, representing most of D2, the pebble long axes trend N 120° and plunge 15° steeper than the bedding (Nilsen 1968). The fabric is well exposed in the poorly cemented division (D1) and has been found from systematic measurements in D2a. Some considerations and observations argue against a sedimentary origin for this fabric; a sedimentary fabric would not display so constant direction through time and space, and the consistency of pebble orientation contrasts with the fluctuating palaeocurrent directions indicated by sedimentary structures in the scarce sandstone bodies (Nilsen 1968). In addition, the associated microstructures (Fig. 6) argue for a tectonically induced fabric.

A N 120° trending *mineral lineation* results from the re-orientation of phyllites and formation of chlorite–quartz–epidote. This lineation develops on the pebble surfaces as *striae lineations*, whose orientations vary according to the pebble shape. Systematic analysis reveals a mean N 120° orientation and a dip-slip motion on the upper and lower pebble surfaces. The continuation of the striae lineation at the tip of the pebbles shows horizontal conical *pressure shadow like structures*, trending N 120° and corresponding to a zone of cementation of the sand and gravels (Fig. 6). An *horizontal cleavage* developed in the sandy matrix and in the scarce reddish marl pebbles which are fine re-worked layers of the Devonian alluvial fan. In the sandy matrix the cleavage is marked by the orientated clasts and by the synkinematic growth of quartz–chlorite fibres in pressure shadows. In the mudstone pebbles, the schistosity, the initiation of which was clearly synchronous with that of the regional Devonian cleavage, is marked by the re-orientation of phyllites and orientated growth of chlorite, epidote and actinolite.

In addition, many of the large Precambrian or Caledonian pebbles contain vertical, N 30° striking, *tension gashes* (Fig. 4), filled with horizontal fibres of quartz and calcite (+ epidote, chlorite) and the conglomerates are cut-off by a number of dip-slip microfaults. Stress tensor determinations (Fig. 7) from microfault analysis employing the automatic method (Etchecopar *et al.* 1981) give a direction of minimum stress, σ_3, orientated horizontal and trending N 120°; a direction of maximum stress, σ_1, vertical and a ratio $R = (\sigma_1 - \sigma_3)/(\sigma_2 - \sigma_3) = 0.75$, i.e. σ_1 close to σ_2. The Mohr circle gives the relative values of σ_1, σ_2, σ_3 and the normal and shear stresses for each

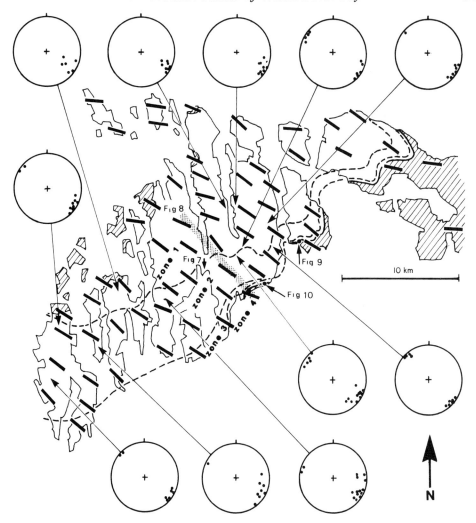

FIG. 4. Structural map of the Solund basin (see text for explanations) with pebble long-axis orientation (after Nilsen 1968, modified) and direction of extension given by tension gashes (Schmidt net, lower hemisphere).

fault plane. The unusual distribution is a result of the unlithified state of the conglomerate (Seranne & Seguret, 1985b).

Zone 2

In this zone the morphological sequence is not expressed, as the poorly cemented division *D1* diminishes laterally southeastwards. The bedding dip and the imbrication angle decrease (Fig. 8), but the preferred orientation of the pebbles strengthens. The same microtectonic structures as in zone 1 are evident from detailed field observation and thin-section studies.

Zone 3

The bedding dip is flatter and there is a horizontal foliation. There is no imbrication, but the pebble preferred orientation is stronger both on bedding planes and on sections striking N 120°. The change in pebble shape suggests internal deformation of the pebbles. This deformation is controlled by lithology and develops as boudinage, ductile deformation, and sliding along pre-existing internal hetero-geneities, such as strata, cleavage and foliation.

Sets of low-angle NE-striking, metre-scale dip-slip shear zones, which dip gently to the NW or the SE and flatten downward, affect the general fabric.

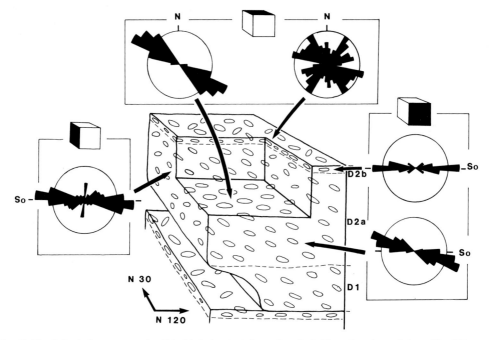

FIG. 5. Morphological sequence and pebble fabric (see text for explanation). The orientations of about 50 pebble long-axes are plotted in each circular diagram referred to the N on the bedding plane and referred to horizontal in the vertical planes. The 25° tilting of the bedding has been removed.

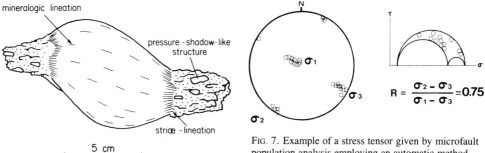

FIG. 6. Microtectonic structures associated with the pebbles.

FIG. 7. Example of a stress tensor given by microfault population analysis employing an automatic method (Etchecopar *et al.* 1981) (Schmidt net, lower hemisphere) and Mohr circle. The *R* ratio characterizes the shape of the stress ellipsoid (for location see Fig. 4).

$$R = \frac{\sigma_2 - \sigma_3}{\sigma_1 - \sigma_3} = 0.75$$

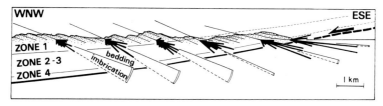

FIG. 8. Schematic cross-section of the Solund basin showing the decrease of the bedding dip and imbrication angle toward the basal contact. Each circular diagram represents about 40 measurements and gives the mean imbrication (stippled line). (For location see Fig. 4.)

They are characterized by the re-orientation of pebbles to the dip-slip direction or by the deflection of the horizontal foliation and they are associated with asymmetrical pressure-shadows around quartz rods. They indicate a conjugated normal sense of motion and a horizontal NW–SE extension.

Some vertical quartz veins, striking N 30°, are folded symmetrically with respect to the horizontal foliation. Giant synkinematic porphyroblasts of epidote (0.20 m mean size, up to 2 m) lie within the horizontal foliation. A crack-seal origin for these porphyroblasts is suggested by horizontal epidote–quartz fibres developed between closely spaced vertical joints (J.P. Brun, pers. comm.). The long, intermediate and short axes of the porphyroblasts are respectively horizontal N 120°, horizontal N 30° and vertical.

Zone 4

A few metres above the basal contact, pebbles are difficult to recognize. There is a grain-size reduction, however, and an increase in clast elongation towards the Devonian/Cambro–Silurian

contact (Fig. 9). The foliation, defined at outcrop scale by the preferred orientation of the deformed clasts, becomes parallel to the contact, which dips 10° NW, and some mylonitic bands occur parallel to the foliation. They are both affected by *C'* shear planes (Berthe *et al.* 1979), dipping 35° NW. In the foliation plane some clasts are broken up into fragmental trails, parallel to the N 120° stretching lineation. The contact itself is marked by a green cohesive schistose rock.

Beneath the contact, the Cambro–Silurian rocks display a foliation parallel to the contact. Some quartz ribbons may be folded into intrafolial recumbent folds. The foliation plane is slightly undulated by oblique shear planes (*C'*), which dip towards the NW (Fig. 10). The stretching lineation, trending N 120°, developed within the foliation and some NW-verging sheath folds are observed.

Further down, the foliation becomes horizontal and the *S*, *C* and *C'* structures become less important. The intensity of the foliation decreases southeastward and, a few 100 m below the contact, it appears to be superimposed on earlier structures related to a WNW-directed ductile shearing of high

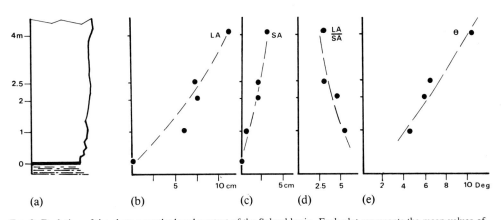

FIG. 9. Evolution of the clasts near the basal contact of the Solund basin. Each plot represents the mean values of about 20 measurements. (a) Section across the contact, (b, c) grain-size reduction, (LA = Long axis; SA = Short axis), (d) stretching of the clasts, (e) reduction of imbrication angle θ (for location see Fig. 4).

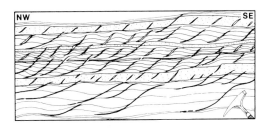

FIG. 10. Example of shear bands (*C'*) within the basal contact of the Solund basin, that indicate a northwestward shearing.

strain. A detailed study of the basement deformation is not the subject of this paper, however, we assume that three major events can be inferred: (i) Caledonian nappe emplacement; (ii) late-Caledonian westward ductile shearing, homogeneous over the area; (iii) heterogeneous Devonian extensional deformation with westward-directed brittle to ductile shearing restricted to a few hundred metres thick zone at the basement/Devonian interface with brittle fracturing below the detachment.

Structural interpretation of the Solund section

In zone 1 the brittle microstructures (microfaults and intrapebble tension gashes) give a stress tensor with σ_3 horizontal N 120°, σ_2 horizontal N 30° and σ_1 vertical. The ductile microstructures (lineation, pressure-shadows, cleavage) result from a finite strain with a N 120° horizontal extension axis (X), a N 30° horizontal intermediate axis (Y), and a vertical shortening axis (Z). The nature of the Y direction (shortening or extension) has not been determined and the strain-ellipsoid shape is not precisely known. There must, however, be a very long extension (X) axis.

The close relationships between the conglomerate fabrics and microtectonics demonstrate that the fabric is not of sedimentary origin. The flattening post-dates both the tilting of the bedding, as the strain and stress axes are not tilted, and the acquisition of the fabric, as the surface of imbricated pebbles are used as normal faults. In fabric-bearing conglomerates, in $D1$ and $D2a$ divisions of the morphological sequence, the pebbles are undeformed apart from the tension gashes and the fabric has been attained by body rotation of the pebbles in an unconsolidated sandy matrix. The characteristics of the microfaults (Guiraud & Seguret, in press) fit this rheological interpretation.

The interbedded levels in the $D2b$ division that do not exhibit a fabric are considered to be previously consolidated layers with a different rheological response to stress.

We propose that the fabric is linked to the tilting of the series and is the result of a southeastwards dip-slip shearing of soft conglomerates (Fig. 11). The shearing occurred parallel to the bedding and was controlled by the previously consolidated levels in the $D2b$ division, which acted as thin undeformable planes interbedded into the soft conglomerate (Seranne & Seguret 1985b). The flattening is superimposed on the shearing. The pebble imbrication angle results from an equilibrium between rotation synthetic to shearing, related to the tilting, and antithetic rotation, related to the flattening. Both shearing and flattening are induced by the vertical maximum stress and the N 120° horizontal minimum stress produces the extension. It has not been possible to establish a relationship between the morphological sequence and a possible sedimentary sequence due to the strong deformation and the poor knowledge of such deposits.

In zone 2, the same structural data as in zone 1 suggest the same deformation mechanisms. The decrease of bedding dip and angle of imbrication results from the down-section increase of flattening (Fig. 11). Bedding and pebbles are rotated and tend to parallel the finite flattening plane; the horizontal schistosity.

In zone 3, rotational deformation criteria have been observed in sections trending N 120°. At outcrop scale, however, the rotational effects are balanced in conjugate structures and the growth of epidote porphyroblasts and the symmetry of the folded quartz veins argue for a finite strain resulting from a coaxial deformation. All the structural data can be interpreted as resulting from a coaxial

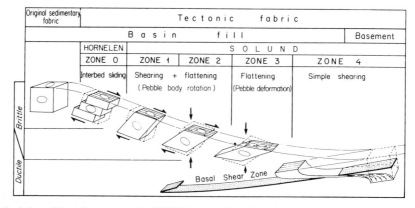

FIG. 11. Evolution of the deformation in the DBWN (see text for explanation).

deformation with principal directions *X, Y, Z* orientated respectively; horizontal N 120°, horizontal N 30° and vertical.

In zone 4, the reliable sense of shear markers indicate that the strain regime is not coaxial. The deformation history of the rocks within the basal contact is of progressive shearing towards the NW, parallel to the contact between Devonian and Cambro–Silurian rocks, with maximum shearing along the contact and motion parallel to the N 120° trending lineation. The microstructures of zone 4 are therefore in agreement with it being a shear zone.

Evolution of the deformation along the DBWN basal contact

From N to S, the Hornelen, Kvamshesten and Solund basins show a different pattern of rock textures at the basal contact, between the Devonian series and the basement. In the northern basin the conglomerates are brecciated through a zone a few metres thick; the contact is marked by a schistose cataclasite (Chester *et al.* 1985) generated by cataclasis on densifying discrete shear planes. This brittle deformation, linked to the formation of the basin, has not affected the well-developed mylonitic fabric of the basement. There is a textural and metamorphic gap between footwall and hanging wall rocks. At the Kvamshesten eastern basal contact, the Devonian Series exhibits the same structures as at Hornelen. The schistose cataclasite is underlain by a 0.3 m thick black glassy rock that locally intrudes fractures, thus suggesting a pseudo-tachylite. The underlying basement consists of polydeformed chloritic gneisses with a consistent mylonitic foliation, showing plastic deformation and recrystallization (Tullis *et al.* 1982). This is overprinted by some discrete cataclastic shear planes that become denser towards the contact. The brittle deformation related to basin formation affected both Devonian and basement rocks. It is still dominated by brittle cataclasis but denotes a higher shear strain than in Hornelen. In contrast to the former examples, the conglomerates of Solund basin are epimetamorphic and ductilely deformed. The fault rocks still resemble the schistose cata-clasites of the Kvamshesten basin, but the extremely fine-grained matrix contains bands of dynamically recrystallized quartz. In the basement, the same close relationships between ductile and brittle processes are observed. There is no tectonometa-morphic gap between hanging wall and foot wall.

At regional scale, the footwall consistently demonstrates the results of ductile deformation. Close to the contact this deformation is progress-ively overprinted by a younger event the effects of which are found both in the basement and in the Devonian Series. This younger event, thus related to the basin formation, displays fault rocks produced under increasing *P/T* conditions, from Hornelen to Solund. This allows us to observe the transition from a brittle to ductile mode of deform-ation (Sibson 1977; Mitra 1984). We conclude that the observed basal contact shows deeper and deeper exposures from N to S.

Metamorphism and magmatism

In Solund basin the deformation is associated with a synkinematic prograde metamorphism and hypo-volcanic intrusions. The petrological studies are still in progress and we present only some prelimi-nary results.

The conglomerate constituents are mostly Precambrian gneisses, and Caledonian meta-sediments and metabasites which have been meta-morphosed into the amphibolites facies. Devonian metamorphism is expressed by; (i) an incomplete retrogression of the gneissic pebbles into the greenschist facies; and (ii) crystallization of index metamorphic minerals in the sandy matrix and into the scarce reddish siltstone pebbles of Devonian age. The blastesis is clearly synchronous with the regional Devonian foliation.

The occurrence of prehnite, zoïsite, clinozoïsite, chlorite, albite and quartz, with possibly pumpel-lyite, characterizes a prehnite–pumpellyite facies (200–300 °C). The occurrence of actinolite marks the beginning of the greenschist facies (300–350 °C). The succession of mineral assemblages is typically of low-pressure type ($P < 3$ Kb) but barometers are poorly defined at low pressure. The metamorphism in the Devonian basins is very unusual, being clearly synkinematic with the extensional tectonics. In that way it differs from other basin-related metamorphism (Muffler & White 1969; Guiraud & Seguret in press), in which minerals are mostly static. In addition, trachytic and rhyolitic lavas are interbedded with the Solund conglomerates (Sigmond *et al.* 1984; Furnes & Lippard 1983) and veins and small bodies of rhyolitic rocks occur within the conglomerates of the Solund basin. The veins and bodies have a granitic composition, with quartz and feldspars and a granophyric texture, typical of hypovolcanic rocks. The bodies (0.1 to 2 m long) have poorly defined and contorted margins. Along the bedding plane they are elongated and well orientated with a similar fabric to that of the pebbles. At the present stage of investigation, we interpret these granitic bodies as synkinematic hypovolcanic intrusions. Only the most differentiated types occur; this may indicate a crustal origin by partial melting but more geochemical data are needed to confirm this.

Kinematic interpretation

Integration of the data obtained from the four basins indicates that deformation of the Devonian sediments resulted from vertical flattening, accommodated by the westward motion of the hanging wall. It consisted of brittle deformation (i.e. interbed sliding) in the upper part of the section, now outcropping at the highest exposed levels (Hornelen, Kvamshesten). At deeper levels (Solund, zones 1 and 2), the conglomerates are ductilely sheared and flattened with pebble-body rotation in a ductile matrix; the eastward shearing is still controlled by the tilted bedding. Close to the bottom of the basin (Solund, zone 3) the flattening increases and the pebbles are ductilely deformed. The basal contact is associated with dip-slip shearing towards the NW (or W), involving both Devonian and basement material. Below this shear zone, the basement was brittly deformed during the development of the basins. Metamorphism and fault-rock associations are consistent with the structural data: deeper and deeper levels are observed from N to S.

Discussion on crustal scale model

One of the main acquisitions of this study is the observation of ductile deformation in the basin fill and on the detachment, over a basement undeformed during basin development. The large offset of the low-angle basal shear zone needs to be accommodated somewhere in the crust or in the lithosphere.

A model associated with a horizontal detachment (Miller *et al.* 1983; Kligfield *et al.* 1984) is not realistic due to; (i) the uniform sense of shear along the detachment and (ii) the huge amount of extension that would be required (stretching factor $\beta = 4.4$, McKenzie 1978) without intense and generalized plutonism and magmatism.

In contrast, all the data support a model with a dipping detachment (Kligfield *et al.* 1984). In a first hypothesis (Fig. 12a), the basal shear zone deepens westward into the crust. There is no ductile deformation of the lower crust and therefore the displacement is preserved down-slip and the offset affects the Moho discontinuity. The deep structure

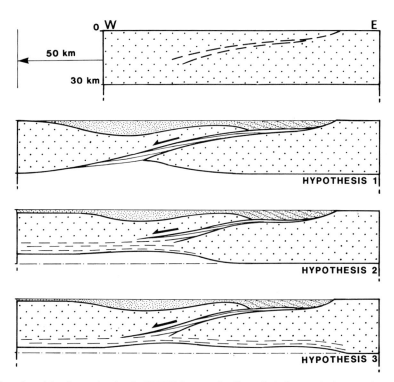

FIG. 12. Crustal models of extension for the DBWN (see text for discussion). Large stipples=continental crust; irregular small dots=syntectonic deposits; dashes parallel to Moho discontinuity=continental crust ductilely stretched.

The sketch illustrates the case of a unique low-angle detachment that implies the development of a large hanging wall syncline, W of the rollover anticline.

may be controlled by a decoupling at the Moho as proposed by Wernicke (1981).

In a second hypothesis (Fig. 12b) the basal shear zone deepens westwards within the crust down to a depth where P/T conditions produce ductile deformation. The horizontal displacement observed in the upper part of the crust is transformed into pervasive ductile stretching of the lower part of the crust at some distance W of the basin. The crustal thinning does not occur directly beneath the basin.

In a third hypothesis (Fig. 12c) the stretching is distributed both beneath the basin and further to the W. In this case, the basin and its undeformed basement overlie a stretched and thinned lower crust.

The petrological studies, now in progress, will supply strong constraints for a choice between the three hypotheses. Precise evaluation of the P/T conditions of the metamorphism will define the geotherm and therefore indicate whether the crust was thinned beneath the basin. Similarly, evidence for partial melting of the lower crust could argue for crustal stretching below the basin.

The model with a dipping detachment is also supported by a comparison with deep seismic reflection profiles (Allmendinger *et al.* 1983; Allmendinger *et al.*, this volume; Brewer & Smythe 1984). These profiles display low-angle reflectors that limit downward-tilted strata of sedimentary basins. Most reflectors are traceable into the upper crust and merge downward into horizontal reflectors, a feature of the lower third of the crust, which may represent the zone of ductile stretching. The transfer of stretching in the lower crust into shearing along the detachment is facilitated by reactivation of pre-existing planes of strength anisotropy, such as thrust planes (Brun & Choukroune 1983). The retrogressive dip-slip shear zone of the DBWN results from the re-working of a previous eastward-dipping Caledonian thrust plane (Hossack 1984; Norton 1984) and/or a late-Caledonian westward shearing.

Finally the DBWN are likely to represent the eastern margin of the Devonian North Sea basin (Fig. 13) (Ziegler 1981), symmetrical to the N Scotland Devonian basin in which a similar geometry has been revealed by the MOIST profile (Brewer & Smythe 1984).

ACKNOWLEDGMENTS: This research was supported by Elf-Aquitaine Norge: we wish to thank J.M. Golberg and Ph. Laurent for their contribution concerning metamorphism and fault-rock associations, respectively. Fruitful discussions with colleagues at the laboratories of Petrology and Structural Geology and with J.P. Brun during a field trip, improved the paper. We are grateful for the comments of two anonymous referees.

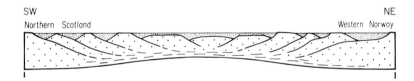

FIG. 13. Proposed section of the North Sea during middle Devonian times. The symmetrical low-angle shear zones bounding the basins at each margin merge in the lower crust within a zone of pervasive ductile flow (not to scale).

References

ALLMENDINGER, R.W., HAUGE, T.A., HAUSER, E.C., POTTER, C.J. & OLIVER, J. This volume. Tectonic heredity in the layered lower crust in the Basin and Range Province, western United States.

——, SHARP, J.W., VON TISH, D., SERPA, L., BROWN, L., KAUFMAN, S., OLIVER, J. & SMITH, R.B. 1983. Cenozoic and Mesozoic Structure of the Eastern Basin and Range province, Utah, from COCORP seismic-reflexion data. *Geology*, **11**, 532–6.

BARTLEY, J.M. & WERNICKE, B.P. 1984. The Snake Range Décollement interpreted as a major extensional shear zone. *Tectonics*, **3**, 647–57.

BERTHE, D., CHOUKROUNE, P. & JEGOUZO, P. 1979. Orthogneiss, mylonite and non-coaxial deformation of granite: the example of the South Armorican Shear zone. *J. struct. Geol.* **1**, 31–42.

BREWER, J.A. & SMYTHE, D.K. 1984. MOIST and the continuity of crustal reflector geometry along the Caledonian-Appalachian orogen. *J. geol. Soc. London*, **141**, 105–20.

BRUN, J.P. & CHOUKROUNE, P. 1983. Normal faulting, block tilting and décollement in a stretched crust. *Tectonics*, **2**, 345–56.

BRYHNI, I. 1964. Migrating basins on the Old Red Continent. *Nature*, **202**, 384–5.

—— 1976. 'Gabbro' in the Solund conglomerates. A Devonian debris flow deposit? *Norsk. Geol. Tidsskift*, **56**, 95–102.

—— 1978. Flood deposit in the Hornelen Basin, West Norway (O.R.S.). *Norsk. Geol. Tidsskift*, **58**, 273–300.

—— & SKJERLIE, F.J. 1975. Syndepositional tectonism in the Kvamshesten district (Old Red Sandstone), Western Norway, *Geol. Mag.* **112**, 593–600.

CHEADLE, M.J., McGEARY, S., WARNER, M.R. & MATTHEWS, D.A. This volume. Extensional structures in the western UK continental shelf; a review of evidence from deep seismic profiling.

CHESTER, F.M., FRIEDMAN, M., LOGAN, J.M. 1985. Foliated cataclasites. *Tectonophysics*, **111**, 139–46.

ETCHECOPAR, A., VASSEUR, G. & DAIGNIERES, M. 1981. An inverse problem in microtectonics for the determination of stress tensors from fault striation analysis. *J. struct. Geol.* **3**, 51–65.

FAUGERE, E. & BRUN, J.P. 1984. Modélisation experimentale de la distension continentale. *C.R. Acad. Sci. Paris*, **299**, 367–70.

FURNES, H. & LIPPARD, S.J. 1983. Devonian lavas from Solund, West Norway. Field relationships and geochemistry. *Nor. Geol. unders.* **383**, 1–15.

GANS, P.B. & MILLER, E.L. 1983. Style of Mid-Tertiary Extension in East Central Nevada; Utah Geol. *Min. Surv. Spec. Stud.* **59**, 107–60.

GLOPPEN, T.G. & STEEL, R.J. 1981. Recent and ancient nonmarine depositional environment: Models for exploration. *S.E.P.M. Spec. Publ.* **31**, 49–69.

GUIRAUD, M. & SEGURET, M. 1986. Releasing solitary overstep model for the Late Jurassic-Early Cretaceous (Wealdian) Soria Strike-slip basin (North Spain). *In: Strike-slip deformation, basin formation and Sedimentation. S.E.P.M. Spec. Publ.* **37**, 159–75.

HOISAETER, T. 1971. Thrust Devonian Sediments in the Kvamshesten area, Western Norway. *Geol. Mag.* **108**, 287–92.

HOSSACK, J.R. 1984. The geometry of listric growth faults in the Devonian basins of Sunnfjord, W. Norway. *J. geol. Soc. London*, **141**, 629–37.

—— & COOPER, M.A. Collision tectonics in the Scandinavian Caledonides. *In: COWARD, M.P. & RIES, A.C. (eds) Collision Tectonics. Spec. Publ. geol. Soc. London*, **19**, 287–304.

INDREAVER, 1980. Unpubl. Thesis, Univ. Bergen.

KILDAL, E. 1970. *Geologisk kart over Norge, berggrunnskart, Maloy. 1: 25000.* Norges Geologiske Undersokelse.

KLIGFIELD, R., CRESPI, J., NARUK, S. & DAVIS, G.H. 1984. Displacement and strain patterns of extensional orogens. *Tectonics*, **3**, 577–606.

KUSZNIR, N.J. & PARK, R.G. 1984. Intraplate lithosphere deformation and the strength of the lithosphere. *Geophys. J.R. astron. Soc.* **79**, 513–38.

MCKENZIE, D. 1978. Some remarks on the development of sedimentary basins. *Earth planet Sci. Lett.* **40**, 25–32.

MILLER, E.L., GANS, P.B. & GARING, J. 1983. The snake Range décollement: an exhumed mid-tertiary ductile-brittle transition. *Tectonics*, **2**, 239–63.

MITRA, G. 1984. Brittle to ductile transition due to large strains along the White Rock Thrust, Wind River

Mountains Wyoming. *J. struct. Geol.* **6**, 57–61.

MUFFLER, L.J.P. & WHITE, D.E. 1969. Active metamorphism of Upper Cenozoic sediments in the Salton Sea geothermal field and Salton trough, southeastern California. *Bull. geol. Soc. Am.* **80**, 157–81.

NILSEN, T.H. 1968. The relationship of sedimentation to tectonics in the Solund area of southwestern Norway. *Nor. Geol. under*, **259**, 108 pp.

NORTON, M.G. 1984. Reactivation of Caledonian thrusts during Devonian extensional faulting, western Norway. *Abstract. Chevauchement et Déformation*, Toulouse, May 84, pp. 81.

ROBERTS, D. 1983. Devonian tectonic deformation in the Norwegian Caledonides and its regional perspectives. *Nor. Geol. Unders.* **380**, 85–96.

SANTARELLI, N. 1977. Le soubassement gneissique des internides Calédoniennes Scandinaves. Limite de la calédonisation. *Rev. geog. phys. Geol.* **19**, 405–20.

SERANNE, M. & SEGURET, M. 1985a. Etirement ductile et cisaillement basal dans les bassins dévoniens de l'Ouest Norvège. *C.R. Acad. Sci. Paris*, **300**, 373–8.

—— & —— 1985b. Ductile deformation of soft conglomerates in Western Norway Devonian Basin, *Abstract, Deformation mechanisms in Sediments and Sedimentary Rocks.* London, pp. 30.

SIBSON, R.H. 1977. Fault rocks and fault mechanisms. *J. geol. Soc. London*, **133**, 191–213.

SIGMOND, E.M.O., GUSTAVSON, M. ROBERTS, D. 1984. *Berggrunnskart over Norge 1 :1 million.* Norges Geologiske Undersokelse.

STEEL, R.J. 1976. Devonian basins of western Norway sedimentary response to tectonism and to varying tectonic context. *Tectonophysics*, **36**, 207–24.

—— & GLOPPEN, T.G. 1980. Late Caledonian (Devonian) basin formation western Norway: signs of strike-slip tectonics during infilling. *Spec. Publ. Int. Ass. Sediment*, **4**, 79–103.

STURT, B.A. 1983. Late Caledonian and possible Variscan stages in the orogenic evolution of the Scandinavian Caledonides. Abstract Symposium Rabat 1983. *In: The Caledonide Orogen IGCP Project N° 27 Morocco and Paleozoic orogenesis.*

TULLIS, J., SNOCKE, A.W. & TODD, V.R. 1982. Significance and petrogenesis of mylonitic rocks (Penrose Conference Report). *Geology*, **10**, 227–30.

WERNICKE, B. 1981. Low-angle normal faults in the Basin and Range province: nappe tectonics in an extending orogen. *Nature*, **291**, 645–8.

ZIEGLER, P.A. 1981. Evolution of Sedimentary Basins in North-West Europe. *In: Petroleum Geology of the Continental Shelf of North West Europe.* Inst. Pet. London.

MICHEL SERANNE & MICHEL SEGURET, Laboratoire de Tectonique, U.S.T.L., Pl. Bataillon, 34060 Montpellier, France.

Extension in the Middle East

Structures associated with extensional tectonics in the Suez rift

P.Y. Chénet, B. Colletta, J. Letouzey, G. Desforges, E. Ousset, & E.A. Zaghloul

SUMMARY: The opening of the Suez rift, which was initiated at the beginning of the Miocene (23 Ma), was the result of a regional extensional stress more or less perpendicular to the rift axis. A detailed study of selected areas within the onshore part of the rift (Abu Durba, Gebel Ekma and Wadi Dib) shows that the fault geometries visible in the Precambrian basement and the overlying sedimentary rocks are distinct; brittle deformation in one, ductile deformation in the other. In the basement (metamorphic and granitic rocks), faults display a rectilinear pattern. Two sets of faults are predominant; (i) N140–150E faults, parallel to the Gulf trend, with pure dip-slip displacement, (ii) cross-faults (transfer faults) trending N00 to N30E with strike-slip component. These faults delineate diamond-shaped tilted blocks. In the overlying sedimentary rocks (Cretaceous–Eocene sands, shales and limestones) faults are spoon-shaped. Spoon faults are generally superimposed over concave wedges of the basement blocks but are decoupled from basement fault sets. The decoupling is accommodated by ductile deformation and detachment in the Cretaceous marls.

The Suez rift (Fig. 1) is a Cenozoic structure of 300 km in length and 50 to 80 km width. The subsidence of the main trough started at the beginning of Miocene times, about 23 Ma. It was followed by a progressive uplift of the shoulders and an increasing subsidence in the central trough. The rifting affected the Afro–Arabian platform which is composed of crystalline Precambrian basement, overlying which are sandstones of the Nubia Formation (Palaeozoic to Lower Cretaceous), followed by interbedded marls, sandstones and limestones of late Cretaceous to Eocene age (Said 1962; Robson 1971).

The structures of the present-day rift result almost entirely from the extension that has been active since rift initiation. No significant deformation affected the Afro–Arabian platform before that. Structures observed in the excellent outcrops of the region give a clue to seismic interpretations in the Gulf of Suez itself, as well as in other continental rifts.

Regional tectonic setting

The ENE-trending folds of the Syrian arc (Fig. 2), N of the Suez rift, result from a NW–SE compression during Eocene times. This compression may have been active later, during Oligocene times, but the paucity of recorded Oligocene sediments prevents a determination of the end of this tectonic phase. Garfunkel & Bartov (1977) have suggested that this compression was responsible for strike-slip movements S of the Syrian arc, in the area of the present Suez rift.

The emplacement of scarce basalt dykes during the Oligocene and early Miocene (ages from 32 to 18 Ma with a 24 My average; Steen 1982) preluded the opening of the rift. They trend generally parallel to the future rift axis, but also N00 to N20, which is a preferred direction for the transverse faulting in the future rift.

The opening of the Suez rift, perpendicular to a NE–SW extension, started in Aquitanian times (23–21 My). The northern Red Sea was also opening at this time (Mart & Hall 1984), but may have been initiated before Aquitanian times. In this case, the Suez rifting would be the consequence of the northward propagation of the Red Sea rifting. The Suez gulf displayed its maximum width during Miocene times. The Levant fault may already have been active at this time, although there is no direct evidence of movement before the Upper Miocene. This movement led to a slight stress reorientation near the fault in the Dead Sea area (Ron & Eyal 1985).

Since Pliocene times, oceanic spreading was active in the northern part of the Red Sea (Cochran 1983) and the opening movement was mainly absorbed by the sinistral displacement along the Dead Sea transform (Garfunkel 1981). This horizontal displacement led to the opening of the Dead Sea and the Aqaba trough and these may be considered as pull-apart basins. At this time, the Suez rift was still active, although its subsidence was restricted to a narrower area, corresponding to the present Gulf of Suez.

Rift fault characteristics

The dominant trend of the normal faults within the Suez rift is N135–150, parallel to the rift axis. In the

From COWARD, M.P., DEWEY, J.F. & HANCOCK, P.L. (eds), 1987, *Continental Extensional Tectonics*, Geological Society Special Publication No. 28, pp. 551–558.

552   *P.Y. Chénet* et al.

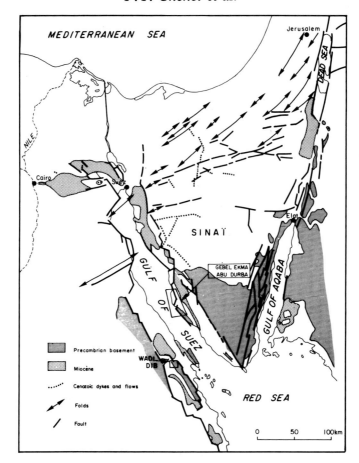

FIG. 1. Schematic geological setting of the Suez rift, the Sinai and the Aqaba–Dead Sea rifts. Locations of the areas studied.

Abu Durba–Gebel Ekma area, previously studied by some of the authors (Chénet *et al.* 1984), these longitudinal faults dip generally between 30 and 60°, while the transverse faults dip more steeply (Fig. 3). The wide range of dips exhibited by the longitudinal faults results from their variety of tilt angles. Typically, the angle between the major faults and the bedding is relatively constant and varies from 60 to 65°.

In the NE–SW extensional regime of the Suez rift (Chénet *et al.* 1984; Angelier & Bergerat 1983), the pitch of the slickenside lineations along the longitudinal faults is nearly vertical, while a wide range of pitches may be found along the transverse faults (Fig. 4). As shown on the stereogramm of several faults of the Abu Durba–Gebel Ekma area (Fig. 5), the dip of the longitudinal faults is in the same range as the pitch along the transverse faults. This shows that the motion along the transverse faults was probably guided by the longitudinal fault planes. It

is thus not necessary to involve strike-slip faulting and horizontal compressive stress to explain the relatively low pitches of slickensides on the transverse fault planes. Furthermore, the horizontal offset along the transverse faults will be mainly related to the horizontal transverse component of the throw on the longitudinal faults and not to any older tectonic event, such as the NW–SE Eocene compression.

Refraction of faulting: the Gebel Ekma example

Refraction of faulting and disharmony are common phenomena where the rocks affected by faulting have contrasting rheologies. In the Gebel Ekma area (Fig. 6), the main longitudinal normal fault, bordering the block to the W, displays a refraction of about 20° when traced from the crystalline base-

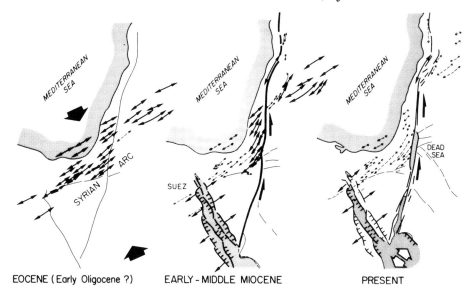

FIG. 2. Synthetic evolution of the stress regime within the Gulf of Suez area, the Sinai shield and the Deaᴅ Sea transcurrent fault (see text). Full double arrows=active folds; dotted double arrows=inactive folds; Suez rift—simple arrows=direction of extension, hatched areas=marine sedimentation.

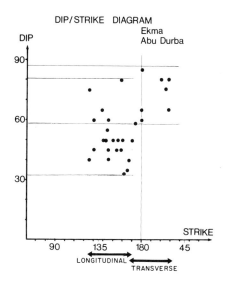

FIG. 3. Dip versus strike diagram of faults in the Abu-Durba–Gebel Ekma area.

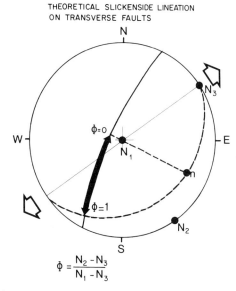

$$\Phi = \frac{N_2 - N_3}{N_1 - N_3}$$

FIG. 4. Theoretical slickenside lineation on a transverse fault in a NE–SW extensional regime on a Wülf (lower hemisphere) stereogram. N1, N2 and N3 = maximum-,

intermediate- and minimum-stresses projection. n = pole of the transverse fault plane.

Following Bott's (1959) theory, the slickenside lineation will be in the plane perpendicular to the fault plane containing the shear stress. When $\Phi=0$, the shear stress is in the N1–n plane. When $\Phi=1$, the shear stress is in the N3–n plane. When $0<\Phi<1$, the theoretical slickenside on the transverse fault plane lies between the two extreme positions (thick stripe with double arrow on the fault plane).

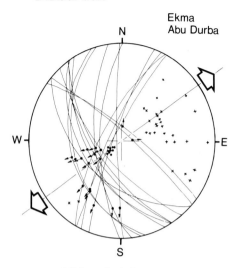

EXTENSION N. 055

Ekma
Abu Durba

Wulf Lower hemisphere

FIG. 5. Wülf stereogram with lower hemisphere projection of faults in the Gebel Ekma–Abu Durba area. Arrows=slickensides on the fault planes. Crosses= poles of fault planes. Dots=poles of bedding.

ment to the overlying more plastic pre-rift series. Well data of the Belayim Land oil field (Ayouti 1961) suggest a mean dip of 60° for the fault, while a 40° dipping fault can be observed in the field.

As shown on the block diagram in Fig. 7, the plastic beds of the pre-rift sedimentary series are folded and slumped and abnormal stratigraphical superpositions occur. These complex structures are the result of downward movement along the non-planar fault surface, which implies a deformation of the overhanging block in the vicinity of the fault. Furthermore they are accentuated by gravity sliding. No compression is required to explain these structures.

The timing of the faulting may be inferred, since the carbonate matrix of the conglomerate which contains pebbles of Eocene limestones, and seals the slumped structure, is of Aquitanian age. Lower Miôcene sands and marls, overlain by middle Miocene gypsum onlap the flank of the palaeoslope.

Transverse faulting and behaviour of the pre-rift substratum

The Wadi Dib example

In the Wadi Dib area (see location, Fig. 1), the pre-rift plastic Cretaceous beds are tilted westward

10 to 15° and locally display vertical dips along a transverse fault zone trending N025. Cretaceous beds appear horizontally offset by about 1 km. Some elongation of the strata along the fault strike leads to thinning. Associated secondary faults display only pure normal dip-slip movement and we suggest that the apparent horizontal displacement results only from the vertical offset of tilted strata (Fig. 9b, c) This kind of deformation along a transverse fault, together with the horizontal offset between layers of the same age on each side of the transverse fault, should not be interpreted as an indication of strike-slip movement, nor as evidence of compression.

Intersection between transverse and longitudinal faults

A study of the slickensides shows that displacement along a transverse fault and a longitudinal fault, bounding a block can be simultaneous. Furthermore, the transverse faults generally have no continuity across the tilted blocks of the Suez rift, but are limited between two-main longitudinal faults. This configuration results in the development of diamond-shaped tilted blocks of variable dimensions within the rift. Careful mapping in the vicinity of a junction between a transverse and a longitudinal fault shows that the structures result mainly from extensional tectonics and are governed by plastic deformations in the sedimentary cover superimposed over diamond-shaped blocks in the crystalline basement at depth.

In the southern border of the Abu Durba block for instance, (Fig. 6) the major transverse fault, trending N20, turns progressively, on the geological map, towards the longitudinal trend. Its dip, which is nearly vertical, decreases progressively where the fault reaches the rift-axis trend. In the vicinity of the change in direction, numerous small splay faults may be observed.

On the block diagram of Fig. 10, the change in direction between the longitudinal and the transverse fault is abrupt at the basement level, while it is more progressive at the sediment level. This is a consequence of the difference of mechanical behaviour and fault-plane refraction between the basement and the sediments. When faulting is active, the plastic sediments are highly deformed near the faults, especially near the area where the trend changes, since the available volume for the sediments decreases downwards. The beds may be locally tilted toward the SE and the NW, while the regional dip is toward the NE. Faults are spoon-shaped in the sedimentary cover and abut against the main transverse fault.

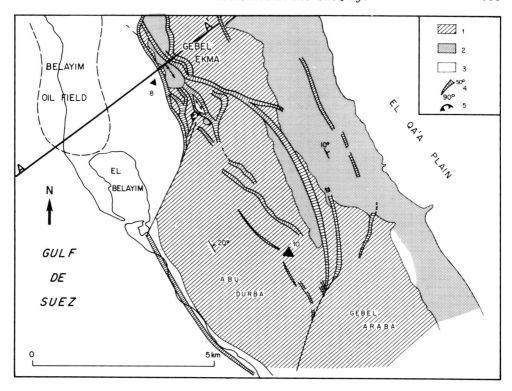

FIG. 6. Structural map of Abu Durba–Gebel Ekma area. 1 = Precambrian crystalline basement and Cambrian to Eocene pre-rift series; 2 = Miocene; 3 = Recent; 4 = Fault dip. The thicker the fault is, the lower is the dip; 5 = Thrust (Gebel Ekma). Arrows and numbers = point of view of the block diagrams of Figs 8 & 10.

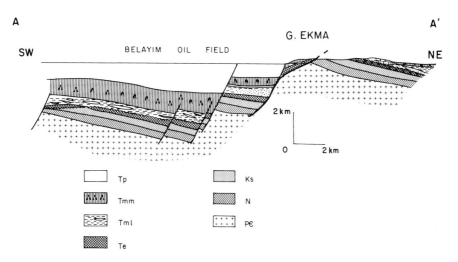

FIG. 7. Belayim oil field–Gebel Ekma cross-section. Tp = Plio–Quaternary (sands, clays and evaporites). Tmm = middle–upper Miocene evaporitic series (Ras Malaab Group in Garfunkel *et al.* 1977). Tml = lower Miocene sands and marls (Gharandal Group) and limestones (E of Gebel Ekma). Te = Eocene cherty limestones. Ks = upper Cretaceous chalk, sands, marls and limestones. N = Nubia sandstones. PC = Precambrian basement.

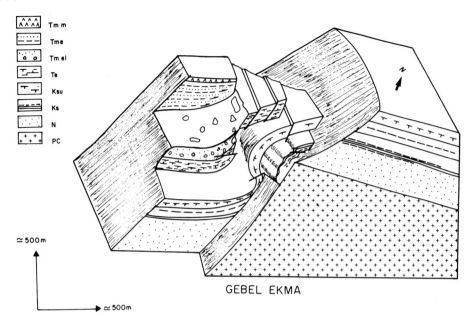

FIG. 8. Block diagram of the western edge of the Gebel Ekma block (see Fig. 6 for location). Tme = Burdigalian sands and marls. Tmel = Aquitanian conglomerates. Ksu = Maestrichtian chalk (see Fig. 7 for the other symbols). Note the onlap of lower Miocene sands and marls against the Aquitanian palaeoslope (arrows).

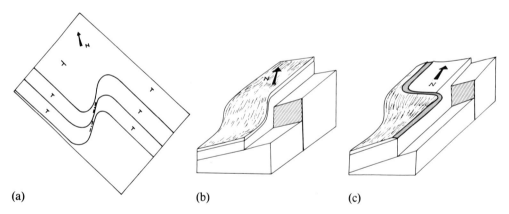

(a)   (b)   (c)

FIG. 9. Schematic geological map of the Wadi Dib area, showing the horizontal offset of the formation boundaries. Beds are vertical when trending N20. (b) Interpretative block diagram of the area showing the relationship between the transverse fault in the basement and the flexured overlying plastic sedimentary series. Note that the sedimentary layers are nearly vertical along the fault strike. (c) The same block diagram as (a), but cut by an horizontal erosion surface showing the horizontal offset of a given layer.

Conclusion

Extensional tectonism within the Suez rift is mainly characterized by the subsidence and tilting of diamond-shaped blocks. Because of the difference of mechanical behaviour between the rifted crystalline basement and the overlying pre- and syn-rift sedimentary series, the diamond-shaped block structure may not be directly observed near the surface and the transition between two blocks often corresponds to ramp-like structures. In some areas, where the pre-rift sedimentary series have not been buried, spectacular structures may appear associated with the normal faulting, such as large-scale

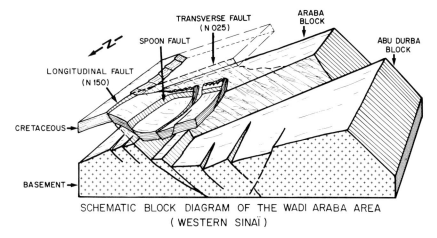

FIG. 10. Schematic block diagram of the southern border of the Abu Durba block, looking towards the SE (see Fig. 6 for location and text for explanation).

slumps, folds and even abnormal stratigraphic superposition; these features are essentially produced by gravity tectonics. The preferred orientation of the transverse faults, toward N00 or N20, in the studied areas, may be related to the fracturing of the platform just before rifting, caused by NW–SE compression, leading to the Syrian Arc formation. Slickenside studies demonstrate that the movements are compatible with rifting events and

there is little evidence of significant displacement before these occurred.

These observations suggest an opening model of the Suez rift (Fig. 11) in which the longitudinal faults may be joined by transverse faults, whose orientation is inherited from older tectonic events that produced a fracturing of the Precambrian shield without significant displacement. These transverse faults have no continuity across the rift.

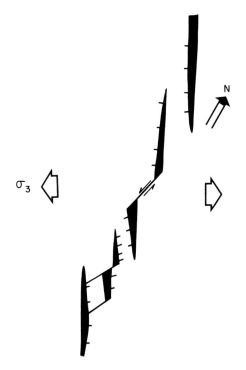

FIG. 11. Simplified model of opening of a rift with 'en échelon' disposed faults trending perpendicular to the extensional stress. The transverse fault, displaying a sinistral component may correspond to older lineaments.

References

ANGELIER, J. & BERGERAT, F. 1983. Système de contraintes et extension intracontinentale. *Bull Centres Rech. Explor. Produc. Elf Aquitaine*, **7**, 137–47.

AYOUTI, M.K. 1961. Geology of Belayim oil fields. *3rd Arab Petr. Cong. Pap. No. 43*, 12 pp.

BOTT, M.H.P. 1959. The mechanics of oblique slip faulting. *Geol. Mag.* **56**, 109–17.

CHÉNET, P.Y., LETOUZEY, J. & ZAGHLOUL, E.S. 1984. Some observations on the rift tectonics in the eastern part of the Suez rift. *Proc. 7th E.G.P.C. Explor. Seminar, Cairo*.

COCHRAN, J. 1983. A model for development of Red Sea. *Bull. Am. Assoc. Pet. Geol.* **67**, 41–69.

GARFUNKEL, Z. 1981. Internal structure of the Dead Sea lealy transform (rift) in relation to plate kinematics. *Tectonophysics*, **80**, 87–108.

—— & BARTOV, Y. 1977. The tectonics of the Suez rift. *Bull. geol. Surv. Isr.* **71**, 1–44.

MART, Y. & HALL, J. 1984. Structural trends in the Northern Red Sea. *J. geophys. Res.* **89**, 11352–64.

ROBSON, D.A. 1971. The structure of the Gulf of Suez (Clysmic rift) with special reference to the eastern side. *J. geol. Soc. London*, **127**, 247–76.

RON, H. & EYAL, Y. 1985. Intraplate deformation by block rotation and mesostructures along the Dead Sea transform, Northern Israel. *Tectonics*, **4**, 85–105.

SAID, R. 1962. *The Geology of Egypt*, Elsevier, Amsterdam.

STEEN, G. 1982. Radiometric age dating and tectonic significance of some Gulf of Suez igneous rocks. *In:* HANTAR, G. (ed.) *The Egyptian General Petroleum Corporation 6th Explo. Seminar, Cairo*, pp. 199–211. EGPC and EPEX Publishers.

P.Y. CHÉNET, B. COLLETTA & J. LETOUZEY, Institut Francais du Pétrole–BP311, 92506 Rueil Malmaison, France.

G. DESFORGES, E. OUSSET & E.A. ZAGHLOUL, TOTAL Proche Orient, Gameat Dowal Arabia 65, Mohandeseen, Cairo, Egypt.

Kinematics of the Sinai triple junction and a two-phase model of Arabia–Africa rifting

V. Courtillot, R. Armijo & P. Tapponnier

SUMMARY: The breakup of Arabia from Africa started at 40–50 Ma in the East African Rift system and concentrated from about 20 Ma around the Red Sea. Presently, the most active system centres along the Gulf of Aden, Red Sea and Dead Sea shear. Two less active features, the Gulf of Suez and East African Rift meet the main boundary at what have often been considered to be active triple junctions (the southern tip of Sinai and Afar). This paper focuses on the continental Sinai triple junction near 27° 30'N. Almost no reliable kinematic data can be found in the Red Sea. Only total motion based on a fit of coastlines is available. Yet, the mechanical basis for this is now known to be wrong. We propose a mechanical interpretation that retains the same pole of ARA–NUB motion, with a reduced amount of total opening. The best data come from the Dead Sea shear: 100 km of left-lateral displacement occurred over the last 20, or more likely 15 Ma (subsidence event in the Gulf of Suez). The pull-apart basins in the Gulf of Elat provide the best constraints on the azimuth of SIN–ARA motion. Four models of SIN–ARA–NUB kinematics are proposed depending on whether the Gulf of Suez is; (i) now extinct, (ii) still opening in the original direction, (iii) in a state of left-lateral shear, (iv) in a state of right-lateral shear. Total SIN–NUB motion is unlikely to exceed 1–2 mm yr^{-1}. We propose a two-phase history of break–up, first along the East African Rift/Red Sea/Gulf of Suez, superseded at ~ 15 Ma by the present Gulf of Aden/Red Sea/Dead Sea shear. Distributed extension now occurs in the Afar and northern Red Sea deforming zones towards which three localized rifts propagate. The Sinai and Afar 'triple junctions' are actually kinks where plate boundaries that were not active at the same time are superimposed.

It has been recognized that the Red Sea and the Gulf of Aden bear witness to the fairly recent rifting of Arabia away from Africa. As a key example of continental rifting in its early, transient stages, the tectonic ensemble consisting of the Red Sea, Gulf of Aden, Levant–Dead Sea shear and the less active Gulf of Suez and East African Rift system, continues to attract the attention of geoscientists (Fig. 1). As soon as plate tectonic concepts were developed, they were applied in attempts to provide a consistent picture of recent kinematics in the area (e.g. Le Pichon 1968; McKenzie *et al.* 1970). In a more recent comprehensive analysis of data from the Gulf of Aden, Red Sea and Dead Sea shear, Le Pichon & Francheteau (1978) proposed a pattern of both instantaneous and total motions since the beginning of plate separation. This analysis rested on the assumption that *large* rigid plates were in relative motion along *narrow* boundaries and indeed provided a good first-order fit to observations. However, the low separation rate and relative youth of the event make a detailed kinematic analysis of the Africa–Arabia rifting particularly difficult.

The Gulf of Aden is the only part of the boundary where the classical plate kinematic data provided by marine geophysics are readily observable. The pattern of magnetic anomalies and transform faults has been known there for over a decade (e.g. Laughton *et al.* 1970). Yet, magnetic anomaly data have been interpreted in very different ways, with Laughton *et al.* (1970) and more recently Courtillot (1980a, b) and Cochran (1981) arguing for a single phase of spreading, whereas Girdler & Styles (1978) advocated two separate phases with a long interruption of spreading between them.

The situation appears to be even more intricate in the Red Sea where the rugged topography, the presence of a salt layer and ill-defined magnetics generate controversy over the extent of oceanic versus continental lithosphere. Proposed transform faults are so short that an accurate identification is actually not possible and identifiable magnetic anomalies extend over only a very small part of the Red Sea. A model of single-phase diffuse extension (Cochran 1983) and rift propagation (Courtillot 1982; Courtillot & Vink 1983) is confronted with a purely oceanic two-phase model (Girdler & Styles 1974). In the case of the Red Sea, it may not be possible to determine an instantaneous pole of rotation and most analyses rely on the pole for total opening derived by McKenzie *et al.* (1970) from a fit of the coastlines (Fig. 2). This fit relied on the assumption that the Red Sea was floored by oceanic lithosphere from coast to coast, an assumption now generally believed to be wrong.

A fit of coastlines or clear identification of plate boundaries may not even be possible in Afar where the Red Sea joins the Gulf of Aden. The original plate tectonic schemes assumed that Afar was a triple-rift junction, the third arm consisting of the East African Rift system. However, global kin-

From COWARD, M.P., DEWEY, J.F. & HANCOCK, P.L. (eds), 1987, *Continental Extensional Tectonics*, Geological Society Special Publication No. 28, pp. 559–573.

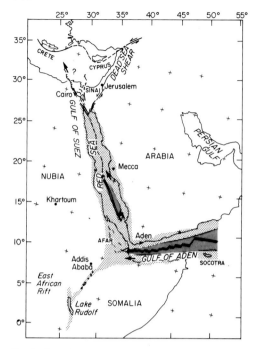 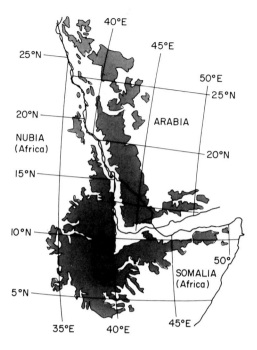

FIG. 1. General setting of the African (Nubia and Somalia), Arabian and Sinai Plates with the intervening deformed zones and plate boundaries. Heavy stippling corresponds to oceanic lithosphere, light to stretched continental lithosphere. The three thick arrows mark the three presently propagating rifts in the Red Sea and Gulf of Aden. Sinuous lines in Afar mark presently active axial volcanic chains.

FIG. 2. A fit of the Red Sea coastlines shows overlap in Afar and good parallelism of the Yemen (Arabia) and Ethiopian (Nubia) plateau scarps. Stippled areas lie above 1000 m. Reconstruction following McKenzie *et al.* (1970).

ematic analyses were unable to resolve Africa in two separate plates. Le Pichon & Francheteau (1978) introduced an additional small plate, termed 'dubious' or Danakil, in order to resolve some ambiguities. Courtillot (1980a, b, 1982) noted that widespread deformation in Afar precluded the identification of such small plates and proposed that Afar was actually a 'locked' zone ('soft' or 'deforming' zone now appear to be more appropriate terms), several hundred kilometres in dimension, in the process of being ruptured by propagating rifts advancing one towards the other from the Gulf of Aden and the Red Sea. The failure of the fit of coastlines in Afar was thus interpreted as being due to the widespread deformation.

Courtillot (1982a, b) and Courtillot & Vink (1983) suggested that another propagating rift was moving northward in the central part of the Red Sea, an analysis followed to some extent by Cochran (1983) and Mart & Hall (1984). The classical view of the northern end of the Red Sea (e.g. Le Pichon & Francheteau 1978) is that is it is a triple junction where the Red Sea meets the Dead Sea shear and the Gulf of Suez rift. As is the case in Afar, and to some extent in other more typical oceanic triple junctions (e.g. Patriat & Courtillot 1984), one arm of the junction is far less active than the other two. Again a number of problems arise in a more detailed analysis. If the Sinai is indeed a triple junction, it is a *continental* one. There is now evidence that there is nothing but continental lithosphere within at least 300 km of the proposed junction. Yet, most of the data relevant to plate kinematic analyses, particularly magnetic anomalies, are only found in oceanic lithosphere. Moreover, there is still ongoing controversy (e.g. abstracts in Ben Avraham 1985b) over the total amount and timing of motion on the Dead Sea shear, the best-defined arm of the Sinai triple junction. It is not yet clear whether tectonic activity on the three boundaries occurred continuously and synchronously or was episodic.

In the light of recent observations and the development of new concepts, a critical reassessment of the following problems seems justified: what are the respective extents of continental and oceanic lithosphere? Is it possible to distinguish between instantaneous and total motions? Where is tectonic deformation distributed and where is it localized?

Do the Afar and Sinai triple junctions exist and are they stable? What is the significance of the 'minor' rifts of Suez and East Africa? We focus here on the Sinai triple junction and discuss which kind of data can be used to construct a kinematic model of a continental triple junction. First we summarize external constraints (i.e. data external to the triple junction area) and more local data. Then, we discuss four kinematic scenarios, with the main differences relating to what kind of data are considered the most relevant for the Gulf of Suez. Finally, we outline a two-phase model for the evolution of rifting of Arabia away from Africa since the Miocene on a more global scale.

Analysis of continental plate kinematics

The principal sources of quantitative information regarding plate kinematics are magnetic anomalies and long transform faults, or on a very different time-scale slip vectors of larger earthquakes. In the case of deformed continental lithosphere magnetic anomalies of oceanic type are of course absent. Similar anomalies can be identified in the early stages of rift propagation, as is the case in Afar (Courtillot *et al.* 1980), but in the very early stages of spreading the magnetic character of rifted margins remains continental (Courtillot 1980a, 1982; Cochran 1981) and the term Magnetic Quiet Zone (or MQZ) is generally used. Strong lineated anomalies associated with basic intrusions have sometimes been mistaken for true oceanic anomalies (see discussion in Cochran 1983).

The identification of the type of plate boundary or azimuth of relative plate motion is not straightforward either. In the case of distensive boundaries, full or half-grabens or depressions bounded by sets of normal faults provide a local indication of the principal strain and stress directions. This is not always identical to the instantaneous motion on a more global scale and these grabens cannot be simply identified as segments of oceanic ridges. In the case of slow-moving plates, the boundary is often not either a narrow or continuous border zone but rather a deforming belt with discontinuous features such as pull-apart basins or *en échelon* deeps or fissures. Missing plate-boundary segments are sometimes hastily interpolated with preconceived ideas as to the local kinematics. Unobserved transform faults have sometimes been added in this way to link *en échelon* fissures.

On the other hand, transcurrent faults of sufficient length, on the order of 50 km or more, act as displacement guides and provide strong constraints on the direction of relative motion. This is mechanically reasonable as soon as the length of the corresponding plate boundary is at least of a dimension comparable to the local thickness of the mechanical layer. The role of strike slip-faulting in collision environments has been emphasized by Tapponnier & Molnar (e.g. 1977) and Tapponnier *et al.* (1982). Although such faulting is of far smaller amplitude in extensional enviroments, it remains a major source of kinematic information. Sufficiently large and active strike-slip faults are often the most conspicuous features on satellite or air photographs for land geology and on detailed bathymetric charts at sea. The primary importance of these topographic data is sometimes underestimated. The determination of the amount of motion and the timing of the motion are difficult to estimate in continental material: the active controversy over the amount and timing of motion along the Dead Sea shear is an example (summarized later in this paper).

Data available for kinematic reconstructions around a continental triple junction include primarily the azimuth of structures of a size comparable to that of plate boundaries (in our case normal faults and particularly strike-slip faults) and the often less reliable estimates of timing of motion along them. At smaller scales, the study of more distributed local deformations constrains the *stress* field. Well-constrained fault-plane solutions of earthquakes also constrain the local fault kinematics. The more classical large-scale 'external' constraints provided by marine geophysics, mostly in close-by oceanic environments, provide valuable additional constraints and allow one to place the kinematic study on a more global scale.

External constraints for Sinai triple-junction kinematics

We can first use published estimates of the relative motion of Africa–Nubia (AFR–NUB) and Arabia (ARA) as derived from 'oceanic'-type data in the Red Sea. Chase (1978) proposed a solution based on three transform-fault azimuths, one earthquake slip vector and four estimates of spreading rates based on magnetic anomalies. The resulting motion at the triple junction (i.e. not far from the Tiran Straights), together with its error estimate, is shown in Fig. 3. It is close to the solution of McKenzie *et al.* (1970), which is a total-opening solution based on the fit of Red Sea coastlines. The McKenzie *et al.* pole involves two assumptions: first, that the motion remained uniform from the beginning of opening up to the present, second that the Red Sea is floored by oceanic lithosphere from coast to coast. However, clear oceanic anomalies are only found between 15 and 21°N (Roeser 1975), and there are convincing arguments that the

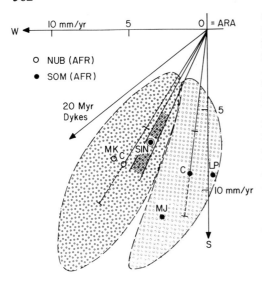

FIG. 3. Velocity data pertaining to the Sinai triple junction. Arabia (ARA) is taken as the origin. Estimates of Nubia (NUB)–Arabia motion by McKenzie *et al.* (1970: MK) and Chase (1978: C) are given by open circles. Estimates of Somalia (SOM)–Arabia motion by Chase (1978: C) and of Africa–Arabia motion by Le Pichon (1968: LP) and Minster & Jordan (1978: MJ) are given by solid circles. Error ovals (95%) are indicated for the Chase (1978) determinations. Sinai (SIN)–Arabia motion is shown as a shaded sector and is discussed in the text. 20 My DYKES is the direction normal to the main Gulf of Suez and Red Sea dykes.

rest of the Red Sea consists of stretched continental crust (Cochran 1983; Courtillot 1982; Courtillot & Vink 1983). In his review of the Red Sea, Cochran (1983) recognized three distinct zones: the deep axial trough with oceanic magnetic anomalies formed in the last 4–5 My (Roeser 1975; Le Pichon & Francheteau 1978; Courtillot 1982) lies between Afar and 21°N. The older outer part is regarded as stretched continental crust by Courtillot (1982) and Cochran (1983) and as oceanic crust by Girdler & Styles (1974), who invoke an older Oligo–Miocene phase of spreading. A transition zone, with a discontinuous axial trough, follows between 21 and 25°N. Further N, there is no axial trough, the main trough is irregular and faulted and Cochran (1983) showed that the lithosphere is everywhere continental, with potentially large amounts of stretching and diffuse deformation. Although recent seismic work in the N might indicate the presence of some older oceanic lithosphere (J. Makris, pers. comm. 1985), the bulk of evidence presently argues against this N of 21°N and shows oceanic material only in a narrow axial band S of it. Thus, the coastlines used in McKenzie *et al.*'s (1970) fit were

never in direct contact. Yet, they do exhibit remarkable similarity over more than two-thirds of their length (Fig. 2). Figure 2 also shows that over the same distance the edges of the Ethiopian and Arabian escarpments, as represented by the 1000 m contour (between 8 and 20°N, and 13 and 24°N respectively), would provide an equally good fit. These escarpments occur where swarms of normal faults resulting from the breakup of Arabia away from Africa have both highest density and largest amplitude. Should they be fitted together, they would play the same role as the 2000 m isobath at the edge of the continental slope, which is often used in continental fits for larger plates. This suggests that the two have the same mechanical interpretation, and implies that the present coastlines are only more or less antithetic normal faults, part of a wide belt of conjugate faults which run rather accurately parallel to the escarpments and breakup line. Note that the concept of fitting continental escarpments on both sides of the Red Sea, although not explicitly stated, is implicity present in McKenzie *et al.* (1970, fig. 3), Le Pichon & Francheteau (1978, fig. 1) and Cochran (1983, fig. 1), where either the 1000 m contour or the nearby boundary of Precambrian outcrops are outlined.

Thus, a mechanical basis is provided for the McKenzie *et al.* (1970) pole of total opening and its similarity with the Chase (1978) instantaneous pole is noted. The same agreement is found by Le Pichon & Francheteau (1978) who incorporate Roeser's (1975) magnetic anomalies and transform faults outlined by Bäcker *et al.* (1975). However, the proposed transforms have markedly small offsets and occur in a very rugged area: most authors would now agree that an accurate determination of their azimuth is not possible and that the original interpretation was heavily biased by the pre-existing pole of McKenzie *et al.* (J. Francheteau, pers. comm. 1984). The divergence or convergence of magnetic anomalies in the southern part of the Red Sea is not significant either, which means that the only reliable constraint on the relative motion of Africa (Nubia) and Arabia is the modulus of velocity near 15/20°N, perpendicular to the mean trend of the axial trough. Moreover, as discussed by Cochran (1983) and Courtillot (1982), the amount of stretching of the continental margins must be added to the amount of oceanic lithosphere in order to evaluate total opening. This becomes a particularly serious problem as one approaches the Afar deforming zone to the S (Courtillot 1982, and Fig. 2).

In view of the lack of strong constraints from the Red Sea, one may think of using better quality oceanic data from the well-developed Gulf of Aden (Courtillot *et al.* 1980; Cochran 1981; Courtillot

1982). This can be done only under the testable hypothesis that recent motion in the East African Rift system can be neglected. For instance, Minster & Jordan (1978) determined a pole for the relative motion of Arabia and Africa, in which Nubia and Somalia are assumed to form a single rigid plate. This pole is based on 13 reasonably reliable data from the Gulf of Aden and two less reliable spreading rates from the Red Sea: it predicts an azimuth of N14°E for the relative motion of these two plates at the Sinai triple junction (MJ in Fig. 3). Indeed Bernard Minster (pers. comm. 1977) did not believe that the relative motion of Somalia and Nubia could be resolved with data available at the time. Chase (1978) did separate the Nubia and Somalia plates and his solution for the Somalia–Arabia motion relied on 10 estimates of spreading rates and two azimuths of larger transform faults all within the Gulf of Aden. The corresponding motion computed at the triple junction has an azimuth of N7°E (C in Fig. 3). The 2σ error ellipse of the Chase solution contains both the Minster–Jordan and the original Le Pichon (1968) solution. The Le Pichon solution, which predicts an azimuth of N3°W at Tiran (LP in Fig. 3), was subsequently used by McKenzie *et al.* (1970) and Cochran (1981).

Inspection of Fig. 3 shows that the predicted Arabia–Nubia and Arabia–Somalia motions computed at Tiran are on the order of 10 mm yr^{-1} and that the confidence ellipses barely intersect each other.

Local constraints for Sinai triple junction kinematics

We can next try and see what bathymetric or geological information is available for each one of the three arms of the tentative Sinai triple junction.

Dead Sea Shear

This tectonic zone, also known as the Dead Sea rift—a rather improper term retained for historical reasons (Garfunkel 1981)—has been the topic of long-lasting reseach and of a number of symposia (Freund & Garfunkel 1981). The most recent meeting (Ben Avraham 1985b) still witnessed lively debate over the total *amount* of displacement along the shear. Some maintain that left-lateral slip was restricted to a few kilometres (Horowitz 1979; Mart & Horowitz 1981; Mart 1982; A. Horowitz, pers. comm. 1985). However, there appears to be an extensive body of evidence in favour of the ~105 km of total slip advocated by Quennell (1959) and Freund (1970): this includes offsets of Precambrian, Triassic and Jurassic rocks, identi-

fication of lower Turonian ammonites, offsets of Pliocene lava flows and alluvial fans, formation of pull-apart basins (i.e. Gulf of Elat, Dead Sea, part of the Lake Kinnereth, Hula Valley) and push-up compressional structures (i.e. Mt Hermon, Lebanon Mountains), displacement of the central Sinai–Negev versus Transjordan shear zones, and of the Negev versus Palmyra fold belts. The amount of opening of the Red Sea itself is another important, yet indirect argument. *Timing* of the motion is another subject of debate. Freund *et al.* (1968) propose that 45 km of motion post-date the Miocene. Garfunkel (1981) convincingly argues that 35–40 km displacement occurred in a 'young' Plio-Pleistocene phase, responsible for most of the opening of the Elat and Dead Sea pull-apart basins (or rhomb-grabens). This implies average slip rates from 7 to 9 mm yr^{-1}. The 'older' phase is well studied on the western margin of the Gulf of Elat by Eyal *et al.* (1981) who describe 24 km of left-lateral offsets in sets of 18–22 Ma basalt dykes (Bartov *et al.* 1980). These dykes intrude Mesozoic and older sediments along the Red Sea and Gulf of Suez margins over hundreds of kilometres and are generally believed to mark the initial stage of development of the Red Sea. Their azimuth is remarkably constant at N143°E (±2°) (Fig. 3). Eyal *et al.* (1981) suggest a similar amount of motion on the less-studied eastern margin of the Gulf of Elat. The remaining 60 km of motion can be taken up in the Gulf itself (Ben Avraham *et al.* 1979; Garfunkel 1981; Ben Avraham 1985a). Thus the entire 105 km of offset occurred since less than 20 Ma, yielding a minimum average slip rate of 5 mm yr^{-1}. Garfunkel & Bartov (1977) suggested that a drastic change in the tectonic regime occurred around 15 Ma in the Gult of Suez: following intensified tectonism and erosion, the fault pattern was rearranged and all mid-Miocene and younger sediments lie with strong unconformities on early Miocene and older rocks (Garfunkel & Bartov 1977). More recently, Michael Steckler (pers. comm. 1985) confirms that a major subsidence event occurred then. If this is taken to mark the onset of strike-slip motion on the Dead Sea shear, a minimum average slip rate of 7 mm yr^{-1} is arrived at. Much of the displacement is thought to post-date the Herod and Hazeva Formations within the rift (e.g. Steinitz *et al.* 1978; Garfunkel 1981) and the age determination of these formations is an important datum. Steinitz *et al.* (1978) and Gideon Steinitz (pers. comm. 1985) argue that the top of the Herod dates from ~5 Ma and that of the Hazeva from ~3 Ma. Depending on whether 40 km or the entire 105 km of offset are thought to have occurred since then, one finds a range from 8 to 30 mm yr^{-1}. Recent findings in the Zemah 1 borehole, S of Lake Kinnereth (Slager & Marcus 1985), would lend credence to the higher values (Gideon Steinitz, pers. comm. 1985). However, these high rates might be related to rather recent accelerations and episodic motion in the shear zone (e.g. Courtillot *et al.* 1984). The detailed analysis of Garfunkel (1981) and the age determinations (Steinitz *et al.* 1978) lead to our preferred estimate of present (Plio–Pleistocene) velocity of 9 ± 3 mm yr^{-1} (Fig. 3, shaded). Finally, the *azimuth* of motions (at the triple junction) must be determined. Garfunkel (1981) stresses that fitting of a circle to the general outline of the Dead Sea shear (as done partly for instance by Le Pichon & Francheteau 1978) provides an erroneous estimate of the slip direction which is best estimated from the strike-slip edges of pull-apart basins. A minor amount of transverse extension may lead to errors of 2° in the estimates of shear motion (Garfunkel 1981). The bathymetric scarps in the Gulf of Elat trend between 20 and 30°E in the S near Tiran (Ben Avraham *et al.* 1979; and Fig. 4). The eastern boundaries of the Elat, Aragonese and Dakar deeps, and the steep scarps extending from the East of Tiran deep to Hume deep and SW of the Sinai (Ben Avraham *et al.* 1979) have a remarkably clear morphology that is assigned to recent strike-slip motion on them. The offsets of the deeps and the general characteristics of motion farther N in the Arava and Dead Sea depressions (Garfunkel 1981) can only be compatible with the left-lateral sense of motion accepted by most authors for many decades. The observations of folding made by Mart (1982) in the Gulf of Elat may seem intriguing but his model does not stand against the bulk of evidence. Drag folding or local warping related to motion on the strike-slip faults and diapir-related tectonics could account for some of Mart's observations. Rotation poles determined by Garfunkel (1981) predict azimuths of 25 and 29°E (at the triple junction) for the older and younger phases respectively. This range between 25 and 30°E is taken to represent the azimuth of Sinai–Arabia motion at the triple junction (Fig. 3).

Northern Red Sea

Bathymetry is among the most revealing available data in the complex northern Red Sea (the area discussed here is located N of 26°N, Fig. 4). It is clear from the early charts that between 26° 30' and 27° 30'N, the central bathymetric axis of the Red Sea shifts from an axial (symmetrical) position to the W, to become more or less aligned with the Gulf of Suez (Laughton 1970; Coleman 1974). This is confirmed by more recent work (Mart & Hall 1984; Cochran *et al.* 1985) and the heat-flow maximum is found to follow the same trend (Hobart *et al.* 1985), an argument used to support the idea that the Gulf of Suez is not yet totally extinct. In his review of Red

Sea data, Cochran (1983) points out that there is no real axial trough N of 25°N, nor are there typical lineated magnetic anomalies. He demonstrates that magnetic and gravity anomalies are best understood if they result from the intrusion of igneous bodies in the basement. This and other data imply that the floor of the Red Sea is still of continental nature almost everywhere N of 26°N (at least). Seismic data show that the continental crust has suffered extensive deformation by block faulting. The more recent bathymetric data show that the northern Red Sea 'axis' actually consists of a series of N10–20°W trending *en échelon* deeps, which Mart & Hall (1984) describe as either symmetrical or asymmetrical active rifts. This is very clear in their fig. 3 (used to construct our Fig. 4), but is somewhat obscured in their complex structural interpretation (their fig. 9a). Even more recent surveys describe similar smaller size *en échelon* deeps (Martinez *et al.* 1985) that are interpreted as resulting from the emplacement of igneous intrusions, marking the transition from block faulting to intrusive extension. This is an example of a northward-propagating rift, as expressed ahead of that part which generates oceanic lithosphere (Courtillot 1982), in an area where spreading is not yet localized (see also McKenzie 1986). Thus presently available morphologic and geophysical data can only be used to demonstrate that separation between Arabia and Africa in the northern Red Sea results in distension with an E–W component. Neither the precise azimuth nor the modulus of

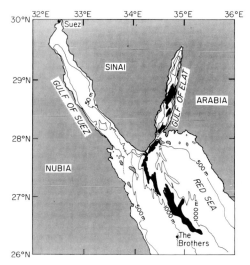

FIG. 4. A summary of bathymetry around the Sinai triple junction with data from Laughton (1970) for the Gulf of Suez, Ben Avraham *et al.* (1979) for the Gulf of Elat and Mart & Hall (1984) for the northern Red Sea. Deeps are shown in black.

present motion can be locally determined. In particular, there is as yet no evidence that strike-slip (transform) faults join the *en échelon* deeps. Note that if the N10–20°W trend of the deeps is used to infer N70–80°E extension, this would be at variance with the N30–40°E motion estimated from the McKenzie *et al.* (1970) or Chase (1978) poles (Fig. 3).

Gulf of Suez

The Gulf of Suez forms the offset northern termination of the Red Sea. This ~ 70-km-wide and 400-km-long structure was considered to be the tectonic boundary between Africa and a Sinai plate by McKenzie *et al.* (1970), who noted that the Dead Sea shear did not correspond to a small circle centred on their Red Sea opening pole. Le Pichon & Francheteau (1978) further discussed the existence of a Sinai sub-plate, although the plate boundary N of Suez was considered hypothetical. Indeed, there is no evidence that the Gulf of Suez structure continues in any simple way in the Eastern Mediterranean (Robson 1971; Tapponnier & Armijo 1985). The total amount of opening of the Gulf of Suez is a matter of debate, with Freund (1970) and Cochran (1981) arguing for 25–30 km, Garfunkel & Bartov (1977) for 15–20 km, and Robson (1971) proposing far-smaller values of order 10 km. A recent calculation based on subsidence considerations yields 25–27 km (Steckler 1985). Timing of this small motion is also a matter of debate. Garfunkel & Bartov (1977) observe that rifting is post-Eocene and was well under way at the beginning of the Miocene (24 Ma). Several authors provide convincing evidence that the Gulf of Suez formed the northern termination of the Red Sea prior to major shear along the Dead Sea rift (Mart & Hall 1984; Tamsett 1984; Steckler & Ten Brink 1985). Opening would have terminated around 15 Ma, when motion was transferred to the E. Considering the 20 Ma dykes discussed previously as an indicator of the beginning of rifting of the Red Sea–Gulf of Suez (Bartov *et al.* 1980) and accepting that the amount of opening in the southern Gulf of Suez is that recently confirmed by Steckler (1985), we find that the mean rate of opening of the Gulf, should it have been complete at the time of the 15 Ma subsidence event (Steckler, pers. comm. 1985), is of the order of 5 mm yr^{-1}. Considering the uncertainties involved, this is about the order of magnitude of 'spreading' at that time in the northern Red Sea. A shorter phase of rifting would imply slightly faster rates.

That there has been no motion between the Sinai and African Plates since the mid-Miocene appears to contradict the McKenzie *et al.* (1970) or Le Pichon & Francheteau (1978) kinematic analyses

(see Fig. 1). On the other hand, Steckler & Ten Brink (1985) and Cochran *et al.* (1985) point out that the offset of the central depression of the far-northern Red Sea towards the Gulf of Suez argues against its being extinct. Finally, further support for present tectonic activity along the Gulf of Suez–Cairo–Alexandria zone is given by the relatively high level of local seismicity, which is documented by a long historical record including several shocks of sizeable magnitude ($M \leqslant 7$) (Tapponnier & Armijo 1985).

Unfortunately, poorly constrained fault-plane solutions of earthquakes in this area lead to contradictory estimates of recent movement. Two local mechanisms for 1969.3.31, $M \approx 7$ earthquake located at the southern tip of the Gulf of Suez, appear to be the most reliable and barely contradict one another, the first favouring normal faulting on NW-trending faults (McKenzie *et al.* 1970), the second some amount of left-lateral motion (Ben Menahem & Aboodi 1971). Other significant earthquakes in the area (1955.9.12, $M = 6.7$, offshore Alexandria; 1972.6.28, $M \approx 5$, Shadwan; 1974.4.29, $M \approx 5$, Zagazig) may indicate left-lateral motion on NNW-trending faults (McKenzie 1972; Ben Menaham *et al.* 1976; Fairhead & Stuart 1982). Garfunkel & Bartov (1977) and Chenet *et al.* (1985) find only limited evidence for left-lateral strike-slip motion along N–S-trending faults. In contrast, Tapponnier & Armijo (1985) argue for some amount of right-lateral strike-slip, based on the study of Landsat images, supplemented by limited fieldwork which indicates recent and probably still active E–W striking thrusts and folds in the Suez–Cairo–Alexandria area. Moreover, the interpretation of Landsat images shows that the most recent normal faults strike N–S, mainly along the eastern coast of the Gulf. Important inconsistencies contained in fault-plane solutions for the three earthquakes above and/or a different set of observations led Maamoun (1976) and Maamoun *et al.* (1980) to alternative possible solutions implying a N–S orientated P axis and right-lateral movement along the NW-trending faults of the Suez–Cairo–Alexandria zone, in good agreement with field and Landsat observations (Tapponnier & Armijo 1985). The same sense of motion was arrived at from more global kinematic considerations by Le Pichon & Francheteau (1978).

Kinematic models of the Sinai triple junction

From the discussion of the two previous sections, we find that data quality pertaining to the kinematics of the African (Nubia), Arabian and Sinai Plates and of their triple junction is very uneven.

Determination of NUB–ARA motion rests on a large-scale analysis of oceanic data of doubtful quality and on the fit of coastlines which may be valid, although the structural analysis and interpretation are totally at variance with the original work (McKenzie *et al.* 1970; see Figs 2 & 3). The ARA–SIN motion is reasonably well determined from an analysis of local morphology, because the boundary is primarily a strike-slip one (Figs 3 & 4). On the other hand, there are almost no clear and direct data from the Gulf of Suez, nor are there global data and we find conflicting interpretations depending on whether seismic or structural data are considered. A good indirect constraint could come from the well-determined motion of Africa (Somalia) with respect to Arabia through the Gulf of Aden (Fig. 3), if motion across the East African Rift system could be either neglected or estimated with confidence. We discuss here various kinematic scenarios that are compatible with part of the data and which demonstrate clearly where additional data are required.

Model A

If we give maximum weight to the McKenzie *et al.* (or almost equivalently Chase) determination of NUB–ARA motion and to the ARA–SIN motion discussed in this paper, we find that the acceptable domain (in velocity space) of the latter lies entirely within the confidence oval of the other (Fig. 3). This would imply that there may be no motion at present between SIN and NUB and that the Gulf of Suez is extinct (Fig. 5a). This would agree with the analyses of Mart & Hall (1984) and Steckler & Ten Brink (1985). This is clearly acceptable to first order since all evidence points to the minor deformation and weak recent activity in the Gulf of Suez. Thus, there would presently be only two plates in relative motion and no triple junction. The apparent triple junction would result from the morphologic superposition of two plate boundaries with a common segment and two distinct kinematic phases. This is very close to the analysis of the Afar 'triple junction' made by Courtillot (1982) and Courtillot & Vink (1983) and is discussed further in the last section. The Gulf of Suez and East African Rift system would both be failed rifts with minor amounts of total displacement. However, the error domains of Fig. 3 leave space for non-zero NUB–SIN motion that is discussed in the following models.

Model B

A further solution is to assume that slow opening motion continues in the Gulf of Suez in the original opening direction and thus in a direction essentially identical to the ARA–SIN and ARA–NUB azimuths. This would result in a flat velocity triangle (Fig. 5b), with a SIN–NUB opening unlikely to exceed 1 mm yr^{-1}. However, there are no field data that support this model.

Model C

If one gives stronger weight to the fault-plane solutions summarized by Fairhead & Stuart (1982), the velocity triangle of Fig. 5c can be constructed, with almost pure left-lateral motion along the trend of the Gulf of Suez. We have already pointed out that for some focal solutions there are conflicting interpretations. Also, it is not clear whether the earthquake cluster at the southernmost end of the Gulf is relevant to AFR(NUB)–SIN tectonics alone. Because the fault-plane solutions may be interpreted in terms of reactivation of pre-existing faults, they are also compatible with NUB–SIN motion intermediate between models B and C, corresponding to NNW to NNE extension in the Gulf of Suez. Finally, model C would imply present EW compression along the dextrally offset parts of the Gulf of Suez and would require errors on the McKenzie *et al.* kinematic determination to be the worst possible at the 95% level (see Fig. 3). In any case, the corresponding AFR(NUB)–SIN motion is most unlikely to exceed 1 mm yr^{-1}.

On the other hand, if one does not place confidence in the McKenzie *et al.* determination of NUB–ARA motion, an alternative method would be to use the far-better-determined AFR (SOM)–ARA motion under the assumption of negligible NUB–SOM recent motion across the East African Rift. This would lead to the dashed velocity triangle of Fig. 5c, where the sense of AFR (NUB)–SIN motion is compatible with the seismic data used for model C. The rate of strike-slip along the Gulf of Suez would, however, have to be 3–4 mm yr^{-1}, implying for instance 15–20 km total motion in the Plio–Pleistocene, coeval with the young phase of motion along the Dead Sea rift (Garfunkel 1981). This cannot be reconciled with available field evidence. Interestingly, this implies that joint consideration of Gulf of Suez and Gulf of Aden data requires resolvable NUB–SOM motion across the East African rift system.

Model D

We can next place more emphasis on the analysis of Landsat images, recent or active tectonics and some (conflicting) fault-plane solutions discussed by Tapponnier & Armijo (1985). Although constraints on the azimuth of horizontal displacements are not as accurate as in the more active Gulf of Elat, directions of inferred right-lateral strike-slip fault segments have values around N30–50°W (Figs 4 & 5d). The modulus, determined from the

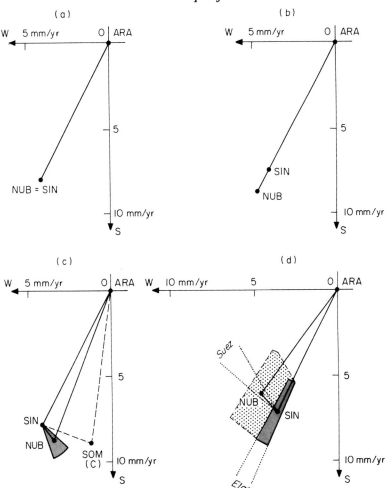

FIG. 5. Various models of Arabia (ARA)–Nubia (NUB)–Sinai (SIN) kinematics. (a) Model A assuming that the Gulf of Suez is extinct. (b) Model B assuming that the Gulf of Suez still opens in its original direction. (c) Model C (continuous lines) assuming left-lateral motion in the Gulf of Suez following the seismic data of Fairhead & Stuart (1982) and an alternative model (dashed lines) assuming that Somalia (SOM) provides a good estimate of Nubia motion (see text for discussion). (d) Model D following the interpretation of Tapponnier & Armijo (1985) that present motion in the Gulf of Suez is right-lateral. Shaded area is error estimate of SIN–ARA motion from Fig. 3, and dotted area is propagated-error estimate of NUB–ARA motion, once error of NUB–SIN motion has been taken into account.

construction of the velocity triangle, is of order 1 mm yr^{-1}. This is essentially the solution proposed on large-scale kinematic considerations by Le Pichon & Francheteau (1978). During the time of the young (Plio–Pleistocene) phase on the Dead Sea shear, ~5 km of strike-slip motion is implied in the Gulf of Suez, which may have contributed to the shape of the Gulf, suggestive of dextrally offset pull-apart basins. However, total motion (Figs 4 & 6) and subsidence would have been far smaller than along the Gulf of Elat, with a

rate of motion 10 times larger (Fig. 5d). The values discussed here are somewhat smaller than those of Tapponnier & Armijo (1985). As noted by these authors, a low rate is compatible with limited evidence on the recurrence of $M \approx 7$ earthquakes in Egypt in the last 4000 years and with the fact that tectonic features in the Gulf are smoothed by sediment deposition.

Models D and A are our preferred ones, although model C might be reconsidered if new focal-plane solutions (or a better reanalysis of old ones) become available. Both models can be partly merged, if the shifting of activity from the Gulf of Suez to the Dead Sea were progressive or even episodic (see for instance Courtillot *et al.* 1984). The problem is then, to determine the typical duration of such episodes. Figure 6 shows our combined morphologic and kinematic interpretation in the case of model D, which interestingly enough shows the *en échelon* deeps of the northern Red Sea extending northwards into the *en échelon* pull-apart depressions of the Gulf of Elat and the far more diffuse possible pull-aparts of the Gulf of Suez. If this model holds, it indicates that around the triple junction all tectonic features on the three plate boundaries (more localized zones of deformation) are compatible with an approximately E–W principal extensive strain. It might be useful to incorporate this kind of analysis of local strain directions in analyses of triple junctions (e.g. Patriat & Courtillot 1984) to see whether triple junctions 'avoid' kinematic solutions that would imply singularities in the strain trajectories. Figure 6 includes an attempt to locate the geographical position of the triple junction, an

attempt which may have limited meaning and chances of success in a continental environment (as opposed to an oceanic one). Following the bathymetric chart of Mart & Hall (1984), the junction may lie near 27° 30′N and 34° to 34° 15′E. The Sinai–Arabia boundary close to the junction is clearly of strike-slip nature, the Arabia–Africa boundary would appear to correspond to one of the N–S-trending deeps and the Sinai–Africa boundary is far less clear, possibly of strike-slip nature if one follows Tapponnier & Armijo (1985). Ongoing work in the area is likely to shed much light on this, as detailed Seabeam maps of the junction will become available. In our model D, the junction would thus be of stable RFF type (McKenzie & Morgan 1969) and would be fixed with respect to the Sinai Plate. The junction is represented in combined geographical–velocity space in Fig. 7 according to the representation of Patriat & Courtillot (1984). Hasty (and in our opinion erroneous) interpretation of the northern Red Sea deeps as a classical mid-ocean spreading centre would seem to imply highly oblique (145°) and asymmetrical (8–2 mm yr^{-1}) spreading, with the spreading rift tip receding at 2–3 mm yr^{-1} from the triple junction. This discussion can only become really useful when the Red Sea will have become a site of oceanic spreading. Note in closing that the area of the velocity triangle, which is proportional to the amount of crust generated in direct relation to the occurrence of the triple junction, is negative (plate circuit and velocity circuit are described in opposing senses), a rather unique case when compared to other (oceanic) triple junctions with only ridge and fault boundaries (Patriat & Courtillot 1984).

A two-phase history of Arabia–Africa rifting

The previous section outlines the present kinematics of the Sinai triple junction. Actually, we have seen that some kinematic data pertain to instantaneous or at least recent motions (such as the pull-apart basins in the Gulf of Elat) whereas others pertain to longer term, finite, and sometimes total motions (such as the fit of Red Sea coastlines). Literature on the subject has always encountered this problem of instantaneous versus finite motions (e.g. Le Pichon & Francheteau 1978; Cochran 1983). In the absence of evidence to the contrary, one is often led to assume that instantaneous and average finite motions are the same: such is for instance the case for the Red Sea. Girdler & Styles (1974) interpreted magnetic and other geophysical data in the Red Sea in terms of two distinct phases of sea-floor spreading, a recent one from about 5 Ma on, and an

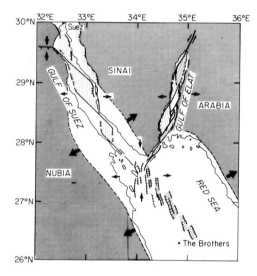

FIG. 6. Structural interpretation of the area mapped in Fig. 4 according to kinematic model D. Strike-slip and normal faults are indicated by heavier lines (with tick marks for normal faults). Light (respectively heavier) stippling indicates areas of moderate (respectively more intense) stretching and subsidence. Small arrows indicate approximate principal strain directions and thin half arrows indicate the sense of motion on strike-slip faults. White areas and large arrows indicate the overall stretched region and the general direction of Africa–Arabia separation respectively (i.e. the first stage of opening in the Gulf of Suez).

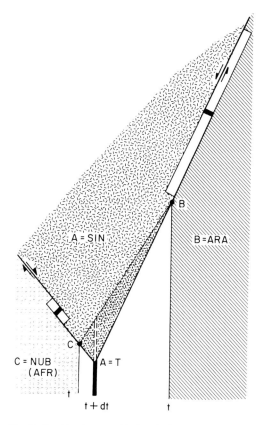

FIG. 7. Combined geographical–velocity space representation of Sinai triple-junction kinematics according to model D, using the representation of Patriat & Courtillot (1984). Possible plate boundaries are shown as thick lines (thicker lines for spreading centres than for transform faults). White areas indicate the amount of new crust generated between times t and $t + dt$. The velocity triangle is that of Fig. 5d.

older one between 30 and 15 Ma, separated by a period of quiescence. This contradicts evidence from the Dead Sea shear that ~ 60 km of motion occurred between ~ 15 and 5 Ma (Garfunkel 1981). It has been criticized by Courtillot (1980, 1982) and Cochran (1981); there are indeed two different types of crust in the Red Sea but they do not necessarily correspond to distinct tectonic phases (Fig. 1). Oceanic lithosphere has been emplaced near 17–18°N about 5 Ma and subsequently two rifts propagated away from this. One has propagated southward at ~ 2–4 cm yr^{-1} and is now located around 15°N. Girdler & Styles (1974) and Styles & Hall (1980) believe that the older lithosphere is already oceanic, but Cochran (1983) shows that it must have propagated through stretched continental crust. Another rift propagated

northward at ~ 10 cm yr^{-1}. The propagation rate and present locations of the rift tip cannot be accurately defined with available data. The rift tip must now lie N of 19°N, possibly around 21°N close to the boundary of the central Red Sea, i.e. the region where the axial trough becomes discontinuous. The rest of the Red Sea is underlain by stretched continental crust, the amount of stretching varying along the Red Sea as a function of distance from the rotation pole and amount of strain relieved by emplacement of oceanic lithosphere (Courtillot 1982; Cochran 1983). The situation is different for other plate boundaries. For instance, we have argued here (following Garfunkel 1981) that there was no displacement along the Dead Sea shear prior to ~ 15 Ma. Yet, on the edges of the Red Sea, the onset of volcanism might be as old as ~ 30 Ma (references in Styles & Hall 1980; Cochran 1983). The best evidence regarding the start of relatively intense deformation is the set of parallel elongated early-Miocene basaltic dykes (e.g. Steinitz *et al.* 1978; Bartov *et al.* 1980; Eyal *et al.* 1981) dated at 18–22 Ma. The interpretation of Garfunkel (1981), Mart & Hall (1984) and Steckler & Ten Brink (1985), which we share, is that the pre ~ 15 Ma activity of the Red Sea includes the development and propagation of the Gulf of Suez. Garfunkel & Bartov (1977) believe that rifting was well underway in the Gulf of Suez in the late Oligocene to early Miocene (20–30 Ma). Further data on this question are clearly desirable. Whether there are really two distinct phases (in the Red Sea), or a single phase which shifts continuously or episodically from one set of boundaries to the other, is not yet resolvable and is an important question related to the mechanical properties of rifting in continental versus oceanic environments (cf. Courtillot *et al.* 1984; Patriat & Courtillot 1984). In any case, there still is a certain amount of activity in the Gulf of Suez, which may correspond to continued (minor) activity or reactivation of an old plate boundary. In either case, the Chasles (vector addition) theorem will apply to the rigid plates separated by deforming zones and the above kinematic (velocity triangle) analysis holds.

A similar situation occurs at the southern end of the Red Sea (Fig. 1). Contradicting an earlier interpretation of Girdler & Styles (1978), Courtillot (1980, 1982) and Cochran (1981) showed that the emplacement of oceanic crust started ~ 10 Ma in the Gulf of Aden to the E of 45°E and propagated westward at 3 cm yr^{-1}, the rift tip being presently located close to 42–43°E. Recent Seabeam data and dives (Cyaden 1986) provide detailed data on the tip morphology and associated *en échelon* deeps, very similar to those found for the early development of the eastern Gulf of Aden (Tamsett 1984) or northern Red Sea (Mart & Hall 1984). Faulting and stretching responsible for the formation of the proto-Gulf of Aden may have started at ~20–25 Ma, which would correspond to dyke injection on the Red Sea margins (Cochran 1981; Stein & Cochran 1985, and references therein). On the other hand, there appears to be some evidence for an older history of faulting and extension in the East African rift system, beginning as early as 40–48 Ma (Baker *et al.* 1972; Davidson & Rex 1980). As is the case for the Gulf of Suez, the East African Rift might have been more active in the older part of its history, and have been reactivated, however mildly, more recently.

This leads us to what appears to be a two-phase history of the separation of Arabia away from the bulk of the African Plate (Figs 1 & 8). Continental rifting would have started in the late Eocene in East Africa and propagated northward through the Red Sea, extending into the Gulf of Suez in the late Oligocene and early Miocene (Fig. 8a). This initial phase is not easy to date and requires further geological work, particularly structural and geochronological study along the entire system. Total separation by 20 Ma may not have been more than a few tens of kilometres. This is important from a geological and thermal point of view but not resolvable by classical plate-kinematic standards. Transient aspects, such as rift propagation, are particularly difficult to document prior to the emplacement of oceanic lithosphere. It seems that at about 20 Ma, stretching in the Gulf of Aden began to prevail over that in the East African Rift, with marked dominance after 15–10 Ma. At about the same time, tectonic activity was transferred from the Gulf of Suez to the Dead Sea shear (Fig. 8b). Three propagating rift tips presently mark the bounds of oceanic lithosphere emplaced after 10 Ma in the Gulf on Aden and 5 Ma in the Red Sea. These ages indicate when and where stretching had reached a level requiring the formation of a true spreading centre. From a global point of view, this stretching is distributed in the Afar area and N of 20°N in the Red Sea and localized elsewhere (Courtillot 1982; McKenzie 1986). At 5 Ma, distributed stretching occurred everywhere along the deforming boundary W and N of 45°E in the Gulf of Aden and was localized only to the E of this point. Yet the total amount of stretching can always be described as a rigid-body rotation between these parts of the African and Arabian Plates that are outside the deforming boundary zone (Courtillot 1982). Minor (?) motion may still occur on the reactivated (?) Gulf of Suez and East African Rift.

The foregoing analysis stresses the fact that, although the Sinai and Afar triple junctions can always be treated kinematically as such, present motion on one plate boundary appears to be an order of magnitude smaller than on the two other plate

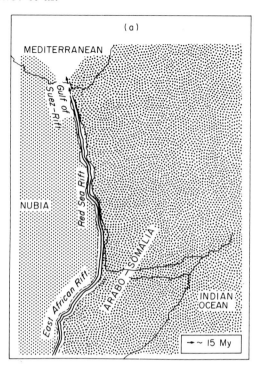

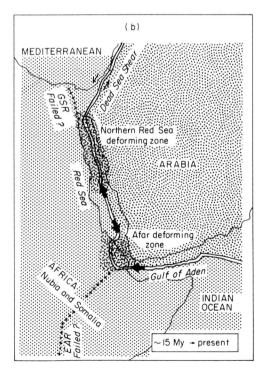

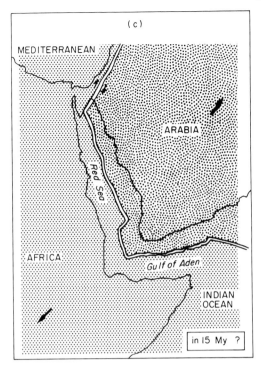

FIG. 8. Two-stage separation model of Arabia away from Africa. (a) Early continental rifting (from about 40 ? to about 15 Ma) along the East African/Red Sea/Gulf of Suez boundary. Northward propagation of rifting is suggested and early deformation in the Gulf of Aden may start towards the end of this period.
(b) Recent continental rifting and oceanic spreading (from about 15 Ma to the present) along the Gulf of Aden/Red Sea/Dead Sea shear boundary. Three propagating rifts, two deforming zones (Afar and northern Red Sea, shaded) and the failing East African Rift and Gulf of Suez are shown. (c) Possible future configuration after total rupture of the deforming zones and extinction of the East African Rift and Gulf of Suez.

boundaries. These triple junctions are better viewed as knees (or kinks) in a single plate boundary which happen to result from the superposition of two successive phases. The old East African Rift/Red Sea/Gulf of Suez boundary has been replaced by a new Gulf of Aden/Red Sea/Dead Sea boundary, with the Red Sea alone recording the entire history of separation. The meaning of the word 'phase' is a slight simplification, as motion may have been time- and space-transgressive. If present motion continues (Fig. 8c), the southern Red Sea and western Gulf of Aden rift tips will eventually meet each other, with deformation becoming everywhere localized in the Afar deforming zone. Similarly, the northern Red Sea rift will propagate to the tip of Sinai and the Dead Sea shear may evolve into a full-

scale continental transform fault. It is not clear whether propagation of deformation of the Suez–Alexandria zone will continue to the N slowly for some time (Tapponnier & Armijo 1985), although this is unlikely to happen extensively for reasons outlined below. Key data required to advance the kinematic analyses presented here concern the semi-quiescent NUB–SOM and SIN–NUB motions.

The remaining question is why deformation has been localized where it is now observed and why has it shifted with time. Development of the East African Rift and of the Dead Sea shear within the continent, close and quasi-parallel to the nearby continent–ocean transition, can be accounted for by comparing the total strength of the two kinds of lithosphere, as performed by Vink *et al.* (1984) following Brace & Kohlstedt (1980) (see also Steckler & Ten Brink 1985). Localization of future plate boundaries is certainly influenced by pre-existing heterogeneities in the continental lithosphere. Such heterogeneities may be responsible for the precise emplacement of the Afar and S Sinai kinks or deformation zones. Morgan (1983) has pointed out the long-lasting thermal effects of pre-existing hot-spot tracks that weaken the continental lithosphere; Morgan's reconstruction shows the trace of the Comoros hot-spot, formed between 180 and 120 Ma, coinciding with the future Gulf of Aden and the trace of the Jebel Marra hot-spot (90–60 Ma) with the Dead Sea shear. Once the East African Rift had developed and started propagating northward, the Red Sea may have been the shortest route to the Mediterranean and to the Alpine subduction zones. Steckler & Ten Brink (1985) propose that the old hinge zone of the Mediterranean continental margin of Africa formed a mechanical barrier to northward propagation. This would have led to (partial) extinction of the Gulf of Suez and to initiation of the Dead Sea shear according to the Vink *et al.* (1984) mechanism. On the other hand, the Gulf of Aden may have superseded the old East African Rift because it formed the shortest route from the western termination of the Central Indian ridge to the Red Sea, by then developed. Cochran (1981) has suggested that the Gulf of Aden formed in response to the renewed northward motion of India in the Oligocene, because Arabia and India would have become locked together across the Owen fracture zone, following the initial collision of India and Eurasia. Recent magnetic data from the Indian Ocean (Patriat *et al.* 1982; Patriat & Achache 1984) seem to document a change in spreading direction occurring at ~40 Ma and completed by ~30 Ma in relation to the Indo–Eurasian collision and first phase of extrusion of Indochina (Tapponnier *et al.* 1985). Wiens *et al.* (1985) argue from recent earthquake and magnetic data in the Indian Ocean that India and Arabia are now locked together, and that the resulting Indo–Arabian Plate converges at ~ 1 cm yr^{-1} towards the Australian Plate across a diffuse boundary near the equator. Courtillot & Besse (1986) show that a major reorganization of plate boundaries occurred at ~ 20 Ma throughout S Eurasia. The end of spreading in the S China Sea, of extrusion of Indochina, the rise of the Tibetan Plateau and the coupling of India with Arabia can all be related to the end of the first phase of India–Eurasia collision. In that way rift propagation from the Arabian Sea to the Dead Sea, through the Gulf of Aden and Red Sea, is a further consequence of the collision.

AKNOWLEDGMENTS: Parts of this paper were presented at the Durham meeting on Continental Extensional Tectonics and at the Gordon Conference on Sedimentary Basins along the Dead Sea and other Rift Zones in Israel, both in April 1985. Invitations to attend extended to V.C. by John Dewey on one hand and Zvi Ben Avraham on the other hand, and discussions with and help from Lois and Gary Karner are gratefully acknowledged. Discussions with participants of both meetings and with M. Steckler were very useful. Helpful comments were made by an anonymous referee. IPGP Contribution NS 879.

References

BÄCKER, H., LANGE, K. & RICHTER, H. 1975. Morphology of the Red Sea Central Graben. *Geol. Jahrb.* **D13**, 79–123.

BAKER, B.H., MOHR, P.A. & WILLIAMS, L.A. 1972. Geology of the Eastern Rift System of Africa. *Geol. Soc. Am. Spec. Pap.* **136**, 67.

BARTOV, Y., STEINITZ, G., EYAL, M. & EYAL, Y. 1980. Sinistral movement along the gulf of Aqaba—its age and relation to the opening of the Red Sea. *Nature*, **285**, 220–1.

BEN AVRAHAM, Z. 1985a. Structural framework of the Gulf of Elat (Aqaba), Northern Red Sea. *J. geophys. Res.* **90**, 703–26.

—— (ed.) 1985b. *International workshop on sedimentary basins along the Dead Sea rift and other rift zones (abstracts)*, International annual Gordon workshop, 45 pp. Tel Aviv University.

——, GARFUNKEL, Z., ALMAGOR, G. & HALL, J.K. 1979. Continental breakup by a leaky transform: The Gulf of Elat (Aqaba). *Science*, **206**, 214–16.

BEN MENAHEM, A. & ABOODI, E. 1971. Tectonic patterns in the northern Red Sea region. *J. geophys. Res.* **76**, 2674–89.

——, NUR, A. & VERED, M. 1976. Tectonics, seismicity and structure of the Afro–Eurasian junction – the breaking of an incoherent plate. *Phys. Earth planet. Inter.* **12**, 1–50.

BRACE, W.F. & KOHLSTEDT, D.L. 1980. Limits on lithospheric stress imposed by laboratory experiments. *J. geophys. Res.* **85**, 6248–52.

CHASE, C.G. 1978. Plate kinematics: the Americas, East Africa, and the Rest of the World. *Earth planet. Sci. Lett.* **37**, 355–68.

CHENET, P.Y., COLLETTA, B., LETOUZEY, J., DESFORGES, G., OUSSET, E. & ZAGHLOUL, E.A. This volume. Structures associated with extensional tectonics in the Suez rift.

COCHRAN, J.R. 1981. The Gulf of Aden: Structure and evolution of a young ocean basin and continental margin. *J. geophys. Res.* **86**, 263–88.

——, 1983. A model for the development of the Red Sea. *Am. Assoc. Pet. Geol.* **67**, 41–69.

——, MARTINEZ, F., STECKLER, M. & HOBART, M. 1985. The northern Red Sea I: Pre-seafloor spreading tectonics. *Eos.* **66**, 365.

COLEMAN, R.G. 1974. Geological background of the Red Sea. *Init. Reps. D.S.D.P.*, **23**, 813–20.

COURTILLOT, V. 1980a. Opening of the Gulf of Aden and Afar by progressive tearing. *Phys. Earth planet. Inter.* **21**, 343–50.

—— 1980b. Plaques, microplaques et déchirures lithosphériques: une hiérarchie de structures tectoniques de l'échelle du globe à celle du terrain. *Bull. Soc. géol. France*, **22**, 981–4.

—— 1982. Propagating rifts and continental breakup. *Tectonics*, **1**, 239–50.

—— & BESSE, J. 1986. Paleogeographic evolution of the Tethys and Indian Ocean bordering continents since the breakup of Gondwanaland. *Eos.* **67**, 845.

—— & VINK, G. 1983. How continents break up. *Sci. Am.* **249**, 42–9.

——, GALDEANO, A. & LE MOUËL, J.L. 1980. Propagation of an accreting plate boundary: a discussion of new aeromagnetic data in the Gulf of Tadjurah and Southern Afar. *Earth planet. Sci. Lett.* **47**, 144–60.

——, ACHACHE, J., LANDRE, F., BONHOMMET, N., GALIBERT, P.Y., MONTIGNY, R. & FÉRAUD, G. 1984. Episodic Spreading and Rift Propagation: new paleomagnetic and geochronologic data from the Afar passive Margin. *J. geophys. Res.* **89**, 3315–33.

CYADEN SCIENTIFIC TEAM. 1986. Tectonics of the Westernmost gulfs of Aden and Tadjourah from submersible observations. *Nature*, **319**, 396–9.

DAVIDSON, A. & REX, D.C. 1980. Age of volcanism and rifting in southwestern Ethiopia. *Nature*, **283**, 657–8.

EYAL, M., EYAL, Y., BARTOV, Y. & STEINITZ, G. 1981. The tectonic development of the western margin of the Gulf of Elat (Aqaba) rift. *Tectonophysics*, **80**, 39–66.

FAIRHEAD, J.D. & STUART, G.W. 1982. The seismicity of the East African rift system and comparison with other continental rifts. *In*: PALMASON, G. (ed.) *Continental and Oceanic Rifts*, pp. 41–61. Am. geophys. Union.

FREUND, R. 1970. Plate tectonics of the Red Sea and East Africa. *Nature*, **228**, 453.

—— & GARFUNKEL, Z. 1981. The Dead Sea Rift. *Tectonophysics*, **80**, 1–303 (special issue).

——, ZAK, I. & GARFUNKEL, Z. 1968. Age and rate of sinistral movement along the Dead Sea rift. *Nature*, **220**, 253–5.

GARFUNKEL, Z. 1981. Internal structure of the Dead Sea leaky transform (rift) in relation to plate kinematics. *Tectonophysics*, **80**, 81–108.

—— & BARTOV, Y. 1977. The tectonics of the Suez rift. *Bull. geol. Surv. Isr.* **71**, 1–44.

GIRDLER, R.W. & STYLES, P. 1974. Two-stage Red Sea floor spreading. *Nature*, **247**, 1–11.

—— & —— 1978. Seafloor spreading in the western Gulf of Aden. *Nature*, **271**, 615–7.

HOBART, M., COCHRAN, J., MARTINEZ, F. & STECKLER, M. 1985. The northern Red Sea III: Heat flow and thermal state of the lithosphere, (abstract). *Eos* **66**, 365.

HOROWITZ, A. 1979. *The Quaternary of Israel*, 365 pp. Academic Press, New York.

LAUGHTON, A.S. 1970. Bathymetric chart of the Red Sea, in Red Sea Discussion. *Phil. Trans. R. Soc. London*, **A267**,

——, WHITMARSH, R.B. & JONES, M.T. 1970. The evolution of the Gulf of Aden. *Phil. Trans. R. Soc. London*, **A267**, 227–66.

LE PICHON, X. 1968. Sea-floor spreading and continental drift. *J. geophys. Res.* **73**, 3661–97.

—— & FRANCHETEAU, J. 1978. A plate-tectonic analysis of the Red Sea–Gulf of Aden area. *Tectonophysics*, **46**, 369–406.

MCKENZIE, D.P. 1972. Active tectonics of the Mediterranean region. *Geophys. J.R. astron. Soc.* **30**, 109–85.

—— 1986. The geometry of propagating rifts. *Earth planet. Sci. Lett.* **77**, 176–86.

—— & MORGAN, W.J. 1969. Evolution of triple junctions. *Nature*, **224**, 125–33.

——, DAVIES, D. & MOLNAR, P. 1970. Plate tectonics of the Red Sea and East Africa. *Nature*, **266**, 243–48.

MAAMOUN, M. 1976. La séismicité du moyen et du proche-orient dans le cadre de la séismotectonique mondiale. Unpubl. Thesis, Univ. Louis Pasteur, Strasbourg.

——, ALLAM, A., MEGAHED, A. & EL ATA, A. 1980. Neotectonics and seismic regionalization of Egypt. *Bull. Int. Inst. Seis. Erthqk. Eng. (Cairo)*, **18**, 27–39.

MART, Y. 1982. Incipient spreading center in the Gulf of Elat, northern Red Sea. *Earth planet. Sci. Lett.* **60**, 117–26.

—— & HALL, J.K., 1984. Structural Trends in the Northern Red Sea. *J. geophys. Res.* **89**, 11352–64.

—— & HOROWITZ, A. 1981. The tectonics of the Timma region in southern Israel and the evolution of the Dead Sea rift. *Tectonophysics*, **79**, 166–99.

MARTINEZ, F., COCHRAN, J., HOBART, M. & STECKLER, M. 1985. The Northern Red Sea II: New deeps and the mechanism of extension, (abstract). *Eos*. **66**, 365.

MINSTER, J.B. & JORDAN, T.H. 1978. Present-day plate motions. *J. geophys. Res.* **83**, 5331–54.

MORGAN, W.J. 1983. Hotspots tracks and the early rifting of the Atlantic. *Tectonophysics*, **94**, 123–39.

PATRIAT, P. & ACHACHE, J. 1984. India–Eurasia collision chronology has implications for crustal shortening and driving mechanism of plates, *Nature*, **311**, 615–21.

—— & COURTILLOT, V. 1984. On the stability of triple Junctions and its Relation to Episodicity in Spreading. *Tectonics*, **3**, 317–32.

—— et al. 1982. Les mouvements relatifs de l'Inde, de l'Afrique et de l'Eurasie. *Bull. Soc. géol. France*, **24**, 363–73.

QUENNELL, A.M. 1959. Tectonics of the Dead Sea rift. *Int. Geol. Cong.* **20**, 384–405.

ROBSON, D.A. 1971. The structure of the Gulf of Suez rift. *Q.J. geol. Soc. London*, **127**, 247–76.

ROESER, H.A. 1975. A detailed magnetic survey of the southern Red Sea. *Geol. Jahrb. Hannover*, **D13**, 131–53.

SLAGER, J. & MARCUS, E. 1985. Neogene–Quaternary stratigraphy and geological history of the Zemah 1 area, abstract. *In:* BEN AVRAHAM, Z. (ed.) *International workshop on sedimentary basins along the Dead Sea rift and other rift zones. (abstracts). International annual Gorden workshop*, 45 pp. Tel Aviv University.

STECKLER, M. 1985. Uplift and extension at the gulf of Suez – Indications of induced mantle convection. *Nature*, **317**, 135–9.

—— & TEN BRINK, U. 1985. Replacement of the gulf of Suez rift by the Dead Sea transform: the role of old hinge zones in rifting. *Eos*. **66**, 364.

STEIN, C.A. & COCHRAN, J.R. 1985. The transition between the Sheba Ridge and Owen Basin: rifting of old oceanic lithosphere. *Geophys. J. R. astron. Soc.* **81**, 47–74.

STEINITZ, G., BARTOV, Y. & HUNZIKER, J.C. 1978. K–Ar age determinations of some Miocene–Pliocene basalts in Israel: their significance to the tectonics of the rift Valley. *Geol. Mag.* **115**, 329–40.

STYLES, P. & HALL, S.A. 1980. A comparison of the seafloor spreading histories of the western Gulf of Aden and the Central Red Sea. *Accad. Naz. Lincei*, **47**, 585–606.

TAMSETT, D. 1984. Comments on the development of rifts and transform faults during continental breakup: examples from the gulf of Aden and northern Red Sea. *Tectonophysics*, **104**, 35–46.

TAPPONNIER, P. & ARMIJO, R. 1985. Seismotectonics of Northern Egypt. *Terra Cognita*, **5**, 171.

—— & MOLNAR, P. 1977. Active faulting and Cenozoic tectonics of China. *J. geophys. Res.* **82**, 2905–30.

——, PELZER, G., LE DAIN, A.Y., ARMIJO, R. & COBBOLD, P. 1982. Propagating Extrusion Tectonics in Asia, new Insights from simple Experiments with Plasticine. *Geology*, **10**, 611–16.

VINK, G., MORGAN, W.J. & WU-LING ZHAO, 1984. Preferential rifting of continents: a source of displaced terranes. *J. geophys. Res.* **89**, 10072–6.

WIENS, D.G. et al. 1985. A diffuse plate boundary model for Indian Ocean tectonics. *Geophys. Res. Lett.* **12**, 429–32.

VINCENT COURTILLOT, ROLANDO ARMIJO & PAUL TAPPONNIER, Institut de Physique du Globe, 75230 Paris Cedex OS, France.

Cross-faults and differential stretching of hanging walls in regions of low-angle normal faulting: examples from western Turkey

A.M.C. Şengör

SUMMARY: Large oblique-throw hinge faults orientated at high angles to the strike of major breakaway faults in W Turkey are examined. They exhibit variable displacements which commonly increase towards the breakaway fault with which they seem to be associated and bound cross-blocks that in places have rotated around vertical axes by differing amounts and senses, and are interpreted in terms of the possibility that hanging walls of major low-angle breakaway faults (extensional allochthons), may exhibit differential internal extension accommodated by transverse faults that may or may not rotate around vertical axes. Such transverse faults, here called *accommodation faults*, are different from transfer faults in that they need not offset the main breakaway fault and may accomplish significant map-view distortions of extensional allochthons.

Irrotational accommodation faults may give rise to horst and graben complexes or may create the image of domino-style, uniformly tilted normal and/or thrust faults at high angles to the strike of major breakaways, thus giving rise to the misleading image of extension in two directions in an extensional zone or shortening at high angles to regional extension. Although strike-slip offsets along irrotational accommodation faults need not bear any relation to the magnitude of regional extension, their strikes must at least be sub-parallel to the orientation of regional extension. Real shortening at high angles to regional extension may give rise to rotational accommodation faults. Neither the strike-slip offset along such faults nor their azimuth need bear any simple relationship to the magnitude and orientation of regional extension. Rotational accommodation faults bring about an equivalent rotation of all structures that form along them, such as pull-apart basins, and the hanging wall blocks they delimit, together with their pre-existing structures.

All three kinds of cross-faults, i.e. transfer faults, irrotational and rotational accommodation faults may coexist in any one extensional region and may grade into one another both in space and in time creating a very complicated structural picture and causing irregular subsidence patterns. It is stressed that cross-faults have an extremely important bearing on our understanding of the geometry and evolution of extensional zones, here called *taphrogens*, and that only a three-dimensional consideration of the structure of taphrogens is likely to lead to a satisfactory understanding of their nature.

A considerable increase of interest in continental extensional regions, here termed *taphrogens**, has characterized tectonic research over the last decade. A significant outcome of mapping along the trend of taphrogens has been the discovery of the common occurrence of *transverse* or *cross*-faults (*oblique faults* of Harding 1983) orientated at high angles to the strike of the main detachment or breakaway faults and other, smaller normal faults, and separating *cross-horsts* and *cross-grabens* (together making up *cross-blocks*) as shown by Gibbs (1984), Etheridge (in press) and Şengör *et al.* (1985).

Many cross-faults separate areas of differential extension (e.g. Şengör *et al.* 1985) and/or areas of opposite block tilting (e.g. Miller *et al.* 1983), although Gibbs (1984) thought that the analogy between cross-faults in normal fault systems and lateral ramps in thrust systems was exact and thus called the former *transfer faults*. Etheridge (in press) also characterized transfer faults as generally steep to vertical features with strikes perpendicular to normal faults. He considered them to be analogous to *oceanic transform faults* 'in that they accommodate differences in normal-fault geometry along the strike of the extended terrane'.

Consideration of cross-faults mapped in the extensional regions of W Turkey, the North Sea, and in the Basin and Range Province suggests that more than one kind of cross-fault may develop in taphrogens, in which most of the extension is taken up on sub-horizontal detachments. The aim of this contribution is to extend the work of Gibbs (1984), Etheridge (in press), and Şengör *et al.* (1985) on cross-faults mainly using W Turkish examples as illustrative material. In the following paragraphs I emphasize the extremely important rôle of 'thin-skinned' cross-faults in accommodating differential stretching in hanging walls above large-scale detachment faults. I show that if different kinds of cross-faults are not correctly identified, erroneous kinematic histories and incorrect estimates of extension in taphrogenic zones may result.

*From η τάφρος = graben; after Krenkel's (1922) usage *taphrogeny* (= trough building) for broadly localized zones of intense extension as opposed to *orogen*.

From COWARD, M.P., DEWEY, J.F. & HANCOCK, P.L. (eds), 1987, *Continental Extensional Tectonics*, Geological Society Special Publication No. 28, pp. 575–589.

Outline geology of the Western Anatolian extensional province

The Western Anatolian extensional province (Fig. 1) is the westernmost of the three major neotectonic provinces in Turkey that formed following the Arabia/Anatolia collision in the late Serravallian (~12 Ma) (Şengör 1980, 1982; Şengör *et al.* 1985). McKenzie (1978) estimated the total amount of extension to be of the order of 50% ($\beta = 2$) in the Aegean, whereas in W Turkey Şengör (1978) argued for a minimum of 30% ($\beta = 1.5$).

The most prominent structural and morphological features of the Western Anatolian extensional province are some 10 E–W-trending grabens with widths varying between a few km and a maximum of 20 km (Fig. 1a). Those around the Sea of Marmara (Gulf of İzmit, İznik, Gemlik, Yenişehir–Bursa–Manyas and Saros) lie along the course of the N and S strands of the N Anatolian fault and have very strong right-lateral strike-slip components (Fig. 1a) (Dewey & Şengör 1979, Şengör *et al.* 1985). As the origin of these circum-Marmara grabens is apparently directly associated with the strike-slip tectonics of the N Anatolian fault (Şengör *et al.* 1985), I shall not consider them here.

The main extensional area S of the circum-Marmara oblique-slip grabens (S of the latitude of Edremit) seems to be divided into two major

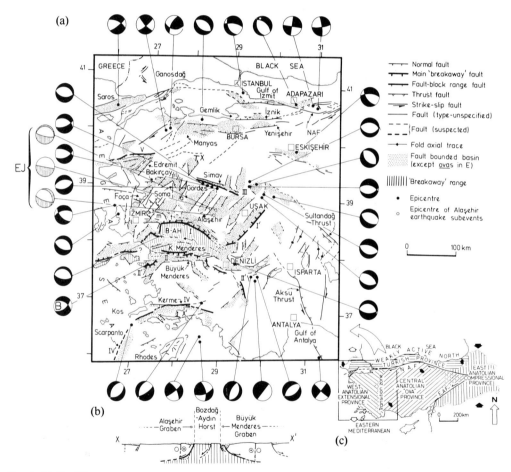

FIG. 1. (a) Simplified neotectonic map of the Western Anatolian extensional province showing the structures discussed in the text (data from Şengör *et al.* 1985). All fault-plane solutions, except those marked EJ were taken from McKenzie (1978); those marked EJ are from Eyidoğan & Jackson (1985). The fault-plane solutions represent lower hemisphere projections: white quadrants—dilatational; black quadrants—compressional. a—Akhisar, m—Manisa, t—Turgutlu. Other details in the text. (b) A highly schematized roughly N–S cross-section along X–X' in part (a) showing the basic structure of the central part of the Western Anatolian extensional province (modified after Şengör *et al.* 1985). (c) Index map showing the location of the region shown on Fig. 1(a) within the context of the neotectonic provinces of Turkey.

domains by the Bozdağ–Aydın horst, N of which most E–W grabens are asymmetric and N-facing (facing of asymmetric grabens is here defined as the dip direction of their master fault) and S of which they are S-facing.

Şengör *et al.* (1985) argued that the structural-divide character of the Bozdağ–Aydın horst was possibly attributable to the fact that the Alaşehir and the Büyük Menderes grabens may constitute the surface expressions of two very large, listric or scoop-shaped, low-angle breakaway faults facing N and S respectively, and that the Bozdağ–Aydın horst bounded by them may be a two-sided break-away range in Wernicke's (1985) classification (Fig. 1b). The following observations support this inference.

Along the N margin of the Büyük Menderes graben, just N of the town of Aydın (N of II in Fig. 1a), J. Jackson (pers. comm. 1982) observed very low-angle normal faults cutting Pliocene *Tmolosschutt* deposits (Erinç 1955; Becker-Platen 1970). The faults are rotated northwards more than 40°, indicating a considerable amount of extension and more than one generation of normal faulting similar to the geometry reported by Proffett (1977) from the Yerington district in Nevada. The S margin of the graben is only moderately broken by small-displacement normal faults, where the total thickness of the Neogene–Quaternary graben fill hardly reaches 100 m. In the N, Quaternary alluvium alone is more than 200 m thick (Koç *et al.* 1975; T. Kozan pers. comm. 1985). These observations indicate a strong S-facing asymmetry of the Büyük Menderes graben. Both westwards and eastwards, the N boundary fault of the Büyük Menderes graben bends strongly southwards suggesting a scoop-shaped geometry. The 16 July 1955 Söke–Balat earthquake (Öcal 1958) occurred near the end of the western bend (Fig. 1a). McKenzie (1972) provided a fault-plane solution for this shock (solution B in Fig. 1a) that indicates a component of right-lateral slip along the fault. McKenzie (1972) assumed that this earthquake had originated in the mantle. If the same solution were employed with a crustal source, as it is now known that all extensional earthquakes in W Turkey and in the Aegean occur at depths not exceeding about 10 km, its strike-slip component would increase. This observation is consistent with the inference that the main N boundary fault of the Büyük Menderes graben may be a S-facing scoop-shaped breakaway fault.

Evidence to suggest that the main S boundary fault of the Alaşehir graben is probably a N-facing scoop-shaped breakaway fault flattening at a depth of about 10 km is stronger than in the case of the Büyük Menderes graben. As Fig. 1(a) shows, the main S boundary fault of the Alaşehir graben has cartographic attributes similar to those of the main Büyük Menderes fault, only with an opposite sense of facing. In a recent seismological study of the normal faulting associated with the 28 March 1969 Alaşehir earthquake along this fault, Eyidoğan & Jackson (1985) documented the multiple nature of the event with at least two discrete sub-events being involved in the production of surface faulting. Eyidoğan & Jackson (1985) also noted that the seismograms of the Alaşehir earthquake contained later, longer period signals that they thought represented source, not structure or propagation complexities. They modelled these later signals by sub-events which took place on sub-horizontal 'detachment-type' faults that connected at depths with the main S boundary fault of the Alaşehir graben. Figure 1a displays the fault-plane solutions generated by Eyidoğan & Jackson (1985) for the Alaşehir sub-events which clearly show the very gentle dip of one of the nodal planes (solutions EJ in Fig. 1a). Eyidoğan & Jackson (1985) estimated the focal depths of the Alaşehir sub-events (and therefore the depth of the detachment fault) to be about 10 km but the data form a constraint only between 6 and 10 km. This range is similar to the 8 km flattening depth of the listric faults in Utah (Smith & Bruhn 1984).

Another seismological observation, supporting the possibility of a major detachment fault underlying most of the region N of the Alaşehir graben, is the anomalously large and diffuse area of the epicentre distribution for aftershocks, with a very large number of events scattered N of the Alaşehir graben following major earthquakes in W Turkey (Ergin *et al.* 1972). A map displaying the epicentre distribution in W Turkey for the 1976–1980 interval (a period of better instrumental control than that reported on by Ergin *et al.* 1972) shows the same pattern (Fig. 2). The very large area of distribution of earthquakes following major shocks may be seen as the result of jostling of loose hanging wall blocks which move along a major and relatively shallow discontinuity.

A much less morphologically prominent structural element of the Western Anatolian extensional province is the family of faults that strike at high angles to the main E–W grabens (Figs 1a & 2). The largest and the best developed of these occur N of the Alaşehir graben and divide the region between it and the Bakırçay and Simav grabens into NNE-trending elongate cross-blocks. A similar, but much smaller set of N–S to NNW–SSE cross-grabens and cross-horsts characterizes the southern shoulder of the Büyük Menderes graben (Fig. 1a).

These transverse structures are as prominent as the E–W grabens on geological maps because they localized Neogene and Quaternary sedimentation. That they do not nucleate major shocks (at least not

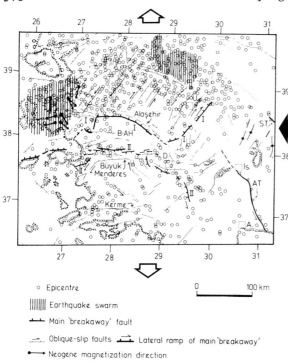

○ Epicentre

||||||| Earthquake swarm

◄–►– Main 'breakaway' fault

⌐–⌐ Oblique-slip faults ⌐⌐ Lateral ramp of main 'breakaway'

●——► Neogene magnetization direction

0   100 km

FIG. 2. Distribution of epicentres of earthquakes that occurred in the Western Anatolian extensional province between 1976 and 1980. Also shown are the major neotectonic structures. Notice the concentration of epicentres N of the main breakaway fault (I) of the Alaşehir graben. Strike-slip components along many of the transverse faults extending N of the Alaşehir and S of the Büyük Menderes grabens are conjectural except near the coast, where they are documented either by field work or by focal-mechanism solutions (see solution B in Fig. 1a). A = Antalya, AT = Aksu thrust, B–AH = Bozdağ–Aydin horst, D = Denizli, I = Izmir, Is = Isparta, ST = Sultandağ thrust, and U = Usak. Large open arrows show the generalized orientation of regional extension, and the solid one shows that of regional shortening since the beginning of the Tortonian (modified from Şengör *et al.* 1985).

as often as do the major E–W normal faults) also correlates well with their more subdued morphology. As the distribution of epicentres in Fig. 2 testifies, however, the transverse faults localize some smaller earthquakes. The paucity of very young (likely historical) fault scarps along the transverse faults (e.g. the Soma scarp) suggests that even some sizeable earthquakes may occasionally occur along them. The orientation of penetrative and semi-penetrative structures in the pre-Neogene basement of the Western Anatolian extensional province shows a remarkable parallelism with the strike of the transverse (and many of the main E–W) faults implying a close control of older trends in localizing younger structures (see Şengör *et al.* 1985, fig. 20).

Ketin (1968, 1970) was the first to emphasize the presence of cross-faults in W Turkey and implied a genetic link between them and the main E–W grabens. Most of the detailed field observations on cross-faults in the Western Anatolian extensional province were gathered by Kaya (1979, 1981). Many of Kaya's observations are not what one would have expected from a simple normal faulted terrain of uniform N–S extension. These 'unexpected observations' form the main basis of the models developed later in this paper.

Kaya (1979, 1981) noticed that the regions between İzmir and the Bakırçay graben and to the S and SE were divided into NNE-trending blocks by steep, oblique-slip faults (Figs 1 & 2). He observed that these faults had both normal and reverse separation depending on locality and all had a considerable left-lateral strike-slip component. Many of them were hinge faults with strong variations of dip-slip magnitude along their strike.

Kaya also mapped smaller E–W- and WNW-striking normal faults between the transverse faults cutting the cross-blocks (Fig. 1a). These smaller faults end abruptly against the main cross-faults and nowhere offset them. He emphasized the difficulty of dating the different fault families, but in a few cases he indicated that the NNE-striking cross-faults seemed older than the E–W to WNW smaller, normal faults between them. Kaya (1979) also stressed that the cross-faults follow older structural trends. For the Foça cross-graben (Fig. 1a), Kaya (1981) documented a subsidence history that had begun in the early Miocene and continued up to the present with a marked break in tectonic activity during the 16 to 11 Ma interval. Şengör *et al.* (1985) pointed out that the subsidence pre-dating 16 Ma clearly belonged to the palaeotectonic evolution of the area (N–S shortening: see Şengör

Şengör *et al.* 1984), whereas the post-11 Ma history was a part of the neotectonic development. They thus concluded that the Foça cross-graben may have been resurrected, and thus inherited, from a palaeotectonic feature, by the neotectonic extensional regime.

In Fig. 3, I have plotted the reported maximum total Neogene thicknesses both from the Alaşehir graben and from the cross-grabens that seem to open into it from the N (Soma–Akhisar and Gördes). The thickness in Soma (Fig. 1a) is 1270 m, which rapidly increases southwards to 3448 m near Akhisar (a in Fig. 1a). Just N of the Manisa horst (m in Fig. 1a) the thickness decreases again to 1085 m and in the Alaşehir graben itself, near Turgutlu (t in Fig. 1a), it is known to exceed 2000 m but it is not known by how many metres (T. Kozan, pers. comm. 1985).

If one connects the top of the pre-Neogene basement in Soma with a point about 2500 m beneath the surface near Turgutlu (assuming that the total Neogene thickness does not exceed that in the Alaşehir graben) a gently sloping (about 8°) basement surface from the Soma-Akhisar cross-graben to the main Alaşehir breakaway fault can be constructed. The 3446-m-thick Neogene section near Akhisar then appears as an anomaly. If, however, the Soma depth is connected with the Akhisar depth, a steeper dip (~ 15°) of the floor of the cross-graben is obtained and the expected depth of the pre-Neogene basement in the Alaşehir graben becomes 6 km.

Although the present data do not permit us to choose between these two hypotheses (preliminary gravity data may be interpreted as indicating very shallow grabens: N. Canıtez pers. comm. 1985), both cases clearly show that the cross-faults bounding the Soma–Akhisar graben must be hinge faults with rather irregular fluctuations of throw along them.

The spatial coincidence of early- and late-Miocene grabens belonging to two fundamentally different tectonic regimes as documented by Kaya (1981) in the Foça graben, and the possibly anomalous Neogene thicknesses, both near Akhisar and Gördes, suggest another kind of control in the localization of the cross-grabens N of the Alaşehir breakaway fault.

Although the transverse faults mapped by Kaya (1979) and the Soma–Akhisar faults may be thought of as offsetting the main Alaşehir breakaway fault to the S (Fig. 1a) those farther to the E, such as at Gördes and N of Alaşehir clearly do not. In Fig. 4 the possible westerly continuation of the main Alaşehir breakaway fault is shown. Beginning to the S of İzmir, a number of what appear to be transfer faults offset it along its entire length well into SE Thessaly in Greece. NE of Euboea a number of NE-striking faults may be cross-faults associated with the main Alaşehir breakaway fault, the only major neotectonic structure, of the Western Anatolian extensional province, continuously traceable across the Aegean Sea. That cross-structures have developed on its N side does not thus appear to be a phenomenon unique to W Turkey and seems to characterize it along its entire strike length. Some of these offset it, whereas others clearly do not.

Where seen, slickenside striae on cross-fault surfaces in W Turkey commonly pitch less than 90° and in places may be curved; on cross-fault surfaces there are commonly at least two distinct generations of slickenside striae, where the older set pitches more gently (A. Poisson pers. comm. 1985 and my own observations).

A further 'unexpected observation' in the region around İzmir is the inconsistency of the observed

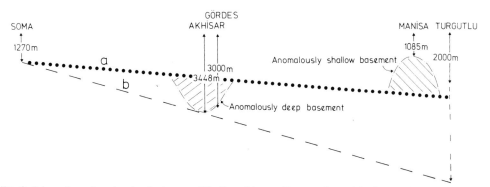

Fig. 3. Schematic section showing the two possible dips of the pre-Neogene floor of the Soma–Akhisar cross-graben (for localities see Fig. 1a) on the basis of measured thicknesses of Neogene sedimentary and volcanic rocks. Thickness values are taken from the following sources: Soma—Brinkmann *et al.* (1970) and Nebert (1978); Akhisar—Kaya (1979); Gördes—Nebert (1961); Manisa—K. Erguvanli, pers. comm. 1984; Turgutlu—T. Kozan, pers. comm. 1985. Discussion is in the text.

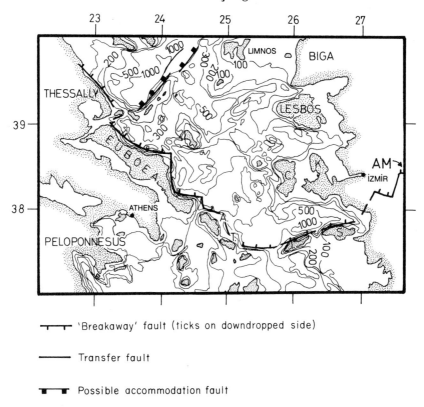

⊤⊤⊤ 'Breakaway' fault (ticks on downdropped side)

⎯⎯⎯ Transfer fault

▮⊤▮ Possible accommodation fault

FIG. 4. Simplified bathymetric map of the central Aegean Sea (simplified from Stanley & Perissoratis 1977) (contours in m) showing the western extension of the Alaşehir main breakaway fault (AM). Discussion is in the text.

Neogene palaeodeclinations, indicating both considerable clockwise and counterclockwise rotations of blocks bounded by the cross-faults mapped by Kaya (1979) (Lauer 1981; Kissel *et al.* 1985 and in prep.) (Fig. 2). Measurements made on the same block appear consistent with one another, whereas between blocks there are significant differences.

In the preceding paragraphs I outlined the overall characteristics of the Western Anatolian extensional province and briefly described some 'unexpected observations' which imply the existence of processes that are not necessary consequences of the simple, uniform N–S extension, believed to have governed the tectonic evolution of the region since the Tortonian. Unfortunately, field data on the large-scale geometry of the major graben structures and mesoscopic observations of both transverse and E–W fault systems are insufficient to derive a unique model of the region's detailed structure and neotectonic evolution. The available data may be used, however, to constrain speculative models, especially for the structure and origin of the observed cross-structures. These speculations may guide future research by predicting a number of

parameters observable either in the field or on seismic reflection profiles or measurable by geophysical techniques.

The models

I develop two models for the origin of cross-faults. The first is for those that do not rotate around vertical axes and the second is for those that do.

Irrotational model

In Fig. 5, four block diagrams (a, b, c & d) demonstrate the evolution of cross-faults that do not offset the main breakaway fault. Block diagram (a) represents a 10-km-thick slab of continental lithosphere. A potential breakaway fault separates a future hanging wall from a future footwall. The former contains zones of weakness that may be controlled by older structures and which trend perpendicular to the strike of the breakaway fault.

If we now extend block diagram (a) by 30% (the minimum amount thought to have affected W

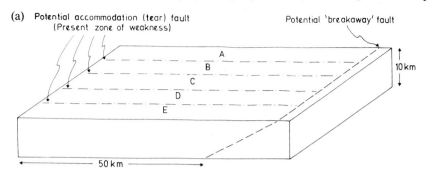

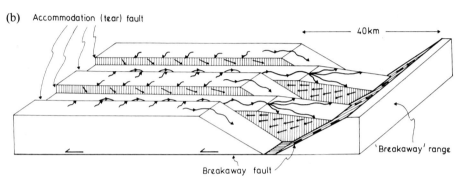

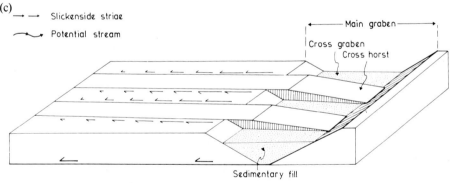

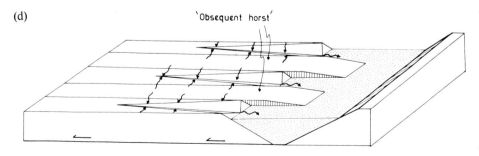

FIG. 5. Balanced block diagrams showing the evolution of accommodation faults separating cross-grabens and cross-horsts. The sizes of half arrows in c give the real amount of strike-slip offset on the accommodation faults. Discussion is in the text.

Turkey), we may obtain the balanced block diagram, (b), by the following procedure: blocks A, C and E undergo no internal stretching and accommodate the extension solely by moving along the main breakaway fault. This motion generates a 40-km-wide, 10-km-deep asymmetric graben. Blocks B and D are allowed to take up 15% of the total extension by internal stretching and the remaining 15% by sliding along the main breakaway fault. For graphic simplicity the internal stretching of blocks B and D is assumed to occur homogeneously. While this assumption is obviously unrealistic, it is a fair approximation of heterogeneous extension along closely spaced, rotational planar normal faults, the most common mode of brittle extension (e.g. Morton & Black 1975; Miller et al. 1983). In block diagram (b) the resulting grabens are shown empty as no erosion is allowed to take place. Block diagram (b) shows the cross-grabens and cross-horsts which form both within the main graben and on the hanging wall. Interestingly, the block that behaves as a cross-horst within the main graben becomes a graben away from the toe region of the hanging wall.

Another aspect of the model, shown in block diagram (b), is the variable pitches of slickenside striae on the cross-faults. The striae pitches in block diagram (b) are parallel to the dip of the main breakaway fault immediately adjacent to it but towards the left they rotate progressively, first towards the horizontal and then past it to 90° where differential stretching between the cross-blocks equals zero.

Even the extremely simplistic situation portrayed in block diagram (b) leads to a fairly complicated structural picture. Calculation of theoretical seismic moments (M_0) on this block diagram shows that the total seismic moment for the total slip, represented by deformation in going from (a) to (b) along the main breakaway fault (assuming that it moves seismically along its entire area shown in the block diagram), is about 80% greater than along the cross-faults. This may be one explanation for why strong earthquakes along cross-faults in W Turkey are not nearly as frequent as those along the main E–W normal faults.

We now continue our line of thought, with the same basic assumptions, by considering the geometry shown in Fig. 6, where the hanging wall is divided into 11 cross-blocks representing different amounts of homogeneous internal stretching parallel to the direction of regional extension. As in Fig. 5, the magnitude of strike-slip offset between different cross-blocks increases away from an imaginary line of no differential extension.

The picture generated in this map is in principle identical to that shown in block diagram (b) of Fig. 5. Notice here the tremendously complicated strike-slip geometry displayed by the cross-faults.

The magnitude of maximum relative strike-slip displacement on any one cross-fault is a function of the ratio of the amount of internal extension in the more-extended cross-block to that in the less-extended adjacent cross-block. If this ratio is 1, the magnitude of maximum relative strike-slip between the two adjacent blocks will be zero; that is no cross-fault need exist. The greater this ratio than 1, the greater will be the amount of maximum strike-slip. Notice in particular that the magnitude of the regional extension need have little to do with the amount of strike-slip on cross-faults, but in the irrotational cases their direction will be parallel to that of regional extension.

The cross-sections AA' and BB' in Fig. 6 exhibit a further complication. If, as seen on these cross-sections, the breakaway fault has a certain amount of tilt parallel to its strike, the cross-faults resting on it may appear to dip, at angles equalling the amount of tilt. In Fig. 6 I assumed a conservative tilt of only 10°, although detachment faults with tilts of more than 25° are not uncommon in the Basin and Range Province of the W United States (Hamilton, this volume).

On proceeding across the strike of the cross-faults in cross-sections AA' and BB' in Fig. 6, an irregularly alternating series of normal and reverse faults would be encountered. This in itself would present a difficult picture to interpret, especially in places where outcrop is scarce. If, for example, only blocks a, b, c and d are mapped along the cross-section BB', the geologist may obtain the image of a series of domino-style tilted rotational planar normal faults and could calculate from this a certain amount of across-strike extension, whereas in reality there would be none.

Even more confusing would be the observation of a series of domino-style tilted normal faults turning into a series of similarly inclined thrust faults along the strike of the cross-faults from cross-section BB' to AA'. These 'thrust faults' would likewise yield an apparent amount of unreal shortening.

Let us now consider the effects of erosion and deposition in the cross-block system. In block diagram (b) of Fig. 5, we see that cross-blocks A, C and E possess the highest relief and thus they are most vulnerable to erosion. Cross-blocks B and D would receive much of the material shed from their neighbours and would further transport this material towards the main graben via rivers flowing along their lengths. Temporary lakes may occur where grabens are themselves faulted as a result of internal stretching.

When rivers flowing along the graben sections of blocks B and D emerge into the main graben they would then flow down the axes of relatively steep-sided horsts (Fig. 5b). Thus much of the debris carried away from blocks A, C and E would eventu-

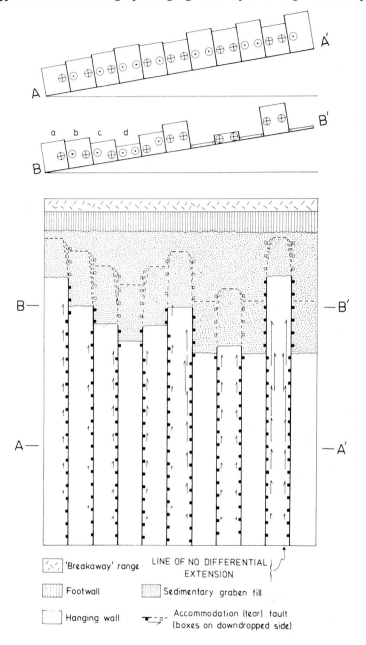

FIG. 6. Map view and two cross-sections (AA' & BB') of an extensional allochthon separated into 11 cross-horsts and grabens. Regional extension is 30% and the blocks accommodate this partly by moving along the main breakaway fault and partly by internally stretching between amounts ranging from zero to 24%. Notice the alternating horst and graben structures both across *and* along the strike and the very variable magnitudes of strike-slip offset along accommodation faults. The sizes of half arrows give the real amount of relative offset along these faults. Discussion is in the text.

ally be deposited in front of them in the lowest regions of the main graben. During denudation of high-standing cross-blocks, their low-lying neighbours are unlikely to be denuded.

The balanced block diagram, c, depicts the situation when the high-standing cross-blocks are denuded to the level of their low-lying neighbours. I have assumed that all the material eroded from blocks A, C and E fills the main graben. The dimensions in plan of the model are similar to the situation N of the Alaşehir graben. Although at this stage all the cross-blocks have the same relief, the gradients on blocks A, C and E are steeper. Therefore fluvial erosion on them will be more vigorous than on cross-blocks B and D. Thus, the originally high-standing blocks will eventually be excavated to levels lower than the originally low-lying, blocks B and D, forming 'obsequent horsts' (Fig. 5d).

At this stage it is appropriate to return to the question of 'inherited grabens' in W Turkey. Fig. 7 shows two block diagrams schematically portraying the pre-Tortonian ('palaeotectonic') and post-Serravallian ('neotectonic') situations in W Turkey. The pre-Tortonian N–S shortening is believed to have generated a compressional (Tibet-type) high plateau in W Turkey that may have had roughly N–S trending Tibet-type (Mercier *et al.* 1984) grabens on it, in which the early-Miocene graben sediments (e.g. the Foça graben; Kaya 1981) may have been deposited. When N–S extension set in during the Tortonian some of these older N–S-trending grabens may have been resurrected in the form of cross-grabens as seen in block diagram (b). In this case these cross-grabens will not only contain their neotectonic graben fill, but an additional, apparently anomalous 'inherited' fill as is shown schematically in cross-section (c). In such cases subsidence curves calculated from total graben fills

may have no bearing on the extensional history of the taphrogenic phase. In W Turkey not only the Foça graben, but also the possibly anomalous thicknesses near Akhisar and Gördes (Fig. 3) may have inherited thicknesses of graben-fill from the palaeotectonic period.

Rotational model

Figure 8 shows a situation where cross-faults, and the blocks they bound, rotate around vertical axes. Extension in one direction is at least partially complemented by shortening at a high angle to it and the rotations of hanging wall blocks are proportional to the magnitude of the sideways shortening. That this kind of sideways shortening is commonly encountered in taphrogens, analogous to along-strike extension in orogens, is shown by the E–W shortening in the Aegean area and W Turkey (Le Pichon & Angelier 1981; Şengör *et al.* 1985) and the N–S shortening in the Mormon Mountains in SE Nevada (Wernicke *et al.* 1985).

Figure 8(a) shows the map view of the pre-extension geometry of the situation displayed in Fig. 8(b). The 'potential fault' may be nucleated on a pre-existing zone of weakness as in Fig. 5. During extension, hanging wall blocks are assumed to be pinned to the breakaway ranges at opposite ends of the cross-fault. As extension and (?complementary) shortening at high angles to it proceed, both the hanging wall blocks and the cross-fault separating them will rotate into the direction of extension. The sides of the rotating hanging wall blocks facing the shortening direction may be marked by complex deformation filling the space generated by the rotation.

It is clear from Fig. 8(b) that the main breakaway faults must be major hinge faults along which throw

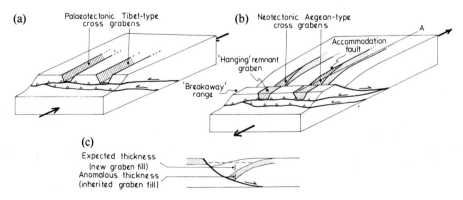

FIG. 7. Block diagrams (a) & (b) and cross-section (c) illustrating the formation of 'inherited' graben fills. Tibet-type grabens are products of longitudinal shortening and sideways extension, whereas Aegean-type cross-grabens have zero sideways extension. Discussion is in the text.

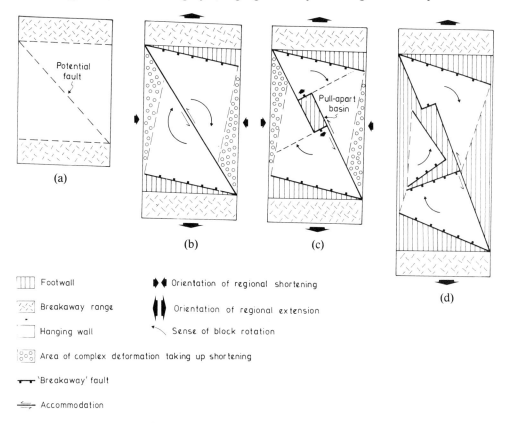

▥ Footwall	▸◂ Orientation of regional shortening	
▨ Breakaway range	▮▮ Orientation of regional extension	
▫ Hanging wall	↖ Sense of block rotation	
▨ Area of complex deformation taking up shortening		
⊤⊤ 'Breakaway' fault		
⇌ Accommodation		

FIG. 8. Sketch maps showing the evolution of rotational cross-faults. Discussion is in the text.

will increase in one direction in concert with the rotation of hanging wall blocks (see Laubach & Marshak, this volume).

If the hanging wall blocks rotate by only 10° (Fig. 8b & c) the cross-faults and other structures, such as the pull-apart basin illustrated in Fig. 8(c), must also rotate by 10° into the direction of extension. The 10° magnitude of rotation is significant, because it can be detected by palaeomagnetic measurement and thus may be independently checked.

An extremely important implication of the kinematic picture displayed in Fig. 8(b) & (c) is that the orientation of such 'thin-skinned' strike-slip faults may not necessarily be parallel to the direction of regional extension. Moreover, if such systematic rotations occur over a large area, they will rotate all structures that pre-date them. Therefore, implicit assumptions that extensional allochthons do not rotate around vertical axes in extensional areas (e.g. Wernicke *et al.* 1985) may be unwarranted and, if made, may lead to serious errors in palinspastic-reconstruction attempts.

Magnitudes of regional extension measured on such rotational cross-faults are also suspect, because even if the total offset along them could be accurately determined, it would still be systematically less than the true amount of regional extension. Therefore strike-slip offset on cross-faults that accommodate differential extension may not necessarily provide a check on the magnitude and orientation of regional crustal extension independent of assumptions on normal fault geometry in a given area as frequently presumed (e.g. Wernicke *et al.* 1982).

If conjugate thin-skinned strike-slip faults disrupting extensional allochthons on sub-horizontal detachment surfaces become active alternately during the course of progressive extension, they may rotate each other around vertical axes up to theoretical limits of 45 or 60° (depending on the original angle they make with the orientation of regional extension) *away* from the direction of regional extension. Rather irregular block rotations around vertical axes reported by Lauer (1981) and Kissel *et al.* (1985) from around Izmir (Fig. 2) may be the result of such alternately active rotational cross-faults. But rotations exceeding 25° are only possible if local extension exceeds 200%. A 49° counterclockwise rotation of a block in the Karaburun peninsula in W Turkey (W of Izmir; Fig. 2) apparently requires a local stretching of about 250% (Kissel *et al.* in prep.).

Figure 8(d) was drawn using Hamilton's model of crustal extension (Hamilton 1982, and this volume). If the footwall block consists of a large number of lenses which continuously slide apart as extension proceeds, it is possible that parts of hanging wall blocks may stick on one or more of the lenses, the differential movement of which may eventually result in the rotation, around vertical axes, of floating pieces of hanging walls. Documentation of such a phenomenon will provide strong corroborative evidence for Hamilton's model.

Hybrid model

The rotational and irrotational models for cross-fault generation need not exclude each other. It is possible that parts of extensional allochthons may undergo differential extension along irrotational cross-faults and that rotational cross-faults may accommodate differential stretching in others. Boundaries between rotational and irrotational domains may be characterized by very complex basin geometries or zones of compressional deformation taking up incompatible strains. Some of the peculiar triangular grabens NE of the Bakırçay graben, or S of Denizli, or N of Uşak (Fig. 1a) may owe their origin to such complications.

Discussion

Types of cross-faults in taphrogens

The most prominent features of the models developed in the preceding section are the three main kinds of cross-faults they require (Fig. 9). In Fig. 9(a) no cross-fault is present and the extensional system is governed by one major breakaway fault. In Fig. 9(b) the main breakaway fault is offset by two strike-slip cross-faults which function like

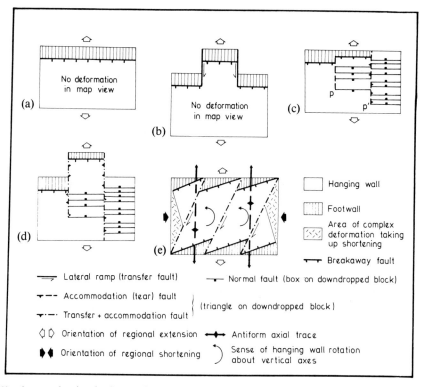

FIG. 9. Sketch maps showing the three main types of cross-faults that may form in environments of extension. (a) Simple geometry with no cross-fault. (b) Transfer faults. (c) Irrotational accommodation faults. (d) Hybrid (transfer + accommodation) faults. (e) Rotational accommodation faults. Discussion is in the text.

ridge–ridge transform faults; the transfer faults of Gibbs (1984). Dip-slip movement on transfer faults is confined to that generated by reverse drag at the toe of the hanging wall. The major faults offsetting the main Alaşehir breakaway fault near its W end, S of Izmir, are probably such transfer fault structures (Fig. 1a).

The cross-faults depicted in Fig. 9(c) are confined entirely to the hanging wall and accommodate the differential internal stretching of its different compartments (the 'cross-blocks'). This is why I suggest that such cross-faults be called *'accommodation faults'*. Their counterparts in thrust systems are tear faults which accommodate differential shortening of the thrust plates they separate. Strike-slip components of displacement on such 'accommodation faults' would systematically decrease away from the main breakaway fault as far as a point of no differential extension between the two cross-blocks they separate (p and p' in Fig. 9c). Dip-slip movement on accommodation faults is more complicated. Near the toe of the extensional allochthon it is governed by the relative magnitudes of subsidence caused by motion along the main breakaway fault and that caused by thinning as a result of internal stretching. Away from the toe region, where the main breakaway fault flattens into a sub-horizontal detachment fault, it is the differential internal stretching of the hanging wall that dominates the amount and sense of the dip-slip motion along the accommodation fault.

Transfer faults may be combined with accommodation faults giving rise to 'hybrid' cross-faults as shown in Fig. 9(d). In this case, if the transfer faults form any sort of relief along the flat part of the main breakaway fault, that relief will be reflected in the topography of the hanging wall and will interfere with that formed by accommodation movement.

Figure 9(e) displays the third main type of transverse fault found in extensional systems, namely the rotational accommodation faults. These faults do not offset the footwall and most commonly occur in regions where extension is accompanied by some shortening at high angles to the stretching direction. They progressively rotate, together with the hanging wall blocks they delimit, into the direction of regional extension. Strike-slip displacement along such rotational accommodation faults will always be less than the total regional extension. Dip-slip motion along them is theoretically confined to that determined by subsidence caused by movement along the main breakaway faults.

I emphasize that the geometries depicted in Fig. 9 commonly grade into each other both in time and in space thereby inheriting the structural complications caused by preceding geometries and influencing the formation of newer geometries.

Subsidence patterns in cross-faulted taphrogens

Figures 5, 6 and 8 demonstrate that the same magnitude of regional extension may give rise to an irregular distribution of crustal thicknesses with widely varying values in the same sedimentary basin related to differential internal stretching of cross-blocks that would result in an extremely complicated subsidence pattern. Because β values, calculated only from local crustal thicknesses without proper attention to the geometry of the entire basin, will vary greatly from place to place within a single basin, they may not necessarily be characteristic of the regional extension.

While calculating β values in any given extensional basin extremely complicated structural geometries resulting from the activity of accommodation faults in taphrogens invite great caution. Inheritance cases such as that illustrated in Fig. 7 may contribute a generally overlooked complication to the picture by increasing β values above their true value. The common failure of many stretching models probably results more from insufficient appreciation of the complexities of extensional basins than from an inherent problem with the models.

Conclusions

A survey of the literature on continental extensional tectonics and the papers in this volume clearly shows that during the last decade we have only just begun to appreciate the complexities of this phenomenon. In addition to the vast amounts of data gathered, by various methods, on the structure of taphrogens, frequent analogies to orogenic belts have helped clarify our views on the geometry and evolution of extensional structures. The availability of high-quality seismic reflection profiles, in places down to 10–15 km, has in particular apparently enhanced the prevalent tendency to consider taphrogens mainly in cross-section, however, as exemplified by the current debate on the dominant mode of extension of the continental lithosphere.

The models presented in this paper imply, however, that many of the parameters critical for an understanding of how continental lithosphere accommodates extension, such as magnitude and direction of stretching and how this stretching effects distribution of crustal thicknesses can only be properly assessed if the third dimension is also taken into consideration. It seems that the lessons learned from the study of orogenic belts concerning the grave dangers of thinking only in terms of cross-sections are not seriously taken into consideration in studies on taphrogens.

Irrotational and rotational accommodation faults may seriously mislead the field geologist trying to obtain magnitudes and directions of stretching by studying offsets along them, especially if their different forms are not properly recognized. Some of the very complicated structural geometries they may generate, such as those shown in Fig. 6 may be difficult to understand if the geologist is unaware of the properties of the various types of cross-faults found in extensional systems.

Because of their very simplistic boundary conditions the models developed here do not do justice to the complexities of cross-faults. The models do, however, illuminate some of their more generalized first-order properties, which may encourage field geologists mapping specific examples to penetrate deeper into their secrets. It is

mostly to that end that current fieldwork in the Western Anatolian extensional province is directed.

Acknowledgments: I thank the convenors of the Durham meeting for inviting this contribution. Professor John F. Dewey introduced me to the beauty of extensional systems while I was his student and never grew tired of warning me and my fellow students against the pitfalls of cross-sectional thinking in tectonics.

I thank Professors B. Clark Burchfiel, Nezihi Canıtez, Kâzım Ergin, Sırrı Ergniç, İhsan Ketin and Dan McKenzie, and Drs Michael A. Etheridge, W. Hamilton, James Jackson, Fuat Şaroğlu and Yücel Yılmaz for helpful discussions. A very thorough review by Dr Paul L. Hancock greatly improved the manuscript.

References

BECKER-PLATEN, J.D. 1970. Lithostratigraphische Untersuchungen in Känozoikum Südwest-Anatoliens (Türkei). *Bh. geol. Jb.* **97**, 244.

BRINKMANN, R., FEIST, R., MARR, W.U., NICKEL, E., SCHLIMM, W. & WALTER, H.R. 1970. Geologie der Soma Dagları. *Maden Tetkik ve Arama Enstitüsü Bülteni*, **74**, 7–23.

DEWEY, J.F. & SENGÖR, A.M.C. 1979. Aegean and surrounding regions: Complex multiplate and continuum tectonics in a convergent zone. *Bull. geol. Soc. Am.* **90** (I), 84–92.

ERGIN, K., UZ, Z. & GÜCLÜ, U. 1972. 8 Mart 1970 Gediz depremi art sarsıntılarının incelenmesi. *İ.T.Ü. Arz Fizigi Enstitüsü Yayınları*, **29**, 50.

ERINÇ, S. 1955. Über die Entstehung und morphologische Bedeutung des Tmolosschutts. *Rev. Univ. Instanbul Geogr. Inst.*, **2**, 57–72.

ETHERIDGE, M.A. In press. On the reactivation of extensional fault systems. *Phil. Trans. R. Soc. London*.

EYİDOĞAN, H. & JACKSON, J.A. 1985. A seismological study of normal faulting in the Demirci, Alaşehir and Gediz earthquakes of 1969–70 in Western Turkey: implications for the nature and geometry of deformation in the continental crust. *Geophys. J. R. astron. Soc.* **81**, 569–607.

GIBBS, A.D. 1984. Structural evolution of extensional basin margins. *J. geol. Soc. London*, **141**, 609–20.

HAMILTON, W.B. 1982. Structural evolution of the Big Maria Mountains, northeastern Riverside county, southeastern California. *In*: FROST, E.G. & MARTIN, D.L. (eds) *Mesozoic–Cenozoic Tectonic Evolution of the Colorado River Region, California, Arizona, and Nevada*, pp. 1–27. Cordillerán Publishers, San Diego.

HAMILTON, W. This volume. Crustal extension in the Basin and Range Province, southwestern United States.

HARDING, T.P. 1983. Graben hydrocarbon plays and structural styles. *Geol. Mijnbouw*, **62**, 3–23.

KAYA, O. 1979. Ortadogu Ege cöküntüsünün (Neojen) stratigrafisi ve tektonigi. *Türk. Jeol. Kur. Bül.* **22**, 35–58.

—— 1981. Miocene reference section for the coastal parts of West Anatolia. *Newsl. Strat.* **10**, 164–91.

KETİN, İ. 1968. Relations between general tectonic features and the main earthquake regions of Turkey. *Bull. Min. Res. Expl. Inst. Turkey*, **71**, 63–7.

—— 1970. Batı Anadolu Neojen havzalarının sismotektonik durumu. *Gediz Depremi Simpozyumu, Tebliğler, Tartışmalar*, pp. 8–16. İnsaat Mühendisleri Odası, Ankara.

KISSEL, C., LAJ, C., MERCIER, J.L., POISSON, A., SAVAŞÇIN, Y. & SIMEAKIS, K. 1985. Tertiary rotational deformations in the Aegean domain, (abstract). *Terra Cognita*, **5**, 139.

KOC, H.F., ERHAN, N., TANSUĞ, Z., AYSAN, D. & UZEL, C. 1975. *Lower Büyük Menderes Basin-Hydrogeological Investigation Report*, 72 pp. Republic of Turkey, Ministry of Energy and Natural Resources, General Directorate of State Hydraulic Works, Geotechnical Services and Groundwater Division, Ankara.

KRENKEL, E. 1922. *Die Bruchzonen Ostafrikas*, 184 pp. Gebrüder Borntraeger, Berlin.

LAUBACH, S.E. & MARSHAK, S. This volume. Fault patterns generated during extensional deformation of crystalline basement, NW Scotland.

LAUER, J.P. 1981. L'évolution géodynamique de la Turqie et de Chypre déduite de l'étude paléomagnetique. 299 pp. Unpubl. Ph.D. Thesis Univ. Louis Pasteur, Strasbourg.

LE PICHON, X. & ANGELIER, J. 1981. The Aegean Sea. *Phil. Trans. R. Soc. London*, **A300**, 357–72.

MCKENZIE, D. 1972. Active tectonics of the Mediterranean region. *Geophys. J. R. astron. Soc.* **30**, 109–85.

—— 1978. Active tectonics of the Alpine–Himalayan belt: The Aegean Sea and surrounding regions. *Geophys. J. R. astron. Soc.* **55**, 217–54.

MERCIER, J.L., TAPPONNIER, P., ARMIJO, R., HAN, T. & ZHOU, J. 1984. Failles normales actives au Tibet: preuves de terrain. *In*: MERCIER, J.L. & GUANGCEN, L. (eds) *Mission Franco-Chinoise au Tibet*, pp. 413–422. Editions du C.N.R.S., Paris.

MILLER, E.L., GANS, P.B. & GARING, J. 1983. The

Snake Range décollement: an exhumed mid-Tertiary ductile–brittle transition. *Tectonics*, **2**, 239–63.

MORTON, W.H. & BLACK, R. 1975. Crustal attenuation in Afar. *In*: PILGER, A. & RÖSLER, A. (eds) *Afar Depression of Ethiopia. Proceedings of the International Symposium on the Afar Region and Related Rift Problems*, pp. 55–65. Schweizerbart 'sche Verlagsbuchhandlung, Stuttgart.

NEBERT, K. 1961. Gördes (Batı Anadolu) bölgesindeki Neojen volkanizması hakkında bazı bilgiler. *Maden Tetkik ve Arama Enstitüsü Bülteni*, **57**, 50–4.

NEBERT, K. 1978. Das braunkohlenführende Neogengebiet von Soma, West-anatolien. *Bull. Min. Res. Expl. Inst. Turkey*, **90**, 20–72.

ÖCAL, N. 1958. 16 Temmuz 1955 Söke-Balat zelzelesi. *Istanbul Kandilli Rasathanesi Sismoloji Yay.* **2**, 8.

PROFFETT, J.M. JR. 1977. Cenozoic geology of the Yerington district, Nevada, and implications for the nature and origin of Basin and Range faulting. *Bull. geol. Soc. Am.* **88**, 247–66.

ŞENGÖR, A.M.C. 1978. Über die angebliche primäre Vertikaltektonik im Agaisraum. *Neues Jahrb. Geol. Palaontol.* **11**, 698–703.

—— 1980. Türkiye'nin neotektoniginin esasları. *Türk. Jeol. Kur. Konf. Ser.* **2**, 40.

—— 1982. Ege'nin neotektonik evrimini yöneten etkenler. *In*: EROL, O. & OYGÜR, V. (eds) *Batı Anadolu'nun Genc Tektoniği ve Volkanizması, Türk Jeol. Kur.* Ankara, pp. 59–72.

——, GÖRÜR, N. & SAROĞLU, F. 1985. Strike-slip faulting and related basin formation in zones of tectonic escape: Turkey as a case study. *In*: BIDDLE, K.T. & CHRISTIE-BLICK, N. (eds) *Strike-slip Faulting and Basin Formation, Soc. econ. Paleontol. and Mineral., Spec. Pub.* **37**, 227–64.

——, SATIR, M. & AKKÖK, R. 1984. Timing of tectonic events in the Menderes Massif, Western Turkey: implications for tectonic evolution and evidence for Pan-African basement in Turkey. *Tectonics*, **3**, 693–707.

SMITH, R.B. & BRUHN, R.L. 1984. Intraplate extensional tectonics of the eastern Basin–Range: Inferences on structural style from seismic reflection data, regional tectonics, and thermal–mechanical models of brittle–ductile deformation. *J. geophys. Res.* **89**, 5733–62.

STANLEY, D.J. & PERISSORATIS, C. 1977. Aegean Sea ridge barrier-and-basin sedimentation patterns. *Mar. Geol.*, **24**, 97–107.

WERNICKE, B. 1985. Uniform sense normal simple shear of the continental lithosphere. *Can. J. Earth Sci.* **22**, 108–25.

——, WALKER, J.D. & BEAUFAIT, M.S. 1985. Structural discordance between Neogene detachments and frontal Sevier thrusts, central Mormon Mountains, southern Nevada. *Tectonics*, **4**, 213–46.

——, SPENCER, J.E., BURCHFIEL, B.C. & GUTH, P.L. 1982. Magnitude of crustal extension in the southern Great Basin. *Geology*, **10**, 499–502.

A.M.C. ŞENGÖR, İ.T.Ü. Maden Fakültesi, Jeoloji Bölümü, Teşvikiye, İstanbul 80394, Turkey.

Extension in Thrust Belts

Extensional tectonics in the Honshu fore-arc, Japan: integrated results of DSDP Legs 57, 87 and reprocessed multichannel seismic reflection profiles

J.K. Leggett, N. Lundberg, C.J. Bray, J.P. Cadet, D.E. Karig, R.J. Knipe & R. von Huene

SUMMARY: Leg 57 drilling on the Honshu fore-arc revealed late-Oligocene arc volcanism at Site 439 just 90 km from the axis of the present Japan Trench, on a basement palaeo-high. This, the Oyashio landmass, is defined by outboard- and inboard-onlapping reflectors in the thick (up to > 2 km) inner trench-slope section. The Neogene section at Site 439 documents subsidence of the Oyashio landmass from a late-Oligocene position at or near wavebase, and subduction erosion was invoked by Leg 57 scientists to explain the anomalously narrow late-Oligocene arc–trench gap. Hole 584, drilled during Leg 87 just upslope from the mid-slope terrace above the outer edge of the Oyashio landmass, produced equally unexpected results. Though it failed to reach basement, penetration of 940 m of slope strata down to middle Miocene revealed below 200 m sub-bottom a progressive down-hole increase in dips to as much as 70°. Palaeomagnetic data indicate that dips are trenchward. Spot-coring in holes 500 m upslope and 700 m downslope revealed a similar peculiar geometry. However, lithostratigraphic and biostratigraphic markers are sub-horizontal or only gently inclined trenchward when correlated between the three holes. Landward-dipping listric normal faults, not imaged in the seismic records available at the time of drilling, are hence required within the slope section. Numbers of such faults, giving step-wise displacements of limited overall vertical displacement, would explain the sub-horizontal markers. This extensional geometry is substantiated by healed, predominantly normal, microfaults which occur throughout the tilted section. Detailed structural analysis reveals that tilting occurred progressively from middle Miocene through earliest Pliocene, was preceded by development of a pervasive vein structure, and was both preceded and accompanied by extensional microfaulting. Microstructural observations, and the apparent restriction of kindred structures in other active margin cores to non-accretionary forearcs, lead us to ascribe the vein structure to an initial response of semi-lithified slope sediments to extension, rather than to hydrofracturing alone.

The multichannel record on which Site 584 drilling was based showed slope-parallel reflectors, and gave no clue to the structure actually encountered with the drill. However, a line through Site 439 some 70 km upslope reveals landward-dipping normal faults, albeit without the rotations required to explain the geometry at Site 584. Subsequent reprocessing of a seismic record crossing the equivalent position of Site 584 40 km S shows considerable small-scale faulting like that around Site 439. This, in concert with the core-scale structural data, suggests tectonic jostling with an extensional fragmentation ranging from microstructure to blocks 300–500 m across. Such tectonism increases in intensity towards the mid-slope terrace until coherent reflections can no longer be resolved.

Basement is either a Cretaceous–Palaeogene accretionary complex akin to the Shimanto Belt of SW Japan (more likely), or old crystalline rocks akin to those exposed onland in the Kitikami massif (less likely). Whatever its nature, low-angle landward-dipping reflectors (LDRs) are a common feature of the basement rocks. The listric landward-dipping faults generated in the slope sediments during Miocene–early-Pliocene subduction erosion may accordingly be explained in two ways. If the LDRs in the basement are old thrusts, they could conceivably have been reactivated as normal faults which propagated up into the cover as it accumulated. Alternatively, the faults in the cover may sole on low-angle detachment faults within the slope section. Present data only allow a first look at what must be a highly complex three-dimensional extensional setting.

A principal result of the DSDP–IPOD programme of active-margin drilling, launched in the mid 1970s, has been to show that subduction accretion is but one of a spectrum of processes operating in forearcs. Some forearcs, such as the Marianas (Hussong & Uyeda 1982) and Guatemala (Aubouin et al. 1982) accrete little or none of the sediment cover of the oceanic plate descending beneath them, and indeed may be receding. This process, known as subduction erosion (Scholl et al. 1980), has profound implications for the evolution of continents and for the reconstruction of orogenic belts. Here we examine the structural effects of a prolonged phase of subduction erosion (≈ 20 My) on an argillaceous slope succession which accumulated on subsiding and extending basement off Honshu, NE Japan, during the subduction of Pacific crust during the Miocene–early Pliocene. This

From COWARD, M.P., DEWEY, J.F. & HANCOCK, P.L. (eds), 1987, *Continental Extensional Tectonics*, Geological Society Special Publication No. 28, pp. 593–609.

paper emphasizes work on core-scale structural features from a critical DSDP site (584, Leg 87) on the modern mid-slope immediately above the outer margin of the basement domain which was affected by subduction erosion, but in addition reviews pertinent aspects of our cumulative experience of the study area on DSDP cruises 57 (R.V.H., J.P.C), 87 (D.E.K., C.J.B., J.P.C., J.K.L.) and our post-cruise studies of structural geology (N.L., J.K.L., R.J.K.), physical properties (D.E.K., C.J.B.) and in reprocessing and interpretation of seismic data in the drilled area, plus subsequent Seabeam mapping (R.V.H., J.P.C.)

Geological history of the Honshu fore-arc

Geological setting

Under NE Honshu, oceanic crust of the Pacific Plate subducts eastward at rates of 8–10 cm yr^{-1}, and has generated a calc-alkaline volcanic arc dating from the late Oligocene or early Miocene

along the spine of Honshu some 300 km from the Japan Trench (Fujioka 1985). The Honshu fore-arc is of the shelved variety (Dickinson & Seely 1979), sloping gently from the coast across a broad deep-sea terrace to reach a depth of 1600 m as much as 140 km offshore. To the E of this point the trench slope dips at an average 4–5° to the trench axis at a depth of 7300 m ≈ 200 km offshore, being divided into upper- and lower-slope domains by a continuous, ≈ 1 km broad mid-slope terrace.

Figure 1 shows the location of seismic lines published to date in the study area, and locations on them of the DSDP sites. These seismic lines, details of which are to be found in Nasu *et al.* (1979, 1980) and von Huene *et al.* (1980, 1982), reveal that the Honshu fore-arc consists of four structural elements. Figure 2, a line drawing of the profile JNOC 1, illustrates three of these. Below the slope and deep-sea terrace a Neogene slope section between ≈ 1 and 1.5 km thick unconformably overlies a basement characterized by common landward-dipping reflectors. The basal-slope strata lap both outboard (near Sites 438/439) and inboard (not visible on JNOC 1: see line P849 of von Huene

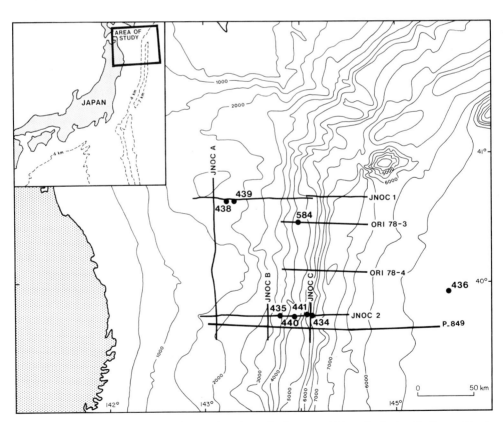

FIG. 1. Regional setting of Deep Sea Drilling Project sites and reference multichannel seismic reflection profiles in the Honshu fore-arc.

et al. 1982), defining a 160 km broad palaeo-high on the basement under the modern upper slope. Rocks of the basement are evidently truncated under the mid-slope terrace, abutting there against much lower velocity rocks (1.7–3.0 km sec^{-1}) under the lower slope. The fourth structural element, a fore-arc basin containing up to 12 km of fill (the Sanriku basin) underlies the innermost 70–80 km of the submarine fore-arc (von Huene *et al.* 1982, fig. 5).

Leg 56 & 57 results

Prior to IPOD drilling, probably the most popular explanation advanced by geophysicists to explain the seismic data was steady-state accretion, a process involving uninterrupted imbrication and uplift of thrust slices of ocean-plate and trench material. Regional geology, in particular that of the Cretaceous–Miocene Shimanto Belt (a subduction–accretion terrane exposed in an equivalent position in the SW Japan fore-arc), and the 'geosynclinal' Cretaceous Yezo Group exposed to the N in Hokkaido, indicated that the Honshu accretionary prism may have grown from Cretaceous to present. However, the drilling data clearly showed a more complicated story. Penetration through the Neogene slope section at Sites 438/439 revealed that:

1 The basement had been at or near sea-level in the late Oligocene, and had subsided since then to its present depth of ≈6 km.
2 Arc volcanism had taken place during the late Oligocene in the immediate vicinity of Sites

438/439, just 90 km from the axis of the modern trench and just 15–20 km above the oceanic crust currently subducting below the Honshu fore-arc.
3 The uppermost part of the basement at Site 439 consists of cleaved Cretaceous siltstones of deep-water (> 2 km) character.

Interpreting these observations and other data from elsewhere in the fore-arc (including industrial wells in the Sanriku basin), Leg 57 scientists proposed the following sequence of events:

1 Construction during Cretaceous times of the Shimanto-type accretionary prism, whose internal fabric gives rise to the landward-dipping reflectors which characterize the basement in seismic reflection records, and behind which the Sanriku fore-arc basin was constructed.
2 A long Palaeogene interval without volcanism: a time of little or no subduction, for which a change in relative plate motion after passage of the Pacific–Kula spreading ridge under Japan may have been responsible.
3 Uplift during the Palaeogene eventually exposing basement in the fore-arc across a 160 km-wide welt known as the Oyashio Landmass (von Huene *et al.* 1978).
4 In the late Oligocene reinitiation of subduction, subsidence of the Oyashio Landmass, and inception of volcanism: first briefly in the E on the Oyashio Landmass itself, and later to the W of the Cretaceous arc volcanics along the present northern Honshu arc.
5 Tectonic removal of the outer part of the fore-

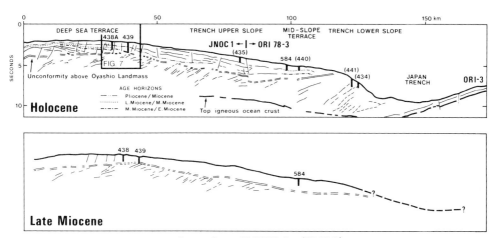

FIG. 2. Line drawing of part of time section JNOC-1 (after von Huene *et al.* 1982) and part of ORI 78-3 (after Kagami *et al.* 1986) showing locations of DSDP Sites (438, 439 and 584 actual, all others in projected along-strike positions—see Fig. 3). Box around upper sites shows location of Fig. 7. Late-Miocene reconstruction of surface of Oyashio Landmass involves an unknown amount of subduction erosion before the onset of Plio-Quaternary accretion and uplift below the lower slope.

arc by subduction erosion from the Miocene to the early Pliocene.

6 Reversion to limited accretion, and uplift, during the late Pliocene.

The fifth point, perhaps the most surprising implication of the Leg 57 drilling campaign, hinges on the following evidence:

1 Fore-arc volcanism on the Oyashio Landmass: namely, rhyolithic and dacitic boulders up to more than a metre across in a 50-m thick, monolithic basal conglomerate in Hole 439, plus local high-velocity rocks of probable igneous origin in the basement.

2 The required removal of a large volume of material to explain subsidence of the margin.

3 The difficulties posed by regional geology in explaining the anomalously narrow arc–trench gap by strike-slip removal of fore-arc elements (von Huene *et al.* 1982).

The evidence, though not completely compelling, is none the less the only explanation offered, especially in the light of the growing catalogue of convergent margins where truncated basement terranes seem to be most easily explained by subduction erosion (e.g. Peru–Chile—Kulm *et al.* 1981; Hussong & Wipperman 1981; von Huene *et al.* 1985; Middle America Trench off Mexico—Watkins *et al.* 1981; Aleutian Trench—Scholl *et al.* 1977).

The late-Pliocene reversion to partial subduction accretion was proposed to explain a wedge of low-velocity strata below the lower slope, possible back-tilting of those strata, and uplift elsewhere in the fore-arc (benthic foraminifera at Site 438/9 reveal a Plio–Quaternary shallowing trend after the prolonged subsidence of Miocene–early-Pliocene times—von Huene *et al.* 1982, fig. 10). But mass-wastage as a result of oversteepening on the lower slope, and local accretion of the slumped debris is a more recent explanation (Cadet *et al.* 1985, in press). This is based on Seabeam bathymetry obtained over 18,000 km² of the Honshu fore-arc during Leg 3 of the French–Japanese KAIKO project.

Leg 87 results

An unsettled facet of the Leg 57 discoveries was whether or not the unconformity seaward of Site 439 was produced by subaerial erosion. Definition of the outboard margin of the Oyashio Landmass is constrained only by the westward onlap of reflectors at the base of the slope section (in a small part of record P849 and perhaps in JNOC 2: von Huene *et al.* 1982, fig. 6). Correlating these reflectors as well as they could, von Huene *et al.* concluded that the subsidence of Oyashio was gradual beginning inboard in the late Oligocene, with the last sub-

mergence of local outboard highs during the early Miocene. If correct, the subsidence rate of the outboard flank of the Oyashio Landmass, currently 40 km from the axis of the trench, would have been at least 5 km in 10–14 My—a rate about as great as the Neogene subsidence rates of the Los Angeles and Ventura basins.

Site 584 was included in Leg 87 to address this problem. Situated immediately upslope from the mid-slope terrace and 42.5 km upslope from the trench axis at a depth of 4078 m, the chosen site overlies the seaward-most resolvable extent of the unconformity on Cretaceous?/Palaeogene basement in a place where the unconformity rises to within 1.4 km of the sea-floor (Fig. 3). Details of the seismic line on which drilling was sited, ORI3, can be found in Nasu *et al.* (1979). Near-horizontal reflectors in the slope sequence progressively lose coherence seaward across this portion of the upper slope, and a reflective package between ≈500 and 825 m sub-bottom at Site 584 is traceable only a short distance further seaward. Shipboard scientists expected to encounter a thick Pliocene and upper Miocene section of deep-water mudrocks, shallowing downward through middle-Miocene strata documenting erosion of the Oyashio Landmass. But 954 m of penetration, to a total depth of 4114 m, saw the drill in middle-Miocene mudrocks with bathyal-to-abyssal trace fossils (*Zoophycos–Teichichnus–Planolites–Nereites* assemblage) and no sign of shallow-marine sediments. The hole caved in leaving ≈400 m of untested sediments above basement, showing that the subsidence of the outboard flank of the Oyashio Landmass had not been delayed as long as had initially been thought to be the case. More importantly, the good recovery of mudrocks through Hole 584 (average 51%) revealed a suite of spectacular core-scale structures, yielding clues to the way in which the sediment section deposited on the Japan Trench inner slope accommodated itself to extensional stresses as the fore-arc subsided in response to subduction erosion.

Detailed descriptions of the sediments recovered are provided by Kagami *et al.* (1986). In brief, the four lithostratigraphic units recognized by shipboard scientists begin with 4 m of Pleistocene diatomaceous mud underlain without lithological contrast by soft lower Pliocene diatomaceous mud, laminated in part and lithifying near 88 m sub-bottom. Beginning 231 m sub-bottom a third lithological unit, also diatomaceous mudstone, is distinguished by fine-sand and silt interlayers. The Pliocene–Miocene boundary, at ≈460 m, is not marked by a lithological contrast. Diatom content is lower in the fourth unit, below 536 m sub-bottom, and this unit is divisible into a very distinctive upper sub-unit of mud turbidites, comprising individual turbidites up to 45 cm thick, and an intensely

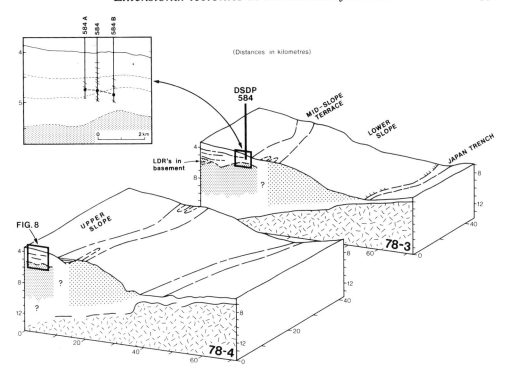

FIG. 3. Schematic block diagram of outer part of Honshu fore-arc, and summary of drilling at Site 584 (inset, after Karig *et al.* 1983). Vertical exaggeration 2.5 times for block diagram, 2 times for inset. Ocean crust dashed. Low-velocity rocks below lower slope dotted, basement grey (for details of velocity structure see text and von Huene *et al.* 1982). Reflectors in upper-slope sequence illustrative only. Note back-tilting of mid-slope terrace strata in 78-4 and uncertainties of the contact relationship between upper-slope and lower-slope domains. Bedding attitudes in Site 584 holes are illustrative; the thickly dashed line between the three closed circles represents the most prominent correlatable horizon—the upper-Miocene/mid-Miocene boundary. The level between the two thinly dashed lines which cross the Site 584 holes mid-way in the slope sequence is a zone of vague slope-parallel reflectors. For further details see text.

bioturbated mudrock of 'Paisley' appearance. Estimates of the sedimentation rate from diatom biostratigraphy and magnetostratigraphy indicate an increase from ≈ 20 m My^{-1} in the middle Miocene to >100 m My^{-1} in the Pliocene (Niitsuma & Akiba 1986).

Regional extension: dipping beds at Site 584

Despite the relative lithological homogeneity of the diatomaceous mudrocks recovered at Site 584, bedding orientation is consistently clear in cores. Marked by primary laminations of silt and fine sand, by colour variations, and by aligned originally sub-horizontal burrows (especially *Zoophycos*), dips vary in a regular fashion. In the upper 250 m beds are horizontal, but below this level they steepen systematically to a maximum of 60 to 70° at 750 m, below which they are slightly less steep (Fig. 3). Detailed data are provided by Lundberg & Leggett (1986, figs 5 & 6).

After persistently good recovery, Hole 584 caved in at 941 m. Two further holes were drilled at Site 584, 584A 524 m upslope and 584B 701 m downslope, to test the regional development of the dipping strata. Spot-cores and wash-cores, shown illustratively in Fig. 3 (after Karig *et al.* 1983) and described in detail by Kagami *et al.* (1986) and Lundberg & Leggett (1986), reveal intervals dipping at essentially the same angle as beds at equivalent depth in Hole 584. Palaeomagnetic measurements show that the direction of dip is consistently to the NE or E, i.e. trenchward (Niitsuma 1986). Given the regular nature of the tilting implied by this observation, it is clear that, unless the slope section is faulted, individual stratigraphic levels in Hole 584 should be encountered considerably shallower in the upslope hole (584A) and considerably deeper in the downslope hole (584B). In fact, lithostratigraphic and biostratigraphic marker horizons traceable between the three holes are not offset by more than 100 m.

We dismiss growth folding as a means of explaining the geometry at 584 on the basis of the lack of folds in seismic records, of the unlikelihood in any case of drilling three E-dipping limbs so close together, and of the implications of the plethora of extensional microstructures described in the next section. At the time of drilling we favoured normal faulting as a means of resolving the problem, even though such faults were not at the time resolvable on seismic lines crossing the mid-slope (Karig *et al.* 1983). Listric normal faults are capable of tilting the section in the manner observed. Either multiple episodes or one protracted phase of listric normal faulting might explain the simple downhole increase in dips, and the more complex zone at the base of the hole made up of small domains with internally consistent dips. Such tilting evidently took place from at least the mid-Miocene to early Pliocene, since the youngest affected strata are lower Pliocene at 250 m. The presence of numerous such faults giving step-wise offset of limited overall vertical displacement would satisfactorily explain the maintenance of comparable depths to correlatable horizons between the 1200 m spread of holes. We shall see in the next two sections that the disposition of small-scale structures is in support of this interpretation and that recent reprocessing of seismic lines has begun to image the kind of large-scale geometry required.

Small-scale extension: structural features at Site 584

Site 584 cores display an abundance of structural features in Miocene (and to a lesser extent in lower Pliocene) sediments. These we categorize principally as 'healed' fractures and veins. Tensional crack fills are minor features of the section. We describe the structural features in turn, using drawings of representative cores, presenting evidence for relative timing of the features, and comparing our data with structural features observed in Leg 56 and 57 cores.

Veins

Closely spaced, irregular, locally anastomosing, claystone-filled veins are ubiquitous in Miocene cores, especially in the lower portion of the section. These are almost all perpendicular to bedding (Fig. 4). The shallowest occurrence is 385 m sub-bottom. They tend to concentrate in particular levels and commonly form bands from several mm to several dm thick (e.g. Fig. 4e). The vein bands may comprise predominantly isolated strands (e.g. Fig. 5) or intense braiding networks (Fig. 4a); the latter especially in cores lower in the section, where

veins commonly permeate the entire length of core-sections.

They strike parallel to the inclined bedding (Fig. 4b), meaning that they are orientated more-or-less N–S parallel to the margin. Individual veins are commonly slightly sigmoidal, with the seams thicker in the middle portions (e.g. Fig. 4c, e). Locally the veins are steeply inclined with respect to bedding. They commonly show minute (< mm) stepped normal displacements of fine laminae (e.g. Fig. 4c) or burrows (e.g. Fig. 4e), but individual offsets only rarely exceed 1 mm. Lithological control on vein formation is evident locally on a small scale. Vein networks terminate in places at fine-sand layers (e.g. Fig. 4d). The veins everywhere post-date bioturbation but pre-date healed fractures (Fig. 5). They greatly resemble the 'beard-like structure' described by Ogawa (1980) in Neogene tuffaceous siltstones from the Shimanto Belt on the Miura and Boso peninsulas.

The same fabric in DSDP cores from previous holes in the Honshu fore-arc has been called 'dewatering veins' (Arthur *et al.* 1980; Carson *et al.* 1982). A kindred fabric retrieved in cores from the Guatemala lower slope has been called 'vein structure' (Cowan 1983). We follow Cowan in choosing a purely descriptive term, since whereas most workers agree that these veins serve as dewatering conduits, we are not convinced of this. Similar features in DSDP cores from the southern Mexico margin grade into true spaced foliation (Lundberg & Moore 1982), and bands of slightly sigmoidal veins at 450 and 930 m sub-bottom are bounded by bedding-parallel shear zones in such a way as to resemble tension gashes (cf. Cowan 1983). Furthermore, microscopic observations have thus far not revealed injection features, and the veins in thin-section are defined by concentrations of realigned phyllosilicates orientated parallel to vein boundaries. The consistent orientation of vein structures perpendicular to bedding in nearly all reported occurrences (Arthur *et al.* 1980; Carson *et al.* 1982; Lundberg & Moore 1982; Cowan 1983; Cowan *et al.* 1984; Ogawa & Miyata 1985) argues that it developed prior to tilting. Vein boundaries detour around quartz grains in a fairly intricate manner, and radiolarian tests are commonly well preserved within veins, so pressure solution is apparently not the primary mechanism for development (Lundberg & Moore 1982).

Two principal mechanisms might lead to the formation of veins in the Honshu fore-arc: dilation of the sediment by an applied stress (e.g. Cowan 1983) or hydrofracturing (Carson *et al.* 1982). Ritger (1985) has emphasized the possibility of both processes operating in concert.

Carson *et al.* (1982), stressing high fluid pressures which characterize fore-arcs (e.g. von

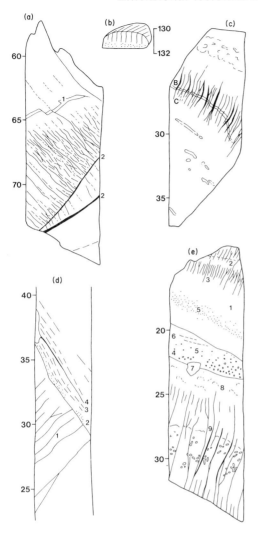

FIG. 4. Drawings of vein arrays in Site 584 cores. Scale in cm, referring to depth within the core section. (a) Intense braided array in homogeneous dark greenish lamination (1), which has both normal and reverse micro-offsets. Dark seams (2) cut microveins at apparent low inclination, being moderately inclined in dip view. 584, Core 95, section 1, 905 m sub-bottom in upper Miocene. (b) Veins commencing above a silty layer form a clear lineation on bedding. 584, Core 57, section 1, 905 m sub-bottom in upper Miocene. (c) Stepped micro-offsets of a paler mudstone lamination (or elongate burrow) by a network of veins. Note sigmoidal shapes and thicker claystone fill in the middle portions of several veins. 584, Core 95, section 3, ≈906 m sub-bottom in mid-Miocene. (d) Veins (1) terminating at a fine-sand bed (2). Silty laminae within the fine-sand bed (3) are truncated by a healed fracture (4) which cuts plane of view in strike section. 584, Core 83, section 3, 790 m sub-bottom in mid-Miocene. (e) Spaced array. Upper homogeneous dark greenish-grey mudstone (1) contains two narrow arrays (2 & 3). A lamination of darker material shows normal micro-offsets (2). A layer of dusky yellow sideritic medium–coarse sand grains has a large angular sideritic clast at the base (7), is graded (4) though very matrix-rich, and shows vague parallel lamination (6). Lower veinlet array terminates in an intensely bioturbated, 'Paisley' mudstone layer (8). Veinlets are slightly sigmoidal as in (c), and cut Chondrites traces.

Huene & Lee 1982), argue that hydrofracturing is the principal contributory factor. Karig *et al.* (1983), Lundberg & Leggett (1986) and Knipe (in press), on the other hand, suggest that the structure developed as a result of primary, regional, extensional stresses on the slope. Evidence for this includes normal micro-offsets, the tension-gash aspect of some vein arrays, their orientation parallel to the margin, the lack of injection features in thin section, and, perhaps most critically, the evident restriction worldwide of veins in DSDP cores to fore-arc regions characterized by normal faulting (the landward reference sites of the Japan transect, of the southern Mexico transect, and in the Mariana and Guatemala fore-arcs: Lundberg & Moore, in press). The structure is absent, or nearly so, in cores from sites that are in clearly compressional regimes: the basal trench slopes of the Nankai fore-arc (Lundberg & Karig 1986), the Barbados fore-arc (Cowan *et al.* 1984) and the Mexico fore-arc (Lundberg & Moore 1982). Elevated pore-pressures resulting from dewatering deposits underthrust beneath the fore-arc should be at least as high and probably higher, below an accretionary lower trench slope as below an extending mid- to upper-slope, and yet vein arrays are not always a feature of slope deposits overlying the former. On balance, then, vein arrays appear to reflect regional extension, and the orientation of veins perpendicular to bedding suggests layer-parallel extension prior to tilting. Furthermore, the fact that veins strike roughly parallel to bedding, in concert with palaeomagnetic evidence for eastward dips of bedding, indicates E–W extension, perpendicular to the

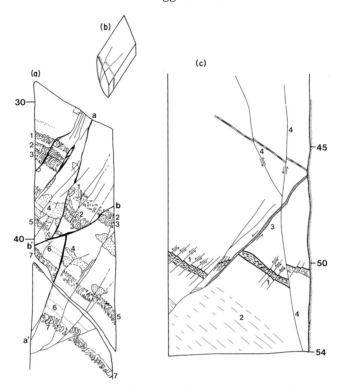

FIG. 5. Drawings of normal microfaults (healed fractures) in Site 584 cores. Scale as Fig. 4. (a) Conjugate set of microfaults (a–a', b+b') cutting burrows and veins. Correlatable components are: 1 sinistral *Zoophycos* trail, 2 & 3 amalgamated dextral *Zoophycos* trails (2 before 3), 4 originally aligned olive burrow mottles, 5 pelleted *Zoophycos*, 6 colour laminations, 7 fat *Zoophycos*.

Sequence of events: (i) burrowing, (ii) anastomosing veins form perpendicular to bedding with only up to several mm, or no, offset; (iii) main fractures form (conjugate, acute-bisector vertical, striking offset); (iv) main fractures heal by deposition of claystone in fractures; (v) strata tilted. 584A, Core 2, section 3.
(b) as (a), core viewed in three dimensions to show strike-parallelism of bedding and normal faults.
(c) Open and filled microfaults cutting granular burrow fill. Bedding is picked out by elongate burrow fill (1) and silty laminae in mudstone (2). Principal offset occurs on the left-dipping fracture (3) accommodated by minor normal offsets on parallel minor filled fractures. Filled fracture, sub-vertical but at a high angle to bedding (4), cuts an earlier very low-angle fracture. 584, Core 49, section 1, 45–54 cm, ≈460 sub-bottom in upper Miocene.

strike of the margin and with the same sense as that required to explain the large-scale normal faults argued for in the previous section.

Microfaults

First observed at 89 m sub-bottom, steeply inclined dark grey claystone-filled seams are a common feature of the 584 section, being in general more abundant down-hole. Lundberg & Leggett (1986, fig. 5) present a detailed structural log and here we comment only on the main features. The seams are commonly straight, generally less than a mm but locally several mm in width. They are in the main part either perpendicular or at a high angle to

bedding, which they cut with offsets which are most commonly small (core-scale) and almost invariably (but not exclusively) normal. Many beds are offset in mm–cm-scale steps (e.g. Fig. 5c) and the largest true throw (i.e. down-dip on the claystone seam) observed is 2.6 cm (Fig. 5a). Some seams show offsets in excess of the part of the fracture recovered in the core, but these are few. Slickensides are common and are predominantly dip-slip (> 70° rake). We referred to these claystone seams in our shipboard descriptions as 'healed fractures', feeling that the initial offsets were most likely made on open fractures in which clays deposited later, perhaps by through-going fluids, caused re-annealing. Here we prefer a description which makes no assumptions about the mode of origin.

Like the vein arrays, the microfaults strike predominantly sub-parallel to bedding (e.g. Fig. 5b) and hence are a further manifestation of E–W extension. Eleven cases of microfaults, broadly conjugate with respect to bedding, and with the angular relationships of the example shown in Fig. 5a, occur in the 584 section; all show normal-fault offsets. This observation provides a strong argument for fracturing prior to tilting of strata. However, seven determinations, near the bottom of the hole, of microfaults conjugate with respect to present orientations suggest a post-tilting origin for at least some (Niitsuma 1986).

Most of the microfaults are straight or nearly so. However, listric normal faults provide a potential mechanism for tilting of the section at Site 584, and they are also represented in at least two instances by core-scale features (Lundberg & Leggett 1986, fig. 11).

Healed fractures are present at a surprisingly shallow level, 89 m, in Site 584. We have noted the absence of upper-Pliocene strata in Hole 584; simple extrapolation of sediment-accumulation rates in lower Pliocene strata suggests that this hiatus may represent the deposition and subsequent erosion of an interval on the order of several hundred metres thick, and thus the shallow fractures may have been more deeply buried when they formed.

Fault zones

A fault zone located at 760 sub-bottom in mid–Miocene diatomaceous claystone exhibits a range of deformation features (Fig. 6a). The fault is 2–3 cm wide and marked by a central, dark movement zone containing mudstone lenses often arranged in discontinuous bands. Bedding is usually preserved in these lenses and is rotated, on a microscopic scale, at their margins towards parallelism with the fault zone. Breccia zones (1 cm thick) are present each side of the central fault zone and thin fracture arrays occur adjacent to these.

A detailed investigation of this fault zone, using electron microscopy, is reported by Knipe (in press). The deformation mechanism involved in the faulting was disaggregation, grain-boundary sliding together with the fracturing of fossils, and Knipe (in press) suggests that the different fabrics preserved reflect deformation at different displacement rates. The microstructures preserved at the edge of the main movement zone are used to discuss the different modes of fault expansion operating during the displacement. All the microstructures present in the

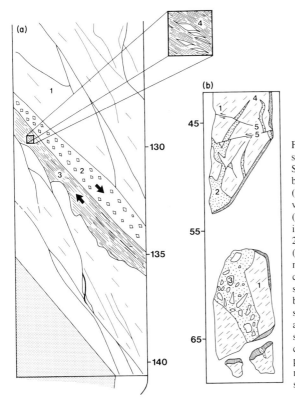

Fig. 6. Drawings of fault zone and crack-fill structures in Site 584 cores. Scale as Fig. 4. (a) Shear zone in steeply dipping mudstone (1) with a bedding-parallel upper brecciated mudstone layer (2) and lower intensely sheared claystone with very fine disseminated pyrite (3). 'Fish' structure (flow-smeared mudstone chips), shown in inset, indicates normal movement. 584, Core 80, section 2, ≈760 m sub-bottom in mid-Miocene. (b) Crack-fill system in grey to dark olive-grey mudstone which manifests bedding as colour-change laminations, shown schematically (1). Fine sand fills a wide, irregular crack perpendicular to bedding. In the upper part of the crack the fill is solely sand (2), but in the lower part highly angular chips of mudstone (3) form a matrix-supported fill. In the upper part other sand-filled cracks penetrate the mudstone, including one parallel to bedding (4). These are cut by microfaults (5). 584, Core 71, section 2, ≈725 m sub-bottom in upper Miocene.

fault zone are indicative of a normal-fault displacement of unknown magnitude.

Crack-fills

A singular sandstone vein system 725 m sub-bottom is up to 5 cm across (Fig. 6b). The main vein is perpendicular to bedding with slightly irregular margins stepped somewhat to one side, tapering down over a ≈ 10-cm exposed length to zero. The section is broken by two thin zones of drilling breccia. In the lower part of the vein angular chips of mudstone, identical to the host rock, are scattered in the fill forming a matrix-supported breccia. In the upper part offshoots of the vein penetrate laterally both parallel to and at a high angle to bedding. The upper part of the vein, and the offshoots, are sand-filled. Unfortunately, the transition between the breccia and sand-filled portions is obscured by the drilling breccia zone.

This feature is best explained as a large tensional-crack system which was filled from above by unconsolidated sand and spalled chips of host mudstone. The angularity of the mudstone chips indicates formation in at least semi-lithified sediment, and that the extension responsible for the feature acted parallel to bedding.

Clastic dykes

Two veins ≈ 1 cm wide, 770 m sub-bottom in mid-Miocene sediment cut bedding at ≈ 70° (in dip section) and have a homogeneous silt fill. Because healed fractures are everywhere filled with material finer than the host mudrock, and almost everywhere show offsets, these silt-filled veins may best be explained as clastic dykes. Thin silt beds, relatively common in the underlying sediment, could have provided the necessary source.

Open fractures

Open fractures, relatively common in the 584 section in consolidated material, may derive from *in situ* fracturing, or from drilling or core-handling processes. Lundberg & Leggett (1986) provide a discussion of criteria useful in distinguishing these categories. In cores from Hole 584 there is no up-section transition from healed to open fractures, as recorded in Leg 57 lower-trench-slope Sites 441 and 434 (Arthur *et al.* 1980).

Slumping and synsedimentary faulting

Features best meriting interpretation as slump phenomena appear in three places. An unconformity at a high angle to bedding 110 m sub-bottom probably represents a slump scar. A probable slumped horizon occurs 557 m sub-bottom and isoclinical microfolds with detached lower limbs define a further slump unit 915 m sub-bottom.

Clear evidence for synsedimentary faulting occurs only in one place, 195 m sub-bottom where silt layers show mm-scale normal displacement on a healed fracture which several cm up-section does not displace bedding.

Comparison with previous Japan Trench sites

Structural features of Japan Trench sites drilled on DSDP Legs 56 and 57, summarized by Arthur *et al.* (1980) and Carson *et al.* (1982), include 'veins', 'fractures' and 'faults'. These are present in upper-trench-slope sites (438, 439) and lower-trench-slope sites with the exception of the shallow-penetration Site 435 (440, 441, 434); they are absent in the ocean-plate reference site (436) (Fig. 1).

Veins occurs in sets up to a maximum length of 10 cm, anastomosing but generally perpendicular to bedding, and are interpreted as dewatering conduits associated with faults. Fractures are mostly healed, dip at between 45 and 90° to bedding, commonly in conjugate sets, and with both normal and reverse offsets of up to several cm. No sediments younger than late Pliocene are deformed. The depth of consolidated sediment (defined as that requiring saw cutting) and to the first occurrence of veins and healed fractures shallows progressively towards the trench. In addition, Arthur *et al.* report that the upper 400 m of section in lower-slope sites is over-consolidated relative to upper-slope sites. They tentatively interpreted these observations as a response to tectonic stress, in addition to lithostatic stress, during consolidation in lower-trench-slope sites. A zone of open fractures (≈ 200–500 m sub-bottom) is interpreted as a corona over a healed fracture network at depth: in it fractures are held open by excess fluid pressure as indicated by the interpretation of down-hole logs and this pressure is maintained by a fine-grained low-permeability sediment cap.

Arthur *et al.* (1980) argue that such an open-fractured zone could provide an over-pressured horizon capable of reducing shear strength in the lower-slope sedimentary cover sufficient to allow downslope mass-movement even at low angles on the trench inner slope. This depends on the interpretation of open fractures in cores from lower-slope sites (440, 441, 434) as *in situ* features. Favouring this interpretation is the correlation between zones of open fractures and reverses in the density gradient, poorer recovery in the fractured intervals and the relative paucity of open fractures in sites away from the lower slope (438, 439, 436).

A confusing factor, however, is the possible role of missing upper-Pliocene and Pleistocene strata in consolidation of the lower-slope section. Holes 441 and 434 are in the axis of a submarine canyon (see JNOC cross-line C, Arthur *et al.*, fig. 7). Based on the depth of this canyon, Arthur *et al.* suggest as much as 450 m of the upper-Pliocene and Pleistocene section may be missing. However, lower-slope Site 440 (on the mid-slope terrace) has no missing section, and the deformational/dewatering features are none the less shallower than at upper-slope sites 438 and 439.

How well do data from Site 584, drilled on the upper part of the lower slope, support the concepts of excess tectonic stress affecting the lower-slope sediment cover and of over-pressuring within the slope section in a zone of open fracturing? Lithification of Site 584 sediments occurs much shallower than in the upper-slope sites and shallower than in previous lower-slope sites. Lithification at mid-slope terrace Site 440 occurred at 175 m in lower-Pleistocene sediment; trenchward at lower-slope Sites 441 and 434 it occurred at 130 and 101 m respectively, in upper-Pliocene sediment. At Site 584, (just upslope from the mid-slope terrace) lithification occurred at ≈ 85 m—though in lower-Pliocene sediment. In total contrast, at Site 438 it occurs at 430 m in upper-Miocene strata.

The first appearance of veins and microfaults in Hole 584 is similarly much higher than in upper-slope sites. Microfaults first appear in Holes 438 and 439 (upper slope) at 603 m in mid-Miocene strata. At Site 440 (mid-slope terrace) they appear at 252 m in lower-Pleistocene sediments. At Site 434 (lower slope) they apparently first appear at 255 m (though recovery was poor) in (?) lower-Pliocene sediments. Microfaults first appear in Site 584 at ≈ 240 m in lower-Pliocene sediments; veins first appear at ≈ 383 m in upper-Miocene sediments.

The data from Site 584 augment previous observations of a strong contrast between the dewatering and deformation histories in the upper- and lower-slope sediment section. Tectonic stress appears to affect the lower-slope section in addition to overburden stress, promoting earlier dewatering, lithification, and deformation. However, quantifying relative variations in these phenomena within the lower-slope domain is difficult using depth to lithification, because of the degree of subjectivity involved in assessing that state; it is further complicated by the difficulty of estimating thicknesses of any missing sediments.

In Hole 584 we detected no precursory zone of open fractures before penetrating the healed fracture networks below 240 m sub-bottom. If the open-fractured corona postulated by Arthur *et al.*, lower down the slope at Sites 441 and 434, once existed at Site 584, it has since been annealed.

The most notable difference between Site 584 and previous mid- and upper-slope sites is the high inclination of strata. In Holes 438 and 439 (upper slope) dips of 0–30° occur below 850 m (mid- and lower-Miocene strata). In Hole 440 (mid-slope terrace dips of up to 10° occur between 254–350 m (lower-Pleistocene–upper-Pliocene strata) and between 15 and 40° below 385 m (Pliocene and upper-Miocene strata). In Hole 441 (lower slope) dips vary irregularly down-hole, ranging from horizontal in the upper part to 35° and locally 70° at depth; however, no intervals of consistently steep dips occur, and near-horizontal to shallow dips persist to the base of the hole (Lundberg & Moore, in press).

Reprocessed seismic data

Two seismic lines reprocessed since the Leg 87 drilling shed new light on the Neogene tectonics of the Honshu fore-arc and go some way towards equating the two main conflicts between previous seismic interpretations (e.g. von Huene *et al.* 1982) and the stratigraphy recovered at Site 584. These new data are discussed fully by von Huene *et al.* (in press) and reviewed in brief here.

JNOC-1, unmigrated at the time Site 439 results were synthesized, was reprocessed recently and made available to the DSDP community. A reinterpretation of seismic stratigraphy capitalizing on reduced uncertainties over correlation across a major fault just seaward of Site 439 (Fig. 7), indicates that total inundation of the Oyashio Landmass was 5–8 My earlier than previously estimated by von Huene *et al.* (1982). This reduces the otherwise very high subsidence rate required of the Oyashio Landmass and equates with the fact that Leg 87 drilling proved the Site 584 area (above the outer flank of the Oyashio Landmass) to be at bathyal- to abyssal-depths by the mid-Miocene.

The second conflict concerns the disparity between seismic stratigraphy and drilled stratigraphy in the Site 584 area. ORI 78-3, the line on which Site 584 was based, shows diffuse, essentially slope-parallel reflections in the cover section (Fig. 3). As we have seen based on the drilling, however, complex predominantly landward-dipping normal faults must cut the slope strata, which are rotated trenchward up to 70°. ORI 78-4, a record equivalent to the one crossing Site 584 but to the S was reprocessed by von Huene *et al.* The sharpened imaging reveals the required structure in the upper 1 sec of data under the slope (Fig. 8). Application of migration before stacking, which can greatly sharpen reflections at bed terminations and dipping layers, reveals between CDP 160 and 300 (Fig. 8) a series of predominantly landward-tilted straight

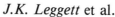

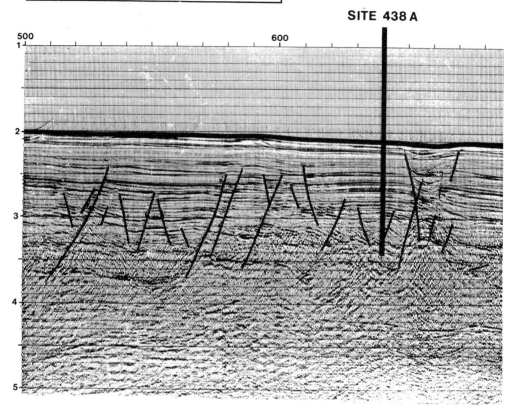

FIG. 7. Reprocessed part of profile JNOC-1. For location see Fig. 2. Depth in sec, 100 shot points=5 km. Note penetration below Cretaceous unconformity of Site 439, and predominantly landward-dipping normal faults tilting slope strata but terminating in Pliocene section. For processing parameters and further geological details see text.

and curved normal faults before reflections became increasingly smeared together.

Steeper dips, not imagable by the seismic technique, can exist at depth. Seaward of CDP 300 the quality of the record deteriorates probably as a result of more complex rotations. The appearance of residual diffraction tails which dip W and were not removed by the migration process indicates that they originate from out of the plane of section. The Cretaceous unconformity is just above 7 sec, and 300–500 m of relief is visible on the erosion surface.

A contributing factor to the explanation for slope-parallel reflections in a moderately- to steeply-dipping sequence of mudrocks in the Site 584 area appears to lie in the lithostratigraphy. Mud turbidites concentrate in the 584 section through the interval in question. Profiles of physical properties reflect the increase in abundance of fine sand and silt through this zone (Kagami *et al.* 1986). Hence, given that overall offsets of stratigraphy are

relatively minor despite the steep inclination of beds in the Site 584 area, the zone of prospective impedance contrasts would be in essence slope-parallel.

Discussion

Extensional stresses appear to have been dominant in the Honshu fore-arc during the accumulation of the mid-Miocene through lower-Pliocene section drilled at Site 584 on the outer part of the upper slope. The study of cores, and a subsequently reprocessed seismic line, shows that large listric normal faults, dipping landward, rotated bedding significantly. This discovery reveals that the large-scale extension, manifested further upslope in the Site 438/439 area by normal faults discernible in seismic section JNOC-1, is a regional attribute of the fore-arc; it furthermore makes sense of dipping strata penetrated in previous DSDP holes on the

SITE 439

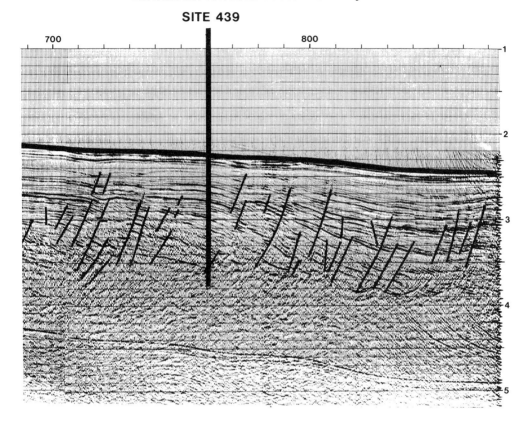

upper slope. Core-scale structures in the Site 584 section comprise vein arrays, microfaults (normal faults including conjugate sets and listric faults), and sand-filled extensional fractures. Palaeomagnetic investigations show that all these reflect E–W, or downslope, extension.

The excellent recovery at Site 584 permits a confident interpretation of the sequence of structures. Primary depositional structures in the slope mudrocks were first extensively reworked by bioturbation, and locally were affected by surficial slumping. Following initial consolidation, microcracks (which would later form vein arrays) developed in response to dilation caused by downslope extension. Locally, larger irregular cracks opened up, and were filled by sand-rich slurries. Once the mudrocks had lithified still further and after clays, probably deposited from dewatering fluids, had sealed the microcracks, through-going normal faults developed. These in turn were sealed by deposition of clay seams along them. After genesis of most (but not all) of the microfaults, the strata began to tilt as listric normal growth faults propagated up through the slope section.

This sequence of structural features is manifested in the whole 584 section below 200 m sub-bottom, and, together with the fact that dips increase progressively down-hole, argues for a continuum of extension and an upward-propagating sequence of structures. Thus, while strata began to tilt against a listric normal fault deeper in the slope section, more recently deposited sediments were dilating, and later failing, before being tilted in their turn. Following tilting, additional healed normal faults attest to continued extension. Minor reverse faults developed below 555 m sub-bottom are difficult to fit into the picture, however, due to a lack of definitive cross-cutting relationships.

Stratigraphic relationships at Site 584 require that the major listric faults are fairly closely spaced and this is confirmed in the seismic line in which the structures are imaged (Fig. 8). Hence, fault planes responsible for rotations must cross the drilled section in Hole 584. Despite overall excellent recovery, several zones of very poor retrieval were encountered (cores 77, 82, 84, 85, 91, 92, 97 and 98). Adjacent to each of these zones recovered cores display intervals more than usually riddled

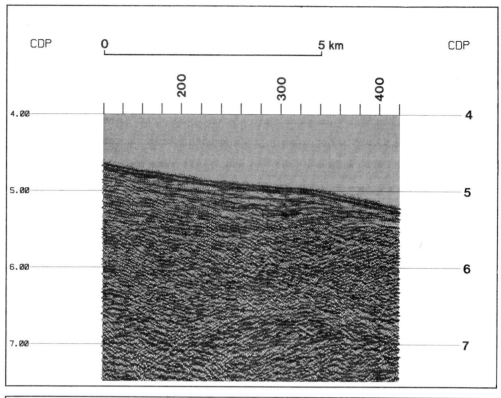

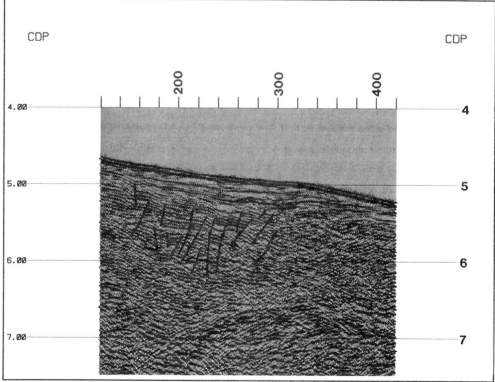

FIG. 8. Uninterpreted and interpreted sections of reprocessed part of profile ORI 73-4. For location see Fig. 3. Vertical exaggeration ≈2.5 × . Note 300–500 m relief on Cretaceous unconformity at 6.7–6.9 sec, and tilting of slope section by landward-dipping normal faults 300–500 m apart, resolvable in upper part of slope section only. For processing parameters and further geological details see text.

with healed fractures. In these the orientations appear random, and the senses of offset vary. Such zones offer candidates for the passage of large-scale faults through the section.

Large-scale listric normal faults such as those in the outer part of the Honshu fore-arc are more usually associated with Biscay-type passive margins. However, on such margins the faults almost all dip oceanward rather than landward (Bally *et al.* 1981). It is not immediately obvious why the faults should not dip oceanward too on a subsiding and extending active margin such as the Miocene–early-Pliocene Honshu fore-arc. However, recent geological and geophysical mapping of extensional systems elsewhere (e.g. Gibbs, this volume, and references therein) leads to the suspicion that closely concentrated listric normal faults, giving rotations of up to 70°, might be expected to sole on a major detachment surface. For example, in the Great Basin of the western USA listric faults bounding tilted half-grabens dip W and sole on low-angle detachment faults (Wernicke & Burchfiel 1982). If this proved to be the case for the Honshu fore-arc there is no *a priori* reason to assume that an underlying detachment surface must dip in the same direction as the listric normal fault which leads up to the surface.

Interestingly, all the holes at Site 584 caved in near 900 m sub-bottom. Was this coincidence, or is there a zone of weak material representing a flat detachment fault within the mid-Miocene strata?

An alternative possibility involves the landward-dipping reflectors observed in the basement below the slope section. This basement represents either a Cretaceous (or Paleogene) accretionary complex (von Huene *et al.* 1982), or old crystalline rocks akin to those exposed onland in the Kitikami massif. In either case, landward-dipping reflectors might be expected: from structural discontinuities such as thrust zones in an ancient accretionary complex, or from lithological changes capable of giving acoustic impedance contrasts in basement rocks, as observed in the Moine Schists off Scotland (Brewer & Smythe 1984). The former case seems more likely, and if so the old planes of weakness in the basement might have been reactivated as normal faults which propagated up into the cover as it accumulated.

We are only able to speculate, though, on the exact causes of the extension: present information, despite representing one of the most complete integrated seismic/drilling data sets available from a fore-arc area, allow only a restricted look at what must be a highly complex three-dimensional extensional geometry.

Structural features in Site 584 cores and the up-dip termination of normal faults within slope sediments on available seismic lines (Figs 2 & 8) show that the extensional regime which affected the slope deposits ended sometime in the early Pliocene. The most attractive explanation for the subsidence of the fore-arc, and extension in the slope deposits, is subduction erosion at the leading edge of the fore-arc (von Huene *et al.* 1980). Subsequent to cessation of the extension in upper-slope sediments, uplift of the deep-sea terrace and the build-up of a prism of low-velocity strata below the lower slope reflect a major change, to an accretionary/mass wastage regime, during Plio–Quaternary times.

References

AUBOUIN, J., VON HUENE, R., BALTUCK, M., ARNOTT, R., BOURGOIS, J., FILEWIEZ, R., HELM, R., KVENEVOLDEN, K., LIENERT, B., MCDONALD, T., MCDOUGALL, K., OGAWA, Y., TAYLOR, E. & WINSBOROUGH, B. 1982. Leg 84 of the Deep Sea Drilling Project, subduction without accretion: Middle America Trench off Guatemala. *Nature*, **297**, 458–60.

ARTHUR, M.A., CARSON, B. & VON HEUNE, R. 1980. Initial tectonic deformation of hemipelagic sediment at the leading edge of the Japan convergent margin. *In: Init. Repts DSDP, 56/57, Pt. 1*, pp. 569–614. U.S. Govt. Printing Office, Washington D.C.

BALLY, A.W., BERNOULLI, D., DAVIS, G.A. & MONTADERT, L. 1981. Listric normal faults. *Ocean. Acta, Spec. Issue: Geology of Continental Margins*, pp. 87–101.

BREWER, J.A. & SMYTHE, D.K. 1984. MOIST and the continuity of crustal reflector geometry along the Caledonian Appalachian orogen. *J. geol. Soc. London*, **141**, 105–20.

CADET, J.P. *et al.* 1985. Oceanographie dynamic de la fosse du Japon a la fosse des Kouriles: premiers resultats de la campagne oceanographique franco-japonais Kaiko (Leg III). *C. R. Acad. Sc. Paris, t. 301, Serie II*, **5**, 287–96.

—— *et al.* In press. The Japan Trench and its junction with the Kuril Trench: cruise results of the KAIKO project, Leg 3. *Earth planet. Sci. Letts.*

CARSON, B., VON HUENE, R. & ARTHUR, M. 1982. Small-scale deformation structures and physical properties related to convergence in Japan Trench slope sediments. *Tectonics*, **1**, 277–302.

COWAN, D.S. 1983. Origin of 'vein structure' in slope sediments on the inner slope of the Middle America Trench off Guatemala. *In: Init. Repts DSDP, 67*, pp. 645–50. U.S. Govt. Printing Office, Washington D.C.

——, MOORE, J.C., ROESKE, S.M., LUNDBERG, N. & LUCAS, S.E. 1984. Structural features at the deformation front of the Barbados Ridge Complex, DSDP Leg 78A. *In: Init. Repts DSDP, 78A*, pp. 535–48. U.S. Govt. Printing Office, Washington D.C.

DICKINSON, W.R. & SEELY, D.R. 1979. Structure and stratigraphy of fore-arc regions. *Bull. Am. Assoc. Pet. Geol.* **63**, 2–31.

FUJIOKA, K. 1985. Geology of vocanogenic sediments of the Japan Trench area and Tertiary explosive volcanism of the NE Japan arc. *Bull. Ocean Res. Inst. Univ. Tokyo*, 276 pp.

GIBBS, A. This volume. Development of extension and mixed-mode sedimentary basins.

HUSSONG, D.M. & UYEDA, S. 1982. Tectonic processes and the history of the Mariana arc: a synthesis of the results of DSDP Leg 60. *In*: *Init. Repts DSDP, 60*, pp. 909–29. U.S. Govt. Printing Office, Washington D.C.

—— & WIPPERMAN, L. 1981. Indications of vertical movement of the continental wall of the Peru–Chile Trench near 9° 30'S. *In*: KULM, L.D., DYMOND, J., DASCH, E.J. & HUSSONG, D.M. (eds) *Nazca plate; crustal formation and Andean convergence*, Mem. geol. Soc. Am. **154**, 509–24.

KAGAMI, H. *et al.* 1986. *Init. Repts DSDP, 87*, 985 pp. U.S. Govt. Printing Office, Washington D.C.

KARIG, D.E. In press. Microstructural evolution of vein arrays preserved in Deep Sea Drilling Project cores from the Japan Trench, Leg 57. *In*: MOORE, J.C. (ed.) *Structural fabrics in DSDP cores from fore-arcs*, *Mem. geol. Soc. Am.* **116**.

——, KAGAMI, H. & DSDP Leg 87 SCIENTIFIC PARTY, 1983. Varied responses to subduction in Nankai Trough and Japan Trench forearcs. *Nature*, **304**, 148–51.

KNIPE, R.J. In press. Faulting mechanisms in slope sediments: examples from DSDP cores. *In*: MOORE, J.C. (ed.) *Structural fabrics in DSDP cores from fore-arcs*, *Mem. geol. Soc. Am.* **116**.

KULK, L.D., PRINCE, R.A., FRENCH, W., JOHNSON, S. & MASIAS, A. 1981. Crustal structure and tectonics of the central Peru continental margin and trench. *Mem. Geol. Soc. Am.* **154**, 445–68.

LUNDBERG, N. In press. Macroscopic structural features in DSDP cores form forearc regions. *In*: MOORE, J.C. (ed.) *Structural fabrics in DSDP cores from fore-arcs*, *Mem. geol. Soc. Am.* **116**.

—— & KARIG, D.C. 1986. Structural features in cores from the Nankai Trough, Deep Sea Drilling Project Leg 87A. *In*: KARIG, D., KAGAMI, H. *et al.* (eds) *Init. Repts DSDP, 87*, pp. 797–808.

—— & LEGGETT, J.K. 1985. Structural features in cores from the slope landward of the Japan Trench, Deep Sea Drilling Project Leg 87B. *In*: *Init. Repts DSDP, 87*, pp. 809–26. U.S. Govt. Printing Office, Washington D.C.

—— & MOORE, J.C. 1982. Structural features of the Middle America Trench slope off southern Mexico, DSDP Leg 66. *In*: *Init. Repts DSDP, 66*, pp. 793–805. U.S. Govt. Printing Office, Washington D.C.

—— & —— In press. Macroscopic structural features in DSDP cores from fore-arc regions. *In*: MOORE, J.C. (ed.) *Structural fabrics in DSDP cores from fore-arcs*. *Mem. geol. Soc. Am.* **116**.

NASU, N., VON HUENE, R., ISHIWADA, Y., LANGSETH, M., BRUNS, T. & HONZA, E. 1980. Interpretation of multichannel seismic reflection data, Legs 56 and 57, Japan Trench transect. *In*: *Init. Repts DSDP, 57*, pp. 489–503. U.S. Govt. Printing Office, Washington D.C.

——, TOMODA, Y., KOBAYASHI, K., KAGAMI, H., UYEDA, S., NAGUMO, S., KURSHIRO, I., OJIMA, M., NAKAZAWA, K., TAKAYANAGI, Y., OKADA, M., MURAUCHI, S., ISHIWADA, Y. & ISHII, Y. 1979. Multichannel seismic reflection data across the Japan Trench. *IPOD Japan Basic Data Series, No. 3*, pp. 1–22. Ocean Research Institute, University of Tokyo.

NIITSUMA, N. 1986. Palaeomagnetic results, Nankai Trough and Japan Trench, DSDP Leg 87. *In*: *Init. Repts DSDP, 87*. pp. 757–86. U.S. Govt. Printing Office, Washington D.C.

NIITSUMA, N. & AKIBA, F. 1986. Sedimentation rates in the Japan Trench, DSDP Site 584, calculated from biostratigraphy and paleomagnetism. *In*: *Init. Repts DSDP, 87*, pp. 555–71. U.S. Govt. Printing Office, Washington D.C.

OGAWA, Y. 1980. Beard-like veinlet structure as fracture cleavage in the Neogene siltstone in the Miura and Boso Peninsulas, central Japan. *Sci. Repts Dept Geol. Kyushu Univ.* **13**, 321–7.

—— & MIYATA, Y. 1985. Vein structure and its deformational history in the sedimentary rocks of the Middle America Trench slope off Guatemala, DSDP Leg 84. *In*: *Init. Repts DSDP, 84*, pp. 811–29. U.S. Govt. Printing Office, Washington D.C.

RITGER, S.D. 1985. Origin of vein structures in the slope deposits of modern accretionary prisms. *Geology*, **13**, 437–9.

SCHOLL, D.W., MARLOW, M.S. & COOPER, A.K. 1977. Sediment subduction and offscraping at Pacific margins. *In*: TALWANI, M. & PITMAN, W.C. III, (eds) *Island Arcs, Deep-Sea Trenches and Back-Arc Basins, Maurice Ewing Series, 1*, pp.199–210. Am. geophys. Union. Washington D.C.

——, VON HUENE, R., VALLIER, T.L. & HOWELL, D.G. 1980. Sedimentary masses and concepts about tectonic processes at underthrust ocean margins. *Geology*, **8**, 564–8.

VON HUENE, R. & LEE, H. 1982. The possible significance of pore fluid pressures in subduction zones. *In*: WATKINS, J.S. & DRAKE, C.L. (eds) *Studies in Continental Margin Geology*, *Am. Assoc. Pet. Geol. Mem.* **34**, 781–91.

——, KULM, L.D. & MILLER, J. 1985. Structure of the frontal part of the Andean convergent margin. *J. geophys. Res.* **90**, 5429–42.

——, R., CADET, J.P., KAGAMI, H. & CULOTTA, R. In press. Interpretation of reprocessed seismic reflection records in the Leg 87B area. *J. geophys. Res.*

——, LANGSETH, M., NASU, N. & OKADA, S. 1980. Summary, Japan Trench Transect. *In*: *Init. Repts DSDP, 56/57*, pp. 473–88. U.S. Govt. Printing Office, Washington D.C.

——, ——, —— & —— 1982. A summary of Cenozoic tectonic history along the IPOD Japan Trench Transect. *Bull. geol. Soc. Am.* **93**, 829–46.

——, NASU, N., ARTHUR, M., CADET, J.P., CARSON, B., MOORE, G.W., HONA, E., FUJIOKA, K., BARRON,

J.A., KELLER, G., REYNOLDS, R., SHAFFER, B.L., SATA, S. & BELL, G. 1978. Japan Trench Transect on Leg 57. *Geotimes 23, No. 4*, 16–21.

WATKINS, J.S. *et al*. 1981. Accretion, underplating, subduction and tectonic erosion, Middle America Trench, southern Mexico: results from DSDP Leg 66. *Ocean. Acta, Spec. Issue, Geology of Continental Margins*, 213–24.

WERNICKE, B. & BURCHFIEL, B.C. 1982. Modes of extensional tectonics. *J. struct. Geol.* **4**, 105–15.

J.K. LEGGETT, Department of Geology, Imperial College, London.
N. LUNDBERG, Department of Geological and Geophysical Sciences, Princeton University, USA.
C.J. BRAY & D.E. KARIG, Department of Geological Sciences, Cornell University, USA.
J.P. CADET, Département des Sciences de la Terre, Université d'Orleans, France.
R.J. KNIPE, Department of Earth Sciences, Leeds University, Leeds.
R. VON HUENE, USGS, Menlo Park, California, USA.

Thin-skinned N–S extension within the convergent Himalayan region: gravitational collapse of a Miocene topographic front

L.H. Royden & B.C. Burchfiel

SUMMARY: Recent work by Burg *et al.* indicates the presence of E–W striking, gently N-dipping normal faults in the High Himalayas and southern Tibet, that formed during the post-collisional convergence of India and Tibet. These faults extend for at least 600 km along strike. We interpret them as probable late (?) Miocene extensional features with perhaps several tens of kilometres downward northerly displacement. A simple elastic model suggests that these normal faults may have formed during gravitational collapse of the Miocene topographic front between India and Tibet. In this interpretation, gravitational collapse occurred by southward motion, relative to India and Tibet, of a wedge of crustal rock bounded above by gently dipping normal faults and below by thrust faults that probably dip N. N–S extension produced in this way is probably confined to upper crustal levels only and does not reflect regional extension of the entire lithosphere. Such faults may be common, but so far mainly unrecognized, features developed during convergence in many orogenic belts.

The Himalayan mountain belt has been formed by N–S shortening and crustal thickening during convergence between the Indian and Asian Plates after their collision at about 45 Ma (Fig. 1). Recent work by Burg *et al.* (1984) indicates the existence of E–W-striking, gently N-dipping normal faults of regional extent in and N of the High Himalayas (Fig. 2). These faults appear to have had down-to-the-N displacement of probable Miocene age and to be a manifestation of N–S sub-horizontal extensional strain within the Himalayan crust. They are coeval with S-directed overthrusting along the Main Boundary Thrust (MBT) or Main Central Thrust (MCT) to the S and roughly coeval with N-directed overthrusting along back-thrusts N of the normal-fault zone.

The existence of E–W extension within the Himalayan mountains and the Tibetan plateau was first recognized by Molnar & Tapponier (1975) and has been still-better documented by more recent studies (Tapponnier & Molnar 1977; Armijo *et al.* 1984). This E–W extension is a young example of the phenomenon of continental escape (Burke 1982, unpublished lecture) that occurs as material within the collision zone escapes laterally (perpendicular to the direction of convergence) towards a zone of lower compressional strain (see also McKenzie 1972). The driving mechanism for continental escape is generally believed to arise from the high confining pressures beneath topographically high areas in the collision zone, relative to the lower confining pressures present at the same depth relative to sea-level in areas adjacent to the collision zone (see discussion in Dalmayrac & Molnar 1981, England & MacKenzie 1982, 1983, and Houseman *et al.* 1981).

Coney & Harms (1984) have suggested that the extensional regime in western North America developed by spreading in an overthickened crust following a reduction of intraplate compressional stress. Other studies have suggested that the same mechanism may lead to extension parallel to the earlier direction of shortening, even before the termination of subduction, giving rise to collapse of the orogenic belt and possible development of an extensional regime (Dalmayrac & Molnar 1981).

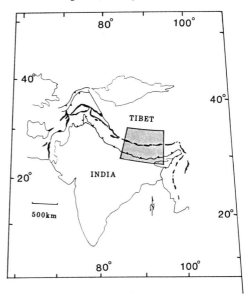

FIG. 1. Location map showing the central Himalayan–southern Tibet region covered in Fig. 2 and its relation to Tibet, India and the Indian–southern Tibet suture (Yarlung–Zangbo suture in black).

From COWARD, M.P., DEWEY, J.F. & HANCOCK, P.L. (eds), 1987, *Continental Extensional Tectonics*, Geological Society Special Publication No. 28, pp. 611–619.

611

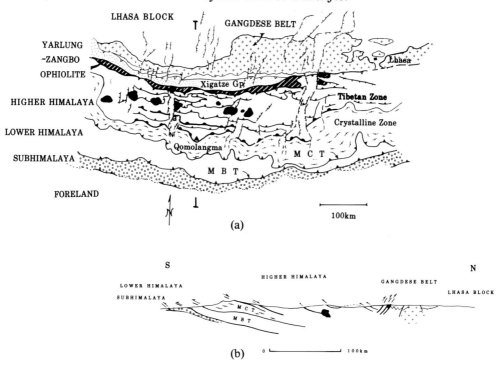

FIG. 2. (a) Major tectonic elements of the central Himalayan–southern Tibet region and location of line of section shown in Fig. 2(b). Lines with closed barbs are thrust faults; lines with open barbs are N-vergent back-thrusts; lines with black semi-circles are N-dipping normal faults; lines with ticks are N-trending normal faults; and the N belt of leucogranites is in black. MCT=Main Central Thrust; MBT=Main Boundary Thrust; N=Nyalam; G=Guzuo.
(b) Generalized cross-section through the Qomolangma area emphasizing the position of the N-dipping normal faults and the S-vergent MCT and MBT and the N-vergent back-thrusts.

Within convergent orogenic belts, significant amounts of synchronous extension and compression in the same direction are not generally observed. Normal faults that are parallel to, and coeval with, compressional structures are generally absent or developed only locally, such as at shallow crustal levels at the crests of anticlines or associated with pull-apart structures along strike-slip faults. The existence of E–W-striking Miocene normal faults within the N–S-convergent regime of the Himalayas seems at first glance to represent a mechanical contradiction, because it implies significant N–S extension within a region of N–S shortening and convergence. In this paper we will show how the development of these normal faults within the High Himalayas may be genetically related to the shortening strain and consequent high topography produced by mountain building in the Himalayas and the Tibetan plateau.

N-dipping normal faults in the Himalayas

The gently N-dipping (15–30°) normal fault or fault zone mapped by Burg *et al.* (1984) in the High Himalayas extends for at least 600 km along strike and separates unmetamorphosed to weakly metamorphosed Ordovician rocks above, from high-grade metamorphic rocks, metamorphosed in Cenozoic time, below (figs 1 & 2, Wang & Zheng 1975). Various shear-sense indicators (mesoscopic S–C fabrics, quartz microfabrics and rotated porphyroblasts and pressure shadows) from a zone 100 to 200 m below the fault contact, consistently show downward northerly displacement of the hanging wall (Burg *et al.* 1984). Rocks of the hanging wall are generally only mildly deformed, contain only a spaced cleavage and do not include the leucogranite dykes and sills that lie immediately below.

Within the hanging wall of the normal fault, described above, are other N-dipping faults with normal displacement. In the area N of Nyalam (Fig. 2), there are two N–dipping faults that place younger rocks in the hanging wall against older rocks in the footwall. We interpret these faults as having normal displacement. About 25 km farther N (S of Guzuo), mesoscopic folds, in a N-dipping section of Jurassic rocks have a down to the N sense of relative displacement (Fig. 2), even though they are on the N flank of an anticline and should show the reverse sense of movement. This suggests that downward northerly displacement within the High Himalayas may be distributed across a zone at least 25 km wide (J.P. Burg, pers. comm. 1984).

In the Qomolangma (Everest) area, Wang & Zheng (1975) have mapped three N-dipping faults, which they interpreted as S-vergent thrust faults. These faults have a gentle dip (5–7°) and are present through about 4–6 km of structural thickness and for 40–50 km across strike. One of these faults separates the Sinian (?) to early Ordovician sedimentary rocks (the Bei Ao Group), at the base of the Tibetan sedimentary sequence, from higher grade metamorphic rocks of the crystalline zone below (Fig. 2) and is the same fault as that described by Burg *et al.* (1984). All three faults, mapped by Wang & Zheng (1975), consistently place younger rocks on older rocks and, where some of the Ordovician rocks are locally marble, place less-metamorphosed rocks on more highly metamorphosed rocks. The thicknesses of stratigraphic units between these faults or near their contacts are highly variable and often thin from N to S. Early ductile structures in the metamorphic rocks and the mylonitic rocks of the hanging wall are S-vergent, suggesting that they developed during S-vergent displacement, but the faults are characteristically marked by breccia up to a few metres thick. Evidence for the thrust sense of displacement on the faults is inferred from the ductile structures, not from structures associated with the brittle deformation that characterizes the faults. Descriptions of these faults are reminiscent of the low-angle normal faults from the Basin and Range Province of the western United States (for example see Davis *et al.* 1980).

Thus from the reconnaissance work of Burg *et al.* (1984) and Wang & Zheng (1975), it appears that there is a major normal fault at the base of the Tibetan sedimentary sequence and that gently dipping normal faults with downward northerly displacement developed across a 25–50 km wide zone (Fig. 2). The fault or fault zone can be traced for more than 600 km along strike in Tibet and may extend for a further 200 km to the W into India, as suggested by the mapping of Valdiya & Goel (1983) in the Kumaum area. The basal fault or faults in this array juxtapose rocks from two different metamorphic environments, which suggests that a significant portion (10–15 km or more) of the crustal sequence is absent. From the gentle dip of these faults, we infer that large displacements (of probably tens of kilometres) are involved.

Location of normal faults relative to other structures

The N-dipping normal faults lie between areas dominated by structures formed as the result of N–S shortening. To the S are the N-dipping thrust faults of the MCT and MBT and to the N are the S-dipping back-thrusts of the Yarlung–Zangbo area (Fig. 2). The normal faults also lie near to or within a zone of N-dipping thrust faults present in or at the base of the Tibetan sedimentary sequence. The N-dipping normal faults and all the thrust faults and folds, observable from the MCT to the southern Lhasa Block, are cut by N-trending normal faults associated with the active E–W extension in the southern part of the Tibetan plateau.

Timing of normal faults relative to other structures

Relative timing constraints suggest that the gently N-dipping normal faults formed during Miocene (perhaps late Miocene) or earliest Pliocene time. They are cut by faults that bound N-trending grabens, giving an upper age limit of 2–4 Ma, according to Armijo *et al.* (1984). The gently N-dipping normal faults cut metamorphic rocks and leucogranites of the crystalline zone in the footwall (Fig. 2) producing a localized fabric. This suggests that the faults may have begun to form at a late stage in the metamorphic and igneous development of the footwall crystalline zone. Unfortunately, the metamorphism and time of leucogranite intrusion is poorly constrained, but the range in radiometric ages suggests the occurrence of an event or events between 30 and 15 Ma (Allegre *et al.* 1984). These relations imply a time for fault formation of between 30 and 15 Ma and 4 Ma (i.e. Miocene to earliest Pliocene time). Similar constraints can be placed on N-vergent back-thrusts that are present 100–150 km farther N (Fig. 2). N-dipping thrusts within Tibet are less-well constrained. Recent work by Burg & Chen (1984) suggests that these faults may be latest Cretaceous to early Tertiary in age and related to a pre-collision event, although some of their movement could be related to convergent events following collision. Our interpretation is that the N-dipping normal faults are, (i) younger than the thrust faults of Tibet; (ii) broadly contemporaneous with movement on either or both the MCT and MBT and the back-thrusts in the Yarlung–Zangbo area and (iii) broadly contemporaneous with but locally outlasting the regional metamorphism and leucogranite intrusion within the exposed part of the crystalline zone of the High Himalayas.

Interpretation

From existing data we interpret the E–W-striking, gently dipping normal faults described above as probable Miocene or earliest Pliocene extensional features, with perhaps several tens of kilometres of downward northerly displacement. This presents mechanical problems because in this area of regional N–S convergence (5 cm yr^{-1} between India and Siberia), the normal faulting and extension were roughly contemporaneous with S-vergent thrusting and subduction along the MCT or MBT and with N-vergent back-thrusting about 100–150 km N of the normal-fault zone (Fig. 2).

Burg *et al.* (1984) interpreted normal faulting as back-sliding on an older thrust fault. They recognized that locally the horizontal N–S compressive stress must have been less than the vertical stress and suggested that this might be due to gravitational effects in the presence of high topographic relief.

In this paper we present an explanation related to the stress orientation in the convergent zone of southern Tibet and northern India.

An idealized cross-section through the High Himalayas at the time that this normal fault zone was active, indicates southward motion, relative to both India and Tibet, of a wedge of crustal rocks (Fig. 3). This wedge was bounded above by gently N-dipping normal faults and below by N-dipping thrust faults. Near the surface, the thrust faults that bounded the base of the southward-moving wedge may be identical to the contemporaneous sub-

duction boundary between India and Tibet, but are not necessarily so. The nature of the geometry of this crustal wedge at depth (shown in Fig. 3) is totally speculative.

We suggest that normal faulting and southward displacement of the crustal wedge (Fig. 3) were the results of gravitational collapse along the Miocene–earliest Pliocene topographic front between the Indian foreland (present average elevation a few hundred metres above sea-level) and the Tibetan plateau (present average elevation about 4–5 km above sea-level). A simple elastic model, described below, suggests that this large, abrupt change in elevation may have produced N–S sub-horizontal extensional stress (or strain) extending for several tens of kilometres N of the topographic front and to 10–20 km depth. Sub-horizontal extensional stresses (or strain), produced in this way, appear to be restricted mainly to crustal levels and do not reflect N–S extension of the lithosphere at greater depths.

The effect of topographic relief on stress distribution

In this paper we present a simple two-dimensional analysis of stress distribution within the lithosphere beneath the Himalayas arising from the differences in topographic elevation N and S of the belt. The lithosphere of the Indian–Tibetan region is treated as a perfectly elastic half-space, initially under horizontal compression and with its surface at sea-level (Fig. 4). The effects of the topographically high areas (Himalayas and Tibet) are approximated by treating material above sea-level as a vertical load applied to the surface of the elastic sheet, so that the assumed load is proportional to the elevation above sea-level at each point. The surface of the infinite half-space is assumed to have no shear stresses. This approximation yields an analytical solution, (see for example, Scott 1963). More complicated models require solution by numerical

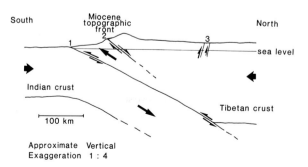

FIG. 3. Diagrammatic cross-section through the Himalayas and southern Tibet showing; (1) thrust faulting along the MCT (or MBT); (2) normal faulting within the High Himalayas; and (3) back-thrusting near the Tsangpo suture zone. Kinematic relationships imply that a shallow wedge of crustal material must have moved southward relative to both India and Tibet. The wedge is bounded above by N-dipping normal fault(s) (2), and below by N-dipping thrust faults, possibly but not necessarily the MCT or MBT (1). The geometry shown at depth is speculative.

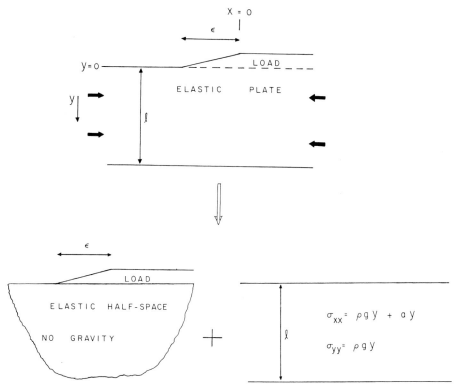

FIG. 4. Simple elastic model used to generate the stress trajectories shown in Fig. 5. The Indian–Tibetan lithosphere is taken to be an infinite elastic sheet with a surface at $y=0$ for $x \leqslant -\epsilon$, $y=h$ for $x \geqslant 0$, and a uniform slope between $x=-\epsilon$ and $x=0$ ($y=-h(x+\epsilon)/\epsilon$). The resulting stresses are approximated by considering the sum of (1) the stresses produced by loading a semi-infinite half-space with a vertical load equivalent to the vertical load of all material above $y=0$ (load$=q=\varrho gh$ for $x \geqslant 0$, load$=\varrho gh(x+\epsilon)\epsilon$ for $-\epsilon \leqslant x \leqslant 0$), and (2) an elastic sheet with a stress distribution $\sigma_{xx}=\varrho gy+ay$, $\sigma_{yy}=\varrho gy$. There is no shear stress on the surface $y=0$. Solutions can be found in the text.

techniques, (see for example, Bott & Dean 1972). Because the effective elastic thickness of the Indian Plate beneath Tibet is estimated to be ~ 80 km (Lyon-Caen & Molnar 1983), this approach should provide reasonable results sufficiently far above the base of the elastic plate, to depths of 40–50 km.

Prior to loading of the elastic half-space, the stress distribution was taken to be $\sigma_{yy} = \varrho gy$, $\sigma_{xx} = \varrho gy + ay$, $\sigma_{xy} = 0$. This choice of initial stress distribution is somewhat arbitrary, but we reason that in the Earth, differential stresses are likely to be smaller near the surface than at depth. The topographic elevation and the associated load, is assumed to have been zero over the Indian shield and 5 km (or $q = 1.25$ kb load) over Tibet and the increase in topographic elevation (or load) is assumed to have occurred linearly across a finite width, ϵ (Table 1).

The resulting stress field is described by:

$$\sigma_{xx} = \frac{q}{\pi} \left\{ \frac{\pi}{2} + \theta_1 + \frac{x}{\epsilon} \; (\theta_1 - \theta_2) \right.$$

$$\left. - \frac{y}{\epsilon} \, \ln \left[\frac{(x+\epsilon)^2 + y^2}{x^2 + y^2} \right] \right\} + \varrho gy + ay \, ,$$

$$\sigma_{yy} = \frac{q}{\pi} \left[\frac{\pi}{2} + \theta_1 + \frac{x}{\epsilon} \; (\theta_1 - \theta_2) \right] + \varrho gy \, ,$$

$$\sigma_{xy} = - \frac{qy}{\pi\epsilon} (\theta_1 - \theta_2)$$

where

$$\theta_1 = \arctan[(x+\epsilon)/y] \text{ and } \theta_2 = \arctan(x/y).$$

Figure 5 shows the calculated stress trajectories for loading of an elastic half-space, with two different assumptions of initial stress and with a 5 km increase in elevation over a 50 km interval. Far from the region of change in topography, σ_1 (maximum compressive stress) is nearly horizontal, but near the topographic slope, the principal stresses are rotated so that σ_1 becomes steep. Figure 5 shows that beneath the northern part of the topographic slope and the southern part of the

TABLE 1.

Symbol	Value	Definition
a	0.01, 0.02 kb km^{-1}	Horizontal stress prior to loading is $\varrho gy + ay$
g	$\varrho g = 0.25$ kb km^{-1}	Gravitational constant
ϱ	$\varrho g = 0.25$ kb km^{-1}	Crustal density
h	5 km	Topographic elevation of plateau
q	1.25 kb	Load equivalent to topographic elevation h
ϵ	50 km	Width of zone of linearly increasing topographic elevation

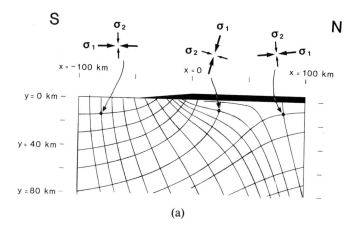

(a)

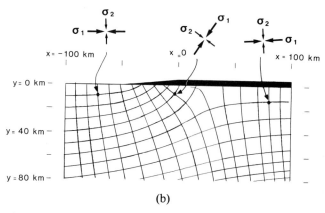

(b)

FIG. 5. Stress trajectories as described in the text. In both cases the load $q=1.25$ kb (corresponds to roughly 5 km elevation) and the width of the zone of linearly increasing load is $\epsilon=50$ km. (a) Horizontal stress prior to loading is $\sigma_{xx}=0.26y$, vertical stress prior to loading is $\sigma_{yy}=0.25y$, y in km, stress in kb. (b) Horizontal stress prior to loading is $\sigma_{xx}=0.27y$, vertical stress prior to loading is $\sigma_{yy}+0.25y$, y in km, stress in kb. North and South refer to compass directions analogous to the topographic differences between India and Tibet. Dark lines show orientation of σ_1 (maximum compressive stress) and σ_2 (minimum compressive stress). Note rotation of principal stress axes near the southern edge of the high-standing region. This effect becomes more pronounced for smaller values of a and ϵ and larger values of q (Table 1).

plateau, σ_1 axes plunge S, with gentle plunges at depth and progressively steeper plunges near the surface. Likewise, σ_2 (minimum compressional stress) axes plunge N in the same area and become horizontal at the surface. Comparing Figs 3 and 5 shows that beneath the northern part of the topographic slope and the southern part of the plateau, the calculated orientation of the principal stress axes is consistent with the sense of movement inferred for the southward-moving crustal wedge from geological field data (Fig. 3). Far away from the topographic slope, the calculated stress field is consistent with sub-horizontal compression and thrust faulting.

The maximum deviatoric stresses calculated within the area, where the vertical compressive stresses exceed the horizontal compressive stresses, are about 800 bars in Fig. 5(a) and 400 bars in Fig. 5(b). This occurs near $x = 0$ in both cases and at depths of about 25–30 km in Fig. 5(a) and about 10–15 km in Fig. 5(b).

The simple model for stress distribution presented in this paper is intended only to explain the apparently incompatible juxtaposition of contemporaneous thrust faults and E–W-striking, N-dipping normal faults in southern Tibet. The stress orientations plotted in Fig. 5 are designed only to illustrate qualitatively the effects of large changes in topographic elevation on a regionally compressive stress regime. They are not intended to be realistic representations of the stress field beneath the Himalayas or any other mountain belt.

It is clear that crustal deformation beneath Tibet is not elastic and that zones of ductile, plastic and viscous flow are important in controlling local and regional deformation, particularly in this area of young magmatic activity. Other potentially significant features ignored in this analysis are the N-dipping main subduction boundary beneath the Himalayas and Tibet, crustal anisotropy produced by N-dipping bedding and foliation in upper-plate rocks, changes in crustal thickness between India and Tibet, stress concentrations at the end of pre-existing cracks, the role of ductile deformation at depth, and the effect of near-surface stresses in the topographically high regions.

We do not mean to imply that a large change in topographic relief necessarily produces sub-horizontal extension, but only that the stresses resulting from such geometries are conducive to sub-horizontal extension as illustrated in Fig. 5. These calculations are intended only as a qualitative explanation for field observations, not as a predictive or quantitative tool. For example, if larger values of horizontal compressional stress are assumed near the surface, the loading effect of the topographically high region will be swamped and sub-horizontal compression will be present almost everywhere.

Discussion

A simplified elastic model shows that large changes in topographic elevation may generate sub-horizontal extensional stresses near the edge of a high-standing plateau that are parallel to the direction of regional compression. Sub-horizontal extensional stresses generated in this way appear to be confined to crustal levels (within several tens of kilometres of the surface) and probably do not extend deep into the lithosphere. The orientations of the principal stress axes near the edge of the high-standing region are consistent with the N–S extension of the southernmost Tibetan plateau and High Himalayas at shallow crustal levels; southward motion of a crustal wedge as shown in Fig. 3 is in reasonable agreement with gently N-plunging T axes (σ_2) as shown in Fig. 5. Thus N–S crustal extension at shallow crustal levels within the High Himalayas and southern Tibet can be mechanically consistent with contemporaneous N–S shortening to the S (along the main subduction boundary) and to the N (back-thrusting in the Tsangpo area).

Normal faults that form in this stress regime could dip either N or S. The well-developed N-dipping structural anisotropy in the High Himalayas may have been responsible for the development of N-dipping normal faults. In fact most mountain belts would have similarly orientated anisotropy which would favour the development of normal faults synthetic to contemporaneous, major thrust faults formed within an overall convergent system.

The sub-horizontal extensional stresses produced in southern Tibet and the High Himalayas can be interpreted as the direct result of gravity acting on the high-standing plateau and extensional faulting can be considered as a type of gravitational collapse of the Himalayan topographic front. Events leading to gravitational collapse of the front may include continued crustal thickening at the leading (southern) edge of the Tibetan Plateau by underplating of the crust with material from the Indian crust that is incompletely subducted (Fig. 3). As the crustal thickness increases beneath the leading edge of the Tibetan Plateau, the topographic elevation increases as well (present average elevation of the High Himalayas is about 6 km) and provides increased vertical stress to drive extension. We suggest that eventually the difference in topographic elevation between the Indian foreland and the southern edge of the Tibetan Plateau increases to the point at which the stresses generated can no longer be supported by the strength of the rocks within the upper crust, and gravitational collapse occurs.

Gravitational collapse may also be related to changes in the coefficient of friction along the

S-dipping subduction boundary in the Himalayas. For example, Dahlen (1984) has shown, theoretically, that by decreasing friction (e.g. by increasing pore-pressure) at the base of an accreting wedge, deformation within the wedge may change from sub-horizontal compression to sub-horizontal extension (figs 12 & 13, Dahlen 1984). Thus a decrease in the effective stresses along the subduction boundary beneath the High Himalayas may also have induced N–S extensional failure within the mountain belt.

Decrease in the effective compressive stresses within the subduction zone could also be caused by changes in the partitioning of deformation between the Himalayan thrust zone and other fault zones farther N in the Tibetan plateau or northern China. Thus from the above considerations, the circumstances that trigger normal faulting could be episodic.

We emphasize that the model proposed here is not the same as those proposed by van Bemmelen (1954) or Ramberg (1967), who proposed that thrust nappes form as secondary consequences of vertical tectonics. Instead, we propose gravitational spreading of the upper to middle crust of the High Himalayas within a primarily convergent regime as crustal material at mid-crustal levels is displaced southward. In some respects our analysis is similar to that of Elliott (1976), but in contrast to Elliott, we believe that the gravity spreading or gravitational collapse inferred for the Miocene Himalayas is a secondary effect superimposed on regional N–S compression. The driving force for this gravitational collapse is similar to that proposed by Dalmayrac & Molnar (1981), where differences in confining pressure at a constant depth (relative to sea-level) tend to drive material from areas of higher topography to those of lower topography. In our interpretation, however, extension is confined to shallow or mid-crustal levels.

Speculation

The relationships outlined above, between normal faulting and thrust faulting imply local shallow decoupling within the lithosphere and may even suggest decoupling on a more regional scale beneath Tibet. Decoupling implies that very different and apparently incompatible structures can develop contemporaneously at different crustal (or sub-crustal) levels in the same region. An ancient situation analogous to that observed in the Himalayas may help to explain paradoxical relations in southern Canada between the Columbia River fault zone, a possible extensional low-angle

normal fault, and the convergent deformation recorded in the adjacent metamorphic rocks of the Monashee and Shuswap Complexes (Reed & Brown 1981). Similar examples would be in the Raft River and Albion Ranges, NW Utah (Allmendinger & Jordan 1981; Compton 1980), the faults in the Drauzug of southern Austria (Tollmann 1963), the Rhone–Simplon line in the Alps (Steck 1984), or the normal faults described by Platt *et al.* (1983) in the Betic Cordillera of southern Spain.

One of the major questions in thrust fault mechanics has been the role of gravity in thrust dynamics. The kinematics and dynamics we envisage for the Himalayan structural development would suggest that displacement on the normal faults that bound the top of the southward-moving crustal wedge in the Himalayas (Fig. 3) and part of the displacement on the thrust faults that bound its base, are the result of gravity acting on a region with considerable topographic relief. Thus a part of the thrust-fault displacement that is contemporaneous with normal faulting may be contributed by gravity. This component, however, is probably small (tens of kilometres?), relative to the total amount of Miocene convergence between India and Siberia ($\sim$1000 km).

Normal faulting within the Himalayan belt may be related to other features. For example, the northern belt of the Himalayan leucogranites is parallel to the zone of normal faulting (Fig. 2) and alignment of the batholiths may have been controlled by the shallow crustal extension and thinning. The locus of granitic intrusion could have been controlled by the site of extension and ascent of magma into the extensional environment above.

Extension in the shallow part of the lithosphere may also have produced a local lowering of the elevation of the highest part of the mountain front, which in turn may have affected the climate in southern Tibet by reducing the rain shadow effect that is so pronounced today. Such an effect might explain the distribution of organisms, such as the Pliocene *Hipperions* in Tibet, which features so prominently in arguments concerning the age of uplift of the Tibetan plateau (Zheng *et al.* 1981).

ACKNOWLEDGMENTS: We would like to thank the geologists of the French–Chinese Tibetan Mission for the opportunity to visit southern Tibet in 1984, and to profit from the results of their scientific cooperation. L.R. is grateful to the Kerr–McGee Foundation, and the Kerr Foundation for their generous support of her research, and Victor Li for helpful discussion and suggestions. B.C.B. would like to thank the Schlumberger Corporation for support of his research on this project.

References

ALLEGRE, C.J. *et al.* 1984. Structure and evolution of the Himalaya–Tibet orogenic belt, *Nature*, **307**, 17–31.

ALLMENDINGER, R.W. & JORDAN, T.E. 1981. Mesozoic evolution, hinterland of the Sevier orogenic belt, Utah. *Geology*, **9**, 308–13.

ARMIJO, R., TAPPONNIER, P., MERCIER, J.L. & HAN, T. 1984. Quaternary extension of the Tibetan Plateau: Field observations and tectonic implications, *Himalayan Geology, International Symposium (Abstracts), Chengdu, China.*

BOTT, M.P.H. & DEAN, D.S. 1972. Stress systems at young continental margins. *Nature*, **235**, 23–5.

BURG, J.P., BRUNEL, M., GAPAIS, D., CHEN, G.M. & LIU. G.H. 1984. Deformation of Leucogranites of the Crystalline Main Central Thrust Sheet in southern Tibet (China), *J. struct. Geol.* **6**, 535–42.

—— & CHEN, J.M. 1984, Tectonics and structural zonation of southern Tibet, China. *Nature*, **311**, 219–23.

COMPTON, R.R. 1980. Fabrics and strains in quartzites of a metamorphic core complex, Raft River Mountains, Utah. *In:* CRITTENDEN, M.D. JR, CONEY, P.J. & DAVIS, G.H., (eds.) *Cordelleran Metamorphic Core Complexes*, Mem. geol. Soc. Am. **153**, 385–98.

CONEY, P.J. & HARMS, T.A. 1984. Cordilleran metamorphic core complexes: Cenozoic extensional relics of Mesozoic compression. *Geology*, **12**, 550–4.

DAHLEN, F.A. 1984. Noncohesive critical couloumb wedges: An exact solution. *J. geophys. res.* **89**, 125–33.

DALMAYRAC, B. & MOLNAR, P. 1981. Parallel thrust and normal faulting in Peru and constraints on the state of stress. *Earth planet. Sci. Lett.* **55**, 473–81.

DAVIS, G.A., ANDERSON, L.J., FROST, E.G. & SHACKELFORD, T.J. 1980. Mylonization and detachment faulting in the Whipple–Buckskin–Rawhide Mountains terrane, south-eastern California and western Arizona. *In:* CRITTENDEN, M.D., JR, CONEY, P.J. & DAVIS, G.H., (eds) *Cordelleran Metamorphic Core Complexes*, Mem. geol. Soc. Am. **153**, 79–130.

ELLIOT, D. 1976. The motion of thrust sheets. *J. geophys. Res.* **81**, 949–63.

ENGLAND, P.C & McKENZIE, D. 1982. A thin viscous sheet model for continental deformation. *Geophys. J. R. astron. Soc.* **70**, 295–321.

—— & —— 1983. Correction to: A thin viscous sheet model for continental deformation. *Geophys. J. R. astron. Soc.* **73**, 523–32.

HOUSEMAN, G.A., McKENZIE, D.P. & MOLNAR, P. 1981. Convective instability of a thickened boundary layer and its relevance for the thermal evolution of continental convergent belts. *J. geophys. Res.* **86**, 6115–32.

LYON-CAEN, H. & MOLNAR, P. 1983. Constraints on the structure of the Himalaya from an analysis of gravity anomalies and a flexural model of the lithosphere. *J. geophys. Res.* **88**, 8171–91.

McKENZIE, D.P. 1972. Active tectonics of the Mediterranean region. *Geophys. J.R. astron. Soc.* **30**, 109–85.

MOLNAR, P. & TAPPONNIER, P. 1975. Effects of a continental collision. *Science*, **189**, 419–26.

PLATT, J.P., VAN DEN EECKHOUT, B., JANZEN, E., KONERT, G., SIMON, O.J. & WEIJERMARS, R. 1983. The structure and tectonic evolution of the Aquilon fold nappe, Sierra Alhamilla, Betic Cordilleras, S.E. Spain. *J. Struct. Geol.* **5**, 519–38.

RAMBERG, H. 1967. *Gravity, Deformation and the Earth's Crust*, 214 pp. Academic Press, London.

REED, P.B. & BROWN, R.L. 1981. Columbia River fault zone: Southeastern margin of the Shuswap and Monashee complexes, southern British Columbia. *Can. J. Earth sci.* **18**, 1127–45.

SCOTT, R.F. 1963. *Principles of Soil Mechanics*, 550 pp. Addison-Wesley Publishing Co., Reading, Massachusetts.

STECK, A. 1984. Structures de deformations tertiaires dans les Alpes centrales. *Eclog. geol. Helv.* **77**, 55–100.

TAPPONNIER, P. & MOLNAR, P. 1977, Active faulting and Cenozoic tectonics of China. *J. Geophys. Res.* **82**, 2905–30.

TOLLMANN, A. 1963. *Ostalpen Syntheses*, 256 pp. Verlag Franz Deuticke, Wein.

VALDIYA, K.S. & GOEL, O.P. 1983. Lithological subdivisions and petrology of the Great Himalayan Vaikrita Group in Kumaun India. *Proc. Ind. Acad. Sci. Earth planet. Sci.* **92**, 141–63.

VAN BEMMELEN, R.W. 1954. *Mountain Building*, 177 pp. Martinus Nijhoff, The Hague.

WANG, Y. & ZHENG, X. 1975. Imbricate structure in the northern slope of Jolmo Lungma and discussion on the uplift of the Himalaya. *Scientific exploration on Jolmo Lungma (1975)*, pp. 199–221. Science Publishing House, Beijing.

ZHENG, Z., FENG, Z., ZHANG, Y. & HU, S. 1981. On the land-vertebrate fauna of Qinghai–Xizang Plateau with considerations concerning its history of transformation. *In: Proc. Symp. Qinghai-Xizang (Tibet) Plateau (Beijing, China),* p. 975–88.

L.H. ROYDEN* & B.C. BURCHFIEL*, Department of Earth, Atmospheric and Planetary Sciences, Massachusetts Institute of Technology, Cambridge, MA 02139, USA.

*B.C.B. was responsible for geologic interpretations of the faults described, including geometrical and timing constraints. L.H.R. was responsible for the kinematic interpretation of these faults within their convergent setting, and for the development of the physical models.

Index

(Figures in italics—Tables in bold)